Everyday Mathematics®

The University of Chicago School Mathematics Project

Teacher's Lesson Guide
Volume 1

Grade

Chicago, IL • Columbus, OH • New York, NY

The University of Chicago School Mathematics Project (UCSMP)

Max Bell, Director, UCSMP Elementary Materials Component; Director, *Everyday Mathematics* First Edition; James McBride, Director, *Everyday Mathematics* Second Edition; Andy Isaacs, Director, *Everyday Mathematics* Third Edition; Amy Dillard, Associate Director, *Everyday Mathematics* Third Edition; Rachel Malpass McCall, Associate Director, *Everyday Mathematics* Common Core State Standards Edition

Authors

Max Bell, John Bretzlauf, Amy Dillard, Robert Hartfield, Andy Isaacs, Rebecca W. Maxcy†, James McBride, Kathleen Pitvorec, Peter Saecker, Robert Balfanz*, William Carroll*, Sheila Sconiers*
**First Edition only* †*Common Core State Standards Edition only*

Technical Art

Diana Barrie

ELL Consultant

Kathryn B. Chval

Third Edition Teachers in Residence

Rebecca W. Maxcy
Carla L. LaRochelle

Mathematics and Technology Advisor

James Flanders

UCSMP Editorial

Laurie K. Thrasher
Kathryn M. Rich

Contributors

Carla LaRochelle, Regina Littleton (Office Manager), Kriszta Miner (Project Manager), David B. Spangler; Deborah Karen Cohen, Maureen Dando, Joseph Dunlap, Serena Hohmann, Joanna Jolly, Carrie Kamm, Colleen Kelly, Sarah Elizabeth Martinek, Claire Doremus Ruch, Laurel Serleth, Nancy Smith, Cynthia G. Somerville, Ingrid Stressenger; Martha Ayala, Virginia J. Bates, Randee Blair, Donna R. Clay, Vanessa Day, Jean Faszholz, Patti Haney, Margaret Phillips Holm, Nancy Kay Hubert, Sybil Johnson, Judith Kiehm, Deborah Arron Leslie, Laura Ann Luczak, Mary O'Boyle, William D. Pattison, Beverly Pilchman, Denise Porter, Judith Ann Robb, Mary Seymour, Laura A. Sunseri-Driscoll

Photo Credits

Cover (l)Tony Hamblin/Frank Lane Picture Agency/CORBIS, (r)Gregory Adams/Lonely Planet Images/Getty Images, (bkgd)John W Banagan/Iconica/Getty Images; **Back Cover** Gregory Adams/Lonely Planet Images/Getty Images; **ii xx** The McGraw-Hill Companies; **xxv** (t c)The McGraw-Hill Companies, (b)George Diebold Photography/Iconica/Getty Images; **xxvi** (t)The McGraw-Hill Companies, (b)Photodisc/Getty Images; **xxvii** (t)The McGraw-Hill Companies, (b)Stockbyte/Getty Images; **xxviii** (t)The McGraw-Hill Companies, (b)Zedcor Wholly Owned/Getty Images/Jupiterimages; **xxix xxx** The McGraw-Hill Companies; **xxxi** Microzoa/The Image Bank/Getty Images; **xxxii xxxiii xxxiv** The McGraw-Hill Companies; **xxxv** Photodisc/Getty Images; **xxxvi** C Squared Studios/Getty Images; **xxxvii** (t)Matthew Ward/Dorling Kindersley/Getty Images, (b)Steven Puetzer/Photonica/Getty Images; **xxxviii** (l)The McGraw-Hill Companies, (r)C Squared Studios/Photodisc/Getty Images; **xxxix** (l)The McGraw-Hill Companies, (r)Stockbyte/Getty Images; **2** (l)Photodisc/Digital Vision/Getty Images, (r)Dorling Kindersley/Getty Images; **3** Eric Meola/Stone/Getty Images; **14** Digital Vision/Getty Images; **15** (t)Lance Nelson/Stock Photos/CORBIS, (b)The McGraw-Hill Companies; **17** Jake Rajs/Stone/Getty Images; **66** (l)Comstock Images/Alamy, (r)David Cook/www.blueshiftstudios.co.uk/Alamy; **67** The McGraw-Hill Companies; **77** Arthur Tilley/Taxi/Getty Images; **78** (t)The McGraw-Hill Companies, (b)Stockbyte/Getty Images; **79 80** The McGraw-Hill Companies; **81** Stockbyte/Getty Images; **142** (l)Dorling Kindersley/Getty Images, (r)mapresources.com; **154** (t c)Tino Soriano/National Geographic/Getty Images, (b)Richard Nowitz/Digital Vision/Getty Images; **224** Photolink/Getty Images; **225** (t)C Squared Studios/Photodisc/Getty Images, (b)Ryan McVay/Photodisc/Getty Images; **236** Stockbyte/Getty Images; **237** Paul Almasy/CORBIS; **298** (l)Burke Triolo Productions/Artville/Getty Images, (r)Asimetrica Juniper/Flickr/Getty Images; **299** The McGraw-Hill Companies; **309** (t)Barry Wong/The Image Bank/Getty Images, (b)Owaki - Kulla/CORBIS; **311** (t)John Rowley/Stone/Getty Images, (b)C Squared Studios/Photodisc/Getty Images; **312** image100/Jupiterimages; **313** (l)Thinkstock/Superstock, (c)Ros Roberts/Riser/Getty Images, (r)Jack Zehrt/Taxi/Getty Images; **382** (l)Brand X Pictures/Jupiterimages, (r)Photodisc/Getty Images; **383** Image Source/PunchStock; **393** The McGraw-Hill Companies; **394** Cover from A REMAINDER OF ONE by Elinor J Pinczes, illustrated by Bonnie MacKain. Jacket art (c) 1995 by Bonnie MacKain. Reprinted by permission of Houghton Mifflin Company. All rights reserved.; **395** PhotoLink/Photodisc/Getty Images; **396** The McGraw-Hill Companies; **397** Ed Freeman/The Image Bank/Getty Images; **398** Adrian Neal/Stone/Getty Images; **399** (t)John W. Gertz/CORBIS, (b)Stockbyte/Getty Images; **Icons** (NCTM l-r)Sharon Hoogstraten/Courtesy of Dave Wyman, Jules Frazier/Photodisc/Getty Images, Comstock/PunchStock, Sundell Larsen/Getty Images, PhotoAlto/PunchStock, Four Elements/V262/CORBIS, Juan Silva/Stockbyte/Getty Images, Digital Vision/Getty Images; (iTLG)C Squared Studios/Getty Images; (Online Content Support)Image Source; (Objective)Brand X Pictures/PunchStock/Getty Images.

This material is based upon work supported by the National Science Foundation under Grant No. ESI-9252984. Any opinions, findings, conclusions, or recommendations expressed in this material are those of the authors and do not necessarily reflect the views of the National Science Foundation.

everyday**math**.com

Send all inquiries to:
McGraw-Hill Education
STEM Learning Solutions Center
P.O. Box 812960
Chicago, IL 60681

ISBN: 978-0-07-657681-4
MHID: 0-07-657681-7

Printed in the United States of America.

2 3 4 5 6 7 8 9 RMN 17 16 15 14 13 12 11

McGraw-Hill is committed to providing instructional materials in Science, Technology, Engineering, and Mathematics (STEM) that give all students a solid foundation, one that prepares them for college and careers in the 21st century.

The University of Chicago School Mathematics Project (UCSMP)

Acknowledgements

The first edition of *Everyday Mathematics* was made possible by sustained support over several years from the GTE Corporation and the National Science Foundation; additional help came from the Amoco Foundation through its support of the University of Chicago School Mathematics Project (UCSMP). Earlier projects supported by the National Science Foundation, the National Institute of Education, and the Benton Foundation provided us with insights into the surprising capabilities of young children.

Development of the second edition of *Everyday Mathematics* was funded by the Everyday Learning Corporation and the authors; development of the third edition was supported by McGraw-Hill, the University of Chicago, and the authors. For all of these editions, many University of Chicago and UCSMP colleagues have been helpful. For this Common Core State Standards edition, Deborah Arron Leslie, Rachel Malpass McCall, Cheryl G. Moran, Mary Ellen Dairyko, Rebecca W. Maxcy, Denise Porter, and Sarah R. Burns formed a committee that provided invaluable guidance on many key issues. Rachel Malpass McCall's work as Associate Director of the Common Core State Standards Edition was especially important to the success of the project. We also acknowledge dedicated and resourceful assistance on production and technical tasks by many people at the University of Chicago and at the McGraw-Hill School Education Group.

Over the years that UCSMP has been working in schools, feedback and advice from teachers willing to take risks in trying development versions of our materials have been essential and enormously helpful. There are too many such teachers to list, but their contributions are gratefully acknowledged.

Andy Isaacs
Director, Third Edition and Common Core State Standards Edition

James McBride
Director, Second Edition

Max Bell
Director, First Edition

Contents

A Mission to Improve Mathematics

The University of Chicago School Mathematics Project

Everyday Mathematics was developed by the University of Chicago School Mathematics Project (UCSMP) in order to enable students in elementary grades to learn more mathematical content and become life-long mathematical thinkers.

- The National Science Foundation and Amoco, GTE, and other leading corporations supported the project through substantial, long-term funding.
- A strong partnership among researchers, mathematics educators, classroom teachers, students, and administrators was developed.
- A consistent, core author team at the University of Chicago School Mathematics Project collaborated on all grade levels to provide a cohesive and well-articulated Pre-K through Grade 6 curriculum.
- The *Everyday Mathematics* curriculum is completely aligned to the NCTM Curriculum Focal Points and the Connections to the Curriculum Focal Points for Grades Pre-K through 6.

"We, our funders, and our users believe strongly that even the best curricula of decades ago are not adequate for today's youth."

University of Chicago School Mathematics Project

Research Foundation

Everyday Mathematics began with the premise that students can, and must, learn more mathematics than has been expected from them in the past. This premise is based on research the UCSMP author team and others undertook prior to writing the curriculum. Following are some major findings of this research:

- The typical U.S. mathematics curriculum is arithmetic-driven, slow-paced, isolated in its instruction, and broad—rather than deep—in its content.
- International studies show that U.S. students learn much less mathematics than students in other countries.
- Children are capable of learning more mathematics in a richer curriculum.
- All children can be successful mathematical thinkers.
- Mathematics is meaningful to children when it is varied, rich, and rooted in real-world problems and applications.

Instructional Design

The *Everyday Mathematics* instructional design was carefully crafted to capitalize on student interest and maximize student learning. Among its features are the following:

- High expectations for all students
- Concepts and skills developed over time and in a wide variety of contexts
- Balance among mathematical strands
- Dynamic applications
- Multiple methods and strategies for problem solving
- Concrete modeling as a pathway to abstract understanding
- Collaborative learning in partner and small-group activities
- Cross-curricular applications and connections
- Built-in professional development for teachers

"Our teachers in Grades 6–8 tell me that students using the *Everyday Mathematics* program in earlier grades are arriving in their classrooms with a deeper understanding of mathematical concepts and are ready to start the year at a much higher level."

Principal Kenneth Tucker,
Pre-K to 8

Meeting Standards, Achieving Results

The *Everyday Mathematics* program is celebrating more than 25 years of research and development. The program offers schools results unmatched by any other elementary mathematics program.

Research, Validation, Results

As part of the research for *Everyday Mathematics,* the authors at the University of Chicago School Mathematics Project examined successful curricula from around the world, researched how children learn mathematics, and studied the actual use of mathematics by people in their everyday lives. The results of this research were used to establish the scope and sequence for the mathematical content of the *Everyday Mathematics* program.

Field Testing

The program was written and field tested one grade-level at a time, beginning with Kindergarten. Field tests gathered information from classroom teachers and students in three main areas: teacher preparation of materials, student response to materials, and student achievement. Based on teacher and student feedback, the authors revised the curriculum before *Everyday Mathematics* was published.

Learner Verification

The best way to show the effectiveness of a program is to study it over time. Several independent research studies have been conducted which provide evidence for the effectiveness of *Everyday Mathematics*. For example, *Everyday Mathematics* was the focus of a five-year longitudinal study conducted by researchers at Northwestern University. Reports from this study and others are available through the University of Chicago School Mathematics Project or McGraw-Hill.

Everyday Mathematics Timeline of Research and Development

	Pre-1989	1989	1990	1991	1992	1993	1994	1995	1996	1997
Pre-K										
Kindergarten	PUBLISH								FEEDBACK ◆ WRITE ◆ FIELD-TEST	
Grade 1	WRITE ◆ FIELD-TEST REWRITE ◆ PUBLISH									◆
Grade 2		WRITE ◆ FIELD-TEST ◆ REWRITE ◆ PUBLISH								◆
Grade 3			WRITE ◆ FIELD-TEST ◆ REWRITE ◆ PUBLISH							◆
Grade 4					WRITE ◆ FIELD-TEST ◆ REWRITE ◆ PUBLISH					
Grade 5						WRITE ◆ FIELD-TEST ◆ REWRITE ◆ PUBLISH				
Grade 6							WRITE ◆ FIELD-TEST ◆ REWRITE ◆ PUBLISH			

Tri-State Student Achievement Study

The ARC Center, a National Science Foundation (NSF) funded project, located at the Consortium for Mathematics and its Applications (COMAP), has carried out a study of the effects of standards-based mathematics programs on student performance on state-mandated standardized tests in Massachusetts, Illinois, and Washington.

The findings of the study are based on the records of over 78,000 students: 39,701 who had used the *Everyday Mathematics* curriculum for at least two years, and 38,481 students from comparison schools. The students were carefully matched by reading level, socioeconomic status, and other variables.

Results showed that the average scores of students in the *Everyday Mathematics* schools were consistently higher than the average scores of students in the comparison schools. (A complete report is available from COMAP or McGraw-Hill.)

A report based on 78,000 students showed that average standardized test scores were significantly higher for students in *Everyday Mathematics* schools than for students in comparison schools.

What Works Clearinghouse

Everyday Mathematics is the only elementary math program found by the What Works Clearinghouse to have potentially positive effects on students' math achievement, among those with a medium to large extent of evidence. The studies of *Everyday Mathematics* cited in the What Works Clearinghouse findings included a total of approximately 12,600 students in Grades 3–5. The students were from a range of socioeconomic backgrounds and attended schools in urban, suburban, and rural communities in multiple states.

Closing the Gap

Many districts, by using the *Everyday Mathematics* program, have helped minority students increase achievement, reducing the minority/majority achievement gap while maintaining growth for all students. This helps schools and districts meet adequate yearly progress requirements set forth by No Child Left Behind legislation. District information is available by contacting McGraw-Hill.

1998	1999	2000	2001	2002	2003	2004	2005	2006	2007	2008	2009	2010
			FEEDBACK ◆ WRITE ◆ FIELD-TEST ◆ PUBLISH				FEEDBACK ◆ WRITE FIELD-TEST ◆ PUBLISH					
PUBLISH — 2ND EDITION					▲	FEEDBACK ◆ WRITE ◆ FIELD-TEST ◆ PUBLISH — 3RD EDITION						●
FEEDBACK ◆ WRITE ◆ FIELD-TEST ◆ PUBLISH — 2ND EDITION					▲	FEEDBACK ◆ WRITE ◆ FIELD-TEST ◆ PUBLISH — 3RD EDITION						●
FEEDBACK ◆ WRITE ◆ FIELD-TEST ◆ PUBLISH — 2ND EDITION					▲	FEEDBACK ◆ WRITE ◆ FIELD-TEST ◆ PUBLISH — 3RD EDITION						●
FEEDBACK ◆ WRITE ◆ FIELD-TEST ◆ PUBLISH — 2ND EDITION					▲	FEEDBACK ◆ WRITE ◆ FIELD-TEST ◆ PUBLISH — 3RD EDITION						●
◆	FEEDBACK ◆ WRITE ◆ FIELD-TEST ◆ PUBLISH — 2ND EDITION				▲	FEEDBACK ◆ WRITE ◆ FIELD-TEST ◆ PUBLISH — 3RD EDITION						●
◆	FEEDBACK ◆ WRITE ◆ FIELD-TEST ◆ PUBLISH — 2ND EDITION				▲	FEEDBACK ◆ WRITE ◆ FIELD-TEST ◆ PUBLISH — 3RD EDITION						●
◆	FEEDBACK ◆ WRITE ◆ FIELD-TEST ◆ PUBLISH — 2ND EDITION				▲	FEEDBACK ◆ WRITE ◆ FIELD-TEST ◆ PUBLISH — 3RD EDITION						●

◆ = 1st edition update ▲ = 2nd edition update ● = 3rd edition update

Everyday Mathematics Grade-Level Goals for Grade 4

Everyday Mathematics structures content into Grade-Level Goals and Program Goals. Grade-Level Goals are then organized by content strand and are carefully articulated across the grades. The content in each grade provides all students with a balanced mathematics curriculum that is rich in real-world problem-solving opportunities. The success of this approach to teaching mathematics is evident in students' improved scores on standardized tests.

The Program Goals and Grade-Level Goals for Grade 4 are listed in the chart below.

Number and Numeration	
Program Goal: Understand the meanings, uses, and representations of numbers.	
Place value and notation	**Goal 1** Read and write whole numbers up to 1,000,000,000 and decimals through thousandths; identify places in such numbers and the values of the digits in those places; translate between whole numbers and decimals represented in words and in base-10 notation.
Meanings and uses of fractions	**Goal 2** Read, write, and model fractions; solve problems involving fractional parts of a region or a collection; describe and explain strategies used; given a fractional part of a region or a collection, identify the unit whole.
Number theory	**Goal 3** Find multiples of whole numbers less than 10; identify prime and composite numbers; find whole-number factors of numbers.
Program Goal: Understand equivalent names for numbers.	
Equivalent names for whole numbers	**Goal 4** Use numerical expressions involving one or more of the basic four arithmetic operations and grouping symbols to give equivalent names for whole numbers.
Equivalent names for fractions, decimals, and percents	**Goal 5** Use numerical expressions to find and represent equivalent names for fractions and decimals; use and explain a multiplication rule to find equivalent fractions; rename fourths, fifths, tenths, and hundredths as decimals and percents.
Program Goal: Understand common numerical relations.	
Comparing and ordering numbers	**Goal 6** Compare and order whole numbers up to 1,000,000,000 and decimals through thousandths; compare and order integers between -100 and 0; use area models, benchmark fractions, and analyses of numerators and denominators to compare and order fractions.

Operations and Computation	
Program Goal: Compute accurately.	
Addition and subtraction facts	**Goal 1** Demonstrate automaticity with addition and subtraction fact extensions.
Addition and subtraction procedures	**Goal 2** Use manipulatives, mental arithmetic, paper-and-pencil algorithms and models, and calculators to solve problems involving the addition and subtraction of whole numbers and decimals through hundredths; describe strategies used and explain how they work.

Operations and Computation (cont.)

Program Goal: Compute accurately. (cont.)	
Multiplication and division facts	**Goal 3** Demonstrate automaticity with multiplication facts through 10 * 10 and proficiency with related division facts; use basic facts to compute fact extensions such as 30 * 60.
Multiplication and division procedures	**Goal 4** Use manipulatives, mental arithmetic, paper-and-pencil algorithms and models, and calculators to solve problems involving the multiplication of multidigit whole numbers by 2-digit whole numbers and the division of multidigit whole numbers by 1-digit whole numbers; describe the strategies used and explain how they work.
Procedures for addition and subtraction of fractions	**Goal 5** Use manipulatives, mental arithmetic, and calculators to solve problems involving the addition and subtraction of fractions and mixed numbers; describe the strategies used.
Program Goal: Make reasonable estimates.	
Computational estimation	**Goal 6** Make reasonable estimates for whole number and decimal addition and subtraction problems and whole number multiplication and division problems; explain how the estimates were obtained.
Program Goal: Understand meanings of operations.	
Models for the operations	**Goal 7** Use repeated addition, skip counting, arrays, area, and scaling to model multiplication and division.

Data and Chance

Program Goal: Select and create appropriate graphical representations of collected or given data.	
Data collection and representation	**Goal 1** Collect and organize data or use given data to create charts, tables, graphs, and line plots.
Program Goal: Analyze and interpret data.	
Data analysis	**Goal 2** Use the maximum, minimum, range, median, mode, and graphs to ask and answer questions, draw conclusions, and make predictions.
Program Goal: Understand and apply basic concepts of probability.	
Qualitative probability	**Goal 3** Describe events using *certain, very likely, likely, unlikely, very unlikely, impossible* and other basic probability terms; use *more likely, equally likely, same chance, 50–50, less likely,* and other basic probability terms to compare events; explain the choice of language.
Quantitative probability	**Goal 4** Predict the outcomes of experiments and test the predictions using manipulatives; summarize the results and use them to predict future events; express the probability of an event as a fraction.

Measurement and Reference Frames

Program Goal: Understand the systems and processes of measurement; use appropriate techniques, tools, units, and formulas in making measurements.	
Length, weight, and angles	**Goal 1** Estimate length with and without tools; measure length to the nearest $\frac{1}{4}$ inch and $\frac{1}{2}$ centimeter; use tools to measure and draw angles; estimate the size of angles without tools.

Measurement and Reference Frames (cont.)

Program Goal: Understand the systems and processes of measurement; use appropriate techniques, tools, units, and formulas in making measurements. (cont.)	
Area, perimeter, volume, and capacity	**Goal 2** Describe and use strategies to measure the perimeter and area of polygons, to estimate the area of irregular shapes, and to find the volume of rectangular prisms.
Units and systems of measure	**Goal 3** Describe relationships among U.S. customary units of measure and among metric units of measure.
Program Goal: Use and understand reference frames.	
Coordinate systems	**Goal 4** Use ordered pairs of numbers to name, locate, and plot points in the first quadrant of a coordinate grid.

Geometry

Program Goal: Investigate characteristics and properties of two- and three-dimensional geometric shapes.	
Lines and angles	**Goal 1** Identify, draw, and describe points, intersecting and parallel line segments and lines, rays, and right, acute, and obtuse angles.
Plane and solid figures	**Goal 2** Describe, compare, and classify plane and solid figures, including polygons, circles, spheres, cylinders, rectangular prisms, cones, cubes, and pyramids, using appropriate geometric terms including *vertex*, *base*, *face*, *edge*, and *congruent*.
Program Goal: Apply transformations and symmetry in geometric situations.	
Transformations and symmetry	**Goal 3** Identify, describe, and sketch examples of reflections; identify and describe examples of translations and rotations.

Patterns, Functions, and Algebra

Program Goal: Understand patterns and functions.	
Patterns and functions	**Goal 1** Extend, describe, and create numeric patterns; describe rules for patterns and use them to solve problems; use words and symbols to describe and write rules for functions that involve the four basic arithmetic operations and use those rules to solve problems.
Program Goal: Use algebraic notation to represent and analyze situations and structures.	
Algebraic notation and solving number sentences	**Goal 2** Use conventional notation to write expressions and number sentences using the four basic arithmetic operations; determine whether number sentences are true or false; solve open sentences and explain the solutions; write expressions and number sentences to model number stories.
Order of operations	**Goal 3** Evaluate numeric expressions containing grouping symbols; insert grouping symbols to make number sentences true.
Properties of the arithmetic operations	**Goal 4** Describe and apply the Distributive Property of Multiplication over Addition.

Common Core State Standards

Everyday Mathematics fully aligns with the national Common Core State Standards for Mathematics. Both are founded on cross-disciplinary skills such as critical thinking and problem solving. The Standards for Mathematical Practice, described in the Common Core State Standards, form a cohesive match with the already-proven instructional design of *Everyday Mathematics*. Both require students to:

- Make sense of problems and persevere in solving them.
- Reason abstractly and quantitatively.
- Construct viable arguments and critique the reasoning of others.
- Model with mathematics.
- Use appropriate tools strategically.
- Attend to precision.
- Look for and make use of structure.
- Look for and express regularity in repeated reasoning.

Everyday Mathematics fully meets all of the Common Core State Standards for Mathematics, Grades K–6.

In *Everyday Mathematics*, the Grade-Level Goals, which state the core content that is assessed at each grade level, align with the Standards for Mathematical Content. *Everyday Mathematics* has a long track record of success resulting from constant revision based on evidence of what works. *Everyday Mathematics* is a world-class mathematics curriculum that fully meets the Common Core State Standards for Grades K–6.

Instruction and Planning

The *Teacher's Lesson Guide* includes a comprehensive grade-level correlation that shows the *Everyday Mathematics* lessons that cover each of the Standards for Mathematical Content. Correlation documents for the complete *Everyday Mathematics* program are available at everydaymathonline.com.

Everyday Mathematics offers a variety of print and technology materials to meet instructional needs and to help incorporate these standards in the classroom curriculum.

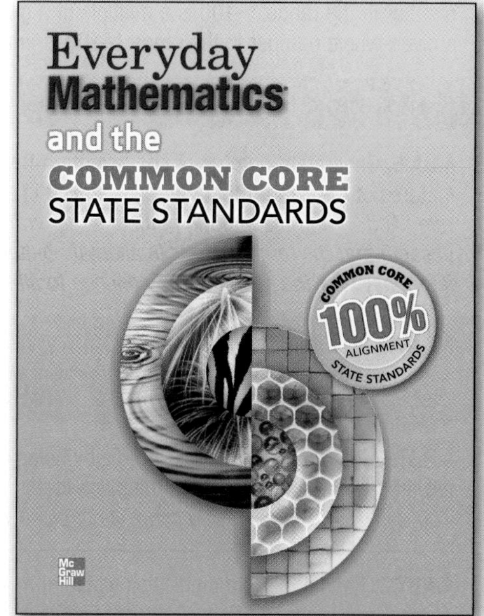

Assessment

Everyday Mathematics provides many opportunities and tools for assessment. Assessment results show students' progress toward the *Everyday Mathematics* Grade-Level Goals and the Common Core State Standards.

Professional Development

Professional Development is offered at implementation, for continued support, and is built into the program materials to help teachers successfully implement the Common Core State Standards with the *Everyday Mathematics* program.

Common Core State Standards and *Everyday Mathematics*

The *Everyday Mathematics* curriculum is completely aligned to the *K-12 Common Core State Standards* for Kindergarten through Grade 6.

Common Core State Standards for Grade 4	*Everyday Mathematics* Grade 4 Lessons*
OPERATIONS AND ALGEBRAIC THINKING 4.OA	
Use the four operations with whole numbers to solve problems.	
4.OA.1. Interpret a multiplication equation as a comparison, e.g., interpret $35 = 5 \times 7$ as a statement that 35 is 5 times as many as 7 and 7 times as many as 5. Represent verbal statements of multiplicative comparisons as multiplication equations.	2•9, **3•2,** 3•3, 3•4, **3•5,** 3•11, **5•1**
4.OA.2. Multiply or divide to solve word problems involving multiplicative comparison, e.g., by using drawings and equations with a symbol for the unknown number to represent the problem, distinguishing multiplicative comparison from additive comparison.	4•5, **4•10, 5•1, 5•8, 6•1, 8•8**
4.OA.3. Solve multistep word problems posed with whole numbers and having whole-number answers using the four operations, including problems in which remainders must be interpreted. Represent these problems using equations with a letter standing for the unknown quantity. Assess the reasonableness of answers using mental computation and estimation strategies including rounding.	2•7, 2•9, **3•8, 5•3, 5•5, 5•6, 5•8,** 5•11, **6•1, 6•2, 6•3, 6•4,** 6•8, **6•10, 8•8,** 9•6, **9•9, 11•7, 12•2, 12•3**
Gain familiarity with factors and multiples.	
4.OA.4. Find all factor pairs for a whole number in the range 1–100. Recognize that a whole number is a multiple of each of its factors. Determine whether a given whole number in the range 1–100 is a multiple of a given one-digit number. Determine whether a given whole number in the range 1–100 is prime or composite.	**3•2, 3•3,** 3•11, **6•2,** 6•4, 7•7, 7•12a, 12•3
Generate and analyze patterns.	
4.OA.5. Generate a number or shape pattern that follows a given rule. Identify apparent features of the pattern that were not explicit in the rule itself. *For example, given the rule "Add 3" and the starting number 1, generate terms in the resulting sequence and observe that the terms appear to alternate between odd and even numbers. Explain informally why the numbers will continue to alternate in this way.*	2•1, 2•3, **3•1,** 3•2, **3•3, 10•3, 10•5, Project 4**
NUMBER AND OPERATIONS IN BASE TEN 4.NBT	
Generalize place value understanding for multi-digit whole numbers.	
4.NBT.1. Recognize that in a multi-digit whole number, a digit in one place represents ten times what it represents in the place to its right. *For example, recognize that $700 \div 70 = 10$ by applying concepts of place value and division.*	**2•3, 2•4, 4•1, 4•7,** 4•8, **5•1, 5•8, 5•9**
4.NBT.2. Read and write multi-digit whole numbers using base-ten numerals, number names, and expanded form. Compare two multi-digit numbers based on meanings of the digits in each place, using $>$, $=$, and $<$ symbols to record the results of comparisons.	1•1, **2•3, 2•4, 2•7,** 3•6, 3•7, 3•8, **3•9, 5•2, 5•8, 5•9,** 5•11, 6•2, 7•12, 8•7
4.NBT.3. Use place value understanding to round multi-digit whole numbers to any place.	**3•6, 5•3, 5•4, 5•6, 5•10,** 6•1, **8•8,** 11•4, **12•3**

***Bold lesson numbers indicate that content from the standard is being taught. Lesson numbers not in bold indicate that content from the standard is being reviewed or practiced.**

Common Core State Standards for Grade 4	*Everyday Mathematics* Grade 4 Lessons
Use place value understanding and properties of operations to perform multi-digit arithmetic.	
4.NBT.4. Fluently add and subtract multi-digit whole numbers using the standard algorithm.	1•3, **2•9** **Algorithm Projects 1 and 3**
4.NBT.5. Multiply a whole number of up to four digits by a one-digit whole number, and multiply two two-digit numbers, using strategies based on place value and the properties of operations. Illustrate and explain the calculation by using equations, rectangular arrays, and/or area models.	**5•1, 5•2, 5•4, 5•5, 5•6, 5•7, 9•8** **Algorithm Project 5**
4.NBT.6. Find whole-number quotients and remainders with up to four-digit dividends and one-digit divisors, using strategies based on place value, the properties of operations, and/or the relationship between multiplication and division. Illustrate and explain the calculation by using equations, rectangular arrays, and/or area models.	**3•5, 6•1, 6•2, 6•3, 6•4,** 6•6, **6•10, 9•9** **Algorithm Projects 7 and 8**
NUMBER AND OPERATIONS—FRACTIONS 4.NF	
Extend understanding of fraction equivalence and ordering.	
4.NF.1. Explain why a fraction $\frac{a}{b}$ is equivalent to a fraction $\frac{(n \times a)}{(n \times b)}$ by using visual fraction models, with attention to how the number and size of the parts differ even though the two fractions themselves are the same size. Use this principle to recognize and generate equivalent fractions.	**7•6, 7•7,** 7•8, **7•9,** 7•10, 8•1, 9•1, **9•2**
4.NF.2. Compare two fractions with different numerators and different denominators, e.g., by creating common denominators or numerators, or by comparing to a benchmark fraction such as $\frac{1}{2}$. Recognize that comparisons are valid only when the two fractions refer to the same whole. Record the results of comparisons with symbols $>$, $=$, or $<$, and justify the conclusions, e.g., by using a visual fraction model.	**7•6, 7•7, 7•9, 7•10,** 8•3, 9•7, 12•5
Build fractions from unit fractions by applying and extending previous understandings of operations on whole numbers.	
4.NF.3. Understand a fraction $\frac{a}{b}$ with $a > 1$ as a sum of fractions $\frac{1}{b}$.	
4.NF.3a. Understand addition and subtraction of fractions as joining and separating parts referring to the same whole.	**7•4, 7•5,** 7•6, **7•7,** 7•10
4.NF.3b. Decompose a fraction into a sum of fractions with the same denominator in more than one way, recording each decomposition by an equation. Justify decompositions, e.g., by using a visual fraction model. *Examples:* $\frac{3}{8} = \frac{1}{8} + \frac{1}{8} + \frac{1}{8}$; $\frac{3}{8} = \frac{1}{8} + \frac{2}{8}$; $2\frac{1}{8} = 1 + 1 + \frac{1}{8} = \frac{8}{8} + \frac{8}{8} + \frac{1}{8}$.	**7•1,** 7•3, **7•4, 7•5,** 7•12
4.NF.3c. Add and subtract mixed numbers with like denominators, e.g., by replacing each mixed number with an equivalent fraction, and/or by using properties of operations and the relationship between addition and subtraction.	**7•5, 7•6, 7•7,** 7•10, 11•3
4.NF.3d. Solve word problems involving addition and subtraction of fractions referring to the same whole and having like denominators, e.g., by using visual fraction models and equations to represent the problem.	**7•5, 7•6, 7•7,** 7•10, 11•3

Common Core State Standards for Grade 4	*Everyday Mathematics* Grade 4 Lessons
4.NF.4. Apply and extend previous understandings of multiplication to multiply a fraction by a whole number.	
4.NF.4a. Understand a fraction $\frac{a}{b}$ as a multiple of $\frac{1}{b}$. *For example, use a visual fraction model to represent $\frac{5}{4}$ as the product $5 \times (\frac{1}{4})$, recording the conclusion by the equation $\frac{5}{4} = 5 \times (\frac{1}{4})$.*	**7•12a, 8•2, 10•4,** 11•3, 11•7
4.NF.4b. Understand a multiple of $\frac{a}{b}$ as a multiple of $\frac{1}{b}$, and use this understanding to multiply a fraction by a whole number. *For example, use a visual fraction model to express $3 \times (\frac{2}{5})$ as $6 \times (\frac{1}{5})$, recognizing this product as $\frac{6}{5}$. (In general, $n \times (\frac{a}{b}) = \frac{(n \times a)}{b}$.)*	**7•12a, 8•2, 10•4,** 11•3, 11•7
4.NF.4c. Solve word problems involving multiplication of a fraction by a whole number, e.g., by using visual fraction models and equations to represent the problem. *For example, if each person at a party will eat $\frac{3}{8}$ of a pound of roast beef, and there will be 5 people at the party, how many pounds of roast beef will be needed? Between what two whole numbers does your answer lie?*	**7•2,** 7•3, **7•12a, 8•2,** 8•6, 8•7, **10•4**
Understand decimal notation for fractions.	
4.NF.5. Express a fraction with denominator 10 as an equivalent fraction with denominator 100, and use this technique to add two fractions with respective denominators 10 and 100. *For example, express $\frac{3}{10}$ as $\frac{30}{100}$, and add $\frac{3}{10} + \frac{4}{100} = \frac{34}{100}$.*	**7•8,** 7•9, **9•2,** 9•6, **10•1,** 10•4
4.NF.6. Use decimal notation for fractions with denominators 10 or 100. *For example, rewrite 0.62 as $\frac{62}{100}$; describe a length as 0.62 meters; locate 0.62 on a number line diagram.*	**4•2, 4•7, 7•8,** 7•12, 8•1, **9•1, 9•2, 9•3,** 9•5, 10•6, 12•1
4.NF.7. Compare two decimals to hundredths by reasoning about their size. Recognize that comparisons are valid only when the two decimals refer to the same whole. Record the results of comparisons with the symbols >, =, or <, and justify the conclusions, e.g., by using a visual model.	**4•3, 4•4, 4•7,** 4•9
MEASUREMENT AND DATA 4.MD	
Solve problems involving measurement and conversion of measurements from a larger unit to a smaller unit.	
4.MD.1. Know relative sizes of measurement units within one system of units including km, m, cm; kg, g; lb, oz.; l, ml; hr, min, sec. Within a single system of measurement, express measurements in a larger unit in terms of a smaller unit. Record measurement equivalents in a two column table. *For example, know that 1 ft is 12 times as long as 1 in. Express the length of a 4 ft snake as 48 in. Generate a conversion table for feet and inches listing the number pairs (1, 12), (2, 24), (3, 36), ...*	2•6, 3•3, 3•6, 4•6, **4•8, 4•9, 4•10, 5•1, 8•4,** 9•4, 10•3, 10•6, **11•1, 11•4, 11•7,** 12•2, **12•3,** 12•4, 12•6
4.MD.2. Use the four operations to solve word problems involving distances, intervals of time, liquid volumes, masses of objects, and money, including problems involving simple fractions or decimals, and problems that require expressing measurements given in a larger unit in terms of a smaller unit. Represent measurement quantities using diagrams such as number line diagrams that feature a measurement scale.	**2•1,** 2•6, 2•7, 2•9, 3•3, 3•5, **3•6, 3•7, 3•8, 3•11, 4•4,** 4•5, **4•6, 5•1, 5•2, 5•3, 5•4, 5•5, 5•6,** 5•7, 5•11, **6•1, 6•3, 6•4, 6•5,** 6•6, **7•2,** 7•4, **8•1, 8•4,** 8•5, **8•8,** 9•4, 9•6, **9•8, 9•9, 11•1, 11•7, 12•2, 12•3, 12•4, 12•5** **Project 5**
4.MD.3. Apply the area and perimeter formulas for rectangles in real world and mathematical problems. *For example, find the width of a rectangular room given the area of the flooring and the length, by viewing the area formula as a multiplication equation with an unknown factor.*	**8•3, 8•5, 8•6, 8•7, 9•2, 11•5**

Common Core State Standards for Grade 4	*Everyday Mathematics* Grade 4 Lessons
Represent and interpret data.	
4.MD.4. Make a line plot to display a data set of measurements in fractions of a unit ($\frac{1}{2}$, $\frac{1}{4}$, $\frac{1}{8}$). Solve problems involving addition and subtraction of fractions by using information presented in line plots. *For example, from a line plot find and interpret the difference in length between the longest and shortest specimens in an insect collection.*	**2•8, 7•10, 11•3**
Geometric measurement: understand concepts of angle and measure angles.	
4.MD.5. Recognize angles as geometric shapes that are formed wherever two rays share a common endpoint, and understand concepts of angle measurement:	
4.MD.5a. An angle is measured with reference to a circle with its center at the common endpoint of the rays, by considering the fraction of the circular arc between the points where the two rays intersect the circle. An angle that turns through $\frac{1}{360}$ of a circle is called a "one-degree angle," and can be used to measure angles.	**6•5, 6•6, 6•7, 6•8** Project 1, **Project 2**
4.MD.5b. An angle that turns through *n* one-degree angles is said to have an angle measure of *n* degrees.	**6•5, 6•6, 6•7, 6•8**
4.MD.6. Measure angles in whole-number degrees using a protractor. Sketch angles of specified measure.	**6•6, 6•7, 6•8,** 7•5, 10•2
4.MD.7. Recognize angle measure as additive. When an angle is decomposed into non-overlapping parts, the angle measure of the whole is the sum of the angle measures of the parts. Solve addition and subtraction problems to find unknown angles on a diagram in real world and mathematical problems, e.g., by using an equation with a symbol for the unknown angle measure.	**6•6, 6•7,** 6•8, **7•9,** 8•6, 9•1, 9•5
GEOMETRY 4.G	
Draw and identify lines and angles, and classify shapes by properties of their lines and angles.	
4.G.1. Draw points, lines, line segments, rays, angles (right, acute, obtuse), and perpendicular and parallel lines. Identify these in two-dimensional figures.	**1•2, 1•3, 1•4, 1•6,** 1•7, **1•8,** 2•1, 2•3, 3•7, 4•1, 5•9, **8•6, 8•7,** 9•9, 10•5
4.G.2. Classify two-dimensional figures based on the presence or absence of parallel or perpendicular lines, or the presence or absence of angles of a specified size. Recognize right triangles as a category, and identify right triangles.	**1•3, 1•4,** 1•5, **1•6,** 1•7, 1•8, 2•1, 2•3, 2•7, 3•7, 4•1, 5•9, **8•7,** 9•9, 10•5
4.G.3. Recognize a line of symmetry for a two-dimensional figure as a line across the figure such that the figure can be folded along the line into matching parts. Identify line-symmetric figures and draw lines of symmetry.	10•1, **10•2,** 10•3, **10•4, 10•5** **Project 4**

Everyday Mathematics

Components at a Glance

Student Materials

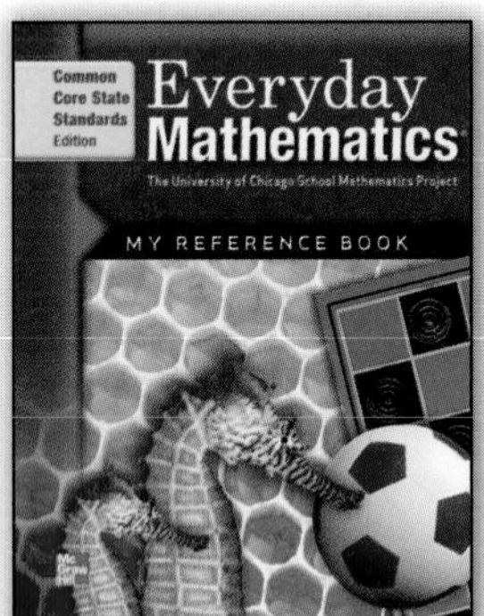

My Reference Book (Grades 1 and 2)
This hardcover book is a child's first mathematical reference book. *My Reference Book* contains explanations of key concepts as well as directions for games.

Student Reference Book (Grades 3–6)
Contains explanations of key mathematical content, along with directions for the *Everyday Mathematics* games. This hardbound book supports student learning in the classroom and at home.

Student Math Journal, Volumes 1 & 2 (Grades 1–6)
These consumable books provide daily support for classroom instruction. They provide a long-term record of each student's mathematical development.

Teacher Materials

Teacher's Lesson Guide, Volumes 1 & 2 (Grades 1–6)
The core of the *Everyday Mathematics* program, the *Teacher's Lesson Guide* provides teachers with easy-to-follow lessons organized by instructional unit, as well as built-in mathematical content support. Lessons include planning and assessment tips and multilevel differentiation strategies to support all learners.

Math Masters (Grades 1–6)
Blackline masters that support daily lesson activities. Includes Home/Study Links, lesson-specific masters, game masters, and project masters.

Minute Math®+ (Grades 1–3)
5-Minute Math (Grades 4–6)
Brief activities for transition time and for spare moments throughout the day.

▶ Teacher Resources

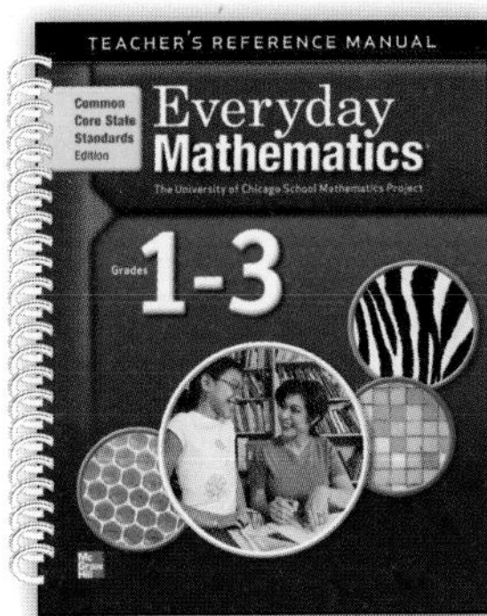

Teacher's Reference Manual Contains comprehensive background information about mathematical content and program management for grades Early Childhood, 1–3, and 4–6.

Home Connection Handbook Enhances home-school communication for teachers and administrators. Includes masters for easy planning for grades Early Childhood, 1–3, and 4–6.

Differentiation Handbook (Grades 1–6)
Grade-specific handbooks that help teachers plan strategically in order to reach the needs of diverse learners.

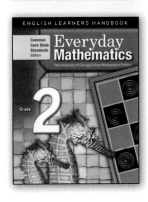

Assessment Handbook (Grades 1–6)
Grade-specific handbooks provide explanations of key features of assessment in the *Everyday Mathematics* program. Includes all assessment masters.

Multilingual Handbook (Grades 1–6) Grade-specific component provides lesson-specific support to help meet the needs of a multilingual classroom. Includes a brief summary and an example for each lesson. Content provided in English, Spanish, traditional Chinese, Vietnamese, Arabic, and Hmong.

English Learners Handbook (Grades 1–6)
Grade-specific component provides lesson-specific comprehension strategies to aid in meeting the needs of a multilingual classroom. Also included are language development notes.

Content by Strand Poster
To help with pacing, the Key Concepts and Skills for each content strand are presented by month. Provides overview of program content for each grade level. Reverse side is a poster of the Grade-Level Goals.

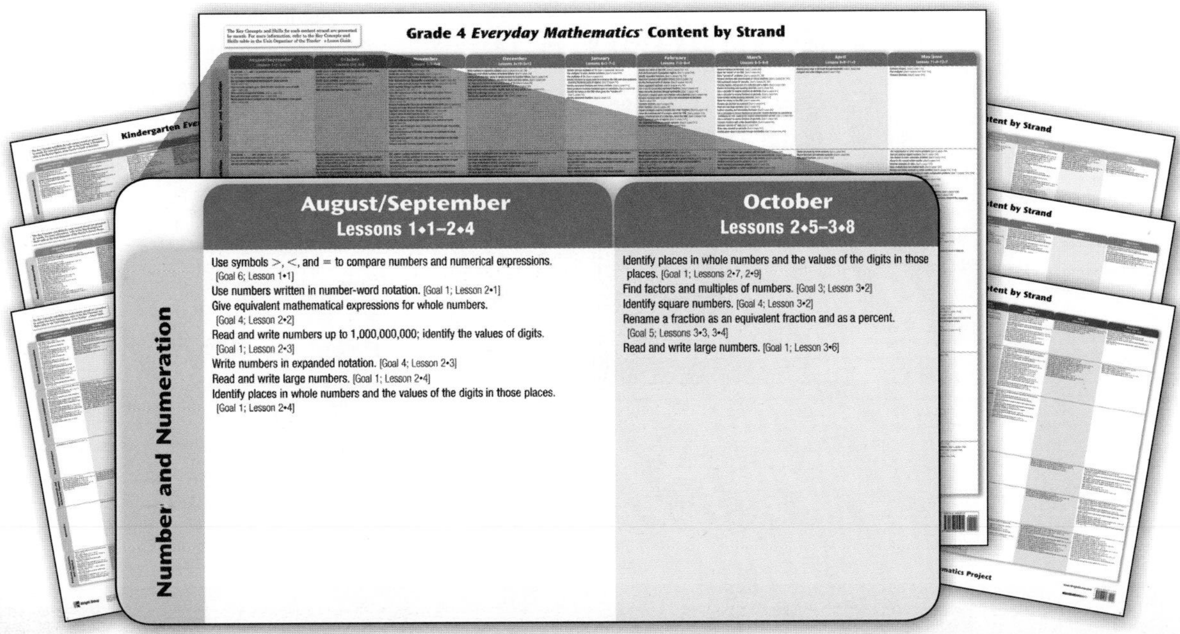

Technology at a Glance

Integrated technology enhances instruction and engages learners. *Everyday Mathematics* offers integrated technology for planning and teaching, practice, assessment, and home connections. Learn more and access all technology resources online at **www.everydaymathonline.com**.

Planning and Teaching

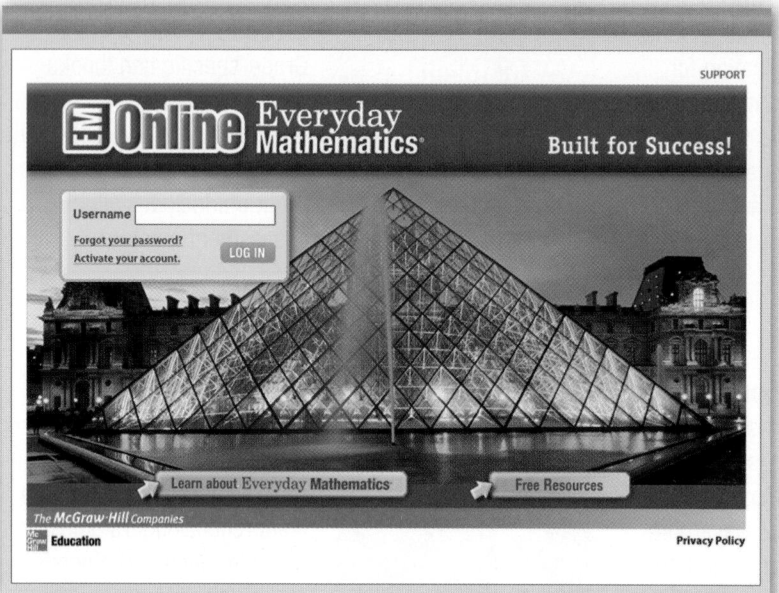

everydaymathonline.com

Offers an eSuite of fully integrated online tools that provide rich, interactive classroom experiences and solutions for students and teachers.

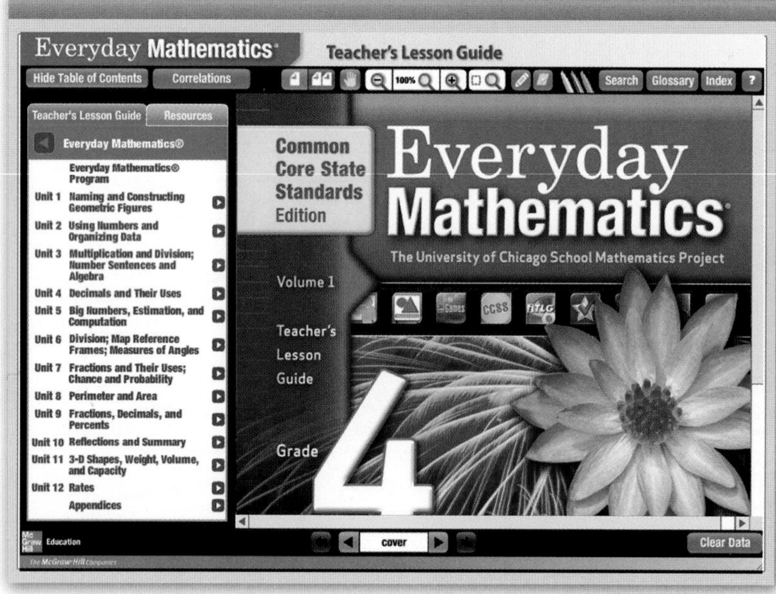

Interactive Teacher's Lesson Guide (iTLG)*

Enables digital access to the entire *Everyday Mathematics* program. Includes access to all components found in the Classroom Resource Package. Content is searchable by word or phase so all pages related to a specific topic can be found quickly and easily. Available online or on CD-ROM.

*Available as separate purchase

Planning and Teaching continued

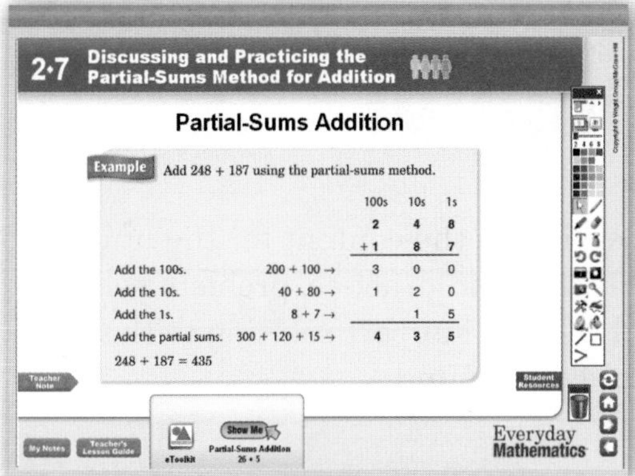

ePresentations*

Provide engaging lessons on your favorite interactive whiteboard for every lesson, except for the Progress Checks. Available online through the ePlanner Deluxe.

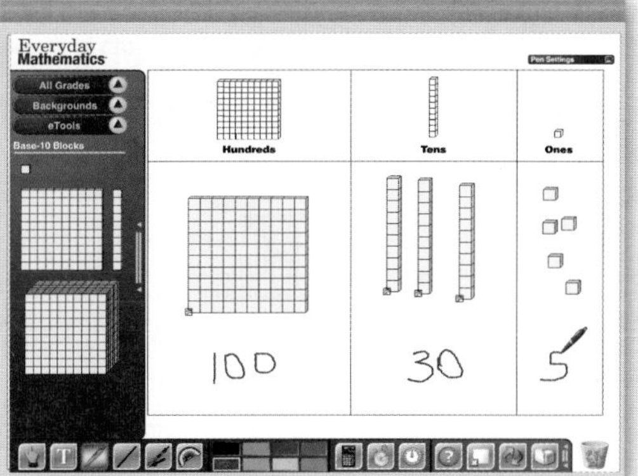

eToolkit*

Includes all the online tools and virtual manipulatives necessary to teach an *Everyday Mathematics* lesson. Available online through the ePlanner Deluxe.

Home Connections

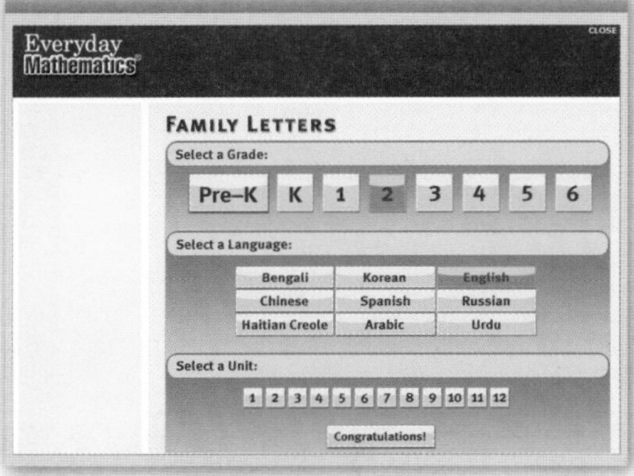

Family Letters** Support students at home by sharing each unit's key content and vocabulary, directions to games, Do-Anytime Activities, and answers to most Home Links/Study Links. Available online in nine different languages.

Practice

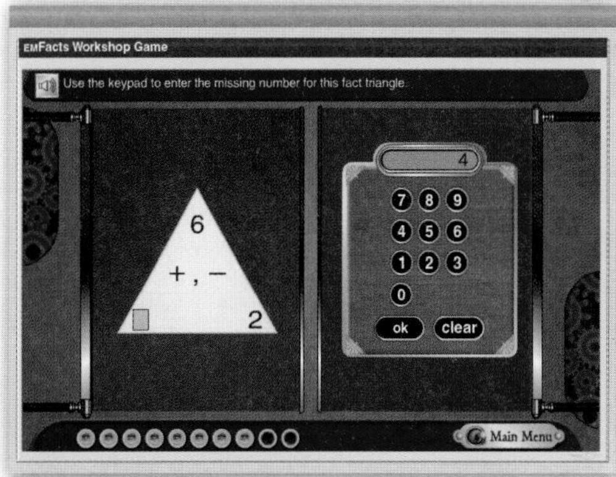

EM Facts Workshop Game

Provides interactive practice for students on basic facts and computation. Available online only.

Assessment

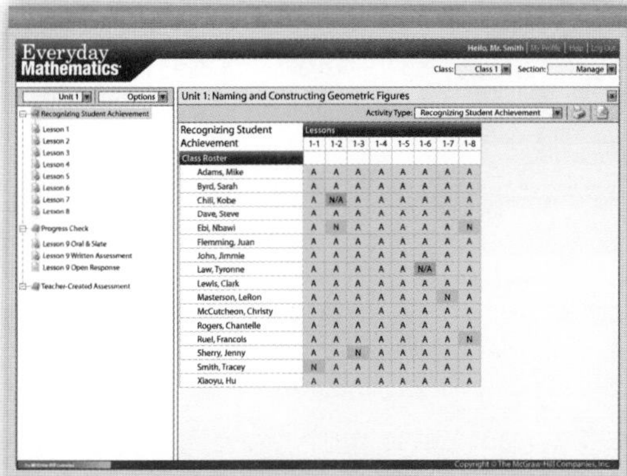

Assessment Management Spreadsheets

This electronic tool can be used to monitor and record students' progress.

After information on student performance is entered, the Assessment Management Spreadsheets provide reports showing students' progress toward Grade-Level Goals. Available online only.

*Available as separate purchase

**Languages other than English and Spanish available as separate purchase

Everyday Mathematics

Planning and Instructional Support

Each unit organizer provides an overview of the content for the unit. Also included is support for ongoing learning and practice, problem solving, and differentiated instruction. Detailed content support relating to the unit instruction is provided in Mathematical Background.

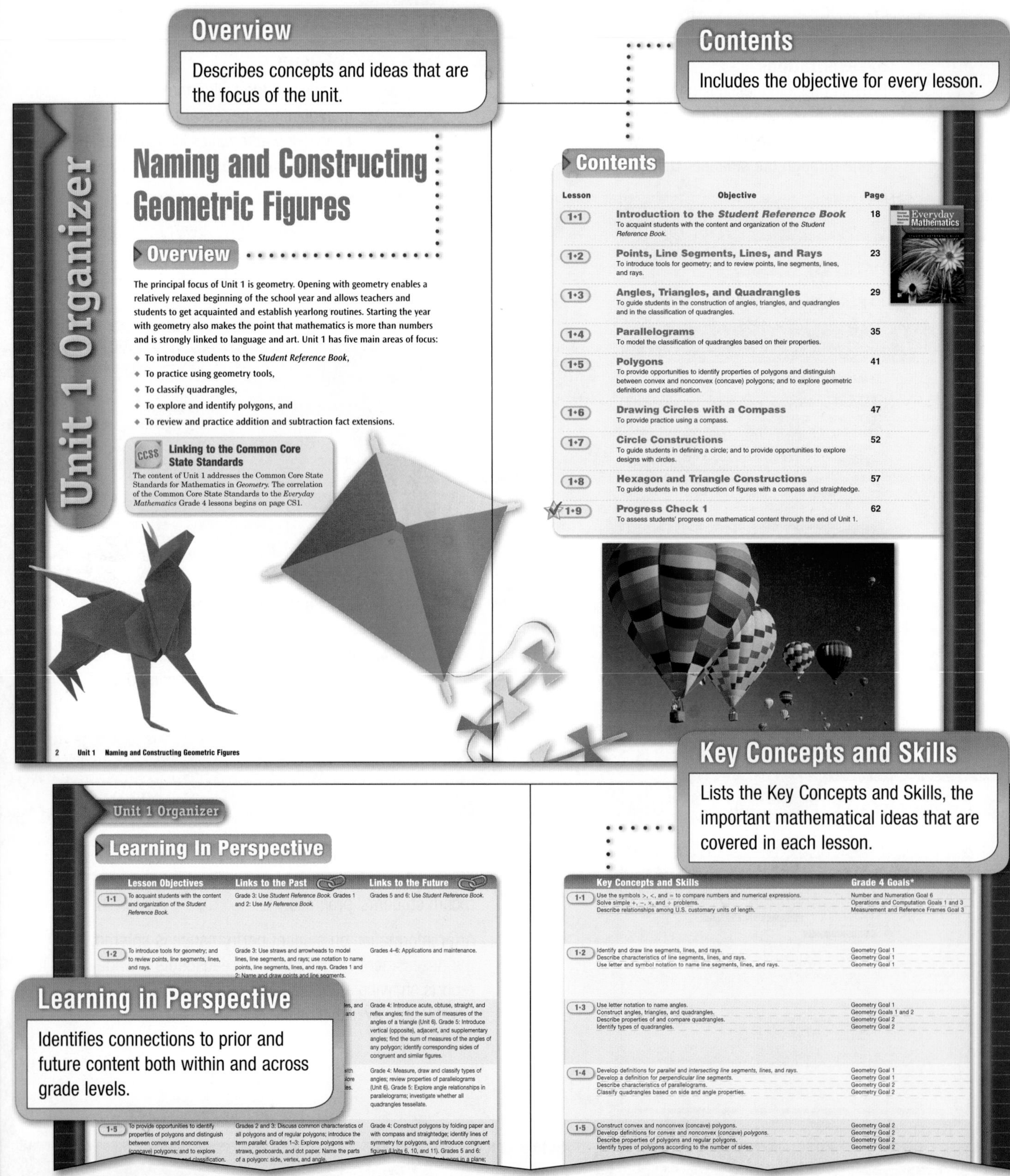

Overview
Describes concepts and ideas that are the focus of the unit.
Contents
Includes the objective for every lesson.
Unit 1 Organizer
Naming and Constructing Geometric Figures
Overview
The principal focus of Unit 1 is geometry. Opening with geometry enables a relatively relaxed beginning of the school year and allows teachers and students to get acquainted and establish yearlong routines. Starting the year with geometry also makes the point that mathematics is more than numbers and is strongly linked to language and art. Unit 1 has five main areas of focus:
To introduce students to the Student Reference Book,
To practice using geometry tools,
To classify quadrangles,
To explore and identify polygons, and
To review and practice addition and subtraction fact extensions.
Linking to the Common Core State Standards
The content of Unit 1 addresses the Common Core State Standards for Mathematics in Geometry. The correlation of the Common Core State Standards to the Everyday Mathematics Grade 4 lessons begins on page CS1.
2 Unit 1 Naming and Constructing Geometric Figures
Contents
Lesson | Objective | Page
1•1 Introduction to the Student Reference Book — To acquaint students with the content and organization of the Student Reference Book. 18
1•2 Points, Line Segments, Lines, and Rays — To introduce tools for geometry; and to review points, line segments, lines, and rays. 23
1•3 Angles, Triangles, and Quadrangles — To guide students in the construction of angles, triangles, and quadrangles and in the classification of quadrangles. 29
1•4 Parallelograms — To model the classification of quadrangles based on their properties. 35
1•5 Polygons — To provide opportunities to identify properties of polygons and distinguish between convex and nonconvex (concave) polygons; and to explore geometric definitions and classification. 41
1•6 Drawing Circles with a Compass — To provide practice using a compass. 47
1•7 Circle Constructions — To guide students in defining a circle; and to provide opportunities to explore designs with circles. 52
1•8 Hexagon and Triangle Constructions — To guide students in the construction of figures with a compass and straightedge. 57
1•9 Progress Check 1 — To assess students' progress on mathematical content through the end of Unit 1. 62
Everyday Mathematics
Key Concepts and Skills
Lists the Key Concepts and Skills, the important mathematical ideas that are covered in each lesson.
Unit 1 Organizer
Learning In Perspective
Lesson Objectives | Links to the Past | Links to the Future
1•1 To acquaint students with the content and organization of the Student Reference Book. | Grade 3: Use Student Reference Book. Grades 1 and 2: Use My Reference Book. | Grades 5 and 6: Use Student Reference Book.
1•2 To introduce tools for geometry; and to review points, line segments, lines, and rays. | Grade 3: Use straws and arrowheads to model lines, line segments, and rays; use notation to name points, line segments, lines, and rays. Grades 1 and 2: Name and draw points and line segments. | Grades 4–6: Applications and maintenance.
Grade 4: Introduce acute, obtuse, straight, and reflex angles; find the sum of measures of the angles of a triangle (Unit 6). Grade 5: Introduce vertical (opposite), adjacent, and supplementary angles; find the sum of measures of the angles of any polygon; identify corresponding sides of congruent and similar figures.
Grade 4: Measure, draw and classify types of angles; review properties of parallelograms (Unit 6). Grade 5: Explore angle relationships in parallelograms; investigate whether all quadrangles tessellate.
1•5 To provide opportunities to identify properties of polygons and distinguish between convex and nonconvex (concave) polygons; and to explore ... classification. | Grades 2 and 3: Discuss common characteristics of all polygons and of regular polygons; introduce the term parallel. Grades 1–3: Explore polygons with straws, geoboards, and dot paper. Name the parts of a polygon: side, vertex, and angle. | Grade 4: Construct polygons by folding paper and with compass and straightedge; identify lines of symmetry for polygons, and introduce congruent figures (Units 6, 10, and 11). Grades 5 and 6:
Learning in Perspective
Identifies connections to prior and future content both within and across grade levels.
Key Concepts and Skills | Grade 4 Goals*
1•1 Use the symbols >, <, and = to compare numbers and numerical expressions. | Number and Numeration Goal 6
Solve simple +, −, ×, and ÷ problems. | Operations and Computation Goals 1 and 3
Describe relationships among U.S. customary units of length. | Measurement and Reference Frames Goal 3
1•2 Identify and draw line segments, lines, and rays. | Geometry Goal 1
Describe characteristics of line segments, lines, and rays. | Geometry Goal 1
Use letter and symbol notation to name line segments, lines, and rays. | Geometry Goal 1
1•3 Use letter notation to name angles. | Geometry Goal 1
Construct angles, triangles, and quadrangles. | Geometry Goals 1 and 2
Describe properties of and compare quadrangles. | Geometry Goal 2
Identify types of quadrangles. | Geometry Goal 2
1•4 Develop definitions for parallel and intersecting line segments, lines, and rays. | Geometry Goal 1
Develop a definition for perpendicular line segments. | Geometry Goal 1
Describe characteristics of parallelograms. | Geometry Goal 2
Classify quadrangles based on side and angle properties. | Geometry Goal 2
1•5 Construct convex and nonconvex (concave) polygons. | Geometry Goal 2
Develop definitions for convex and nonconvex (concave) polygons. | Geometry Goal 2
Describe properties of polygons and regular polygons. | Geometry Goal 2
Identify types of polygons according to the number of sides. | Geometry Goal 2

Unit 1 Organizer

A Balanced Curriculum

Ongoing Practice

Everyday Mathematics provides numerous opportunities for ongoing practice. These activities are embedded throughout the lessons:

Mental Math and Reflexes activities promote speed and accuracy in mental computation.

Math Boxes offer mixed practice and are paired across lessons as shown in the brackets below. This makes them useful as assessment tools. The last one or two boxes on each page preview the next unit's content.

Mixed practice	[1•1, 1•3], [1•2, 1•4], [1•5, 1•7], [1•6, 1•8]
Mixed practice with multiple choice	1•1, 1•4, 1•5, 1•8
Mixed practice with writing/reasoning opportunity	1•3, 1•4, 1•6, 1•7

Study Links are daily homework assignments that review the content of the lesson and often contain ongoing facts practice or computation practice.

5-Minute Math problems are offered for additional practice in Lesson 1•3.

EM Facts Workshop Game provides online practice of basic facts and computation.

EXTRA PRACTICE **Extra Practice** activities are included in Lessons 1•3, 1•6, and 1•8.

Ongoing Practice

Highlights essential activities that provide review and practice for maintaining skills. These activities include Math Boxes, Home/Study Links, games, and Extra Practice.

Daily Assessments

Includes the assessment opportunities in each lesson to assess progress toward Grade-Level Goals.

Assessment Support

Identifies useful pages in the *Assessment Handbook* for each unit.

Unit 1 Organizer

Balanced Assessment

Daily Assessments

- **Recognizing Student Achievement** – A daily assessment that is included in every lesson to evaluate students' progress toward the Grade 4 Grade-Level Goals.
- **Informing Instruction** – Notes that appear throughout the unit to help anticipate students' common errors and suggest appropriate problem-solving strategies.

Lesson	Recognizing Student Achievement	Informing Instruction
1•1	Demonstrate automaticity with addition fact extensions. [OC Goal 1]	
1•2	Describe a line segment and a line. [GEO Goal 1]	Connect points to other points.
1•3	Compare and contrast plane figures. [GEO Goal 2]	Consider the measures of angles rather than the lengths of rays.
1•4	Understand parallel line segments. [GEO Goal 1]	
1•5	Explain the properties of polygons. [GEO Goal 2]	Distinguish regular polygons from other polygons.
1•6	Understand right angles. [GEO Goal 1]	
1•7	Construct circles with a compass. [GEO Goal 2]	
1•8	Demonstrate automaticity with subtraction fact extensions. [OC Goal 1]	Connect consecutive marks to form a regular hexagon.

[NN] Number and Numeration [OC] Operations and Computation [DC] Data and Chance
[MRF] Measurement and Reference Frames [GEO] Geometry [PFA] Patterns, Functions, and Algebra

Portfolio Opportunities

The following lessons provide opportunities to gather samples of students' mathematical writings, drawings, and creations to add balance to the assessment process: Lessons 1•3, 1•4, 1•5, 1•6, 1•7, and 1•9.

See pages 16 and 17 in the *Assessment Handbook* for more information about portfolios and how to use them.

Unit Assessment

Progress Check 1 – A cumulative assessment of concepts and skills taught in Unit 1, providing information for evaluating students' progress and planning for future instruction. These assessments include oral/slate, written, and open-response activities, as shown below in the sample Progress Check lesson opener.

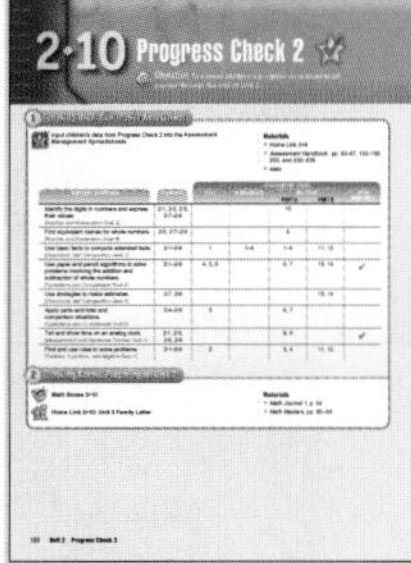

Core Assessment Resources

Assessment Handbook

- **Unit 1 Assessment Overview,** pages 52–59
- **Unit 1 Assessment Masters,** pages 154–158
- **Unit 1 Individual Profiles of Progress,** pages 246, 247, and 302
- **Unit 1 Class Checklists,** pages 248, 249, and 303
- **Beginning-of-Year Assessment,*** pages 227A–227D
- **Math Logs,** pages 306–308
- **Exit Slip,** page 311
- **Other Student Assessment Forms,** pages 304, 305, 309, and 310

*The Beginning-of-Year Assessment is one of the screening tools that can be used to help identify which concepts and skills students have learned and to help plan instruction for the upcoming year.

Assessment Management Spreadsheets

The Assessment Management Spreadsheets consist of the Digital Class Checklists and Individual Profile of Progress Checklists. Use them to monitor, record, and report student progress.

8 Unit 1 Naming and Constructing Geometric Figures

Unit Organizer 9

Unit 1 Organizer

Addressing All Needs

Differentiated Instruction

Adjusting the Activity – suggests adaptations that target advanced learners, English language learners, or learners who need additional instructional support.

ELL SUPPORT / ELL – provides lesson-specific suggestions to help English language learners understand and process the mathematical content.

READINESS – accesses students' prior knowledge or previews content that prepares students to engage in the lesson's Part 1 activities.

EXTRA PRACTICE – provides additional opportunities to apply the mathematical content of the lesson.

ENRICHMENT – enables students to apply or further explore the mathematical content of the lesson.

Lesson	Adjusting the Activity	ELL Support/ ELL	Readiness	Extra Practice	Enrichment
1•1	•	•	•		•
1•2	•	•	•		•
1•3	•	•	•	•	•
1•4	•	•	•		•
1•5	•	•	•		•
1•6	•			•	•
1•7	•	•			•
1•8	•		•	•	•

Differentiated Instruction

Highlights the many facets of differentiated instruction in each unit. Includes English language learner support, as well as Enrichment, Readiness, and Extra Practice activities.

Everyday Mathematics

3-Part Lesson Plan

3-Part Lesson

1. **Teaching the Lesson** Provides main instructional activities for the lesson.
2. **Ongoing Learning and Practice** Supports previously introduced concepts and skills; essential for maintaining skills.
3. **Differentiation Options** Includes options for supporting the needs of all students; usually an extension of Part 1, Teaching the Lesson.

Technology Resources

Suggests appropriate digital resources that support instruction of the lesson.

Lesson Opener

At-a-glance view of the 3-part lesson, highlighting materials, vocabulary, assessment, and more!

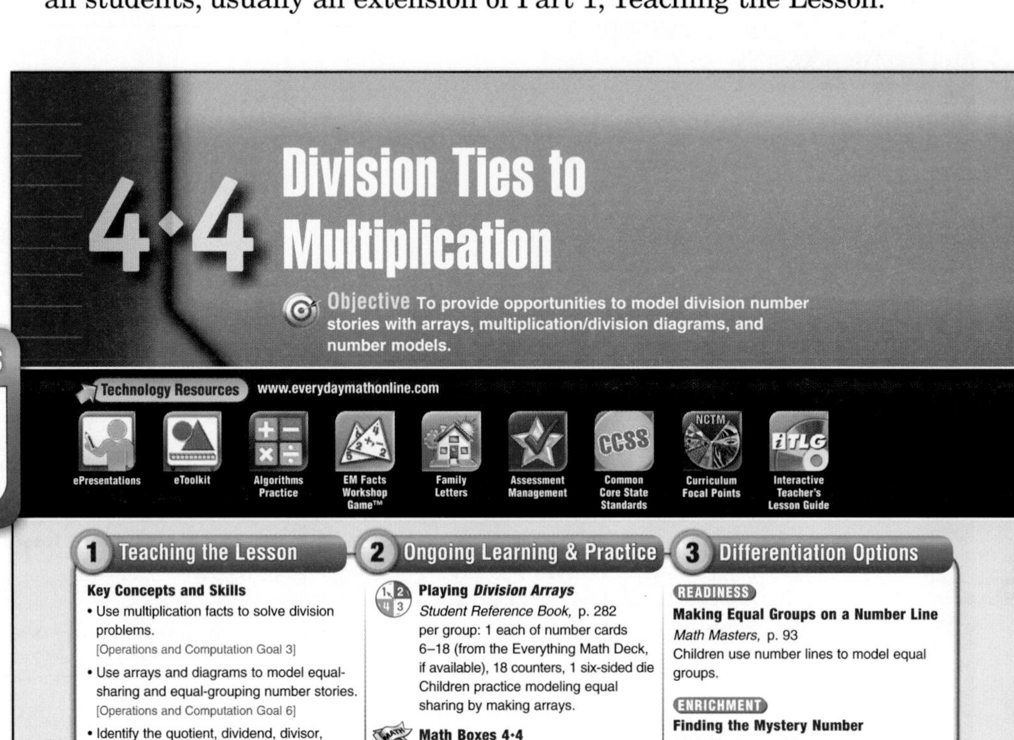

4•4 Division Ties to Multiplication

Objective To provide opportunities to model division number stories with arrays, multiplication/division diagrams, and number models.

Technology Resources www.everydaymathonline.com

ePresentations | eToolkit | Algorithms Practice | EM Facts Workshop Game™ | Family Letters | Assessment Management | Common Core State Standards | Curriculum Focal Points | Interactive Teacher's Lesson Guide

1 Teaching the Lesson

Key Concepts and Skills
- Use multiplication facts to solve division problems. [Operations and Computation Goal 3]
- Use arrays and diagrams to model equal-sharing and equal-grouping number stories. [Operations and Computation Goal 6]
- Identify the quotient, dividend, divisor, and remainder. [Operations and Computation Goal 6]
- Write number sentences to model number stories. [Patterns, Functions, and Algebra Goal 2]

Key Activities
Children draw arrays, fill in multiplication/division diagrams, and write number models to solve division number stories.

Ongoing Assessment: Recognizing Student Achievement Use the Math Message. [Operations and Computation Goal 6]

Ongoing Assessment: Informing Instruction See page 263.

Key Vocabulary
quotient • dividend • divisor • remainder

Materials
Math Journal 1, p. 86
Student Reference Book, p. 250 (optional)
Home Link 4•3
Math Masters, p. 406 (optional); pp. 407 and 419
pennies or other counters • calculator (optional)

2 Ongoing Learning & Practice

Playing *Division Arrays*
Student Reference Book, p. 282
per group: 1 each of number cards 6–18 (from the Everything Math Deck, if available), 18 counters, 1 six-sided die
Children practice modeling equal sharing by making arrays.

Math Boxes 4•4
Math Journal 1, p. 87
Children practice and maintain skills through Math Box problems.

Home Link 4•4
Math Masters, p. 92
Children practice and maintain skills through Home Link activities.

3 Differentiation Options

READINESS
Making Equal Groups on a Number Line
Math Masters, p. 93
Children use number lines to model equal groups.

ENRICHMENT
Finding the Mystery Number
Math Masters, p. 94
counters • calculator
Children find mystery numbers using multiplication and division.

ELL SUPPORT
Building a Math Word Bank
Differentiation Handbook, p. 132
Children add the term *quotient* to their Math Word Banks.

Advance Preparation
Post the Guide to Solving Number Stories. Make multiple copies of *Math Masters,* page 419 for each child to use during Part 1.

***Teacher's Reference Manual,* Grades 1–3** p. 84

260 Unit 4 Multiplication and Division

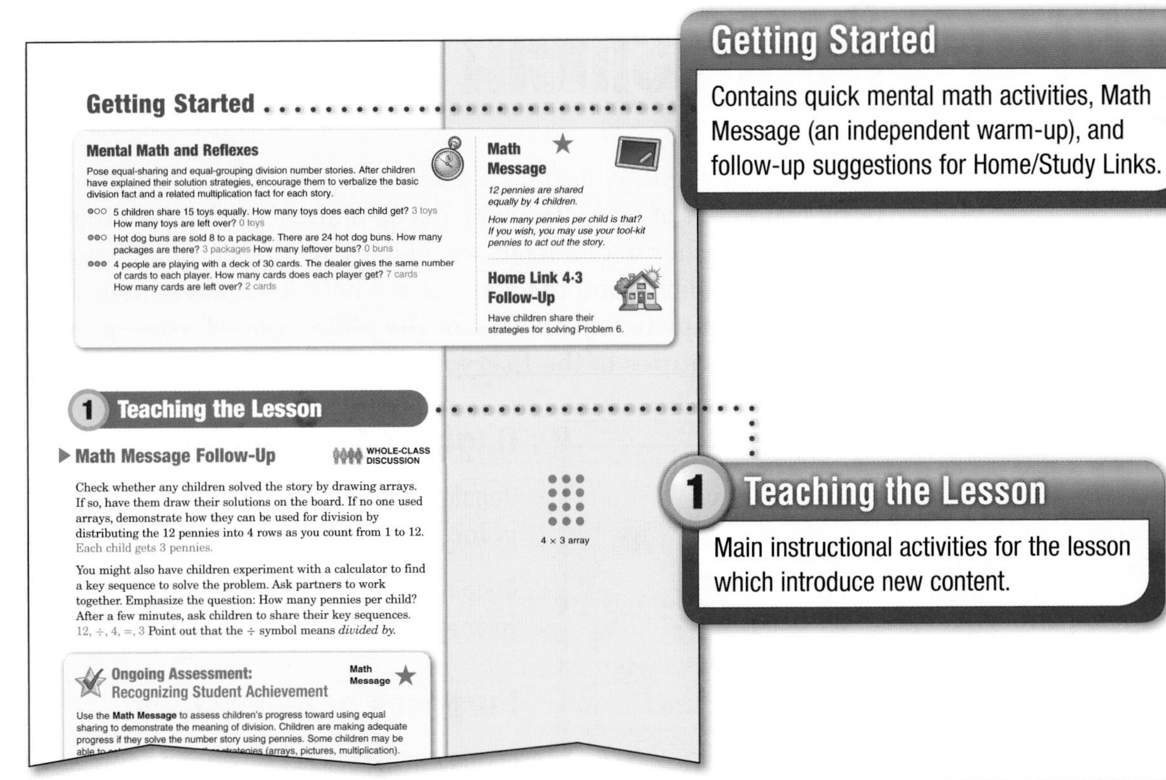

Getting Started . . . .

Mental Math and Reflexes

Pose equal-sharing and equal-grouping division number stories. After children have explained their solution strategies, encourage them to verbalize the basic division fact and a related multiplication fact for each story.

●○○ 5 children share 15 toys equally. How many toys does each child get? 3 toys How many toys are left over? 0 toys

●●○ Hot dog buns are sold 8 to a package. There are 24 hot dog buns. How many packages are there? 3 packages How many leftover buns? 0 buns

●●● 4 people are playing with a deck of 30 cards. The dealer gives the same number of cards to each player. How many cards does each player get? 7 cards How many cards are left over? 2 cards

Math Message

12 pennies are shared equally by 4 children.

How many pennies per child is that? If you wish, you may use your tool-kit pennies to act out the story.

Home Link 4·3 Follow-Up

Have children share their strategies for solving Problem 6.

1 Teaching the Lesson

▶ Math Message Follow-Up

WHOLE-CLASS DISCUSSION

Check whether any children solved the story by drawing arrays. If so, have them draw their solutions on the board. If no one used arrays, demonstrate how they can be used for division by distributing the 12 pennies into 4 rows as you count from 1 to 12. Each child gets 3 pennies.

You might also have children experiment with a calculator to find a key sequence to solve the problem. Ask partners to work together. Emphasize the question: How many pennies per child? After a few minutes, ask children to share their key sequences. 12, ÷, 4, =, 3 Point out that the ÷ symbol means *divided by.*

4 × 3 array

Ongoing Assessment: Recognizing Student Achievement Math Message

Use the **Math Message** to assess children's progress toward using equal sharing to demonstrate the meaning of division. Children are making adequate progress if they solve the number story using pennies. Some children may be able to ...

Getting Started

Contains quick mental math activities, Math Message (an independent warm-up), and follow-up suggestions for Home/Study Links.

1 Teaching the Lesson

Main instructional activities for the lesson which introduce new content.

Student Page

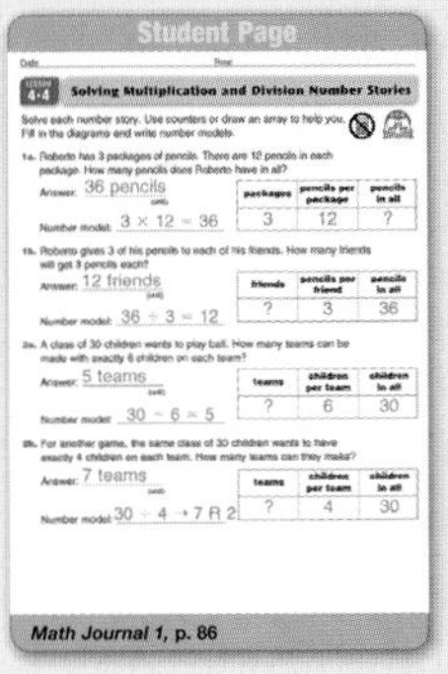

Math Journal 1, p. 86

2 Ongoing Learning & Practice

▶ Playing *Division Arrays*

SMALL-GROUP ACTIVITY

(*Student Reference Book*, p. 282)

Children practice modeling equal sharing by making arrays in *Division Arrays*. For detailed instructions, see page 282 in the *Student Reference Book.*

▶ Math Boxes 4·4

INDEPENDENT ACTIVITY

(*Math Journal 1*, p. 87)

Mixed Practice Math Boxes in this lesson are paired with Math Boxes in Lesson 4-2. The skill in Problem 6 previews Unit 5 content.

▶ Home Link 4·4

INDEPENDENT ACTIVITY

(*Math Masters*, p. 92)

Home Connection Children use division to solve number stories.

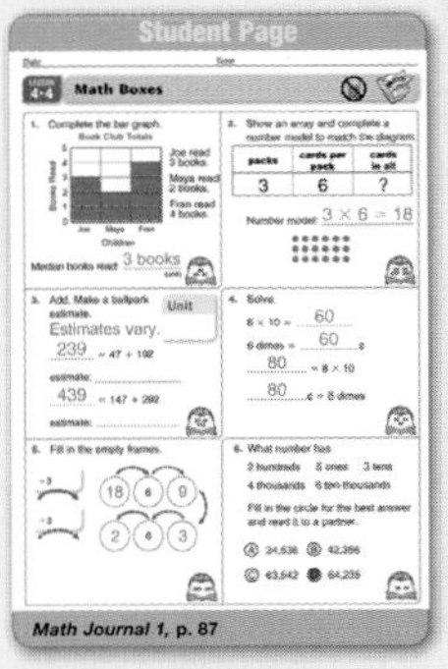

Student Page

Math Journal 1, p. 87

Home Link Master

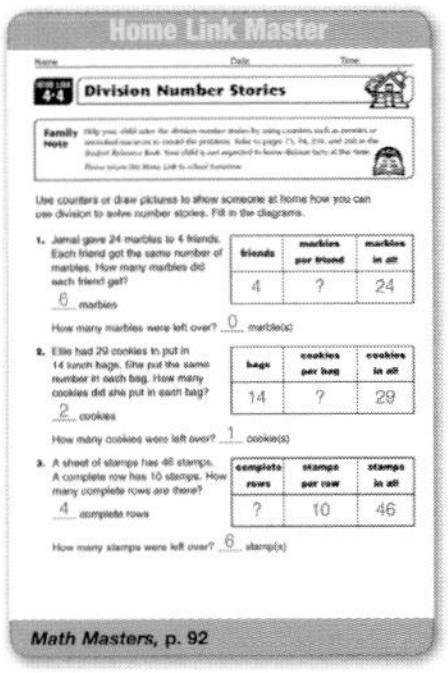

Math Masters, p. 92

3 Differentiation Options

READINESS

▶ Making Equal Groups on a Number Line

INDEPENDENT ACTIVITY 5–15 Min

(*Math Masters*, p. 93)

To provide experience with equal-grouping situations using a number-line model, have children solve equal-grouping problems by marking and counting hops on a number line.

ENRICHMENT

▶ Finding the Mystery Number

INDEPENDENT ACTIVITY 15–30 Min

(*Math Masters*, p. 94)

To apply children's understanding of the relationship between multiplication and division, have them find mystery numbers and identify patterns on *Math Masters*, page 94. When children have finished the page, have them share their ideas on why the Mystery Number is the same as the first number. Sample answer: First you multiply a number, then you subtract that number one time and divide by one less than you multiplied by.

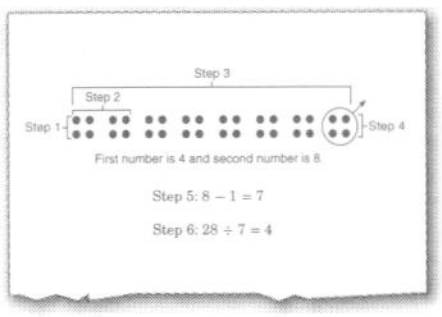

Step 5: 8 − 1 = 7

Step 6: 28 ÷ 7 = 4

Sample answer for Start Number 4 and 2nd number 8

ELL SUPPORT

▶ Building a Math Word Bank

SMALL-GROUP ACTIVITY 5–15 Min

(*Differentiation Handbook*, p. 132)

To provide language support for division, have children use the Word Bank template found on *Differentiation Handbook*, page 132. Ask children to write *quotient* and *remainder*, draw a picture representing each word, and write other related words. See the *Differentiation Handbook* for more information.

Teaching Master

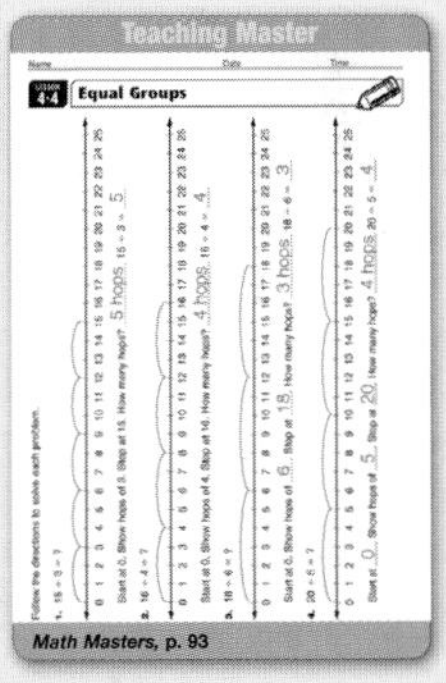

Math Masters, p. 93

Teaching Master

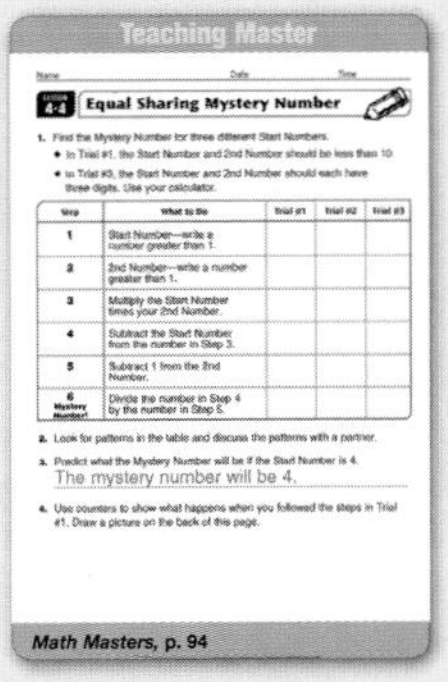

Math Masters, p. 94

264 Unit 4 Multiplication and Division

Lesson 4·4 265

2 Ongoing Learning & Practice

Activities provide essential review and practice for maintaining skills. Includes *Everyday Mathematics* games appropriate for revisiting mathematics skills, as well as Math Boxes and Home/Study Links.

3 Differentiation Options

Includes Readiness activities which cover mathematical content necessary for student success in the lesson. English language learner support, Enrichment, and Extra Practice are also key features of the Differentiation Options.

Assessment

In *Everyday Mathematics,* assessment is like a motion picture revealing the development of each student's mathematical understanding over time, while giving the teacher useful feedback about the instructional needs of both individual students and the class as a whole. The *Assessment Handbook* contains a complete explanation of the philosophy of assessment and assessment features of the *Everyday Mathematics* program.

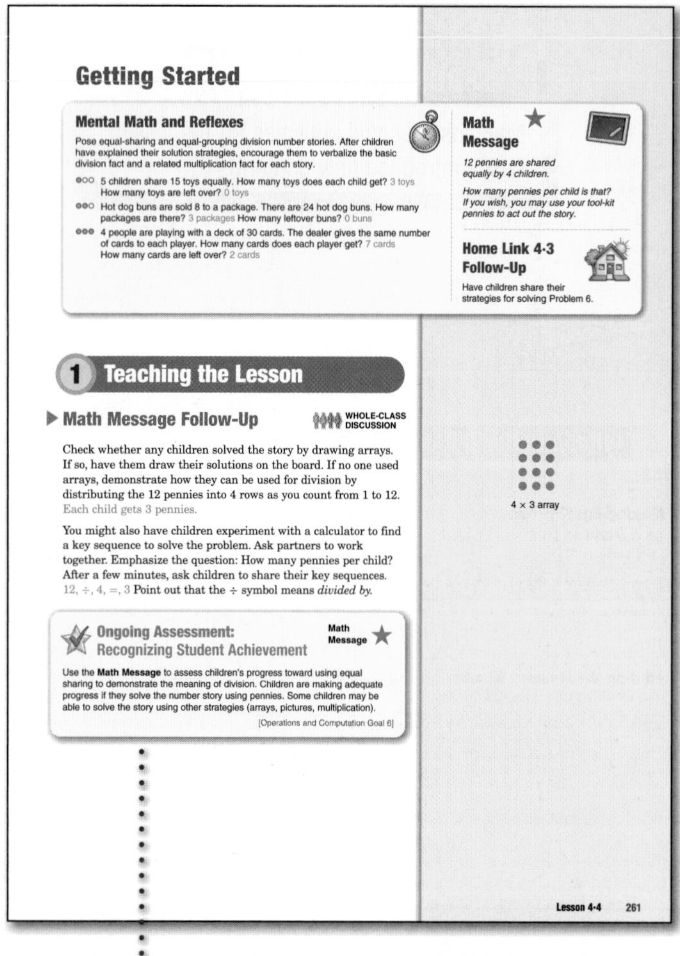

Getting Started

Mental Math and Reflexes

Pose equal-sharing and equal-grouping division number stories. After children have explained their solution strategies, encourage them to verbalize the basic division fact and a related multiplication fact for each story.

●○○ 5 children share 15 toys equally. How many toys does each child get? 3 toys How many toys are left over? 0 toys

●●○ Hot dog buns are sold 8 to a package. There are 24 hot dog buns. How many packages are there? 3 packages How many leftover buns? 0 buns

●●● 4 people are playing with a deck of 30 cards. The dealer gives the same number of cards to each player. How many cards does each player get? 7 cards How many cards are left over? 2 cards

Math Message

12 pennies are shared equally by 4 children.

How many pennies per child is that? If you wish, you may use your tool-kit pennies to act out the story.

Home Link 4·3 Follow-Up

Have children share their strategies for solving Problem 6.

1 Teaching the Lesson

▶ Math Message Follow-Up WHOLE-CLASS DISCUSSION

Check whether any children solved the story by drawing arrays. If so, have them draw their solutions on the board. If no one used arrays, demonstrate how they can be used for division by distributing the 12 pennies into 4 rows as you count from 1 to 12. Each child gets 3 pennies.

4 × 3 array

You might also have children experiment with a calculator to find a key sequence to solve the problem. Ask partners to work together. Emphasize the question: How many pennies per child? After a few minutes, ask children to share their key sequences. 12, ÷, 4, =, 3 Point out that the ÷ symbol means *divided by.*

Ongoing Assessment: Recognizing Student Achievement Math Message

Use the **Math Message** to assess children's progress toward using equal sharing to demonstrate the meaning of division. Children are making adequate progress if they solve the number story using pennies. Some children may be able to solve the story using other strategies (arrays, pictures, multiplication).

[Operations and Computation Goal 6]

Lesson 4·4 261

Recognizing Student Achievevment

Each lesson contains a Recognizing Student Achievement note. The notes highlight tasks that can be used to monitor student progress.

Ongoing Assessment

Ongoing Assessment: Recognizing Student Achievement is included in every lesson.

Ongoing Assessment: Informing Instruction is included in many lessons to help you guide instruction.

Purposes of Assessment

Formative Assessments provide information about students' current knowledge and abilities that can be used to plan or inform instruction. Information from almost any assessment task in *Everyday Mathematics* might be useful for planning future instruction.

Summative Assessments measure student growth and achievement and provide information that may be used to assign grades or otherwise evaluate students' performance. Summative assessments in *Everyday Mathematics* include the Recognizing Student Achievement tasks in each lesson, Part A of the written assessments in each unit, and other assessments labeled "fair to grade."

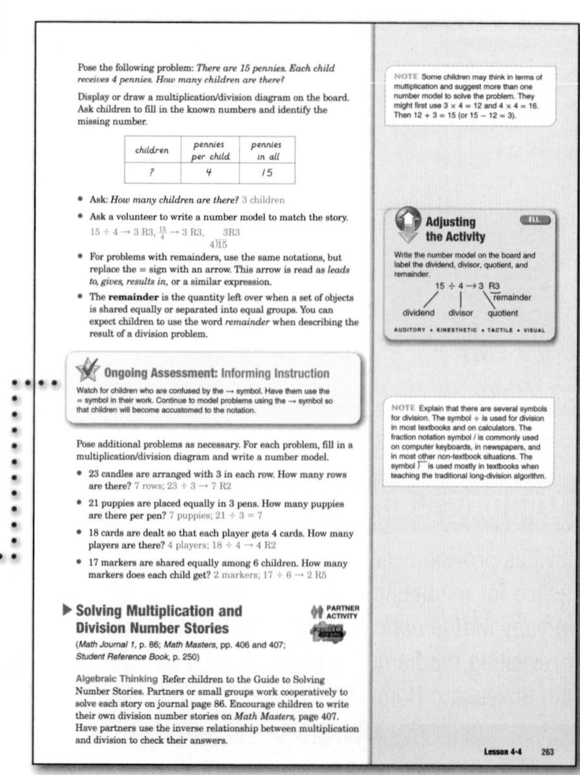

Pose the following problem: *There are 15 pennies. Each child receives 4 pennies. How many children are there?*

Display or draw a multiplication/division diagram on the board. Ask children to fill in the known numbers and identify the missing number.

children	pennies per child	pennies in all
?	4	15

- Ask: *How many children are there?* 3 children
- Ask a volunteer to write a number model to match the story. 15 ÷ 4 → 3 R3, $\frac{15}{4}$ → 3 R3, $4\overline{)15}$ 3R3
- For problems with remainders, use the same notations, but replace the = sign with an arrow. This arrow is read as *leads to, gives, results in,* or a similar expression.
- The **remainder** is the quantity left over when a set of objects is shared equally or separated into equal groups. You can expect children to use the word *remainder* when describing the result of a division problem.

NOTE Some children may think in terms of multiplication and suggest more than one number model to solve the problem. They might first use 3 × 4 = 12 and 4 × 4 = 16. Then 12 + 3 = 15 (or 15 − 12 = 3).

Adjusting the Activity ELL

Write the number model on the board and label the dividend, divisor, quotient, and remainder.

15 ÷ 4 → 3 R3 (dividend, divisor, quotient, remainder)

AUDITORY • KINESTHETIC • TACTILE • VISUAL

Ongoing Assessment: Informing Instruction

Watch for children who are confused by the → symbol. Have them use the = symbol in their work. Continue to model problems using the → symbol so that children will become accustomed to the notation.

Pose additional problems as necessary. For each problem, fill in a multiplication/division diagram and write a number model.

- 23 candles are arranged with 3 in each row. How many rows are there? 7 rows; 23 ÷ 3 → 7 R2
- 21 puppies are placed equally in 3 pens. How many puppies are there per pen? 7 puppies; 21 ÷ 3 = 7
- 18 cards are dealt so that each player gets 4 cards. How many players are there? 4 players; 18 ÷ 4 → 4 R2
- 17 markers are shared equally among 6 children. How many markers does each child get? 2 markers; 17 ÷ 6 → 2 R5

NOTE Explain that there are several symbols for division. The symbol ÷ is used for division in most textbooks and on calculators. The fraction notation symbol / is commonly used on computer keyboards, in newspapers, and in most other non-textbook situations. The symbol $\overline{)}$ is used mostly in textbooks when teaching the traditional long-division algorithm.

▶ Solving Multiplication and Division Number Stories PARTNER ACTIVITY

(*Math Journal 1*, p. 86; *Math Masters*, pp. 406 and 407; *Student Reference Book*, p. 250)

Algebraic Thinking Refer children to the Guide to Solving Number Stories. Partners or small groups work cooperatively to solve each story on journal page 86. Encourage children to write their own division number stories on *Math Masters*, page 407. Have partners use the inverse relationship between multiplication and division to check their answers.

Lesson 4·4 263

Informing Instruction

Suggests how to use observation of students' work to effectively adapt instruction.

Periodic Assessment

The Progress Check lessons, included for each unit, provide several types of periodic assessment.

Online Assessment Tools

The Assessment Management Spreadsheets provide additional opportunities to monitor student progress and inform instruction.

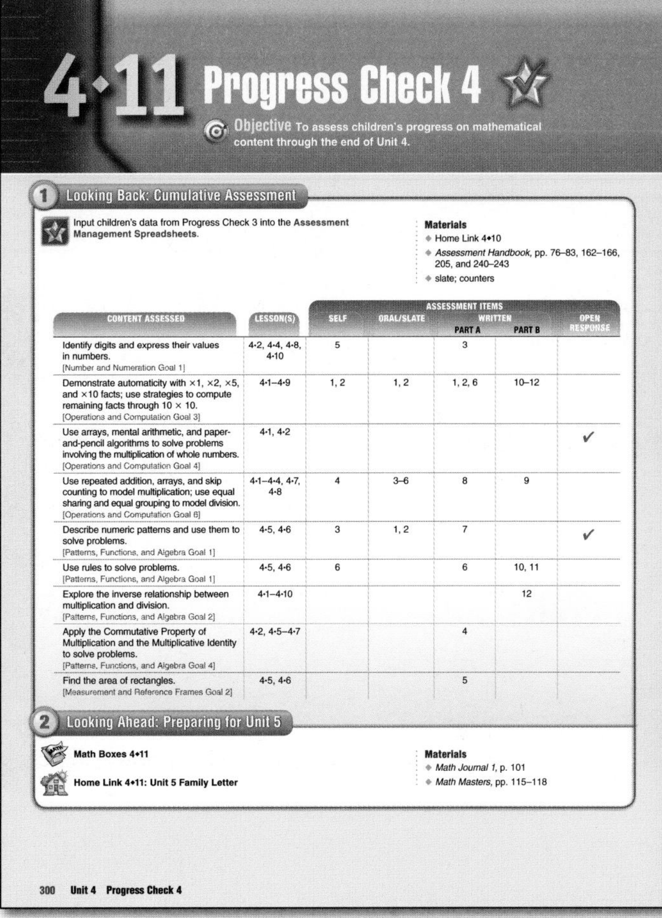

4•11 Progress Check 4

Objective To assess children's progress on mathematical content through the end of Unit 4.

1 Looking Back: Cumulative Assessment

Input children's data from Progress Check 3 into the Assessment Management Spreadsheets.

Materials
- Home Link 4•10
- *Assessment Handbook*, pp. 76–83, 162–166, 205, and 240–243
- slate; counters

CONTENT ASSESSED	LESSON(S)	SELF	ORAL/SLATE	WRITTEN PART A	WRITTEN PART B	OPEN RESPONSE
Identify digits and express their values in numbers. [Number and Numeration Goal 1]	4-2, 4-4, 4-8, 4-10	5		3		
Demonstrate automaticity with ×1, ×2, ×5, and ×10 facts; use strategies to compute remaining facts through 10 × 10. [Operations and Computation Goal 3]	4-1–4-9	1, 2	1, 2	1, 2, 6	10–12	
Use arrays, mental arithmetic, and paper-and-pencil algorithms to solve problems involving the multiplication of whole numbers. [Operations and Computation Goal 4]	4-1, 4-2					✓
Use repeated addition, arrays, and skip counting to model multiplication; use equal sharing and equal grouping to model division. [Operations and Computation Goal 6]	4-1–4-4, 4-7, 4-8	4	3–6	8	9	
Describe numeric patterns and use them to solve problems. [Patterns, Functions, and Algebra Goal 1]	4-5, 4-6	3	1, 2	7		✓
Use rules to solve problems. [Patterns, Functions, and Algebra Goal 1]	4-5, 4-6	6		6	10, 11	
Explore the inverse relationship between multiplication and division. [Patterns, Functions, and Algebra Goal 2]	4-1–4-10				12	
Apply the Commutative Property of Multiplication and the Multiplicative Identity to solve problems. [Patterns, Functions, and Algebra Goal 4]	4-2, 4-5–4-7			4		
Find the area of rectangles. [Measurement and Reference Frames Goal 2]	4-5, 4-6			5		

2 Looking Ahead: Preparing for Unit 5

Math Boxes 4•11

Home Link 4•11: Unit 5 Family Letter

Materials
- *Math Journal 1*, p. 101
- *Math Masters*, pp. 115–118

300 Unit 4 Progress Check 4

Progress Check

Provides multiple assessment options. Includes Oral and Slate Assessments, Written Assessment, Open Response, and Self Assessment.

Written Assessment

Each Written Assessment has two parts: Part A Recognizing Student Achievement (summative assessment), and Part B Informing Instruction (formative assessment).

Open Response

Each unit provides an Open Response question. Sample student responses as well as rubrics for every Open Response question are found in the *Assessment Handbook.*

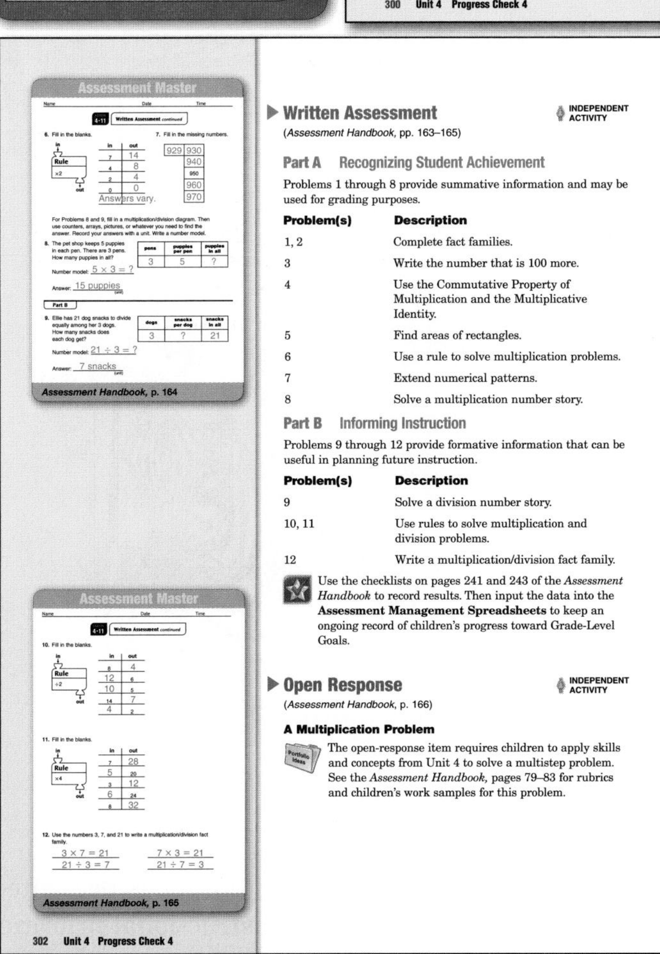

Assessment Master — *Assessment Handbook*, p. 164

Assessment Master — *Assessment Handbook*, p. 165

▶ Written Assessment INDEPENDENT ACTIVITY

(*Assessment Handbook*, pp. 163–165)

Part A Recognizing Student Achievement

Problems 1 through 8 provide summative information and may be used for grading purposes.

Problem(s)	Description
1, 2	Complete fact families.
3	Write the number that is 100 more.
4	Use the Commutative Property of Multiplication and the Multiplicative Identity.
5	Find areas of rectangles.
6	Use a rule to solve multiplication problems.
7	Extend numerical patterns.
8	Solve a multiplication number story.

Part B Informing Instruction

Problems 9 through 12 provide formative information that can be useful in planning future instruction.

Problem(s)	Description
9	Solve a division number story.
10, 11	Use rules to solve multiplication and division problems.
12	Write a multiplication/division fact family.

Use the checklists on pages 241 and 243 of the *Assessment Handbook* to record results. Then input the data into the **Assessment Management Spreadsheets** to keep an ongoing record of children's progress toward Grade-Level Goals.

▶ Open Response INDEPENDENT ACTIVITY

(*Assessment Handbook*, p. 166)

A Multiplication Problem

The open-response item requires children to apply skills and concepts from Unit 4 to solve a multistep problem. See the *Assessment Handbook*, pages 79–83 for rubrics and children's work samples for this problem.

302 Unit 4 Progress Check 4

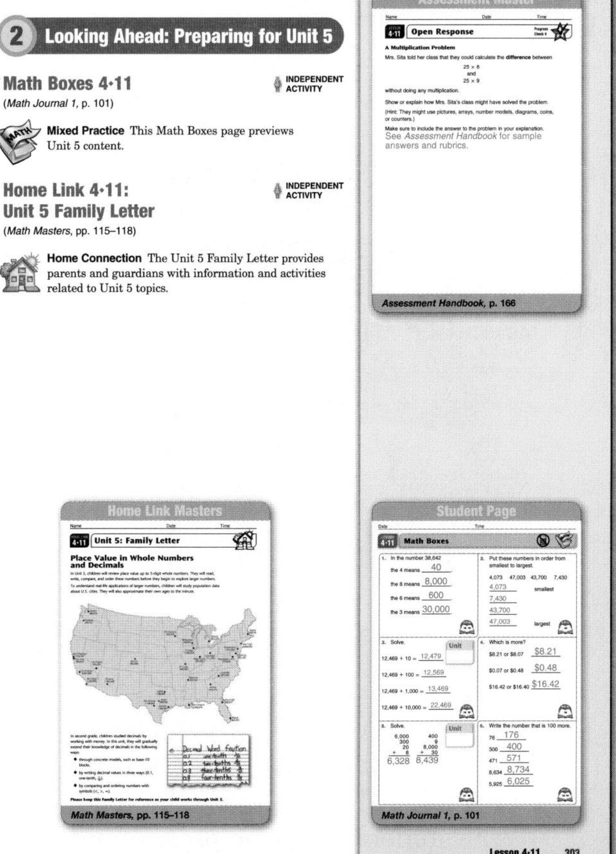

2 Looking Ahead: Preparing for Unit 5

▶ Math Boxes 4•11 INDEPENDENT ACTIVITY

(*Math Journal 1*, p. 101)

Mixed Practice This Math Boxes page previews Unit 5 content.

▶ Home Link 4•11: Unit 5 Family Letter INDEPENDENT ACTIVITY

(*Math Masters*, pp. 115–118)

Home Connection The Unit 5 Family Letter provides parents and guardians with information and activities related to Unit 5 topics.

Assessment Master — *Assessment Handbook*, p. 166

Home Link Masters — *Math Masters*, pp. 115–118

Student Page — *Math Journal 1*, p. 101

Lesson 4•11 303

Professional Development

Everyday Mathematics believes it is critical to support teachers with the materials necessary to enable students to meet higher expectations of mathematical achievement. In addition to district-specific training offered at implementation and for continued support, numerous professional development opportunities are built into the *Everyday Mathematics* program.

Teacher's Reference Manual

An invaluable resource that contains comprehensive background information about mathematical content as well as a guide to help organize the curriculum, the students, and the program materials.

Teacher's Lesson Guide

Professional development is embedded throughout, including Mathematical Background in each unit organizer to highlight the major content ideas presented and to help establish instructional priorities.

Supporting Students and Home

Family Involvement

Within *Everyday Mathematics* there are several opportunities for supporting the home–school connection.

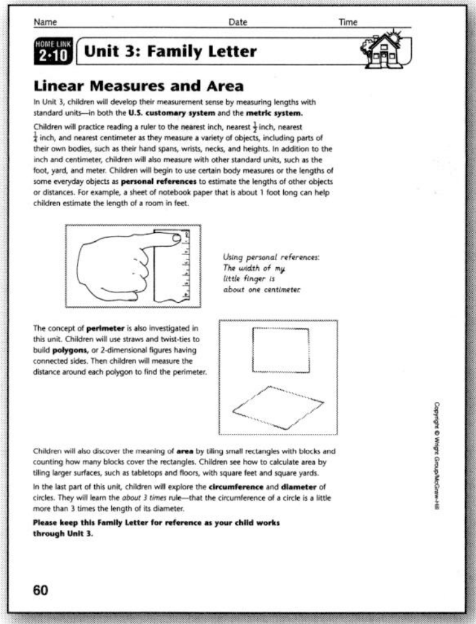

Name Date Time

HOME LINK 2·10 **Unit 3: Family Letter**

Linear Measures and Area

In Unit 3, children will develop their measurement sense by measuring lengths with standard units—in both the **U.S. customary system** and the **metric system.**

Children will practice reading a ruler to the nearest inch, nearest $\frac{1}{2}$ inch, nearest $\frac{1}{4}$ inch, and nearest centimeter as they measure a variety of objects, including parts of their own bodies, such as their hand spans, wrists, necks, and heights. In addition to the inch and centimeter, children will also measure with other standard units, such as the foot, yard, and meter. Children will begin to use certain body measures or the lengths of some everyday objects as **personal references** to estimate the lengths of other objects or distances. For example, a sheet of notebook paper that is about 1 foot long can help children estimate the length of a room in feet.

Using personal references: The width of my little finger is about one centimeter.

The concept of **perimeter** is also investigated in this unit. Children will use straws and twist-ties to build **polygons,** or 2-dimensional figures having connected sides. Then children will measure the distance around each polygon to find the perimeter.

Children will also discover the meaning of **area** by tiling small rectangles with blocks and counting how many blocks cover the rectangles. Children see how to calculate area by tiling larger surfaces, such as tabletops and floors, with square feet and square yards.

In the last part of this unit, children will explore the **circumference** and **diameter** of circles. They will learn the *about 3 times* rule—that the circumference of a circle is a little more than 3 times the length of its diameter.

Please keep this Family Letter for reference as your child works through Unit 3.

Copyright © Wright Group/McGraw-Hill

60

Family Letters

Each unit's Family Letter explains the unit's key content and vocabulary and provides directions for appropriate games, Do-Anytime Activities, and answers to most Home/Study Links for the unit.

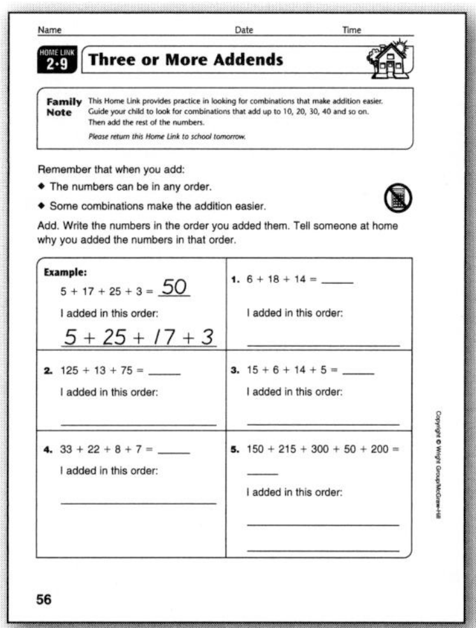

Name Date Time

HOME LINK 2·9 **Three or More Addends**

Family Note This Home Link provides practice in looking for combinations that make addition easier. Guide your child to look for combinations that add up to 10, 20, 30, 40 and so on. Then add the rest of the numbers.

Please return this Home Link to school tomorrow.

Remember that when you add:

- The numbers can be in any order.
- Some combinations make the addition easier.

Add. Write the numbers in the order you added them. Tell someone at home why you added the numbers in that order.

Example: 5 + 17 + 25 + 3 = 50 I added in this order: 5 + 25 + 17 + 3	**1.** 6 + 18 + 14 = ____ I added in this order: ______
2. 125 + 13 + 75 = ____ I added in this order: ______	**3.** 15 + 6 + 14 + 5 = ____ I added in this order: ______
4. 33 + 22 + 8 + 7 = ____ I added in this order: ______	**5.** 150 + 215 + 300 + 50 + 200 = ____ I added in this order: ______

Copyright © Wright Group/McGraw-Hill

56

Home Links/Study Links

Each lesson has a Home/Study Link. They show families what students are doing in mathematics.

Student Reference Book and My Reference Book

These books are resources that can be sent home to provide parents with support on lesson content. The reference books include explanations and examples of mathematical topics, as well as directions for *Everyday Mathematics* games.

Home Connection Handbook

This teacher- and administrator-focused handbook provides support for communicating with families. Includes blackline masters for easier communication.

EM Online Access all technology resources online at everydaymathonline.com

NCTM Curriculum Focal Points and *Everyday Mathematics*

The *Everyday Mathematics* curriculum is completely aligned to the NCTM Curriculum Focal Points and the Connections to the Curriculum Focal Points for Pre-Kindergarten through Grade 6.

NCTM Curriculum Focal Points for Grade 4	*Everyday Mathematics* Grade 4 Lessons
Number and Operations and Algebra: Developing quick recall of multiplication facts and related division facts and fluency with whole number multiplication.	
Students use understandings of multiplication to develop quick recall of the basic multiplication facts and related division facts.	3•2, 3•3, 3•4, 3•5, 3•6, 3•7, 3•9, 3•10, 5•1, 5•2, 5•7
Students apply their understanding of models for multiplication (i.e., equal sized groups, arrays, area models, equal intervals on the number line), place value, and properties of operations (in particular, the distributive property) as they develop, discuss, and use efficient, accurate, and generalizable methods to multiply multidigit whole numbers.	2•3, 3•2, 3•3, 3•5, 3•7, 5•1, 5•5, 12•1
Students select appropriate methods and apply them accurately to estimate products or calculate them mentally, depending on the context and numbers involved.	4•8, 4•10, 5•4, 9•8, 12•1, 12•2, 12•3
Students develop fluency with efficient procedures, including the standard algorithm, for multiplying whole numbers, understand why the procedures work (on the basis of place value and properties of operations), and use them to solve problems.	5•2, 5•5, 5•6, 5•7, 9•8, 12•2 Project 3, Project 7 Algorithm Project 5
Number and Operations: Developing an understanding of decimals, including the connections between fractions and decimals.	
Students understand decimal notation as an extension of the base-ten system of writing whole numbers that is useful for representing more numbers, including numbers between 0 and 1, between 1 and 2, and so on.	4•1, 4•2, 4•4, 4•6, 4•7, 6•4
Students relate their understanding of fractions to reading and writing decimals that are greater than or less than 1, identifying equivalent decimals, comparing and ordering decimals, and estimating decimal or fractional amounts in problem solving.	4•2, 4•3, 4•4, 4•7, 9•2, 9•5, 9•6, 12•5
Students connect equivalent fractions and decimals by comparing models to symbols and locating equivalent symbols on the number line.	4•2, 4•3, 7•8, 9•1, 9•2, 9•5, 9•6
Measurement: Developing an understanding of area and determining the areas of two-dimensional shapes.	
Students recognize area as an attribute of two-dimensional regions. They learn that they can quantify area by finding the total number of same-sized units of area that cover the shape without gaps or overlaps. They understand that a square that is 1 unit on a side is the standard unit for measuring area.	8•3, 8•4, 8•5
Students select appropriate units, strategies (e.g., decomposing shapes), and tools for solving problems that involve estimating or measuring area.	8•3, 8•4, 8•5, 8•6, 8•7, 8•8
Students connect area measure to the area model that they have used to represent multiplication, and they use this connection to justify the formula for the area of a rectangle.	8•5, 8•6, 8•7, 9•8

NCTM Connections to the Curriculum Focal Points for Grade 4	*Everyday Mathematics* Grade 4 Lessons
Algebra	
Students continue identifying, describing, and extending numeric patterns involving all operations and nonnumeric growing or repeating patterns.	2•1, 3•1, 8•5, 10•5, 11•3 Project 4
Students develop an understanding of the use of a rule to describe a sequence of numbers or objects.	3•1, 10•5, 11•3, 12•2 Project 4
Geometry	
Students extend their understanding of properties of two-dimensional shapes as they find the areas of polygons. They build on their earlier work with symmetry and congruence in grade 3 to encompass transformations, including those that produce line and rotational symmetry. By using transformations to design and analyze simple tilings and tessellations, students deepen their understanding of two-dimensional space.	1•5, 10•1, 10•2, 10•3, 10•4, 10•5 Project 4
Measurement	
Students measure and classify angles, as part of understanding two-dimensional shapes.	6•5, 6•6, 6•7 Project 1 Project 2
Data Analysis	
Students continue to use tools from grade 3, solving problems by making frequency tables, bar graphs, picture graphs, and line plots. They apply their understanding of place value to develop and use stem-and-leaf plots.	2•5, 2•6, 2•8, 3•4, 5•10, 8•1, 9•6, 12•1
Number and Operations	
Students extend their understanding of place value and ways of representing numbers to 100,000 in various contexts, building on their work in grade 3.	2•3, 2•4, 2•7, 2•9, 4•5, 4•7, 5•8, 5•9, 5•10, 5•11
Students use estimation in determining the relative sizes of amounts or distances.	2•1, 2•5, 2•7, 2•9, 3•6, 5•3, 5•8, 5•10, 11•7
Students develop understandings of strategies for multidigit division by using models that represent division as the inverse of multiplication, as partitioning, or as successive subtraction.	3•1, 6•1, 6•2, 6•3, 6•4, 6•10, 9•9, 12•4,12•6 Project 7
Students extend their ability to recognize equivalent fractions, by working with decimals.	7•8, 9•1, 9•2
Students' earlier work in grade 3 with models of fractions and multiplication and division facts supports their understanding of techniques for generating equivalent fractions and simplifying fractions.	7•4, 7•5, 7•6, 7•7, 7•8, 7•9

The Curriculum Focal Points identify key mathematical ideas for these grades. They are not discrete topics or a checklist to be mastered; rather, they provide a framework for the majority of instruction at a particular grade level and the foundation for future mathematics study.

Contents

Volume 1

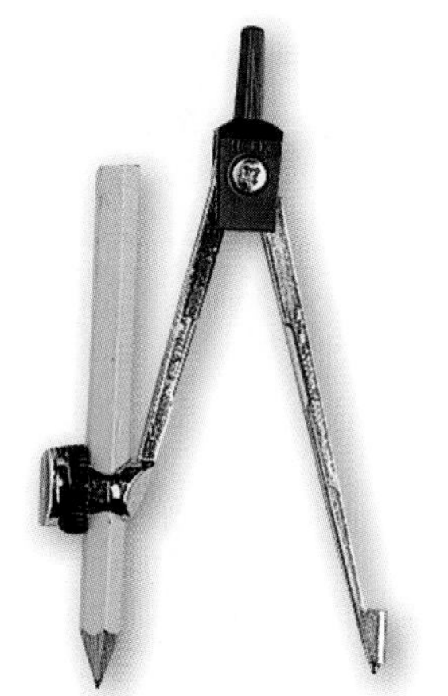

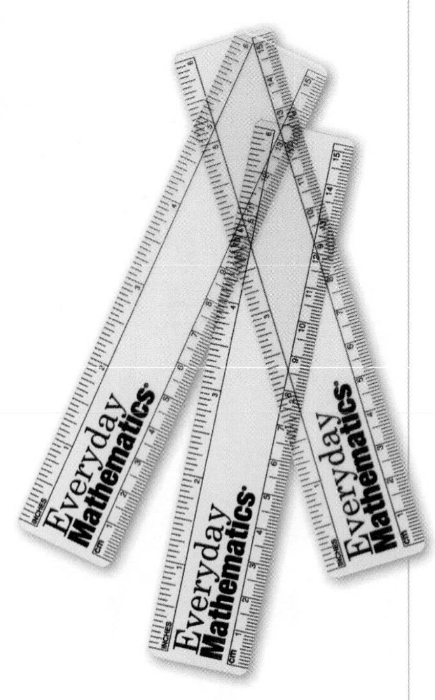
Everyday Mathematics
Everyday Mathematics
Everyday Mathematics

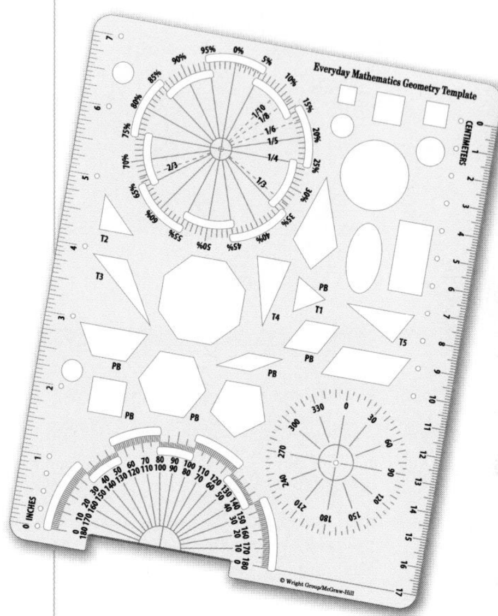
Everyday Mathematics Geometry Template
CENTIMETERS
INCHES

Volume 2

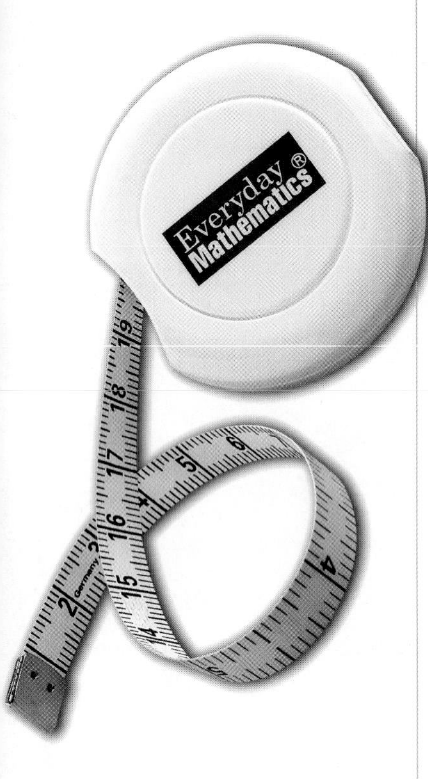
Everyday Mathematics®

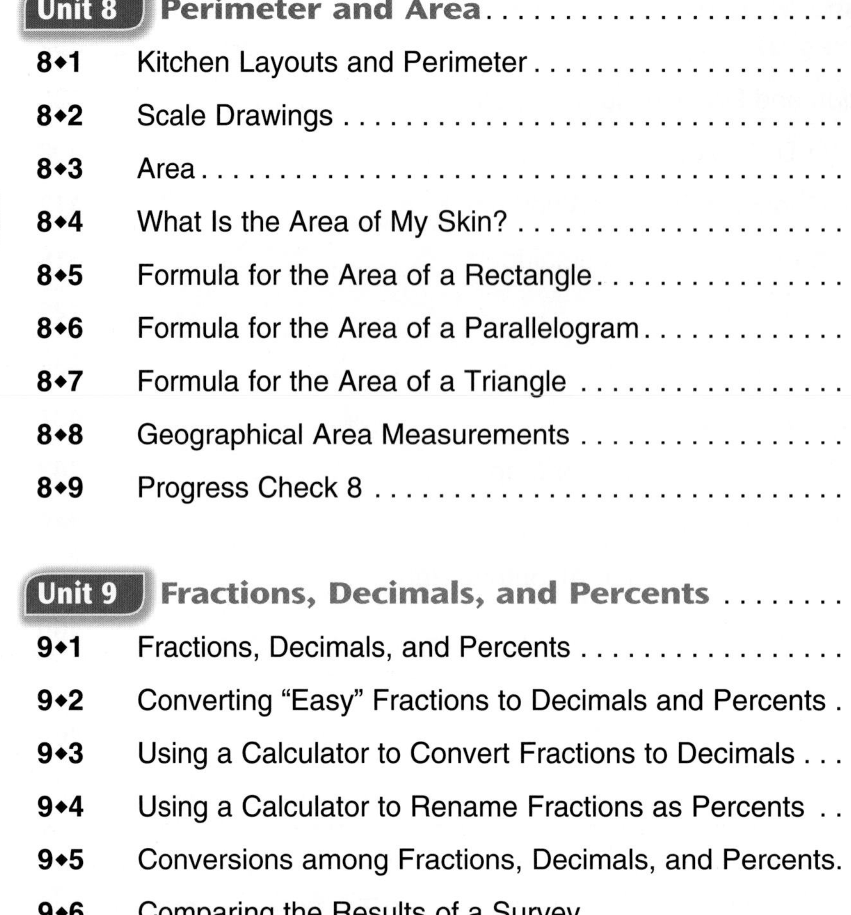

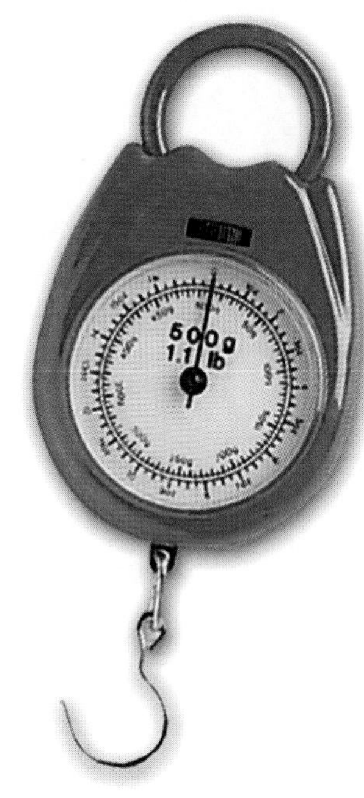

Welcome to *Everyday Mathematics*, the elementary school mathematics curriculum developed by the University of Chicago School Mathematics project (UCSMP). *Everyday Mathematics* offers you and your students a broad, rich, and balanced experience in mathematics.

Fourth Grade Everyday Mathematics emphasizes the following content strands, skills, and concepts:

- **Number and Numeration** Reading, writing, and comparing whole numbers up to 1,000,000,000, decimals through thousandths, negative numbers to −100, and fractions; understanding relations between fractions, decimals, and percents; locating fractions and mixed numbers on a number line; generating equivalent fractions.
- **Operations and Computation** Using paper-and-pencil algorithms to add, subtract, multiply, and divide multidigit whole numbers and decimals; using mental arithmetic to compute exact answers and to estimate; rounding from millions to hundredths; modeling multiplication with arrays and area; using several methods to add and subtract fractions and mixed numbers.
- **Data and Chance** Creating, reading, and interpreting graphs; identifying landmarks in data sets, including range, median, mode, and mean; listing all possible outcomes in simple situations; using fractions to quantify probabilities; using experimental results to make predictions.
- **Measurement and Reference Frames** Measuring length, area, volume, weight, temperature, and time; developing personal references for inches, centimeters, feet, meters, and yards; estimating lengths and weights; finding areas and perimeters of rectangles, parallelograms, and triangles; finding volumes of rectangular prisms by counting cubic units; calculating elapsed time; using correct units in all measurements; calculating distances using map scales.
- **Geometry** Locating points on a coordinate grid; drawing and measuring angles; classifying angles as acute, obtuse, or right; classifying lines as parallel, intersecting, or perpendicular; recognizing and using transformations, including reflections and rotations; understanding the relationship between reflections and line symmetry; building 3-dimensional shapes; describing, comparing, and analyzing 2-dimensional and 3-dimensional figures.
- **Patterns, Functions, and Algebra** Using letters and other symbols for unknowns; simplifying expressions containing parentheses; creating, extending, and describing patterns; using formulas for finding the areas of simple geometric figures; determining rules that relate numbers in pairs; finding missing numbers in tables; translating among verbal, numerical, and graphical representations; understanding and writing number models for number stories.

Everyday Mathematics is a comprehensive program that will help you and your students experience mathematical processes as a part of everyday work and play. These processes will gradually shape your students' ways of thinking about mathematics and will foster the development of their mathematical intuitions and understandings. By the end of the year, we think you will agree that the rewards are worth the effort.

Everyday Mathematics emphasizes the following:

- A realistic approach to problem solving in everyday situations, applications, and purely mathematical contexts.
- Frequent and distributed practice of basic skills through ongoing program routines and mathematical games.
- An instructional approach that revisits topics regularly to ensure full concept development and long-term retention of learning.
- Activities that explore a wide variety of mathematical content and offer opportunities for students to apply their skills and understandings to geometry, measurement, and algebra.

Professional Preparation

Components for Fourth Grade *Everyday Mathematics*

Go to...	When you need...	
Teacher's Lesson Guide	• daily lessons • daily assessment suggestions • readiness, enrichment, and extra practice suggestions	• unit support information • key vocabulary • scope and sequence • Grade-Level Goals • English language learners support
Teacher's Reference Manual	• background on mathematical content	• ideas for curriculum and classroom management
Assessment Handbook	• suggestions for ongoing and periodic assessment • Grade-Level Goals across all grades	• assessment masters • sample rubrics for open response items
Differentiation Handbook	• suggestions for meeting diverse needs	• unit specific ideas
5-Minute Math	• brief activities for transition time and extra practice	
Content-by-Strand Poster	• key concepts and skills organized by content strand and paced by month	• Program Goals and Grade-Level Goals
Home Connection Handbook	• suggestions for home-school communication	• masters for easy planning
Student Reference Book	• concise explanations of fundamental mathematics • worked examples	• game directions • a reference for students, parents, and others
Student Math Journal	• a yearlong record of each student's mathematical development	• paired Math Boxes for mixed practice • activity sheets
Math Masters	• blackline masters for lessons, Study Links, projects, teaching aids, and games	
English Learners Handbook	• comprehensive instructional strategies that maximize understanding	• methods that accelerate the acquisition of academic language and improve students' comprehension
Multilingual Handbook	• brief lesson summaries with examples in 6 languages	• lesson vocabulary in 11 languages

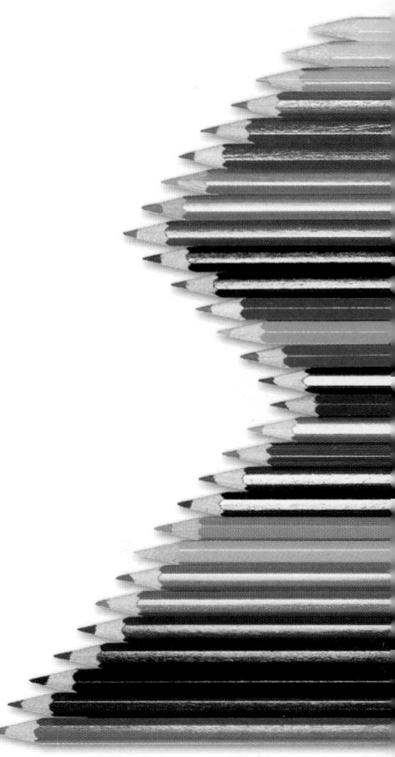

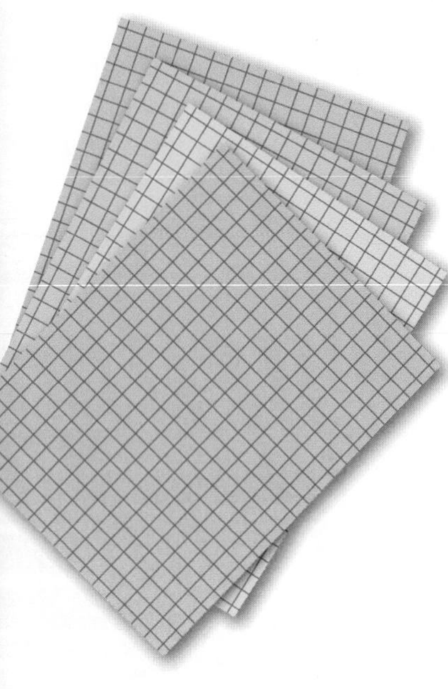

Suggested Reading & Lesson Preparation

In order to prepare for effective classroom and curriculum management, we suggest the following before you teach *Everyday Mathematics* for the first time.

- ☐ Review each component in your Classroom Resource Package (CRP). Locate information and materials so that you can find them as needed throughout the school year.
- ☐ Browse through the *Teacher's Reference Manual,* the *Assessment Handbook,* the *Differentiation Handbook,* the *Home Connection Handbook,* and the *Student Reference Book.*
- ☐ Read the Management Guide in the *Teacher's Reference Manual,* which has many useful tips and explanations.
- ☐ Before you teach each unit, read the Unit Organizer in the *Teacher's Lesson Guide* and refer to the Advance Preparation section in each lesson. Also read the relevant sections of the *Teacher's Reference Manual,* the *Assessment Handbook,* and the *Differentiation Handbook.*
- ☐ Prepare a daily math schedule. *Everyday Mathematics* lessons have several parts, which can be done at different times throughout the day. Your schedule should include time for Getting Started activities (Math Message, Mental Math and Reflexes, and Study Link Follow-Up); Teaching the Lesson; Ongoing Learning & Practice activities, including Math Boxes and games; and possibly Differentiation Options.
- ☐ Prepare materials that will be used throughout the year. Special items for consideration include:
    - For the Mental Math and Reflexes routine, gather slates and chalk (or dry erase boards and markers) and old socks for erasers.
    - Prepare a lost-and-found box for misplaced items.
    - Assign an ID number to each student to simplify matching students and manipulatives. See *Teacher's Lesson Guide,* Lesson 1-2, page 23.
- ☐ Prepare a supply of paper: Blank $8\frac{1}{2}$-by-11 (full, half, and quarter size sheets); Graph paper (1 centimeter; see *Math Masters,* page 403)
- ☐ Obtain the optional books listed in the literature links section of the Unit Organizer for upcoming units.

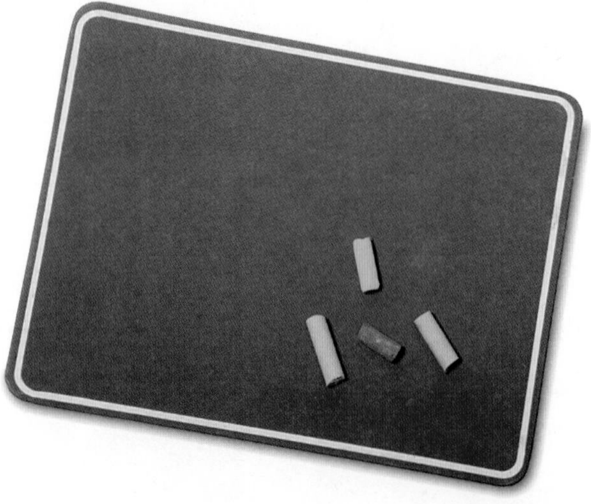

Organizing Your Classroom

Items for Display

Before the school year begins, we suggest that you gather the following items for classroom display. By taking time to prepare these items your first year and laminating them if possible, you will be able to reuse them year after year. See the given sections of the Management Guide in your *Teacher's Reference Manual* for more information and suggestions.

- ☐ Number Line (−35 to 180)
- ☐ Poster 1: 3-D Geometry (English/Spanish)
- ☐ Poster 2: 2-D Geometry (English/Spanish)
- ☐ Poster 3: *,/ Facts Table (English/Spanish)
- ☐ Poster 4: Class Number Grid (English/Spanish)
- ☐ A Class Data Pad (for example, chart paper on an easel)

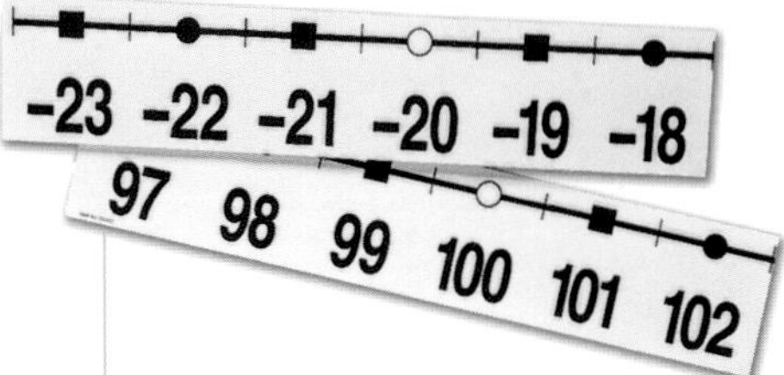

Classroom Setup

The following items should be considered as you set up your classroom for *Everyday Mathematics*. Try several arrangements until you find one that is comfortable and effective for you and your students. Visit other classrooms in your building to observe and discuss what works for your colleagues.

- ☐ Prepare and label a location in the classroom where students can deposit their written work such as Math Messages, Study Links, Exit Slips, and so on.
- ☐ Arrange classroom desks/tables to allow for easy access to manipulatives and to facilitate efficient transitions for individual, partner, and small-group activities.
- ☐ Organize class and individual manipulatives for easy access and efficient use of storage space.
- ☐ Allow (table) space for math center(s). Selected games and activities can then be left in this space for ongoing practice or free exploration.
- ☐ Identify a place where the daily Math Message will be posted. See the *Teacher's Reference Manual* for information about the Math Message.
- ☐ One or more computers with Internet access allows students to use software and Web sites that are recommended in *Fourth Grade Everyday Mathematics.*

Manipulatives

The table below lists the materials that are used throughout *Fourth Grade Everyday Mathematics*. Some lessons call for minor additional materials, which you or your students can bring in at the appropriate time.

Additional Valuable Classroom Resources

- Overhead Projector Materials
- Class Data Pad (a 12" by 15" spiral flip chart)
- World Map

Quantity	Item
1 set	Base-10 Blocks
1 per student	Calculators (Texas Instruments TI-15 or Casio *fx*-55 recommended)
1 per student	Compass, Helix
1 pkg (2,000)	Connectors (twist-ties)
1	Cup Set, standard
1 per student	Dice, Dot
3 pkgs (18 total)	Dice, Polyhedral
15 decks	Everything Math Decks
2 pkgs (20 total)	Eyedroppers
2 sets	Graduated Beakers
1	Liter Pitcher
1	Liter Volume Cube
1 per student	Geometry Template (in student materials set)
8	Geoboards, Two-Sided, 7" × 7"
10	Meterstick, Dual Scale
1	Number Line, −35 to 180
2 sets	Pattern Blocks
2 sets	Play Money Coin Sets
1	Rocker Balance
1 pkg (400)	Rubber Bands
1 per student	Slate or Marker Boards
1 pkg (500)	Straws
15	Tape Measures, Retractable
1	Tape Measure, 30m /100'
1 per student	Tool-Kit Bags
15	Transparent Mirror

All of the items above are available from McGraw-Hill. They may be purchased either as a comprehensive classroom manipulatives kit or by individual components. The manipulatives kit provides multiple classroom quantities and comes packaged in durable plastic tubs with labels.

Instruction

The following sections introduce instructional procedures and suggestions for implementing *Everyday Mathematics.* Teachers are encouraged to read these pages and refer to them as needed throughout the school year.

Program Routines

Everyday Mathematics uses a number of program routines that are incorporated throughout all grade levels. These routines provide a consistent and familiar format for ongoing practice and applications.

Below is a list of the program routines you will encounter in *Fourth Grade Everyday Mathematics.* The lesson in which each routine is first used has been noted. Refer to the Management Guide in the *Teacher's Reference Manual* for more information.

Math Message (Lesson 1-1)
Mental Math and Reflexes (Lesson 1-1)
Study Links (Lesson 1-1)
Games (Lesson 1-2)
Name-Collection Boxes (Lesson 2-2)
Math Boxes (Lesson 1-1)
Fact Triangles (+,−) (Lesson 1-1)
Fact Triangles (∗,/) (Lesson 3-2)
"What's My Rule?"/Function Machines (Lesson 3-1)

Students who have used *Third Grade Everyday Mathematics* will be familiar with the above routines, so most can be reintroduced with a minimum of explanation.

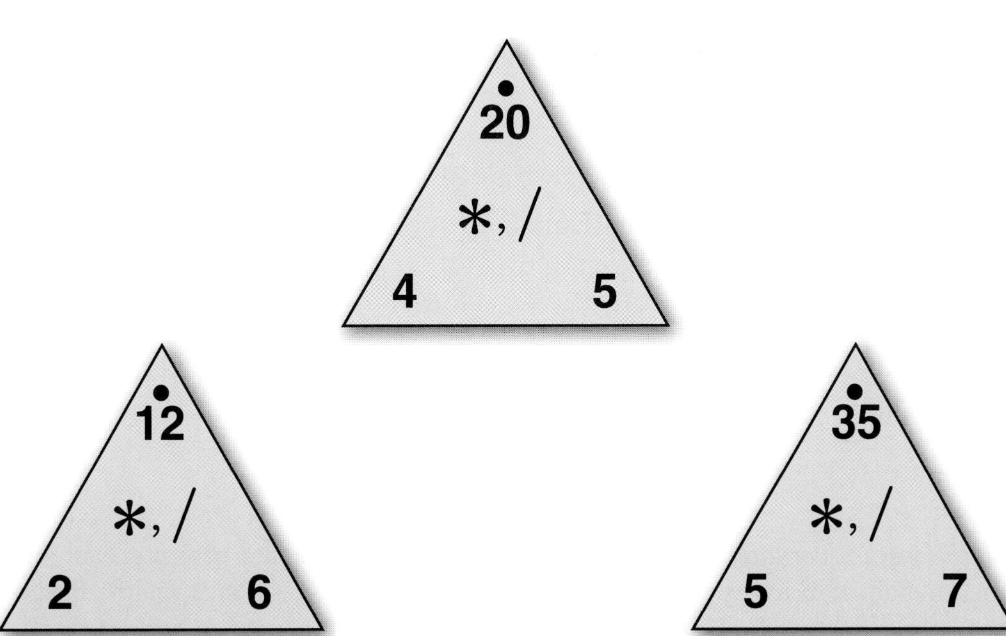

Games

A significant amount of practice in *Everyday Mathematics* is formatted as games, which are accordingly integral to the program and must not be omitted. Establish a games routine during the first unit and maintain it throughout the year. Once established, the routine will become self-sustaining, as much by the students' enthusiasm as by your effort. Make sure that all students are afforded time to play the games, especially those students who require the most practice.

Suggestions for building games into your instructional program:

- Include games as part of your daily morning routine.
- Devote the first or last 10 minutes of each math class to playing games from the current unit.
- Designate one math class per week as Games Day. Set up stations that feature the unit games. Ask parent volunteers to assist in the rotation of students though these stations.
- Set up a Games Corner that features some of the students' favorite games. Encourage students to visit this corner during free time. Change the games frequently to maintain student interest.

The World Tour

In fourth grade, students also go on a yearlong World Tour, collecting, analyzing, and representing information about the countries of the world. The tour is easily linked to geography and other social studies and language arts topics. The *Fourth Grade Everyday Mathematics Student Reference Book* has a special World Tour section, which is a source of information for the yearlong project. This section contains maps, data about countries in the World Tour, essays of interest, and games. The World Tour is introduced in Lesson 2-1.

Museums

Everyday Mathematics encourages the development of classroom museums using a bulletin board or table where related items can be collected, categorized, and labeled. *Fourth Grade Everyday Mathematics* includes the following museums:

- Numbers and Their Uses Museum (Unit 2)
- Decimals All Around Museum (Unit 4)
- Percents All Around Museum (Unit 9)
- Line Symmetry Museum (Unit 10)
- Gram and Ounce Museum; Liter and Milliliter Museum (Unit 11)
- Rates Museum (Unit 12)

Projects

Fourth Grade Everyday Mathematics provides seven optional projects, each of which includes an array of mathematics activities that focus on a theme that interests students. The Unit Organizers in the *Teacher's Lesson Guide* include reminders about these projects at appropriate times throughout the year. With the exception of the yearlong World Tour, projects typically take one to two days to complete, depending upon how many of the suggested activities you incorporate. Projects involve a range of concepts and skills; integrate mathematics with science, social studies, art, and language arts; and allow the teacher to assess students' abilities to apply the mathematics they have learned in cross-curricular contexts. Projects are also often memorable for students.

Refer to the Management Guide in the *Teacher's Reference Manual* and the Unit Organizers in the *Teacher's Lesson Guide* for more information. Detailed explanations for the projects are found at the back of the *Teacher's Lesson Guides*.

Assessment

Everyday Mathematics supports a balanced approach to assessment, one that provides information both for guiding instruction and for evaluating student performance. Assessment takes place on an ongoing basis as students complete their everyday work and in special periodic assessments, such as the Progress Check lesson at the end of each unit. Information for assessment is gathered both through teacher observations while students are working and through students' written products.

Refer to the *Assessment Handbook* and the Unit Organizers in the *Teacher's Lesson Guide* for detailed information regarding student assessment.

Differentiation

Everyday Mathematics has been designed to accommodate a wide range of student backgrounds and abilities, including English language learners. The program also includes many tools and suggestions to help teachers differentiate instruction to meet students' diverse needs, including Enrichment, Readiness, ELL, and Extra Practice activities in Part 3 of the lessons and Adjusting the Activity suggestions in Parts 1 and 2. Differentiated instruction gives students multiple options for taking in information, making sense of ideas, building skills, and communicating what they have learned.

Refer to the *Differentiation Handbook* and the Unit Organizers in the *Teacher's Lesson Guide* for detailed information about differentiation in *Everyday Mathematics*.

Providing for Home-School Connections

Comprehensive and consistent home-school communication is essential for successful implementation of *Everyday Mathematics*. *Everyday Mathematics* provides a number of support materials to facilitate this communication. The *Home Connection Handbook* has many suggestions and tools that can help you introduce parents and primary caregivers to the *Everyday Mathematics* curriculum. Grade-specific Family Letters and Study Links in the *Math Masters* facilitate ongoing communication and engage parents as partners in the learning process. Individual assessment checklists in the *Assessment Handbook* enable teachers to document in detail the progress of each student and are a valuable communication tool during parent conferences.

Refer to the *Home Connection Handbook* for more information.

4–6 Games Correlation Chart

Games	Grade 4 Lesson	Grade 5 Lesson	Grade 6 Lesson	Basic Facts	Operations	Calculator	Numeration	Geometry	Data	Algebra	Measurement/ Ref. Frames	Mental Math	Strategy
				Skill and Concept Areas									
Addition Top-It (Extended-Facts Version)	1•2			●	●		●					●	
Addition Top-It (Decimal Version)		2•2			●		●					●	
Algebra Election		4•7	6•11		●	●			●	●	●		●
Angle Add-Up	6•6				●			●			●		
Angle Tangle	6•6	3•6	5•1		●			●			●		
Base-10 Exchange	4•2						●						
Baseball Multiplication	3•3	*		●	●							●	
Beat the Calculator	3•5	*		●	●	●						●	
Beat the Calculator (Extended-Facts Version)		1•3		●	●	●						●	
Build-It		8•1	4•2				●						●
Buzz and *Bizz Buzz*	3•2				●		●						
Calculator 10,000	*				●	●							
Chances Are	7•11								●				
Coin Top-It	4•3				●		●					●	
Coordinate Search		12•8									●		●
Credits/Debits Game	10•6		3•7		●							●	
Credits/Debits Game (Advanced Version)	11•6	7•8	6•3		●							●	
Divisibility Dash		4•4	2•6	●	●		●					●	●
Division Arrays	3•5			●	●							●	
Division Dash	6•3	4•2			●							●	
Division Top-It	*	4•5	2•7		●		●					●	
Doggone Decimal			2•4		●	●	●					●	●
Estimation Squeeze		5•5				●	●					●	
Exponent Ball		7•1	2•10		●	●	●					●	
Factor Bingo		1•7		●	●		●					●	
Factor Captor		1•4	3•2	●	●		●					●	●
Factor Top-It		*		●	●		●					●	
Finish First		6•2		●	●							●	
First to 100		4•7	8•12	●	●					●		●	
Fishing for Digits	2•4				●	●	●						●
500		7•8			●								
Frac-Tac-Toe		5•7	4•8		●		●					●	●
Fraction Action, Fraction Friction		8•4	4•4		●		●					●	
Fraction Capture		6•9	4•1		●							●	●
Fraction Match	7•6						●					●	●
Fraction Of	7•2	5•11			●		●					●	●
Fraction/Percent Concentration	9•3	5•8				●	●					●	
Fraction Spin		8•5			●		●						●
Fraction Top-It	7•9	5•1					●					●	
Fraction Top-It (Advanced Version)		6•8			●		●					●	
Fraction/Whole Number Top-It		*	6•1		●		●					●	

Number indicates first exposure at grade level. *Available in the Games section of the *Student Reference Book.*

;ames Correlation Chart *continued*

ames	Grade 4 Lesson	Grade 5 Lesson	Grade 6 Lesson	Basic Facts	Operations	Calculator	Numeration	Geometry	Data	Algebra	Measurement/ Ref. Frames	Mental Math	Strategy
				Skill and Concept Areas									
etting to One	7•10	*	3•10			●	●						●
rab Bag	7•3		7•1		●				●	●		●	●
reedy			7•7						●			●	●
rid Search	6•8										●		●
idden Treasure		9•1									●		●
igh-Number Toss	2•7	2•10	1•2				●						●
igh-Number Toss (Decimal Version)		2•5	1•11		●		●						●
andmark Shark			1•5						●			●	●
lixed-Number Spin		8•3	4•7		●		●			●		●	●
lultiplication Bull's-Eye		2•7	2•5		●	●	●					●	
lultiplication Top-It	3•3	3•3	2•5	●	●		●					●	
lultiplication Top-It (Extended-Facts Version)		1•8		●	●		●					●	
lultiplication Wrestling	5•2	*	9•1		●		●			●		●	●
ame That Number	2•2	1•9	1•8		●		●			●		●	●
umber Top-It (7-Digit Numbers)	5•11	2•10	2•1				●						●
umber Top-It (Decimals)	4•4	5•6					●						●
ver and Up Squares	6•9		1•6								●		●
ercent/Sector Match-Up			1•9				●						●
olygon Capture		3•7	5•8					●					
olygon Pair-Up	1•6							●					
roduct Pile-Up	4•3			●			●					●	●
ugs and Fences	8•7	11•4								●	●	●	●
cientific Notation Toss		7•3	2•9				●						●
eega	3•6												●
ides and Angles: Triangles		3•6						●			●		
olution Search			6•12		●					●			●
poon Scramble		12•6	5•4				●					●	
preadsheet Scramble			3•7		●							●	●
prouts	1•2							●					●
ubtraction Target Practice	2•9	*			●	●							●
ubtraction Target Practice (Decimal Version)		2•3			●	●							●
ubtraction Top-It (Extended-Facts Version)	1•4			●	●		●					●	
z'kwa	1•4							●					●
-D Shape Sort		11•2	5•10					●					
op-It with Positive and Negative Numbers		7•11	6•4		●		●					●	
riangle Sort		3•6						●					
enn Diagram Challenge			7•6					●	●				●
/hat's My Attribute Rule?		3•7						●					●
/here Do I Fit In?		3•6						●					
and O—Tic-Tac-Toe			5•4								●		●

Number indicates first exposure at grade level. *Available in the Games section of the *Student Reference Book*.

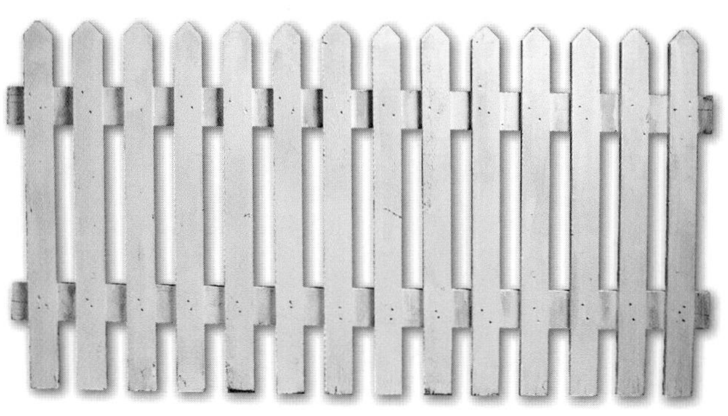

Unit 1 Organizer

Naming and Constructing Geometric Figures

Overview

The principal focus of Unit 1 is geometry. Opening with geometry enables a relatively relaxed beginning of the school year and allows teachers and students to get acquainted and establish yearlong routines. Starting the year with geometry also makes the point that mathematics is more than numbers and is strongly linked to language and art. Unit 1 has five main areas of focus:

- To introduce students to the *Student Reference Book*,
- To practice using geometry tools,
- To classify quadrangles,
- To explore and identify polygons, and
- To review and practice addition and subtraction fact extensions.

Linking to the Common Core State Standards

The content of Unit 1 addresses the Common Core State Standards for Mathematics in *Geometry.* The correlation of the Common Core State Standards to the *Everyday Mathematics* Grade 4 lessons begins on page CS1.

Contents

Learning In Perspective

	Lesson Objectives	Links to the Past	Links to the Future
1•1	To acquaint students with the content and organization of the *Student Reference Book.*	Grade 3: Use *Student Reference Book.* Grades 1 and 2: Use *My Reference Book.*	Grades 5 and 6: Use *Student Reference Book.*
1•2	To introduce tools for geometry; and to review points, line segments, lines, and rays.	Grade 3: Use straws and arrowheads to model lines, line segments, and rays; use notation to name points, line segments, lines, and rays. Grades 1 and 2: Name and draw points and line segments.	Grades 4–6: Applications and maintenance.
1•3	To guide students in the construction of angles, triangles, and quadrangles and in the classification of quadrangles.	Grade 3: Use straws to model angles, triangles, and quadrangles. Grade 2: Trace pattern blocks, and use geoboards to construct polygons.	Grade 4: Introduce acute, obtuse, straight, and reflex angles; find the sum of measures of the angles of a triangle (Unit 6). Grade 5: Introduce vertical (opposite), adjacent, and supplementary angles; find the sum of measures of the angles of any polygon; identify corresponding sides of congruent and similar figures.
1•4	To model the classification of quadrangles based on their properties.	Grade 3: Use straws to construct polygons with specific characteristics. Grades 1 and 2: Explore similarities and differences among quadrangles.	Grade 4: Measure, draw and classify types of angles; review properties of parallelograms (Unit 6). Grade 5: Explore angle relationships in parallelograms; investigate whether all quadrangles tessellate.
1•5	To provide opportunities to identify properties of polygons and distinguish between convex and nonconvex (concave) polygons; and to explore geometric definitions and classification.	Grades 2 and 3: Discuss common characteristics of all polygons and of regular polygons; introduce the term *parallel.* Grades 1–3: Explore polygons with straws, geoboards, and dot paper. Name the parts of a polygon: side, vertex, and angle.	Grade 4: Construct polygons by folding paper and with compass and straightedge; identify lines of symmetry for polygons, and introduce congruent figures (Units 6, 10, and 11). Grades 5 and 6: Explore transformations of polygons in a plane; investigate congruent and similar figures; determine which regular polygons tessellate.
1•6	To provide practice using a compass.	Grades 1 and 3: Use a ruler, Pattern-Block Template, and dot paper to draw figures and create designs.	Grade 4: Construct equilateral triangles, parallelograms, and parallel lines. Grades 5 and 6: Review and extend compass and straightedge constructions.
1•7	To guide students in defining a circle; and to provide opportunities to explore designs with circles.	Grade 3: Explore relationship of diameter to circumference.	Grades 5 and 6: Use formulas to find circumference and area of a circle.
1•8	To guide students in the construction of figures with a compass and straightedge.	Grades 1 and 3: Use a ruler, Pattern-Block Template, and dot paper to draw figures and create designs.	Grade 4: Construct equilateral triangles, parallelograms, and parallel lines. Grades 5 and 6: Review and extend compass and straightedge constructions.

	Key Concepts and Skills	Grade 4 Goals*
1•1	Use the symbols >, <, and = to compare numbers and numerical expressions.	Number and Numeration Goal 6
	Solve simple +, −, ×, and ÷ problems.	Operations and Computation Goals 1 and 3
	Describe relationships among U.S. customary units of length.	Measurement and Reference Frames Goal 3
1•2	Identify and draw line segments, lines, and rays.	Geometry Goal 1
	Describe characteristics of line segments, lines, and rays.	Geometry Goal 1
	Use letter and symbol notation to name line segments, lines, and rays.	Geometry Goal 1
1•3	Use letter notation to name angles.	Geometry Goal 1
	Construct angles, triangles, and quadrangles.	Geometry Goals 1 and 2
	Describe properties of and compare quadrangles.	Geometry Goal 2
	Identify types of quadrangles.	Geometry Goal 2
1•4	Develop definitions for *parallel* and *intersecting line segments, lines,* and *rays.*	Geometry Goal 1
	Develop a definition for *perpendicular line segments.*	Geometry Goal 1
	Describe characteristics of parallelograms.	Geometry Goal 2
	Classify quadrangles based on side and angle properties.	Geometry Goal 2
1•5	Construct convex and nonconvex (concave) polygons.	Geometry Goal 2
	Develop definitions for *convex* and *nonconvex* (*concave*) *polygons.*	Geometry Goal 2
	Describe properties of polygons and regular polygons.	Geometry Goal 2
	Identify types of polygons according to the number of sides.	Geometry Goal 2
1•6	Use a compass to measure distance.	Measurement and Reference Frames Goal 1
	Use a compass to draw circles.	Geometry Goal 2
	Construct an inscribed square.	Geometry Goal 2
	Verify that the sides of a square are the same length.	Geometry Goal 2
1•7	Measure line segments to the nearest centimeter.	Measurement and Reference Frames Goal 1
	Demonstrate and explain the meaning of *intersect.*	Geometry Goal 1
	Use a compass to draw circles.	Geometry Goal 2
	Demonstrate and explain the meanings of *concentric, radius,* and *congruent.*	Geometry Goal 2
1•8	Use a compass as a tool to measure distance.	Measurement and Reference Frames Goal 1
	Copy a line segment with a compass and straightedge.	Geometry Goal 1
	Use a compass to draw circles; construct a regular hexagon inscribed in a circle.	Geometry Goal 2
	Verify that the sides of regular polygons are the same length.	Geometry Goal 2

*See the Appendix for a complete list of Grade 4 Goals.

A Balanced Curriculum

Ongoing Practice

Everyday Mathematics provides numerous opportunities for ongoing practice. These activities are embedded throughout the lessons:

Mental Math and Reflexes activities promote speed and accuracy in mental computation.

Math Boxes offer mixed practice and are paired across lessons as shown in the brackets below. This makes them useful as assessment tools. The last one or two boxes on each page preview the next unit's content.

Mixed practice	[1•1, 1•3], [1•2, 1•4], [1•5, 1•7], [1•6, 1•8]
Mixed practice with multiple choice	1•1, 1•4, 1•5, 1•8
Mixed practice with writing/reasoning opportunity	1•3, 1•4, 1•6, 1•7

Study Links are daily homework assignments that review the content of the lesson and often contain ongoing facts practice or computation practice.

5-Minute Math problems are offered for additional practice in Lesson 1•3.

EM Facts Workshop Game provides online practice of basic facts and computation.

EXTRA PRACTICE **Extra Practice** activities are included in Lessons 1•3, 1•6, and 1•8.

Practice through Games

Games are an essential component of practice in the *Everyday Mathematics* program. Games offer skills practice and promote strategic thinking. See the *Differentiation Handbook* for ways to adapt games to meet students' needs.

Lesson	Game	Skill Practiced
1•1	*Top-It*	**Use symbols to compare numbers** [NN Goal 6]
1•2	*Addition Top-It* (Extended-Facts Version)	**Solve addition fact extensions** [OC Goal 1]
1•2	*Sprouts*	**Explore line segments and points** [GEO Goal 1]
1•4	*Subtraction Top-It* (Extended-Facts Version)	**Solve subtraction fact extensions** [OC Goal 1]
1•4	*Sz'kwa*	**Explore intersecting line segments** [GEO Goal 1]
1•6, 1•7	*Polygon Pair-Up*	**Describe properties of polygons** [GEO Goal 2]

[NN] Number and Numeration
[MRF] Measurement and Reference Frames
[OC] Operations and Computation
[GEO] Geometry
[DC] Data and Chance
[PFA] Patterns, Functions, and Algebra

Problem Solving 

Experts at problem solving and mathematical modeling generally do these things:

- Identify the problem.
- Decide what information is needed to solve the problem.
- Play with and study the data to find patterns and meaning.
- Identify and use mathematical procedures to solve the problem.
- Decide whether the solution makes sense and whether it can be applied to other problems.

The table below lists some of the opportunities in this unit for students to practice these strategies.

Lesson	Activity
1•3	Make triangles and different types of quadrangles with straws and twist-ties.
1•4	Classify geometric shapes according to their properties.
1•5	Explain what a polygon is.
1•6	Discuss ways to draw a large circle on the playground.
1•7	Use a compass to draw three designs that involve more than one circle.
1•8	Construct a regular hexagon inscribed in a circle.

Lessons that teach *through* problem solving, not just *about* problem solving

See Chapter 18: Problem Solving in the *Teacher's Reference Manual* for more information.

The Language of Mathematics

Everyday Mathematics provides lesson-specific suggestions to help all students acquire, process, and express mathematical ideas. Throughout Unit 1, there are lesson-specific language development notes that address the needs of English language learners, indicated by ELL.

ELL SUPPORT Activities to support English language learners are in Part 3 of Lessons 1•2, 1•3, and 1•7.

The *English Learners Handbook* and the *Differentiation Handbook* have suggestions for promoting language development and acquisition of mathematics vocabulary. See Unit 1 in each handbook.

Literacy Connection

Lesson 1•5 *The Greedy Triangle,* by Marilyn Burns, Scholastic Inc., 1995

Lesson 1•6 *Ed Emberley's Picture Pie: A Cut and Paste Drawing Book,* by Ed Emberley, Little Brown, 2006

For more literacy connections, see the *Home Connection Handbook,* Grades 4–6.

Unit 1 Vocabulary

angle
center (of a circle)
circle
compass
concentric circles
congruent
convex
endpoint
equilateral triangle
heptagon
hexagon
inscribed square
interior
intersect
kite
line
line segment
n-gon
nonagon
nonconvex or concave
octagon
parallel line segments
parallel lines
parallel rays
parallelogram
pentagon
perpendicular line segments
point
polygon
quadrangle
quadrilateral
radius
ray
rectangle
regular polygon
rhombus
right angle
side
square
trapezoid
triangle
vertex (vertices)

Cross-Curricular Links

Language Arts – Lessons 1•1, 1•5, 1•8

Literature – Lesson 1•5

Art – Lessons 1•6, 1•8

Balanced Assessment

Daily Assessments

- **Recognizing Student Achievement** – A daily assessment that is included in every lesson to evaluate students' progress toward the Grade 4 Grade-Level Goals.
- **Informing Instruction** – Notes that appear throughout the unit to help anticipate students' common errors and suggest appropriate problem-solving strategies.

Lesson	Recognizing Student Achievement	Informing Instruction
1•1	Demonstrate automaticity with addition fact extensions. [OC Goal 1]	
1•2	Describe a line segment and a line. [GEO Goal 1]	Connect points to other points.
1•3	Compare and contrast plane figures. [GEO Goal 2]	Consider the measures of angles rather than the lengths of rays.
1•4	Understand parallel line segments. [GEO Goal 1]	
1•5	Explain the properties of polygons. [GEO Goal 2]	Distinguish regular polygons from other polygons.
1•6	Understand right angles. [GEO Goal 1]	
1•7	Construct circles with a compass. [GEO Goal 2]	
1•8	Demonstrate automaticity with subtraction fact extensions. [OC Goal 1]	Connect consecutive marks to form a regular hexagon.

[NN] Number and Numeration [OC] Operations and Computation [DC] Data and Chance
[MRF] Measurement and Reference Frames [GEO] Geometry [PFA] Patterns, Functions, and Algebra

Portfolio Opportunities

The following lessons provide opportunities to gather samples of students' mathematical writings, drawings, and creations to add balance to the assessment process: Lessons 1•3, 1•4, 1•5, 1•6, 1•7, and 1•9.

See pages 16 and 17 in the *Assessment Handbook* for more information about portfolios and how to use them.

Unit Assessment

Progress Check 1 – A cumulative assessment of concepts and skills taught in Unit 1, providing information for evaluating students' progress and planning for future instruction. These assessments include oral/slate, written, and open-response activities, as shown below in the sample Progress Check lesson opener.

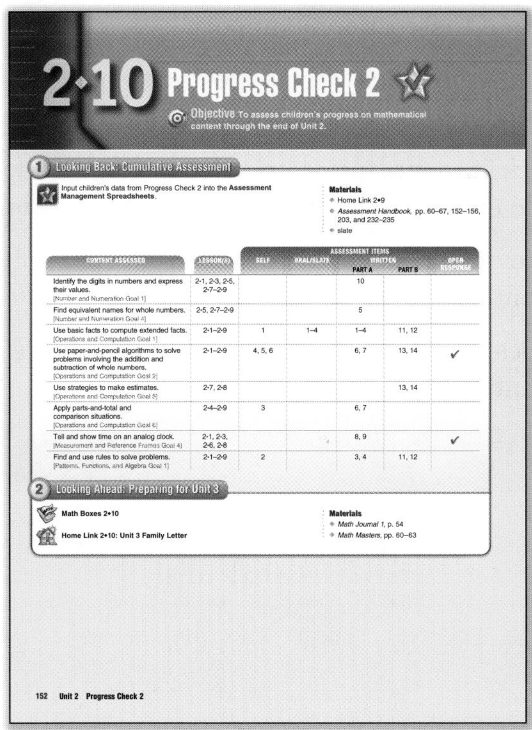

2·10 Progress Check 2

Objective To assess children's progress on mathematical content through the end of Unit 2.

1 Looking Back: Cumulative Assessment

Input children's data from Progress Check 2 into the **Assessment Management Spreadsheets**.

Materials
- Home Link 2•9
- *Assessment Handbook*, pp. 60–67, 152–156, 203, and 232–235
- slate

Content Assessed	Lesson(s)	Assessment Items: Self	Oral/Slate	Written: Part A	Written: Part B	Open Response
Identify the digits in numbers and express their values. [Number and Numeration Goal 1]	2·1, 2·3, 2·5, 2·7–2·9			10		
Find equivalent names for whole numbers. [Number and Numeration Goal 4]	2·5, 2·7–2·9			5		
Use basic facts to compute extended facts. [Operations and Computation Goal 1]	2·1–2·9	1	1–4	1–4	11, 12	
Use paper-and-pencil algorithms to solve problems involving the addition and subtraction of whole numbers. [Operations and Computation Goal 2]	2·1–2·9	4, 5, 6		6, 7	13, 14	✓
Use strategies to make estimates. [Operations and Computation Goal 5]	2·7, 2·8				13, 14	
Apply parts-and-total and comparison situations. [Operations and Computation Goal 6]	2·4–2·9	3		6, 7		
Tell and show time on an analog clock. [Measurement and Reference Frames Goal 4]	2·1, 2·3, 2·6, 2·8			8, 9		✓
Find and use rules to solve problems. [Patterns, Functions, and Algebra Goal 1]	2·1–2·9	2		3, 4	11, 12	

2 Looking Ahead: Preparing for Unit 3

Math Boxes 2•10

Home Link 2•10: Unit 3 Family Letter

Materials
- *Math Journal 1*, p. 54
- *Math Masters*, pp. 60–63

152 Unit 2 Progress Check 2

Core Assessment Resources

Assessment Handbook

- **Unit 1 Assessment Overview,** pages 52–59
- **Unit 1 Assessment Masters,** pages 154–158
- **Unit 1 Individual Profiles of Progress,** pages 246, 247, and 302
- **Unit 1 Class Checklists,** pages 248, 249, and 303
- **Beginning-of-Year Assessment,*** pages 227A–227D
- **Math Logs,** pages 306–308
- **Exit Slip,** page 311
- **Other Student Assessment Forms,** pages 304, 305, 309, and 310

*The Beginning-of-Year Assessment is one of the screening tools that can be used to help identify which concepts and skills students have learned and to help plan instruction for the upcoming year.

Assessment Management Spreadsheets

The Assessment Management Spreadsheets consist of the Digital Class Checklists and Individual Profile of Progress Checklists. Use them to monitor, record, and report student progress.

Addressing All Needs

Differentiated Instruction

Adjusting the Activity – suggests adaptations that target advanced learners, English language learners, or learners who need additional instructional support.

ELL SUPPORT / **ELL** – provides lesson-specific suggestions to help English language learners understand and process the mathematical content.

READINESS – accesses students' prior knowledge or previews content that prepares students to engage in the lesson's Part 1 activities.

EXTRA PRACTICE – provides additional opportunities to apply the mathematical content of the lesson.

ENRICHMENT – enables students to apply or further explore the mathematical content of the lesson.

Lesson	Adjusting the Activity	ELL Support/ ELL	Readiness	Extra Practice	Enrichment
1•1	•	•	•		•
1•2	•	•	•		•
1•3	•	•	•	•	•
1•4	•	•	•		•
1•5	•	•	•		•
1•6	•			•	•
1•7	•	•			•
1•8	•		•	•	•

Additional Resources

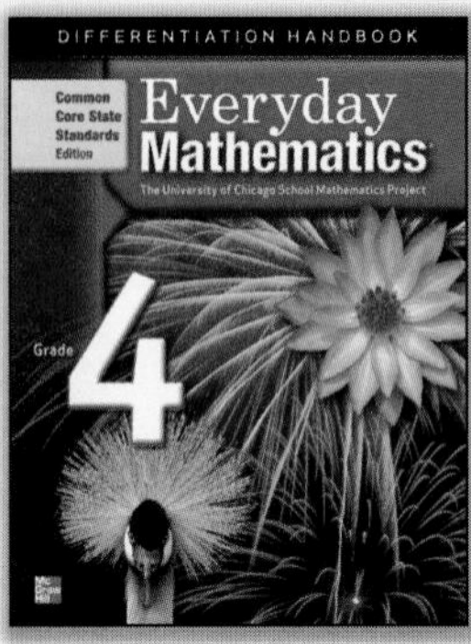

Differentiation Handbook
Provides ideas and strategies for differentiating instruction.
Pages 48–54

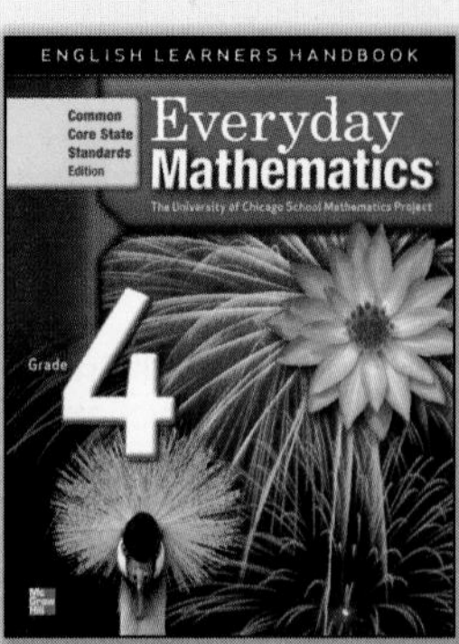

English Learners Handbook
Contains lesson-specific comprehension strategies.
Pages 1–8

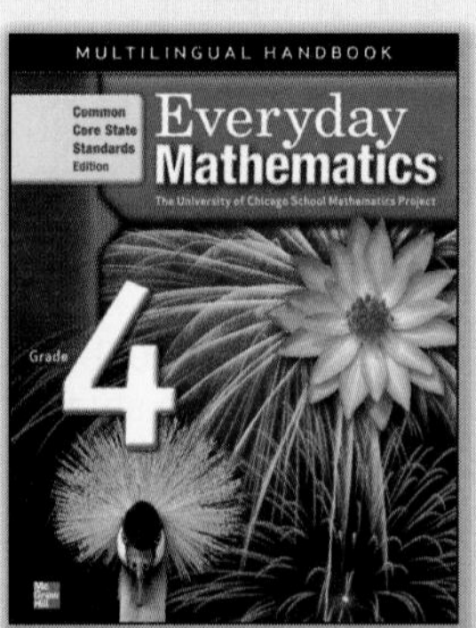

Multilingual Handbook
Previews concepts and vocabulary. It is written in six languages.
Pages 1–16

Planning Tips

Multiage Classroom

Companion Lessons from Grades 3 and 5 can help you meet instructional needs of a multiage classroom. The full Scope and Sequence can be found in the Appendix.

Grade 3	1•3	6•1, 6•2	3•4, 3•5, 6•3–6•8	3•4, 6•5	1•4, 5•6, 6•5, 6•6	3•9	1•4, 3•9	1•4, 3•4, 3•6
Grade 4	**1•1**	**1•2**	**1•3**	**1•4**	**1•5**	**1•6**	**1•7**	**1•8**
Grade 5	1•1	3•4, 3•5	3•3–3•5, 3•7	3•4–3•5, 3•7	3•7	3•5	5•10, 5•11	9•5, 9•6

Pacing for Success

Pacing depends on a number of factors, such as students' individual needs and how long your school has been using *Everyday Mathematics*. At the beginning of Unit 1, you may want to use tools available at www.everydaymathonline.com to help you set your pace.

Home Support

Unit 1 Family Letter (English/Spanish) provides families with an overview, Do-Anytime Activities, Building Skills through Games, a list of vocabulary, and answers to the daily homework (Study Links). Family Letters in English, Spanish, and seven other languages are also available online.

Study Links are the daily homework assignments. They consist of active projects and ongoing review problems.

Home Support Resources

Home Connection Handbook
Offers ideas and reproducible masters for communicating with families. See Table of Contents for unit information.

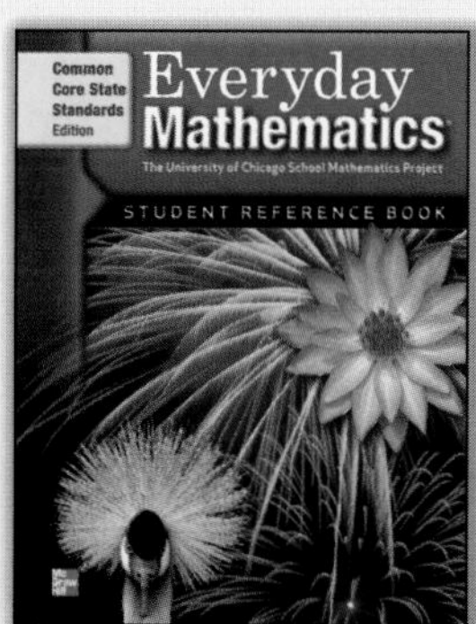

Student Reference Book
Provides a resource for students and parents.

Pages 88–91, 97, 100, 114, 117, 118, 258, 263, 264, 310, 313

Technology Resources

Materials

Technology Resources www.everydaymathonline.com

ePresentations

eToolkit

Algorithms Practice

EM Facts Workshop Game™

Family Letters

Assessment Management

Common Core State Standards

Curriculum Focal Points

Interactive Teacher's Lesson Guide

Lesson	Masters	Manipulative Kit	Other Items
1•1	Study Link Masters, pp. 2–5 Teaching Aid Masters, pp. 384–387 Teaching Masters, pp. 6 and 7	per group: 4 each of number cards 0–9	stick-on notes*; paper clips; small resealable plastic bags or regular envelopes; scissors
1•2	Teaching Aid Master, p. 388* or 389* Study Link Master, p. 8 Game Master, p. 506 Teaching Masters, pp. 9 and 10	slate or marker board; per group: 4 each of number cards 1–10; geoboard; rubber bands; compass	chalk or dry-erase marker; socks brought by students; yardstick or ruler; calculator; Geometry Template
1•3	Teaching Aid Masters, pp. 388* or 389* and 390 Study Link Master, p. 11 Teaching Masters, pp. 12 and 13	slate; straws and twist-ties; pattern blocks	straightedge; chart paper; tape*; Geometry Template
1•4	Teaching Masters, pp. 14, 16, and 17 Study Link Master, p. 15 Game Masters, pp. 505 and 506	slate; 4 each of number cards 1–10; geoboard; rubber bands; straws	straightedge; 40 counters (20 each of 2 different colors); Geometry Template*
1•5	Study Link Master, p. 18 Teaching Masters, pp. 19–22	slate; straws; twist-ties; geoboard; rubber bands	straightedge; *The Greedy Triangle*
1•6	Study Link Master, p. 23 Game Masters, pp. 496 and 497 Teaching Master, p. 24	slate; compass	paper (colored*); straightedge; cardboard; scissors; glue; *Ed Emberley's Picture Pie: A Cut and Paste Drawing Book*
1•7	Teaching Masters, pp. 25 and 27–29 Study Link Master, p. 26 *Polygon Pair-Up* Property Cards and Polygon Cards, pp. 496 and 497 *Differentiation Handbook,* p. 140	slate; compass	tape; scissors; board compass; straightedge; Geometry Template
1•8	Study Link Master, p. 30 Teaching Masters, pp. 31–33	slate; compass	straightedge; tape; scissors; board compass; crayons or markers; paper; Geometry Template
1•9	Assessment Masters, pp. 154–158 and 227A–227D Study Link Masters, pp. 34–37	compass	Geometry Template

*Denotes optional materials

Mathematical Background

The discussion below highlights the major content ideas presented in Unit 1 and helps establish instructional priorities.

Why Geometry?

The title of this series is *Everyday Mathematics,* not *Everyday Arithmetic.* This title reflects the authors' belief that arithmetic, though important, is only a fraction of what most people should know about mathematics to cope intelligently with today's world.

High school students often have a great deal of trouble in geometry courses because they have had little prior experience that builds spatial reasoning. *Everyday Mathematics* provides a remedy to that situation with geometry-oriented action and experience in elementary school. The activities, written so that they are interesting and fun for elementary students, build a foundation for geometry—an intuition about geometry. In *Everyday Mathematics,* informal geometry is featured throughout Grades K–3, along with other mathematical ideas beyond arithmetic.

Note

Research on child development supports the belief that waiting too long to provide experience with such things as geometric figures and relationships may be harmful. Many pathways to thinking that are easy to build with young children may be lost permanently if appropriate and timely experiences are not provided.

The *Student Reference Book*

(Lesson 1◆1)

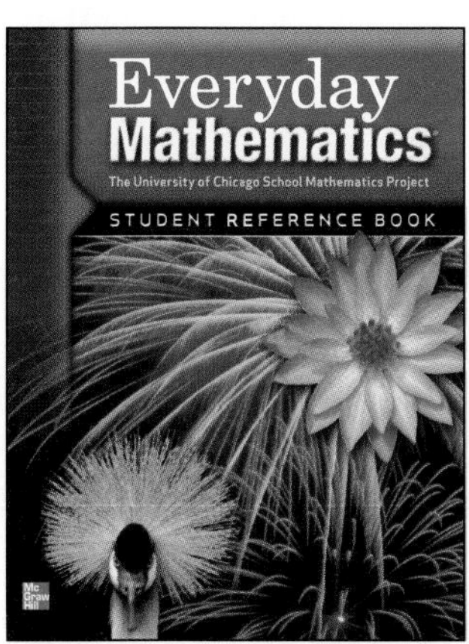

The *Student Reference Book* is a resource book containing summaries of the principal concepts and skills that students encounter in their study of mathematics. It provides review and reinforcement of critical mathematics topics and calculator usage, as well as rules for mathematical games, a reference table, a glossary of mathematical terms, and other helpful information. These materials, presented in a concise, reference-oriented format, invite students to look up information on their own, thereby encouraging them to take responsibility for their own learning. The book also serves as a resource for students who must make up work and for parents, or others, who help students at home.

From time to time, an icon (SRB) appears in the journal to indicate *Student Reference Book* pages on which there is information on the topic at hand.

See Section 1.2.9 of the *Teacher's Reference Manual* for additional information about using the *Student Reference Book.*

Note

The *Everyday Mathematics* authors believe that students should learn and practice the special skills involved in obtaining information from mathematics books, almanacs, encyclopedias,and other resources. Regular use of the *Student Reference Book* can be an important asset for your language arts program.

Beyond Informal Geometry

(Lessons 1◆2–1◆5)

Geometric figures are all well-defined sets of points. Geometry deals with the properties of those sets of points and the relationships between and among them. As *Everyday Mathematics* begins a more systematic study of figures in fourth grade, the lessons will emphasize more rigorous geometry:

- clear notations (naming),
- clear definitions, and
- clear statements of properties and relationships.

The standard notations used in secondary school geometry are introduced in Lessons 1-2 and 1-3. The symbols that distinguish lines, line segments, rays, and angles are used. Basic geometric figures are named with letters. All of these naming conventions have proven to be quite accessible to fourth graders.

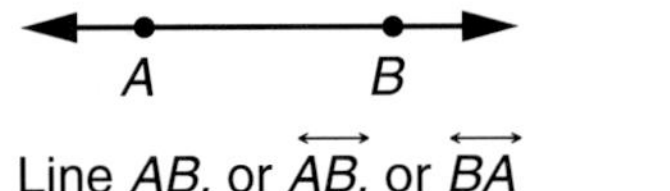

Line *AB*, or $\overleftrightarrow{AB}$, or $\overleftrightarrow{BA}$

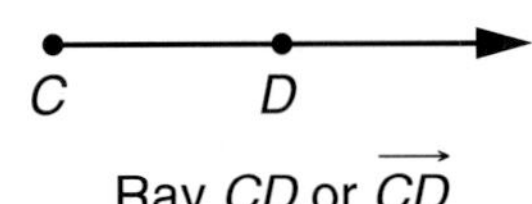

Ray *CD* or $\overrightarrow{CD}$

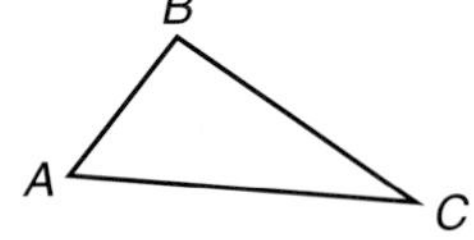

Triangle *ABC, ACB, BAC, BCA, CAB,* or *CBA*

Students quickly realize that the same figure can have many names. Triangle *ABC,* for example, may also be named *ACB, BAC, BCA, CAB,* or *CBA.* The idea that many equivalent names can be used for the same thing appears throughout *Everyday Mathematics.* The equivalent names are like synonyms, or multiple names, in language arts.

Lessons 1-4 and 1-5 help students develop more precise definitions of figures and their properties than was possible in earlier grades. The main emphasis in these lessons is on developing a grasp of how geometric figures are classified and of the relationships among figures. In Lesson 1-4, for example, students explore the properties of parallelograms. They apply their understanding of these properties by listing the similarities and differences between and among various quadrangles. In Lesson 1-5, students examine the properties that characterize polygons and regular polygons.

Feel free to use the vocabulary of geometry. Although students may not be familiar with all of the terms, consistent and frequent use of these terms enables students to develop the working vocabulary that is essential for discussing the characteristics of figures, as well as the similarities and differences among them.

Whenever you have the opportunity, take time to discuss the meanings of roots, prefixes, and suffixes of geometric terms (see Lessons 1-5 and 1-8).

For additional information about standard notation and definitions of figures and their properties, see Section 13.4 of the *Teacher's Reference Manual.*

Using a Compass and Straightedge

(Lessons 1•6–1•8)

Note

The main difficulty in using a straightedge or ruler to draw segments and rays is allowing for the width of the pencil lead. The straightedge should be placed slightly off the points. Again, there is no substitute for trial and error and then practice.

Using a compass skillfully requires quite a bit of practice, and doing so is easier for some students than for others. Since "practice makes perfect," there is no substitute for it. Good tools help a lot, too. A compass should have a sharp anchor point to prevent slipping; it should hold the pencil securely. Use a sharp, soft lead pencil that is short enough so that it does not interfere with the rotation of the compass.

Make certain that when students use a compass, they draw on a piece of cardboard, pad of paper, or the like so that the compass anchor does not slip and damage the desk or tabletop. Two methods for drawing circles with a compass are described in Lesson 1-6. Practice both methods yourself before teaching them.

Section 13.13.1 of the *Teacher's Reference Manual* contains additional information about using a compass and a straightedge to construct figures on paper.

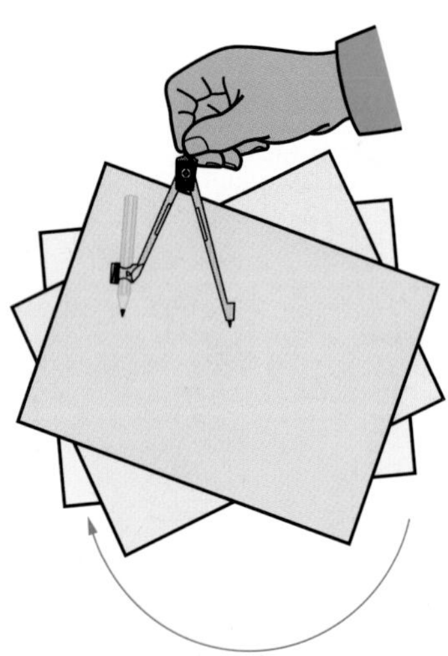

Rotating the paper is one way to use a compass.

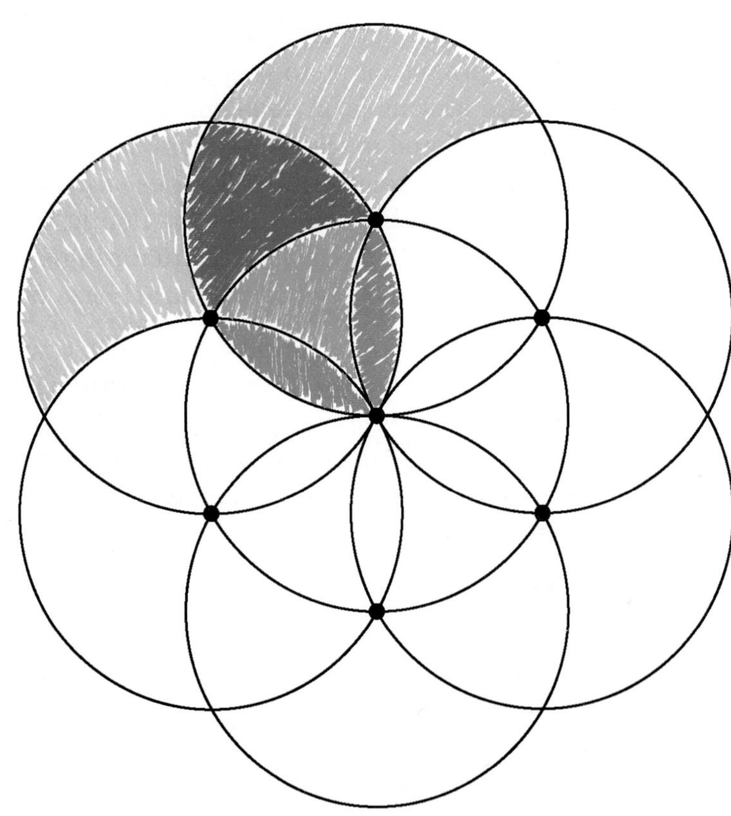

On journal page 19, students use compasses to create circle designs.

Addition and Subtraction Fact Extensions

By now, all students are expected to have achieved automatic recall of the basic addition and subtraction facts. In fourth grade, students will work toward achieving automaticity with addition and subtraction fact extensions. Students have been exposed to these fact extensions in previous grades of *Everyday Mathematics.* Fluency with fact extensions is important because they provide powerful mental arithmetic strategies when working with large numbers.

For additional information about addition and subtraction fact extensions, refer to Section 16.3.3 of the *Teacher's Reference Manual.*

Calculators

Calculators are useful teaching tools. Encourage students to use their calculators whenever they encounter interesting numbers or problems that may be easier to handle with a calculator.

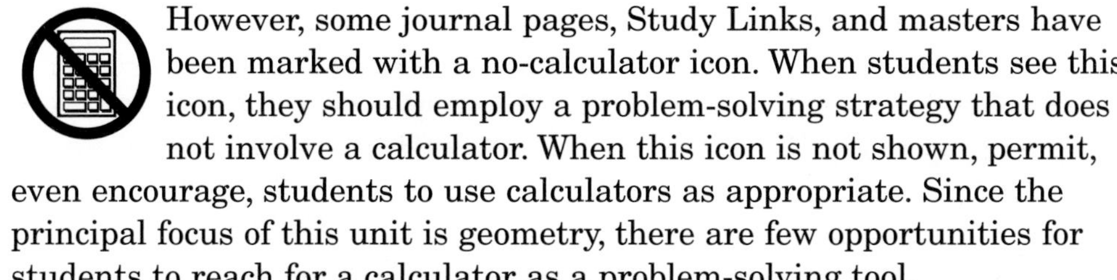

However, some journal pages, Study Links, and masters have been marked with a no-calculator icon. When students see this icon, they should employ a problem-solving strategy that does not involve a calculator. When this icon is not shown, permit, even encourage, students to use calculators as appropriate. Since the principal focus of this unit is geometry, there are few opportunities for students to reach for a calculator as a problem-solving tool.

Section 3.1.1 of the *Teacher's Reference Manual* contains additional information about using calculators.

1·1 Introduction to the *Student Reference Book*

Objective To acquaint students with the content and organization of the *Student Reference Book.*

Technology Resources www.everydaymathonline.com

ePresentations

eToolkit

Algorithms Practice

EM Facts Workshop Game™

Family Letters

Assessment Management

Common Core State Standards

Curriculum Focal Points

Interactive Teacher's Lesson Guide

1 Teaching the Lesson

Key Concepts and Skills

- Use the symbols >, <, and = to compare numbers and numerical expressions. [Number and Numeration Goal 6]
- Solve simple +, −, ×, and ÷ problems. [Operations and Computation Goals 1 and 3]
- Describe relationships among U.S. customary units of length. [Measurement and Reference Frames Goal 3]

Key Activities

Students explore the *Student Reference Book.*

Ongoing Assessment: Recognizing Student Achievement
Use Mental Math and Reflexes.
[Operations and Computation Goal 1]

Materials

Math Journal 1, p. 2
Student Reference Book
stick-on notes (optional)

2 Ongoing Learning & Practice

Using Fact Triangles

Math Masters, pp. 384–387
paper clips ◆ small, resealable plastic bags or regular envelopes ◆ scissors
Students work with +, − Fact Triangles.

Math Boxes 1·1

Math Journal 1, p. 3
Students practice and maintain skills through Math Box problems.

Study Link 1·1: Unit 1 Family Letter

Math Masters, pp. 2–5
Students take home the Study Link Family Letter introducing *Everyday Mathematics* and Unit 1.

3 Differentiation Options

READINESS

Using Relation Symbols to Compare Numbers

Math Masters, p. 6
per partnership: 4 each of number cards 0–9 (from the Everything Math Deck, if available) ◆ scissors
Students use the relation symbols >, <, and = to compare numbers.

ENRICHMENT

Searching for Symbols

Student Reference Book
Math Masters, p. 7
Students look for mathematical symbols in the *Student Reference Book.*

Advance Preparation

For Part 2, copy onto cardstock the +, − Fact Triangles on *Math Masters,* pages 384–387. Have students use plastic bags or envelopes to store them.

***Teacher's Reference Manual,* Grades 4–6** pp. 11, 12, 15, 56

Getting Started

Mental Math and Reflexes ★

Pose addition facts and extended facts. *Suggestions:*

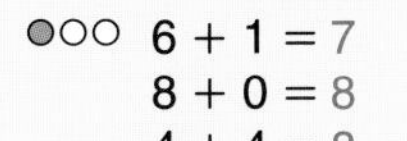

●○○	●●○	●●●
6 + 1 = 7	6 + 7 = 13	50 + 50 = 100
8 + 0 = 8	60 + 70 = 130	20 + 30 = 50
4 + 4 = 8	7 + 9 = 16	60 + 80 = 140
9 + 2 = 11	70 + 90 = 160	90 + 90 = 180

FACTS PRACTICE

Math Message

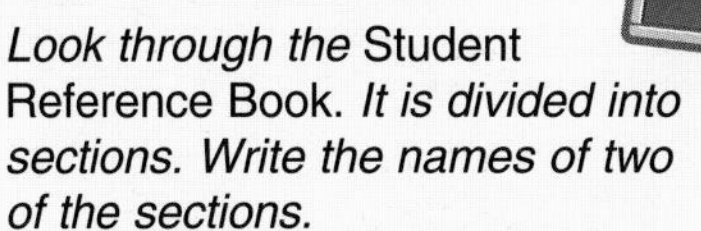

Look through the Student Reference Book. *It is divided into sections. Write the names of two of the sections.*

Find a page that looks interesting to you. Record the page number. Be prepared to share.

Ongoing Assessment: Recognizing Student Achievement

Mental Math and Reflexes ★

Use **Mental Math and Reflexes** to assess students' automaticity with extended addition facts. Students are making adequate progress if they are able to solve the ●○○ and ●●○ problems. Some students may already be able to solve the ●●● problems, which do not include a basic fact prompt.

[Operations and Computation Goal 1]

1 Teaching the Lesson

NOTE Readiness activities help students gain prerequisite skills so that they can be successful in the lesson. Some students may benefit from doing the **Readiness** activity before you begin Part 1 of the lesson. See the Readiness activity in Part 3 for details.

Interactive whiteboard-ready ePresentations are available at www.everydaymathonline.com to help you teach the lesson.

▸ Math Message Follow-Up

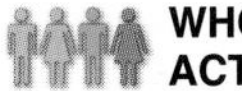

WHOLE-CLASS ACTIVITY

(*Student Reference Book*)

Have partners look through the *Student Reference Book* and share interesting pages. Invite students to name different sections of the *Student Reference Book,* and have the others indicate "thumbs-up" if they named the same section.

Tell students that in this lesson they will have the opportunity to explore the *Student Reference Book* and learn how it can be used to investigate topics in mathematics.

▸ Investigating the *Student Reference Book*

WHOLE-CLASS ACTIVITY

(*Student Reference Book*)

Language Arts Link Discuss the sections of the *Student Reference Book.* As each section is discussed, write its name on the board.

▷ Tell students that the Table of Contents can be used to find an essay about a certain topic. The table also lists the first page number of each essay.

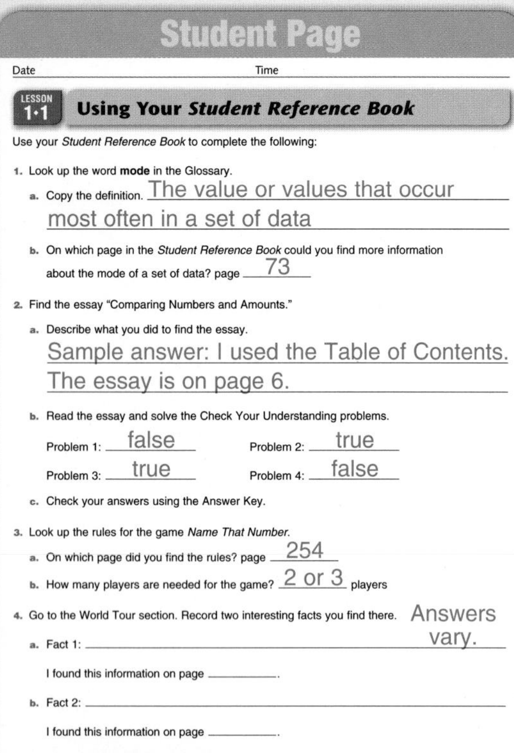
Student Page

Date Time

LESSON 1·1 **Using Your *Student Reference Book***

Use your *Student Reference Book* to complete the following:

1. Look up the word **mode** in the Glossary.
   a. Copy the definition. The value or values that occur most often in a set of data
   b. On which page in the *Student Reference Book* could you find more information about the mode of a set of data? page 73
2. Find the essay "Comparing Numbers and Amounts."
   a. Describe what you did to find the essay. Sample answer: I used the Table of Contents. The essay is on page 6.
   b. Read the essay and solve the Check Your Understanding problems.
      Problem 1: false Problem 2: true
      Problem 3: true Problem 4: false
   c. Check your answers using the Answer Key.
3. Look up the rules for the game *Name That Number.*
   a. On which page did you find the rules? page 254
   b. How many players are needed for the game? 2 or 3 players
4. Go to the World Tour section. Record two interesting facts you find there. Answers vary.
   a. Fact 1: ______
      I found this information on page ______.
   b. Fact 2: ______
      I found this information on page ______.

***Math Journal 1,* p. 2**

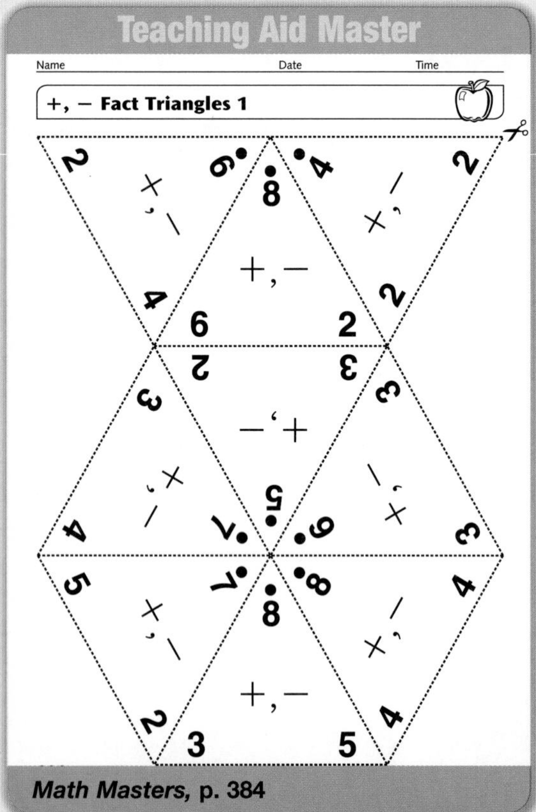

***Math Masters,* p. 384**

▷ Have students use the Table of Contents to look up "Extended Multiplication Facts," which is on page 17. Point out the Check Your Understanding problems. Explain that these problems check students' understanding of the content of the essay. When students read an essay, they should do the Check Your Understanding problems and then check their answers using the Answer Key.

▷ Discuss the Glossary. Explain that it lists important math terms in alphabetical order and defines each one. Ask students to look up *line of symmetry*.

▷ Turn to the Index. Explain that an index lists key words in alphabetical order and gives pages on which those words appear. Ask students to use it to find the rules for the game *Baseball Multiplication*.

▷ Finally, turn to the World Tour section. Explain that it contains information that students will use on an imaginary world tour.

Adjusting the Activity

Have students put labeled stick-on notes on key sections of the *Student Reference Book* that they will refer to often, such as Table of Contents, Answer Key, Glossary, Index, and Games.

AUDITORY ◆ KINESTHETIC ◆ TACTILE ◆ VISUAL

▶ Using the *Student Reference Book*

(*Math Journal 1*, p. 2; *Student Reference Book*)

Ask students to complete a journal page that takes them on a tour of the *Student Reference Book*.

Adjusting the Activity

ELL

Work together to identify and mark key terms, such as *mode, Name That Number, Comparing Numbers and Amounts,* or *World Tour* in each question. Model how students might look up these words in the Index or Table of Contents.

AUDITORY ◆ KINESTHETIC ◆ TACTILE ◆ VISUAL

2 Ongoing Learning & Practice

▶ Using Fact Triangles

(*Math Masters*, pp. 384–387)

Fact Triangles are an alternative to traditional flash cards. They will be used as a screening tool to identify students who need additional practice with basic addition and subtraction facts. Using the cards reminds students that subtracting is like asking "How much do I add?"

When a student uses a Fact Triangle for a subtraction problem, the student receives two visual messages—a subtraction message (such as 17 − 9 = ?) and an addition message (such as 9 + ? = 17). The triangles help reinforce the idea that a student who knows one fact also knows three other related facts.

- ▷ Have students cut out the Fact Triangles on the masters.
- ▷ One partner covers a corner of a Fact Triangle with a finger.
- ▷ The other partner tells the addition or subtraction fact containing the numbers that are left uncovered.

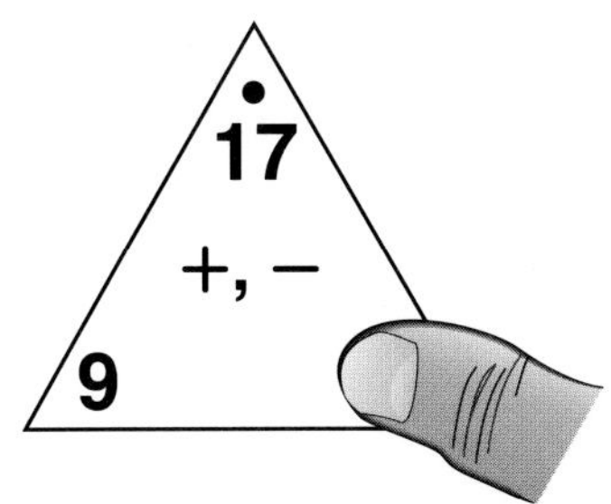

17 − 9 = ? and 9 + ? = 17

- ▷ To practice the facts alone, students turn the cards facedown, pick up a card by a corner so that a finger covers the number in the corner, and tell which number is covered.
- ▷ Encourage students to sort their Fact Triangles into two piles—"OK" and "Try Again." Use this Fact Triangle activity to determine which students are proficient with the basic addition and subtraction facts. Students with triangles in the Try Again pile will need additional support. Although basic addition and subtraction facts are not addressed again in the Part 1 sections of *Fourth Grade Everyday Mathematics,* games and Fact Triangles are available to provide opportunities for students to practice these facts. See the *Teacher's Reference Manual* for ideas about establishing a game routine in your classroom.

Student Page

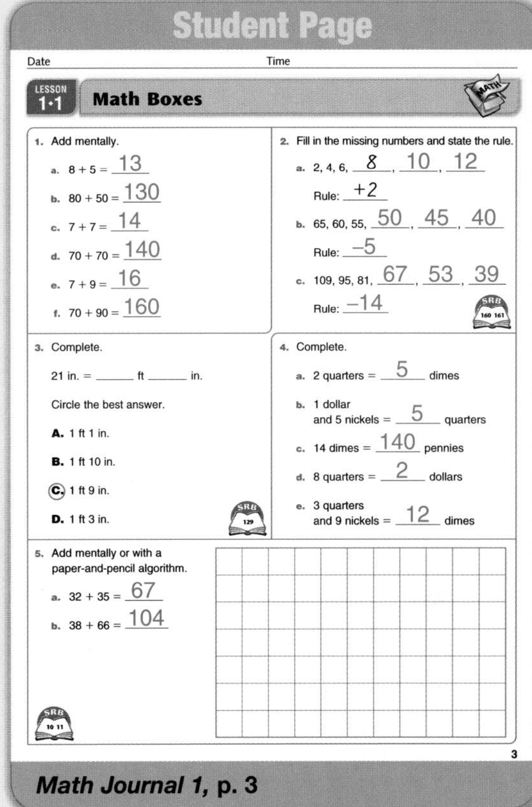
Date Time

LESSON 1•1 **Math Boxes**

1. Add mentally.
   a. 8 + 5 = 13
   b. 80 + 50 = 130
   c. 7 + 7 = 14
   d. 70 + 70 = 140
   e. 7 + 9 = 16
   f. 70 + 90 = 160

2. Fill in the missing numbers and state the rule.
   a. 2, 4, 6, 8, 10, 12
   Rule: +2
   b. 65, 60, 55, 50, 45, 40
   Rule: −5
   c. 109, 95, 81, 67, 53, 39
   Rule: −14

SRB 160 161

3. Complete.
   21 in. = ____ ft ____ in.
   Circle the best answer.
   A. 1 ft 1 in.
   B. 1 ft 10 in.
   C. 1 ft 9 in.
   D. 1 ft 3 in.

SRB 129

4. Complete.
   a. 2 quarters = 5 dimes
   b. 1 dollar and 5 nickels = 5 quarters
   c. 14 dimes = 140 pennies
   d. 8 quarters = 2 dollars
   e. 3 quarters and 9 nickels = 12 dimes

5. Add mentally or with a paper-and-pencil algorithm.
   a. 32 + 35 = 67
   b. 38 + 66 = 104

SRB 10 11

3

Math Journal 1, **p. 3**

NOTE Consider sending home a set of Fact Triangles for students who require additional practice.

Math Boxes 1•1

INDEPENDENT ACTIVITY

(*Math Journal 1,* p. 3)

Mixed Practice Math Boxes in this lesson are paired with Math Boxes in Lesson 1-3. The skill in Problem 5 previews Unit 2 content.

Study Link 1•1: Unit 1 Family Letter

INDEPENDENT ACTIVITY

(*Math Masters,* pp. 2–5)

Home Connection Study Links contain a follow-up to material presented in the lesson. Most Study Links should be taken home, while others can be done in school. Some Study Links are letters to parents. Note that the last page of each Family Letter includes answers to the unit's Study Link problems.

Many Study Links end with a Practice section that provides a cumulative review of concepts and skills. Students should complete this section without the help of a calculator.

Study Link Masters

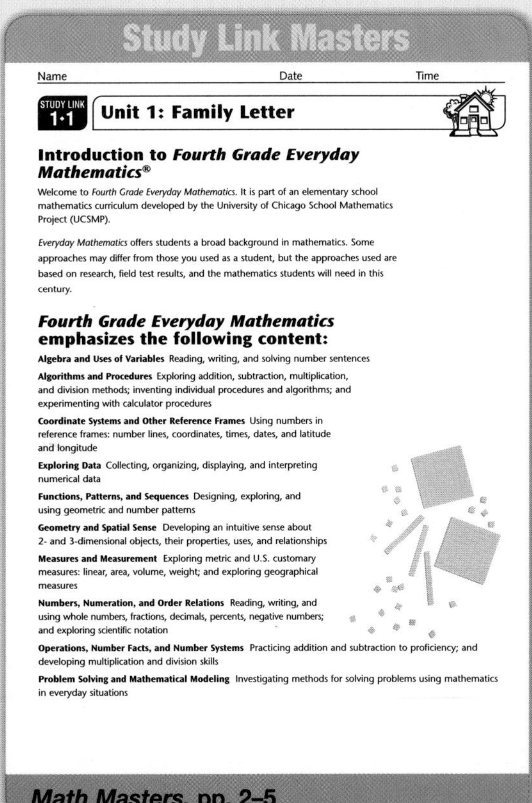
Name Date Time

STUDY LINK 1•1 **Unit 1: Family Letter**

Introduction to *Fourth Grade Everyday Mathematics*®

Welcome to *Fourth Grade Everyday Mathematics.* It is part of an elementary school mathematics curriculum developed by the University of Chicago School Mathematics Project (UCSMP).

Everyday Mathematics offers students a broad background in mathematics. Some approaches may differ from those you used as a student, but the approaches used are based on research, field test results, and the mathematics students will need in this century.

***Fourth Grade Everyday Mathematics* emphasizes the following content:**

Algebra and Uses of Variables Reading, writing, and solving number sentences

Algorithms and Procedures Exploring addition, subtraction, multiplication, and division methods; inventing individual procedures and algorithms; and experimenting with calculator procedures

Coordinate Systems and Other Reference Frames Using numbers in reference frames: number lines, coordinates, times, dates, and latitude and longitude

Exploring Data Collecting, organizing, displaying, and interpreting numerical data

Functions, Patterns, and Sequences Designing, exploring, and using geometric and number patterns

Geometry and Spatial Sense Developing an intuitive sense about 2- and 3-dimensional objects, their properties, uses, and relationships

Measures and Measurement Exploring metric and U.S. customary measures: linear, area, volume, weight; and exploring geographical measures

Numbers, Numeration, and Order Relations Reading, writing, and using whole numbers, fractions, decimals, percents, negative numbers; and exploring scientific notation

Operations, Number Facts, and Number Systems Practicing addition and subtraction to proficiency; and developing multiplication and division skills

Problem Solving and Mathematical Modeling Investigating methods for solving problems using mathematics in everyday situations

Math Masters, **pp. 2–5**

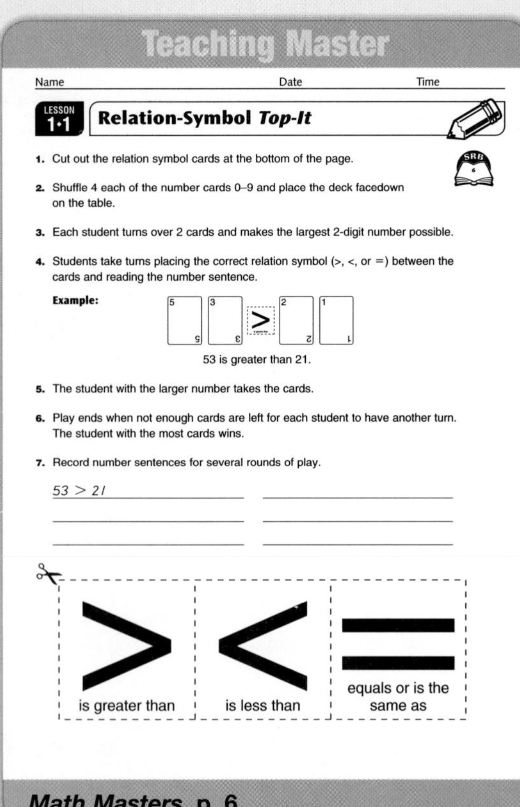

Teaching Master

Name Date Time

LESSON 1·1 **Relation-Symbol *Top-It***

1. Cut out the relation symbol cards at the bottom of the page.
2. Shuffle 4 each of the number cards 0–9 and place the deck facedown on the table.
3. Each student turns over 2 cards and makes the largest 2-digit number possible.
4. Students take turns placing the correct relation symbol (>, <, or =) between the cards and reading the number sentence.

Example: 5 3 > 2 1

53 is greater than 21.

5. The student with the larger number takes the cards.
6. Play ends when not enough cards are left for each student to have another turn. The student with the most cards wins.
7. Record number sentences for several rounds of play.

53 > 21

> is greater than | < is less than | = equals or is the same as

***Math Masters,* p. 6**

3 Differentiation Options

READINESS

5–15 Min

▶ Using Relation Symbols to Compare Numbers

(*Math Masters,* p. 6)

To explore the use of the relation symbols >, <, and =, have students play *Top-It* using *Math Masters,* page 6. Students use cards to create 2-digit numbers. One student places the correct relation symbol (>, <, or =) between the numbers and reads the resulting number sentence. Have students record number sentences for several rounds of play.

ENRICHMENT

INDEPENDENT ACTIVITY

▶ Searching for Symbols

(*Student Reference Book; Math Masters,* p. 7)

To further explore mathematical symbols, have students search the *Student Reference Book* for other symbols used by mathematicians. Have them record the symbols and their meanings.

Planning Ahead

Ask students to bring one or two old socks to school tomorrow. These will be used as erasers for slate activities throughout the year.

Name Date Time

LESSON 1·1 **Symbols Scavenger Hunt**

Mathematicians use symbols instead of writing out words such as *is greater than, is less than,* and *equals.* Search the *Student Reference Book* to find as many symbols as you can. Record the symbols and the words they stand for in the table below.

Symbol	Meaning
>	*is greater than*
Sample answers:	
//	is parallel to
⊥	is perpendicular to
π	pi–the ratio of the
	circumference of a circle
	to its diameter

Math Masters, page 7

1·2 Points, Line Segments, Lines, and Rays

Objectives To introduce tools for geometry; and to review points, line segments, lines, and rays.

www.everydaymathonline.com

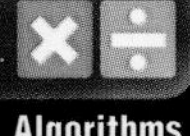

Presentations | eToolkit | Algorithms Practice | EM Facts Workshop Game™ | Family Letters | Assessment Management | Common Core State Standards | Curriculum Focal Points | Interactive Teacher's Lesson Guide

1 Teaching the Lesson

Key Concepts and Skills

- Identify and draw line segments, lines, and rays. [Geometry Goal 1]
- Describe characteristics of line segments, lines, and rays. [Geometry Goal 1]
- Use letter and symbol notation to name line segments, lines, and rays. [Geometry Goal 1]

Key Activities

Students review points, line segments, lines, and rays.

Ongoing Assessment: Informing Instruction See page 26.

Ongoing Assessment: Recognizing Student Achievement Use a Math Log or Exit Slip (*Math Masters,* page 388 or 389). [Geometry Goal 1]

Key Vocabulary

point ◆ line segment ◆ endpoint ◆ line ◆ ray

Materials

Math Journal 1, p. 4
Student Reference Book, pp. 88–91
Math Masters, p. 388 or 389 (optional)
slate or marker board ◆ chalk or dry-erase marker ◆ socks brought by students ◆ ruler or yardstick for demonstration purposes ◆ Geometry Template ◆ compass ◆ calculator

2 Ongoing Learning & Practice

Playing *Addition Top-It* (Extended-Facts Version)
Student Reference Book, p. 263
Math Masters, p. 506
per partnership: 4 each of number cards 1–10 (from the Everything Math Deck, if available)
Students practice addition fact extensions.

Math Boxes 1·2
Math Journal 1, p. 5
Students practice and maintain skills through Math Box problems.

Study Link 1·2
Math Masters, p. 8
Students practice and maintain skills through Study Link activities.

3 Differentiation Options

READINESS

Modeling Line Segments
Math Masters, p. 9
geoboard ◆ rubber bands
Students model line segments with rubber bands on a geoboard.

ENRICHMENT

Solving a Collinear-Points Puzzle
Math Masters, p. 10
Students solve a collinear-points puzzle.

ENRICHMENT

Playing *Sprouts*
Student Reference Book, p. 313
Students explore line segments and points with simple vertex-edge graphs.

ELL SUPPORT

Building Background for Mathematics Words
Students discuss the meaning of *tools* in a mathematical context.

Advance Preparation

For Part 1, assign and record an ID number for each student. Label students' math tools with their ID numbers. Have extra socks for students to use as slate erasers.

***Teacher's Reference Manual,* Grades 4–6** pp. 9, 10, 14, 15, 176, 177

Getting Started

Mental Math and Reflexes

FACTS PRACTICE

Pass out a slate and piece of chalk (or a marker board and dry-erase marker) to each student and explain how they are to be used:

1. You pose a problem. (*How much is 12 – 7?*)
2. Students write the answer on their slates.
3. When you give the signal, they show their answers.
4. Students then erase their answers with the socks they brought from home.
5. At the end of the session, they store their chalk (or markers) in the socks.

Suggestions:

●○○	●●○	●●●
9 – 0 = 9	14 – 6 = 8	90 – 40 = 50
7 – 2 = 5	16 – 9 = 7	70 – 30 = 40
11 – 1 = 10	12 – 7 = 5	60 – 20 = 40
12 – 6 = 6	17 – 8 = 9	140 – 70 = 70

Math Message

Read Student Reference Book, *pages 88 and 89 with a partner. List three places where geometry can be found in our world.*

NOTE Some students may benefit from doing the **Readiness** activity before you begin Part 1 of the lesson. See the Readiness activity in Part 3 for details.

Interactive whiteboard-ready ePresentations are available at www.everydaymathonline.com to help you teach the lesson.

Student Page

Geometry and Constructions

Geometry in Our World

The world is filled with geometry. There are angles, segments, lines, and curves everywhere you look. There are 2-dimensional and 3-dimensional shapes of every type.

Many wonderful geometric patterns can be seen in nature. You can find patterns in flowers, spider webs, leaves, seashells, even your own face and body.

The ideas of geometry are also found in the things people create. Think of the games you play. Checkers is played with round pieces. The gameboard is covered with squares. Basketball and tennis are played with spheres. They are played on rectangular courts that are painted with straight and curved lines. The next time you play or watch a game, notice how geometry is important to the way the game is played.

The places we live in are built from plans that use geometry. Buildings almost always have rectangular rooms. Outside walls and roofs often include sections that have triangular shapes. Archways are curved and are often shaped like semicircles (half circles). Staircases may be straight or spiral. Buildings and rooms are often decorated with beautiful patterns. You see these decorations on doors and windows; on walls, floors, and ceilings; and on railings of staircases.

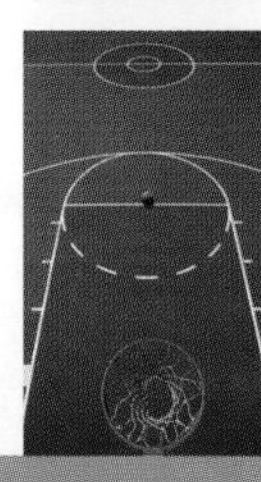

Student Reference Book, **p. 88**

1 Teaching the Lesson

▶ Math Message Follow-Up

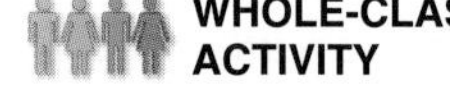

WHOLE-CLASS ACTIVITY

(*Student Reference Book,* pp. 88 and 89)

Have students share their answers in small groups. Then ask them to look around the classroom for other geometric shapes and patterns. Point out the line segments found in objects such as windows, doors, and bulletin boards.

▶ Discussing the Care of Students' Math Tools

WHOLE-CLASS ACTIVITY

In Lesson 1-1, students were introduced to the *Student Reference Book* as a resource tool. Tell them that in this lesson they will be given additional tools. Students will use one of these tools to draw line segments, lines, and rays.

Pass out the rulers, Geometry Templates, compasses, and calculators to students.

Remind students of the following:

- ▷ The numbers on the tools identify each student's tools and other materials borrowed during the school year. Other fourth graders will use them next year, so they should take good care of them.
- ▷ They should put misplaced tools in a lost-and-found box.
- ▷ A *straightedge* and a *ruler* are different. A straightedge is any tool used for drawing straight lines. A ruler is a measuring tool as well as a straightedge. A straightedge may not be used as a ruler unless it is divided into unit intervals.

Reviewing Points, Line Segments, Lines, and Rays

WHOLE-CLASS ACTIVITY

1. Draw two dots on the board and label them *A* and *B*. Tell students that the dots represent **points.** Use a straightedge to connect the dots. Remind the class that this figure is called a **line segment** and that letters are often used to name line segments.

   Point out the following:

   ▷ One name for this line segment is "line segment *AB*." Write $\overline{AB}$ on the board and say that this is a short way to write "line segment *AB*."

   ▷ Another name for this line segment is "line segment *BA*." Write $\overline{BA}$ on the board. Explain that points *A* and *B* are called the **endpoints** of the line segment.

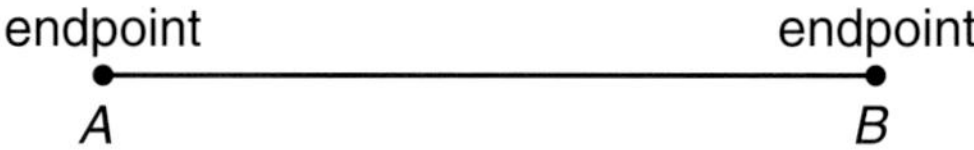

Line segment *AB*, line segment *BA*, $\overline{AB}$, or $\overline{BA}$

   ▷ Although there are two ways of naming a line segment by its endpoints, both names refer to the *same* segment.

   • How would you describe a line segment to someone who has never seen one before? Sample answers: It is straight and thin. It has a beginning and an end. Its length can be measured.

2. Review how a **line** can be represented by extending line segment *AB* in both directions and drawing an arrowhead at each end.

   ▷ Explain that this line is called "line *AB*" or "line *BA*."

   ▷ Write $\overleftrightarrow{AB}$ and $\overleftrightarrow{BA}$ on the board, and say that these are short for "line *AB*" and "line *BA*."

Line *AB*, line *BA*, $\overleftrightarrow{AB}$, or $\overleftrightarrow{BA}$

   • How is a line different from a line segment? Sample answers: It is like a line segment except that it has no beginning and no end. One way to think of a line is to imagine a line segment that goes on without end in both directions. A line segment is part of a line.

3. Finally, ask students to imagine a line segment that goes on without end in only one direction. This is called a **ray.**

   To support English language learners, ask: *Have you ever heard the word* ray? *What are some different ways you have heard it used?* Sample answers: A ray of sunshine, my neighbor Ray

Student Page

Geometry and Constructions

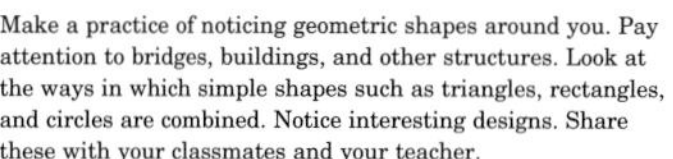

The clothes people wear are often decorated with geometric shapes. So are the things they use every day. Everywhere in the world, people create things using geometric patterns. Examples include quilts, pottery, baskets, and tiles. Some patterns are shown here. Which are your favorites?

Make a practice of noticing geometric shapes around you. Pay attention to bridges, buildings, and other structures. Look at the ways in which simple shapes such as triangles, rectangles, and circles are combined. Notice interesting designs. Share these with your classmates and your teacher.

In this section, you will study geometric shapes and learn how to construct them. As you learn, try to create your own beautiful designs.

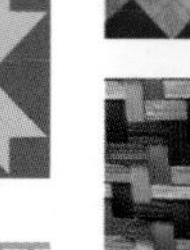

Student Reference Book, **p. 89**

Adjusting the Activity

As the class participates in this activity, label the drawings on the board as *line segment, line,* and *ray.* Display these drawings throughout the unit as a visual reference for students.

AUDITORY ♦ KINESTHETIC ♦ TACTILE ♦ VISUAL

▷ Draw a picture of ray CD on the board, and write its name $\overrightarrow{CD}$.

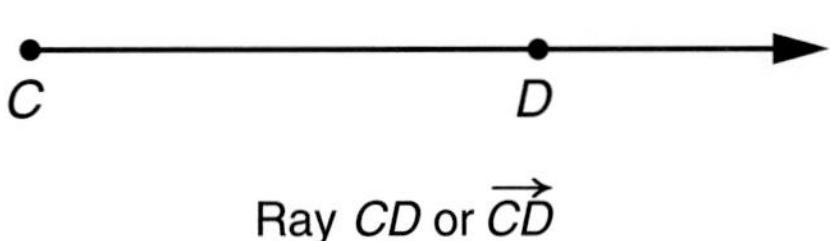

Ray CD or $\overrightarrow{CD}$

▷ Tell students that point C is the endpoint of ray CD.

▷ Remind students that the letter that names the endpoint of a ray is always written first. Ask someone to draw a picture of ray BA.

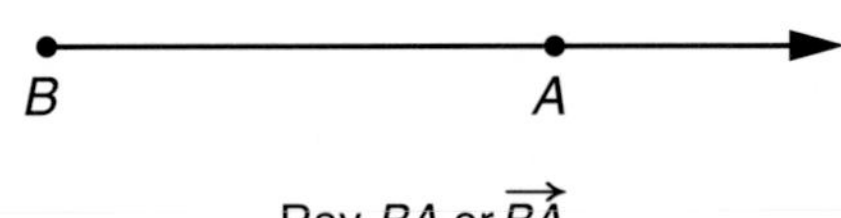

Ray BA or $\overrightarrow{BA}$

- Is it ever possible to draw all of a line? no All of a line segment? yes All of a ray? no

To summarize, draw the line shown below on the board.

- How many line segments can you name using the points marked on this line? Give alternative names. 3 line segments: $\overline{XY}$, $\overline{YZ}$, and $\overline{XZ}$; alternative names: $\overline{YX}$, $\overline{ZY}$, and $\overline{ZX}$
- How many rays can you name? 4 rays: $\overrightarrow{XY}$ (or $\overrightarrow{XZ}$), $\overrightarrow{ZX}$ (or $\overrightarrow{ZY}$), $\overrightarrow{YZ}$, and $\overrightarrow{YX}$

Be sure students understand the following:

▷ $\overrightarrow{XY}$ and $\overrightarrow{XZ}$ name the same ray.

▷ Point X is the endpoint of the ray.

▷ The endpoint is always the first letter in the name of a ray. The second letter can be any other point on the ray.

▷ Points Y and Z are both on the ray. The same is true for $\overrightarrow{ZX}$ and $\overrightarrow{ZY}$.

▶ Drawing Line Segments, Lines, and Rays

(*Math Journal 1,* p. 4; *Student Reference Book,* pp. 90 and 91)

Students practice drawing and labeling line segments, lines, and rays. Model how students can refer to pages 90 and 91 of the *Student Reference Book* to review points, line segments, lines, and rays.

Ongoing Assessment: Informing Instruction

Watch for students who draw only four line segments for Problem 4 on journal page 4. Encourage them to focus on connecting each point to each of the other points rather than making a shape.

Student Page

Date Time

LESSON 1·2 **Points, Line Segments, Lines, and Rays**

Use a straightedge to draw the following:

1. a. Draw and label line segment RT ($\overline{RT}$).
   R T
   b. What is another name for $\overline{RT}$? $\overline{TR}$
2. a. Draw and label line BN ($\overleftrightarrow{BN}$). Draw and label point T on it.
   B T N
   b. What are 2 other names for $\overleftrightarrow{BN}$? $\overleftrightarrow{BT}$, $\overleftrightarrow{NT}$, $\overleftrightarrow{TN}$, $\overleftrightarrow{TB}$, $\overleftrightarrow{NB}$
3. a. Draw and label ray SL ($\overrightarrow{SL}$). Draw and label point R on it.
   S R L
   b. What is another name for $\overrightarrow{SL}$? $\overrightarrow{SR}$
4. a. Draw a line segment from each point to each of the other points.
   M N O P
   b. How many line segments did you draw? 6
   c. Write a name for each line segment you drew.
   $\overline{OM}$, $\overline{ON}$, $\overline{OP}$, $\overline{MP}$, $\overline{MN}$, $\overline{NP}$
   (Or letters may be in reverse order.)

Math Journal 1, p. 4

Ongoing Assessment: Recognizing Student Achievement

Math Log or Exit Slip

Use a **Math Log** or an **Exit Slip** (*Math Masters,* page 388 or 389) to assess students' ability to describe a line segment and a line. Have students explain the difference between a line segment and a line. Students are making adequate progress if they are able to explain that a line segment has a beginning and an end, and a line continues in both directions without end. Some students may include drawings and symbols as part of their explanations.

[Geometry Goal 1]

2 Ongoing Learning & Practice

Playing *Addition Top-It* (Extended-Facts Version)

PARTNER ACTIVITY

(*Student Reference Book,* p. 263; *Math Masters,* p. 506)

Students play an extended-facts version of *Addition Top-It* to develop automaticity with addition fact extensions. Students will attach a 0 to both cards before finding the sum. For example, a student who draws a 2 and a 4 would solve the extended fact 20 + 40. Consider having students record several rounds of play on *Math Masters,* page 506.

Adjusting the Activity

Sketch a diagram like the one below on the board for students to copy and use as a gameboard.

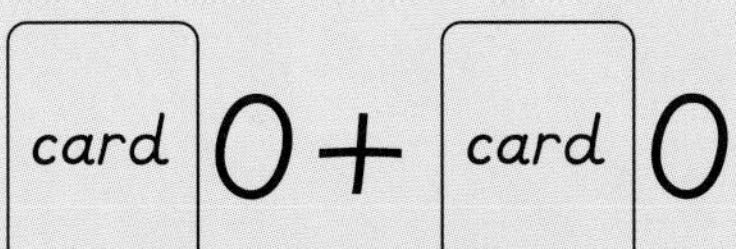

AUDITORY ◆ KINESTHETIC ◆ TACTILE ◆ VISUAL

Math Boxes 1•2

INDEPENDENT ACTIVITY

(*Math Journal 1,* p. 5)

Mixed Practice Math Boxes in this lesson are paired with Math Boxes in Lesson 1-4. The skill in Problem 5 previews Unit 2 content.

Study Link 1•2

INDEPENDENT ACTIVITY

(*Math Masters,* p. 8)

Home Connection Students list at least five things that remind them of line segments. They draw and label lines, line segments, and rays, and write about the differences.

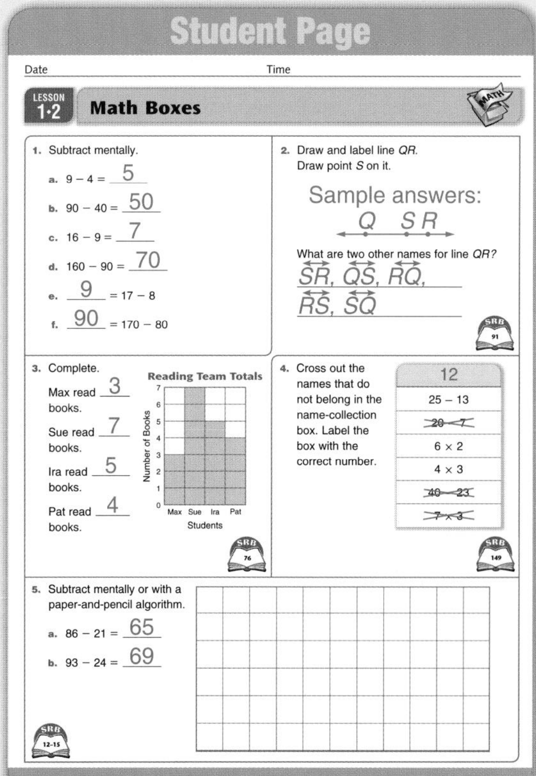

Student Page

Date Time

LESSON 1•2 **Math Boxes**

1. Subtract mentally.
   a. 9 − 4 = 5
   b. 90 − 40 = 50
   c. 16 − 9 = 7
   d. 160 − 90 = 70
   e. 9 = 17 − 8
   f. 90 = 170 − 80

2. Draw and label line *QR*. Draw point *S* on it.
   Sample answers: Q S R
   What are two other names for line *QR*?
   $\overleftrightarrow{SR}$, $\overleftrightarrow{QS}$, $\overleftrightarrow{RQ}$, $\overleftrightarrow{RS}$, $\overleftrightarrow{SQ}$

3. Complete.
   Max read 3 books.
   Sue read 7 books.
   Ira read 5 books.
   Pat read 4 books.

4. Cross out the names that do not belong in the name-collection box. Label the box with the correct number.

12
25 − 13
~~20 − 7~~
6 × 2
4 × 3
~~40 − 23~~
~~7 × 3~~

5. Subtract mentally or with a paper-and-pencil algorithm.
   a. 86 − 21 = 65
   b. 93 − 24 = 69

Math Journal 1, p. 5

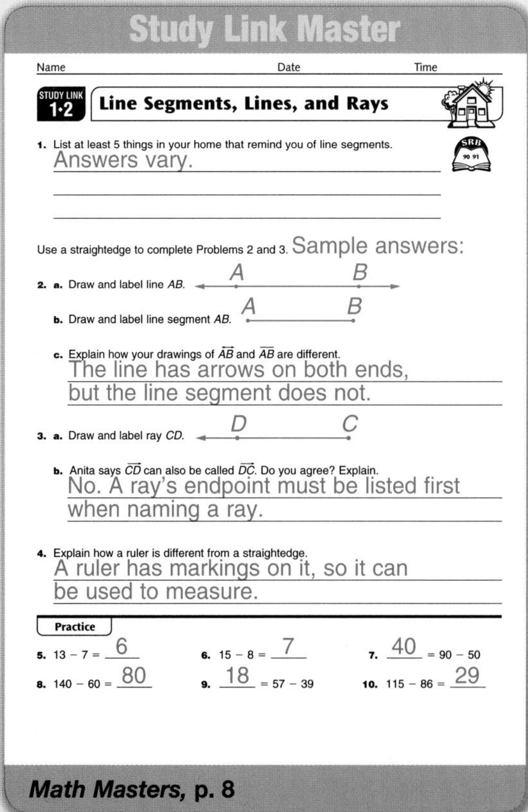

Study Link Master

Name Date Time

STUDY LINK 1•2 **Line Segments, Lines, and Rays**

1. List at least 5 things in your home that remind you of line segments.
   Answers vary.

Use a straightedge to complete Problems 2 and 3. Sample answers:

2. a. Draw and label line *AB*. A B
   b. Draw and label line segment *AB*. A B
   c. Explain how your drawings of $\overleftrightarrow{AB}$ and $\overline{AB}$ are different.
   The line has arrows on both ends, but the line segment does not.

3. a. Draw and label ray *CD*. D C
   b. Anita says $\overrightarrow{CD}$ can also be called $\overrightarrow{DC}$. Do you agree? Explain.
   No. A ray's endpoint must be listed first when naming a ray.

4. Explain how a ruler is different from a straightedge.
   A ruler has markings on it, so it can be used to measure.

Practice

5. 13 − 7 = 6
6. 15 − 8 = 7
7. 40 = 90 − 50
8. 140 − 60 = 80
9. 18 = 57 − 39
10. 115 − 86 = 29

Math Masters, p. 8

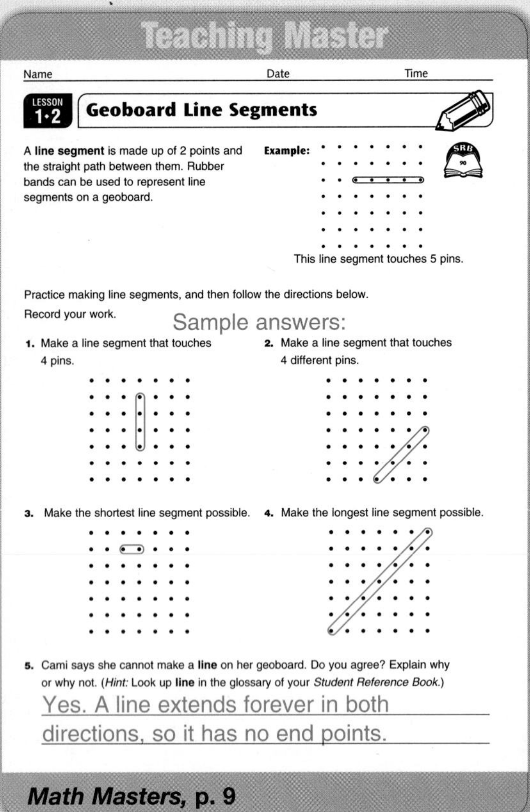
Teaching Master

Name Date Time

LESSON 1·2 **Geoboard Line Segments**

A **line segment** is made up of 2 points and the straight path between them. Rubber bands can be used to represent line segments on a geoboard.

Example: This line segment touches 5 pins.

Practice making line segments, and then follow the directions below. Record your work.

Sample answers:

1. Make a line segment that touches 4 pins.
2. Make a line segment that touches 4 different pins.
3. Make the shortest line segment possible.
4. Make the longest line segment possible.
5. Cami says she cannot make a **line** on her geoboard. Do you agree? Explain why or why not. (*Hint:* Look up **line** in the glossary of your *Student Reference Book.*)
Yes. A line extends forever in both directions, so it has no end points.

***Math Masters,* p. 9**

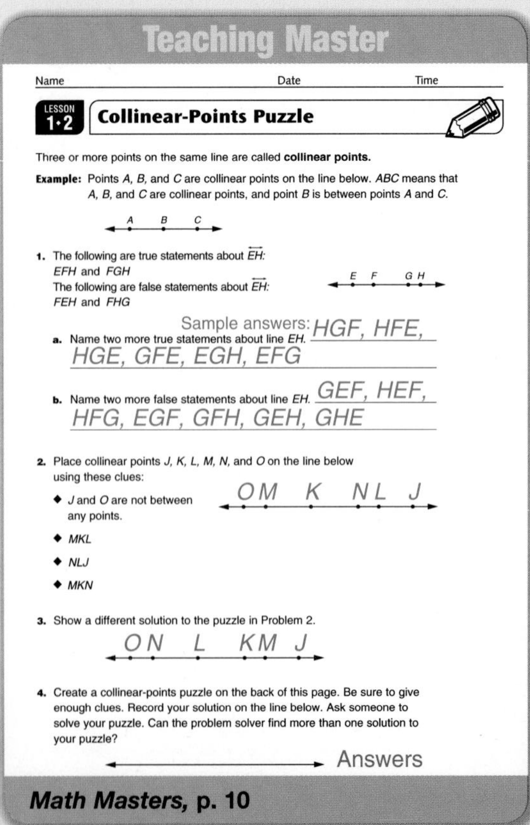
Teaching Master

Name Date Time

LESSON 1·2 **Collinear-Points Puzzle**

Three or more points on the same line are called **collinear points.**

Example: Points *A*, *B*, and *C* are collinear points on the line below. *ABC* means that *A*, *B*, and *C* are collinear points, and point *B* is between points *A* and *C*.

A B C

1. The following are true statements about $\overleftrightarrow{EH}$: *EFH* and *FGH*
The following are false statements about $\overleftrightarrow{EH}$: *FEH* and *FHG*
E F G H
   a. Name two more true statements about line *EH*. Sample answers: HGF, HFE, HGE, GFE, EGH, EFG
   b. Name two more false statements about line *EH*. GEF, HEF, HFG, EGF, GFH, GEH, GHE
2. Place collinear points *J*, *K*, *L*, *M*, *N*, and *O* on the line below using these clues:
   - *J* and *O* are not between any points.
   - *MKL*
   - *NLJ*
   - *MKN*

   OM K NL J
3. Show a different solution to the puzzle in Problem 2.
ON L KM J
4. Create a collinear-points puzzle on the back of this page. Be sure to give enough clues. Record your solution on the line below. Ask someone to solve your puzzle. Can the problem solver find more than one solution to your puzzle?
Answers

***Math Masters,* p. 10**

3 Differentiation Options

READINESS

PARTNER ACTIVITY

5–15 Min

▶ Modeling Line Segments

(*Math Masters,* p. 9)

To explore the characteristics of line segments using a concrete model, have students make line segments on a geoboard. The limited size of the geoboard reinforces the notion that a line segment is part of a line, while a line goes on without end in both directions.

ENRICHMENT

PARTNER ACTIVITY

15–30 Min

▶ Solving a Collinear-Points Puzzle

(*Math Masters,* p. 10)

To further explore characteristics of lines, have students solve puzzles involving *collinear points.*

ENRICHMENT

PARTNER ACTIVITY

15–30 Min

▶ Playing *Sprouts*

(*Student Reference Book,* p. 313)

To further explore line segments and points, have students play *Sprouts*. Although the rules of *Sprouts* are quite simple, the game involves subtle strategies and gives students experience with simple *vertex-edge graphs*. The dots are the vertices, and the lines are the edges.

ELL SUPPORT

SMALL-GROUP ACTIVITY

5–15 Min

▶ Building Background for Mathematics Words

To provide language support for mathematical *tools,* ask students to generate a list of mathematical tools they know. Write the name of each tool on the board. When you introduce a compass, explain the distinction between a compass that tells direction and a compass used to draw geometric figures. Have students discuss how they use each tool.

Planning Ahead

Note that Part 1 of Lesson 1-3 requires straws and twist-ties.

1·3 Angles, Triangles, and Quadrangles

Objective To guide students in the construction of angles, triangles, and quadrangles and in the classification of quadrangles.

Technology Resources www.everydaymathonline.com

Presentations

eToolkit

Algorithms Practice

EM Facts Workshop Game™

Family Letters

Assessment Management

Common Core State Standards

Curriculum Focal Points

Interactive Teacher's Lesson Guide

1 Teaching the Lesson

Key Concepts and Skills

- Use letter notation to name angles. [Geometry Goal 1]
- Construct angles, triangles, and quadrangles. [Geometry Goals 1 and 2]
- Describe properties of and compare quadrangles. [Geometry Goal 2]
- Identify types of quadrangles. [Geometry Goal 2]

Key Activities

Students construct and name angles; construct triangles and quadrangles; and classify quadrangles.

Ongoing Assessment: Recognizing Student Achievement Use a Math Log or Exit Slip (*Math Masters,* page 388 or 389). [Geometry Goal 2]

Ongoing Assessment: Informing Instruction See page 33.

Key Vocabulary

angle ◆ vertex ◆ right angle ◆ triangle ◆ quadrangle ◆ quadrilateral ◆ square ◆ rhombus ◆ rectangle ◆ parallelogram ◆ trapezoid ◆ kite

Materials

Math Journal 1, p. 6
Student Reference Book, p. 100
Study Link 1•2
Math Masters, p. 388 or 389 (optional)
straightedge ◆ slate ◆ straws ◆ twist-ties ◆ chart paper ◆ tape (optional)

2 Ongoing Learning & Practice

Adding and Subtracting Whole Numbers
Math Journal 1, p. 7
Students add and subtract whole numbers.

Math Boxes 1•3
Math Journal 1, p. 8
Students practice and maintain skills through Math Box problems.

Study Link 1•3
Math Masters, p. 11
Students practice and maintain skills through Study Link activities.

3 Differentiation Options

READINESS
Sorting Pattern Blocks
Math Masters, p. 12
Geometry Template ◆ pattern blocks
Students sort pattern blocks according to properties.

ENRICHMENT
Solving a Polygon Puzzle
Math Masters, p. 13
Students solve a geometry puzzle involving polygons embedded in a figure.

EXTRA PRACTICE
5-Minute Math
5-Minute Math™, pp. 56, 57, 61, and 64
Students identify characteristics of 2-dimensional shapes.

ELL SUPPORT
Comparing and Contrasting Quadrangles
Math Masters, p. 390
Students use a Venn diagram to compare and contrast quadrangles.

Advance Preparation

For Part 1, place twist-ties and full-length, half-length, and $\frac{3}{4}$-length straws in 4 separate boxes near the Math Message. Each student will need 4 of each size straw and 4 twist-ties. Have extras available.

***Teacher's Reference Manual,* Grades 4–6** pp. 178–185, 212

Getting Started

Mental Math and Reflexes

Pose place-value questions. Students write the value of the digit on their slates. *Suggestions:*

●○○ The 6 in 67 60
The 7 in 47 7
The 9 in 903 900

●●○ The 4 in 1,416 400
The 5 in 5,890 5,000
The 2 in 3,128 20

●●● The 4 in 14,002 4,000
The 1 in 10,234 10,000
The 3 in 346,041 300,000

Math Message

Take 4 of each size straw. Take 4 twist-ties. Make a design or geometric shape. Do not bend the straws.

Study Link 1·2 Follow-Up

Have small groups compare examples of line segments found at home. Ask volunteers to share answers for Problems 2c, 3b, and 4.

NOTE Some students may benefit from doing the **Readiness** activity before you begin Part 1 of the lesson. See the Readiness activity in Part 3 for details.

Interactive whiteboard-ready ePresentations are available at www.everydaymathonline.com to help you teach the lesson.

NOTE Set up a procedure for students to follow when using straws and twist-ties. Give them the responsibility for quickly getting these materials for themselves and sorting and putting them away when they have finished.

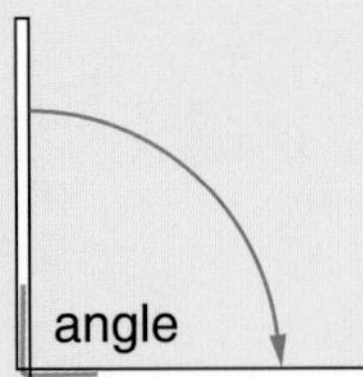

Use straws and a twist-tie to form an angle.

1 Teaching the Lesson

▶ Math Message Follow-Up

Give students a few minutes to play with the straws; they will be better able to concentrate on the lesson if they are allowed some free time with the materials first. Have students share their designs or geometric shapes with a partner.

Discuss how it is possible to represent 2-dimensional shapes in different ways: with concrete materials such as straws and twist-ties or rubber bands on a geoboard, with pictures or constructions, and with verbal descriptions.

Tell students that in this lesson and in Lesson 1-5 they will construct a number of 2-dimensional shapes with straws and discuss how the shapes are similar and different.

▶ Constructing Angles

Ask students to each take 2 straws and 1 twist-tie. Have students insert the twist-tie into one end of each straw to join them. Lead the class in a discussion of angles. As angle-related terms are introduced in the discussion, write them on the board. *For example*:

▷ The straws form an **angle.** They meet at a point called the **vertex** of the angle.

▷ A **right angle** is a square corner. Have students use their straws to show a right angle, an angle larger than a right angle, and an angle smaller than a right angle.

To support English language learners, differentiate the terms *right* answer, *right* turn, and *right* angle.

▷ Draw an angle on the board. Relate that the angle is made of two rays that have the same endpoint—the vertex of the angle. An angle can also be made of two line segments that share the same endpoint.

▷ Label the vertex *B*. Mark and label a point *A* on one of the rays and a point *C* on the other ray. One name for this angle is angle *ABC* (written ∠*ABC*). The middle letter in the name of the angle always names the vertex. (*See margin.*)

- What is another name for angle *ABC*? ∠*CBA*
- Is angle *BAC* another name for this angle? no Why or why not? The name of the vertex must be in the middle.

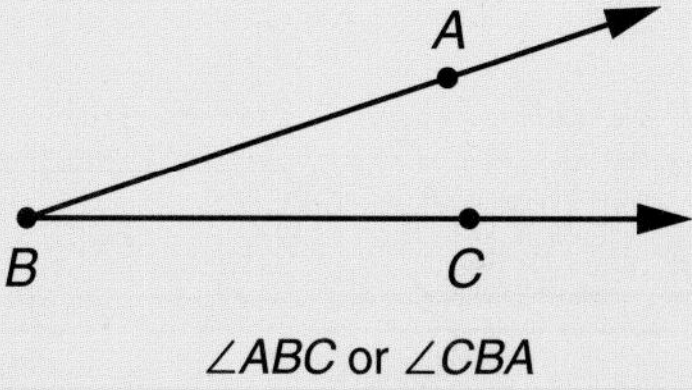

∠*ABC* or ∠*CBA*

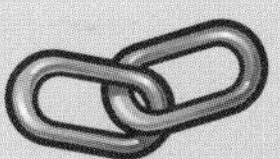

Links to the Future

Do not expect students to be able to identify obtuse and acute angles at this time. Students will have additional opportunities to work with these types of angles in Unit 6 of *Fourth Grade Everyday Mathematics*.

Constructing Triangles and Quadrangles

(*Student Reference Book,* p. 100)

Ask students to join three straws of different lengths and lay their constructions flat on their desks.

- What is this shape called? **triangle**

Write *triangle* on the board. As the class discusses the different types of quadrangles that follow, also write those names on the board.

Next have students make a straw construction out of any four straws and lay their constructions flat on their desks.

- What is a four-sided shape called? **Quadrangle,** or **quadrilateral**

Have students follow the directions below to make and name a variety of quadrangles.

- Make a quadrangle with all four sides equal in length and all right angles. What is this shape called? **square**
- Pull two opposite corners of the square in opposite directions. (Model this for students.) Are the angles still right angles? no Are the pairs of opposite sides still the same length? yes What is the new shape called? **rhombus**

ELL

As you make each straw model in this lesson, tape the model to a piece of chart paper and use a marker to clearly label it with the name of the figure. Display this poster throughout the unit.

AUDITORY ◆ KINESTHETIC ◆ TACTILE ◆ VISUAL

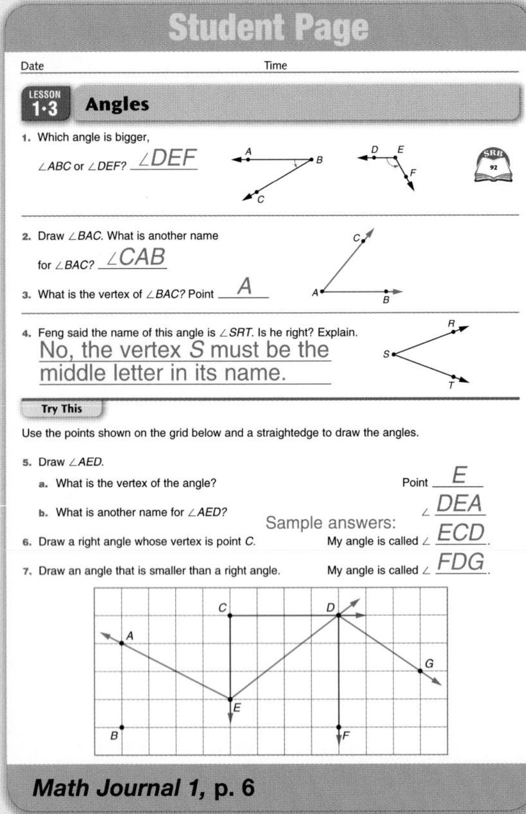

Student Page

Date ____ Time ____

LESSON 1·3 Angles

1. Which angle is bigger, ∠ABC or ∠DEF? ∠DEF

2. Draw ∠BAC. What is another name for ∠BAC? ∠CAB

3. What is the vertex of ∠BAC? Point A

4. Feng said the name of this angle is ∠SRT. Is he right? Explain. No, the vertex S must be the middle letter in its name.

Try This

Use the points shown on the grid below and a straightedge to draw the angles.

5. Draw ∠AED.
   a. What is the vertex of the angle? Point E
   b. What is another name for ∠AED? ∠DEA

Sample answers:

6. Draw a right angle whose vertex is point C. My angle is called ∠ECD.

7. Draw an angle that is smaller than a right angle. My angle is called ∠FDG.

Math Journal 1, p. 6

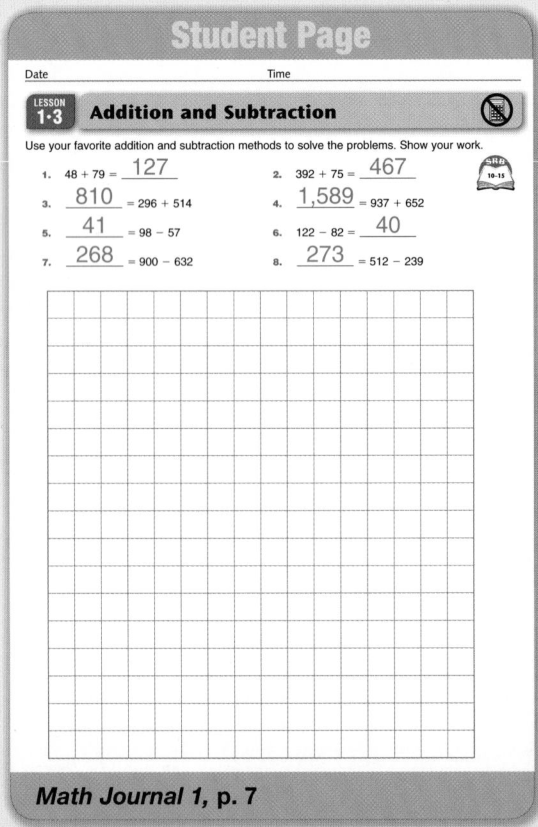

Student Page

Date ____ Time ____

LESSON 1·3 Addition and Subtraction

Use your favorite addition and subtraction methods to solve the problems. Show your work.

1. 48 + 79 = 127
2. 392 + 75 = 467
3. 810 = 296 + 514
4. 1,589 = 937 + 652
5. 41 = 98 − 57
6. 122 − 82 = 40
7. 268 = 900 − 632
8. 273 = 512 − 239

Math Journal 1, p. 7

- Use two straws of one length and two straws of another length. Make a quadrangle with pairs of opposite sides the same length and all right angles. What is this shape called? **rectangle**
- Pull two opposite corners of the rectangle in opposite directions. Are the angles still right angles? no Are the pairs of opposite sides still the same length? yes What is the new shape called? **parallelogram**
- Make a **trapezoid.** Are the angles right angles? Probably not, but two angles in a trapezoid may be right angles. Are any of the sides the same length? Possibly, but all sides in a trapezoid may have different lengths.

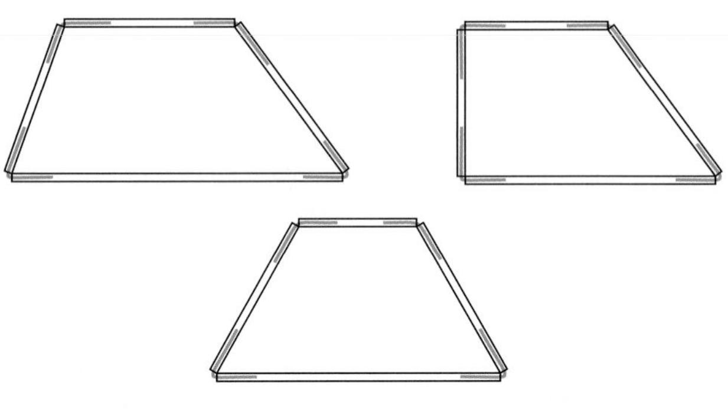

Trapezoids

- Look at the pictures of the parallelograms and the **kite** on page 100 of your *Student Reference Book*. How are these two figures alike? They each have two pairs of sides that are the same length. How are they different? In a parallelogram, the opposite sides are equal in length. In a kite, sides equal in length are next to each other.

To support English language learners, discuss the everyday and mathematical meanings of the word *kite*.

Ongoing Assessment: Recognizing Student Achievement

Math Log or Exit Slip

Use a **Math Log** or **Exit Slip** (*Math Masters*, page 388 or 389) to assess students' ability to compare and contrast plane figures. Have students choose two of the quadrangles they made in this lesson and explain how they are alike and how they are different. Students are making adequate progress if their explanations include information about the lengths of the sides and the measures of the angles. Some students may note whether or not pairs of sides of the quadrangles are parallel or perpendicular.

[Geometry Goal 2]

Drawing and Naming Angles

INDEPENDENT ACTIVITY

(*Math Journal 1,* p. 6)

Ask students to complete journal page 6. Discuss students' responses to Problem 4. Determine how many different answers they found for Problem 7. Record them on the board.

Ongoing Assessment: Informing Instruction

Watch for students who think angle *ABC* in Problem 1 on journal page 6 is bigger because the rays that form the angle are longer. Remind students to consider the *measures* of the angles, not the lengths of the rays.

2 Ongoing Learning & Practice

Adding and Subtracting Whole Numbers

INDEPENDENT ACTIVITY

(*Math Journal 1,* p. 7)

Students add and subtract whole numbers.

Links to the Future

Lessons 2-7 and 2-9 of *Fourth Grade Everyday Mathematics* provide a formal review of addition and subtraction algorithms for multidigit numbers.

Math Boxes 1·3

INDEPENDENT ACTIVITY

(*Math Journal 1,* p. 8)

Mixed Practice Math Boxes in this lesson are paired with Math Boxes in Lesson 1-1. The skill in Problem 5 previews Unit 2 content.

Writing/Reasoning Have students write a response to the following: *Describe how you might solve Problem 5b mentally.* Sample answer: Take 3 from 56 and add it to 97; 97 + 3 = 100 and 100 + 53 = 153.

Study Link 1·3

INDEPENDENT ACTIVITY

(*Math Masters,* p. 11)

Home Connection Students draw and compare quadrangles and draw and label angles.

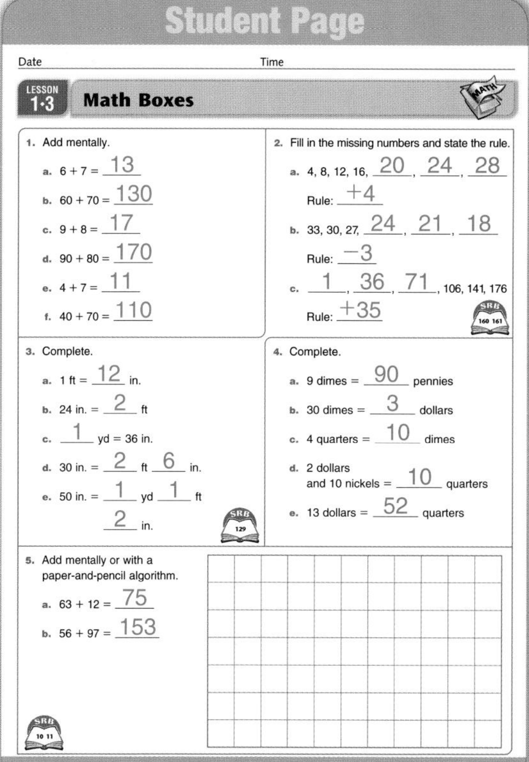

Student Page

Date Time

LESSON 1·3 **Math Boxes**

1. Add mentally.
a. 6 + 7 = 13
b. 60 + 70 = 130
c. 9 + 8 = 17
d. 90 + 80 = 170
e. 4 + 7 = 11
f. 40 + 70 = 110

2. Fill in the missing numbers and state the rule.
a. 4, 8, 12, 16, 20, 24, 28
Rule: +4
b. 33, 30, 27, 24, 21, 18
Rule: −3
c. 1, 36, 71, 106, 141, 176
Rule: +35

SRB 160 161

3. Complete.
a. 1 ft = 12 in.
b. 24 in. = 2 ft
c. 1 yd = 36 in.
d. 30 in. = 2 ft 6 in.
e. 50 in. = 1 yd 1 ft 2 in.

SRB 129

4. Complete.
a. 9 dimes = 90 pennies
b. 30 dimes = 3 dollars
c. 4 quarters = 10 dimes
d. 2 dollars and 10 nickels = 10 quarters
e. 13 dollars = 52 quarters

5. Add mentally or with a paper-and-pencil algorithm.
a. 63 + 12 = 75
b. 56 + 97 = 153

SRB 10 11

Math Journal 1, p. 8

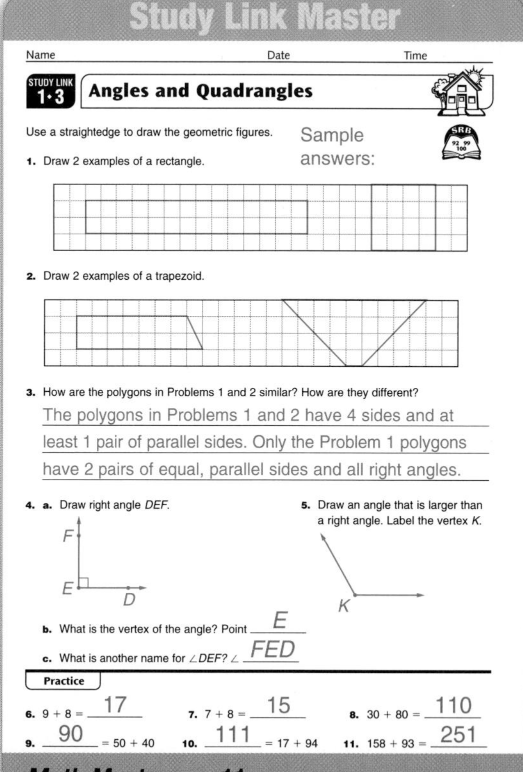

Study Link Master

Name Date Time

STUDY LINK 1·3 **Angles and Quadrangles**

Use a straightedge to draw the geometric figures. Sample answers:

SRB 92 99 100

1. Draw 2 examples of a rectangle.

2. Draw 2 examples of a trapezoid.

3. How are the polygons in Problems 1 and 2 similar? How are they different?
The polygons in Problems 1 and 2 have 4 sides and at least 1 pair of parallel sides. Only the Problem 1 polygons have 2 pairs of equal, parallel sides and all right angles.

4. a. Draw right angle *DEF*.
F E D
b. What is the vertex of the angle? Point E
c. What is another name for ∠*DEF*? ∠ FED

5. Draw an angle that is larger than a right angle. Label the vertex *K*.
K

Practice

6. 9 + 8 = 17
7. 7 + 8 = 15
8. 30 + 80 = 110
9. 90 = 50 + 40
10. 111 = 17 + 94
11. 158 + 93 = 251

Math Masters, p. 11

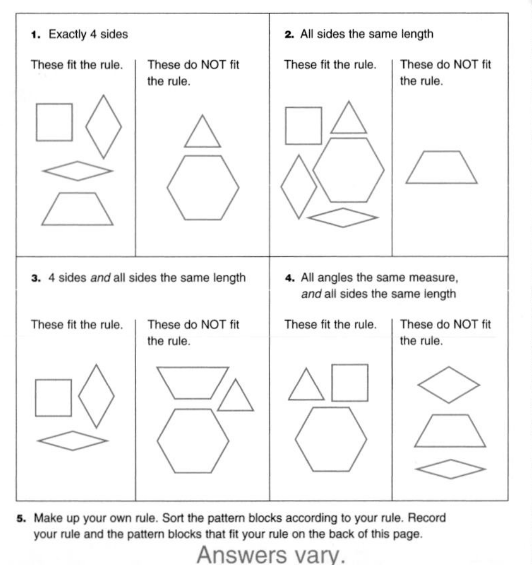

1. Exactly 4 sides		2. All sides the same length	
These fit the rule.	These do NOT fit the rule.	These fit the rule.	These do NOT fit the rule.
3. 4 sides *and* all sides the same length		**4.** All angles the same measure, *and* all sides the same length	
These fit the rule.	These do NOT fit the rule.	These fit the rule.	These do NOT fit the rule.

5. Make up your own rule. Sort the pattern blocks according to your rule. Record your rule and the pattern blocks that fit your rule on the back of this page.

Answers vary.

***Math Masters,* p. 12**

ACTIVITY

▶ Sorting Pattern Blocks

15–30 Min

(*Math Masters,* p. 12)

To explore properties of quadrangles, have students sort pattern blocks according to rules. When students have finished the sorts, ask them to share the rules they wrote for Problem 5. Other students in the group can sort the pattern blocks according to the new rules.

ENRICHMENT

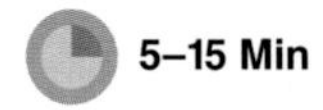

INDEPENDENT ACTIVITY

▶ Solving a Polygon Puzzle

5–15 Min

(*Math Masters,* p. 13)

To apply students understanding of properties of rectangles, triangles, and squares, have them search for those shapes embedded in polygon puzzles. Students use line segments to create an embedded-polygon puzzle for others to solve.

EXTRA PRACTICE

SMALL-GROUP ACTIVITY

▶ *5-Minute Math*

5–15 Min

To offer students more experience with identifying characteristics of 2-dimensional shapes, see *5-Minute Math,* pages 56, 57, 61, and 64.

ELL SUPPORT

PARTNER ACTIVITY

▶ Comparing and Contrasting Quadrangles

5–15 Min

(*Math Masters,* p. 390)

To provide language support for *quadrangles,* have students use a Venn diagram as a tool to compare and contrast the attributes of different categories of quadrangles. *For example:*

Some Properties of Parallelograms and Kites

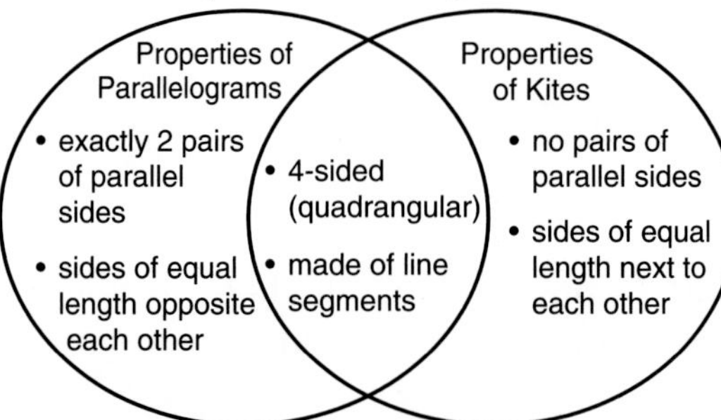

Teaching Master

Name Date Time

LESSON 1·3 **Polygon Search**

1. Study the figure at the right.
   a. How many triangles do you see? 12
   b. How many triangles have a right angle? 8
2. Study the figure at the right.
   a. How many squares do you see? 6
   b. How many triangles? 12
   c. How many rectangles that are *not* squares? 4
3. Make up a geometry puzzle like the one in Problem 2. Use a straightedge to draw line segments to connect some of the dots in the array. Write the answers on the back of this page. Then ask someone to count the number of different polygons in your puzzle.

Answers vary.

***Math Masters,* p. 13**

1•4 Parallelograms

Objective To model the classification of quadrangles based on their properties.

www.everydaymathonline.com

ePresentations

eToolkit

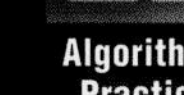
Algorithms Practice

EM Facts Workshop Game™

Family Letters

Assessment Management

Common Core State Standards

Curriculum Focal Points

Interactive Teacher's Lesson Guide

1 Teaching the Lesson

Key Concepts and Skills

- Develop definitions for *parallel* and *intersecting line segments, lines,* and *rays.* [Geometry Goal 1]
- Develop a definition for *perpendicular line segments.* [Geometry Goal 1]
- Describe characteristics of parallelograms. [Geometry Goal 2]
- Classify quadrangles based on side and angle properties. [Geometry Goal 2]

Key Activities

Students review the meanings of *parallel lines, line segments,* and *rays.* They compare various parallelograms and quadrangles.

Ongoing Assessment: Recognizing Student Achievement
Use journal page 10. [Geometry Goal 1]

Key Vocabulary

parallel lines ◆ intersect ◆ parallel line segments ◆ parallel rays ◆ perpendicular line segments

Materials

Math Journal 1, pp. 10 and 11
Student Reference Book, p. 100 (optional)
Study Link 1•3
Math Masters, p. 14
slate ◆ Geometry Template or straightedge

2 Ongoing Learning & Practice

Playing *Subtraction Top-It* (Extended-Facts Version)
Student Reference Book, pp. 263 and 264
Math Masters, p. 506
per partnership: 4 each of number cards 1–10 (from the Everything Math Deck, if available)
Students practice subtraction fact extensions.

Math Boxes 1•4
Math Journal 1, p. 9
Students practice and maintain skills through Math Box problems.

Study Link 1•4
Math Masters, p. 15
Students practice and maintain skills through Study Link activities.

3 Differentiation Options

READINESS

Exploring Parallel Line Segments with Geoboards
Math Masters, p. 16
geoboard ◆ rubber bands
Students explore parallel line segments using a concrete model.

ENRICHMENT

Solving a Straw-Squares Puzzle
Math Masters, p. 17
straws ◆ straightedge
Students solve a puzzle involving properties of parallelograms.

ENRICHMENT

Playing *Sz'kwa*
Student Reference Book, p. 310
Math Masters, p. 505
40 counters (20 each of 2 different colors)
Students apply their understanding of intersecting line segments.

Advance Preparation

For Part 1, place copies of *Math Masters,* page 14 near the Math Message.

***Teacher's Reference Manual,* Grades 4–6** pp. 192, 193

Getting Started

Mental Math and Reflexes

Pose addition facts and extended facts. *Suggestions:*

●○○ 5 + 4 = 9
7 + 6 = 13
8 + 9 = 17

●●○ 20 + 30 = 50
40 + 60 = 100
70 + 50 = 120

●●● 300 + 400 = 700
800 + 200 = 1,000
300 + 900 = 1,200

Math Message

Take a Properties of Polygons sheet (Math Masters, *page 14*) *and follow the directions.*

Study Link 1·3 Follow-Up

Have students compare answers with a partner. Ask volunteers to share how the rectangles and trapezoids they drew in Problems 1 and 2 are similar and different.

NOTE Some students may benefit from doing the **Readiness** activity before you begin Part 1 of the lesson. See the Readiness activity in Part 3 for details.

Interactive whiteboard-ready ePresentations are available at www.everydaymathonline.com to help you teach the lesson.

1 Teaching the Lesson

▶ Math Message Follow-Up

(*Math Masters,* p. 14)

Invite volunteers to identify what the shapes have in common and indicate which shapes have that property. Students indicate thumbs-up if they agree. Have partners share the polygons they drew for Problem 3.

Explain that geometric shapes can be classified by their properties. For example, any polygon with four sides is a quadrangle. As illustrated on *Math Masters,* page 14, some quadrangles are squares, some are trapezoids, and so on.

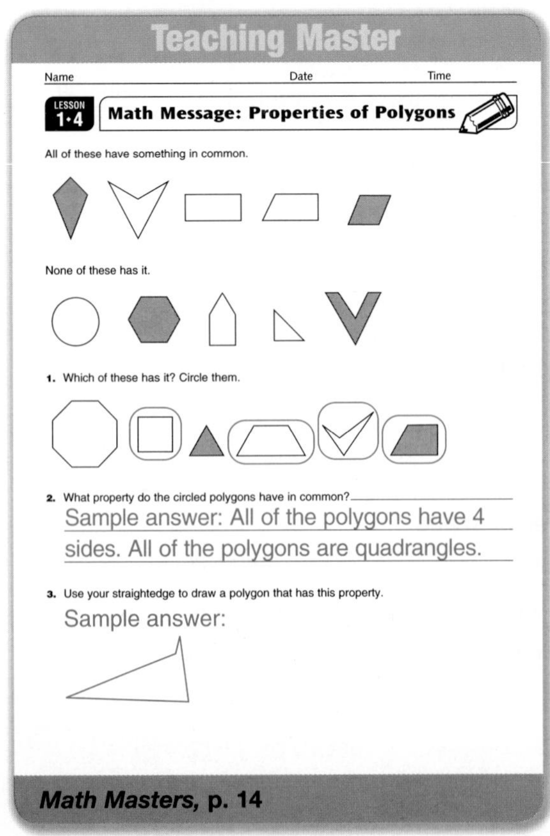
Teaching Master

Name Date Time

LESSON 1·4 Math Message: Properties of Polygons

All of these have something in common.

None of these has it.

1. Which of these has it? Circle them.

2. What property do the circled polygons have in common? Sample answer: All of the polygons have 4 sides. All of the polygons are quadrangles.

3. Use your straightedge to draw a polygon that has this property. Sample answer:

Math Masters, p. 14

Developing Definitions of Parallel Lines, Line Segments, and Rays

Tell students that the number of sides is an obvious property of a shape, but there are many other properties that are less obvious. This lesson involves one of those properties.

1. Draw two **parallel lines** on the board, and ask students what these lines are called. Remind them that a line goes on without end in both directions.

Parallel lines

- When you look at a long stretch of straight railroad tracks, the tracks appear to meet far in the distance. Do they actually meet? no Do two parallel lines ever meet or cross? no

  Parallel lines are lines on a flat surface that never meet or cross; they do not **intersect.**

- What would happen if railroad tracks were not parallel? Sample answer: The train's wheels could not stay on the tracks.

2. Draw two **parallel line segments** on the board. Two line segments in the same plane are parallel if they do not intersect and they will never intersect no matter how far they are extended. Parallel line segments are parts of lines that are parallel. Have students demonstrate parallel line segments with their arms—either by holding them straight up or by lining up their forearms, elbow to finger, with a small distance between them.

Parallel line segments

3. Draw two **parallel rays** on the board. Two rays in the same plane are parallel if they do not intersect, and they will never intersect no matter how far they are extended. Parallel rays are parts of parallel lines.

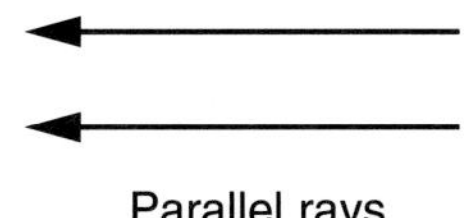

Parallel rays

Adjusting the Activity

ELL

To help students remember the definition of *parallel,* point out that the three *l*'s in the word ***parallel*** are, in fact, parallel.

Some students may be interested in the mathematical symbols used to indicate parallel lines or line segments. For example, instead of writing "Line segment *AB* is parallel to line segment *CD,*" students can write $\overline{AB} \parallel \overline{CD}$.

AUDITORY ◆ KINESTHETIC ◆ TACTILE ◆ VISUAL

Links to the Future

In Unit 11 of *Fourth Grade Everyday Mathematics,* students apply their understanding of the term *parallel* as they describe the relationships between the faces and edges of geometric solids.

NOTE To be parallel, lines must be in the same plane. Two lines that do not meet and are not in the same plane are called *skew lines.* Lay a pencil on a table and stand another pencil upright a few inches away. The two pencils suggest skew lines.

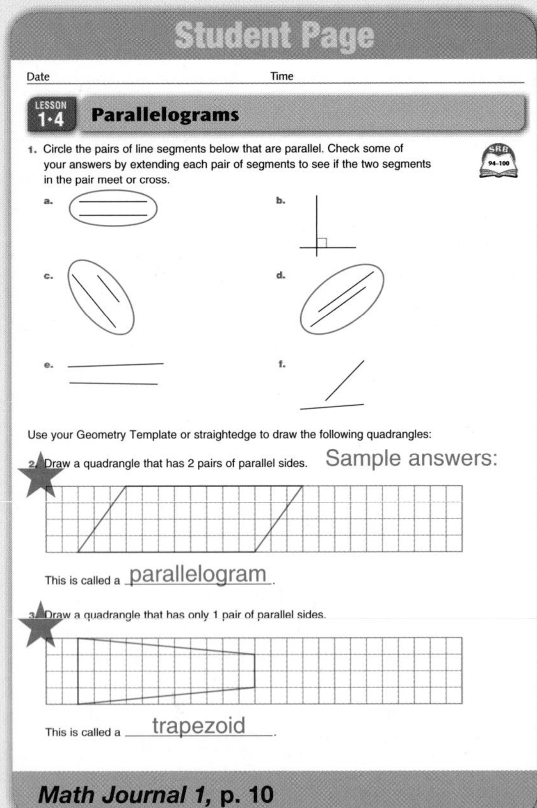
Student Page

Date Time

LESSON 1·4 **Parallelograms**

1. Circle the pairs of line segments below that are parallel. Check some of your answers by extending each pair of segments to see if the two segments in the pair meet or cross.

a. b. c. d. e. f.

Use your Geometry Template or straightedge to draw the following quadrangles:

2. Draw a quadrangle that has 2 pairs of parallel sides. Sample answers:

This is called a parallelogram.

3. Draw a quadrangle that has only 1 pair of parallel sides.

This is called a trapezoid.

Math Journal 1, p. 10

NOTE The term *rhombus* comes from Greek by way of Latin. The plural is either *rhombuses* or *rhombi*.

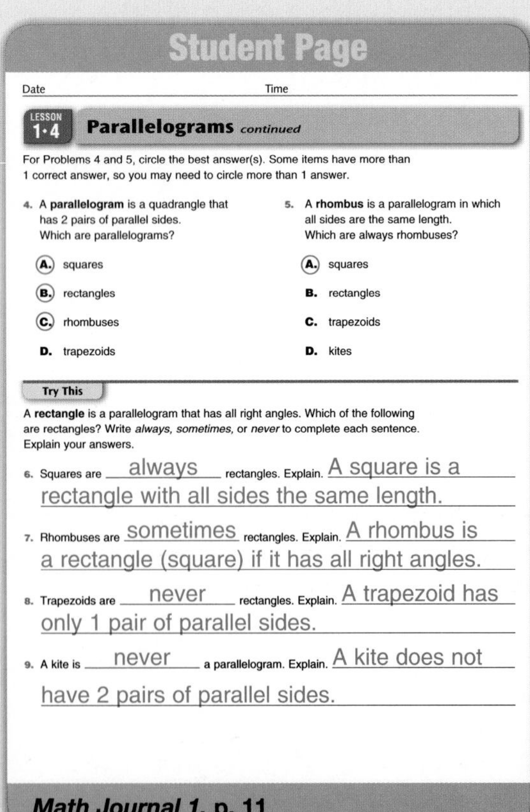
Student Page

Date Time

LESSON 1·4 **Parallelograms** *continued*

For Problems 4 and 5, circle the best answer(s). Some items have more than 1 correct answer, so you may need to circle more than 1 answer.

4. A **parallelogram** is a quadrangle that has 2 pairs of parallel sides. Which are parallelograms?

A. squares
B. rectangles
C. rhombuses
D. trapezoids

5. A **rhombus** is a parallelogram in which all sides are the same length. Which are always rhombuses?

A. squares
B. rectangles
C. trapezoids
D. kites

Try This

A **rectangle** is a parallelogram that has all right angles. Which of the following are rectangles? Write *always*, *sometimes*, or *never* to complete each sentence. Explain your answers.

6. Squares are always rectangles. Explain. A square is a rectangle with all sides the same length.

7. Rhombuses are sometimes rectangles. Explain. A rhombus is a rectangle (square) if it has all right angles.

8. Trapezoids are never rectangles. Explain. A trapezoid has only 1 pair of parallel sides.

9. A kite is never a parallelogram. Explain. A kite does not have 2 pairs of parallel sides.

Math Journal 1, p. 11

▶ Exploring Parallelograms

PARTNER ACTIVITY

(*Math Journal 1,* pp. 10 and 11)

Have students identify the parallel line segments in Problem 1 on journal page 10. Ask why the other pairs of line segments are not parallel. If the line segments in Problems 1e and 1f are extended, they will meet or cross. The line segments in Problem 1b intersect. Line segments (or lines) that intersect and form right angles, like those in Problem 1b, are called **perpendicular line segments** (or lines).

Have students do Problems 2 and 3 on their own before completing journal page 11 with a partner.

Ongoing Assessment: Recognizing Student Achievement

Journal page 10 Problems 2 and 3

Use **journal page 10, Problems 2 and 3** to assess students' understanding of parallel line segments. Students are making adequate progress if they are able to draw appropriate quadrangles. Some students may be able to draw more than one example.

[Geometry Goal 1]

Ask students to help you list relationships, similarities, and differences among various quadrangles. *For example:*

- ▷ Parallelograms are quadrangles with two pairs of parallel sides.
- ▷ Squares, rectangles, and rhombuses are parallelograms, but trapezoids and kites are not.
- ▷ All squares are rectangles, but not all rectangles are squares.
- ▷ All four sides of a square or rhombus are the same length. Squares have right angles; rhombuses can have right angles but usually do not.
- ▷ All squares are rhombuses, but not all rhombuses are squares. (Rhombuses are usually thought of as "slanted" or diamond shaped.) A rhombus that is not a square is also not a rectangle.

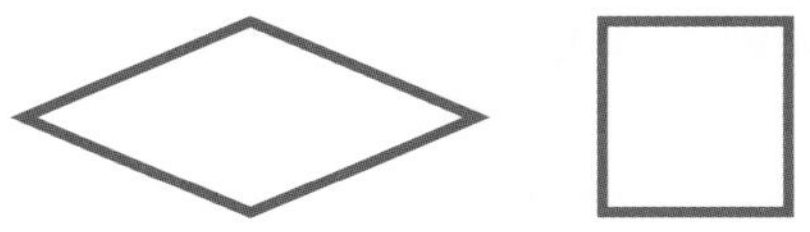

Rhombuses

- ▷ The key difference between a kite and a rhombus is that all the sides of a rhombus are equal, but a kite has two adjacent sides of one length and two adjacent sides of another length.

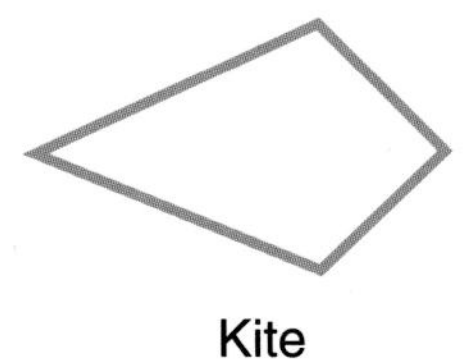

Kite

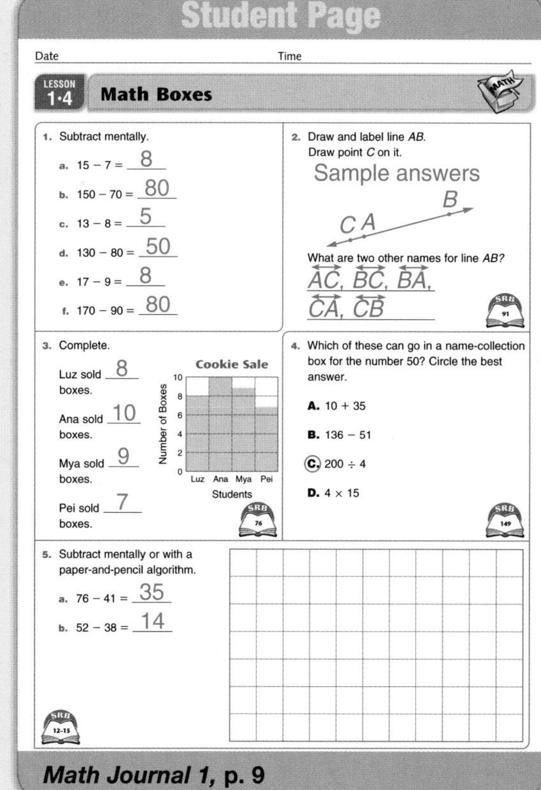
Student Page

Date Time

LESSON 1·4 **Math Boxes**

1. Subtract mentally.
   a. 15 − 7 = 8
   b. 150 − 70 = 80
   c. 13 − 8 = 5
   d. 130 − 80 = 50
   e. 17 − 9 = 8
   f. 170 − 90 = 80

2. Draw and label line *AB*. Draw point *C* on it.
   Sample answers
   What are two other names for line *AB*?
   $\overleftrightarrow{AC}$, $\overleftrightarrow{BC}$, $\overleftrightarrow{BA}$, $\overleftrightarrow{CA}$, $\overleftrightarrow{CB}$

3. Complete.
   Luz sold 8 boxes.
   Ana sold 10 boxes.
   Mya sold 9 boxes.
   Pei sold 7 boxes.

4. Which of these can go in a name-collection box for the number 50? Circle the best answer.
   A. 10 + 35
   B. 136 − 51
   C. 200 ÷ 4 (circled)
   D. 4 × 15

5. Subtract mentally or with a paper-and-pencil algorithm.
   a. 76 − 41 = 35
   b. 52 − 38 = 14

Math Journal 1, p. 9

Adjusting the Activity

Have students open their *Student Reference Book* to page 100 to see a visual organizer displaying relationships among quadrangles.

AUDITORY ◆ KINESTHETIC ◆ TACTILE ◆ VISUAL

2 Ongoing Learning & Practice

Playing *Subtraction Top-It* (Extended-Facts Version)

(*Student Reference Book*, pp. 263 and 264; *Math Masters*, p. 506)

Students play an extended-facts version of *Subtraction Top-It* to develop automaticity with subtraction fact extensions. Students will attach a 0 to both cards before finding the difference. (*See margin.*) For example, a student who draws a 3 and a 7 would solve the extended fact 70 – 30. Consider having students record several rounds of play on *Math Masters*, page 506.

Adjusting the Activity

Sketch a diagram like the one shown below on the board for students to copy and use as a gameboard.

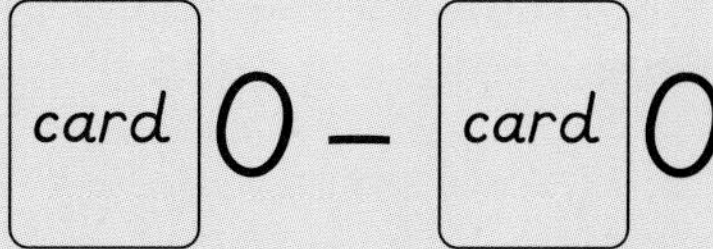

AUDITORY ◆ KINESTHETIC ◆ TACTILE ◆ VISUAL

Math Boxes 1·4

(*Math Journal 1*, p. 9)

Mixed Practice Math Boxes in this lesson are paired with Math Boxes in Lesson 1-2. The skill in Problem 5 previews Unit 2 content.

Writing/Reasoning Have students write a response to the following: *For Problem 3, some students wrote that Mya sold $4\frac{1}{2}$ boxes of cookies. Explain the mistake they might have made when reading the graph.* Sample answer: They counted the number of squares. They did not look at the scale to see that one square represents two boxes of cookies.

Study Link 1·4

(*Math Masters*, p. 15)

Home Connection Students answer questions and draw figures to demonstrate their understanding of the classifications of different quadrangles.

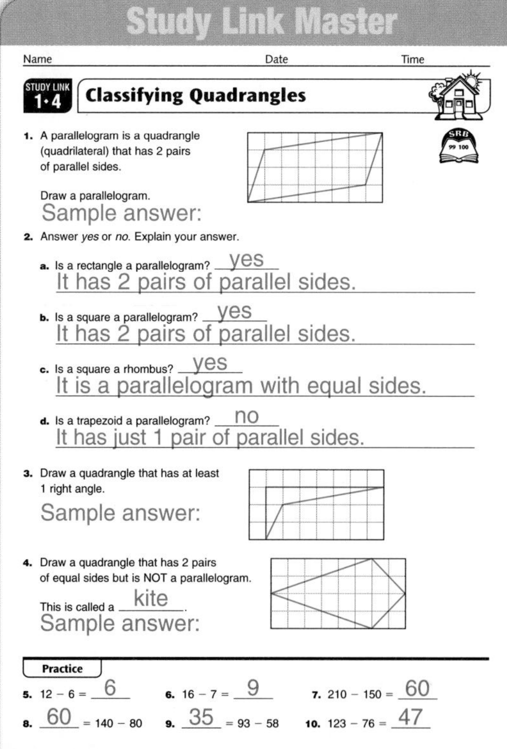
Study Link Master

Name Date Time

STUDY LINK 1·4 **Classifying Quadrangles**

1. A parallelogram is a quadrangle (quadrilateral) that has 2 pairs of parallel sides.
   Draw a parallelogram.
   Sample answer:

2. Answer *yes* or *no*. Explain your answer.
   a. Is a rectangle a parallelogram? yes
      It has 2 pairs of parallel sides.
   b. Is a square a parallelogram? yes
      It has 2 pairs of parallel sides.
   c. Is a square a rhombus? yes
      It is a parallelogram with equal sides.
   d. Is a trapezoid a parallelogram? no
      It has just 1 pair of parallel sides.

3. Draw a quadrangle that has at least 1 right angle.
   Sample answer:

4. Draw a quadrangle that has 2 pairs of equal sides but is NOT a parallelogram.
   This is called a kite.
   Sample answer:

Practice

5. 12 − 6 = 6
6. 16 − 7 = 9
7. 210 − 150 = 60
8. 60 = 140 − 80
9. 35 = 93 − 58
10. 123 − 76 = 47

Math Masters, p. 15

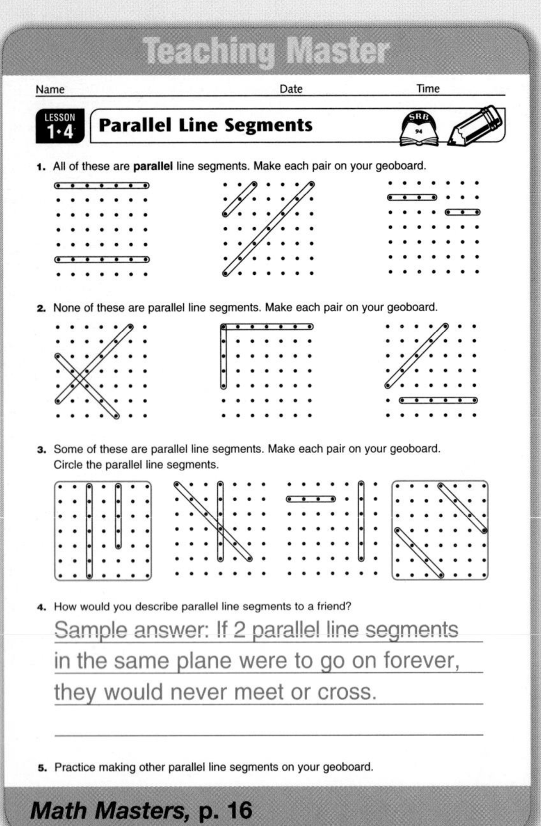

Teaching Master

Name Date Time

LESSON 1·4 **Parallel Line Segments**

1. All of these are **parallel** line segments. Make each pair on your geoboard.

2. None of these are parallel line segments. Make each pair on your geoboard.

3. Some of these are parallel line segments. Make each pair on your geoboard. Circle the parallel line segments.

4. How would you describe parallel line segments to a friend?
Sample answer: If 2 parallel line segments in the same plane were to go on forever, they would never meet or cross.

5. Practice making other parallel line segments on your geoboard.

Math Masters, **p. 16**

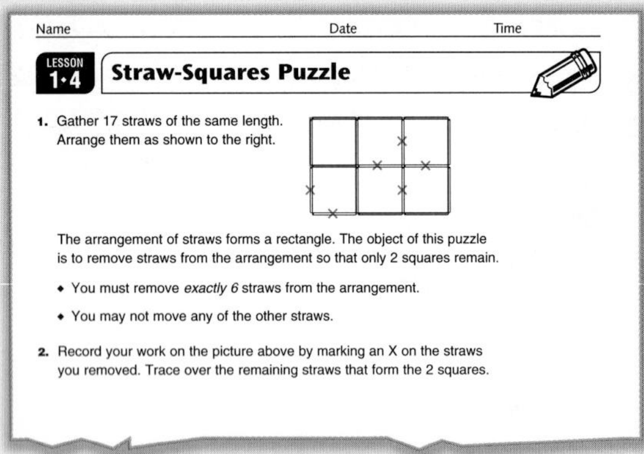

Name Date Time

LESSON 1·4 **Straw-Squares Puzzle**

1. Gather 17 straws of the same length. Arrange them as shown to the right.

The arrangement of straws forms a rectangle. The object of this puzzle is to remove straws from the arrangement so that only 2 squares remain.

- You must remove *exactly 6* straws from the arrangement.
- You may not move any of the other straws.

2. Record your work on the picture above by marking an X on the straws you removed. Trace over the remaining straws that form the 2 squares.

Math Masters, page 17

3 Differentiation Options

READINESS

PARTNER ACTIVITY

5–15 Min

▶ Exploring Parallel Line Segments with Geoboards

(*Math Masters,* p. 16)

To explore the concept of parallel line segments using a concrete model, have students make line segments on a geoboard. Ask them to share their answers to Problem 4. Some students might use gestures to support their words.

ENRICHMENT

PARTNER ACTIVITY

15–30 Min

▶ Solving a Straw-Squares Puzzle

(*Math Masters,* p. 17)

To apply students' understanding of the properties of parallelograms, have them solve a puzzle that requires altering a rectangular arrangement of straws to create two squares.

ENRICHMENT

PARTNER ACTIVITY

15–30 Min

▶ Playing *Sz'kwa*

(*Student Reference Book,* p. 310; *Math Masters,* p. 505)

To apply students' understanding of intersecting line segments, have them play *Sz'kwa*. Students take turns placing markers on the *Sz'kwa* game mat (*Math Masters,* page 505) at any intersection that is not already covered by a marker. The goal is to capture the most markers.

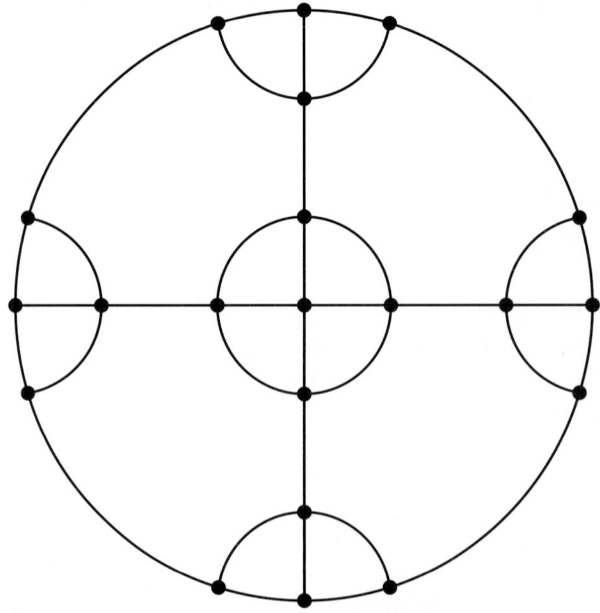

Sz'kwa Game Mat from *Math Masters,* page 505

1•5 Polygons

Objectives To provide opportunities to identify properties of polygons and distinguish between convex and nonconvex (concave) polygons; and to explore geometric definitions and classification.

www.everydaymathonline.com

ePresentations

eToolkit

Algorithms Practice

EM Facts Workshop Game™

Family Letters

Assessment Management

Common Core State Standards

Curriculum Focal Points

Interactive Teacher's Lesson Guide

1 Teaching the Lesson

Key Concepts and Skills

- Construct convex and nonconvex (concave) polygons. [Geometry Goal 2]
- Develop definitions for *convex* and *nonconvex* (*concave*) polygons. [Geometry Goal 2]
- Describe properties of polygons and regular polygons. [Geometry Goal 2]
- Identify types of polygons according to the number of sides. [Geometry Goal 2]

Key Activities

Students construct convex and concave polygons. They identify the characteristics that various polygons have in common and develop definitions of a *polygon* and a *regular polygon.*

Ongoing Assessment: Recognizing Student Achievement
Use journal page 12. [Geometry Goal 2]

Ongoing Assessment: Informing Instruction See page 45.

Key Vocabulary

side ◆ angle ◆ pentagon ◆ polygon ◆ vertex (vertices) ◆ convex ◆ nonconvex or concave ◆ hexagon ◆ heptagon ◆ octagon ◆ nonagon ◆ *n*-gon ◆ interior ◆ regular polygon ◆ equilateral triangle

Materials

Math Journal 1, p. 12
Student Reference Book, p. 97
Study Link 1•4
slate ◆ straws ◆ twist-ties

2 Ongoing Learning & Practice

Math Boxes 1•5
Math Journal 1, p. 13
Students practice and maintain skills through Math Box problems.

Study Link 1•5
Math Masters, p. 18
Students practice and maintain skills through Study Link activities.

3 Differentiation Options

READINESS

Constructing Polygons on a Geoboard
Math Masters, p. 19
geoboard ◆ rubber bands ◆ straightedge
Students explore the properties of a polygon using a concrete model.

READINESS

Exploring Side Angle Properties
Math Masters, p. 20
straws ◆ twist-ties
Students use straws to create polygons found in *The Greedy Triangle.*

ENRICHMENT

Identifying Properties of Kites and Rhombuses
Math Masters, pp. 21 and 22
Students identify properties of kites and rhombuses.

Advance Preparation

For Part 1, place twist-ties and full-length, half-length, and $\frac{3}{4}$-length straws in 4 separate boxes. Each student will need 8 twist-ties and 3 of each size straw. Have extras on hand.

For the optional Readiness activity in Part 3, obtain the book ***The Greedy Triangle*** by Marilyn Burns (Scholastic, 1995).

***Teacher's Reference Manual,* Grades 4–6** pp. 180–185

Getting Started

Mental Math and Reflexes

Pose addition facts and extended facts. *Suggestions:*

●○○ 7 + 8 = 15
6 + 3 = 9
9 + 9 = 18

●●○ 90 + 70 = 160
80 + 60 = 140
50 + 60 = 110

●●● 800 + 500 = 1,300
600 + 900 = 1,500
4,000 + 7,000 = 11,000

Math Message

Take 3 of each size straw and 8 twist-ties. Make a shape with 5 sides.

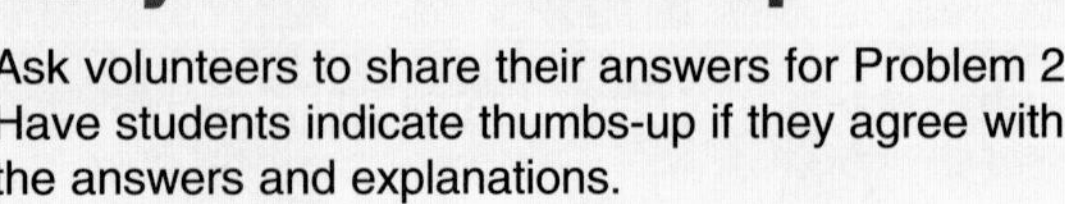

Study Link 1•4 Follow-Up

Ask volunteers to share their answers for Problem 2. Have students indicate thumbs-up if they agree with the answers and explanations.

NOTE Some students may benefit from doing the **Readiness** activity before you begin Part 1 of the lesson. See the Readiness activity in Part 3 for details.

Interactive whiteboard-ready ePresentations are available at www.everydaymathonline.com to help you teach the lesson.

1 Teaching the Lesson

▶ Math Message Follow-Up

NOTE Although this lesson's vocabulary list is extensive, many of the words have been used in *Everyday Mathematics* prior to fourth grade and should be familiar to many students. Do not insist that students memorize these words. They will become part of their vocabulary through repeated use. As geometric terms are discussed in this lesson, write them on the board, and include drawings, to support English language learners.

Ask students to look at the shape they made with the straws and recall the name of a shape that has five **sides** and five **angles.** pentagon Students may remember that triangles, quadrangles, and **pentagons** are examples of **polygons.**

Language Arts Link The word *polygon* comes from the Greek words *polu,* meaning "many," and *gonia,* meaning "angle." Many geometric terms are derived from Greek and Latin words. Breaking these terms into parts can make learning them easier and promotes useful word analysis skills.

Ask students to push one **vertex** or several **vertices** of their pentagons toward the inside. This new shape is also a pentagon, but it has a special name: It is called a nonconvex or concave pentagon.

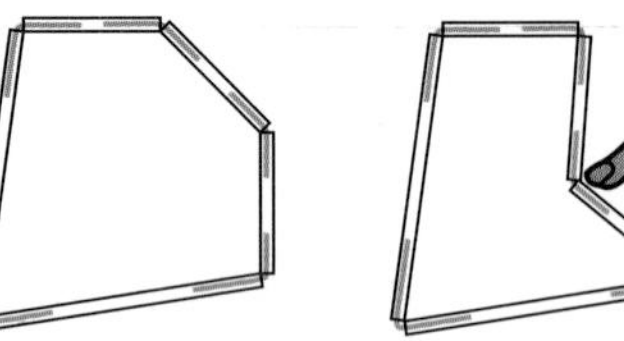

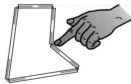

convex nonconvex, or concave

NOTE A line segment connecting any two points on a convex polygon lies entirely inside or on the polygon. That is not always the case for concave polygons.

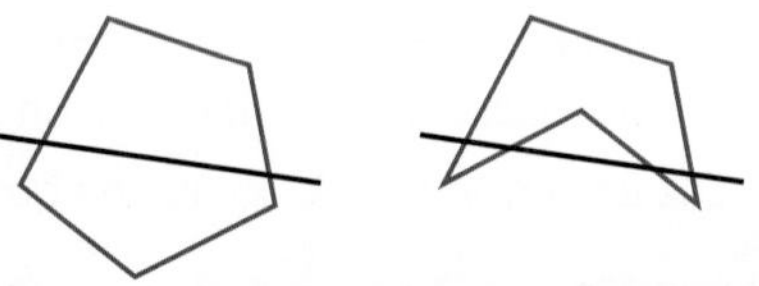

Point out the following:

- ▷ A polygon in which all vertices are pushed outward is called a **convex** polygon.
- ▷ A polygon in which at least one vertex is pushed inward ("caves in") is called a **nonconvex,** or **concave,** polygon.

To support English language learners, explain the meaning of *cave in* so that the hint is understood.

Adjusting the Activity

Ask students if it is possible to create a concave triangle no or a concave quadrangle. yes Have them explain their reasoning.

AUDITORY ◆ KINESTHETIC ◆ TACTILE ◆ VISUAL

Constructing Convex and Concave Polygons

Have students work in groups of four. Ask each group to make polygons with 6 straws, 7 straws, 8 straws, and 9 straws. (That is, each student in a group makes one of the polygons. Some should have all sides equal, some not. Students will need to share straws and twist-ties.) Bring the class together and review the names of the polygons: A polygon with 6 sides is a **hexagon,** with 7 sides a **heptagon,** with 8 sides an **octagon,** and with 9 sides a **nonagon.**

Ask students who made hexagons to hold up their constructions for all to see. Ask them to distinguish between convex and nonconvex (concave) polygons. Repeat with the other kinds of polygons.

- Is it possible to make a polygon out of 25 straws? yes Out of 100 straws? yes

A nonconvex (concave) 25-gon

Polygons are sometimes called ***n*-gons.** For example, a 25-sided polygon can be called a 25-gon.

Language Arts Link Remind students of the prefixes in the names of polygons: *tri-* in *triangle* means "three"; *quad-* in *quadrilateral* and *quadrangle* means "four"; *penta-* means "five"; *hexa-* means "six"; *hepta-* means "seven"; *octa-* means "eight"; *nona-* means "nine"; *deca-* means "ten"; and *dodeca-* means "twelve" (two and ten).

NOTE The **interior** (inside) of a polygon is not part of the polygon. A polygon with its interior is known as a polygonal region.

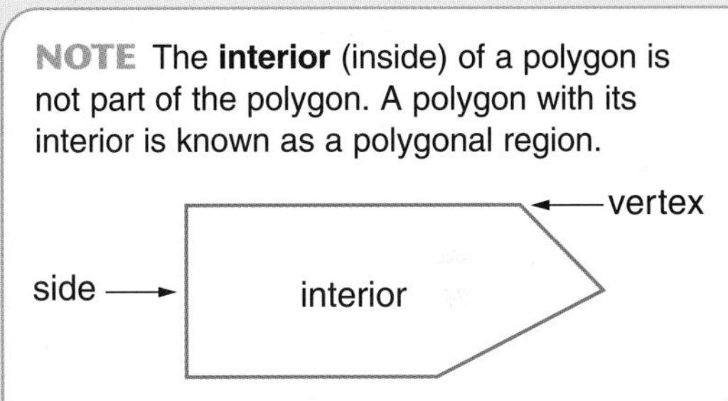

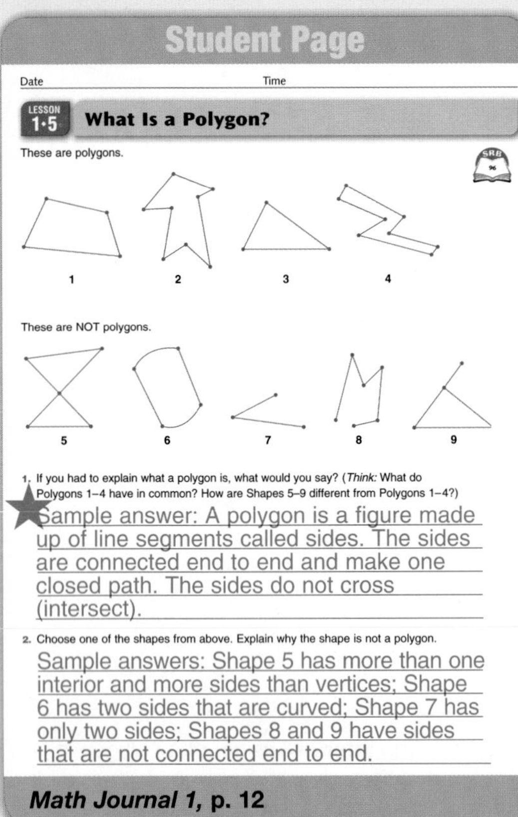

Student Page
Date
Time
LESSON 1·5
What Is a Polygon?
These are polygons.
These are NOT polygons.
1. If you had to explain what a polygon is, what would you say? (Think: What do Polygons 1–4 have in common? How are Shapes 5–9 different from Polygons 1–4?)
Sample answer: A polygon is a figure made up of line segments called sides. The sides are connected end to end and make one closed path. The sides do not cross (intersect).
2. Choose one of the shapes from above. Explain why the shape is not a polygon.
Sample answers: Shape 5 has more than one interior and more sides than vertices; Shape 6 has two sides that are curved; Shape 7 has only two sides; Shapes 8 and 9 have sides that are not connected end to end.

Math Journal 1, p. 12

▶ Defining Properties of Polygons

(*Math Journal 1,* p. 12)

Working in pairs, have students examine the two sets of shapes at the top of journal page 12. Suggest that they use these shapes to help them discuss the properties of polygons. Then ask students to complete journal page 12 on their own.

Ongoing Assessment: Recognizing Student Achievement

Journal page 12 Problem 1

Use **journal page 12, Problem 1** to assess students' understanding of the properties of polygons. Students are making adequate progress if responses include the following:

▷ A polygon is made up of line segments; curved lines are not line segments.

▷ The sides of a polygon must form one closed path.

▷ The sides of a polygon must not cross.

▷ A polygon can have only one interior (inside).

Some students may include additional information such as the following:

▷ The number of sides is the same as the number of angles and vertices.

▷ A polygon must have at least three sides.

[Geometry Goal 2]

▶ Defining the Properties of Regular Polygons

(*Student Reference Book,* p. 97)

Ask pairs of students to look at the **regular polygons** on page 97 of the *Student Reference Book.*

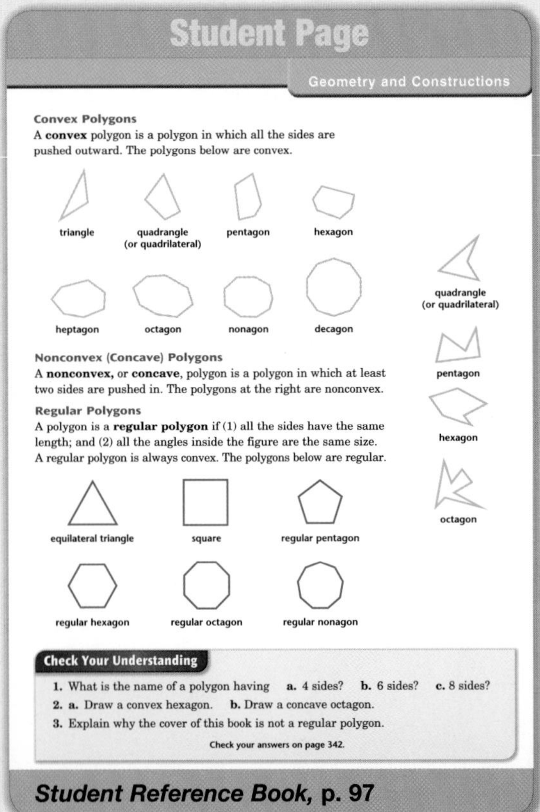

Student Page
Geometry and Constructions
Convex Polygons
A convex polygon is a polygon in which all the sides are pushed outward. The polygons below are convex.
triangle
quadrangle (or quadrilateral)
pentagon
hexagon
heptagon
octagon
nonagon
decagon
Nonconvex (Concave) Polygons
A nonconvex, or concave, polygon is a polygon in which at least two sides are pushed in. The polygons at the right are nonconvex.
quadrangle (or quadrilateral)
pentagon
hexagon
octagon
Regular Polygons
A polygon is a regular polygon if (1) all the sides have the same length; and (2) all the angles inside the figure are the same size. A regular polygon is always convex. The polygons below are regular.
equilateral triangle
square
regular pentagon
regular hexagon
regular octagon
regular nonagon
Check Your Understanding
1. What is the name of a polygon having a. 4 sides? b. 6 sides? c. 8 sides?
2. a. Draw a convex hexagon. b. Draw a concave octagon.
3. Explain why the cover of this book is not a regular polygon.
Check your answers on page 342.

Student Reference Book, p. 97

Adjusting the Activity

Discuss the everyday and mathematical meanings of the word *regular.* Write *regular polygons* on the board. Label and draw pictures of the regular and nonregular polygons you discuss in class. Display these labeled illustrations throughout the unit.

AUDITORY ♦ KINESTHETIC ♦ TACTILE ♦ VISUAL

Ask students to make a list of things that regular polygons have in common. The list should include the following:

- ▷ All sides of a regular polygon have the same length.
- ▷ The angles inside the figure are the same size.
- ▷ Regular polygons are convex.
- ▷ Regular polygons are symmetric.

Ongoing Assessment: Informing Instruction

Watch for students who list properties of *all* polygons (for example, sides are line segments, there is only one interior, and so on). Ask them to focus on what makes regular polygons different from other polygons.

Call attention to the two regular polygons with special names: An **equilateral triangle** is a regular triangle, and a square is a regular quadrangle. Other regular polygon names are always preceded by the adjective *regular:* regular pentagon, regular 13-gon, and so on.

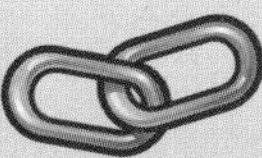

Links to the Future

In Unit 11 of *Fourth Grade Everyday Mathematics*, students apply their knowledge of polygons as they identify and construct *polyhedrons*—geometric solids whose surfaces are all flat and formed by polygons.

2 Ongoing Learning & Practice

▸ Math Boxes 1•5

INDEPENDENT ACTIVITY

(*Math Journal 1,* p. 13)

Mixed Practice Math Boxes in this lesson are paired with Math Boxes in Lesson 1-7. The skill in Problem 6 previews Unit 2 content.

▸ Study Link 1•5

INDEPENDENT ACTIVITY

(*Math Masters,* p. 18)

Home Connection Students solve polygon riddles and write one of their own.

Student Page

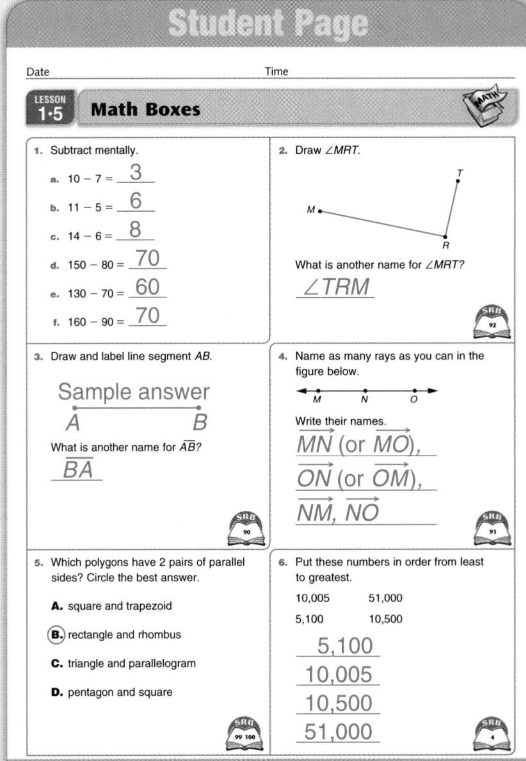

Date Time

LESSON 1•5 **Math Boxes**

1. Subtract mentally.
   a. 10 − 7 = 3
   b. 11 − 5 = 6
   c. 14 − 6 = 8
   d. 150 − 80 = 70
   e. 130 − 70 = 60
   f. 160 − 90 = 70

2. Draw ∠MRT.
   What is another name for ∠MRT? ∠TRM

3. Draw and label line segment AB.
   Sample answer
   What is another name for $\overline{AB}$? $\overline{BA}$

4. Name as many rays as you can in the figure below.
   Write their names.
   $\overrightarrow{MN}$ (or $\overrightarrow{MO}$), $\overrightarrow{ON}$ (or $\overrightarrow{OM}$), $\overrightarrow{NM}$, $\overrightarrow{NO}$

5. Which polygons have 2 pairs of parallel sides? Circle the best answer.
   A. square and trapezoid
   (B.) rectangle and rhombus
   C. triangle and parallelogram
   D. pentagon and square

6. Put these numbers in order from least to greatest.
   10,005 51,000 5,100 10,500
   5,100
   10,005
   10,500
   51,000

Math Journal 1, p. 13

Study Link Master

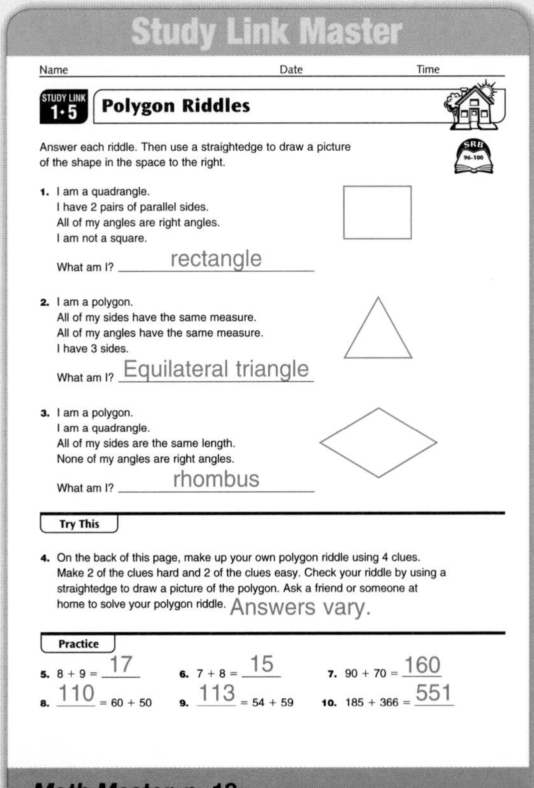

Name Date Time

STUDY LINK 1•5 **Polygon Riddles**

Answer each riddle. Then use a straightedge to draw a picture of the shape in the space to the right.

1. I am a quadrangle.
   I have 2 pairs of parallel sides.
   All of my angles are right angles.
   I am not a square.
   What am I? rectangle

2. I am a polygon.
   All of my sides have the same measure.
   All of my angles have the same measure.
   I have 3 sides.
   What am I? Equilateral triangle

3. I am a polygon.
   I am a quadrangle.
   All of my sides are the same length.
   None of my angles are right angles.
   What am I? rhombus

Try This

4. On the back of this page, make up your own polygon riddle using 4 clues. Make 2 of the clues hard and 2 of the clues easy. Check your riddle by using a straightedge to draw a picture of the polygon. Ask a friend or someone at home to solve your polygon riddle. Answers vary.

Practice

5. 8 + 9 = 17
6. 7 + 8 = 15
7. 90 + 70 = 160
8. 110 = 60 + 50
9. 113 = 54 + 59
10. 185 + 366 = 551

Math Master, p. 18

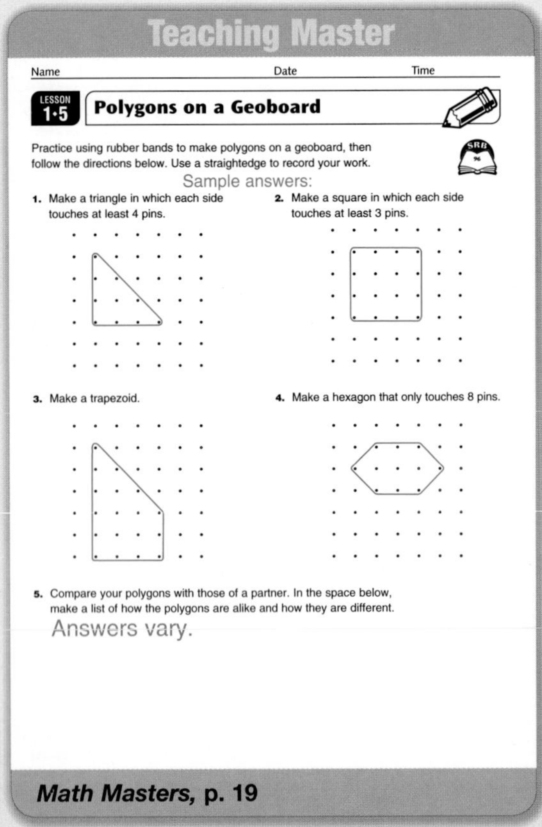

Teaching Master

Name Date Time

LESSON 1·5 **Polygons on a Geoboard**

Practice using rubber bands to make polygons on a geoboard, then follow the directions below. Use a straightedge to record your work.

Sample answers:

1. Make a triangle in which each side touches at least 4 pins.
2. Make a square in which each side touches at least 3 pins.
3. Make a trapezoid.
4. Make a hexagon that only touches 8 pins.
5. Compare your polygons with those of a partner. In the space below, make a list of how the polygons are alike and how they are different.

Answers vary.

Math Masters, p. 19

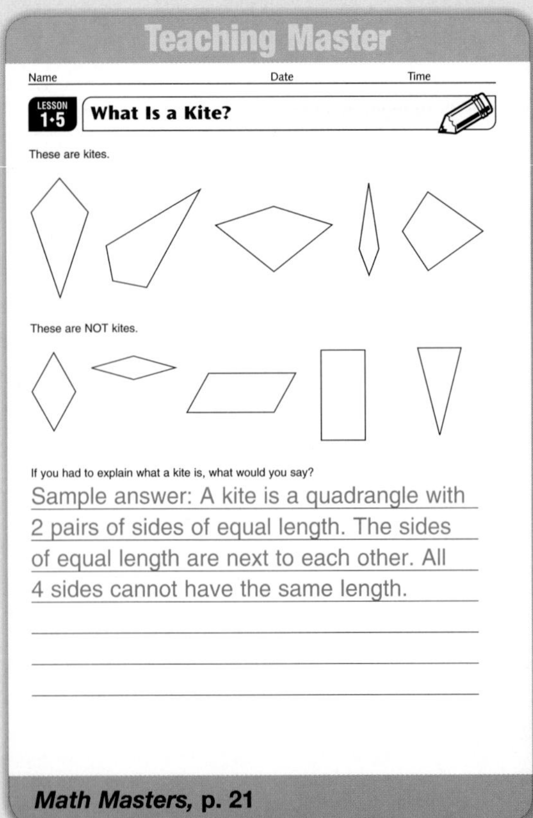

Teaching Master

Name Date Time

LESSON 1·5 **What Is a Kite?**

These are kites.

These are NOT kites.

If you had to explain what a kite is, what would you say?

Sample answer: A kite is a quadrangle with 2 pairs of sides of equal length. The sides of equal length are next to each other. All 4 sides cannot have the same length.

Math Masters, p. 21

3 Differentiation Options

READINESS

▶ Constructing Polygons on a Geoboard

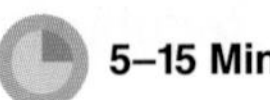

(*Math Masters,* p. 19)

To explore the properties of polygons using a concrete model, have students use rubber bands to construct polygons on a geoboard. Partners look for similarities and differences among the polygons they made.

READINESS

▶ Exploring Side Angle Properties

(*Math Masters*, p. 20)

Literature Link To explore classifying polygons according to their number of sides, have students read or listen to the story ***The Greedy Triangle*** by Marilyn Burns (Scholastic, 1995) and build the polygons from the story using straws and twist-ties. Ask students to record their work on *Math Masters,* page 20.

Shape	Drawing of Shape	Number of Sides	Number of Angles
equilateral triangle		3	3
quadrilateral		4	

ENRICHMENT

▶ Identifying Properties of Kites and Rhombuses

15–30 Min

(*Math Masters,* pp. 21 and 22)

To apply students' understanding of the properties of kites and rhombuses, have them compare examples and nonexamples of each. They use this information to describe the properties of both kinds of polygons.

Planning Ahead

Students play *Polygon Pair-Up* in Part 2 of Lesson 1-6. They will need to cut apart the Polygon Deck and Property Deck found on *Math Masters,* pages 496 and 497. Consider copying the cards on cardstock.

1•6 Drawing Circles with a Compass

Objective To provide practice using a compass.

Technology Resources www.everydaymathonline.com

Presentations

eToolkit

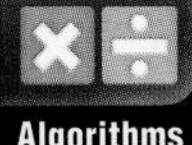
Algorithms Practice

EM Facts Workshop Game™

Family Letters

Assessment Management

Common Core State Standards

Curriculum Focal Points

Interactive Teacher's Lesson Guide

1 Teaching the Lesson

Key Concepts and Skills

- Use a compass to measure distance. [Measurement and Reference Frames Goal 1]
- Use a compass to draw circles. [Geometry Goal 2]
- Construct an inscribed square. [Geometry Goal 2]
- Verify that the sides of a square are the same length. [Geometry Goal 2]

Key Activities

Students draw circles with a compass and construct a square inscribed in a circle by folding paper.

Key Vocabulary

compass ◆ circle ◆ center (of a circle) ◆ inscribed square

Materials

Math Journal 1, pp. 14 and 15
Study Link 1•5
slate ◆ compass ◆ paper (colored, if available) ◆ straightedge ◆ cardboard ◆ scissors (optional)

2 Ongoing Learning & Practice

Playing *Polygon Pair-Up*
Student Reference Book, p. 258
Math Masters, pp. 496 and 497
scissors
Students practice identifying properties of polygons.

Math Boxes 1•6
Math Journal 1, p. 16
Students practice and maintain skills through Math Box problems.

Ongoing Assessment: Recognizing Student Achievement
Use Math Boxes, Problem 3.
[Geometry Goal 1]

Study Link 1•6
Math Masters, p. 23
Students practice and maintain skills through Study Link activities.

3 Differentiation Options

ENRICHMENT

Solving an Inscribed-Square Puzzle
Math Masters, p. 24
straightedge
Students apply their understanding of inscribing polygons within circles.

EXTRA PRACTICE

Creating Circle Designs
straightedge ◆ compass ◆ scissors ◆ glue ◆ colored paper (optional)
Students use a compass to create circle designs based on examples in *Ed Emberley's Picture Pie: A Cut and Paste Drawing Book.*

Advance Preparation

In Part 2, students cut apart the Polygon Deck and Property Deck from *Math Masters,* pages 496 and 497. Consider copying the cards on cardstock for students and making overhead transparency cards for demonstrations.

For the optional Extra Practice activity in Part 3, obtain the book ***Ed Emberley's Picture Pie: A Cut and Paste Drawing Book*** by Ed Emberley (Little Brown, 2006).

***Teacher's Reference Manual,* Grades 4–6** pp. 42–44, 209–211

Getting Started

Mental Math and Reflexes

Write numbers such as those listed below on the board.

●○○	●●○	●●●
2,510	32,756	7,682,041
9,246	172,908	4,502,639
3,082	530,175	67,314,851

For each number, ask questions such as the following:

- What is the value of the digit *x*?
- Which digit is in the thousands place?

Math Message

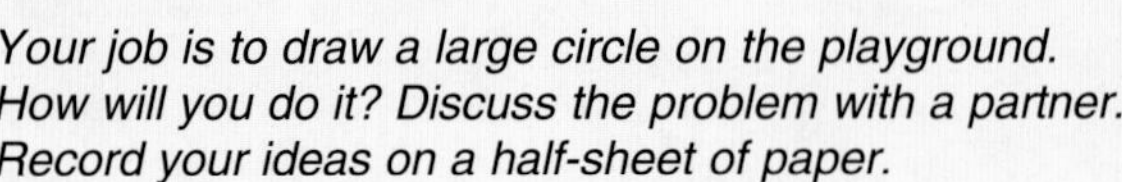

Your job is to draw a large circle on the playground. How will you do it? Discuss the problem with a partner. Record your ideas on a half-sheet of paper.

Study Link 1·5 Follow-Up

Have small groups of students compare answers to Problems 1–3. Then ask students to pose their own riddles to the group.

Interactive whiteboard-ready ePresentations are available at www.everydaymathonline.com to help you teach the lesson.

1 Teaching the Lesson

▶ Math Message Follow-Up

Encourage students to share ideas. One method is to anchor one end of a rope to the ground, attach a piece of chalk to the other end, pull the rope taut, and then rotate it around the anchor to draw the circle. Let students judge for themselves the relative effectiveness of the methods they suggest. You might have them try out their methods on the playground.

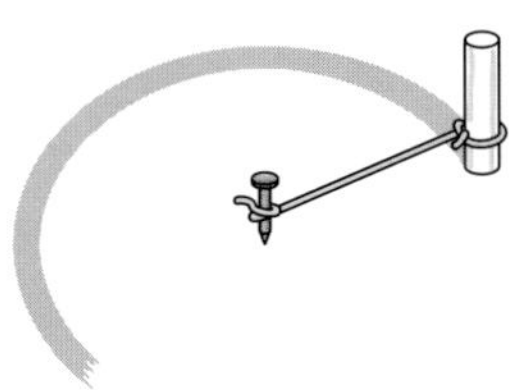

One way of drawing a circle without a compass

Tell students that in this lesson they will learn how to use a **compass** to draw circles. Students who have never used a compass will need plenty of practice with the most basic construction—that of a **circle**—before attempting more difficult constructions.

▶ Drawing Circles with a Compass

Demonstrate two methods for drawing circles with a compass. (These directions are for right-handed students.) Students should draw on top of cardboard or several sheets of paper to prevent damage to the desk or tabletop and to keep the anchor from slipping as the pencil is rotated. For either method, the compass should be held at the top, not by its arms. (*See margin on page 49.*)

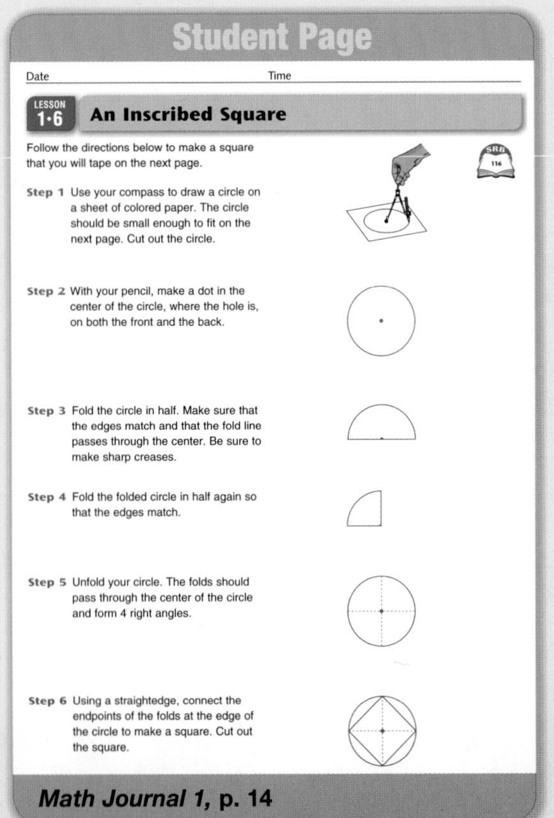

Student Page

Date Time

LESSON 1·6 **An Inscribed Square**

SRB 116

Follow the directions below to make a square that you will tape on the next page.

Step 1 Use your compass to draw a circle on a sheet of colored paper. The circle should be small enough to fit on the next page. Cut out the circle.

Step 2 With your pencil, make a dot in the center of the circle, where the hole is, on both the front and the back.

Step 3 Fold the circle in half. Make sure that the edges match and that the fold line passes through the center. Be sure to make sharp creases.

Step 4 Fold the folded circle in half again so that the edges match.

Step 5 Unfold your circle. The folds should pass through the center of the circle and form 4 right angles.

Step 6 Using a straightedge, connect the endpoints of the folds at the edge of the circle to make a square. Cut out the square.

Math Journal 1, p. 14

Students should experiment with both methods and use the one with which they feel more comfortable. Have them draw circles of various sizes.

Remind students of the following:

- ▷ As with polygons, the interior of a circle is not part of the circle.
- ▷ The point located at the anchor of the compass is called the **center** of the circle; the center is not part of the circle.
- ▷ All points on a circle are the same distance from the center of the circle.

Constructing an Inscribed Square

INDEPENDENT ACTIVITY

(*Math Journal 1,* pp. 14 and 15)

Construction of an **inscribed square** (a square whose vertices all lie on a circle) relies on paper folding. Demonstrate the construction while students follow your directions, or have students follow the directions on their own.

Adjusting the Activity

Have students construct an inscribed regular octagon. One way to do this is to draw and cut out a circle and fold it into eighths. The fold lines meet the circle in eight equally spaced points. These points become the vertices of the octagon. If students need a hint, you might tell them to start as though they were making a square using the method on journal page 14.

AUDITORY ◆ KINESTHETIC ◆ TACTILE ◆ VISUAL

Student Page

Date Time

LESSON 1·6 **An Inscribed Square** *continued*

Now use your compass to find out whether the 4 sides of your square are about the same length.

Place the anchor on one endpoint of a side and the pencil point on the other endpoint of the side. Then, *without changing the compass opening,* try to place the anchor and pencil point on the endpoints of each of the other sides.

If the sides of your square are about the same length, tape the square in the space below. If not, follow the directions on page 14 again. Tape your best square in the space below.

***Math Journal 1*, p. 15**

Method 1:

1. Press the anchor of the compass firmly onto the paper. (Some teachers find it helpful to tape the paper to the work surface.)
2. Rotate the pencil point of the compass around the anchor, keeping the paper fixed in place.
3. If the pencil is rotated clockwise, start with the pencil close to where the 5 would be located on a clock face. (If rotating counterclockwise, start near the 7.)

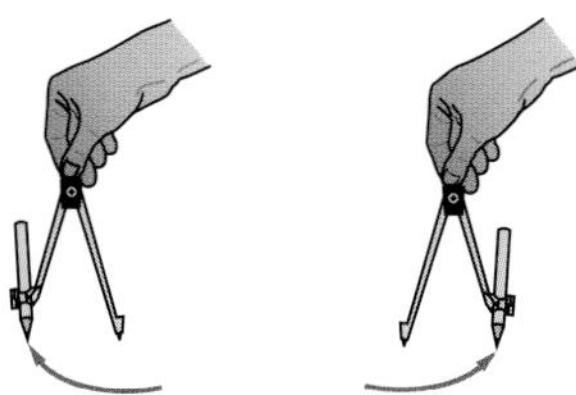

Method 1

Method 2:

Rotate a single sheet of paper, keeping the anchor and pencil point fixed in place. This method is especially useful when drawing smaller circles.

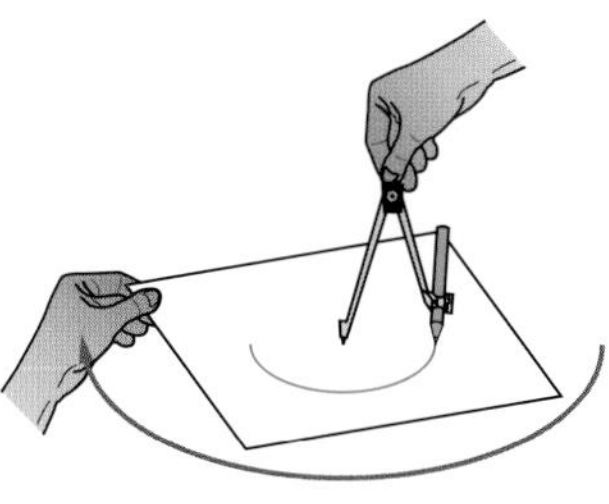

Method 2

NOTE These directions are for a traditional, two-arm compass. Other compasses are available, including ruler-type compasses. These methods work with both types of compasses.

2 Ongoing Learning & Practice

▶ Playing *Polygon Pair-Up*

(*Student Reference Book,* p. 258; *Math Masters,* pp. 496 and 497)

Students play *Polygon Pair-Up* to practice identifying properties of polygons. Consider playing a game or two against the class on the overhead projector to help students learn the rules.

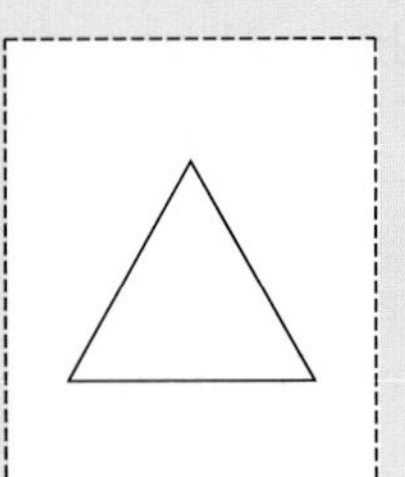

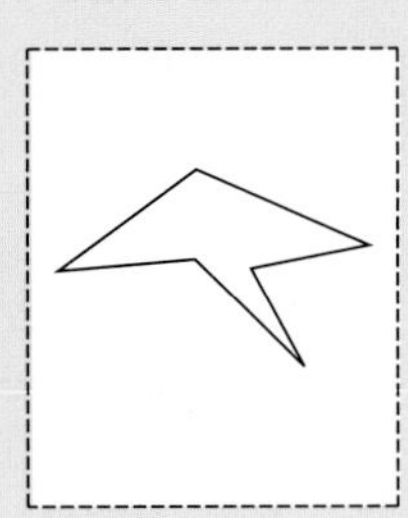

Polygon Cards from *Math Masters,* page 496

All sides are the same length.

All angles are right angles.

Property Cards from *Math Masters,* page 497

Adjusting the Activity

Use these game variations as appropriate:

Variation 1:

- ▷ Use only the Property Cards.
- ▷ Players take turns drawing cards and tracing a shape from their Geometry Template that matches the property described on the card.
- ▷ The first time a shape from the Geometry Template is used, a player earns 3 points for a correct match. If the same shape is traced again, players earn only 1 point.
- ▷ When time runs out, the player with the highest score wins.

Variation 2:

- ▷ Place all the Polygon Cards faceup. Place the Property Cards facedown between the players.
- ▷ Players take turns drawing a Property Card and searching the Polygon Cards to find a match.
- ▷ The player with the most pairs wins.

AUDITORY ◆ KINESTHETIC ◆ TACTILE ◆ VISUAL

▶ Math Boxes 1·6

(*Math Journal 1,* p. 16)

Mixed Practice Math Boxes in this lesson are paired with Math Boxes in Lesson 1-8. The skill in Problem 6 previews Unit 2 content.

Writing/Reasoning Have students write a response to the following: *Explain why the shapes you chose in Problem 2 are not polygons.* Sample answer: B has curved sides, and A does not have sides that connect end to end.

Student Page

Date Time

LESSON 1·6 **Math Boxes**

1. Subtract mentally.
   a. 11 − 2 = 9
   b. 110 − 20 = 90
   c. 8 = 12 − 4
   d. 120 − 40 = 80
   e. 30 = 120 − 90
   f. 160 − 80 = 80

2. Which of the shape(s) below are NOT polygons? B and C
   A B C

3. Draw a quadrangle with only 1 right angle. Draw in the right angle symbol.
   Sample answers:
   How do you know it is a right angle?
   It is a square corner.

4. Circle the convex polygon(s).

5. Draw and label ray *HA*. Draw point *T* on it.
   Sample answer
   H A T
   What is another name for $\overrightarrow{HA}$? $\overrightarrow{HT}$

6. In the numeral 42,318, the 2 stands for 2,000.
   a. The 1 stands for 10.
   b. The 8 stands for 8.
   c. The 4 stands for 40,000.
   d. The 3 stands for 300.

Math Journal 1, p. 16

Ongoing Assessment: Recognizing Student Achievement

Math Boxes Problem 3

Use **Math Boxes, Problem 3** to assess students' understanding of right angles. Students are making adequate progress if they are able to draw an appropriate quadrangle. Some students may be able to explain how they know the angle is a right angle.

[Geometry Goal 1]

Study Link 1•6

INDEPENDENT ACTIVITY

(*Math Masters,* p. 23)

Home Connection Students match geometric figures and properties.

3 Differentiation Options

ENRICHMENT

INDEPENDENT ACTIVITY

Solving an Inscribed-Square Puzzle

15–30 Min

(*Math Masters,* p. 24)

To apply students' understanding of inscribing polygons within circles, have them solve an inscribed-square puzzle. Polygon 1 is said to be inscribed in Polygon 2 if all of the vertices of Polygon 1 are on Polygon 2.

Have students describe the squares they drew. Encourage words like *center of circle* and *inscribed.*

EXTRA PRACTICE

INDEPENDENT ACTIVITY

Creating Circle Designs

30+ Min

Portfolio Ideas

Art Link To provide practice using a compass to draw circles, have students create circle designs based on the ones in ***Ed Emberley's Picture Pie: A Cut and Paste Drawing Book*** by Ed Emberley (Little Brown, 2006). Circles that have been constructed with a compass and cut into halves, fourths, or eighths are the basis for the artwork in the book. The circles can be constructed on paper of various colors and can be used to form elaborate designs.

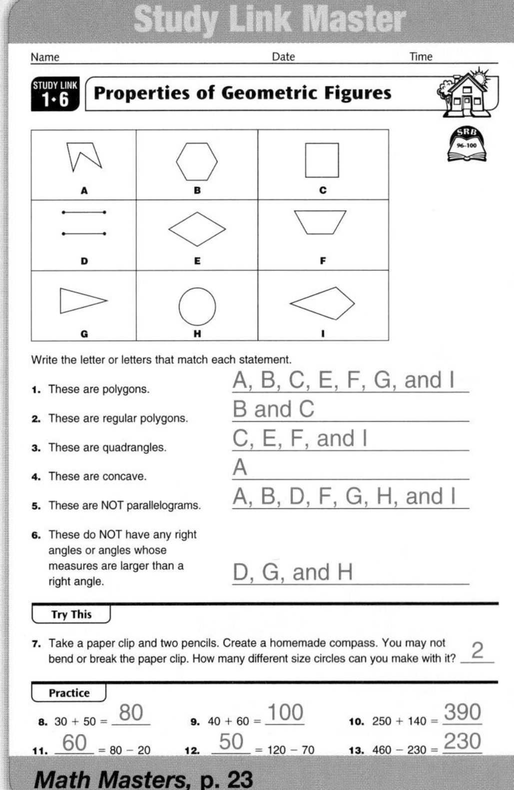

Study Link Master

Name Date Time

STUDY LINK 1•6 **Properties of Geometric Figures**

SRB 96–100

Write the letter or letters that match each statement.

1. These are polygons. A, B, C, E, F, G, and I
2. These are regular polygons. B and C
3. These are quadrangles. C, E, F, and I
4. These are concave. A
5. These are NOT parallelograms. A, B, D, F, G, H, and I
6. These do NOT have any right angles or angles whose measures are larger than a right angle. D, G, and H

Try This

7. Take a paper clip and two pencils. Create a homemade compass. You may not bend or break the paper clip. How many different size circles can you make with it? 2

Practice

8. 30 + 50 = 80
9. 40 + 60 = 100
10. 250 + 140 = 390
11. 60 = 80 − 20
12. 50 = 120 − 70
13. 460 − 230 = 230

Math Masters, p. 23

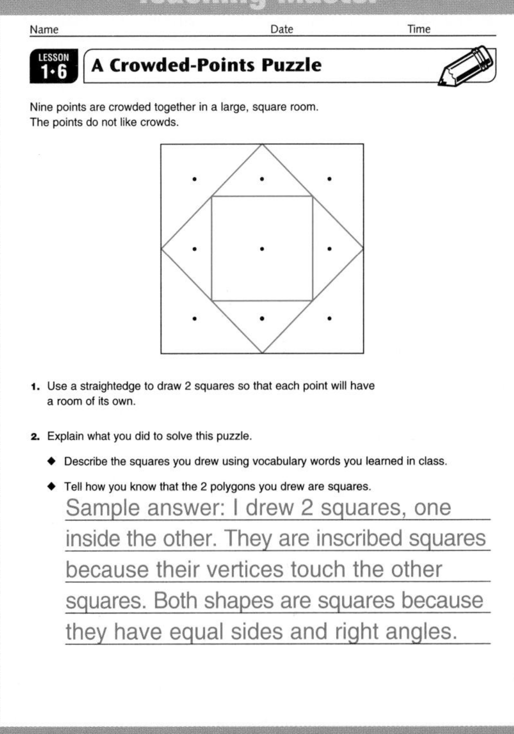

Teaching Master

Name Date Time

LESSON 1•6 **A Crowded-Points Puzzle**

Nine points are crowded together in a large, square room. The points do not like crowds.

1. Use a straightedge to draw 2 squares so that each point will have a room of its own.
2. Explain what you did to solve this puzzle.
   - Describe the squares you drew using vocabulary words you learned in class.
   - Tell how you know that the 2 polygons you drew are squares.

Sample answer: I drew 2 squares, one inside the other. They are inscribed squares because their vertices touch the other squares. Both shapes are squares because they have equal sides and right angles.

Math Masters, p. 24

1•7 Circle Constructions

Objectives To guide students in defining a circle; and to provide opportunities to explore designs with circles.

www.everydaymathonline.com

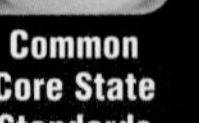

ePresentations | eToolkit | Algorithms Practice | EM Facts Workshop Game™ | Family Letters | Assessment Management | Common Core State Standards | Curriculum Focal Points | Interactive Teacher's Lesson Guide

1 Teaching the Lesson

Key Concepts and Skills

- Measure line segments to the nearest centimeter. [Measurement and Reference Frames Goal 1]
- Demonstrate and explain the meaning of *intersect.* [Geometry Goal 1]
- Use a compass to draw circles. [Geometry Goal 2]
- Demonstrate and explain the meanings of *concentric, radius,* and *congruent.* [Geometry Goal 2]

Key Activities

Students explore constructions that involve more than one circle.

Ongoing Assessment: Recognizing Student Achievement
Use journal page 17. [Geometry Goal 2]

Key Vocabulary

circle ◆ radius ◆ congruent ◆ concentric circles ◆ intersect

Materials

Math Journal 1, pp. 17–19
Study Link 1•6
Math Masters, p. 25
slate ◆ Geometry Template ◆ compass ◆ tape ◆ scissors ◆ board compass for demonstration purposes

2 Ongoing Learning & Practice

Playing *Polygon Pair-Up*
Student Reference Book, p. 258
Math Masters, pp. 496 and 497
Students practice identifying properties of polygons.

Math Boxes 1•7
Math Journal 1, p. 20
Students practice and maintain skills through Math Box problems.

Study Link 1•7
Math Masters, p. 26
Students practice and maintain skills through Study Link activities.

3 Differentiation Options

ENRICHMENT

Drawing Tangent Circles
Math Masters, pp. 27 and 28
compass ◆ straightedge
Students use a compass to construct tangent circles.

ENRICHMENT

Using Diameters, Chords, and Radii
Math Masters, p. 29
straightedge
Students inscribe polygons in circles.

ELL SUPPORT

Building a Math Word Bank
Differentiation Handbook, p. 140
Students add the term *intersect* to their Math Word Banks.

Advance Preparation

For Part 1, be sure students have plenty of paper for constructions. Copy and cut apart *Math Masters,* page 25 so that each student has one answer sheet. Place the sheets near the Math Message.

***Teacher's Reference Manual,* Grades 4–6** pp. 185, 186, 209–211

Getting Started

Mental Math and Reflexes

FACTS PRACTICE

Pose addition facts and extended facts. *Suggestions:*

●○○ 9 + 3 = 12
8 + 6 = 14
5 + 8 = 13

●●○ 50 + 40 = 90
60 + 70 = 130
70 + 80 = 150

●●● 600 + 200 = 800
500 + 500 = 1,000
400 + 900 = 1,300

Math Message

Take an answer sheet (Math Masters, *page 25*) *and complete it.*

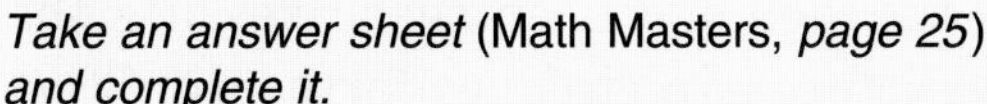

Study Link 1·6 Follow-Up

Have partners compare answers. Ask volunteers to share solutions to the Try This problem. Students should be able to construct circles with two different radii.

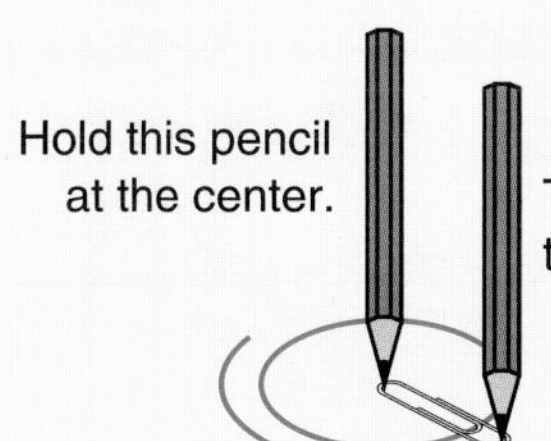
Hold this pencil at the center.
This pencil traces the circles.

1 Teaching the Lesson

Interactive whiteboard-ready ePresentations are available at www.everydaymathonline.com to help you teach the lesson.

Math Message Follow-Up

WHOLE-CLASS ACTIVITY
ELL

(*Math Masters,* p. 25)

Have partners compare results. A **circle** is the set of all points that are a given distance from a given point called the center of the circle. All of the 20 points on the paper that are 2 centimeters from point A form a circle with center A.

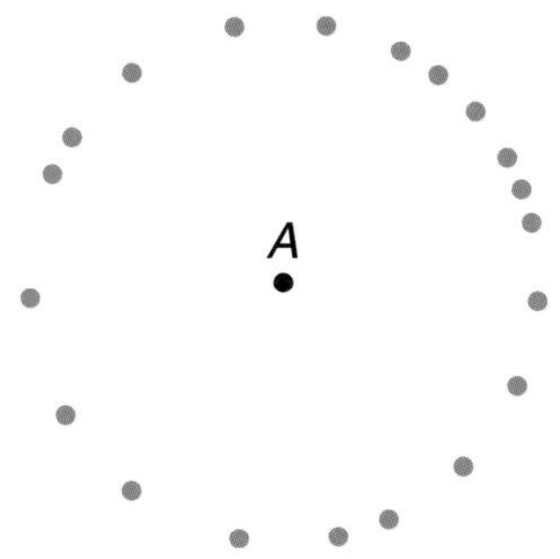
A

A circular pattern of points

The **radius** of a circle is a line segment from the center of a circle to any point on the circle. (It is also the length of such a line segment.) Ask students to connect one of the 20 points to the center point and label the line segment *radius*. To support English language learners, draw a picture of a circle on the board. Draw and label the *radius* of the circle.

Ask students to draw another circle with their compasses. Have them mark the center point and a point on the circle and connect them with a line segment. Ask students to measure the radius to the nearest centimeter. Suggest that they measure another radius to emphasize that all points on the same circle are the same distance from the center.

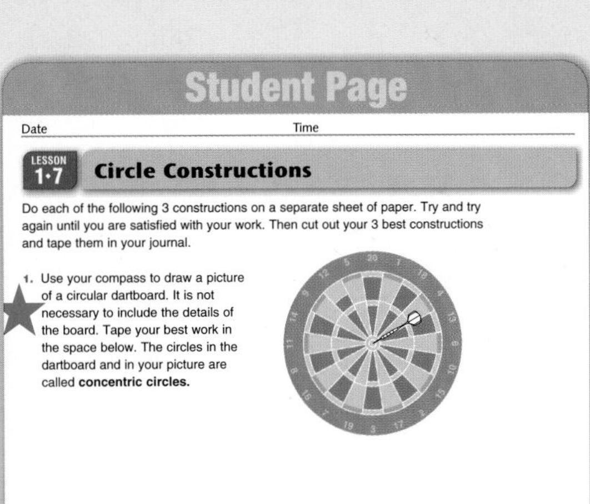

Student Page

Date Time

LESSON 1•7 **Circle Constructions**

Do each of the following 3 constructions on a separate sheet of paper. Try and try again until you are satisfied with your work. Then cut out your 3 best constructions and tape them in your journal.

1. Use your compass to draw a picture of a circular dartboard. It is not necessary to include the details of the board. Tape your best work in the space below. The circles in the dartboard and in your picture are called **concentric circles.**

***Math Journal 1*, p. 17**

Adjusting the Activity

Have students use a straightedge to draw the radius of each of the circles they drew on journal page 17. Have them measure each radius to the nearest centimeter and record it on the journal page.

AUDITORY ♦ KINESTHETIC ♦ TACTILE ♦ VISUAL

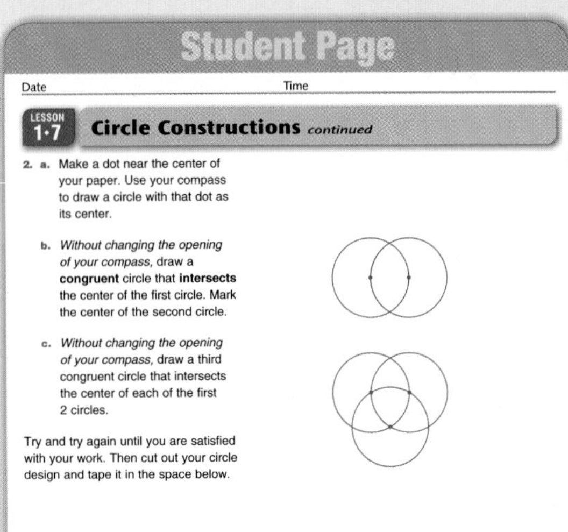

Student Page

Date Time

LESSON 1•7 **Circle Constructions** *continued*

2. a. Make a dot near the center of your paper. Use your compass to draw a circle with that dot as its center.

   b. *Without changing the opening of your compass,* draw a **congruent** circle that **intersects** the center of the first circle. Mark the center of the second circle.

   c. *Without changing the opening of your compass,* draw a third congruent circle that intersects the center of each of the first 2 circles.

Try and try again until you are satisfied with your work. Then cut out your circle design and tape it in the space below.

***Math Journal 1*, p. 18**

▶ Practicing Circle Constructions

INDEPENDENT ACTIVITY

(*Math Journal 1,* pp. 17–19)

Tell students that this lesson consists of activities designed to give them practice using a compass to draw circles. Students should practice the constructions on sheets of paper until they are satisfied with the results and then tape their final work onto pages 17–19 in their journals.

Write the word *constructions* on the board. To support English language learners, discuss the distinction between the everyday and mathematical meanings of *constructions*.

Drawing a Dartboard

To introduce students to the idea of concentric circles, ask them to use a compass to draw a picture of a circular dartboard. Students do not need to include details on the dartboard.

Ongoing Assessment: Recognizing Student Achievement

Journal page 17 Problem 1

Use **journal page 17, Problem 1** to assess students' ability to construct circles with a compass. Students are making adequate progress if the concentric circles they draw have the same center point. Some students may be able to compare the area of the smallest circle with the area of the entire dartboard.

[Geometry Goal 2]

Drawing Three Circles That Pass through One Another's Centers

On journal page 18, students construct two **congruent** circles (circles of the same size) so that each circle passes through the center of the other circle. Then they add a third congruent circle that passes through the center of each of the first two circles.

Making Circle Designs

Have students construct and color a circle design that extends the three-circle construction from journal page 18.

▶ Drawing Conclusions about Circles

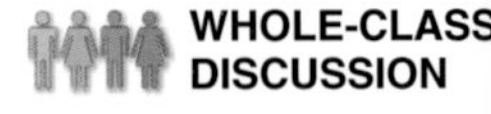

WHOLE-CLASS DISCUSSION

Bring the class together to discuss students' work. Students should recognize that each circle on the dartboard has the same center, but the *radius*—the distance from the center to the points on the circle—is different for each circle.

Tell students that circles with the same center are called **concentric circles.** Concentric circles do not **intersect** (touch or cross).

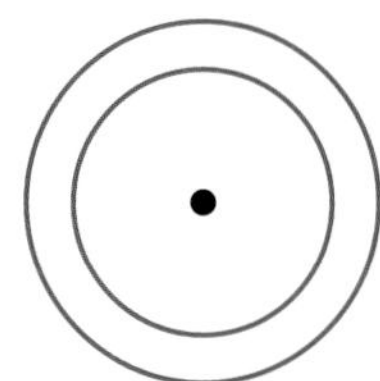

Concentric circles
do not intersect

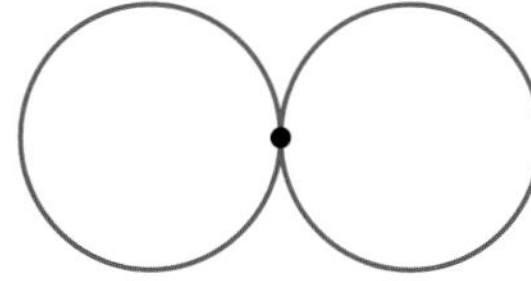

Not concentric circles
can intersect at 1 point

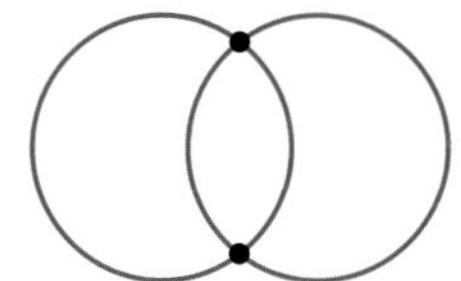

Not concentric circles
can intersect at 2 points

Ask students to give other examples of things that suggest concentric circles. Sample answers: archery target, saucer, doughnut, CD, ripples in a pond, merry-go-round, car wheel, sewer cover

NOTE The word *concentric* is derived from the Greek words *con*, which means "same," and *centrom*, which means "center."

2 Ongoing Learning & Practice

Playing *Polygon Pair-Up*

PARTNER ACTIVITY

(*Student Reference Book,* p. 258; *Math Masters,* pp. 496 and 497)

Students play *Polygon Pair-Up* to practice identifying properties of polygons. See Lesson 1-6 for additional information.

Math Boxes 1•7

INDEPENDENT ACTIVITY

(*Math Journal 1,* p. 20)

Mixed Practice Math Boxes in this lesson are paired with Math Boxes in Lesson 1-5. The skill in Problem 6 previews Unit 2 content.

Writing/Reasoning Have students write a response to the following: *How can you use a basic subtraction fact like 9 – 7 in Problem 1 to solve an extended subtraction fact like 900 – 700?* Sample answer: 900 – 700 is the same as **9** hundreds – **7** hundreds. **9** hundreds – **7** hundreds = 2 hundreds. 2 hundreds = 200, so 900 – 700 = 200.

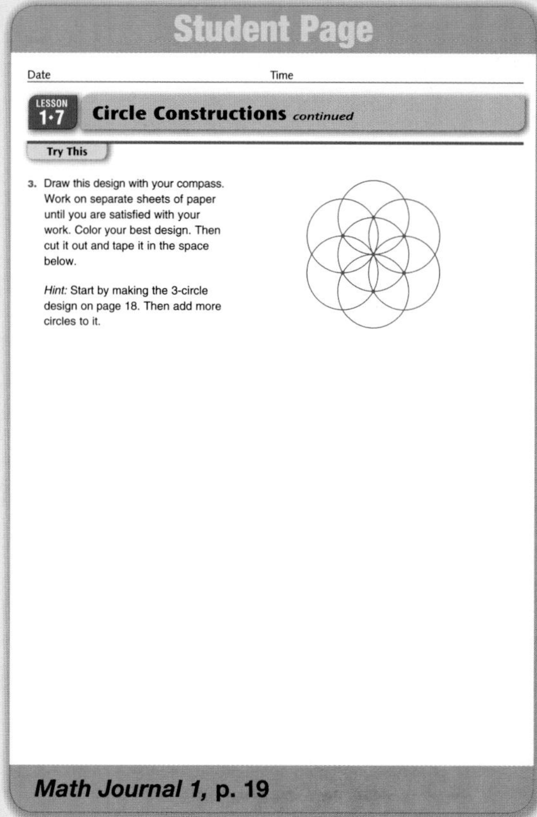

Student Page

Date Time

LESSON 1•7 **Circle Constructions** *continued*

Try This

3. Draw this design with your compass. Work on separate sheets of paper until you are satisfied with your work. Color your best design. Then cut it out and tape it in the space below.

Hint: Start by making the 3-circle design on page 18. Then add more circles to it.

Math Journal 1, p. 19

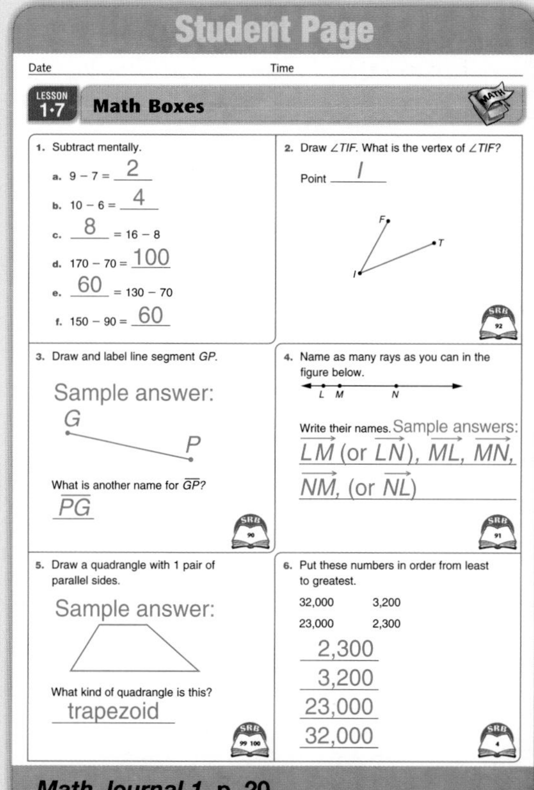

Student Page

Date Time

LESSON 1•7 **Math Boxes**

1. Subtract mentally.
a. 9 – 7 = 2
b. 10 – 6 = 4
c. 8 = 16 – 8
d. 170 – 70 = 100
e. 60 = 130 – 70
f. 150 – 90 = 60

2. Draw ∠TIF. What is the vertex of ∠TIF?
Point I

3. Draw and label line segment GP.
Sample answer:
What is another name for $\overline{GP}$? PG

4. Name as many rays as you can in the figure below.
Write their names. Sample answers: $\overrightarrow{LM}$ (or $\overrightarrow{LN}$), $\overrightarrow{ML}$, $\overrightarrow{MN}$, $\overrightarrow{NM}$, (or $\overrightarrow{NL}$)

5. Draw a quadrangle with 1 pair of parallel sides.
Sample answer:
What kind of quadrangle is this? trapezoid

6. Put these numbers in order from least to greatest.
32,000 3,200
23,000 2,300
2,300
3,200
23,000
32,000

Math Journal 1, p. 20

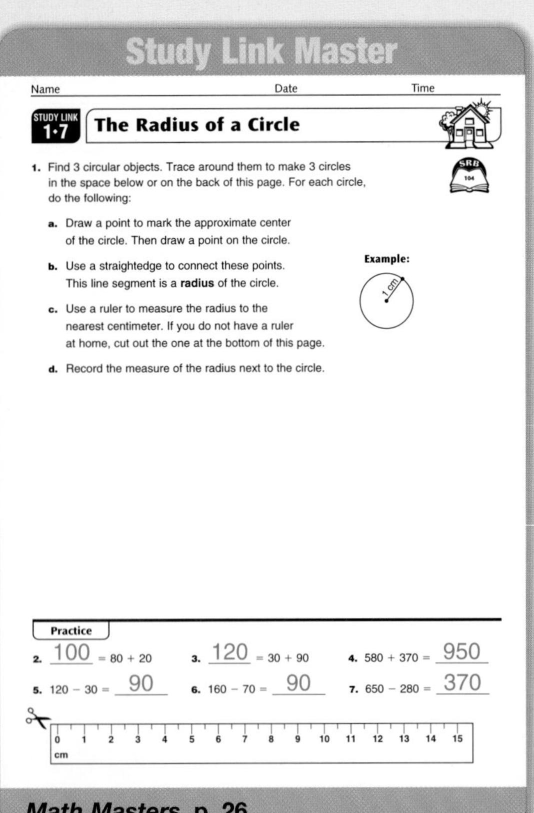
Study Link Master

Name Date Time

STUDY LINK 1·7 **The Radius of a Circle**

1. Find 3 circular objects. Trace around them to make 3 circles in the space below or on the back of this page. For each circle, do the following:
   a. Draw a point to mark the approximate center of the circle. Then draw a point on the circle.
   b. Use a straightedge to connect these points. This line segment is a **radius** of the circle.
   c. Use a ruler to measure the radius to the nearest centimeter. If you do not have a ruler at home, cut out the one at the bottom of this page.
   d. Record the measure of the radius next to the circle.

Example: 1 cm

Practice

2. 100 = 80 + 20
3. 120 = 30 + 90
4. 580 + 370 = 950
5. 120 − 30 = 90
6. 160 − 70 = 90
7. 650 − 280 = 370

0 1 2 3 4 5 6 7 8 9 10 11 12 13 14 15 cm

Math Masters, p. 26

▶ Study Link 1·7

INDEPENDENT ACTIVITY

(*Math Masters,* p. 26)

Home Connection Students draw circles and measure each radius to the nearest centimeter.

3 Differentiation Options

ENRICHMENT

INDEPENDENT ACTIVITY

▶ Drawing Tangent Circle

15–30 Min

(*Math Masters,* pp. 27 and 28)

To apply students' understanding of circle constructions, have them explore tangent circles. Two circles that barely touch (touch at just one point) are said to be *tangent* to each other. Students first construct two tangent circles of the same size (radius). Then they construct a third circle of the same size so that each circle is tangent to the other two circles.

ENRICHMENT

INDEPENDENT ACTIVITY

▶ Using Diameters, Chords, and Radii

5–15 Min

(*Math Masters,* p. 29)

To apply students' understanding of attributes of polygons, have them inscribe polygons in circles using line segments that represent chords and radii of the circles. When they have finished the page, have students share their strategies and describe how they know they have correctly constructed the specified polygons.

ELL SUPPORT

SMALL-GROUP ACTIVITY

▶ Building a Math Word Bank

5–15 Min

(*Differentiation Handbook,* p. 140)

To provide language support for geometry, have students use the Word Bank Template found on *Differentiation Handbook,* page 140. Ask students to write the term *intersect,* draw pictures relating to the term, and write other related words. See the *Differentiation Handbook* for more information.

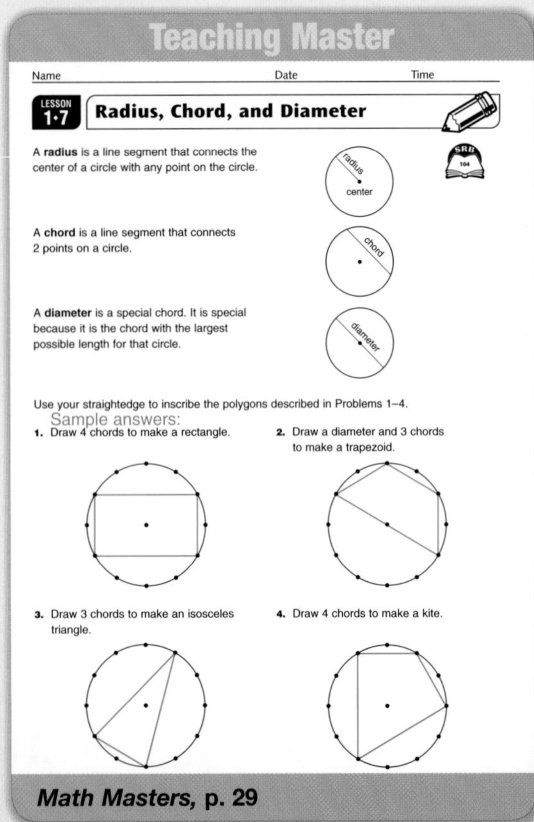
Teaching Master

Name Date Time

LESSON 1·7 **Radius, Chord, and Diameter**

A **radius** is a line segment that connects the center of a circle with any point on the circle.

A **chord** is a line segment that connects 2 points on a circle.

A **diameter** is a special chord. It is special because it is the chord with the largest possible length for that circle.

Use your straightedge to inscribe the polygons described in Problems 1–4.

Sample answers:

1. Draw 4 chords to make a rectangle.
2. Draw a diameter and 3 chords to make a trapezoid.
3. Draw 3 chords to make an isosceles triangle.
4. Draw 4 chords to make a kite.

Math Masters, p. 29

1•8 Hexagon and Triangle Constructions

Objective To guide students in the construction of figures with a compass and straightedge.

Technology Resources www.everydaymathonline.com

ePresentations

eToolkit

Algorithms Practice

EM Facts Workshop Game™

Family Letters

Assessment Management

Common Core State Standards

Curriculum Focal Points

Interactive Teacher's Lesson Guide

1 Teaching the Lesson

Key Concepts and Skills

- Use a compass as a tool to measure distance. [Measurement and Reference Frames Goal 1]
- Copy a line segment with a compass and straightedge. [Geometry Goal 1]
- Use a compass to draw circles; construct a regular hexagon inscribed in a circle. [Geometry Goal 2]
- Verify that the sides of regular polygons are the same length. [Geometry Goal 2]

Key Activities

Students continue their work with a compass and straightedge. They copy line segments, construct regular hexagons inscribed in circles, and divide a hexagon into six equilateral triangles.

Ongoing Assessment: Informing Instruction See page 59.

Materials

Math Journal 1, pp. 21–24
Student Reference Book, pp. 114, 117, and 118 (optional)
Study Link 1•7
slate ◆ Geometry Template ◆ straightedge ◆ compass ◆ tape ◆ scissors ◆ board compass for demonstration purposes

2 Ongoing Learning & Practice

Defining Geometric Figures
Math Journal 1, p. 25
Students match descriptions of geometric figures with their names.

Math Boxes 1•8
Math Journal 1, p. 26
Students practice and maintain skills through Math Box problems.

Ongoing Assessment: Recognizing Student Achievement
Use Math Boxes, Problem 1.
[Operations and Computation Goal 1]

Study Link 1•8
Math Masters, p. 30
Students practice and maintain skills through Study Link activities.

3 Differentiation Options

READINESS

Identifying a Regular Hexagon
Math Masters, p. 31
straightedge ◆ crayons or markers
Students identify and describe a regular hexagon inscribed in a circle.

ENRICHMENT

Creating 6-Point Designs
Math Masters, p. 32
compass ◆ straightedge ◆ crayons or markers ◆ paper
Students create designs by inscribing hexagons in circles.

EXTRA PRACTICE

Inscribing an Equilateral Triangle in a Circle
Math Masters, p. 33
compass ◆ straightedge ◆ paper
Students practice inscribing polygons in a circle.

Advance Preparation

For Parts 1 and 3, students should have plenty of paper for constructions.

***Teacher's Reference Manual,* Grades 4–6** pp. 209–211

Getting Started

Mental Math and Reflexes

Pose addition facts and extended facts. *Suggestions:*

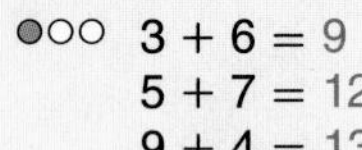

●○○ 3 + 6 = 9
5 + 7 = 12
9 + 4 = 13

●●○ 70 + 90 = 160
60 + 70 = 130
40 + 80 = 120

●●● 500 + 400 = 900
800 + 800 = 1,600
6,000 + 7,000 = 13,000

Math Message

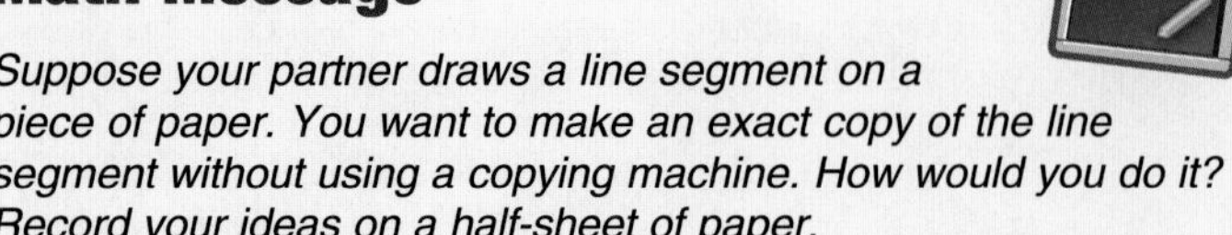

Suppose your partner draws a line segment on a piece of paper. You want to make an exact copy of the line segment without using a copying machine. How would you do it? Record your ideas on a half-sheet of paper.

Study Link 1•7 Follow-Up

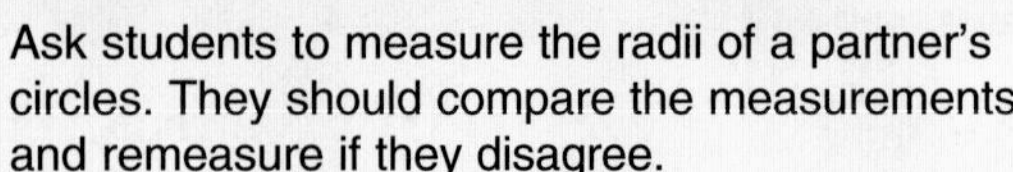

Ask students to measure the radii of a partner's circles. They should compare the measurements and remeasure if they disagree.

NOTE Some students may benefit from doing the **Readiness** activity before you begin Part 1 of the lesson. See the Readiness activity in Part 3 for details.

Interactive whiteboard-ready ePresentations are available at www.everydaymathonline.com to help you teach the lesson.

1 Teaching the Lesson

▶ Math Message Follow-Up

Before discussing the Math Message problem as a class, have partners discuss how they would copy the line segment. Strategies might include the following:

▷ Use tracing paper and trace the line segment.

▷ Measure the line segment with a ruler, and then draw another line segment that is the same length.

If no student mentions the use of a compass and straightedge, ask if anyone can think of a way that these tools could be used to copy the line segment. Allow several minutes for partners to discuss the question. Then tell students that in this lesson they will learn how to use a compass and straightedge to copy a line segment.

▶ Making Constructions with a Compass and Straightedge

INDEPENDENT ACTIVITY

(*Math Journal 1,* pp. 21–24)

The constructions in the previous lessons consisted mainly of drawing circles with a compass. The compass-and-straightedge constructions in this lesson involve marking equal distances between points on a circle.

At first, you probably will need to demonstrate the constructions on the board or overhead projector. The directions also appear in the journal.

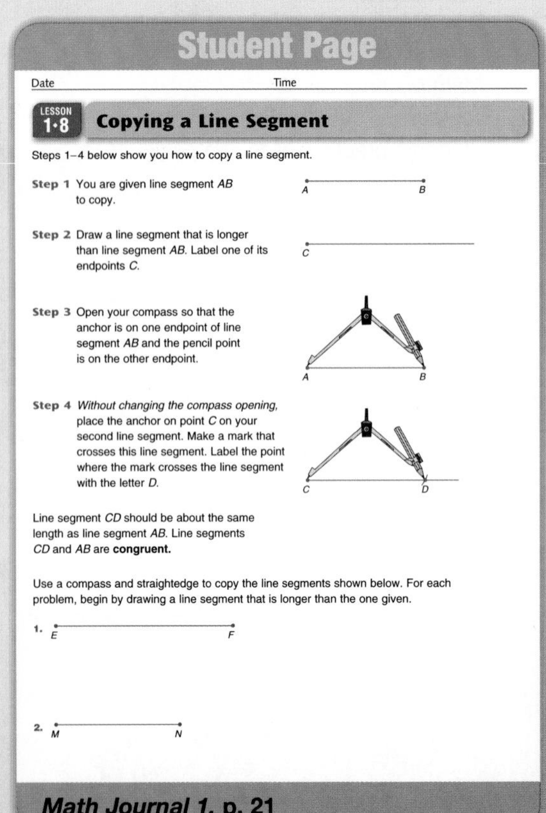

Student Page

Date Time

LESSON 1•8 **Copying a Line Segment**

Steps 1–4 below show you how to copy a line segment.

Step 1 You are given line segment *AB* to copy.

Step 2 Draw a line segment that is longer than line segment *AB*. Label one of its endpoints *C*.

Step 3 Open your compass so that the anchor is on one endpoint of line segment *AB* and the pencil point is on the other endpoint.

Step 4 *Without changing the compass opening,* place the anchor on point *C* on your second line segment. Make a mark that crosses this line segment. Label the point where the mark crosses the line segment with the letter *D*.

Line segment *CD* should be about the same length as line segment *AB*. Line segments *CD* and *AB* are **congruent.**

Use a compass and straightedge to copy the line segments shown below. For each problem, begin by drawing a line segment that is longer than the one given.

1. *E* *F*

2. *M* *N*

Math Journal 1, p. 21

Copying a Line Segment

Go over the steps for copying a line segment shown on journal page 21. Students should practice this construction several times. Then have students copy line segments *EF* and *MN* onto the journal page. Remind them that their straightedges are for drawing straight lines, not for measuring.

Constructing an Inscribed Regular Hexagon

Discuss the examples of regular hexagons shown on journal page 22. Then demonstrate how to construct an inscribed regular hexagon while students follow the directions on page 23.

Language Arts Link Explain that the root word *scribe* comes from the Latin word that means "to write." In mathematics, the word *inscribe* means "to write or draw a figure inside another figure such that every vertex of the inside figure touches the outside figure."

After completing Step 3, there should be 6 arcs. The points where these 6 arcs cross the circle will become the 6 vertices of the hexagon. Before going on to Step 4, ask the following questions:

- What do you notice about the 6 marks? They divide the circle into 6 equal parts.
- Without measuring, how do you know that the marks are the same distance apart? The compass opening did not change.
- What do you think the next step should be? Connect the 6 marks.

After Step 4, ask the following question:

- How do we know that all the vertices of the hexagon are the same distance from the center of the circle? All the vertices of the hexagon are on the circle. Because all points on a circle are the same distance from the center, all the vertices must be the same distance from the center.

After students have practiced this construction several times, they should tape their best work onto journal page 23.

Ongoing Assessment: Informing Instruction

Watch for students who have difficulty connecting *consecutive* marks in Step 4 to form the regular hexagon. If students completed the Readiness activity in Part 3, refer them to the regular hexagon outlined in red. This will provide them with a visual image of the design they are trying to create.

Dividing a Regular Hexagon

Have students construct another inscribed hexagon and then divide it into six equilateral triangles by drawing appropriate diagonals. Encourage them to keep trying until they have one they can tape onto journal page 24.

Student Page

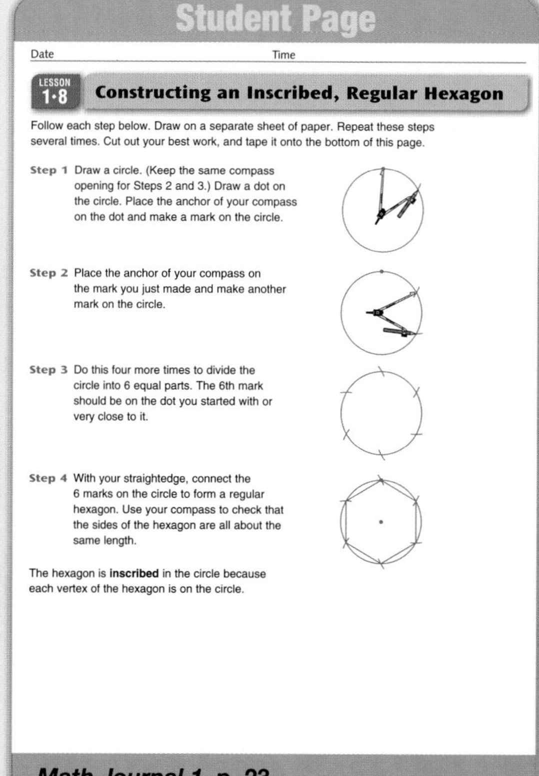

Date Time

LESSON 1•8 **Constructing an Inscribed, Regular Hexagon**

Follow each step below. Draw on a separate sheet of paper. Repeat these steps several times. Cut out your best work, and tape it onto the bottom of this page.

Step 1 Draw a circle. (Keep the same compass opening for Steps 2 and 3.) Draw a dot on the circle. Place the anchor of your compass on the dot and make a mark on the circle.

Step 2 Place the anchor of your compass on the mark you just made and make another mark on the circle.

Step 3 Do this four more times to divide the circle into 6 equal parts. The 6th mark should be on the dot you started with or very close to it.

Step 4 With your straightedge, connect the 6 marks on the circle to form a regular hexagon. Use your compass to check that the sides of the hexagon are all about the same length.

The hexagon is **inscribed** in the circle because each vertex of the hexagon is on the circle.

Math Journal 1, p. 23

Adjusting the Activity

Encourage students to do additional constructions from pages 114, 117, and 118 of the *Student Reference Book.*

AUDITORY ◆ KINESTHETIC ◆ TACTILE ◆ VISUAL

Student Page

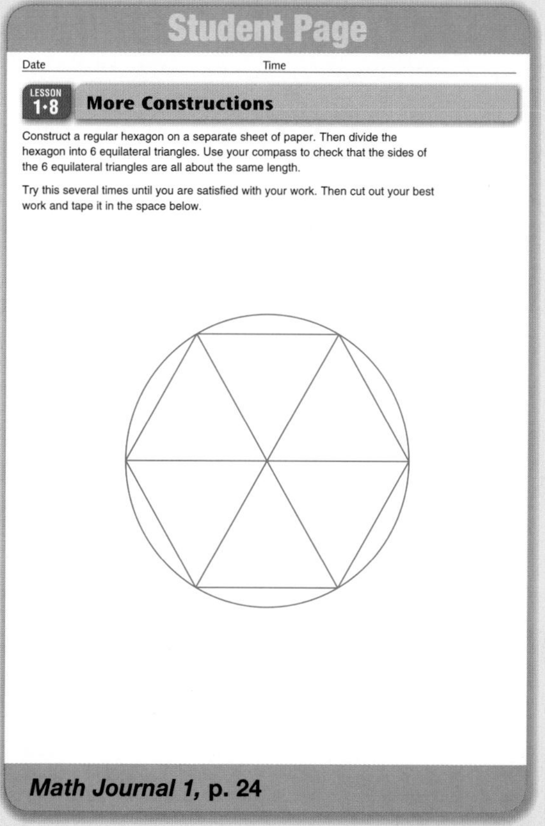

Date Time

LESSON 1•8 **More Constructions**

Construct a regular hexagon on a separate sheet of paper. Then divide the hexagon into 6 equilateral triangles. Use your compass to check that the sides of the 6 equilateral triangles are all about the same length.

Try this several times until you are satisfied with your work. Then cut out your best work and tape it in the space below.

Math Journal 1, p. 24

2 Ongoing Learning & Practice

▶ Defining Geometric Figures

INDEPENDENT ACTIVITY

(*Math Journal 1*, p. 25)

Students match descriptions of geometric figures with names.

▶ Math Boxes 1•8

INDEPENDENT ACTIVITY

(*Math Journal 1*, p. 26)

Mixed Practice Math Boxes in this lesson are paired with Math Boxes in Lesson 1-6. The skill in Problem 6 previews Unit 2 content.

Ongoing Assessment: Recognizing Student Achievement

Math Boxes Problem 1 

Use **Math Boxes, Problem 1** to assess students' automaticity with subtraction fact extensions. Students are making adequate progress if they compute the differences in Problems 1a–1d correctly. Some students may already be able to solve Problems 1e and 1f, which do not include a basic fact prompt.

[Operations and Computation Goal 1]

▶ Study Link 1•8

INDEPENDENT ACTIVITY

(*Math Masters*, p. 30)

Home Connection Students inscribe polygons in circles.

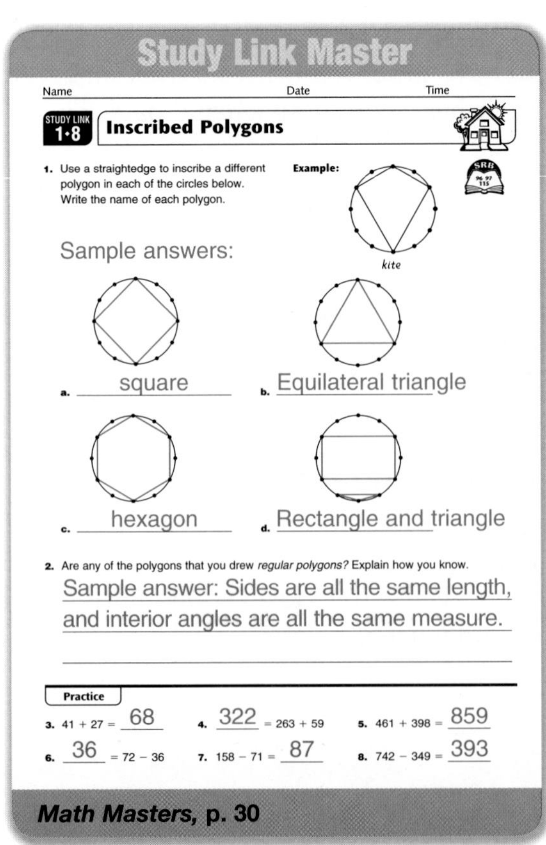

Study Link Master

Name Date Time

STUDY LINK 1•8 **Inscribed Polygons**

1. Use a straightedge to inscribe a different polygon in each of the circles below. Write the name of each polygon.

Example: kite

Sample answers:

a. square

b. Equilateral triangle

c. hexagon

d. Rectangle and triangle

2. Are any of the polygons that you drew *regular polygons?* Explain how you know.

Sample answer: Sides are all the same length, and interior angles are all the same measure.

Practice

3. 41 + 27 = 68

4. 322 = 263 + 59

5. 461 + 398 = 859

6. 36 = 72 − 36

7. 158 − 71 = 87

8. 742 − 349 = 393

Math Masters, p. 30

Student Page

Date Time

LESSON 1•8 **Definition Match**

Match each description of a geometric figure in Column I with its name in Column II. Some of the items in Column II do not have a match.

I	II
a. a polygon with 4 right angles and 4 sides of the same length	f octagon
	e rhombus
b. a polygon with 4 sides, none of which are the same length	h right angle
c. a quadrilateral with exactly 1 pair of opposite sides that is parallel	c trapezoid
	___ hexagon
d. lines that never intersect	a square
e. a parallelogram with all sides the same length, but not a rectangle	i equilateral triangle
f. a polygon with 8 sides	___ perpendicular lines
g. a polygon with 5 sides	d parallel lines
h. an angle that measures 90°	g pentagon
	___ isosceles triangle
i. a triangle with all sides the same length	b quadrangle

Math Journal 1, p. 25

Student Page

Date Time

LESSON 1•8 **Math Boxes**

1. Subtract mentally.
   a. 14 − 9 = 5
   b. 140 − 90 = 50
   c. 9 = 18 − 9
   d. 180 − 90 = 90
   e. 40 = 110 − 70
   f. 90 = 150 − 60

2. Which of the shape(s) below are polygons? A and C

   A B C

3. Draw a quadrangle that has 2 pairs of parallel sides and no right angles.

   Sample answer:

   What kind of quadrangle is this? parallelogram

4. Circle the concave (nonconvex) polygon(s).

5. Draw and label ray *CA*. Draw point *R* on it.

   Sample answer

   C A R

   What is another name for ray *CA*? $\overrightarrow{CR}$

6. In the numeral 30,516, what does the 3 stand for? Circle the best answer.

   A. 3,000

   B. 30

   (C.) 30,000

   D. 300,000

Math Journal 1, p. 26

3 Differentiation Options

READINESS

INDEPENDENT ACTIVITY

Identifying a Regular Hexagon

5–15 Min

(*Math Masters,* p. 31)

To explore the concept of regular polygons, have students identify and describe a regular hexagon inscribed in a circle. Ask them to outline the regular hexagon in a design and then color the design in an interesting way. Have students share their definitions of a regular polygon.

ENRICHMENT

INDEPENDENT ACTIVITY

Creating 6-Point Designs

15–30 Min

(*Math Masters,* p. 32)

Art Link To apply students' ability to inscribe hexagons in circles, have them create hexagram designs. Suggestions are on *Math Masters,* page 32. Students can work on these designs first and then create some of their own as an ongoing project for the next few weeks. Their finished work could be displayed in a Geometry Art Exhibit.

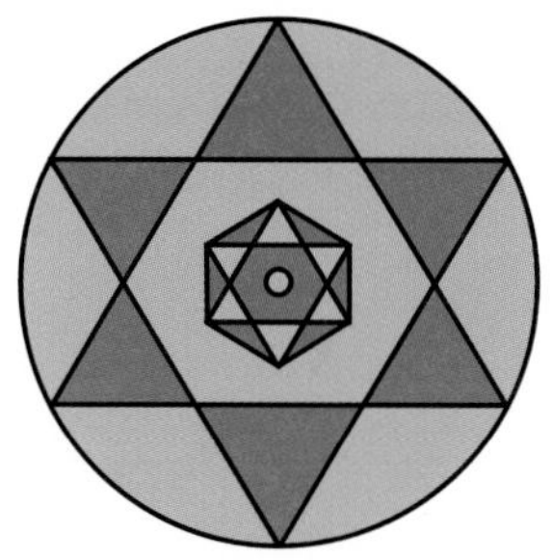

Sample hexagram design from *Math Masters,* page 32

EXTRA PRACTICE

INDEPENDENT ACTIVITY

Inscribing an Equilateral Triangle in a Circle

5–15 Min

(*Math Masters,* p. 33)

To provide practice inscribing polygons in circles, students use a compass to divide a circle into six equal parts. Then they inscribe an equilateral triangle by connecting three alternating points on the circle.

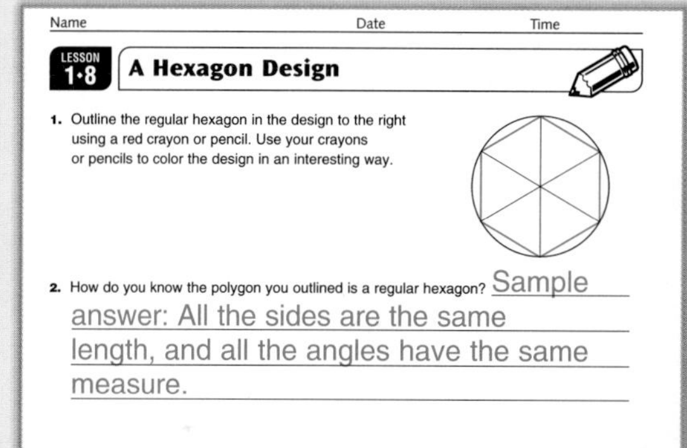

Name Date Time

LESSON 1·8 **A Hexagon Design**

1. Outline the regular hexagon in the design to the right using a red crayon or pencil. Use your crayons or pencils to color the design in an interesting way.

2. How do you know the polygon you outlined is a regular hexagon? Sample answer: All the sides are the same length, and all the angles have the same measure.

Math Masters, page 31

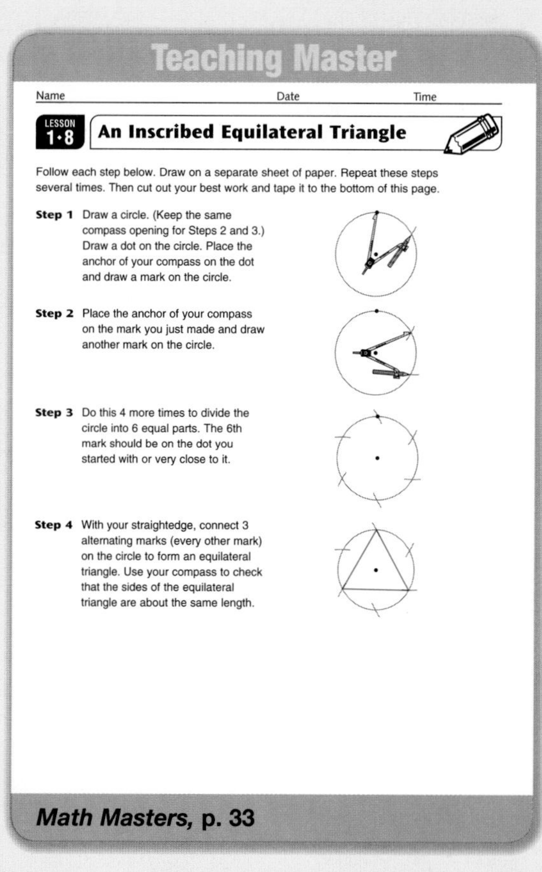

Teaching Master

Name Date Time

LESSON 1·8 **An Inscribed Equilateral Triangle**

Follow each step below. Draw on a separate sheet of paper. Repeat these steps several times. Then cut out your best work and tape it to the bottom of this page.

Step 1 Draw a circle. (Keep the same compass opening for Steps 2 and 3.) Draw a dot on the circle. Place the anchor of your compass on the dot and draw a mark on the circle.

Step 2 Place the anchor of your compass on the mark you just made and draw another mark on the circle.

Step 3 Do this 4 more times to divide the circle into 6 equal parts. The 6th mark should be on the dot you started with or very close to it.

Step 4 With your straightedge, connect 3 alternating marks (every other mark) on the circle to form an equilateral triangle. Use your compass to check that the sides of the equilateral triangle are about the same length.

Math Masters, p. 33

1•9 Progress Check 1

Objective To assess students' progress on mathematical content through the end of Unit 1.

1 Looking Back: Cumulative Assessment

The **Beginning-of-Year Assessment** in the *Assessment Handbook* is a written assessment that you may use to gauge students' readiness for the content they will encounter early in fourth grade.

Input student data from Progress Check 1 and the Beginning-of-Year Assessment into the **Assessment Management Spreadsheets**.

Materials

- Study Link 1•8
- *Assessment Handbook,* pp. 52–59, 154–158, 216, and 226–229
- Beginning-of-Year Assessment (*Assessment Handbook,* pp. 51A, 51B, 242, and 227A–227D)
- Geometry Template; compass

CONTENT ASSESSED	LESSON(S)	ASSESSMENT ITEMS				
		SELF	ORAL/SLATE	WRITTEN PART A	WRITTEN PART B	OPEN RESPONSE
Demonstrate automaticity with addition and subtraction fact extensions. [Operations and Computation Goal 1]	1•1–1•8	1	4	10, 11		
Identify, draw, and describe points, intersecting and parallel line segments and lines, rays, and right angles. [Geometry Goal 1]	1•2–1•8	2, 3	1, 2, 3	1, 2, 3, 4, 5, 6	13	
Describe and classify plane figures, including polygons and circles using appropriate geometric terms including *congruent.* [Geometry Goal 2]	1•3–1•8	4, 5	1, 3	1, 2, 7, 8, 9	12, 14, 15, 16	✓

2 Looking Ahead: Preparing for Unit 2

Math Boxes 1•9

Home Link 1•9: Unit 2 Family Letter

Materials

- *Math Journal 1,* p. 27
- *Math Masters,* pp. 34–37

Getting Started

Math Message • Self Assessment

Complete the Self Assessment (Assessment Handbook, *page 154).*

Study Link 1•8 Follow-Up

Have partners compare answers. Ask volunteers to explain how they know whether the polygons they drew are regular.

1 Looking Back: Cumulative Assessment

Math Message Follow-Up

(Self Assessment, *Assessment Handbook,* p. 154)

The Self Assessment offers students the opportunity to reflect upon their progress.

Oral and Slate Assessments

Problems 2–4 provide summative information and can be used for grading purposes. Problem 1 provides formative information that can be useful in planning future instruction.

Oral Assessment

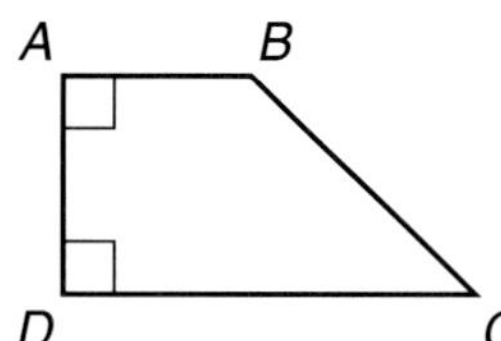

1. Draw a geometric figure on the board. Ask students to describe it. For example, you may want to draw a trapezoid such as the one shown to the right.

   Sample answers: The figure has four sides. Angles *A* and *D* are right angles. The figure is a (polygon, quadrangle, trapezoid). It is convex. The figure has one pair of parallel sides, $\overline{AB}$ and $\overline{DC}$.

2. Ask students to look around the classroom and point out examples of line segments, lines, rays, right angles, and parallel line segments. Sample answers: the edge of a chalkboard is a line segment, the top and bottom edges of a chalkboard are parallel line segments, and the corner of a chalkboard is a right angle.

Slate Assessment

3. Ask students to draw these geometric figures on their slates:
   - rhombus
   - right angle
   - hexagon
   - parallel line segments
   - trapezoid
   - triangle

4. Pose addition and subtraction facts and fact extensions. *Suggestions:*
   - $7 + 5 = 12$ $\quad 6 + 6 = 12$ $\quad 50 + 90 = 140$ $\quad 80 + 70 = 150$
   - $18 - 9 = 9$ $\quad 14 - 7 = 7$ $\quad 130 - 40 = 90$ $\quad 170 - 90 = 80$

Assessment Master

Name Date Time

LESSON 1•9 **Self Assessment** Progress Check 1

Think about each skill listed below. Assess your own progress by checking the most appropriate box.

Skills	I can do this on my own and explain how to do it.	I can do this on my own.	I can do this if I get help or look at an example.
1. Know addition and subtraction fact extensions.			
2. Identify, draw, and label line segments, lines, and rays.			
3. Identify and draw parallel and intersecting line segments.			
4. Describe sides and angles of polygons.			
5. Use a compass and straightedge to construct geometric figures.			

Assessment Handbook, **p. 154**

Assessment Master

Name Date Time

LESSON 1•9 **Written Assessment** Progress Check 1

Part A

Use a straightedge or the Geometry Template to complete Problems 1–4.

1. Draw a quadrangle that has 4 right angles and is not a square.
   Sample answer:
   What kind of quadrangle is this? rectangle

2. Draw a quadrangle with 1 pair of parallel sides and no right angles.
   Sample answer:
   What kind of quadrangle is this? trapezoid

3. Draw $\overline{AB}$ parallel to $\overline{CD}$.
   A B
   C D

4. Draw $\overleftrightarrow{EM}$. Draw $\overleftrightarrow{TX}$ so that $\overleftrightarrow{EM}$ and $\overleftrightarrow{TX}$ intersect.
   E X T M

For Problems 5–8, there may be more than one correct name for the geometric figure. Put a check mark beside all of the correct names.

5. ___ $\overline{OP}$ ✓ $\overleftrightarrow{OP}$ ✓ $\overleftrightarrow{PO}$ (P, O)

6. ___ $\overline{LA}$ ___ $\overrightarrow{AL}$ ✓ $\overrightarrow{LA}$ (A, L)

7. ✓ quadrangle ✓ polygon ✓ parallelogram

8. ___ square ✓ rhombus ✓ parallelogram

Assessment Handbook, **p. 155**

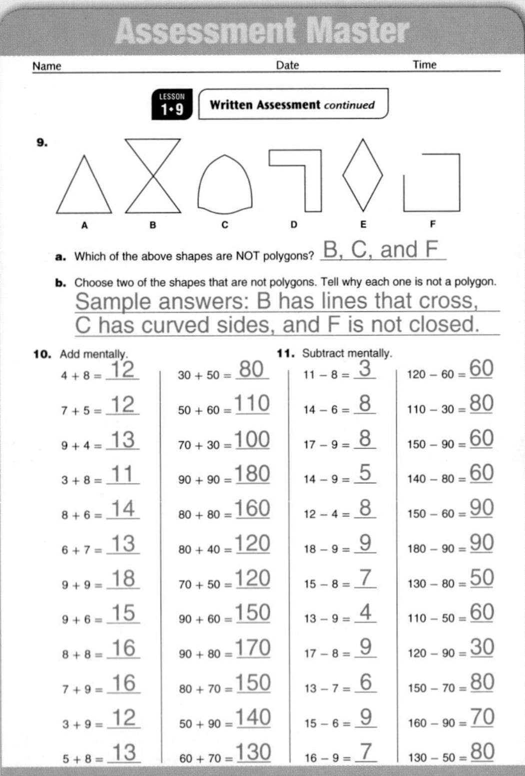

Assessment Master

Name Date Time

LESSON 1·9 Written Assessment *continued*

9.

A B C D E F

a. Which of the above shapes are NOT polygons? B, C, and F

b. Choose two of the shapes that are not polygons. Tell why each one is not a polygon.
Sample answers: B has lines that cross, C has curved sides, and F is not closed.

10. Add mentally.

11. Subtract mentally.

4 + 8 = 12	30 + 50 = 80	11 − 8 = 3	120 − 60 = 60
7 + 5 = 12	50 + 60 = 110	14 − 6 = 8	110 − 30 = 80
9 + 4 = 13	70 + 30 = 100	17 − 9 = 8	150 − 90 = 60
3 + 8 = 11	90 + 90 = 180	14 − 9 = 5	140 − 80 = 60
8 + 6 = 14	80 + 80 = 160	12 − 4 = 8	150 − 60 = 90
6 + 7 = 13	80 + 40 = 120	18 − 9 = 9	180 − 90 = 90
9 + 9 = 18	70 + 50 = 120	15 − 8 = 7	130 − 80 = 50
9 + 6 = 15	90 + 60 = 150	13 − 9 = 4	110 − 50 = 60
8 + 8 = 16	90 + 80 = 170	17 − 8 = 9	120 − 90 = 30
7 + 9 = 16	80 + 70 = 150	13 − 7 = 6	150 − 70 = 80
3 + 9 = 12	50 + 90 = 140	15 − 6 = 9	160 − 90 = 70
5 + 8 = 13	60 + 70 = 130	16 − 9 = 7	130 − 50 = 80

Assessment Handbook, p. 156

Use the checklists on pages 247 and 249 of the *Assessment Handbook* to record results. Then input the data into the **Assessment Management Spreadsheets** to keep an ongoing record of students' progress toward Grade-Level Goals.

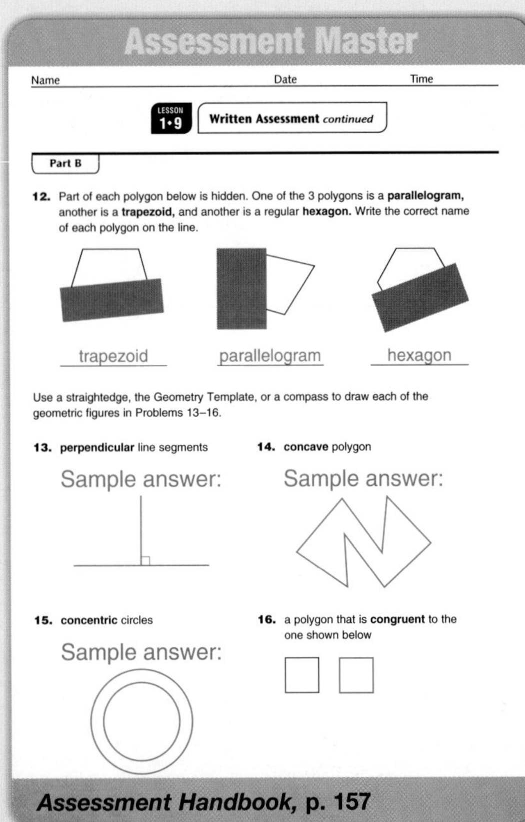

Assessment Master

Name Date Time

LESSON 1·9 Written Assessment *continued*

Part B

12. Part of each polygon below is hidden. One of the 3 polygons is a **parallelogram,** another is a **trapezoid,** and another is a regular **hexagon.** Write the correct name of each polygon on the line.

trapezoid parallelogram hexagon

Use a straightedge, the Geometry Template, or a compass to draw each of the geometric figures in Problems 13–16.

13. **perpendicular** line segments
Sample answer:

14. **concave** polygon
Sample answer:

15. **concentric** circles
Sample answer:

16. a polygon that is **congruent** to the one shown below

Assessment Handbook, p. 157

▶ Written Assessment

(*Assessment Handbook,* pp. 155–157)

Everyday Mathematics students are expected to master a variety of mathematical concepts and skills over time. The curriculum frequently revisits topics, concepts, and skills. For this reason, the written assessment includes items recently introduced as well as items that assess long-term retention and mastery.

The written assessment is only one part of a balanced assessment plan. Use it along with other assessment tools in the program. See the *Assessment Handbook* for additional information.

Part A Recognizing Student Achievement

The Recognizing Student Achievement, or *summative,* part of the written assessment is designed to help teachers assess students' progress toward Grade 4 Goals. The items in this section can be used for grading purposes since the curriculum to this point has provided multiple exposures to the content of these problems.

Problem(s)	Description
1, 2	Draw quadrangles.
3, 4	Draw parallel and intersecting lines and line segments.
5, 6	Name lines and rays.
7, 8	Name polygons.
9	Identify properties of polygons.
10, 11	Solve addition and subtraction facts and fact extensions.

Part B Informing Instruction

The Informing Instruction, or *formative,* part of the written assessment can help teachers make decisions about how best to approach concepts and skills the next time they appear. The items in this part of the written assessment are intended to inform future instruction.

Problem(s)	Description
12	Identify polygons.
13	Draw perpendicular line segments.
14	Draw a concave polygon.
15	Draw concentric circles.
16	Draw a polygon congruent to a given polygon.

▶ Open Response

(*Assessment Handbook,* p. 158)

Properties of Polygons

The open-response item requires students to apply concepts and skills from Unit 1 to solve a multistep problem. See *Assessment Handbook,* pages 55–59 for rubrics and students' work samples for this problem.

Looking Ahead: Preparing for Unit 2

Math Boxes 1•9

INDEPENDENT ACTIVITY

(*Math Journal 1,* p. 27)

Mixed Practice This Math Boxes page previews Unit 2 content.

Study Link 1•9: Unit 2 Family Letter

INDEPENDENT ACTIVITY

(*Math Masters,* pp. 34–37)

Home Connection The Unit 2 Family Letter provides parents and guardians with information and activities related to Unit 2 topics.

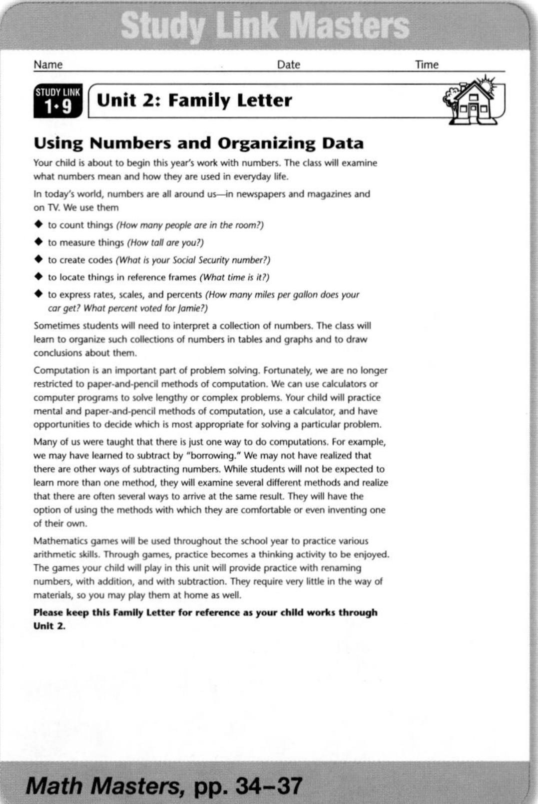

Study Link Masters

Name Date Time

STUDY LINK 1•9 **Unit 2: Family Letter**

Using Numbers and Organizing Data

Your child is about to begin this year's work with numbers. The class will examine what numbers mean and how they are used in everyday life.

In today's world, numbers are all around us—in newspapers and magazines and on TV. We use them

- to count things *(How many people are in the room?)*
- to measure things *(How tall are you?)*
- to create codes *(What is your Social Security number?)*
- to locate things in reference frames *(What time is it?)*
- to express rates, scales, and percents *(How many miles per gallon does your car get? What percent voted for Jamie?)*

Sometimes students will need to interpret a collection of numbers. The class will learn to organize such collections of numbers in tables and graphs and to draw conclusions about them.

Computation is an important part of problem solving. Fortunately, we are no longer restricted to paper-and-pencil methods of computation. We can use calculators or computer programs to solve lengthy or complex problems. Your child will practice mental and paper-and-pencil methods of computation, use a calculator, and have opportunities to decide which is most appropriate for solving a particular problem.

Many of us were taught that there is just one way to do computations. For example, we may have learned to subtract by "borrowing." We may not have realized that there are other ways of subtracting numbers. While students will not be expected to learn more than one method, they will examine several different methods and realize that there are often several ways to arrive at the same result. They will have the option of using the methods with which they are comfortable or even inventing one of their own.

Mathematics games will be used throughout the school year to practice various arithmetic skills. Through games, practice becomes a thinking activity to be enjoyed. The games your child will play in this unit will provide practice with renaming numbers, with addition, and with subtraction. They require very little in the way of materials, so you may play them at home as well.

Please keep this Family Letter for reference as your child works through Unit 2.

Math Masters, pp. 34–37

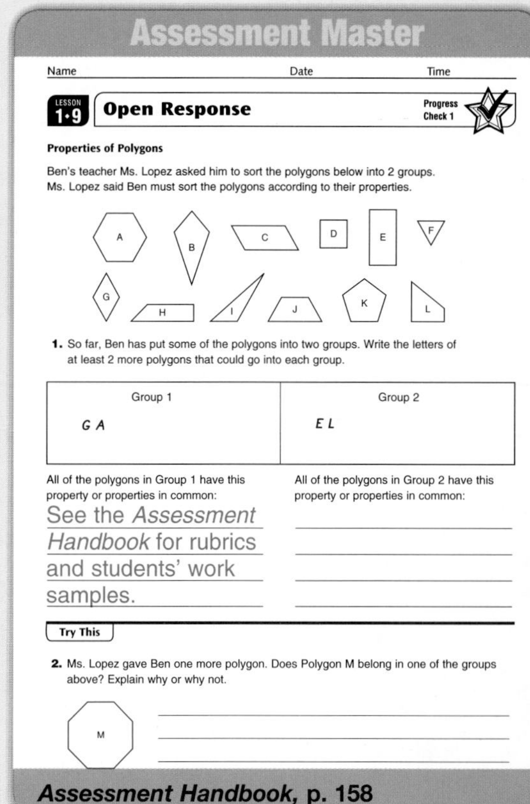

Assessment Master

Name Date Time

LESSON 1•9 **Open Response** Progress Check 1

Properties of Polygons

Ben's teacher Ms. Lopez asked him to sort the polygons below into 2 groups. Ms. Lopez said Ben must sort the polygons according to their properties.

1. So far, Ben has put some of the polygons into two groups. Write the letters of at least 2 more polygons that could go into each group.

Group 1	Group 2
G A	E L

All of the polygons in Group 1 have this property or properties in common:

See the *Assessment Handbook* for rubrics and students' work samples.

All of the polygons in Group 2 have this property or properties in common:

Try This

2. Ms. Lopez gave Ben one more polygon. Does Polygon M belong in one of the groups above? Explain why or why not.

M

Assessment Handbook, p. 158

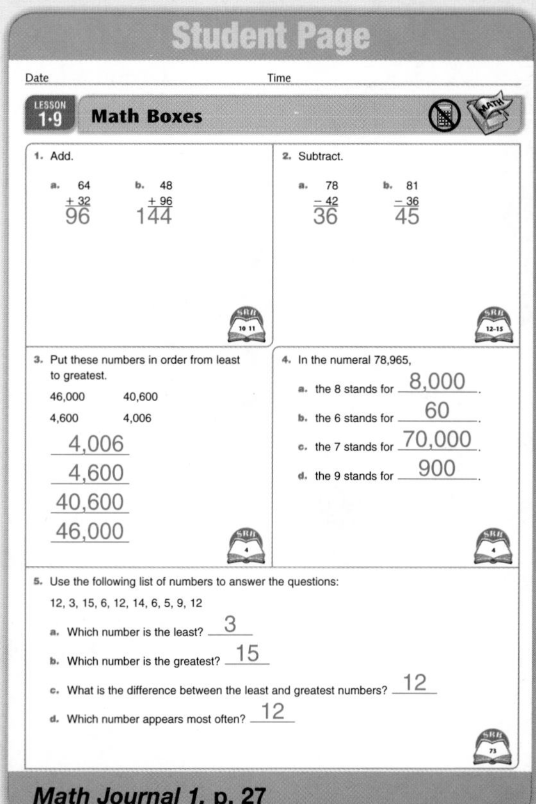

Student Page

Date Time

LESSON 1•9 **Math Boxes**

1. Add.

a. $64 + 32 = 96$

b. $48 + 96 = 144$

2. Subtract.

a. $78 - 42 = 36$

b. $81 - 36 = 45$

3. Put these numbers in order from least to greatest.

46,000 40,600
4,600 4,006

4,006
4,600
40,600
46,000

4. In the numeral 78,965,

a. the 8 stands for 8,000.

b. the 6 stands for 60.

c. the 7 stands for 70,000.

d. the 9 stands for 900.

5. Use the following list of numbers to answer the questions:

12, 3, 15, 6, 12, 14, 6, 5, 9, 12

a. Which number is the least? 3

b. Which number is the greatest? 15

c. What is the difference between the least and greatest numbers? 12

d. Which number appears most often? 12

Math Journal 1, p. 27

Using Numbers and Organizing Data

Overview

In this unit, the yearlong World Tour project is introduced. Besides providing links to social studies and language arts topics, the tour offers many opportunities to apply the mathematical content of this unit. Unit 2 has three main areas of focus:

- To examine different uses and equivalent names for numbers and review the base-ten place-value system,
- To review procedures for addition and subtraction of multidigit whole numbers, and
- To reintroduce and extend ideas about data collection, organization, display, and analysis.

Linking to the Common Core State Standards

The content of Unit 2 addresses the Common Core State Standards for Mathematics in *Number and Operations in Base Ten.* The correlation of the Common Core State Standards to the *Everyday Mathematics* Grade 4 lessons begins on page CS1.

Contents

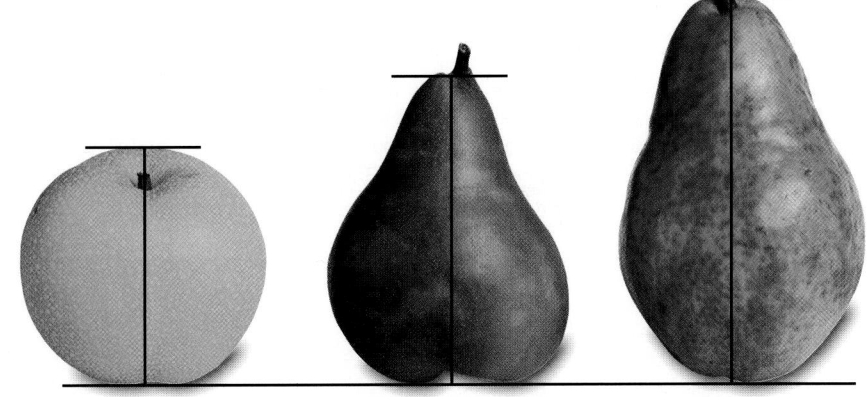

Unit 2 Organizer

Learning In Perspective

	Lesson Objectives	Links to the Past	Links to the Future
2•1	To review examples of the various ways in which numbers are used; and to introduce the World Tour Project.	Grades 2 and 3: Discuss and sort different kinds of numbers by how they are used.	Grade 4: Find lines of latitude and longitude (Unit 6). Grade 5: Applications and maintenance; conduct American Tour Project.
2•2	To review equivalent names for whole numbers and name-collection boxes.	Grades 1–3: Use name-collection box routines to express numbers in many ways, including pictures, tallies, and words.	Grade 4: Find equivalent names for decimals; rename numbers using exponential notation and powers of 10; start a table of equivalent fractions and decimals (Units 5 and 9). Grades 5 and 6: Applications and extensions.
2•3	To provide practice identifying values of digits in numbers up to one billion; and to provide practice reading and writing numbers up to one billion.	Grades 1–3: Practice place-value skills with base-10 blocks, place-value books, slate routines, and through games.	Grade 4: Read, write, and compare numbers up to billions; introduce exponential notation for powers of 10 (Unit 5). Grades 5 and 6: Extend place-value facility beyond billions; use exponential and scientific notation.
2•4	To provide practice with place-value skills using a calculator routine; and to review reading and writing large numbers.	Grades 1–3: Introduce and practice calculator routines; practice place-value skills with base-10 blocks, place-value books, slate routines, and through games.	Grade 4: Read, write, and compare numbers up to billions; introduce exponential notation for powers of 10 (Unit 5). Grade 5: Extend place-value facility beyond billions; use exponential and scientific notation.
2•5	To provide practice organizing and displaying data with a tally chart and determining the maximum, minimum, range, and mode of a set of data.	Grades 1 and 2: Define and calculate minimum, maximum, median, and mode. Grade 3: Define and calculate mean (average) and range. Use lists, tally charts, line plots, and graphs to determine landmarks.	Grade 4: Use side-by-side graphs and color-coded maps to compare data (Unit 9). Grade 5: Use stem-and-leaf plots to list and sort data and to calculate landmarks. Grade 6: Applications and maintenance.
2•6	To review how to display a set of data with a line plot; and to review how to find the median of a set of data.	Grades 1 and 2: Use tally charts and bar graphs to sort, display, and describe data. Grade 3: Use line plots to sort and display data; use tally charts, bar graphs, and line plots to find landmarks and interpret data.	Grade 4: Compare the mean and median of data sets; convert average rates to more easily understood rates (Units 3 and 4). Grade 5: Use stem-and-leaf plots. Grade 6: Applications and maintenance.
2•7	To review the partial-sums algorithm used to solve multidigit addition problems; and to introduce a column-addition method similar to the traditional addition algorithm.	Grades 1–3: Use invented (student-generated) algorithms to solve multidigit addition problems; begin to practice the partial-sums focus algorithm for addition. Grades 2 and 3: Use ballpark estimates.	Grade 4: Develop strategies for addition of decimals (Unit 4). Grades 4–6: Applications and maintenance to develop proficiency with the focus algorithms, including adding multidigit numbers with mental strategies.
2•8	To provide practice measuring length to the nearest half-centimeter; and to guide the construction and use of graphs for a set of collected data.	Grades 1–3: Choose and use appropriate measuring tools; refer to tables of equivalent units of metric measure. Grades 1 and 2: Use tally charts and bar graphs to sort, display, and describe data.	Grades 4–6: Repeated opportunities to measure in metric units. Grade 5: Use stem-and-leaf plots, broken-line graphs, and circle graphs. Grade 6: Use step graphs.
2•9	To review the trade-first and counting-up methods, and to introduce the partial-differences method of solving multidigit subtraction problems; and to provide practice estimating differences for multidigit subtraction problems.	Grades 1–3: Use invented (student-generated) algorithms to solve multidigit subtraction problems; begin to practice the trade-first and counting-up focus algorithms. Grades 2 and 3: Use ballpark estimates.	Grade 4: Develop strategies for subtraction of decimals (Unit 4). Grades 4–6: Develop proficiency with the focus algorithms, including subtracting with mental strategies.

	Key Concepts and Skills	Grade 4 Goals*
2•1	Use numbers written in number-word notation.	Number and Numeration Goal 1
	Compare uses of estimates and exact counts.	Operations and Computation Goal 6
	Locate points on a letter-number coordinate map.	Measurement and Reference Frames Goal 4
	Extend numerical patterns.	Patterns, Functions, and Algebra Goal 1
2•2	Give equivalent mathematical expressions for whole numbers.	Number and Numeration Goal 4
	Use conventional notation to write expressions using the four basic arithmetic operations.	Patterns, Functions, and Algebra Goal 2
	Insert grouping symbols to make number sentences true.	Patterns, Functions, and Algebra Goal 3
2•3	Read and write numbers up to 1,000,000,000; identify the values of digits.	Number and Numeration Goal 1
	Write numbers in expanded notation.	Number and Numeration Goal 4
	Find the sum of numbers written in expanded notation.	Operations and Computation Goal 2
	Use and describe patterns to find sums.	Patterns, Functions, and Algebra Goal 1
2•4	Read and write large numbers.	Number and Numeration Goal 1
	Identify places in whole numbers and the values of the digits in those places.	Number and Numeration Goal 1
	Add and subtract multidigit whole numbers.	Operations and Computation Goal 2
	Solve open sentences.	Patterns, Functions, and Algebra Goal 2
2•5	Create a tally chart.	Data and Chance Goal 1
	Find the maximum, minimum, range, mode, median, and mean for a set of data.	Data and Chance Goal 2
	Use data landmarks to make a prediction.	Data and Chance Goal 2
	Use and describe a strategy for estimating volume; describe the difference between an estimate and a guess.	Measurement and Reference Frames Goal 2
2•6	Create a line plot.	Data and Chance Goal 1
	Find the maximum, minimum, range, mode, median, and mean for a set of data.	Data and Chance Goal 2
	Use data landmarks and representations to answer questions and draw conclusions.	Data and Chance Goal 2
2•7	Identify places in whole numbers and the values of the digits in those places.	Number and Numeration Goal 1
	Apply extended addition facts.	Operations and Computation Goal 1
	Use the partial-sums and column-addition algorithms to solve multidigit addition problems; choose an appropriate paper-and-pencil algorithm to solve multidigit addition problems.	Operations and Computation Goal 2
	Make ballpark estimates for multidigit addition problems.	Operations and Computation Goal 6
2•8	Create a bar graph and line plot.	Data and Chance Goal 1
	Determine the maximum, minimum, range, mode, and median of a data set.	Data and Chance Goal 2
	Ask and answer questions and draw conclusions based on data landmarks, a bar graph, and a line plot.	Data and Chance Goal 2
	Measure to the nearest half-centimeter.	Measurement and Reference Frames Goal 1
2•9	Identify places in whole numbers and the values of the digits in those places.	Number and Numeration Goal 1
	Apply extended subtraction facts.	Operations and Computation Goal 1
	Use the trade-first and partial-differences algorithms to solve multidigit subtraction problems; choose an appropriate paper-and-pencil algorithm to solve multidigit subtraction problems.	Operations and Computation Goal 2
	Make ballpark estimates for multidigit subtraction problems.	Operations and Computation Goal 6

*See the Appendix for a complete list of Grade 4 Goals.

A Balanced Curriculum

Ongoing Practice

Everyday Mathematics provides numerous opportunities for ongoing practice. These activities are embedded throughout the lessons:

Mental Math and Reflexes activities promote speed and accuracy in mental computation.

Math Boxes offer mixed practice and are paired across lessons as shown in the brackets below. This makes them useful as assessment tools. The last one or two boxes on each page preview the next unit's content.

Mixed practice	[2•1, 2•3], [2•2, 2•4], [2•5, 2•7, 2•9], [2•6, 2•8]
Mixed practice with multiple choice	2•1, 2•4, 2•6, 2•9
Mixed practice with writing/reasoning opportunity	2•1, 2•2, 2•3, 2•5, 2•6, 2•7, 2•8, 2•9

Study Links are daily homework assignments that review the content of the lesson and often contain ongoing facts practice or computation practice.

5-Minute Math problems are offered for additional practice in Lessons 2•2, 2•3, and 2•5.

EM Facts Workshop Game provides online practice of basic facts and computation.

EXTRA PRACTICE **Extra Practice** activities are included in Lessons 2•1, 2•2, 2•3, and 2•5.

Practice through Games

Games are an essential component of practice in the *Everyday Mathematics* program. Games offer skills practice and promote strategic thinking. See the *Differentiation Handbook* for ways to adapt games to meet students' needs.

Lesson	Game	Skill Practiced
2•1	*Polygon Pair-Up*	Identifying properties of polygons [GEO Goal 2]
2•2	*Name That Number*	Representing numbers in different ways [NN Goal 4]
2•4	*Fishing for Digits*	Identifying digits and expressing values of digits in whole numbers [NN Goal 1]
2•5	*Addition Top-It* (Extended-Facts Version)	Developing automaticity with addition fact extensions [OC Goal 1]
2•6	*Subtraction Top-It* (Extended-Facts Version)	Developing automaticity with subtraction fact extensions [OC Goal 1]
2•7	*High-Number Toss*	Comparing numbers [NN Goal 6]
2•9	*Subtraction Target Practice*	Developing place-value and subtraction skills [NN Goal 1 and OC Goal 2]

[NN] Number and Numeration
[MRF] Measurement and Reference Frames
[OC] Operations and Computation
[GEO] Geometry
[DC] Data and Chance
[PFA] Patterns, Functions, and Algebra

Problem Solving 

Experts at problem solving and mathematical modeling generally do these things:

- Identify the problem.
- Decide what information is needed to solve the problem.
- Play with and study the data to find patterns and meaning.
- Identify and use mathematical procedures to solve the problem.
- Decide whether the solution makes sense and whether it can be applied to other problems.

The table below lists some of the opportunities in this unit for students to practice these strategies.

Lessons that teach *through* problem solving, not just *about* problem solving

Lesson	Activity
2•1	Examine numerical information about Washington, D.C.
2•2	Name a target number using numbers 1 through 30 and the four operations.
2•4	Practice place-value using a calculator.
2•5	Determine about how many raisins are in a typical $\frac{1}{2}$ ounce box of raisins.
2•6	Find landmarks in family-size data for the class.
2•8	Determine the median head size for the class.

See Chapter 18: Problem Solving in the *Teacher's Reference Manual* for more information.

The Language of Mathematics

Everyday Mathematics provides lesson-specific suggestions to help all students acquire, process, and express mathematical ideas. Throughout Unit 2, there are lesson-specific language development notes that address the needs of English language learners, indicated by ELL.

ELL SUPPORT Activities to support English language learners are in Part 3 of Lessons 2•1, 2•3, 2•6, and 2•7.

The *English Learners Handbook* and the *Differentiation Handbook* have suggestions for promoting language development and acquisition of mathematics vocabulary. See Unit 2 in each handbook.

Literacy Connection

12 Ways to Get to 11, by Eve Merriam, Aladdin Paperbacks, 1996

If You Made a Million, by David M. Schwartz, HarperCollins, 1994

How Tall, How Short, How Far Away?, by David A. Adler, Holiday House, 2000

The History of Counting, by Denise Schmandt-Besserat, HarperCollins, 1999

For more literacy connections, see the *Home Connection Handbook,* Grades 4–6.

Unit 2 Vocabulary

ballpark estimate
bar graph
column-addition method
counting number
digit
equivalent name
estimate
expanded notation
guess
landmark
line plot
maximum
median
minimum
mode
name-collection box
partial-differences method
partial-sums method
place
range
tally chart
trade-first method
whole number

Cross-Curricular Links 

Social Studies
Lesson 2•1 Students begin the yearlong World Tour Project.

Consumer
Lesson 2•8 Students verify an advertising claim.

Balanced Assessment

Daily Assessments

- **Recognizing Student Achievement** – A daily assessment that is included in every lesson to evaluate students' progress toward the Grade 4 Grade-Level Goals.
- **Informing Instruction** – Notes that appear throughout the unit to help anticipate students' common errors and suggest appropriate problem-solving strategies.

Lesson	Recognizing Student Achievement	Informing Instruction
2•1	Compute extended addition facts. [OC Goal 1]	Distinguish between measurements and counts.
2•2	Give equivalent names for whole numbers. [NN Goal 4]	
2•3	Identify the values of digits in whole numbers. [NN Goal 1]	Use the word *and* correctly when reading numbers.
2•4	Identify places in whole numbers and the values of the digits in those places. [NN Goal 1]	
2•5	Compute extended addition facts. [OC Goal 1]	Correctly place the fifth tally mark.
2•6	Identify the maximum, minimum, range, and mode of a data set. [DC Goal 2]	Order numbers to find the median of a data set.
2•7	Solve multidigit addition problems. [OC Goal 2]	
2•8	Use data landmarks and bar graphs to draw conclusions about a data set. [DC Goal 2]	Measure length to the nearest half-centimeter.
2•9	Solve multidigit subtraction problems. [OC Goal 2]	

[NN] Number and Numeration
[OC] Operations and Computation
[DC] Data and Chance
[MRF] Measurement and Reference Frames
[GEO] Geometry
[PFA] Patterns, Functions, and Algebra

Portfolio Opportunities

The following lessons provide opportunities to gather samples of students' mathematical writings, drawings, and creations to add balance to the assessment process: Lessons 2•1, 2•2, 2•4, 2•5, 2•6, 2•7, 2•8, 2•9, and 2•10.

See pages 16 and 17 in the *Assessment Handbook* for more information about portfolios and how to use them.

Unit Assessment

Progress Check 2 – A cumulative assessment of concepts and skills taught in Unit 2 and in the previous unit, providing information for evaluating students' progress and planning for future instruction. These assessments include oral/slate, written, and open-response activities, as shown below in the sample Progress Check lesson opener.

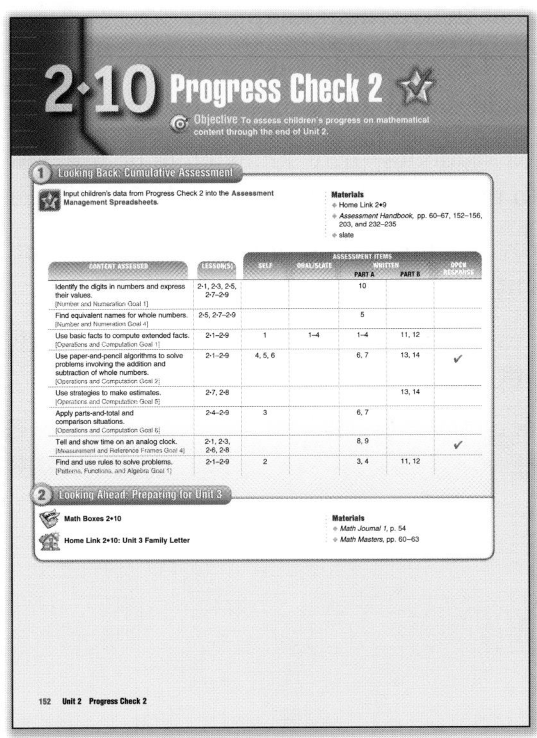

2·10 Progress Check 2

Objective To assess children's progress on mathematical content through the end of Unit 2.

1 Looking Back: Cumulative Assessment

Input children's data from Progress Check 2 into the **Assessment Management Spreadsheets.**

Materials
- Home Link 2•9
- *Assessment Handbook,* pp. 60–67, 152–156, 203, and 232–235
- slate

CONTENT ASSESSED	LESSON(S)	ASSESSMENT ITEMS: SELF	ORAL/SLATE	WRITTEN: PART A	WRITTEN: PART B	OPEN RESPONSE
Identify the digits in numbers and express their values. [Number and Numeration Goal 1]	2·1, 2·3, 2·5, 2·7–2·9			10		
Find equivalent names for whole numbers. [Number and Numeration Goal 4]	2·5, 2·7–2·9			5		
Use basic facts to compute extended facts. [Operations and Computation Goal 1]	2·1–2·9	1	1–4	1–4	11, 12	
Use paper-and-pencil algorithms to solve problems involving the addition and subtraction of whole numbers. [Operations and Computation Goal 2]	2·1–2·9	4, 5, 6		6, 7	13, 14	✓
Use strategies to make estimates. [Operations and Computation Goal 5]	2·7, 2·8				13, 14	
Apply parts-and-total and comparison situations. [Operations and Computation Goal 6]	2·4–2·9	3		6, 7		
Tell and show time on an analog clock. [Measurement and Reference Frames Goal 4]	2·1, 2·3, 2·6, 2·8			8, 9		✓
Find and use rules to solve problems. [Patterns, Functions, and Algebra Goal 1]	2·1–2·9	2		3, 4	11, 12	

2 Looking Ahead: Preparing for Unit 3

Math Boxes 2•10

Home Link 2•10: Unit 3 Family Letter

Materials
- *Math Journal 1,* p. 54
- *Math Masters,* pp. 60–63

152 **Unit 2 Progress Check 2**

Core Assessment Resources

Assessment Handbook

- **Unit 2 Assessment Overview,** pages 60–67
- **Unit 2 Assessment Masters,** pages 159–163
- **Unit 2 Individual Profiles of Progress,** pages 250, 251, and 302
- **Unit 2 Class Checklists,** pages 252, 253, and 303
- **Math Logs,** pages 306–308
- **Exit Slip,** page 311
- **Other Student Assessment Forms,** pages 304, 305, 309, and 310

Assessment Management Spreadsheets

The Assessment Management Spreadsheets consist of the Digital Class Checklists and Individual Profile of Progress Checklists. Use them to monitor, record, and report student progress.

Addressing All Needs

Differentiated Instruction

Adjusting the Activity – suggests adaptations that target advanced learners, English language learners, or learners who need additional instructional support.

ELL SUPPORT / **ELL** – provides lesson-specific suggestions to help English language learners understand and process the mathematical content.

READINESS – accesses students' prior knowledge or previews content that prepares students to engage in the lesson's Part 1 activities.

EXTRA PRACTICE – provides additional opportunities to apply the mathematical content of the lesson.

ENRICHMENT – enables students to apply or further explore the mathematical content of the lesson.

Lesson	Adjusting the Activity	ELL Support/ ELL	Readiness	Extra Practice	Enrichment
2•1	•	•	•	•	•
2•2	•		•	•	•
2•3	•	•		•	•
2•4	•	•	•		•
2•5	•	•	•	•	•
2•6	•	•	•		•
2•7	•	•	•		•
2•8	•	•	•		•
2•9	•	•	•		•

Additional Resources

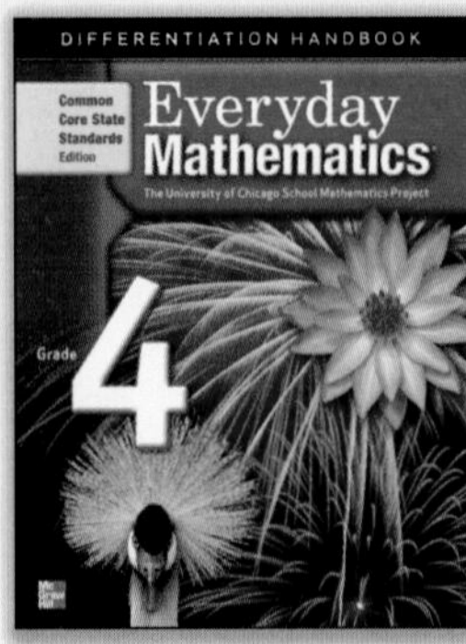

Differentiation Handbook
Provides ideas and strategies for differentiating instruction.
Pages 55–61

English Learners Handbook
Contains lesson-specific comprehension strategies.
Pages 9–17

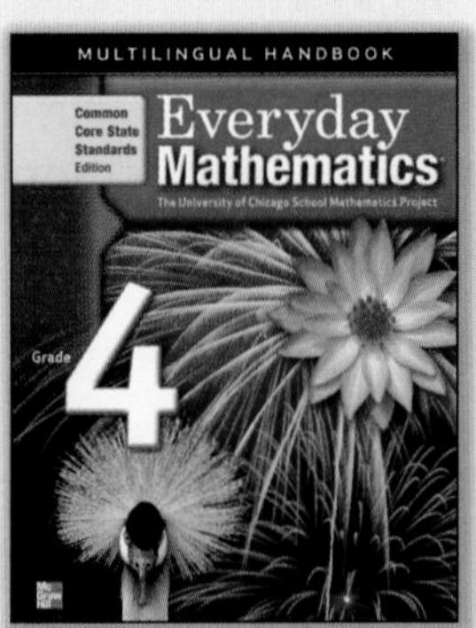

Multilingual Handbook
Previews concepts and vocabulary. It is written in six languages.
Pages 17–34

Planning Tips

Multiage Classroom

Companion Lessons from Grades 3 and 5 can help you meet instructional needs of a multiage classroom. The full Scope and Sequence can be found in the Appendix.

Grade 3		1•1, 1•6	5•1, 5•3	1•9	1•5, 10•7	1•5, 10•6, 10•7	2•1, 2•7	1•5	2•1, 2•8
Grade 4	**2•1**	**2•2**	**2•3**	**2•4**	**2•5**	**2•6**	**2•7**	**2•8**	**2•9**
Grade 5	3•1	2•4	2•2, 2•3	2•2, 2•3	6•1, 6•3, 12•7	10•4, 10•7	2•2, 2•3	5•9	2•3

Pacing for Success

Pacing depends on a number of factors, such as students' individual needs and how long your school has been using *Everyday Mathematics*. At the beginning of Unit 2, you may want to use tools available at www.everydaymathonline.com to help you set your pace.

Home Support

Unit 2 Family Letter (English/Spanish) provides families with an overview, Do-Anytime Activities, Building Skills through Games, a list of vocabulary, and answers to the daily homework (Study Links). Family Letters in English, Spanish, and seven other languages are also available online.

Study Links are the daily homework assignments. They consist of active projects and ongoing review problems.

Home Support Resources

Home Connection Handbook
Offers ideas and reproducible masters for communicating with families. See Table of Contents for unit information.

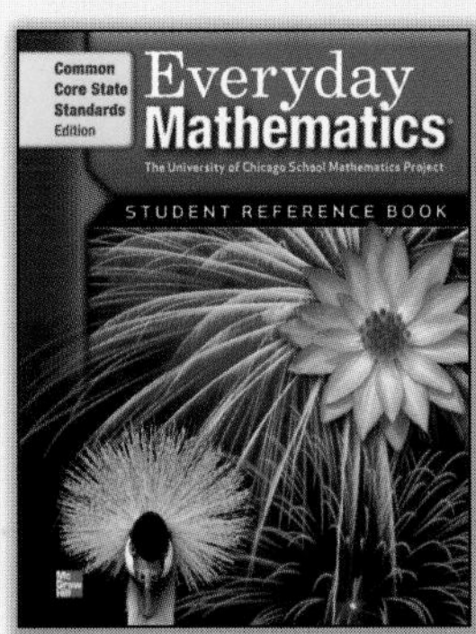

Student Reference Book
Provides a resource for students and parents.

Pages 2, 4, 10–12, 14, 15, 71, 242, 252, 254, 258, 262–264, 267–270

Technology Resources

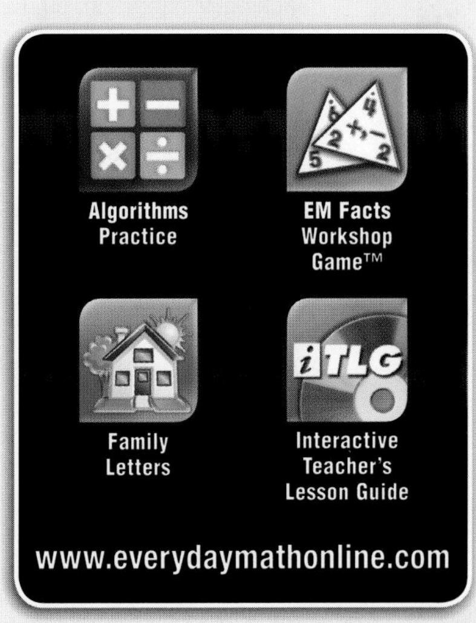

Lesson	Masters	Manipulative Kit	Other Items
2•1	Teaching Masters, pp. 38, 40, and 41 Study Link Master, p. 39 Game Masters, pp. 496 and 497 Teaching Aid Master, p. 393	slate	straightedge; scissors
2•2	Teaching Aid Masters, pp. 389 and 394–397 Study Link Master, p. 42 Game Master, p. 489 Teaching Masters, pp. 43 and 44	slate; deck of number cards; 1 each of number cards 0–18	index cards*; calculator*; scissors
2•3	Transparency of *Math Masters,* p. 398* Study Link Master, p. 45 Teaching Master, p. 46 *Differentiation Handbook*, p. 140	slate	calculator
2•4	Teaching Aid Masters, pp. 388* or 389* and 399–402 Transparency of *Math Masters,* p. 47* Study Link Master, p. 48 Game Master, p. 472 Teaching Masters, pp. 49 and 50	slate	overhead calculator*; scissors; stapler; calculator
2•5	Study Link Master, p. 51 Game Master, p. 506 Teaching Masters, pp. 52 and 53	slate; per partnership: deck of number cards; 2 six-sided dice	per student: small box of raisins (or 3-ounce cup of raisin substitute); 1 large box of raisins (12 or 15 ounces)
2•6	Study Link Master, p. 54 Game Master, p. 506 Teaching Masters, pp. 55 and 56 *Differentiation Handbook*, p. 140	slate; per partnership: 4 each of number cards 1–10; deck of number cards	3-inch-square stick-on notes; tape*
2•7	Teaching Aid Masters, pp. 403* or 404* and 405 Study Link Masters, pp. 57 and 58 Game Master, p. 487 Teaching Master, p. 59 *Differentiation Handbook*, p. 140	base-10 blocks; per partnership: 1 six-sided die	quarter-sheet of paper; 3-section paper dinner plates*
2•8	Teaching Masters, pp. 60, 62, and 63 Study Link Master, p. 61 Teaching Aid Master, p. 406	per partnership: tape measure; slate; compass; pattern blocks	ruler; stick-on notes; computer with Internet access*; straightedge; tape; adjustable baseball caps
2•9	Teaching Aid Master, p. 403* or 404* Study Link Masters, pp. 64 and 65 Game Master, p. 504 Teaching Masters, pp. 66 and 67	slate; base-10 blocks*; 4 each of number cards 0–9	quarter-sheet of paper; scissors; calculator
2•10	Assessment Masters, pp. 159–163 Study Link Masters, pp. 68–71	slate	Geometry Template

*Denotes optional materials

Mathematical Background

The discussion below highlights the major content ideas presented in Unit 2 and helps establish instructional priorities.

Introduction to the World Tour; Number Uses (Lesson 2◆1)

This lesson introduces the yearlong World Tour Project that focuses on the study of number uses. Students begin the tour by traveling from their hometowns to Washington, D.C. (They will not travel to foreign countries until Unit 3.) They use the tourist information about Washington, D.C., which appears in the *Student Reference Book,* and consider different uses of numbers.

Most of these numbers fall into one of five major categories.

- counts (5 people; 10,200,000 cars)
- measures (2.6 kilograms; 35 mph; $7\frac{3}{8}$ inches)
- locations in reference frames (36°F; A.D. 1266; 5:41 P.M.)
- ratios, percents, and scale numbers (95%; $\frac{2}{3}$ as many)
- identification numbers and codes (1-312-555-9816; ZIP code 08648)

Although it is not important that students know this classification scheme, they should be exposed to everyday uses of numbers in each of these categories. As the examples listed above suggest, it is difficult to know how a number is being used without looking at its label. "Miles per hour" is a measurement unit label, and "degrees Fahrenheit" identifies a temperature scale. On the bar graph shown below, "days" is a counting unit label.

For additional information about number uses, see Section 9.1 of the *Teacher's Reference Manual.*

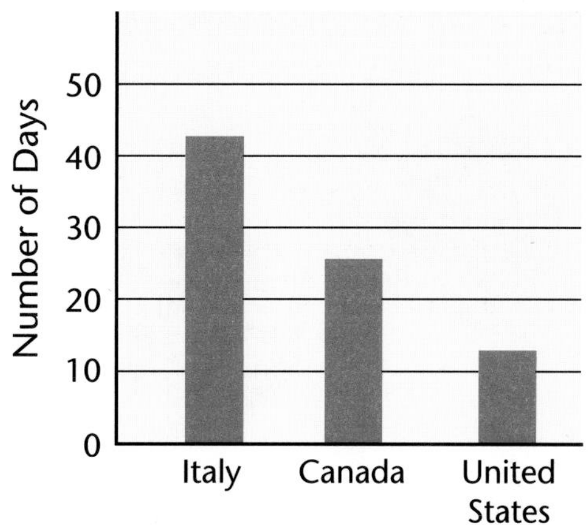

Note

Encourage students to include examples from all the major use categories by making a classroom display of some of the more interesting number-use examples that students collect.

Many Names for Numbers

(Lesson 2•2)

16
26 − 10
4 + 4 + 4 + 4
4^2
116 − 100
8 + (4 × 2)
32 ÷ 2

16-box

The name-collection box, which is used to record equivalent names for numbers, is reviewed in this lesson. The idea that a number can be represented in many (equivalent) ways is so important that it is taught and practiced throughout the *Everyday Mathematics* program. By now, students should be very familiar with the idea of equivalent names for numbers, for they have been filling in name-collection boxes since the middle of first grade.

See the *Teacher's Reference Manual,* Chapter 9, for additional information about number names.

Playing Games

(Lessons 2•1, 2•2, 2•4–2•7, and 2•9)

Practice through games is an integral part of the *Everyday Mathematics* curriculum. The authors believe that games are an efficient means of building number skills. Games allow the frequent practice that is necessary to attain mastery of many skills, and games do not tend to become tedious, as drills so often do.

Note

Games are featured in all of the units. They should be played not only when they are introduced, but at other times and on a regular basis as well.

Additional information about games may be found in Section 1.2.2 of the *Teacher's Reference Manual.*

Name That Number Record Sheet

Name ____ Date ____ Time ____

Round 1
Target Number: ____ My Cards: ____
My best solution (number sentence): ____
Number of cards used: ____

Round 2
Target Number: ____ My Cards: ____
My best solution (number sentence): ____
Number of cards used: ____

Name That Number Record Sheet

Name ____ Date ____ Time ____

Round 1
Target Number: ____ My Cards: ____
My best solution (number sentence): ____
Number of cards used: ____

Round 2
Target Number: ____ My Cards: ____
My best solution (number sentence): ____
Number of cards used: ____

The Base-Ten Place-Value System
(Lessons 2•3 and 2•4)

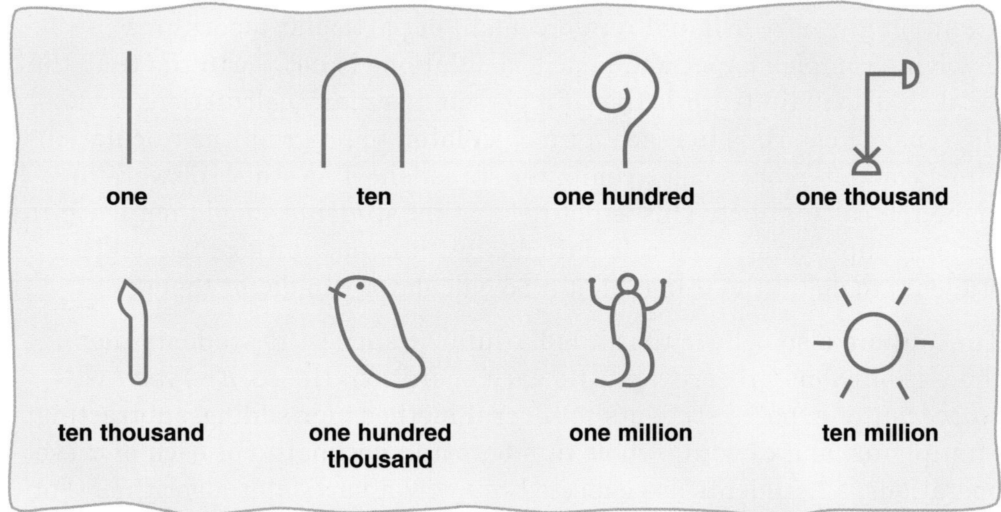

The earliest human societies devised systems for counting objects. These systems evolved into a variety of methods for recording the number of objects counted. They ranged from simple tallies to the more sophisticated Egyptian, Babylonian, and Roman notational systems. More recently, the base-ten place-value system, which is in widespread use today, was invented. This system is based on three principles:

- Using the digits 0 through 9, one can write any whole number, no matter how large.
- The value of each digit in a numeral depends on its position, or place, in the numeral.
- Place values increase tenfold from each place to the next higher place.

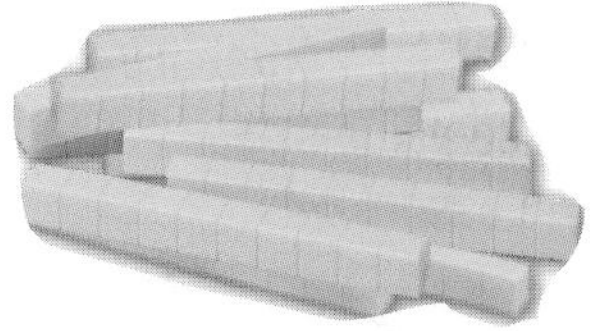

In Lesson 2-3, students review and practice these underlying concepts, with a special focus on reading and writing whole numbers to one billion. In Lesson 2-4, they practice place-value skills by using a calculator to change one or more digits in a number. They also play *Fishing for Digits,* a game that involves identifying digits in whole numbers and expressing their value.

For additional information about place value and the base-ten numeration system, see Section 9.9.1 of the *Teacher's Reference Manual.*

Algorithms for Adding and Subtracting Numbers (Lessons 2•7 and 2•9)

Numbers make the most sense when they are in a real-world context. However, students need to practice computation, and to do this, they frequently operate with numbers that have no context and no label or unit of measure.

The focus of Lessons 2-7 and 2-9 is on methods for adding and subtracting multidigit numbers. The review of place value in Lessons 2-3 and 2-4 prepares students for the addition and subtraction methods that the program presents.

Project Note

To teach U.S. traditional addition and subtraction, see Algorithm Projects 1 and 3.

Unit 2 Organizer

Computational algorithms are systematic procedures that are important in mathematics. In programming computers, for example, systematic procedures are developed for working out complex calculations. However, in this calculator and computer age, the authors believe that the usual attention given to drill and reinforcement of particular algorithms involving complex paper-and-pencil calculations is not worth the time that it takes. The plain truth is that if a person has many calculations to do, the sensible choice is to reach for a calculator, to program the calculations into a computer, or to use a computer spreadsheet or other software to make the calculations. This is not to say that students should not learn to perform paper-and-pencil calculations. But it is not our goal to enable students to do all the things that a $5 calculator can do for them.

Note

Students should not use their calculators while exploring and practicing the algorithms for adding and subtracting multidigit numbers. The journal pages, Study Links, and Masters used for assessment with these lessons are marked with the no-calculator icon to remind students of this. However, calculator usage is encouraged in other parts of the program. For example, students use a calculator to practice place-value skills in Lesson 2-4.

The authors also believe that it is harmful to suggest to students that there is only one proper way to do each operation. Hence, *Everyday Mathematics* exposes students to several methods for adding, subtracting, multiplying, and dividing whole numbers and decimals. For each of these operations, all students are expected to know a particular algorithm. (For addition, it is the partial-sums algorithm; for subtraction, the trade-first algorithm.) But students are encouraged to use whatever algorithm they like to solve problems, or even to invent one of their own.

For students who have already learned reliable addition and subtraction algorithms, these lessons remind them that there is more than one way to solve a problem. For students who are still struggling, these lessons provide an opportunity to learn reliable methods that will work for them.

See Sections 11.2.1 and 11.2.2 in the *Teacher's Reference Manual* for additional information about addition and subtraction algorithms.

Partial-Sums Method Using Base-10 Blocks

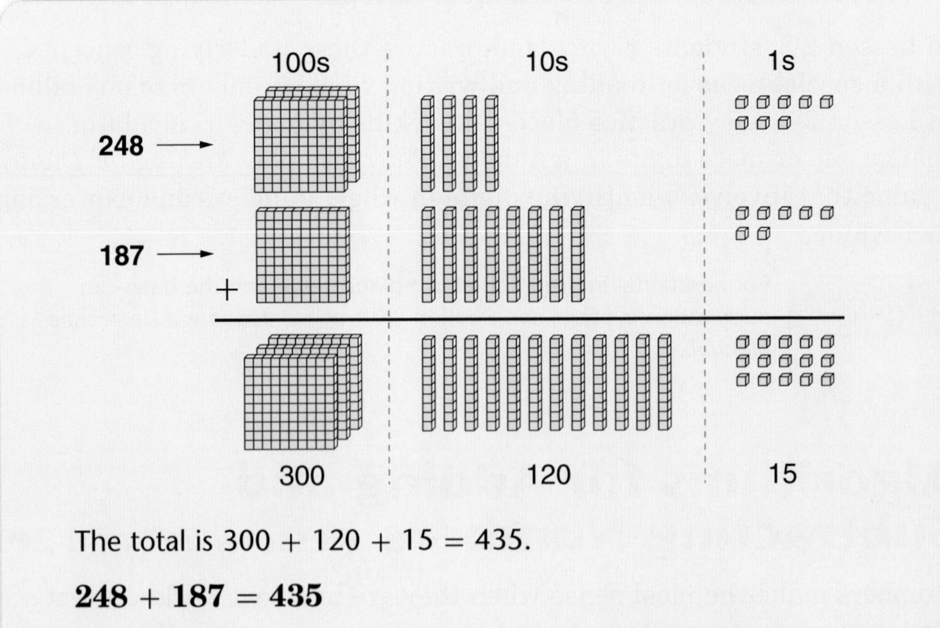

Collecting, Organizing, and Describing Data (Lessons 2•5, 2•6, and 2•8)

These first data lessons review and introduce several devices that enable students to organize their data. Such organization makes it easier to understand the data.

The simple tally chart and bar graph should be familiar to students who have used *Everyday Mathematics* in earlier grades. Line plots (also called *sketch graphs*) are introduced and are used extensively to organize and display data.

One of the simplest devices for displaying data is to arrange the data in order from largest to smallest data value. Such an arrangement often can be done without using a tally table or line plot. For example, on a tangible level, students can line up by either age or height.

Once the data are organized in some way, encourage students at every opportunity to discuss things they notice about their data. Their discussions generally should include the following "landmarks" in the data: the maximum, minimum, median, mode, and range. Students can use these landmarks as reference points when they discuss other features of the data, just as cartographers use landmarks when they discuss map facts.

For additional information about data and landmarks of data, see Section 12.2 of the *Teacher's Reference Manual.*

Note

During the school year, many sources of data are used, and students gather their data in different ways. The lessons in this unit rely on counting and measuring in the classroom. In future lessons, students collect data in other ways, such as by observing and measuring at home, by taking surveys, and by recording information from reference books.

Tally Chart

Number of Students	Head Size (cm)
/	49
/	49.5
//	50
///	50.5
	51
///	51.5
////	52
	52.5
~~////~~	53
	53.5
/	54

Head Sizes in 4th Grade Class

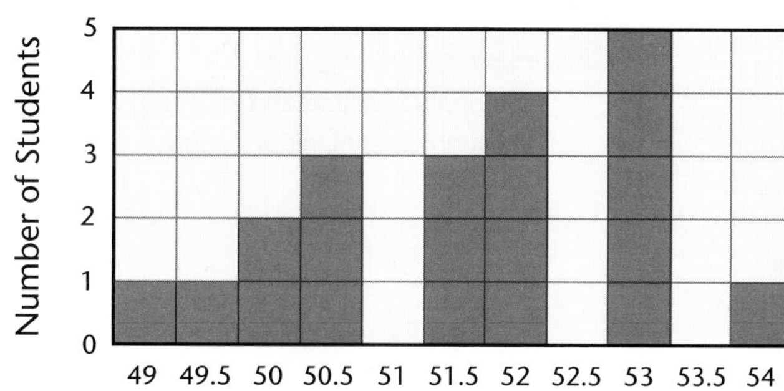

Head Sizes to the Nearest $\frac{1}{2}$ cm

2·1 A Visit to Washington, D.C.

Objectives To review examples of the various ways in which numbers are used; and to introduce the World Tour Project.

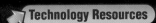

www.everydaymathonline.com

ePresentations

eToolkit

Algorithms Practice

EM Facts Workshop Game™

Family Letters

Assessment Management

Common Core State Standards

Curriculum Focal Points

Interactive Teacher's Lesson Guide

1 Teaching the Lesson

Key Concepts and Skills

- Use numbers written in number-word notation.
  [Number and Numeration Goal 1]
- Compare uses of estimates and exact counts.
  [Operations and Computation Goal 6]
- Locate points on a letter-number coordinate map.
  [Measurement and Reference Frames Goal 4]
- Extend numerical patterns.
  [Patterns, Functions, and Algebra Goal 1]

Key Activities

Students start the yearlong World Tour Project by traveling from their hometown to Washington, D.C. They identify uses of numbers in the tourist information on Washington, D.C., provided in the *Student Reference Book.*

Ongoing Assessment: Recognizing Student Achievement Use Mental Math and Reflexes.
[Operations and Computation Goal 1]

Ongoing Assessment: Informing Instruction See page 85.

Materials

Math Journal 1, pp. 28, 172, and 173
Student Reference Book, pp. 2 and 267–270
Math Masters, p. 38
straightedge ◆ slate

2 Ongoing Learning & Practice

Playing *Polygon Pair-Up*
Student Reference Book, p. 258
Math Masters, pp. 496 and 497
scissors
Students practice identifying properties of polygons.

Math Boxes 2·1
Math Journal 1, p. 29
Students practice and maintain skills through Math Box problems.

Study Link 2·1
Math Masters, p. 39
Students practice and maintain skills through Study Link activities.

3 Differentiation Options

READINESS

Solving Frames-and-Arrows Problems
Math Masters, p. 40
Students explore using rules to find linear intervals.

ENRICHMENT

Finding Missing Numbers
Math Masters, p. 41
Students find missing numbers on a number line using intervals.

EXTRA PRACTICE

Solving Frames-and-Arrows Problems
Math Masters, p. 393
Students practice extending numerical patterns.

ELL SUPPORT

Sharing Country Information
Math Journal 1, pp. 172 and 173
Students look at a world map and share interesting things about other countries.

Advance Preparation

For Part 1, copy and cut apart *Math Masters,* page 38. Place these sheets near the Math Message.
Before starting the lesson, read about the World Tour Project on page 266 in the *Student Reference Book.*

***Teacher's Reference Manual,* Grades 4–6** pp. 13, 57–59

Getting Started

Mental Math and Reflexes  

Pose extended addition-fact problems. *Suggestions:*

●○○ 2 + 7 = 9
20 + 70 = 90
200 + 700 = 900

●●○ 4 + 9 = 13
40 + 90 = 130
400 + 900 = 1,300

●●● 500 + 700 = 1,200
5,000 + 7,000 = 12,000
50,000 + 70,000 = 120,000

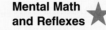

Math Message 

Complete Math Masters, *page 38.*

Ongoing Assessment: Recognizing Student Achievement

Mental Math and Reflexes

Use **Mental Math and Reflexes** to assess students' automaticity with extended addition facts. Students are making adequate progress if they can solve the ●○○ and ●●○ problems. Some students may be able to solve the ●●● problems, which do not include a basic fact prompt.

[Operations and Computation Goal 1]

1 Teaching the Lesson

Math Message Follow-Up

WHOLE-CLASS ACTIVITY

(*Student Reference Book,* p. 2; *Math Masters,* p. 38)

Direct students to the "Uses of Numbers" essay on page 2 in the *Student Reference Book*. Discuss the five categories of uses of numbers and write them on the board.

Then have students work in small groups to match their Math Message answers to the five categories. 1. count, 2. identification and code, 3. reference system, 4. measure, 5. reference system, 6. compare, 7. Answers vary.

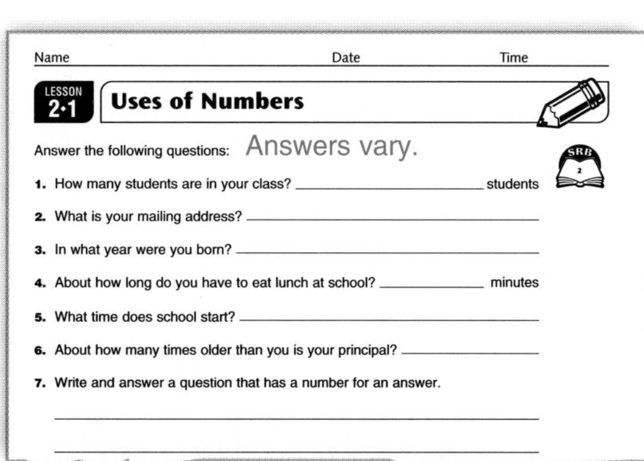

Name ______ Date ______ Time ______

LESSON 2·1 **Uses of Numbers**

Answer the following questions: Answers vary.

1. How many students are in your class? ______ students
2. What is your mailing address? ______
3. In what year were you born? ______
4. About how long do you have to eat lunch at school? ______ minutes
5. What time does school start? ______
6. About how many times older than you is your principal? ______
7. Write and answer a question that has a number for an answer.

______

______

Math Masters, page 38

Interactive whiteboard-ready ePresentations are available at www.everydaymathonline.com to help you teach the lesson.

NOTE To review Fahrenheit and Celsius temperatures, see www.everydaymathonline.com.

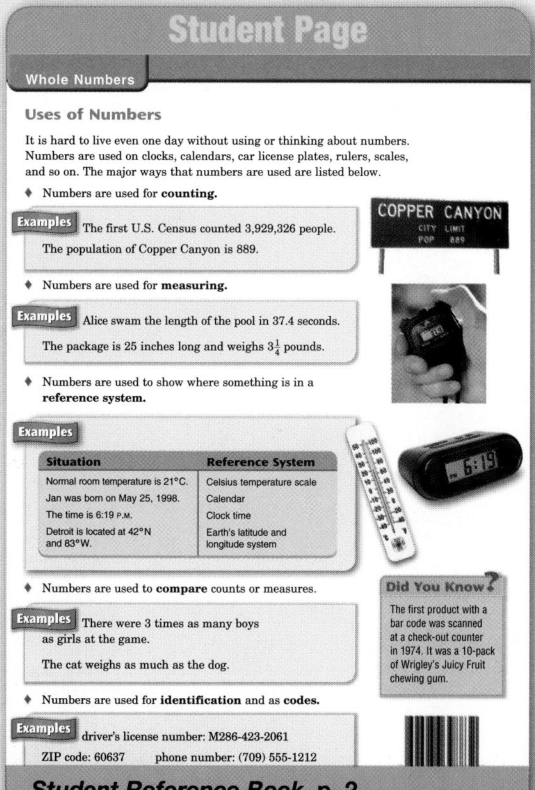

Student Page

Whole Numbers

Uses of Numbers

It is hard to live even one day without using or thinking about numbers. Numbers are used on clocks, calendars, car license plates, rulers, scales, and so on. The major ways that numbers are used are listed below.

- Numbers are used for **counting.**

Examples The first U.S. Census counted 3,929,326 people.
The population of Copper Canyon is 889.

- Numbers are used for **measuring.**

Examples Alice swam the length of the pool in 37.4 seconds.
The package is 25 inches long and weighs $3\frac{1}{4}$ pounds.

- Numbers are used to show where something is in a **reference system.**

Examples

Situation	Reference System
Normal room temperature is 21°C.	Celsius temperature scale
Jan was born on May 25, 1998.	Calendar
The time is 6:19 P.M.	Clock time
Detroit is located at 42°N and 83°W.	Earth's latitude and longitude system

- Numbers are used to **compare** counts or measures.

Examples There were 3 times as many boys as girls at the game.
The cat weighs as much as the dog.

Did You Know?
The first product with a bar code was scanned at a check-out counter in 1974. It was a 10-pack of Wrigley's Juicy Fruit chewing gum.

- Numbers are used for **identification** and as **codes.**

Examples driver's license number: M286-423-2061
ZIP code: 60637 phone number: (709) 555-1212

***Student Reference Book,* p. 2**

Washington, D.C. Facts

Washington, D.C., is the **capital** of the United States of America. The capital is where our country's laws are made. It is also where our president lives.

Washington, D.C., has been the capital of the United States since 1800. Before that, the capital was in Philadelphia, Pennsylvania. The capital city was named "Washington, the District of Columbia" in honor of George Washington and Christopher Columbus. "District of Columbia" is usually abbreviated as D.C.

Washington, D.C., has an area of 68 square miles. With a population of about 600,000 people, more people live in our capital city than in the state of Wyoming!

There are many interesting things to do in Washington, D.C. The facts below will help you plan your visit.

Average High/Low Temperatures (°F)			Average Precipitation (in.)	
Month	High	Low	Month	Precipitation
Jan	42	25	Jan	3.1
Feb	46	28	Feb	2.7
Mar	55	35	Mar	3.6
Apr	66	43	Apr	3.0
May	75	53	May	4.0
Jun	83	62	Jun	3.6
Jul	88	67	Jul	3.6
Aug	86	66	Aug	3.6
Sep	79	59	Sep	3.8
Oct	68	46	Oct	3.3
Nov	57	37	Nov	3.2
Dec	46	29	Dec	3.1

The White House
Every U.S. president except George Washington has lived here. The White House sits on 18 acres of land. It has 132 rooms, five of which can be seen on a 20-minute public tour. Every year more than 1,500,000 people tour the White House. Web site: http://www.whitehouse.gov

***Student Reference Book*, p. 267**

Introducing the World Tour Project

ACTIVITY

(*Math Journal 1,* pp. 172 and 173)

Social Studies Link Tell students that for the entire school year they will be embarking on an imaginary tour of the world. In the course of their travels, students will learn about the countries they visit and the people who live there. They will collect and examine numerical data (with uses such as those discussed in the Math Message Follow-Up) about the countries they visit. Students may use reference books to find this information, but their primary source will be the World Tour section of the *Student Reference Book.*

Look over the World Tour section with students. It includes detailed information about 50 countries. The map on pages 172 and 173 of *Math Journal 1* shows the locations of these countries and their capitals. (Additional countries are named, but their capitals are not shown.) During the World Tour, students' travels will be limited to these 50 countries.

Tell students that they will first travel from their hometown to Washington, D.C. Ask students to find the approximate location of their hometown on the Route Map on journal pages 172 and 173, mark it with a dot, and then draw a straight line from the dot to Washington, D.C.

Student Pages

Date Time

Route Map

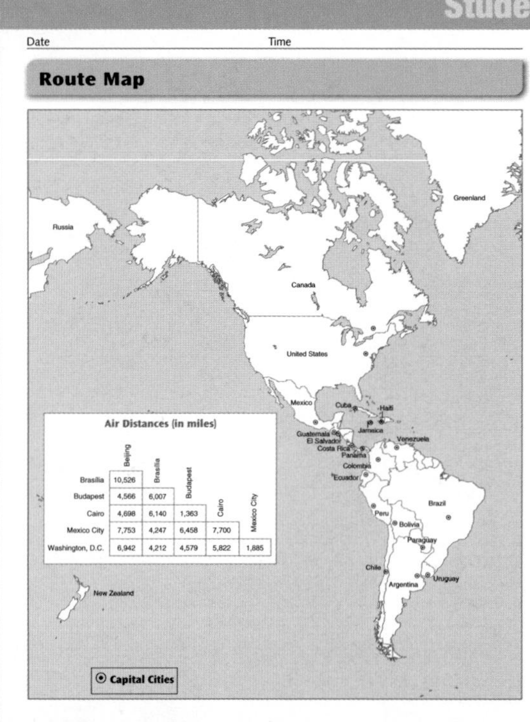

Air Distances (in miles)

	Beijing	Brasília	Budapest	Cairo	Mexico City
Brasília	10,526				
Budapest	4,566	6,007			
Cairo	4,698	6,140	1,363		
Mexico City	7,753	4,247	6,458	7,700	
Washington, D.C.	6,942	4,212	4,579	5,822	1,885

Date Time

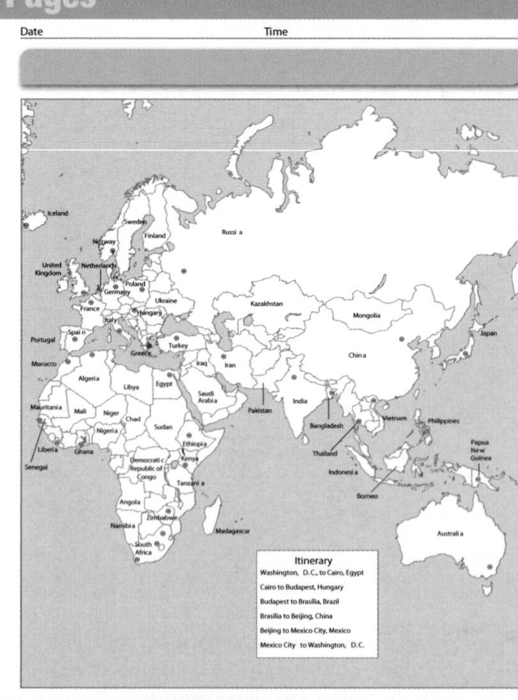

***Math Journal 1,* pp. 172 and 173**

Examining Numerical Information about Washington, D.C.

(*Student Reference Book,* pp. 2 and 267–270)

Use the numerical data about Washington, D.C., shown on pages 267–270 in the *Student Reference Book* to illustrate uses of numbers. Refer to the five categories on the board and ask students to find examples for each category.

- Find examples of numbers that are used to count things. Sample answers: The White House has 132 rooms. More than 1,500,000 people tour the White House every year. On an average weekday, about 500,000 people ride the Washington Metrorail electric trains. Abraham Lincoln was the 16th U.S. president. There are 78 Metrorail Stations in the Washington area.

Ongoing Assessment: Informing Instruction

Watch for students who think that certain numbers, such as the total length of the bookshelves in the Library of Congress (535 miles), are counts rather than measurements. Discuss that the unit *miles* refers to a specific unit of measurement.

- Which of the numbers listed so far are exact counts? Sample answers: The number of rooms in the White House; the number of Metrorail stations
- Which of the numbers listed are estimates? Sample answers: The population of Washington, D.C.; the number of comic books in the Library of Congress
- Why are estimates more appropriate for some of the counts than exact numbers? For example, why isn't it possible to give the exact population of Washington, D.C.? The count changes daily because of births, deaths, and people moving in or out of the city.
- Why is it not possible to give the exact attendance at a museum? Would such a figure be useful? Answers vary.
- Do you think it is possible to count how many people rode the Washington Metrorail in 2000? Why? Answers vary.
- Find examples of measurements. Sample answers: The length of the giant squid in the Museum of Natural History; the weight of the iron dome in the Capitol Building; the average monthly amounts of rainfall; the number of carats in the Hope Diamond

Student Page

World Tour

Washington, D.C. Facts

Washington Metrorail
This system of underground electric trains opened in 1976. There are 83 stations in the Washington area; some are decorated with beautiful artwork. They are connected by more than 103 miles of train lines. On an average weekday, about 500,000 people ride the Metro trains.
Web site: http://www.wmata.com

Washington Monument
This 555-foot-tall monument was built to honor George Washington, the first president of the United States. It is one of the tallest masonry structures in the world. You can take an elevator to a viewing area at the 500-foot level. The monument's cornerstone was laid in 1848, but building was interrupted by the Civil War (1861–1865). Construction workers started building again in 1880 and completed it in 1884. The Washington Monument receives more than 800,000 visitors each year.
Web site: http://www.nps.gov/wamo

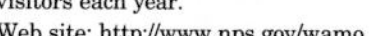

Jefferson Memorial
This memorial was built in honor of Thomas Jefferson. Jefferson was the third president of the United States and the author of the *Declaration of Independence.* The memorial was dedicated in 1943, exactly 200 years after Jefferson was born. Inside the memorial, a statue of Jefferson stands 19 feet tall.
Web site: http://www.nps.gov/thje/home.htm

Lincoln Memorial
This memorial was built in 1922 in honor of Abraham Lincoln. Lincoln was the 16th U.S. president. Inside the memorial is a 19-foot-high statue of Lincoln seated in a large armchair. The statue is made of 28 blocks of white marble from the state of Georgia.
Web site: http://www.nps.gov/linc/home.htm

Student Reference Book, **p. 268**

Student Page

World Tour

The United States Capitol
The Capitol Building is where the senators and representatives in Congress meet to make laws. George Washington laid its cornerstone in 1793. The building's cast iron dome weighs 9 million pounds. Brass doors that weigh 10 tons lead to the rotunda, which is 180 feet high and 96 feet in diameter.
Web site: http://www.aoc.gov

Library of Congress
The Library of Congress is the world's largest library. It contains more than 128 million items in 450 languages. It has about 535 miles of bookshelves. The Library is composed of three buildings. One of these, the James Madison Building, encloses an area greater than 35 football fields. The Library has more than 18 million books, 12 million photographs, 3 million sound recordings, and 5 million maps. It also has about 125,000 telephone books and 100,000 comic books. The Library of Congress collection grows by more than 10,000 items every day. Web site: http://www.loc.gov

National Museum of Natural History
Exhibits in the National Museum of Natural History include an 8-ton African bull elephant, the 45.5-carat Hope Diamond, a 360 million-year-old fossilized fish, a 90-foot-long skeleton of a diplodocus, a 30-foot-long giant squid, moon rocks, a mural of a 3.5 billion-year-old shoreline, and a life-size 92-foot model of a blue whale. The Insect Zoo has live insects as well as scorpions and tarantulas. In the Discovery Room, you can try on costumes from around the world. The museum is part of the Smithsonian Institution. Web site: http://www.mnh.si.edu

National Air and Space Museum
The National Air and Space Museum is the most popular museum in the world. Every year more than 10 million people visit it. Its collection includes the *Wright Flyer,* which is the original plane flown by the Wright brothers at Kitty Hawk, North Carolina, in 1903. It also includes the *Spirit of St. Louis,* the plane in which Charles Lindbergh made the first nonstop flight across the Atlantic in 1927. *Columbia,* the Apollo 11 command module that brought back the first men to walk on the moon in 1969, is also on display.

Student Reference Book, **p. 269**

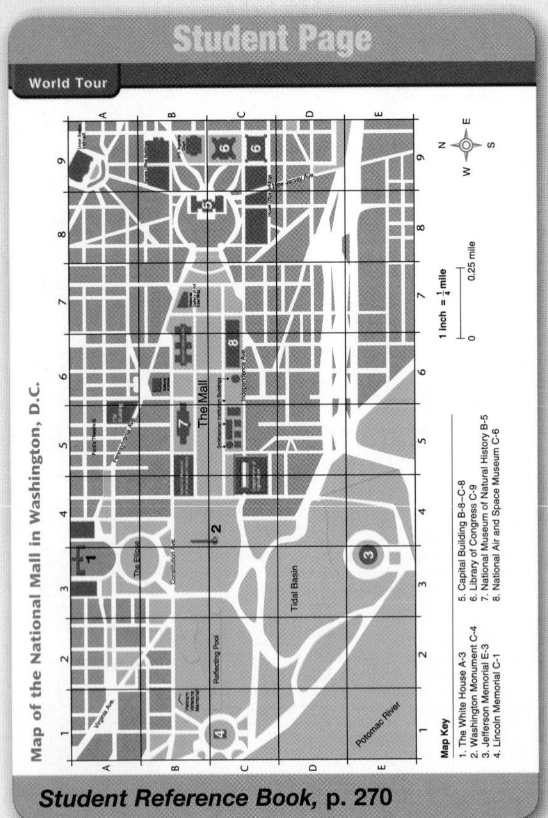

Student Reference Book, p. 270

Adjusting the Activity

Have students use the map scale (1 inch = $\frac{1}{4}$ mile) on *Student Reference Book,* page 270 to estimate the distances between attractions on the National Mall and to plot a course to see all of the attractions while walking the shortest distance.

AUDITORY ◆ KINESTHETIC ◆ TACTILE ◆ VISUAL

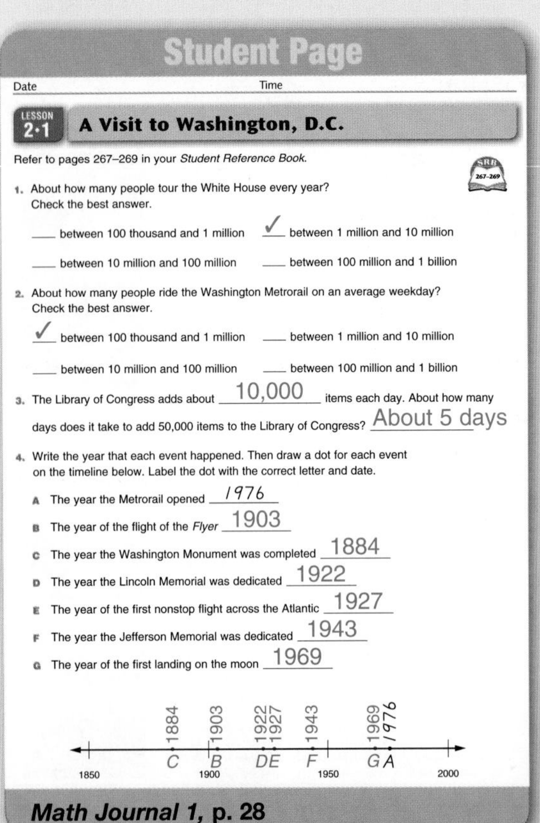
Student Page

Date Time

LESSON 2•1 **A Visit to Washington, D.C.**

Refer to pages 267–269 in your *Student Reference Book.*

1. About how many people tour the White House every year? Check the best answer.
   - ___ between 100 thousand and 1 million
   - ✓ between 1 million and 10 million
   - ___ between 10 million and 100 million
   - ___ between 100 million and 1 billion
2. About how many people ride the Washington Metrorail on an average weekday? Check the best answer.
   - ✓ between 100 thousand and 1 million
   - ___ between 1 million and 10 million
   - ___ between 10 million and 100 million
   - ___ between 100 million and 1 billion
3. The Library of Congress adds about 10,000 items each day. About how many days does it take to add 50,000 items to the Library of Congress? About 5 days
4. Write the year that each event happened. Then draw a dot for each event on the timeline below. Label the dot with the correct letter and date.
   - A The year the Metrorail opened 1976
   - B The year of the flight of the *Flyer* 1903
   - C The year the Washington Monument was completed 1884
   - D The year the Lincoln Memorial was dedicated 1922
   - E The year of the first nonstop flight across the Atlantic 1927
   - F The year the Jefferson Memorial was dedicated 1943
   - G The year of the first landing on the moon 1969

Timeline: 1850, 1900, 1950, 2000; 1884 C, 1903 B, 1922 1927 DE, 1943 F, 1969 1976 GA

Math Journal 1, p. 28

- **Find examples of codes.** Sample answers: The number codes for the various Washington sites shown on the map on *Student Reference Book,* page 270; the number 11 in the name of the *Apollo* command module can be either a count or a code—it stands for the 11th *Apollo* mission, but it is also part of the name of the mission.
- **Find examples of reference frames.** Sample answers: For temperatures above and below zero; for dates B.C. and A.D.; for locating points on the National Mall map

Ask students to locate a few sites on the National Mall map using the map coordinates and the number codes displayed in the map key. For example, the White House can be found in region A-3, and its code is 1. To support English language learners, clarify the meaning of *mall* in this context.

▶ Finding and Using Numerical Information about Washington, D.C.

SMALL-GROUP ACTIVITY

(*Math Journal 1,* p. 28; *Student Reference Book,* pp. 267–269)

Have students use *Student Reference Book,* pages 267–269 to complete journal page 28.

Adjusting the Activity

For Problem 4, have students provide additional reference points by locating the years halfway between the given years. Encourage students to think in terms of the Frames-and-Arrows problems they have solved since *First Grade Everyday Mathematics* to find the additional dates.

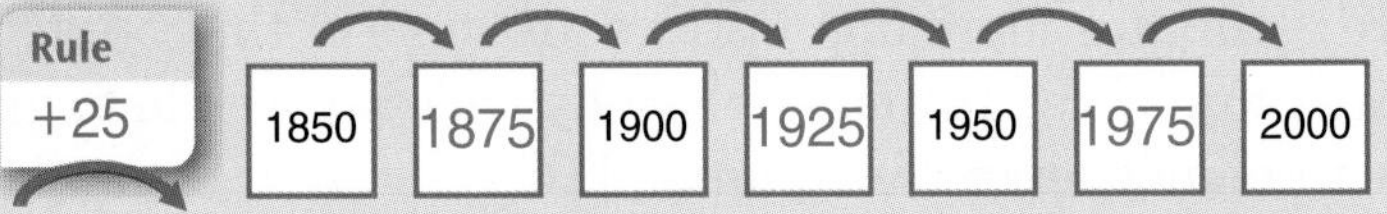

Ask students to explain how they found the rule. Sample answer: There are 50 years between 1850 and 1900. There are 2 jumps between 1850 and 1900. If I divide the 50 years by the 2 jumps, then each jump must be 25 years. So the rule is +25. Have students record the years halfway between the given dates below the timeline on journal page 28.

AUDITORY ◆ KINESTHETIC ◆ TACTILE ◆ VISUAL

Pose questions using the dates in Problem 4 of journal page 28. Encourage students to use the timeline at the bottom of the journal page to help them calculate the answers. *Suggestions:*

- How soon after the first landing on the moon was the Metrorail opened? 7 years
- How much older is the Lincoln Memorial than the Jefferson Memorial? 21 years older
- How many years after the first flight across the Atlantic was the first landing on the moon? 42 years

2 Ongoing Learning & Practice

▸ Playing *Polygon Pair-Up*

PARTNER ACTIVITY

(*Student Reference Book,* p. 258; *Math Masters,* pp. 496 and 497)

Students play *Polygon Pair-Up* to practice identifying properties of polygons. See Lesson 1-6 for additional information.

▸ Math Boxes 2·1

INDEPENDENT ACTIVITY

(*Math Journal 1,* p. 29)

Mixed Practice Math Boxes in this lesson are paired with Math Boxes in Lesson 2-3. The skills in Problems 5 and 6 preview Unit 3 content.

Writing/Reasoning Have students write a response to the following: *Look at Problem 5. About how many days longer can the giant tortoise live than the elephant?* 26,280 days *How many hours?* 630,720 hours *Explain what you did to find your answers.* Sample answer: There are about 365 days in a year, so 72 × 365 = 26,280 days. There are 24 hours in a day, so 26,280 × 24 = 630,720 hours.

▸ Study Link 2·1

INDEPENDENT ACTIVITY

(*Math Masters,* p. 39)

Home Connection Students begin to look for numbers for a Numbers and Their Uses Museum. They should continue to collect numbers throughout the unit and add them to the museum.

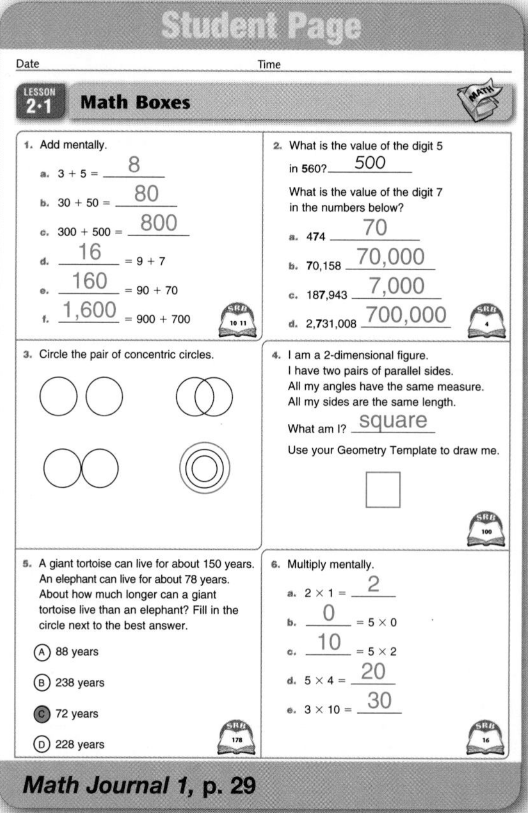

Student Page

Date Time

LESSON 2·1 **Math Boxes**

1. Add mentally.
 a. 3 + 5 = 8
 b. 30 + 50 = 80
 c. 300 + 500 = 800
 d. 16 = 9 + 7
 e. 160 = 90 + 70
 f. 1,600 = 900 + 700

2. What is the value of the digit 5 in 560? 500
 What is the value of the digit 7 in the numbers below?
 a. 474 70
 b. 70,158 70,000
 c. 187,943 7,000
 d. 2,731,008 700,000

3. Circle the pair of concentric circles.

4. I am a 2-dimensional figure.
 I have two pairs of parallel sides.
 All my angles have the same measure.
 All my sides are the same length.
 What am I? square
 Use your Geometry Template to draw me.

5. A giant tortoise can live for about 150 years. An elephant can live for about 78 years. About how much longer can a giant tortoise live than an elephant? Fill in the circle next to the best answer.
 (A) 88 years
 (B) 238 years
 (C) 72 years
 (D) 228 years

6. Multiply mentally.
 a. 2 × 1 = 2
 b. 0 = 5 × 0
 c. 10 = 5 × 2
 d. 5 × 4 = 20
 e. 3 × 10 = 30

Math Journal 1, p. 29

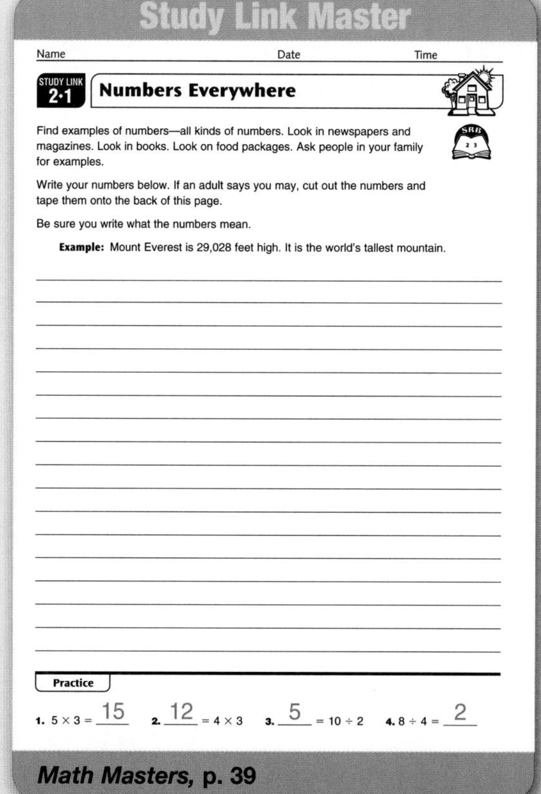

Study Link Master

Name Date Time

STUDY LINK 2·1 **Numbers Everywhere**

Find examples of numbers—all kinds of numbers. Look in newspapers and magazines. Look in books. Look on food packages. Ask people in your family for examples.

Write your numbers below. If an adult says you may, cut out the numbers and tape them onto the back of this page.

Be sure you write what the numbers mean.

Example: Mount Everest is 29,028 feet high. It is the world's tallest mountain.

Practice

1. 5 × 3 = 15
2. 12 = 4 × 3
3. 5 = 10 ÷ 2
4. 8 ÷ 4 = 2

Math Masters, p. 39

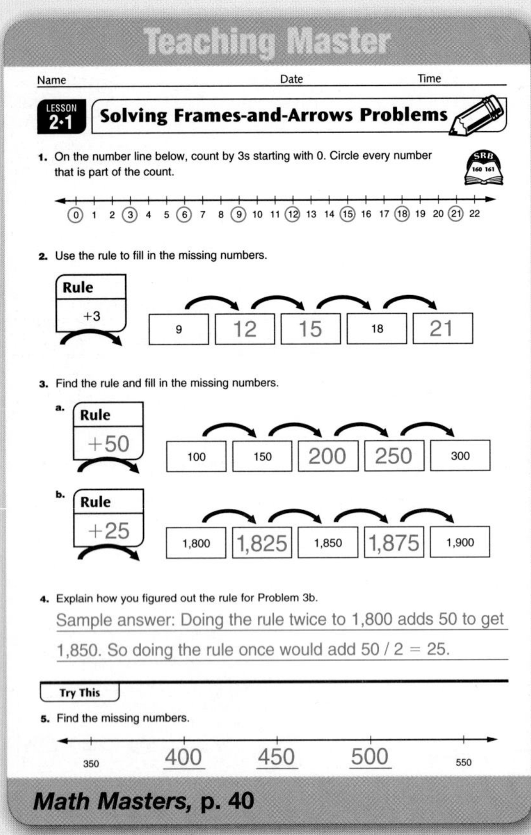
Teaching Master

Name Date Time

LESSON 2·1 **Solving Frames-and-Arrows Problems**

1. On the number line below, count by 3s starting with 0. Circle every number that is part of the count.

SRB 160 161

(0) 1 2 (3) 4 5 (6) 7 8 (9) 10 11 (12) 13 14 (15) 16 17 (18) 19 20 (21) 22

2. Use the rule to fill in the missing numbers.

Rule +3

9, 12, 15, 18, 21

3. Find the rule and fill in the missing numbers.

a. Rule +50

100, 150, 200, 250, 300

b. Rule +25

1,800, 1,825, 1,850, 1,875, 1,900

4. Explain how you figured out the rule for Problem 3b.

Sample answer: Doing the rule twice to 1,800 adds 50 to get 1,850. So doing the rule once would add 50 / 2 = 25.

Try This

5. Find the missing numbers.

350, 400, 450, 500, 550

Math Masters, p. 40

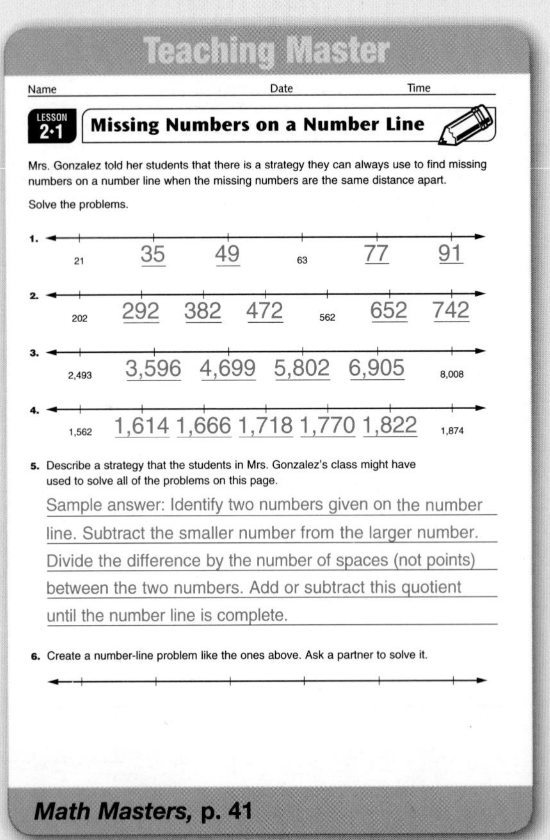
Teaching Master

Name Date Time

LESSON 2·1 **Missing Numbers on a Number Line**

Mrs. Gonzalez told her students that there is a strategy they can always use to find missing numbers on a number line when the missing numbers are the same distance apart.

Solve the problems.

1. 21, 35, 49, 63, 77, 91
2. 202, 292, 382, 472, 562, 652, 742
3. 2,493, 3,596, 4,699, 5,802, 6,905, 8,008
4. 1,562, 1,614, 1,666, 1,718, 1,770, 1,822, 1,874
5. Describe a strategy that the students in Mrs. Gonzalez's class might have used to solve all of the problems on this page.

Sample answer: Identify two numbers given on the number line. Subtract the smaller number from the larger number. Divide the difference by the number of spaces (not points) between the two numbers. Add or subtract this quotient until the number line is complete.

6. Create a number-line problem like the ones above. Ask a partner to solve it.

Math Masters, p. 41

3 Differentiation Options

READINESS

PARTNER ACTIVITY

▶ Solving Frames-and-Arrows Problems

5–15 Min

(*Math Masters,* p. 40)

To explore using rules to find linear intervals, have students solve a set of Frames-and-Arrows problems. Discuss how the problems are similar and different. Sample answers: All of the problems work with sequences of numbers. You can always find the missing numbers by applying the same rule over and over. Some problems are on number lines, and some are in other contexts. Have students share how they solved Problem 5.

ENRICHMENT

INDEPENDENT ACTIVITY

▶ Finding Missing Numbers

5–15 Min

(*Math Masters,* p. 41)

To apply students' understanding of using intervals to find missing numbers on a number line, have them solve number-line problems. Ask students to share their strategies.

EXTRA PRACTICE

INDEPENDENT ACTIVITY

▶ Solving Frames-and-Arrows Problems

5–15 Min

(*Math Masters,* p. 393)

To provide practice extending numerical patterns, have students complete Frames-and-Arrows problems. Use *Math Masters,* page 393 to create problems to meet the needs of individual students, or have students create and solve their own problems.

ELL SUPPORT

SMALL-GROUP DISCUSSION

▶ Sharing Country Information

5–15 Min

(*Math Journal 1,* pp. 172 and 173)

To provide language support for the World Tour, have students look at the world map on journal pages 172 and 173. Invite students who have lived in another country to share something about these countries. Have students locate each of these countries on the map in their journals.

Planning Ahead

Set aside space for a Numbers and Their Uses Museum.

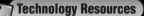

2·2 Many Names for Numbers

Objective To review equivalent names for whole numbers and name-collection boxes.

Technology Resources www.everydaymathonline.com

ePresentations

eToolkit

Algorithms Practice

EM Facts Workshop Game™

Family Letters

Assessment Management

Common Core State Standards

Curriculum Focal Points

Interactive Teacher's Lesson Guide

1 Teaching the Lesson

Key Concepts and Skills

- Give equivalent mathematical expressions for whole numbers.
  [Number and Numeration Goal 4]
- Use conventional notation to write expressions using the four basic arithmetic operations.
  [Patterns, Functions, and Algebra Goal 2]
- Insert grouping symbols to make number sentences true.
  [Patterns, Functions, and Algebra Goal 3]

Key Activities

Students use name-collection boxes to practice representing whole numbers in different ways.

Ongoing Assessment: Recognizing Student Achievement
Use journal page 30.
[Number and Numeration Goal 4]

Key Vocabulary

equivalent name ◆ name-collection box

Materials

Math Journal 1, p. 30
Study Link 2•1
Math Masters, p. 389
slate ◆ calculator (optional) ◆ index cards (optional)

2 Ongoing Learning & Practice

Playing *Name That Number*
Student Reference Book, p. 254
Math Masters, p. 489
deck of number cards (the Everything Math Deck, if available) ◆ index cards (optional)
Students practice representing numbers in different ways.

Math Boxes 2•2
Math Journal 1, p. 31
Students practice and maintain skills through Math Box problems.

Study Link 2•2
Math Masters, p. 42
Students practice and maintain skills through Study Link activities.

3 Differentiation Options

READINESS

Sorting Dominoes
Math Masters, pp. 43 and 394–396
1 each of number cards 0–18 (from the Everything Math Deck, if available) ◆ scissors
Students sort dominoes into collections according to the sums of the dominoes' dots.

ENRICHMENT

Solving Pan-Balance Problems
Math Masters, p. 44
Students investigate a pan-balance approach to find equivalent names for numbers.

EXTRA PRACTICE

Completing Name-Collection Boxes
Math Masters, p. 397
Students practice representing numbers in different ways.

EXTRA PRACTICE

5-Minute Math
5-Minute Math™, pp. 4–6
Students solve problems involving Roman numerals.

Advance Preparation

For Part 1, set aside space for a Numbers and Their Uses Museum. (See the Study Link 2•1 Follow-Up.)

***Teacher's Reference Manual,* Grades 4–6** pp. 16, 87, 88

Getting Started

Mental Math and Reflexes

Pose extended subtraction-fact problems. *Suggestions:*

●○○ 7 – 1 = 6
70 – 10 = 60
700 – 100 = 600

●●○ 14 – 7 = 7
140 – 70 = 70
1,400 – 700 = 700

●●● 170 – 80 = 90
1,700 – 800 = 900
17,000 – 8,000 = 9,000

Math Message

On an Exit Slip, write as many names as you can for the number 10.

Study Link 2·1 Follow-Up

Have students share examples of numbers they found. Ask them to record a few interesting numbers on index cards. Add the cards to your Numbers and Their Uses Museum. Encourage students to continue to collect and record additional interesting number facts for the display.

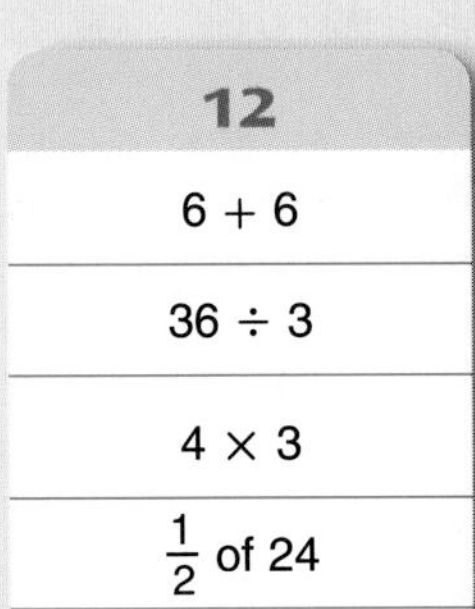

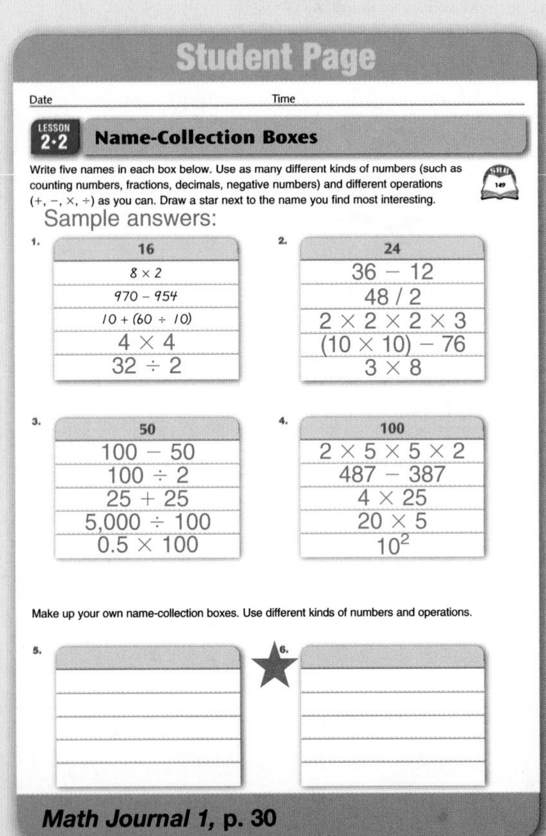

Student Page

Date Time

LESSON 2·2 **Name-Collection Boxes**

Write five names in each box below. Use as many different kinds of numbers (such as counting numbers, fractions, decimals, negative numbers) and different operations (+, –, ×, ÷) as you can. Draw a star next to the name you find most interesting.

Sample answers:

1.

16
8 × 2
970 – 954
10 + (60 ÷ 10)
4 × 4
32 ÷ 2

2.

24
36 – 12
48 / 2
2 × 2 × 2 × 3
(10 × 10) – 76
3 × 8

3.

50
100 – 50
100 ÷ 2
25 + 25
5,000 ÷ 100
0.5 × 100

4.

100
2 × 5 × 5 × 2
487 – 387
4 × 25
20 × 5
10^2

Make up your own name-collection boxes. Use different kinds of numbers and operations.

5.

6. ★

Math Journal 1, p. 30

1 Teaching the Lesson

▶ Math Message Follow-Up

Students share names for the number 10 as you record them on the board. For example: 3 + 7, 48 – 38, 2 × 5, 2 + 2 + 2 + 4, and 20 ÷ 2 are all names for the number 10. Have students indicate "thumbs-up" if they agree with each answer.

Introduce the term **equivalent names.** Names for the same number are called equivalent names. In this lesson students will use numbers and operations to generate equivalent names for whole numbers.

NOTE Equivalent names may be defined broadly to include all kinds of names, including names that do not use numbers and operations. For example, the words *dozen* and *doce,* the Roman numeral XII, 12 tally marks, and a 4-by-3 array of dots are all names for the number 12. Encourage students to look for other names that consist of numbers and operations. In mathematics, such names are called *mathematical expressions.*

▶ Reviewing the Idea that Numbers Have Many Names

(*Math Journal 1,* p. 30)

Draw a **name-collection box** for the number 12 on the board. (*See margin.*) Have students suggest operations (+, –, ×, ÷) and numbers (whole numbers, fractions, decimals, negative numbers) they might use when completing a name-collection box. Record their suggestions on the board.

Ask the class to make up names for 12 as you record them in the name-collection box. Encourage students to come up with unusual names. For example, some students might offer mathematical expressions that include multiple operations, parentheses, or exponents.

Adjusting the Activity

To focus on the goal of representing numbers in equivalent ways, have students use a calculator to help them complete the name-collection boxes.

AUDITORY ◆ KINESTHETIC ◆ TACTILE ◆ VISUAL

Give more examples if needed. Then have students work with a partner to complete Problems 1–5 on journal page 30. Ask students to complete Problem 6 independently.

Have students share their favorite answers from journal page 30. List some of them on the board, especially the most inventive.

Ongoing Assessment: Recognizing Student Achievement

Journal page 30 Problem 6

Use **journal page 30, Problem 6** to assess students' ability to give equivalent names for whole numbers. Students are making adequate progress if they are able to name the box and generate correct mathematical expressions involving one or more of the basic four arithmetic operations. Some students may give mathematical expressions involving grouping symbols or exponents.

[Number and Numeration Goal 4]

2 Ongoing Learning & Practice

Playing *Name That Number*

PARTNER ACTIVITY

(*Student Reference Book,* p. 254; *Math Masters,* p. 489)

Students play *Name That Number* to practice representing numbers in different ways. Consider having them record rounds of play on *Math Masters,* page 489.

Adjusting the Activity

Suggest that students write the operation symbols (+, −, ×, and ÷) and parentheses symbols on separate index cards. Then they can arrange the numbers, operations cards, and parentheses cards in various ways to help them find solutions.

AUDITORY ◆ KINESTHETIC ◆ TACTILE ◆ VISUAL

Student Page

Games

Name That Number

Materials □ 1 complete deck of number cards

Players 2 or 3

Skill Naming numbers with expressions

Object of the game To collect the most cards.

Directions

1. Shuffle the cards and deal 5 cards to each player. Place the remaining cards number-side down on the table between the players. Turn over the top card and place it beside the deck. This is the **target number** for the round.
2. Players try to match the target number by adding, subtracting, multiplying, or dividing the numbers on as many of their cards as possible. A card may only be used once.
3. Players write their solutions on a sheet of paper. When players have written their best solutions:
   - Each player sets aside the cards they used to match the target number.
   - Each player replaces the cards they set aside by drawing new cards from the top of the deck.
   - The old target number is placed on the bottom of the deck.
   - A new target number is turned over, and another round is played.
4. Play continues until there are not enough cards left to replace all of the players' cards. The player who has set aside the most cards wins the game.

Example Target number: 16

Player 1's cards:

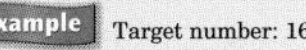

Some possible solutions:

10 + 8 − 2 = 16 (3 cards used)

7 ∗ 2 + 10 − 8 = 16 (4 cards used)

8 / 2 + 10 + 7 − 5 = 16 (all 5 cards used)

The player sets aside the cards used to make a solution and draws the same number of cards from the top of the deck.

***Student Reference Book,* p. 254**

Links to the Future

Lesson 3-10 of *Fourth Grade Everyday Mathematics* reviews the use of parentheses in number sentences. Until students are able to insert parentheses into their recorded solutions for *Name That Number*, have them write each calculation separately. Without parentheses, students may record number sentences that do not follow the order of operations. Describing and applying the order of operations is a Grade 6 Goal.

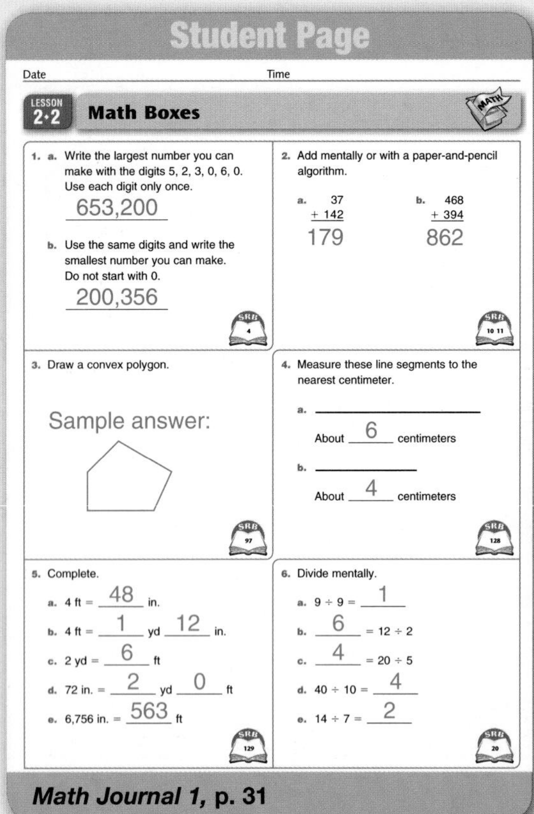
Student Page

Date Time

LESSON 2·2 **Math Boxes**

1. a. Write the largest number you can make with the digits 5, 2, 3, 0, 6, 0. Use each digit only once.
   653,200
   b. Use the same digits and write the smallest number you can make. Do not start with 0.
   200,356

2. Add mentally or with a paper-and-pencil algorithm.
   a. 37 + 142 = 179
   b. 468 + 394 = 862

3. Draw a convex polygon.
   Sample answer:

4. Measure these line segments to the nearest centimeter.
   a. About 6 centimeters
   b. About 4 centimeters

5. Complete.
   a. 4 ft = 48 in.
   b. 4 ft = 1 yd 12 in.
   c. 2 yd = 6 ft
   d. 72 in. = 2 yd 0 ft
   e. 6,756 in. = 563 ft

6. Divide mentally.
   a. 9 ÷ 9 = 1
   b. 6 = 12 ÷ 2
   c. 4 = 20 ÷ 5
   d. 40 ÷ 10 = 4
   e. 14 ÷ 7 = 2

Math Journal 1, p. 31

▶ Math Boxes 2·2

INDEPENDENT ACTIVITY

(*Math Journal 1*, p. 31)

Mixed Practice Math Boxes in this lesson are paired with Math Boxes in Lesson 2-4. The skill in Problem 6 previews Unit 3 content.

Writing/Reasoning Have students write a response to the following: *Explain how you know that the polygon you drew in Problem 3 is convex and not concave.* Sample answer: All of the vertices are "pushed out."

▶ Study Link 2·2

INDEPENDENT ACTIVITY

(*Math Masters*, p. 42)

Home Connection Students complete name-collection boxes and solve broken-calculator problems.

3 Differentiation Options

READINESS

▶ Sorting Dominoes

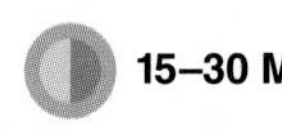

SMALL-GROUP ACTIVITY

15–30 Min

(*Math Masters*, pp. 43 and 394–396)

To explore equivalent names for whole numbers using manipulatives, have students sort dominoes according to sums. Ask each group to make a list of all the addition facts shown by the dominoes.

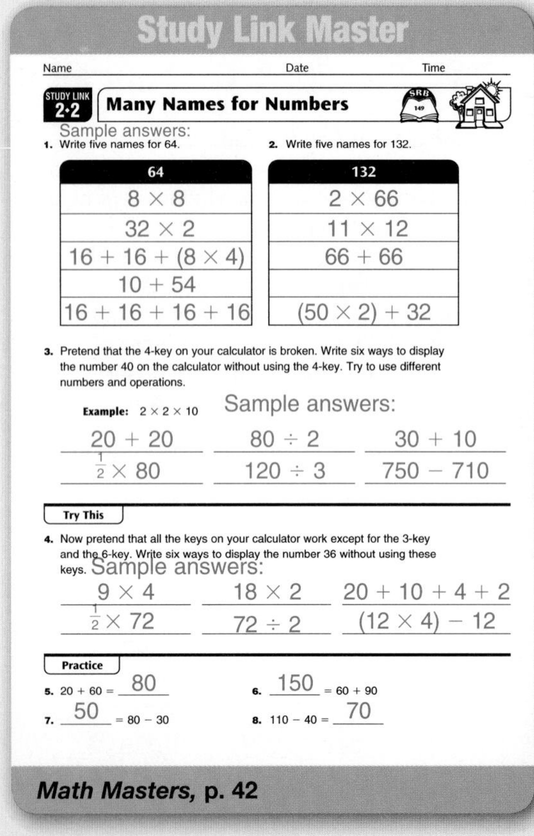
Study Link Master

Name Date Time

STUDY LINK 2·2 **Many Names for Numbers**

Sample answers:

1. Write five names for 64.

64
8 × 8
32 × 2
16 + 16 + (8 × 4)
10 + 54
16 + 16 + 16 + 16

2. Write five names for 132.

132
2 × 66
11 × 12
66 + 66
(50 × 2) + 32

3. Pretend that the 4-key on your calculator is broken. Write six ways to display the number 40 on the calculator without using the 4-key. Try to use different numbers and operations.

   Example: 2 × 2 × 10 Sample answers:
   20 + 20 80 ÷ 2 30 + 10
   $\frac{1}{2}$ × 80 120 ÷ 3 750 − 710

Try This

4. Now pretend that all the keys on your calculator work except for the 3-key and the 6-key. Write six ways to display the number 36 without using these keys. Sample answers:
   9 × 4 18 × 2 20 + 10 + 4 + 2
   $\frac{1}{2}$ × 72 72 ÷ 2 (12 × 4) − 12

Practice

5. 20 + 60 = 80
6. 150 = 60 + 90
7. 50 = 80 − 30
8. 110 − 40 = 70

Math Masters, p. 42

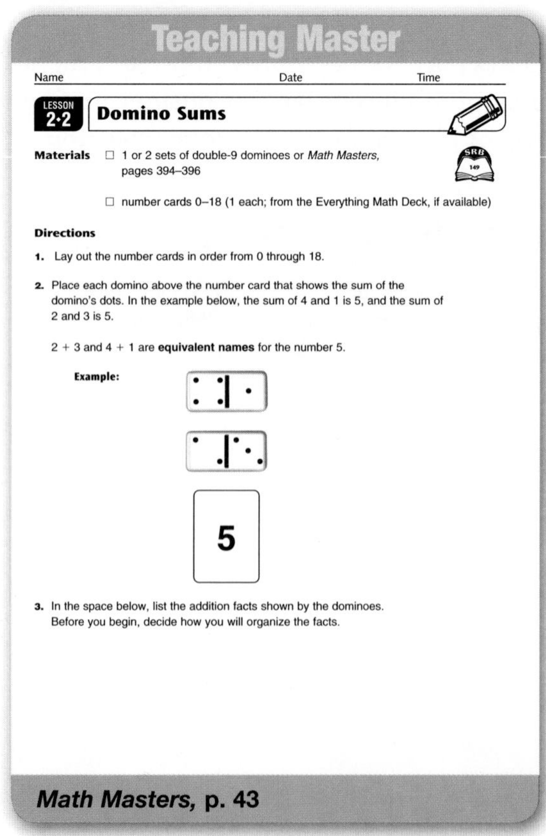
Teaching Master

Name Date Time

LESSON 2·2 **Domino Sums**

Materials □ 1 or 2 sets of double-9 dominoes or *Math Masters*, pages 394–396
□ number cards 0–18 (1 each; from the Everything Math Deck, if available)

Directions

1. Lay out the number cards in order from 0 through 18.
2. Place each domino above the number card that shows the sum of the domino's dots. In the example below, the sum of 4 and 1 is 5, and the sum of 2 and 3 is 5.

   2 + 3 and 4 + 1 are **equivalent names** for the number 5.

   Example:

   5

3. In the space below, list the addition facts shown by the dominoes. Before you begin, decide how you will organize the facts.

Math Masters, p. 43

ENRICHMENT

PARTNER ACTIVITY

Solving Pan-Balance Problems

15–30 Min

(*Math Masters,* p. 44)

To apply students' understanding of equivalent names for whole numbers, have them solve pan-balance problems. Ask students to describe the pan-balance problems and explain their solution strategies.

EXTRA PRACTICE

INDEPENDENT ACTIVITY

Completing Name-Collection Boxes

5–15 Min

(*Math Masters,* p. 397)

To provide practice representing numbers in different ways, have students complete name-collection boxes. Use *Math Masters,* page 397 to create problems to meet the needs of individual students, or have students create and solve their own problems.

EXTRA PRACTICE

SMALL-GROUP ACTIVITY

5-Minute Math

5–15 Min

To offer students more experience with Roman numerals, see *5-Minute Math,* pages 4–6.

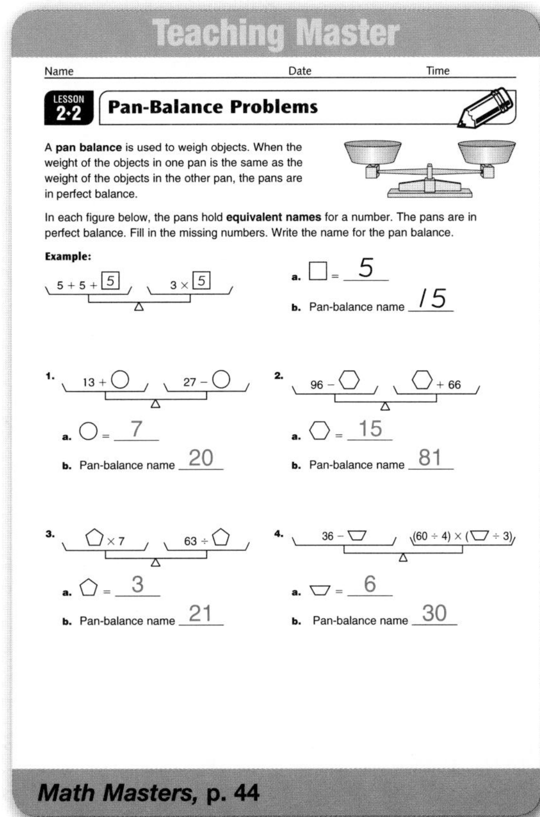

Teaching Master

Name Date Time

LESSON 2·2 **Pan-Balance Problems**

A **pan balance** is used to weigh objects. When the weight of the objects in one pan is the same as the weight of the objects in the other pan, the pans are in perfect balance.

In each figure below, the pans hold **equivalent names** for a number. The pans are in perfect balance. Fill in the missing numbers. Write the name for the pan balance.

Example: 5 + 5 + [5] | 3 × [5]

a. □ = 5

b. Pan-balance name 15

1. 13 + ○ | 27 − ○

a. ○ = 7

b. Pan-balance name 20

2. 96 − ⬡ | ⬡ + 66

a. ⬡ = 15

b. Pan-balance name 81

3. ⬠ × 7 | 63 ÷ ⬠

a. ⬠ = 3

b. Pan-balance name 21

4. 36 − ▽ | (60 ÷ 4) × (▽ ÷ 3)

a. ▽ = 6

b. Pan-balance name 30

Math Masters, p. 44

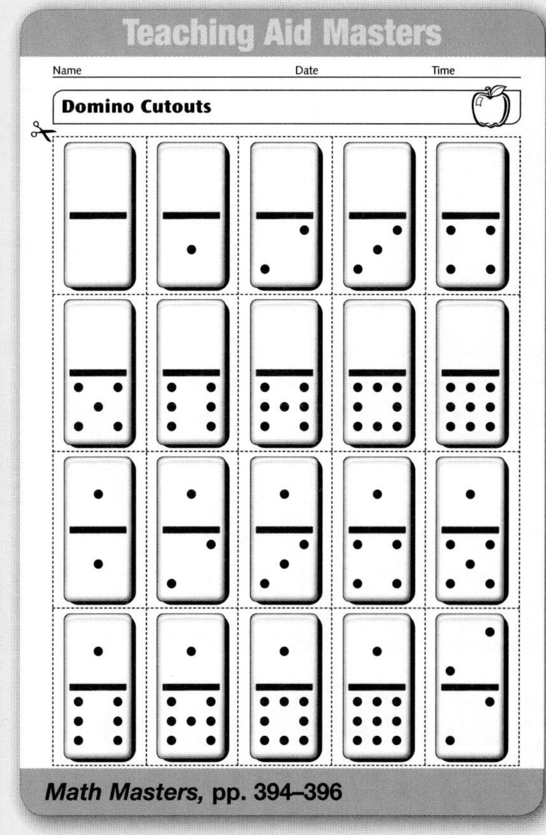

Teaching Aid Masters

Name Date Time

Domino Cutouts

Math Masters, pp. 394–396

Math Masters, pages 394–396 are domino cutouts.

Teaching Aid Master

Name Date Time

Name-Collection Boxes

Name

Date

Name

Date

Name

Date

Name

Date

Math Masters, p. 397

2·3 Place Value in Whole Numbers

Objectives To provide practice identifying values of digits in numbers up to one billion; and to provide practice reading and writing numbers up to one billion.

Technology Resources www.everydaymathonline.com

ePresentations

eToolkit

Algorithms Practice

EM Facts Workshop Game™

Family Letters

Assessment Management

Common Core State Standards

Curriculum Focal Points

Interactive Teacher's Lesson Guide

1 Teaching the Lesson

Key Concepts and Skills

- Read and write numbers up to 1,000,000,000; identify the values of digits.
  [Number and Numeration Goal 1]
- Write numbers in expanded notation.
  [Number and Numeration Goal 4]
- Find the sum of numbers written in expanded notation.
  [Operations and Computation Goal 2]
- Use and describe patterns to find sums.
  [Patterns, Functions, and Algebra Goal 1]

Key Activities

Students review basic place-value concepts for whole numbers. They express whole numbers as sums of ones, tens, hundreds, and so on, and observe the relationship between such sums and the way numbers are read.

Ongoing Assessment: Informing Instruction See page 97.

Ongoing Assessment: Recognizing Student Achievement Use journal page 33.
[Number and Numeration Goal 1]

Key Vocabulary

counting number ◆ whole number ◆ digit ◆ place ◆ expanded notation

Materials

Math Journal 1, pp. 32 and 33
Student Reference Book, p. 4
Study Link 2•2
transparency of *Math Masters,* p. 398 (optional) ◆ calculator ◆ slate

2 Ongoing Learning & Practice

Identifying Polygon Properties

Math Journal 1, p. 34
Students identify properties of polygons.

Math Boxes 2•3

Math Journal 1, p. 35
Students practice and maintain skills through Math Box problems.

Study Link 2•3

Math Masters, p. 45
Students practice and maintain skills through Study Link activities.

3 Differentiation Options

ENRICHMENT

Solving Number-Grid Puzzles

Math Masters, p. 46
Students apply their understanding of the base-ten place-value system to solve number-grid puzzles.

EXTRA PRACTICE

5-Minute Math

5-Minute Math™, pp. 12 and 18
Students practice place-value skills.

ELL SUPPORT

Building a Math Word Bank

Differentiation Handbook, p. 140
Students add the terms *counting numbers* and *whole numbers* to their Math Word Banks.

Advance Preparation

For Part 1, make an overhead transparency of *Math Masters,* page 398, or copy the place-value chart on the board.

***Teacher's Reference Manual,* Grades 4–6** pp. 59, 60, 259, 260

Getting Started

Mental Math and Reflexes

Have students skip count by 10s, 100s, 1,000s, and 10,000s on their calculators, counting both up and down starting with different numbers. For example, ask students to count up by 10s beginning with 40 and to count down by 10s beginning with 293.

Pay special attention to transitions. For example, point out what happens when you go from 95 to 105 or from 203 to 193.

Math Message

Write the largest number you can using the digits 0, 3, 9, and 7. Use each digit only once.

Study Link 2·2 Follow-Up

Ask students to draw a star next to their most inventive solutions to the broken-calculator problems and share them with a partner.

1 Teaching the Lesson

Math Message Follow-Up

WHOLE-CLASS ACTIVITY

Have partners compare answers. 9,730 Ask students to respond to the following questions on their slates:

- Which digit is in the ones place? 0
- Which digit is in the tens place? 3 How much is that digit worth? 30
- How much is the digit 7 worth? 700
- What is the smallest whole number you can write using the digits 9, 7, 3, and 0? Do not use 0 in the thousands place. 3,079

Tell students that in this lesson they will look at the digits and the values of digits in numbers through hundred-millions.

Reviewing Place Value for Whole Numbers

WHOLE-CLASS ACTIVITY

ELL

(*Math Journal 1,* p. 32; *Math Masters,* p. 398)

Ask someone to describe the **counting numbers.** The numbers 1, 2, 3, and so on Remind students that zero is usually not considered a counting number. Explain that all of the counting numbers as well as the number zero are called **whole numbers;** that is, the whole numbers are the numbers 0, 1, 2, 3, and so on.

- Is every counting number also a whole number? yes

Adjusting the Activity

Have students use the digits 9, 7, 3, and 0 to write decimal numbers less than one. Remind them to use zero in the ones place. 0.379; 0.397; 0.739; 0.793; 0.937; 0.973 Ask students to identify the value of each digit.

AUDITORY ◆ KINESTHETIC ◆ TACTILE ◆ VISUAL

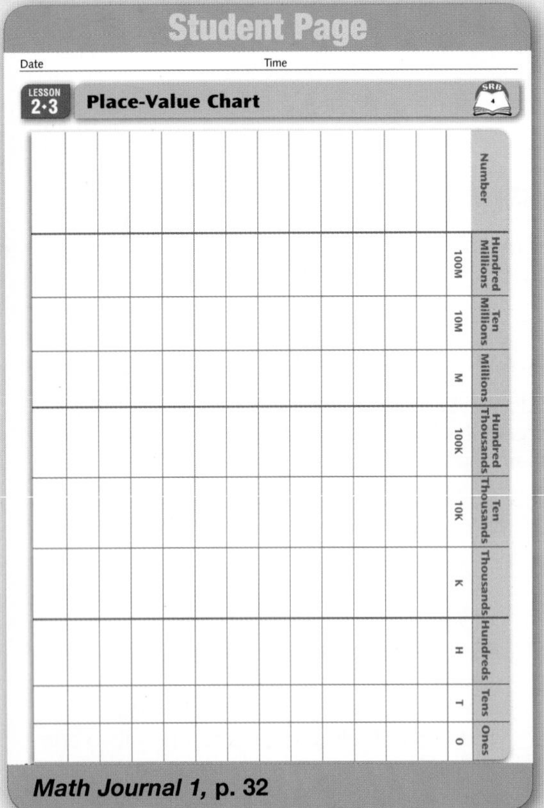

Math Masters, page 398 is identical to journal page 32.

Remind students that any number in our base-ten numeration system can be written by using one or more of the **digits** 0, 1, 2, 3, 4, 5, 6, 7, 8, and 9. What makes this possible is that digits take on different values, depending on their positions or **places** in a number.

To support English language learners, discuss the different meanings of the homonyms *whole* and *hole.* Discuss the everyday and mathematical uses of the word *place.*

Display the place-value chart (*Math Masters,* page 398) on the overhead projector or draw it on the board, and write the numbers as shown below.

Number	Hundred Thousands	Ten Thousands	Thousands	Hundreds	Tens	Ones
	100K	10K	K	H	T	O
2						2
20					2	0
200				2	0	0
2,000			2	0	0	0
20,000		2	0	0	0	0
200,000	2	0	0	0	0	0

To support English language learners, explain the meaning of the symbols. For example, *100K* means *one hundred-thousand.* The symbol *K* for *thousand* is derived from the prefix *kilo-,* as in *kilometer* in the metric system. The symbol *M* for *million* is derived from the prefix *mega-*. Continue to use the full name of a place in oral work.

Remind students that the value of a digit in a numeral depends on its position in the place-value chart. *For example:*

▷ A 2 in the ones column stands for 2 ones. It is worth 2.

▷ A 2 in the tens column stands for 2 tens. It is worth 20.

▷ A 2 in the hundreds column stands for 2 hundreds. It is worth 200 (and so on).

When you get to the hundred-thousands place, ask students to name the three places to the left. Millions, ten-millions, and hundred-millions

Point out that each number in the table is 10 times the number in the line before it. You can illustrate this relationship using both multiplication and division. For example, $2{,}000 \times 10 = 20{,}000$ and $200 \div 20 = 10$.

Write a number such as 5,607,481 in the place-value chart. Have students write this number in the place-value chart on page 32 in their journals. Ask questions such as the following:

- How do you say this number? Five million, six hundred seven thousand, four hundred eighty-one
- What is the value of the digit 6? 6 hundred thousand
- What is the value of the digit in the millions place? 5 million

Write additional numbers such as the following in the place-value chart, and pose questions similar to the ones above:

763	902,352	614,729,351
941	771,964	823,457,019
5,872	2,371,145	550,291,370

Adjusting the Activity

ELL

Remind students that numbers are divided into groups of digits separated by commas. Each group of digits is read as though it is a separate number; then the name of the group is read (with the exception of the ones group). Illustrate this with a diagram like the one below.

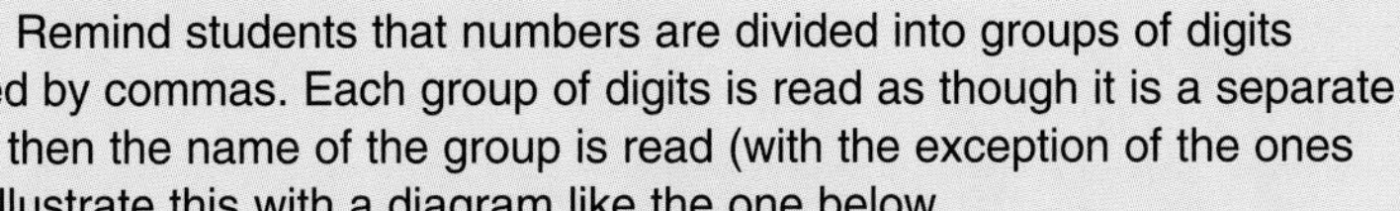

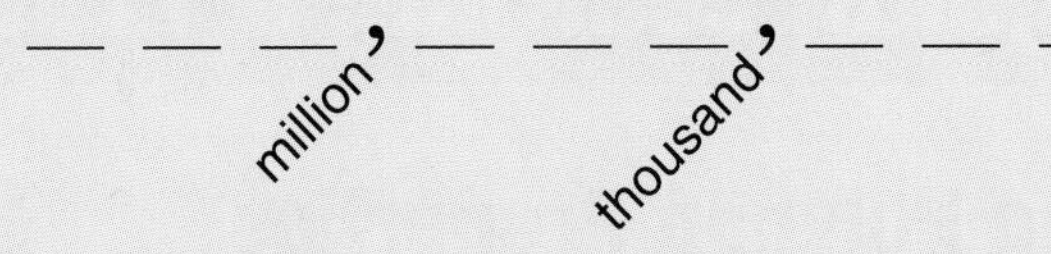

AUDITORY • KINESTHETIC • TACTILE • VISUAL

Ongoing Assessment: Informing Instruction

Watch for students who insert the word *and* when reading a whole number. A number such as 4,009 should be read as "four thousand nine," not "four thousand *and* nine." Proper use of the word *and* is especially important in reading decimals.

Writing Numbers as Sums of Ones, Tens, and Hundreds

WHOLE-CLASS ACTIVITY

(*Student Reference Book,* p. 4)

Write a number, such as 853, on the board. Ask what each digit in the number is worth, and record the values as a vertical sum. For 853, you would write:

853	8 is worth 800	800
	5 is worth 50	50
	3 is worth 3	+ 3
		853

Recording numbers in this way is an example of **expanded notation.** Repeat this process using up to six digits in a number if students are ready. Then write vertical sums, such as those shown in the margin, and ask students to add them mentally.

Students will discover the pattern that the sum is the number obtained by reading the individual addends from largest to smallest. For example, 700 + 60 + 5 equals seven hundred sixty-five, or 765. See *Student Reference Book,* page 4 for another example of expanded notation.

NOTE There are various ways to write a number in expanded notation. For example, 853 may be written as $8 * 100 + 5 * 10 + 3 * 1$ or as 8[100s] + 5[10s] + 3[1s].

$$\begin{array}{r} 700 \\ 60 \\ +\ \ 5 \\ \hline 765 \end{array} \qquad \begin{array}{r} 4{,}000 \\ 600 \\ 90 \\ +\ \ 2 \\ \hline 4{,}692 \end{array}$$

$$\begin{array}{r} 50{,}000 \\ 300 \\ +\ \ 10 \\ \hline 50{,}310 \end{array} \qquad \begin{array}{r} 200{,}000 \\ 50{,}000 \\ 8{,}000 \\ +\ \ 20 \\ \hline 258{,}020 \end{array}$$

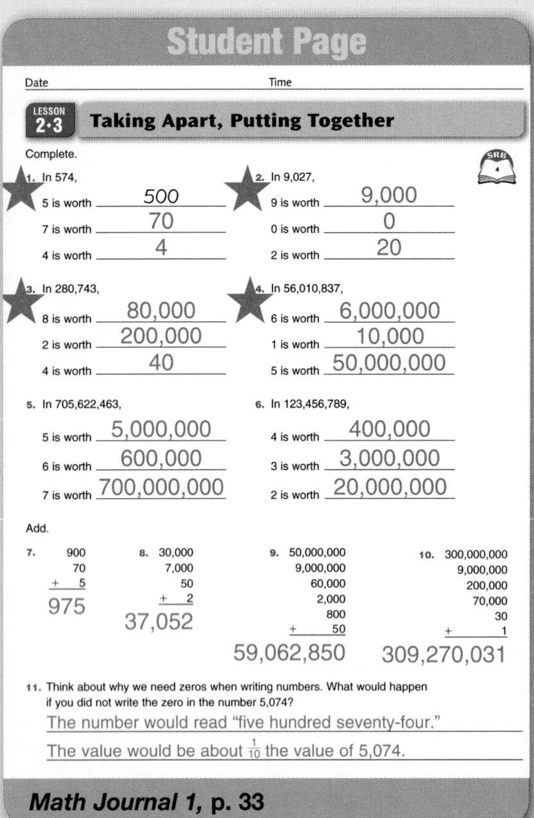

Student Page

Date ______ Time ______

LESSON 2·3 **Taking Apart, Putting Together**

Complete.

1. In 574,
   5 is worth 500
   7 is worth 70
   4 is worth 4
2. In 9,027,
   9 is worth 9,000
   0 is worth 0
   2 is worth 20
3. In 280,743,
   8 is worth 80,000
   2 is worth 200,000
   4 is worth 40
4. In 56,010,837,
   6 is worth 6,000,000
   1 is worth 10,000
   5 is worth 50,000,000
5. In 705,622,463,
   5 is worth 5,000,000
   6 is worth 600,000
   7 is worth 700,000,000
6. In 123,456,789,
   4 is worth 400,000
   3 is worth 3,000,000
   2 is worth 20,000,000

Add.

7. 900 + 70 + 5 = 975
8. 30,000 + 7,000 + 50 + 2 = 37,052
9. 50,000,000 + 9,000,000 + 60,000 + 2,000 + 800 + 50 = 59,062,850
10. 300,000,000 + 9,000,000 + 200,000 + 70,000 + 30 + 1 = 309,270,031

11. Think about why we need zeros when writing numbers. What would happen if you did not write the zero in the number 5,074?
    The number would read "five hundred seventy-four."
    The value would be about $\frac{1}{10}$ the value of 5,074.

Math Journal 1, p. 33

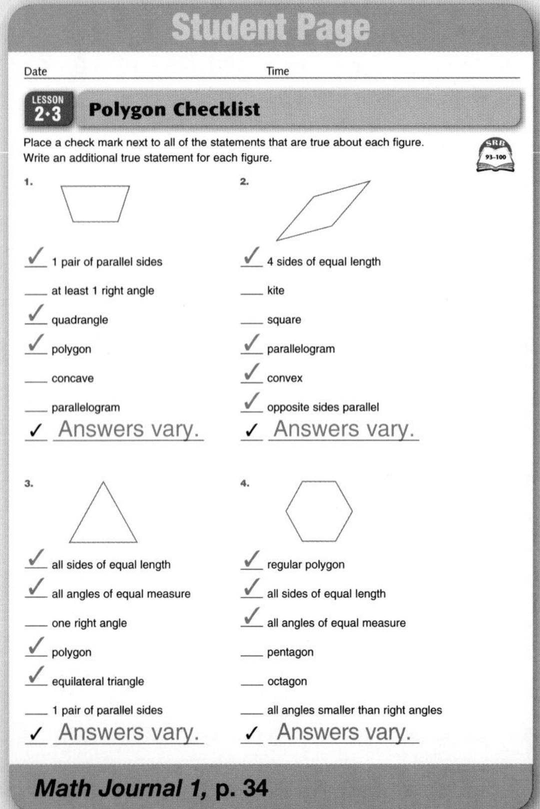

Student Page

Date ______ Time ______

LESSON 2·3 **Polygon Checklist**

Place a check mark next to all of the statements that are true about each figure. Write an additional true statement for each figure.

1.
- ✓ 1 pair of parallel sides
- ___ at least 1 right angle
- ✓ quadrangle
- ✓ polygon
- ___ concave
- ___ parallelogram
- ✓ Answers vary.

2.
- ✓ 4 sides of equal length
- ___ kite
- ___ square
- ✓ parallelogram
- ✓ convex
- ✓ opposite sides parallel
- ✓ Answers vary.

3.
- ✓ all sides of equal length
- ✓ all angles of equal measure
- ___ one right angle
- ✓ polygon
- ✓ equilateral triangle
- ___ 1 pair of parallel sides
- ✓ Answers vary.

4.
- ✓ regular polygon
- ✓ all sides of equal length
- ✓ all angles of equal measure
- ___ pentagon
- ___ octagon
- ___ all angles smaller than right angles
- ✓ Answers vary.

Math Journal 1, p. 34

▶ Expressing Values of Digits

(*Math Journal 1*, p. 33)

Ask students to complete Problems 1–4 independently before completing the rest of journal page 33 with a partner. Have them share their responses to Problem 11.

Ongoing Assessment: Recognizing Student Achievement

Journal page 33 Problems 1–4

Use **journal page 33, Problems 1–4** to assess students' ability to identify the values of digits in whole numbers. Students are making adequate progress if they correctly identify the values of digits through hundred-thousands. Some students may be able to identify the values of digits in whole numbers up to 1,000,000,000.

[Number and Numeration Goal 1]

2 Ongoing Learning & Practice

▶ Identifying Polygon Properties

(*Math Journal 1*, p. 34)

Students check all statements that apply to a given polygon and write an additional true statement for each. Ask students to explain why they did not check some of the statements.

▶ Math Boxes 2·3

(*Math Journal 1*, p. 35)

Mixed Practice Math Boxes in this lesson are paired with Math Boxes in Lesson 2-1. The skills in Problems 5 and 6 preview Unit 3 content.

Writing/Reasoning Have students write a response to the following: *Explain how you know that the circles you drew for Problem 3 are concentric.* Sample answer: The circles have the same center but different radii.

▶ Study Link 2·3

(*Math Masters*, p. 45)

Home Connection Students review place-value skills. They use place value to compare numbers and to transform given numbers by changing a single digit.

3 Differentiation Options

ENRICHMENT

INDEPENDENT ACTIVITY

Solving Number-Grid Puzzles

5–15 Min

(*Math Masters,* p. 46)

To apply students' understanding of the base-ten place-value system, have them solve number-grid puzzles. Ask students to share patterns and compare features of the grid puzzle pieces.

EXTRA PRACTICE

SMALL-GROUP ACTIVITY

5-Minute Math

5–15 Min

To offer students more experience with place value, see *5-Minute Math,* pages 12 and 18.

ELL SUPPORT

SMALL-GROUP ACTIVITY

Building a Math Word Bank

5–15 Min

(*Differentiation Handbook,* p. 140)

To provide language support for numbers, have students use the Word Bank Template found on *Differentiation Handbook,* page 140. Ask students to write the terms *counting numbers* and *whole numbers,* draw pictures representing the terms, and write other related words that describe them. See the *Differentiation Handbook* for more information.

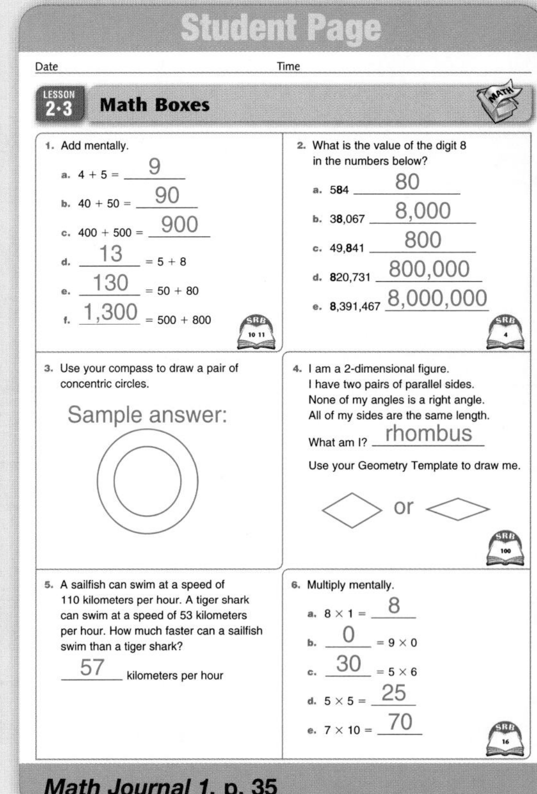

Student Page

Date Time

LESSON 2·3 **Math Boxes**

1. Add mentally.
   a. 4 + 5 = 9
   b. 40 + 50 = 90
   c. 400 + 500 = 900
   d. 13 = 5 + 8
   e. 130 = 50 + 80
   f. 1,300 = 500 + 800

2. What is the value of the digit 8 in the numbers below?
   a. 584 80
   b. 38,067 8,000
   c. 49,841 800
   d. 820,731 800,000
   e. 8,391,467 8,000,000

3. Use your compass to draw a pair of concentric circles.
   Sample answer:

4. I am a 2-dimensional figure. I have two pairs of parallel sides. None of my angles is a right angle. All of my sides are the same length.
   What am I? rhombus
   Use your Geometry Template to draw me.
   or

5. A sailfish can swim at a speed of 110 kilometers per hour. A tiger shark can swim at a speed of 53 kilometers per hour. How much faster can a sailfish swim than a tiger shark?
   57 kilometers per hour

6. Multiply mentally.
   a. 8 × 1 = 8
   b. 0 = 9 × 0
   c. 30 = 5 × 6
   d. 5 × 5 = 25
   e. 7 × 10 = 70

Math Journal 1, p. 35

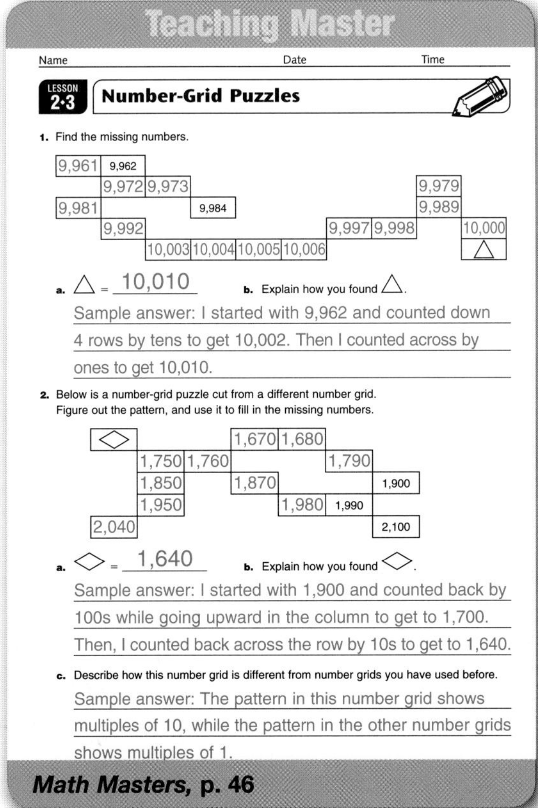

Teaching Master

Name Date Time

LESSON 2·3 **Number-Grid Puzzles**

1. Find the missing numbers.

9,961 9,962 9,972 9,973 9,979 9,981 9,984 9,989 9,992 9,997 9,998 10,000 10,003 10,004 10,005 10,006

a. △ = 10,010
b. Explain how you found △.
Sample answer: I started with 9,962 and counted down 4 rows by tens to get 10,002. Then I counted across by ones to get 10,010.

2. Below is a number-grid puzzle cut from a different number grid. Figure out the pattern, and use it to fill in the missing numbers.

1,670 1,680 1,750 1,760 1,790 1,850 1,870 1,900 1,950 1,980 1,990 2,040 2,100

a. ◇ = 1,640
b. Explain how you found ◇.
Sample answer: I started with 1,900 and counted back by 100s while going upward in the column to get to 1,700. Then, I counted back across the row by 10s to get to 1,640.

c. Describe how this number grid is different from number grids you have used before.
Sample answer: The pattern in this number grid shows multiples of 10, while the pattern in the other number grids shows multiples of 1.

Math Masters, p. 46

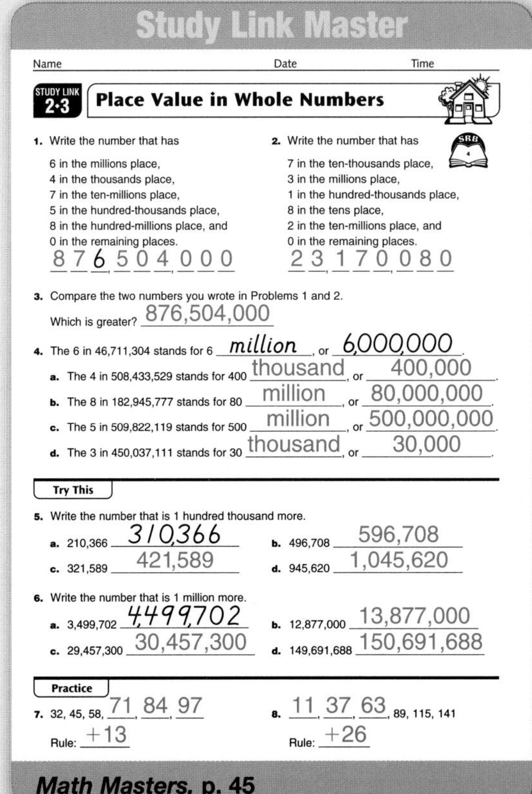

Study Link Master

Name Date Time

STUDY LINK 2·3 **Place Value in Whole Numbers**

1. Write the number that has
   6 in the millions place,
   4 in the thousands place,
   7 in the ten-millions place,
   5 in the hundred-thousands place,
   8 in the hundred-millions place, and
   0 in the remaining places.
   8 7 6, 5 0 4, 0 0 0

2. Write the number that has
   7 in the ten-thousands place,
   3 in the millions place,
   1 in the hundred-thousands place,
   8 in the tens place,
   2 in the ten-millions place, and
   0 in the remaining places.
   2 3, 1 7 0, 0 8 0

3. Compare the two numbers you wrote in Problems 1 and 2.
   Which is greater? 876,504,000

4. The 6 in 46,711,304 stands for 6 million, or 6,000,000.
   a. The 4 in 508,433,529 stands for 400 thousand, or 400,000.
   b. The 8 in 182,945,777 stands for 80 million, or 80,000,000.
   c. The 5 in 509,822,119 stands for 500 million, or 500,000,000.
   d. The 3 in 450,037,111 stands for 30 thousand, or 30,000.

Try This

5. Write the number that is 1 hundred thousand more.
   a. 210,366 310,366
   b. 496,708 596,708
   c. 321,589 421,589
   d. 945,620 1,045,620

6. Write the number that is 1 million more.
   a. 3,499,702 4,499,702
   b. 12,877,000 13,877,000
   c. 29,457,300 30,457,300
   d. 149,691,688 150,691,688

Practice

7. 32, 45, 58, 71, 84, 97
   Rule: +13

8. 11, 37, 63, 89, 115, 141
   Rule: +26

Math Masters, p. 45

2•4 Place Value with a Calculator

Objectives To provide practice with place-value skills using a calculator routine; and to review reading and writing large numbers.

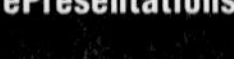
Technology Resources www.everydaymathonline.com

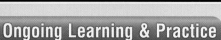

ePresentations

eToolkit

Algorithms Practice

EM Facts Workshop Game™

Family Letters

Assessment Management

Common Core State Standards

Curriculum Focal Points

Interactive Teacher's Lesson Guide

1 Teaching the Lesson

Key Concepts and Skills

- Read and write large numbers. [Number and Numeration Goal 1]
- Identify places in whole numbers and the values of the digits in those places. [Number and Numeration Goal 1]
- Add and subtract multidigit whole numbers. [Operations and Computation Goal 2]
- Solve open sentences. [Patterns, Functions, and Algebra Goal 2]

Key Activities

Students enter a number in their calculators and then change one or more digits in the display by adding or subtracting one or more numbers.

Ongoing Assessment: Recognizing Student Achievement
Use a Math Log or Exit Slip (*Math Masters,* page 388 or 389).
[Number and Numeration Goal 1]

Materials

Math Journal 1, p. 36
Study Link 2•3
Math Masters, p. 388 or 389 (optional)
transparency of *Math Masters,* p. 47 (optional) ◆ calculator ◆ slate

2 Ongoing Learning & Practice

Playing *Fishing for Digits*
Student Reference Book, p. 242
Math Masters, p. 472 (optional)
calculator ◆ overhead calculator (optional)
Students identify digits in whole numbers and express their values.

Math Boxes 2•4
Math Journal 1, p. 37
Students practice and maintain skills through Math Box problems.

Study Link 2•4
Math Masters, p. 48
Students practice and maintain skills through Study Link activities.

3 Differentiation Options

READINESS

Using a Place-Value Tool
Math Masters, pp. 49 and 399–402
scissors ◆ stapler
Students find numbers that are 10 more or less, 100 more or less, or 1,000 more or less than a given number.

ENRICHMENT

Deciphering a Place-Value Code
Math Masters, p. 50
Students apply their understanding of place value to break a code.

Advance Preparation

For the optional Readiness activity in Part 3, decide whether you will prepare Compact Place-Value Flip Books (*Math Masters,* pp. 399–402) ahead of time or have students make them.

***Teacher's Reference Manual,* Grades 4–6** pp. 29–35

Getting Started

Mental Math and Reflexes

Students display a number on their calculators for their partners to read. They also take turns dictating numbers for their partners to display on their calculators.

Math Message

(Write 56,385 and 7,490,613 on the board.)

Be prepared to read the numbers aloud.

Study Link 2·3 Follow-Up

Have partners compare answers. Ask students to draw a star next to any problems they wish to discuss with the whole class.

1 Teaching the Lesson

▶ Math Message Follow-Up

WHOLE-CLASS ACTIVITY

Have pairs of students read the numbers to each other. Then ask someone to read the number 56,385 aloud. Students indicate thumbs-up if they agree with the reading.

Ask students to respond to the following questions on their slates and refer to a place-value chart if necessary.

- Which digit is in the tens place? 8 How much is that digit worth? 80
- Which digit is in the hundreds place? 3 How much is that digit worth? 300
- Which digit is in the ones place? 5 How much is that digit worth? 5

Ask someone to read 7,490,613 to the class and pose questions similar to the ones above.

- Which digit is in the ten-thousands place? 9 How much is that digit worth? 90,000
- Which digit is in the millions place? 7 How much is that digit worth? 7,000,000
- Which digit is worth 200 times as much as the 3 in the ones place? The 6 in the hundreds place is worth 600.

Tell students that in this lesson they will solve calculator problems that require them to focus on the digits and values of digits in numbers.

▶ Practicing Place-Value Skills with a Calculator

(*Math Journal 1,* p. 36; *Math Masters,* p. 47)

Make a chart on the board or use a transparency of *Math Masters,* page 47. (*See below.*) For each problem, provide the "Change to" digit and the "Operation" sign for students to record on journal page 36 as you guide the class through the examples.

Students solve each problem on their calculators. *Only* the given digit may be changed. All of the other digits in the starting number must remain the same. Discuss students' solutions.

	Start with	Place of Digit	Change to	Operation	New Number
a.	570	Tens	0	–	500
b.	409	Hundreds	8	+	809
c.	54,463	Thousands	9	+	59,463
d.	760,837	Tens	0	–	760,807
e.	52,036,458	Ones	9	+	52,036,459
f.		Ten Thousands	5	+	52,056,459
g.		Millions	1	–	51,056,459

Say:

Problem 1

- Enter 570 in your calculator.
- Underline the digit in the tens place on your chart. 7
- Change the digit in the tens place to 0. Use the [–] key. Write "0" in the "Change to" column and "–" in the "Operation" column.
- (Give students time to carry out the operation on the calculator.) How did you do that? Press [–] 70 [=].
- What is the new number? 500 (Students record the new number on their chart.)

Problem 2

- Enter 409.
- Use the [+] key to change the digit in the hundreds place to 8.
- How did you do that? Press [+] 400 [=].
- What is the new number? 809

Problem 3

- Enter 54,463.
- Use the [+] key to change the digit in the thousands place to 9.
- How did you do that? Press [+] 5,000 [=].
- What is the new number? 59,463

Adjusting the Activity

ELL

Have students build the starting number with base-10 blocks and take away or add the necessary blocks to show the new number. Ask students to take note of how many blocks they added or subtracted and translate that into what they would do on the calculator.

AUDITORY ◆ KINESTHETIC ◆ TACTILE ◆ VISUAL

Links to the Future

Solving these problems requires students to informally identify solutions to open sentences and explain the strategies they used. The solutions, for example, to Problems 1 and 3 can be more formally expressed as $570 - x = 500$; $x = 70$ and $54{,}463 + x = 59{,}463$; $x = 5{,}000$. Lesson 3-11, Open Sentences, will provide students with further instruction regarding Patterns, Functions, and Algebra Goal 2.

Problem 4

- Enter 760,837.
- Use the [−] key to change the digit in the tens place to 0.
- How did you do that? Press [−] 30 [=].
- What is the new number? 760,807

Problem 5

- Enter 52,036,458.
- Use the [+] key to change the digit in the ones place to 9. Press [+] 1 [=].
- Use the [+] key to change the digit in the ten-thousands place to 5. Press [+] 20,000 [=].
- Use the [−] key to change the digit in the millions place to 1. Press [−] 1,000,000 [=].
- What is the new number? 51,056,459

Solving Change Problems

INDEPENDENT ACTIVITY

(*Math Journal 1,* p. 36)

Students solve the calculator "change" problems in Problem 2 on journal page 36.

Ongoing Assessment: Recognizing Student Achievement

Math Log or Exit Slip

Portfolio Ideas

Use a **Math Log** or an **Exit Slip** (*Math Masters,* page 388 or 389) to assess students' ability to identify places in whole numbers and the values of the digits in those places. Have students explain how they solved Problem 2f on journal page 36. Students are making adequate progress if their responses include that the digit in the ten-millions place in 873,562,003 is 7. The value of the 7 is 70,000,000. To change the digit in the ten-millions place to a 1, subtract 60,000,000. Some students may respond that another way to solve the problem is to add –60,000,000.

[Number and Numeration Goal 1]

Adjusting the Activity

Pose similar problems, but do not indicate which operation key ([+] or [−]) should be used. Remind students that *only* the given digit may change.

AUDITORY ♦ KINESTHETIC ♦ TACTILE ♦ VISUAL

Student Page

Date Time

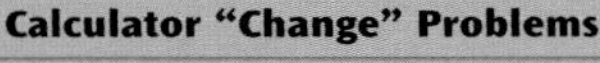

LESSON 2·4 **Calculator "Change" Problems**

1. Follow your teacher's directions to complete the "change" problems below. Use your calculator.

	Start with	Place of Digit	Change to	Operation	New Number
a.	570	Tens	0	–	500
b.	409	Hundreds	8	+	809
c.	54,463	Thousands	9	+	59,463
d.	760,837	Tens	0	–	760,807
e.	52,036,458	Ones	9	+	52,036,459
f.		Ten Thousands	5	+	52,056,459
g.		Millions	1	–	51,056,459

2. Complete these calculator "change" problems on your own.

	Start with	Place of Digit	Change to	Operation	New Number
a.	893	Tens	3	–	833
b.	5,489	Hundreds	7	+	5,789
c.	94,732	Thousands	6	+	96,732
d.	218,149	Ten Thousands	0	–	208,149
e.	65,307,000	Millions	9	+	69,307,000
★ f.	873,562,003	Ten Millions	1	–	813,562,003
g.	103,070,651	Hundred Millions	8	+	803,070,651

Math Journal 1, p. 36

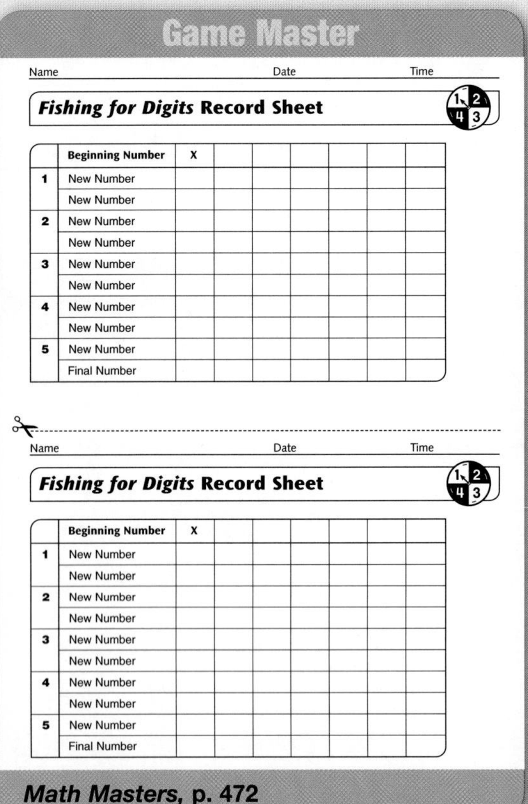

Game Master

Name Date Time

***Fishing for Digits* Record Sheet**

	Beginning Number	X						
1	New Number							
	New Number							
2	New Number							
	New Number							
3	New Number							
	New Number							
4	New Number							
	New Number							
5	New Number							
	Final Number							

Name Date Time

***Fishing for Digits* Record Sheet**

	Beginning Number	X						
1	New Number							
	New Number							
2	New Number							
	New Number							
3	New Number							
	New Number							
4	New Number							
	New Number							
5	New Number							
	Final Number							

Math Masters, p. 472

2 Ongoing Learning & Practice

▶ Playing *Fishing for Digits*

PARTNER ACTIVITY

(*Student Reference Book,* p. 242; *Math Masters,* p. 472; optional)

Fishing for Digits combines place-value and calculator skills. The steps in the game are similar to the calculator practice done in this lesson. Go over the game directions on page 242 in the *Student Reference Book*. Play a sample round as a class using an overhead calculator, if available. If you want students to use the *Fishing for Digits* Record Sheet (*Math Masters,* page 472), model its use first.

▶ Math Boxes 2•4

INDEPENDENT ACTIVITY

(*Math Journal 1,* p. 37)

Mixed Practice Math Boxes in this lesson are paired with Math Boxes in Lesson 2-2. The skill in Problem 6 previews Unit 3 content.

▶ Study Link 2•4

INDEPENDENT ACTIVITY

(*Math Masters,* p. 48)

Home Connection Students practice place-value skills and reading, writing, and ordering numbers up to one billion.

Student Page

Date Time

LESSON 2•4 **Math Boxes**

1. What is the largest number you can make with the digits 3, 0, 3, 8, and 0? Fill in the circle next to the best answer.
   - (A) 83,003
   - (B) 83,030
   - (C) 83,300 (filled)
   - (D) 80,033

   SRB 4

2. Add mentally or with a paper-and-pencil algorithm.
   - a. 145 + 34 = 179
   - b. 297 + 136 = 433

   SRB 10 11

3. Draw a concave pentagon.

   Sample answer:

   SRB 97

4. Measure these line segments to the nearest centimeter.
   - a. About 5 centimeters
   - b. About 3 centimeters

   SRB 128

5. Complete.
   - a. 14 in. = 1 ft 2 in.
   - b. 24 in. = 2 ft
   - c. 21 ft = 7 yd
   - d. 1 yd 1 ft = 48 in.
   - e. 413 ft = 137 yd 2 ft

   SRB 129

6. Divide mentally.
   - a. 16 ÷ 2 = 8
   - b. 20 ÷ 10 = 2
   - c. 8 = 40 ÷ 5
   - d. 60 ÷ 10 = 6
   - e. 9 = 45 ÷ 5

   SRB 20

Math Journal 1, p. 37

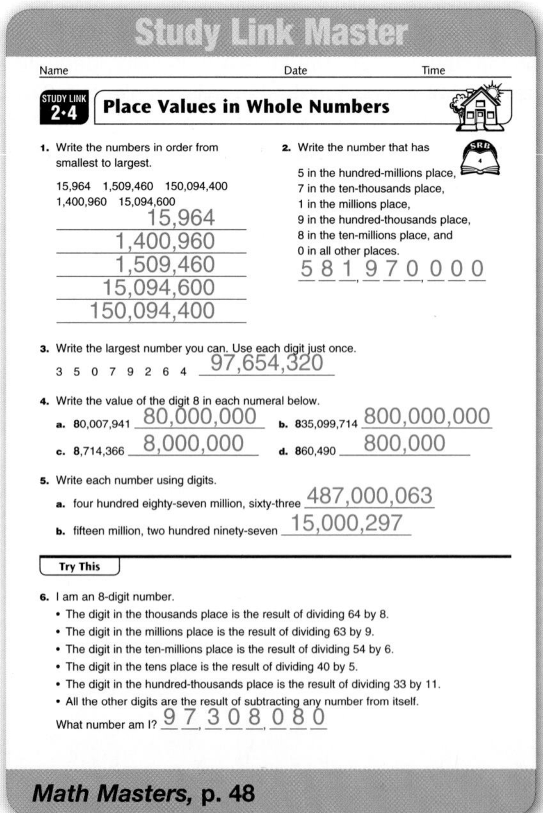

Study Link Master

Name Date Time

STUDY LINK 2•4 **Place Values in Whole Numbers**

1. Write the numbers in order from smallest to largest.
   15,964 1,509,460 150,094,400 1,400,960 15,094,600
   15,964
   1,400,960
   1,509,460
   15,094,600
   150,094,400

2. Write the number that has
   5 in the hundred-millions place,
   7 in the ten-thousands place,
   1 in the millions place,
   9 in the hundred-thousands place,
   8 in the ten-millions place, and
   0 in all other places.
   5 8 1, 9 7 0, 0 0 0

3. Write the largest number you can. Use each digit just once.
   3 5 0 7 9 2 6 4 97,654,320

4. Write the value of the digit 8 in each numeral below.
   - a. 80,007,941 80,000,000
   - b. 835,099,714 800,000,000
   - c. 8,714,366 8,000,000
   - d. 860,490 800,000

5. Write each number using digits.
   - a. four hundred eighty-seven million, sixty-three 487,000,063
   - b. fifteen million, two hundred ninety-seven 15,000,297

Try This

6. I am an 8-digit number.
   - The digit in the thousands place is the result of dividing 64 by 8.
   - The digit in the millions place is the result of dividing 63 by 9.
   - The digit in the ten-millions place is the result of dividing 54 by 6.
   - The digit in the tens place is the result of dividing 40 by 5.
   - The digit in the hundred-thousands place is the result of dividing 33 by 11.
   - All the other digits are the result of subtracting any number from itself.

   What number am I? 9 7, 3 0 8, 0 8 0

Math Masters, p. 48

3 Differentiation Options

READINESS

 PARTNER ACTIVITY

Using a Place-Value Tool

 15–30 Min

(*Math Masters,* pp. 49 and 399–402)

To provide experience identifying the place value of digits in large numbers, have students use a Compact Place-Value Flip Book to solve problems. The flipping of the digits in the place-value tool provides a hands-on way for students to see the operation that occurs when the digit within a number changes. Have students describe how they would change the original number to make the new number for each prompt.

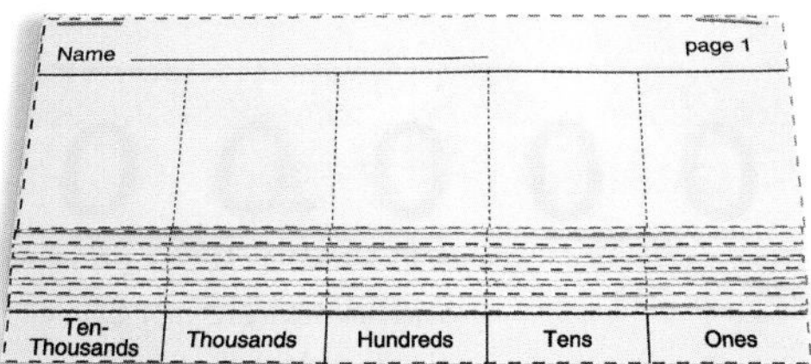

The Compact Place-Value Flip Book can be used to display whole numbers up to 99,999. It can also be adapted to show decimals. When students have completed the activity, collect and save the books for use in Unit 4—Decimals and Their Uses.

ENRICHMENT

 PARTNER ACTIVITY

Deciphering a Place-Value Code

 15–30 Min

(*Math Masters,* p. 50)

Portfolio Ideas

To apply students' understanding of place value, have them decipher the packing-system code used at a bakery. Encourage students to use a visual organizer such as the following to help them solve the problem. Students might begin by asking "How many boxes of x muffins?" beginning with 27, then 9, and so on.

Total Muffins	Boxes of 27	Boxes of 9	Boxes of 3	Boxes of 1

Have students describe how the chart they used to solve the problem is different from and similar to a base-ten place-value chart. In this problem, you multiply by 3 to get the next column. In the base-ten place-value chart, you multiply by 10. In both charts, each time you have enough in one column, that column becomes 0 and the next column becomes 1.

Teaching Master

Name Date Time

LESSON 2·4 **Use a Place-Value Tool**

1. Display each number below in your place-value flip book. Then display, read, and record the numbers that are 10 more, 100 more, and 1,000 more. Circle the digit that changed.

Number	10 more	100 more	1,000 more
146	1⑤6	②46	①,146
508	5①8	⑥08	①,508
2,368	2,3⑦8	2,④68	③,368
4,571	4,5⑧1	4,⑥71	⑤,571
15,682	15,6⑨2	15,⑦82	1⑥,682

2. Display each number below in your place-value flip book. Then display, read, and record the numbers that are 10 less, 100 less, and 1,000 less. Circle the digit that changed.

Number	10 less	100 less	1,000 less
2,345	2,3③5	2,②45	①,345
3,491	3,4⑧1	3,③91	②,491
6,839	6,8②9	6,⑦39	⑤,839
12,367	12,3⑤7	12,②67	1①,367
45,130	45,1②0	45,⓪30	4④,130

3. Use your place-value flip book to help you answer the following questions.
   a. What number is 50 more than 329? 379
   b. What number is 300 more than 517? 817
   c. What number is 60 less than 685? 625
   d. What number is 400 less than 932? 532

Math Masters, p. 49

Teaching Master

Name Date Time

LESSON 2·4 **Crack the Muffin Code**

Daniel takes orders at the Marvelous Muffin Bakery. The muffins are packed into boxes that hold 1, 3, 9, or 27 muffins. When a customer asks for muffins, Daniel fills out an order slip.

- If a customer orders 5 muffins, Daniel writes CODE 12 on the order slip.
- If a customer orders 19 muffins, Daniel writes CODE 201 on the order slip.
- If a customer orders 34 muffins, Daniel writes CODE 1021 on the order slip.

1. What would Daniel write on the order slip if a customer asked for 47 muffins? Explain.
   CODE 1202
   Sample answer: Daniel needs 1 box of 27 muffins (the "1" in the code), 2 boxes of 9 muffins (18 muffins; the first "2" in the code); zero boxes of 3 muffins (the "0" in the code), and 2 boxes of 1 muffin (2 muffins; the last "2" in the code).

2. If the Marvelous Muffin Bakery always packs its muffins into the fewest number of boxes possible, what is a code Daniel would never write on an order slip? Explain.
   CODE Sample answer: 300
   CODE 300 means that the bakery would be using 3 boxes of 9 to pack 27 muffins instead of using 1 box of 27 to pack 27 muffins (CODE 1000).

3. The largest box used by the bakery holds 27 muffins. Daniel thinks the bakery should have a box one size larger. How many muffins would the new box hold? Explain.
   81 muffins Sample answer:
   There is a pattern in the numbers 1, 3, 9, 27. The rule is ×3. So, the next number in the pattern is 27 × 3 = 81.

Math Masters, p. 50

2•5 Organizing and Displaying Data

Objective To provide practice organizing and displaying data with a tally chart and determining the maximum, minimum, range, and mode of a set of data.

Technology Resources www.everydaymathonline.com

ePresentations

eToolkit

Algorithms Practice

EM Facts Workshop Game™

Family Letters

Assessment Management

Common Core State Standards

Curriculum Focal Points

Interactive Teacher's Lesson Guide

1 Teaching the Lesson

Key Concepts and Skills

- Create a tally chart.
  [Data and Chance Goal 1]
- Find the maximum, minimum, range, mode, median, and mean for a set of data.
  [Data and Chance Goal 2]
- Use data landmarks to make a prediction.
  [Data and Chance Goal 2]
- Use and describe a strategy for estimating volume; describe the difference between an estimate and a guess.
  [Measurement and Reference Frames Goal 2]

Key Activities

Students guess, estimate, and then count the number of objects in a container. They tally the class results in a chart and find the minimum, maximum, range, and mode for the data.

Ongoing Assessment: Informing Instruction See page 108.

Key Vocabulary

guess ◆ estimate ◆ tally chart ◆ landmark ◆ maximum ◆ minimum ◆ range ◆ mode

Materials

Math Journal 1, p. 38
Study Link 2•4
small boxes of raisins (or 3-ounce cups of raisin substitute) ◆ slate

2 Ongoing Learning & Practice

Playing *Addition Top-It* (Extended-Facts Version)
Student Reference Book, p. 263
Math Masters, p. 506
per partnership: deck of number cards (the Everything Math Deck, if available)
Students practice addition fact extensions.

Ongoing Assessment: Recognizing Student Achievement
Use *Math Masters,* page 506.
[Operations and Computation Goal 1]

Math Boxes 2•5
Math Journal 1, p. 39
Students practice and maintain skills through Math Box problems.

Study Link 2•5
Math Masters, p. 51
Students practice and maintain skills through Study Link activities.

3 Differentiation Options

READINESS

Recording Data with Tally Marks
Math Masters, p. 52
2 six-sided dice
Students use tally marks to record dice sums.

ENRICHMENT

Making a Prediction Based on a Sample
Math Journal 1, p. 38
Math Masters, p. 53
1 large box of raisins (12 or 15 ounces)
Students use data landmarks to predict how many raisins are in a large box.

EXTRA PRACTICE

5-Minute Math
5-Minute Math™, pp. 34, 37, 38, and 40
Students find data landmarks.

Advance Preparation

For Part 1, use $\frac{1}{2}$-ounce boxes of raisins, one box for each student. Or have at least 14 boxes for students to share to get a representative set of data.

Place an unopened $\frac{1}{2}$-ounce box of raisins near the Math Message.

***Teacher's Reference Manual,* Grades 4–6** pp. 161–169

Getting Started

Mental Math and Reflexes

Pose addition problems. *Suggestions:*

●○○ 10 + 10 = 20
12 + 10 = 22
15 + 10 = 25

●●○ 30 + 13 = 43
40 + 56 = 96
24 + 61 = 85

●●● 175 + 426 = 601
238 + 546 = 784
693 + 168 = 861

Math Message

Guess how many raisins are in the box. Write your guess in Problem 1a on page 38 in your journal.

Study Link 2·4 Follow-Up

Ask partners to read the numbers in Problem 1 to each other. Remind students that the word *and* is not used when reading whole numbers.

Encourage students to add interesting number facts to the Numbers and Their Uses Museum.

1 Teaching the Lesson

Math Message Follow-Up

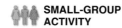

Ask students to share their guesses in small groups. Emphasize that guessing, estimating, and organizing are skills they use on a daily basis. In this lesson students will gather, organize, and summarize data on the number of raisins in a box.

Collecting, Organizing, and Interpreting a Set of Data

(*Math Journal 1,* p. 38)

Pass out a box of raisins to each student. Then guide the class through the following activity.

Collecting the Data

1. Ask students to open their box of raisins and, without emptying it, count the number of raisins they see at the top of the box. Tell them to use this count to estimate the total number of raisins in the box. Ask them to record their estimate in Problem 1b.
2. Encourage students to describe their estimation strategies. For example: "I saw 7 raisins on top and figured 5 rows. Five rows of 7 is about 35 raisins."
3. Discuss the difference between a **guess** and an **estimate.** An estimate is a guess that employs a strategy. To support English language learners, point out that the Math Message answer is a *guess* because students did not have any information about the raisins in the box. When students looked into the box, they could use a strategy for making an *estimate* because they saw the size of the raisins and how they were packed inside.

Student Page

Date ______ Time ______

LESSON 2·5 **Counting Raisins**

1. Use your $\frac{1}{2}$-ounce box of raisins. Complete each step when the teacher tells you. Stop after you complete each step. Answers vary.
   a. Don't open your box yet. **Guess** about how many raisins are in the box. About ______ raisins
   b. Open the box. Count the number of raisins in the top layer. Then **estimate** the total number of raisins in the box. About ______ raisins
   c. Now **count** the raisins in the box. How many? ______ raisins
2. Make a tally chart of the class data.

Number of Raisins	Number of Boxes

3. Find the following **landmarks** for the class data. Answers vary.
   a. What is the **maximum,** or largest, number of raisins found? ______
   b. What is the **minimum,** or smallest, number of raisins found? ______
   c. What is the **range?** (Subtract the minimum from the maximum.) ______
   d. What is the **mode,** or most frequent number of raisins found? ______

Try This

4. What is the **median** number of raisins found? Answers vary.
5. What is the **mean** number of raisins found? Answers vary.

Math Journal 1, p. 38

of Raisins	of Boxes
29	/
30	//
31	
32	
33	///
34	
35	///
36	~~////~~
37	//
38	////
39	
40	/
41	
42	
43	
44	
45	/
46	

Tally Chart

NOTE Stem-and-leaf plots are covered in Grade 5. If your curriculum requires that this concept be covered in Grade 4, see www.everydaymathonline.com.

NOTE If graphing software is available, this would be a good time to familiarize students with the features that allow them to analyze data.

that they count the raisins as many times as they need to, until they get the same number more than once. Have them record the total in Problem 1c.

5. Discuss counting techniques. Some students may have lost track of the count when counting the raisins by 1s. Suggest that a more accurate and efficient way might be to count by 2s or to group the raisins by 5s or 10s.

Organizing the Data

Ask students to report the exact number of raisins in their boxes. Record the numbers on the board in the order in which they are reported. Partners then use the class data to complete the **tally chart** in Problem 2 in their journals.

To help students get started, ask them to complete the first column by writing the numbers in order, beginning with the smallest number of raisins and ending with the largest number of raisins. Students then make a tally mark on the appropriate line in the second column for each number on the board.

Ongoing Assessment: Informing Instruction

Watch for students who do not use the fifth tally mark to cross the first four. Point out that tally marks organize counts by 5s and show each number between 5 and 10 as five *plus* one or more ones.

Analyzing the Data

Use questions such as the following to elicit discussion:

- Does anyone know what a **landmark** is? An object or feature that stands out
- What are some examples of ways we use landmarks? Sample answers: When giving directions, we might say, “Go straight ahead, turn right at the second stoplight, then go until you see the playground.” When describing a location, we might say “The tallest building you see is right next to the city square.”

Following this discussion, students complete Problems 3–5 in their journals on their own. Tell them that they will use landmarks to describe their raisin data.

Have students look for the following. To support English language learners, write the key terms on the board along with their definitions and examples.

▷ The largest number of raisins found—the **maximum**

▷ The smallest number of raisins found—the **minimum**

▷ The difference between the maximum and the minimum—the **range**

▷ The most frequent number of raisins found—the **mode**

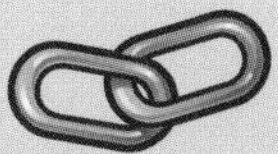

Links to the Future

The median is reviewed in Lesson 2-6. The mean, introduced in *Third Grade Everyday Mathematics,* is reviewed in Lesson 3-4. Calculating the mean of a data set is a Grade 5 Goal.

Encourage students to talk about the distribution of the data in their tally charts. Terms like *clumps, bumps, holes, way-out number,* and *all-alone number* are fine for describing these data. *For example:*

▷ "The most anybody got was 45. But 45 is way out by itself, and the next biggest is 40."

▷ "The smallest is 29. There's a little group near the bottom—one 29 and two 30s."

▷ "There's a big clump of tally marks between 35 and 39."

▷ "The table has some holes—at 31, 32, 34, and 39."

Finally, ask students what they think is the typical number of raisins in a box. Expect a variety of answers, such as the number that occurs most often or a number where the counts cluster most heavily.

Adjusting the Activity

Have students describe how the mean, median, and mode of the data are similar and different. Ask them to explain which landmark they think provides the best possible picture of the raisin data and why.

AUDITORY ◆ KINESTHETIC ◆ TACTILE ◆ VISUAL

2 Ongoing Learning & Practice

Playing *Addition Top-It* (Extended-Facts Version)

PARTNER ACTIVITY

FACTS PRACTICE

(*Student Reference Book,* p. 263; *Math Masters,* p. 506)

Students play an extended-facts version of *Addition Top-It* to develop automaticity with addition fact extensions. See Lesson 1-2 for additional information.

Ongoing Assessment: Recognizing Student Achievement

***Math Masters* Page 506**

Use the number sentences on *Math Masters,* page 506 generated in the *Addition Top-It* game to assess students' automaticity with extended addition facts. Students are making adequate progress if they are able to find the correct sum for each number sentence. Some students may be able to explain how they would use subtraction to check their answers.

[Operations and Computation Goal 1]

NOTE The word *range* is sometimes defined as the interval between the smallest and the largest number in a set of data—for example, the interval from 29 to 45. *Everyday Mathematics* defines range as "a number—the difference between the minimum and the maximum." For example, if the minimum is 29 and the maximum is 45, the range is 16.

If one single number or value occurs most often in a set of data, that number or value is called the *mode*. Sometimes two or more numbers occur most often. All of these numbers or values are called modes.

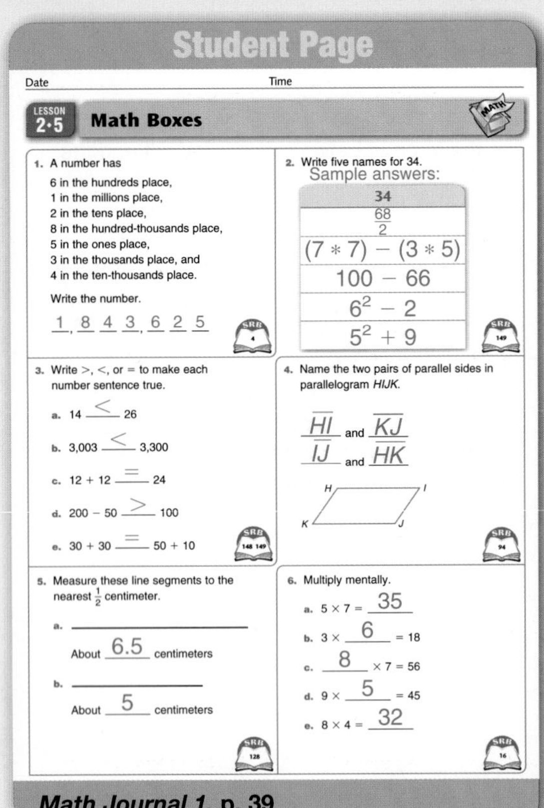

Student Page

Date ____ Time ____

LESSON 2·5 **Math Boxes**

1. A number has
6 in the hundreds place,
1 in the millions place,
2 in the tens place,
8 in the hundred-thousands place,
5 in the ones place,
3 in the thousands place, and
4 in the ten-thousands place.
Write the number.
1, 8 4 3, 6 2 5

2. Write five names for 34.
Sample answers:

34
$\frac{68}{2}$
$(7 * 7) - (3 * 5)$
$100 - 66$
$6^2 - 2$
$5^2 + 9$

3. Write >, <, or = to make each number sentence true.
a. 14 < 26
b. 3,003 < 3,300
c. 12 + 12 = 24
d. 200 − 50 > 100
e. 30 + 30 = 50 + 10

4. Name the two pairs of parallel sides in parallelogram *HIJK*.
$\overline{HI}$ and $\overline{KJ}$
$\overline{IJ}$ and $\overline{HK}$

5. Measure these line segments to the nearest $\frac{1}{2}$ centimeter.
a. About 6.5 centimeters
b. About 5 centimeters

6. Multiply mentally.
a. 5 × 7 = 35
b. 3 × 6 = 18
c. 8 × 7 = 56
d. 9 × 5 = 45
e. 8 × 4 = 32

Math Journal 1, p. 39

▶ Math Boxes 2·5

INDEPENDENT ACTIVITY

(*Math Journal 1,* p. 39)

Mixed Practice Math Boxes in this lesson are linked with Math Boxes in Lessons 2-7 and 2-9. The skill in Problem 6 previews Unit 3 content.

Writing/Reasoning Have students write a response to the following: *Explain how you know that the pairs of sides you chose in Problem 4 are parallel.* Sample answer: No matter how far the sides are extended, they will never meet or cross.

▶ Study Link 2·5

INDEPENDENT ACTIVITY

(*Math Masters,* p. 51)

Home Connection Students collect data about the sizes of their families. Go over in class the definition of *family* as described on the page. Students also answer questions about data displayed in a tally chart.

NOTE A few teachers have reported that family size is a sensitive topic with some students in their classrooms. If you anticipate this to be an issue, consider replacing family size with the number of radios, televisions, pets, or smoke detectors in the home. Adjust the activities in Lesson 2-6 accordingly.

Study Link Master

Name ____ Date ____ Time ____

STUDY LINK 2·5 **Collecting Data**

1. Make a list of all the people in your family. Include all the people living at home now. Also include any brothers or sisters who live somewhere else. The people who live at home do not have to be related to you. Do not forget to write your name in the list.

You will need this information to learn about the sizes of families in your class.

How many people are in your family? ____ people

The tally chart at the right shows the number of books that some students read over the summer. Use the information to answer the questions below.

Number of Books Reported	Number of Students
2	///
3	~~////~~
4	
5	~~////~~ //
6	~~////~~ /
7	//
8	////

2. How many students reported the number of books they read? 27
3. What is the **maximum** (the largest number of books reported)? 8
4. What is the **minimum** (the smallest number of books reported)? 2
5. What is the **range?** 6
6. What is the **mode** (the most frequent number of books reported)? 5

Practice

7. 30 + 50 = 80
8. 210 = 70 + 70 + 70
9. 230 = 90 + 80 + 60
10. 100 + 40 + 70 = 210

Math Masters, p. 51

3 Differentiation Options

READINESS

PARTNER ACTIVITY

Recording Data with Tally Marks

5–15 Min

(*Math Masters,* p. 52)

To provide experience with tally marks, have students complete a tally chart of dice rolls. When students have finished, discuss why tallies are an easy way to keep track of data and how they make it easier to compare results. Tallies are grouped in fives and make it easier to count. It is easier to compare groups of five rather than a lot of single marks.

ENRICHMENT

PARTNER ACTIVITY

Making a Prediction Based on a Sample

5–15 Min

(*Math Journal 1,* p. 38; *Math Masters,* p. 53)

To apply students' understanding of data landmarks, have them predict, based on the data collected from the half-ounce raisin boxes, how many raisins are in a 12- or 15-ounce box. Ask students to describe how they made their predictions.

EXTRA PRACTICE

SMALL-GROUP ACTIVITY

5-Minute Math

5–15 Min

To offer students more experience with data landmarks, see *5-Minute Math,* pages 34, 37, 38, and 40.

Teaching Master

Name Date Time

LESSON 2·5 **Dice-Roll Tally Chart**

Tally marks are vertical marks used to keep track of a count. The fifth tally mark crosses the first four.

Examples:

/ one	// two	/// three	//// four	𝍸 five
𝍸 / six	𝍸 // seven	𝍸 /// eight	𝍸 //// nine	𝍸 𝍸 ten

1. Roll a pair of dice and find the sum.
2. Make a tally mark next to the sum in the chart below.
3. Set a timer for 3 minutes. Roll the dice and make a tally mark for each sum until the timer goes off.

Sum	Tallies
2	
3	
4	
5	
6	
7	
8	
9	
10	
11	
12	

4. Answer the questions below. Answers vary.
   a. How many times did you roll a sum of
      4? ____ times
      7? ____ times
      11? ____ times
   b. Which sum was rolled the most number of times? ____
   c. Which sum was rolled the least number of times? ____
   d. How many times did you roll the dice in all? ____ times
   e. On the back of this page, write two more things that you notice about the data you collected.

Math Masters, p. 52

Teaching Master

Name Date Time

LESSON 2·5 **Making a Prediction Based on a Sample**

Sometimes large numbers of people or things are impossible to count or take too much time to count. A smaller **sample** of data is often used to make predictions about a larger group or **population.**

You and your class collected, recorded, and analyzed data about the number of raisins found in $\frac{1}{2}$-ounce boxes of raisins.

Use the raisin data you collected on journal page 38 to answer the following questions.

1. Without opening it, how many raisins do you think are in a large box (12 or 15 ounces) of raisins?

   About ______ raisins are in a ______-ounce box. Answers vary.

2. Explain the strategy you used to make your prediction.
   Sample answer: I took the median number of raisins from a $\frac{1}{2}$-ounce box and multiplied by 24 (12-oz box) or 30 (15-oz box).

3. Suppose you only knew the number of raisins in a single $\frac{1}{2}$-ounce box of raisins. Would that affect your prediction about the number of raisins in the large box? Why or why not?
   Sample answer: My prediction would not be as reliable, but it would still be close. There wasn't a big difference between the minimum and maximum in our class data.

Math Masters, p. 53

2·6 The Median

Objectives To review how to display a set of data with a line plot; and to review how to find the median of a set of data.

Technology Resources www.everydaymathonline.com

ePresentations

eToolkit

Algorithms Practice

EM Facts Workshop Game™

Family Letters

Assessment Management

Common Core State Standards

Curriculum Focal Points

Interactive Teacher's Lesson Guide

1 Teaching the Lesson

Key Concepts and Skills

- Create a line plot. [Data and Chance Goal 1]
- Find the maximum, minimum, range, mode, median, and mean for a set of data. [Data and Chance Goal 2]
- Use data landmarks and representations to answer questions and draw conclusions. [Data and Chance Goal 2]

Key Activities

Students construct a line plot to organize and summarize data about the sizes of their families. They find the minimum, maximum, range, mode, and median for the data.

Ongoing Assessment: Recognizing Student Achievement Use journal page 40. [Data and Chance Goal 2]

Key Vocabulary

line plot ◆ median

Materials

Math Journal 1, p. 40
Student Reference Book, p. 71
Study Link 2•5
3-inch-square stick-on notes ◆
tape (optional) ◆ slate

2 Ongoing Learning & Practice

Playing *Subtraction Top-It* (Extended-Facts Version)
Student Reference Book, pp. 263 and 264
Math Masters, p. 506
per partnership: 4 each of number cards 1–10 (from the Everything Math Deck, if available)
Students practice subtraction fact extensions.

Math Boxes 2•6
Math Journal 1, p. 41
Students practice and maintain skills through Math Box problems.

Study Link 2•6
Math Masters, p. 54
Students practice and maintain skills through Study Link activities.

Ongoing Assessment: Informing Instruction See page 117.

3 Differentiation Options

READINESS

Finding the Middle Value
Math Masters, p. 55
deck of number cards (the Everything Math Deck, if available)
Students order number cards and find the median.

ENRICHMENT

Comparing Family-Size Data
Math Masters, p. 56
Students organize and compare family-size data for two or more classes.

ELL SUPPORT

Building a Math Word Bank
Differentiation Handbook, p. 140
Students add the term *median* to their Math Word Banks.

Advance Preparation

***Teacher's Reference Manual,* Grades 4–6** pp. 160–169

Getting Started

Mental Math and Reflexes

Write the problem 50 − 26 on the board. Ask students to solve it mentally and write the answer on their slates. Have students share their strategies. Present the following counting-up strategy if it is not brought up during discussion:

Start at 26. Add up to the next 10 and then to 50:

26 + **4** = 30, and 30 + **20** = 50. That is **4** + **20** = 24.

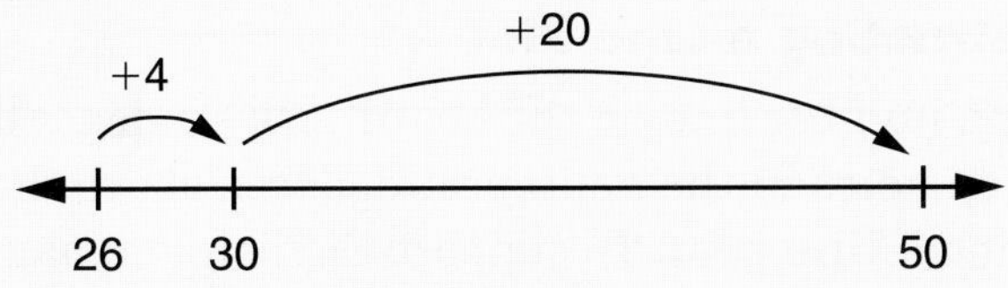

Pose additional problems such as the following:

●○○ 40 − 27 = 13
30 − 16 = 14
60 − 33 = 27

●●○ 67 − 10 = 57
51 − 20 = 31
84 − 30 = 54

●●● 110 − 52 = 58
180 − 143 = 37
240 − 136 = 104

Math Message

Find the line plot on page 71 of your Student Reference Book. *Write two things you notice about students' scores on Mr. Jackson's spelling test.*

Study Link 2•5 Follow-Up

Ask partners to compare answers to Problems 2–6. Check to see that all students know the number of people in their families (or the number of radios, televisions, pets, or smoke detectors in their home).

1 Teaching the Lesson

▸ Math Message Follow-Up

WHOLE-CLASS ACTIVITY

(*Student Reference Book,* p. 71)

Invite volunteers to share observations about the data shown in the "Scores on a 5-Word Spelling Test" line plot. Have students stand up if they made a similar observation.

▸ Investigating the Sizes of Students' Families

WHOLE-CLASS ACTIVITY

(*Math Journal 1,* p. 40; Study Link 2•5)

Tell students that in this lesson they will organize data about the number of people in their families. Then they will identify landmarks in the data.

Reviewing Students' Family-Size Data

Remind students that in conducting their survey, all people living at home now and any siblings living elsewhere are to be included. Resolve any questions students might have. *For example:*

- Do I count my brother who is away at college? yes
- We have a boarder who has rented a room for the last 10 years. We think of her as part of the family. Should I count her? yes

Student Page

Data and Probability

Organizing Data

Once the data have been collected, it helps to organize them to make them easier to understand. **Line plots** and **tally charts** are two methods of organizing data.

Example Mr. Jackson's class got the following scores on a five-word spelling test. Make a line plot and a tally chart to show the data below.

5 3 5 0 4 4 5 4 4 4 2 3 4 5 3 5 4 3 4 4

Scores on a 5-Word Spelling Test

Number of Students

0	1	2	3	4	5
X		X	XXXX	XXXXXXXXX	XXXXX

Number Correct

In this **line plot,** there are 4 Xs above the number 3.

Four students got a score of 3 on the test.

Scores on a 5-Word Spelling Test

Number Correct	Number of Students
0	/
1	
2	/
3	////
4	HHT ////
5	HHT

In this **tally chart,** there are 4 tallies to the right of 3.

Four students got a score of 3 on the test.

Both the line plot and the tally chart help to organize the data. They make it easier to describe the data. For example,

- Five students had 5 words correct.
- 4 correct is the score that came up most often.
- 0 correct and 2 correct are scores that came up least often.
- No student got exactly 1 correct.

Check Your Understanding

Here are the number of hits made by 14 players in a baseball game.

4 1 0 2 1 3 2 1 0 2 0 2 0 3

Organize the data. 1. Make a tally chart. 2. Make a line plot.

Check your answers on page 341.

***Student Reference Book,* p. 71**

- My parents are divorced. I live with my mother during the school year and with my father during summer vacations. How should I count them? Count only those people living in your present household.
- I have a cousin who lives in France. Should he be counted? no

After questions have been resolved, students may need to revise their family lists. Then have students record their family size in Problem 1 on journal page 40 and on a stick-on note.

Constructing a Line Plot

Draw a number line on the board. Ask students to attach their stick-on notes in the appropriate places above the number line, creating a **line plot.** To support English language learners, discuss the everyday as well as the mathematical meaning of the word *plot.*

NOTE A line plot is a quick and easy way to organize and display data. You can think of it as a rough sketch of a bar graph. If graphing software is available, have students create their line plots using the software.

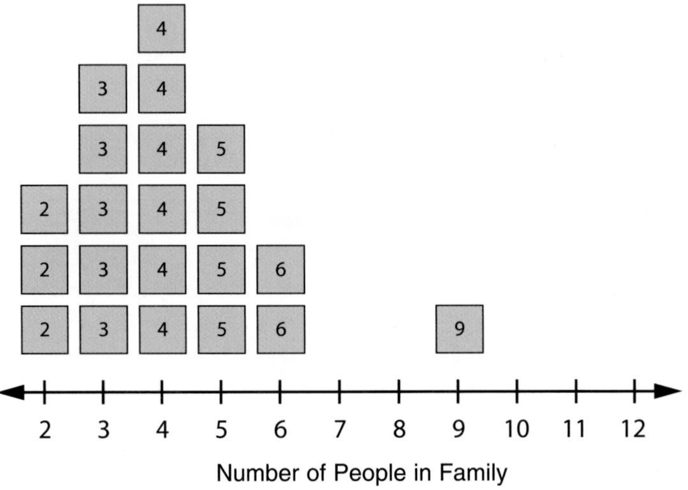

After everyone's stick-on note has been posted on the board, students copy the line plot on their journal pages. Have them use Xs in place of the stick-on notes.

Analyzing the Data

Ask students to complete Problem 3 on journal page 40 on their own. Then have students share their observations about the data. In discussing the data landmarks, students can use informal terms, but you should refer to these terms as *maximum, minimum, range,* and *mode*.

Adjusting the Activity ELL

As you discuss each landmark, have a volunteer label the number on the class line plot. Consider having students do the same on journal page 40.

AUDITORY ◆ KINESTHETIC ◆ TACTILE ◆ VISUAL

Here are some other questions for discussion:

- How are the landmarks reflected in the shape and distribution of the data in the line plot? Sample answers: The mode is the family size that occurs most frequently. The number with the most stick-on notes is the mode. If two or more family sizes have the tallest columns of stick-on notes, they are all modes.
- Where are the clusters, bumps, holes, and far-out numbers? Answers vary.

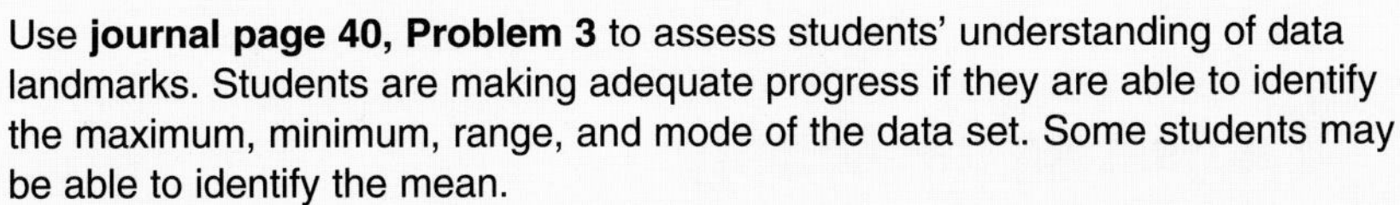

Ongoing Assessment: Recognizing Student Achievement

Journal page 40 Problem 3

Use **journal page 40, Problem 3** to assess students' understanding of data landmarks. Students are making adequate progress if they are able to identify the maximum, minimum, range, and mode of the data set. Some students may be able to identify the mean.

[Data and Chance Goal 2]

Finding the Median of the Class Data

Review ways of finding a middle value for family size; that is, about half the families should be smaller and half should be larger than this middle number. Remind students that the middle number is called the **median.** Here is one way to find the median:

1. List all the data from smallest to largest (or largest to smallest).
2. Count from each end to the number (or pair of numbers) in the middle.
3. If two numbers are in the middle, the median number is the average of the two numbers. This happens when there is an even number of data.

Ages of 5 boys: **9 10 11↓ 11 12**

The median age of the boys is 11.

Ages of 6 girls: **9 10 10 ↓ 11 11 12**

The median age of the girls is $10\frac{1}{2}$ —the value halfway between the two middle numbers.

Student Page

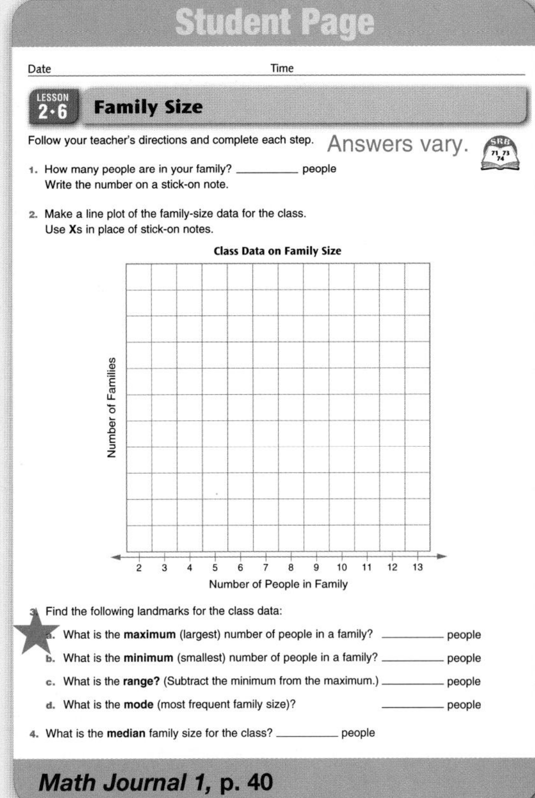

Date Time

LESSON 2·6 **Family Size**

Follow your teacher's directions and complete each step. Answers vary.

1. How many people are in your family? ______ people
   Write the number on a stick-on note.
2. Make a line plot of the family-size data for the class.
   Use **Xs** in place of stick-on notes.

3. Find the following landmarks for the class data:
   a. What is the **maximum** (largest) number of people in a family? ______ people
   b. What is the **minimum** (smallest) number of people in a family? ______ people
   c. What is the **range?** (Subtract the minimum from the maximum.) ______ people
   d. What is the **mode** (most frequent family size)? ______ people
4. What is the **median** family size for the class? ______ people

Math Journal 1, p. 40

NOTE Stem-and-leaf plots are covered in Grade 5. If your curriculum requires that this concept be covered in Grade 4, see www.everydaymathonline.com.

To find the median family size for the class, you can remove the stick-on notes from the line plot and line them up single file in ascending order on the board. (Have tape available to secure stick-on notes that fall off.) Then have two students remove the stick-on notes two at a time, one from each end, until only one or two notes are left on the board. Students then record the median on journal page 40, Problem 4.

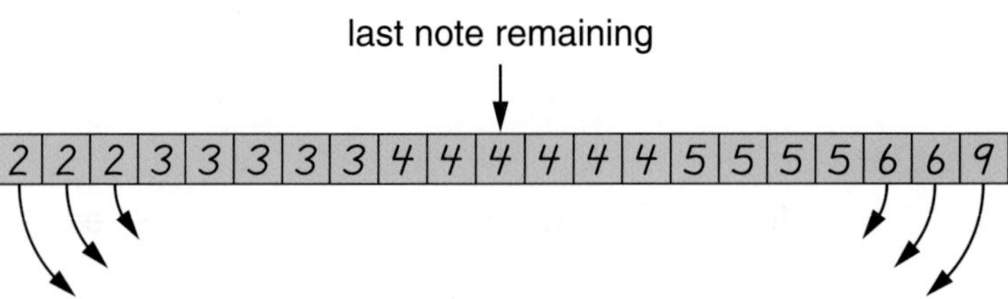

Adjusting the Activity

ELL

Instead of lining up stick-on notes on the board, have each student take a stick-on note and line up in order. Model finding the median by asking one student from each end of the line to come together as a pair and then sit down. Repeat this until one or two students are left standing and identify the median.

AUDITORY ♦ KINESTHETIC ♦ TACTILE ♦ VISUAL

After finding the median family size for your class, ask the following questions:

- Are the median and the mode for family size the same?
- How does your own family size compare with the median size? Is your family size equal to the median size? Less than the median size? Greater than the median size?

Explain that the median is the most useful landmark for describing the middle point of a data set, and it is often called a *typical value.*

Adjusting the Activity

Ask students to find the mean of the data set and explain how the mean is similar to or different from the median. Then ask them to explain which landmark they think better represents the data.

AUDITORY ♦ KINESTHETIC ♦ TACTILE ♦ VISUAL

2 Ongoing Learning & Practice

▶ Playing *Subtraction Top-It* (Extended-Facts Version)

PARTNER ACTIVITY

(*Student Reference Book,* pp. 263 and 264; *Math Masters,* p. 506)

Students play an extended-facts version of *Subtraction Top-It* to develop automaticity with subtraction fact extensions. See Lesson 1-4 for additional information. Consider having students record several rounds of play on *Math Masters,* page 506.

▶ Math Boxes 2·6

(*Math Journal 1,* p. 41)

Mixed Practice Math Boxes in this lesson are paired with Math Boxes in Lesson 2-8. The skills in Problems 5 and 6 preview Unit 3 content.

Writing/Reasoning Have students write a response to the following: *Suppose the data set in Problem 2 represents the number of hours each volunteer at an animal shelter worked during the month of July. What was the median number of minutes worked?* 780 minutes *Explain how you found your answer.* Sample answer: There are 60 minutes in an hour, so $60 \times 13 = 780$. *Do you think it makes make more sense to report data like this in hours or in minutes? Why?* Sample answer: It makes more sense to report it in hours. I understand what 13 hours feels like, but 780 minutes doesn't mean as much to me. The larger unit makes more sense.

▶ Study Link 2·6

(*Math Masters,* p. 54)

Home Connection Students construct a line plot from data given in a tally chart. Then they find landmarks of the data set.

Ongoing Assessment: Informing Instruction

Watch for students who think that the median number of hours spent watching television is 19.5. Students need to order the actual numbers of hours reported by Sylvia's class to find the median of the data set.

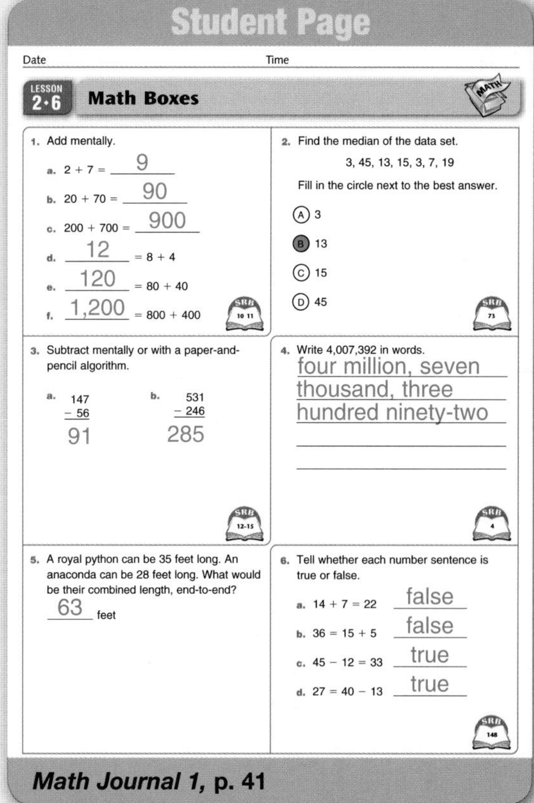

Student Page

Date Time

LESSON 2·6 **Math Boxes**

1. Add mentally.
   a. 2 + 7 = 9
   b. 20 + 70 = 90
   c. 200 + 700 = 900
   d. 12 = 8 + 4
   e. 120 = 80 + 40
   f. 1,200 = 800 + 400

2. Find the median of the data set.
   3, 45, 13, 15, 3, 7, 19
   Fill in the circle next to the best answer.
   Ⓐ 3
   Ⓑ 13 (filled)
   Ⓒ 15
   Ⓓ 45

3. Subtract mentally or with a paper-and-pencil algorithm.
   a. 147 − 56 = 91
   b. 531 − 246 = 285

4. Write 4,007,392 in words.
   four million, seven thousand, three hundred ninety-two

5. A royal python can be 35 feet long. An anaconda can be 28 feet long. What would be their combined length, end-to-end?
   63 feet

6. Tell whether each number sentence is true or false.
   a. 14 + 7 = 22 false
   b. 36 = 15 + 5 false
   c. 45 − 12 = 33 true
   d. 27 = 40 − 13 true

Math Journal 1, p. 41

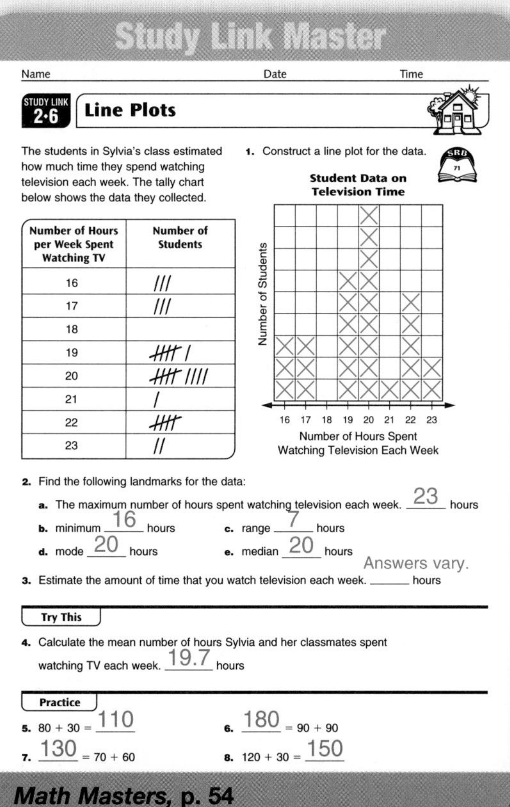

Study Link Master

Name Date Time

STUDY LINK 2·6 **Line Plots**

The students in Sylvia's class estimated how much time they spend watching television each week. The tally chart below shows the data they collected.

Number of Hours per Week Spent Watching TV	Number of Students
16	///
17	///
18	
19	HHT /
20	HHT ////
21	/
22	HHT
23	//

1. Construct a line plot for the data.

Student Data on Television Time

Number of Students

16 17 18 19 20 21 22 23

Number of Hours Spent Watching Television Each Week

2. Find the following landmarks for the data:
   a. The maximum number of hours spent watching television each week. 23 hours
   b. minimum 16 hours
   c. range 7 hours
   d. mode 20 hours
   e. median 20 hours

3. Estimate the amount of time that you watch television each week. Answers vary. hours

Try This

4. Calculate the mean number of hours Sylvia and her classmates spent watching TV each week. 19.7 hours

Practice

5. 80 + 30 = 110
6. 180 = 90 + 90
7. 130 = 70 + 60
8. 120 + 30 = 150

Math Masters, p. 54

The number in the middle of an ordered set of data is called the **middle value**, or **median**.

For Problems 1–3,

- Draw nine cards from a deck of number cards.
- Arrange the cards in order from smallest to largest.
- Record the numbers in the boxes below.
- Circle the number in the middle.

Example: 0 2 5 5 (7) 8 9 13 18 (smallest ... largest)

Answers vary.

1. [| | | | | | | |] smallest largest The median of my nine cards is ______.

2. [| | | | | | | |] smallest largest The median of my nine cards is ______.

3. [| | | | | | | |] smallest largest The median of my nine cards is ______.

4. Describe how you found the middle number in the problems above.
Sample answer: With 9 cards total, the middle card has 4 cards on each side of it. So the fifth card is the middle one.

5. If you arranged the cards in Problem 1 in order from *largest* to *smallest*, would the middle number stay the same? yes Explain.
The order of the numbers would be reversed, but the middle number would remain the same.

***Math Masters,* p. 55**

Teaching Master

Name Date Time

LESSON 2·6 **Comparing Family-Size Data**

1. Create a display that compares the family-size data from your class with those of other fourth-grade classes.
Answers vary.
2. Compare the maximum, minimum, range, mode, and median for family size for each class. Write about the similarities and differences. Use the back of this page if you need more space.

Combine and organize the data from all of the classes. Then answer the following questions.

3. What is the *median* family size for all of the classes? ______ people
4. How does your class median compare with the larger sample?
5. What is the *mean* family size for all of the classes? ______ people
6. If you had to predict the family size of a student from your school that you did not know, what would you predict? Explain your answer.

***Math Masters,* p. 56**

3 Differentiation Options

READINESS

PARTNER ACTIVITY

▶ Finding the Middle Value

15–30 Min

(*Math Masters,* p. 55)

To provide experience with finding the median of a data set using a concrete model, have students order number cards and find the middle value.

ENRICHMENT

PARTNER ACTIVITY

▶ Comparing Family-Size Data

30+ Min

(*Math Masters,* p. 56)

Portfolio Ideas

To further investigate organizing and summarizing data, have students compare the family-size data of their class with those of other fourth-grade classes. If graphing software is available, encourage students to use it to create their displays.

ELL SUPPORT

SMALL-GROUP ACTIVITY

▶ Building a Math Word Bank

5–15 Min

(*Differentiation Handbook,* p. 140)

To provide language support for data landmarks, have students use the Word Bank Template found on *Differentiation Handbook,* page 140. Ask students to write the term *median,* draw a picture representing the term, and write other related words. See the *Differentiation Handbook* for more information.

2•7 Addition of Multidigit Numbers

Objectives To review the partial-sums algorithm used to solve multidigit addition problems; and to introduce a column-addition method similar to the traditional addition algorithm.

Technology Resources www.everydaymathonline.com

ePresentations

eToolkit

Algorithms Practice

EM Facts Workshop Game™

Family Letters

Assessment Management

Common Core State Standards

Curriculum Focal Points

Interactive Teacher's Lesson Guide

1 Teaching the Lesson

Key Concepts and Skills

- Identify places in whole numbers and the values of the digits in those places. [Number and Numeration Goal 1]
- Apply extended addition facts. [Operations and Computation Goal 1]
- Use the partial-sums and column-addition algorithms to solve multidigit addition problems; choose an appropriate paper-and-pencil algorithm to solve multidigit addition problems. [Operations and Computation Goal 2]
- Make ballpark estimates for multidigit addition problems. [Operations and Computation Goal 6]

Key Activities

Students make ballpark estimates for addition problems. They use the partial-sums and column-addition methods for addition.

Ongoing Assessment: Recognizing Student Achievement
Use journal page 42.
[Operations and Computation Goal 2]

Key Vocabulary

partial-sums method ◆ column-addition method ◆ ballpark estimate

Materials

Math Journal 1, pp. 42 and 43
Student Reference Book, pp. 10 and 11
Study Link 2•6
Math Masters, p. 403 or 404 (optional)
quarter-sheet of paper ◆ base-10 blocks (optional)

2 Ongoing Learning & Practice

Playing *High-Number Toss*
Student Reference Book, p. 252
Math Masters, p. 487
per partnership: 1 six-sided die
Students practice comparing numbers.

Math Boxes 2•7
Math Journal 1, p. 44
Students practice and maintain skills through Math Box problems.

Study Link 2•7
Math Masters, pp. 57 and 58
Students practice and maintain skills through Study Link activities.

3 Differentiation Options

READINESS

Solving Addition Number Stories
Math Masters, pp. 59 and 405
base-10 blocks ◆ 3-section paper dinner plates (optional)
Students use base-10 blocks to model the partial-sums method for addition.

ENRICHMENT

Writing Addition Number Stories
Students write and solve addition number stories.

ELL SUPPORT

Building a Math Word Bank
Differentiation Handbook, p. 140
Students add the term *ballpark estimate* to their Math Word Banks.

Advance Preparation

Plan to spend a total of two days on this lesson. Place quarter-sheets of paper near the Math Message. If students need computation grids in Part 1, make copies of *Math Masters,* page 403 or 404.

***Teacher's Reference Manual,* Grades 4–6** pp. 119–122, 256–261

Getting Started

Mental Math and Reflexes

Pose extended addition-facts problems. *Suggestions:*

●○○ 50 + 50 = 100
300 + 300 = 600
400 + 100 = 500
2,000 + 6,000 = 8,000

●●○ 60 + 70 = 130
200 + 700 = 900
3,000 + 8,000 = 11,000
70,000 + 30,000 = 100,000

●●● 900 + 400 = 1,300
6,000 + 5,000 = 11,000
90,000 + 80,000 = 170,000
70,000 + 50,000 = 120,000

Math Message

Solve the problems on a quarter-sheet of paper. Show your work.

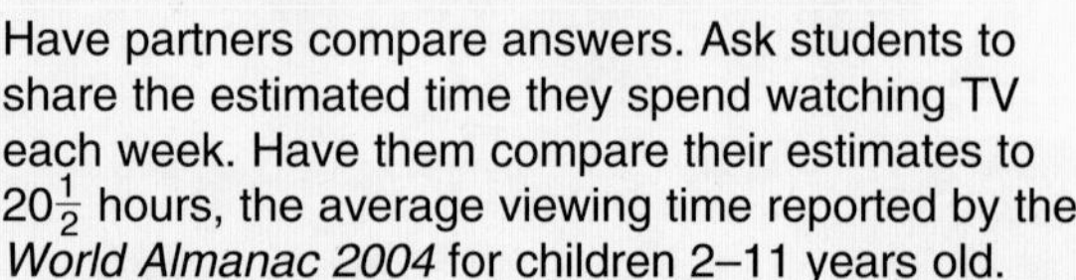

46	233
+ 37	+158
83	391

Study Link 2·6 Follow-Up

Have partners compare answers. Ask students to share the estimated time they spend watching TV each week. Have them compare their estimates to $20\frac{1}{2}$ hours, the average viewing time reported by the *World Almanac 2004* for children 2–11 years old.

1 Teaching the Lesson

▶ Math Message Follow-Up

Have students share their solution strategies. Tell them that in this lesson they will review the **partial-sums method** and explore the **column-addition method.** To support English language learners, explain the meaning of the word *partial.* Some students may have used these algorithms to solve the Math Message problems.

▶ Making Ballpark Estimates

Remind students that they should always check their answers to see whether they make sense. This is true for number stories and for computation problems like those in the Math Message.

Whether done in advance or as a final check, it is often desirable to make a rough **ballpark estimate** of the answer. One way to estimate a sum is to change the addends to "close-but-easier" numbers and then add them. To support English language learners, discuss the mathematical as well as the everyday meanings of the terms *ballpark* and *estimate.*

Ask students to give ballpark estimates rather than exact answers for sums. (*See examples on page 121.*) Have them tell how they arrived at their estimates. Encourage students to use terms such as *closer to, between,* and *a little more than* to refine their estimates. Note that often more than one estimate is acceptable.

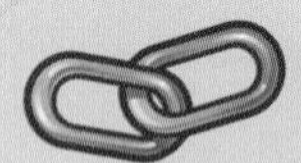

Links to the Future

In Unit 4 of *Fourth Grade Everyday Mathematics* students apply these addition algorithms to decimal numbers.

Sample answers:

- ▷ **44 + 87** 40 + 80 = 120; 40 + 90 = 130; 50 + 80 = 130; 50 + 90 = 140
- ▷ **23 + 77** 20 + 80 = 100; 30 + 70 = 100
- ▷ **147 + 56** 150 + 60 = 210; 140 + 50 = 190
- ▷ **342 + 281** 350 + 300 = 650; 300 + 300 = 600
- ▷ **459 + 809** 450 + 800 = 1,250; 500 + 800 = 1,300

Discussing and Practicing the Partial-Sums Method for Addition

(*Student Reference Book,* p. 10; *Math Journal 1,* p. 42)

The partial-sums method (algorithm) for addition was introduced in *Second Grade Everyday Mathematics*. Discuss the example of the partial-sums method that appears on page 10 of the *Student Reference Book*. It involves more steps than some standard algorithms, but it is also more explicit; for this reason, it might be easier to use. Addition is performed from left to right and column by column. The sum of each column is recorded on a separate line. The partial sums can be added following each step or at the end.

NOTE Addition by the partial-sums method can be performed from right to left. The advantage of working from left to right is that this is consistent with the approach used in estimating sums.

Write several 2-digit and 3-digit addition problems on the board. Have volunteers use and describe the partial-sums method to solve these problems. Remind students that the value of each digit is determined by its place in the numeral. Thus, they should keep in mind what numbers they are adding. For example, in the first problem below, they should think "40 + 30," not "4 + 3"; in the second problem, they should think "200 + 100," not "2 + 1," and "30 + 50," not "3 + 5."

Addition Using the Partial-Sums Method

		46
		+ 37
Add the 10s:	40 + 30 →	70
Add the 1s:	6 + 7 →	+ 13
Add the partial sums:	70 + 13 →	83

		233
		+ 158
Add the 100s:	200 + 100 →	300
Add the 10s:	30 + 50 →	80
Add the 1s:	3 + 8 →	+ 11
Add the partial sums:	300 + 80 + 11 →	391

Algorithm Project The focus of this lesson is the partial-sums and column-addition algorithms for addition. To teach U.S. traditional addition, see Algorithm Project 1 on page A1.

NOTE An *algorithm* is a step-by-step set of instructions for solving a problem. In classroom discussion, simply refer to algorithms as "methods." The partial-sums algorithm is an example of what is sometimes called a "low-stress" algorithm. Such algorithms are not necessarily the most efficient, but they are easy to use, and they reveal important underlying concepts.

Have base-10 blocks readily available for students to use while solving the addition problems.

AUDITORY ◆ KINESTHETIC ◆ TACTILE ◆ VISUAL

Student Page

Whole Numbers

Addition Methods

Partial-Sums Method

The **partial-sums method** is used to find sums mentally or with paper and pencil. Here is the partial-sums method for adding 2-digit or 3-digit numbers:

1. Add the 100s. **2.** Add the 10s. **3.** Add the 1s.

4. Then add the sums you just found (the partial sums).

Example Add 248 + 187 using the partial-sums method.

		100s	10s	1s
		2	**4**	**8**
		+ 1	**8**	**7**
Add the 100s.	200 + 100 →	3	0	0
Add the 10s.	40 + 80 →	1	2	0
Add the 1s.	8 + 7 →		1	5
Add the partial sums.	300 + 120 + 15 →	**4**	**3**	**5**

248 + 187 = 435

Note Larger numbers with 4 or more digits are added the same way.

Use base-10 blocks to show the partial-sums method.

Example Use base-10 blocks to add 248 + 187.

100s | 10s | 1s
248
187
+
300 | 120 | 15

The total is 300 + 120 + 15 = 435.

248 + 187 = 435

A cube is worth 1.
A long is worth 10.
A flat is worth 100.

***Student Reference Book,* p. 10**

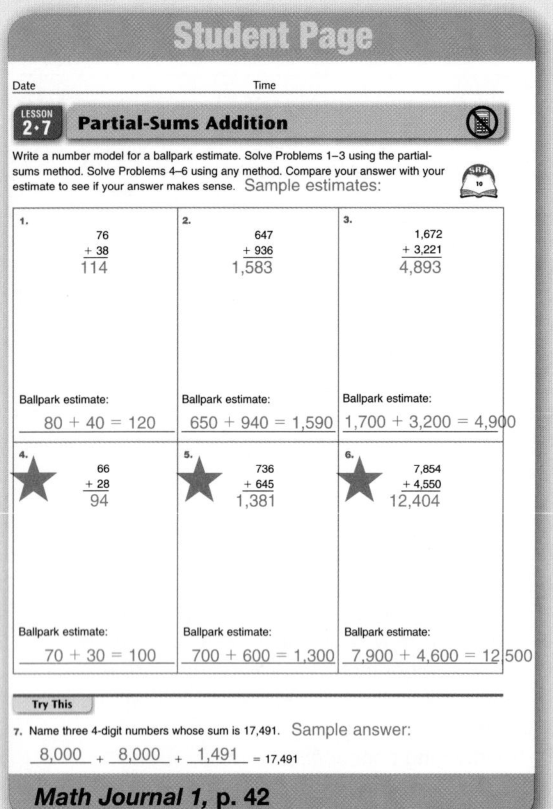
Student Page

Date Time

LESSON 2·7 **Partial-Sums Addition**

Write a number model for a ballpark estimate. Solve Problems 1–3 using the partial-sums method. Solve Problems 4–6 using any method. Compare your answer with your estimate to see if your answer makes sense. Sample estimates:

1.	2.	3.
76 + 38 = 114	647 + 936 = 1,583	1,672 + 3,221 = 4,893
Ballpark estimate: 80 + 40 = 120	Ballpark estimate: 650 + 940 = 1,590	Ballpark estimate: 1,700 + 3,200 = 4,900
4. 66 + 28 = 94	5. 736 + 645 = 1,381	6. 7,854 + 4,550 = 12,404
Ballpark estimate: 70 + 30 = 100	Ballpark estimate: 700 + 600 = 1,300	Ballpark estimate: 7,900 + 4,600 = 12,500

Try This

7. Name three 4-digit numbers whose sum is 17,491. Sample answer:
8,000 + 8,000 + 1,491 = 17,491

Math Journal 1, p. 42

Ask students to turn to journal page 42. Have computation grids available (*Math Masters,* page 403 or 404) for those students who prefer to use them to help keep the digits in the proper columns. Assign Problems 1–7 for students to complete on their own.

Have students share their solutions to Problem 7 and indicate thumbs-up if they agree with an answer.

Ongoing Assessment: Recognizing Student Achievement

Journal page 42 Problems 4–6

Use **journal page 42, Problems 4–6** to assess students' ability to solve multidigit addition problems. Students are making adequate progress if they are able to use a paper-and-pencil algorithm to calculate the correct sums. Some students may be able to use more than one method to solve the problems or demonstrate how the relationship between + and − can be used to check their answers.

[Operations and Computation Goal 2]

▶ Discussing and Practicing the Column-Addition Method

WHOLE-CLASS ACTIVITY

COMPUTATION PRACTICE

(*Student Reference Book,* p. 11; *Math Journal 1,* p. 43)

Column addition is another method for adding numbers. It can become a reliable method for students who are still struggling with addition. Column addition is similar to the traditional addition algorithm that most adults know.

Discuss the example of the column-addition method that appears on page 11 of the *Student Reference Book*. In this algorithm, each column of numbers is added separately in any order.

- ▷ If this results in a single digit in each column, the sum has been found.
- ▷ If the sum of any column is a 2-digit number, that column sum is adjusted by "trading" part of the sum into the column to the left.
- ▷ The concept of trading is equivalent to the idea of carrying in the traditional algorithm. In some cultures, the words used to describe what we call *trading* translate into *making* and *breaking*. For example, when you have ten 1s, you *make* a 10. When you need more 1s, you *break* a 10.

Write several 2-digit and 3-digit addition problems on the board. Have volunteers use and describe the column-addition method to solve these problems.

Before students solve each problem, ask for and record ballpark estimates.

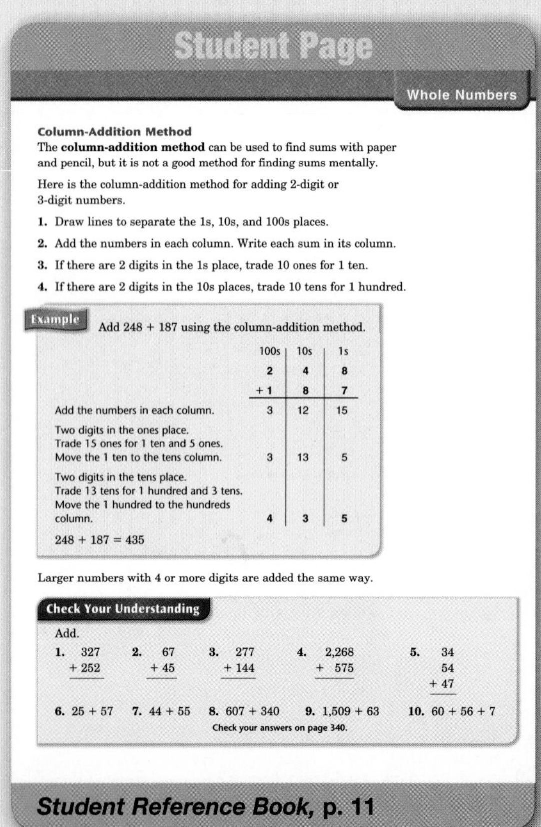
Student Page

Whole Numbers

Column-Addition Method

The **column-addition method** can be used to find sums with paper and pencil, but it is not a good method for finding sums mentally.

Here is the column-addition method for adding 2-digit or 3-digit numbers.

1. Draw lines to separate the 1s, 10s, and 100s places.
2. Add the numbers in each column. Write each sum in its column.
3. If there are 2 digits in the 1s place, trade 10 ones for 1 ten.
4. If there are 2 digits in the 10s places, trade 10 tens for 1 hundred.

Example Add 248 + 187 using the column-addition method.

	100s	10s	1s
	2	4	8
	+ 1	8	7
Add the numbers in each column.	3	12	15
Two digits in the ones place. Trade 15 ones for 1 ten and 5 ones. Move the 1 ten to the tens column.	3	13	5
Two digits in the tens place. Trade 13 tens for 1 hundred and 3 tens. Move the 1 hundred to the hundreds column.	4	3	5

248 + 187 = 435

Larger numbers with 4 or more digits are added the same way.

Check Your Understanding

Add.

1. 327 + 252
2. 67 + 45
3. 277 + 144
4. 2,268 + 575
5. 34 + 54 + 47
6. 25 + 57
7. 44 + 55
8. 607 + 340
9. 1,509 + 63
10. 60 + 56 + 7

Check your answers on page 340.

Student Reference Book, p. 11

Ask students to solve Problems 1–3 on journal page 43, using the column-addition method. They can do the remaining problems using any method they choose. Bring small groups of students together to share solutions.

Adjusting the Activity

ELL

Have students use base-10 blocks to model the meaning of *trading* in the context of addition.

AUDITORY ◆ KINESTHETIC ◆ TACTILE ◆ VISUAL

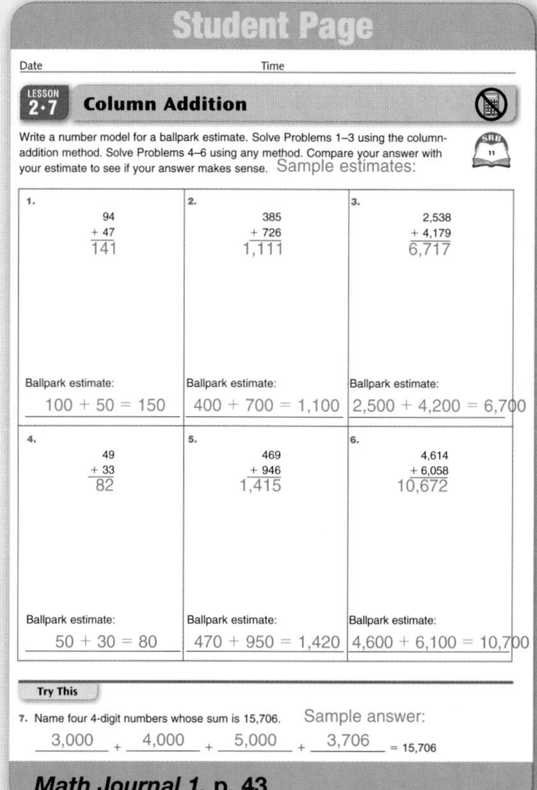

Student Page

Date Time

LESSON 2·7 **Column Addition**

Write a number model for a ballpark estimate. Solve Problems 1–3 using the column-addition method. Solve Problems 4–6 using any method. Compare your answer with your estimate to see if your answer makes sense. Sample estimates:

1. 94 + 47 = 141	2. 385 + 726 = 1,111	3. 2,538 + 4,179 = 6,717
Ballpark estimate: 100 + 50 = 150	Ballpark estimate: 400 + 700 = 1,100	Ballpark estimate: 2,500 + 4,200 = 6,700
4. 49 + 33 = 82	5. 469 + 946 = 1,415	6. 4,614 + 6,058 = 10,672
Ballpark estimate: 50 + 30 = 80	Ballpark estimate: 470 + 950 = 1,420	Ballpark estimate: 4,600 + 6,100 = 10,700

Try This

7. Name four 4-digit numbers whose sum is 15,706. Sample answer:
3,000 + 4,000 + 5,000 + 3,706 = 15,706

Math Journal 1, p. 43

2 Ongoing Learning & Practice

Playing *High-Number Toss*

PARTNER ACTIVITY

(*Student Reference Book*, p. 252; *Math Masters*, p. 487)

Students play *High-Number Toss* to practice comparing numbers.

Adjusting the Activity

Have students play *High-Number Toss* in groups of three or more to practice ordering numbers. Have them adjust the scoring accordingly.

AUDITORY ◆ KINESTHETIC ◆ TACTILE ◆ VISUAL

Math Boxes 2·7

INDEPENDENT ACTIVITY

(*Math Journal 1*, p. 44)

Mixed Practice Math Boxes in this lesson are linked with Math Boxes in Lessons 2-5 and 2-9. The skill in Problem 6 previews Unit 3 content.

Writing/Reasoning Have students write a response to the following: *Shaneel said, "I can draw a rhombus, rectangle, square, or kite for Problem 4." Do you agree or disagree? Explain your answer.* Sample answer: I disagree. A parallelogram has two pairs of parallel sides. A rhombus, rectangle, and square have two pairs of parallel sides, but a kite doesn't have any parallel sides.

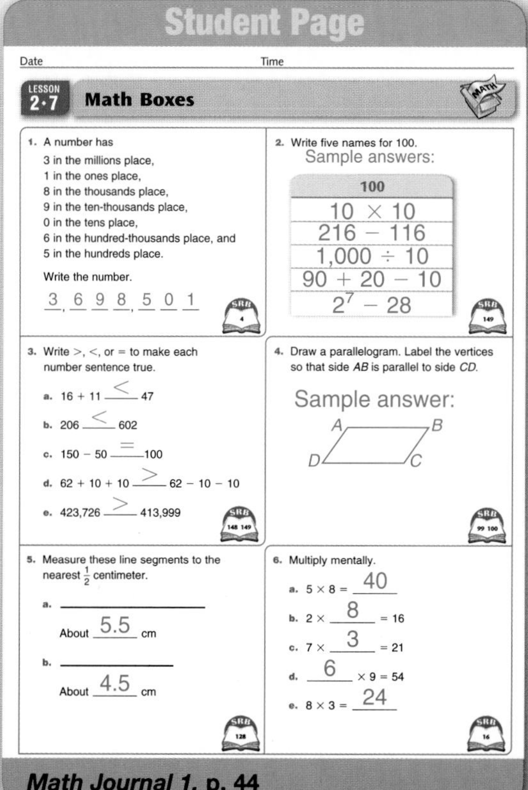

Student Page

Date Time

LESSON 2·7 **Math Boxes**

1. A number has
3 in the millions place,
1 in the ones place,
8 in the thousands place,
9 in the ten-thousands place,
0 in the tens place,
6 in the hundred-thousands place, and
5 in the hundreds place.
Write the number. 3, 6 9 8, 5 0 1

2. Write five names for 100. Sample answers:

100
10 × 10
216 − 116
1,000 ÷ 10
90 + 20 − 10
2^7 − 28

3. Write >, <, or = to make each number sentence true.
a. 16 + 11 < 47
b. 206 < 602
c. 150 − 50 = 100
d. 62 + 10 + 10 > 62 − 10 − 10
e. 423,726 > 413,999

4. Draw a parallelogram. Label the vertices so that side *AB* is parallel to side *CD*.
Sample answer:

5. Measure these line segments to the nearest $\frac{1}{2}$ centimeter.
a. About 5.5 cm
b. About 4.5 cm

6. Multiply mentally.
a. 5 × 8 = 40
b. 2 × 8 = 16
c. 7 × 3 = 21
d. 6 × 9 = 54
e. 8 × 3 = 24

Math Journal 1, p. 44

▶ Study Link 2·7

(*Math Masters,* pp. 57 and 58)

Home Connection Students solve addition problems and show someone at home how to use the methods they used in this lesson. Note that this Study Link consists of two pages—students use the partial-sums method on the first page and the column-addition method on the second page.

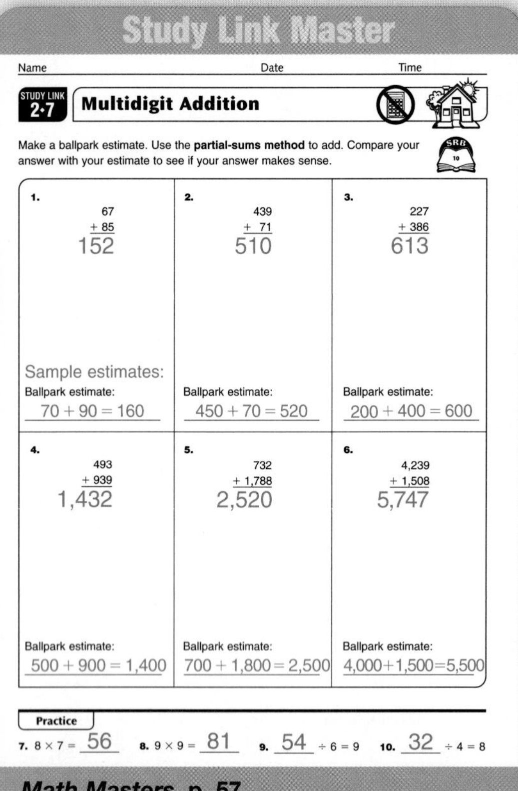

Study Link Master

Name Date Time

STUDY LINK 2·7 **Multidigit Addition**

Make a ballpark estimate. Use the **partial-sums method** to add. Compare your answer with your estimate to see if your answer makes sense.

1.	2.	3.
67 + 85 = 152	439 + 71 = 510	227 + 386 = 613
Sample estimates: Ballpark estimate: 70 + 90 = 160	Ballpark estimate: 450 + 70 = 520	Ballpark estimate: 200 + 400 = 600
4. 493 + 939 = 1,432	**5.** 732 + 1,788 = 2,520	**6.** 4,239 + 1,508 = 5,747
Ballpark estimate: 500 + 900 = 1,400	Ballpark estimate: 700 + 1,800 = 2,500	Ballpark estimate: 4,000 + 1,500 = 5,500

Practice

7. 8 × 7 = 56 8. 9 × 9 = 81 9. 54 ÷ 6 = 9 10. 32 ÷ 4 = 8

Math Masters, p. 57

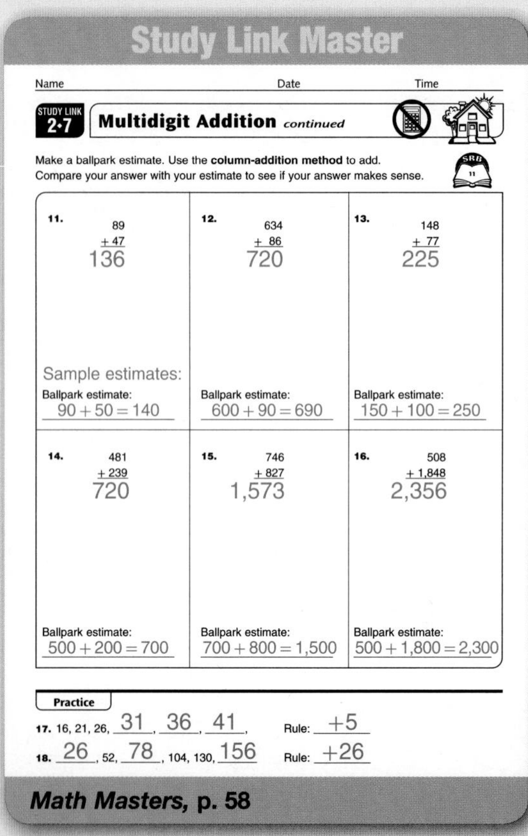

Study Link Master

Name Date Time

STUDY LINK 2·7 **Multidigit Addition** *continued*

Make a ballpark estimate. Use the **column-addition method** to add. Compare your answer with your estimate to see if your answer makes sense.

11.	12.	13.
89 + 47 = 136	634 + 86 = 720	148 + 77 = 225
Sample estimates: Ballpark estimate: 90 + 50 = 140	Ballpark estimate: 600 + 90 = 690	Ballpark estimate: 150 + 100 = 250
14. 481 + 239 = 720	**15.** 746 + 827 = 1,573	**16.** 508 + 1,848 = 2,356
Ballpark estimate: 500 + 200 = 700	Ballpark estimate: 700 + 800 = 1,500	Ballpark estimate: 500 + 1,800 = 2,300

Practice

17. 16, 21, 26, 31, 36, 41 Rule: +5

18. 26, 52, 78, 104, 130, 156 Rule: +26

Math Masters, p. 58

3 Differentiation Options

READINESS

▶ Solving Addition Number Stories

SMALL-GROUP ACTIVITY

15–30 Min

(*Math Masters,* pp. 59 and 405)

To explore solving addition problems using a concrete model, have students solve parts-and-total number stories using base-10 blocks and *Math Masters,* page 405. For each number story, students put base-10 blocks in each of the Part sections, then move the Parts into the Total section to solve the problem.

Example:

The class had 43 blue crayons and 15 red crayons. How many crayons did they have in all? Students first put 4 longs and 3 cubes in one of the Part sections and 1 long and 5 cubes in the other Part section. To solve the problem, they move all of the base-10 blocks to the Total section.

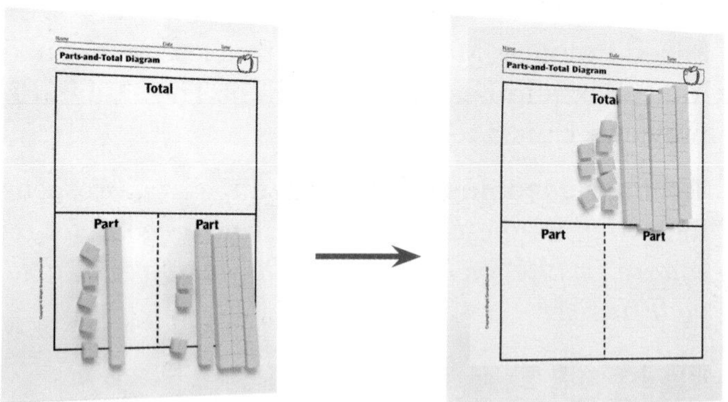

NOTE Instead of *Math Masters,* page 405, consider using paper dinner plates divided into three sections. Label each of the two smaller sections *Part* and the larger section *Total.*

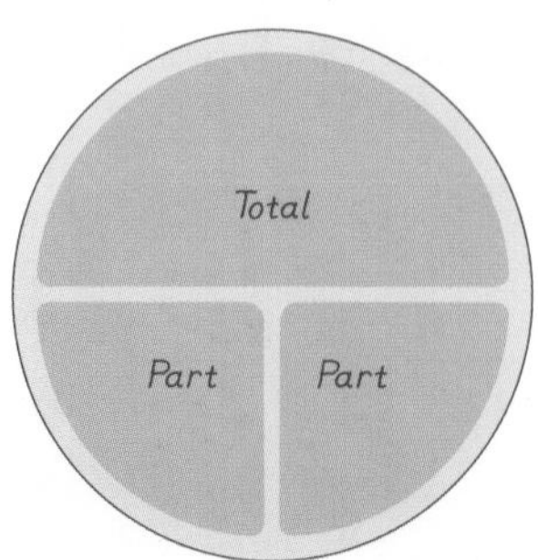

ENRICHMENT

Writing Addition Number Stories

15–30 Min

To apply students' understanding of addition algorithms, have them write and solve addition number stories. Then have them record a number model using a letter for the unknown. Encourage students to write multistep number stories. Stories may look similar to the following:

▷ Ian is shelving books in the library. He shelves 25 science fiction books, 18 biographies, and 36 mystery books. How many books did he shelve in all? Answer: 79 books; Number model: $25 + 18 + 36 = b$

Some students may be interested in writing and solving problems that involve distances, intervals of time, liquid volumes, masses of objects, or money. Stories may look similar to the following:

▷ Kendra bought some school supplies. She spent \$1.75 on folders, \$2.40 on pens, and \$3.80 on notebooks. How much did she spend in all? Answer: \$7.95; Number model: $\$1.75 + \$2.40 + \$3.80 = c$

▷ Marco wanted to make three different kinds of cookies for the school bake sale. The first recipe called for $2\frac{1}{2}$ cups of milk. The second called for $\frac{1}{2}$ cup of milk. The last called for $1\frac{1}{2}$ cups of milk. How much milk did Marco need in all? Answer: $4\frac{1}{2}$ cups of milk; Number model: $2\frac{1}{2} + \frac{1}{2} + 1\frac{1}{2} = m$

Provide opportunities for students to revise and share their writing. Then have partners solve each other's problems.

ELL SUPPORT

Building a Math Word Bank

5–15 Min

(*Differentiation Handbook,* p. 140)

To provide language support for estimation, have students use the Word Bank Template found on *Differentiation Handbook,* page 140. Ask students to write the term *ballpark estimate,* draw a picture representing the term, and write other related words. See the *Differentiation Handbook* for more information.

Planning Ahead

For Part 3 in Lesson 2-8, you will need several baseball caps with adjustable headbands—one cap to be used by each small group of students. Ask students to bring baseball caps to school if they can. To be on the safe side, bring in one or more caps.

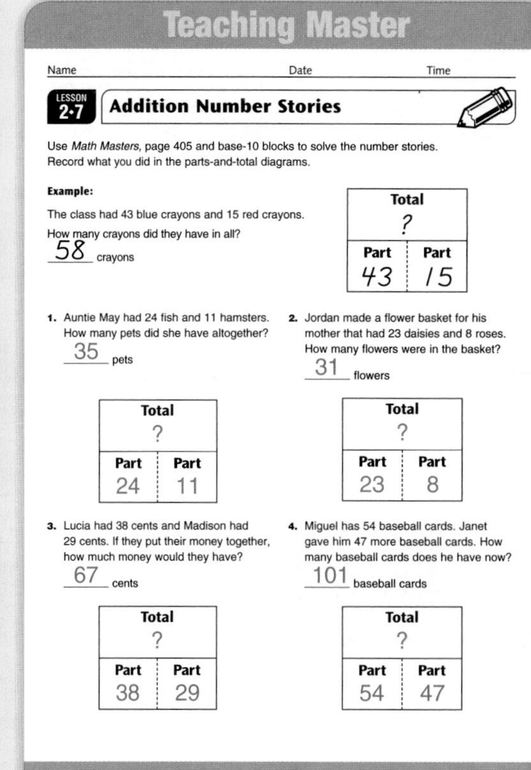

Teaching Master

Name Date Time

LESSON 2·7 **Addition Number Stories**

Use *Math Masters,* page 405 and base-10 blocks to solve the number stories. Record what you did in the parts-and-total diagrams.

Example:

The class had 43 blue crayons and 15 red crayons. How many crayons did they have in all?
58 crayons

Total	
?	
Part	Part
43	15

1. Auntie May had 24 fish and 11 hamsters. How many pets did she have altogether?
35 pets

Total	
?	
Part	Part
24	11

2. Jordan made a flower basket for his mother that had 23 daisies and 8 roses. How many flowers were in the basket?
31 flowers

Total	
?	
Part	Part
23	8

3. Lucia had 38 cents and Madison had 29 cents. If they put their money together, how much money would they have?
67 cents

Total	
?	
Part	Part
38	29

4. Miguel has 54 baseball cards. Janet gave him 47 more baseball cards. How many baseball cards does he have now?
101 baseball cards

Total	
?	
Part	Part
54	47

Math Masters, p. 59

2•8 Displaying Data with Graphs

Objectives To provide practice measuring length to the nearest half-centimeter; and to guide the construction and use of graphs for a set of collected data.

www.everydaymathonline.com

ePresentations

eToolkit

Algorithms Practice

EM Facts Workshop Game™

Family Letters

Assessment Management

Common Core State Standards

Curriculum Focal Points

Interactive Teacher's Lesson Guide

1 Teaching the Lesson

Key Concepts and Skills

- Create a bar graph and line plot. [Data and Chance Goal 1]
- Determine the maximum, minimum, range, mode, and median of a data set. [Data and Chance Goal 2]
- Ask and answer questions and draw conclusions based on data landmarks, a bar graph, and a line plot. [Data and Chance Goal 2]
- Measure to the nearest half-centimeter. [Measurement and Reference Frames Goal 1]

Key Activities

Students measure their head sizes to the nearest half-centimeter. They find the median head size and make a bar graph and line plot of the data.

Ongoing Assessment: Informing Instruction See page 127.

Ongoing Assessment: Recognizing Student Achievement Use journal page 46. [Data and Chance Goal 2]

Key Vocabulary

bar graph

Materials

Math Journal 1, pp. 46, 47, 47A, and 47B
Student Reference Book, p. 71
Study Link 2•7 ◆ *Math Masters,* p. 60
per partnership: tape measure ◆ ruler ◆ stick-on notes ◆ slate ◆ computer with Internet access (optional)

2 Ongoing Learning & Practice

Constructing a Kite

Math Journal 1, p. 48
compass ◆ straightedge
Students construct a kite with a compass and straightedge.

Math Boxes 2•8

Math Journal 1, p. 45
Students practice and maintain skills through Math Box problems.

Study Link 2•8

Math Masters, p. 61
Students practice and maintain skills through Study Link activities.

3 Differentiation Options

READINESS

Constructing a "Real Graph"

Math Masters, pp. 62 and 406
pattern blocks ◆ tape
Students use pattern blocks to construct a real graph.

ENRICHMENT

Determining the Validity of the "One Size Fits All" Claim

Math Journal 1, pp. 46 and 47
Math Masters, p. 63
baseball caps with adjustable headbands ◆ tape measure
Students analyze a product claim by using the class head-size data.

Advance Preparation

Place copies of *Math Masters,* page 60 near the Math Message. For the optional Readiness activity in Part 3, cut apart and tape together four copies of *Math Masters,* page 406 for students to use as a graph mat and get the pattern blocks specified on page 131.

***Teacher's Reference Manual,* Grades 4–6** pp. 161–167, 216–219

Getting Started

Mental Math and Reflexes

Pose addition problems such as the following. Encourage students to share their strategies.

●○○ 20 + 5 = 25
8 + 40 = 48
14 + 6 = 20
7 + 23 = 30

●●○ 12 + 9 = 21
15 + 8 = 23
18 + 4 = 22
27 + 6 = 33

●●● 331 + 179 = 510
627 + 266 = 893
218 + 572 = 790
644 + 548 = 1,192

Math Message

Take out your ruler. Complete Math Masters, *page 60.*

Study Link 2·7 Follow-Up

Have partners compare answers. Encourage students to add any interesting number facts to the Numbers and Their Uses Museum.

1 Teaching the Lesson

Math Message Follow-Up

INDEPENDENT ACTIVITY

(*Math Masters,* p. 60)

As students are measuring and drawing the line segments, circulate and observe. Have them check each other's work and remeasure line segments to resolve any disagreements.

Ongoing Assessment: Informing Instruction

Watch for students who are having difficulty measuring to the nearest half-centimeter. Look for common errors such as measuring from a point other than the 0-mark on the ruler, rounding incorrectly, or failing to recognize the millimeter mark halfway between the two whole numbers.

Collecting and Organizing Head-Size Data

PARTNER ACTIVITY

(*Math Journal 1,* pp. 46, 47, 47A, and 47B; *Student Reference Book,* p. 71)

To introduce this activity, read the first two paragraphs on journal page 46 as a class. To help solve Ms. Woods's problem, have partners measure the distance around each other's heads and *record* the measurement in Problem 1 on journal page 46. When students measure head size, the tape measure should measure the maximum distance around the skull. Then ask students to organize these measurements, using some of the techniques from the previous lessons. This activity can be done in a number of ways, one of which is described on the next page.

Adjusting the Activity

ELL

Discuss the different meanings and pronunciations of the word *record.* For example, compare the phrase "record their head sizes" with the phrase "holds the record for the fastest 100-meter dash."

AUDITORY ◆ KINESTHETIC ◆ TACTILE ◆ VISUAL

Teaching Master

Name Date Time

LESSON 2·8 **Measuring and Drawing Line Segments**

SRB 128

Measure the following line segments to the nearest $\frac{1}{2}$ centimeter.

1. About 7 cm
2. About 9 cm
3. About 7.5 cm
4. About 11.5 cm

Draw line segments having the following lengths:

5. 8 centimeters
6. 10 centimeters
7. 3.5 centimeters

Try This

8. Draw a line segment having the following length: 46 millimeters

Math Masters, p. 60

Student Page

Date Time

LESSON 2·8 **Head Sizes**

Ms. Woods owns a clothing store. She is trying to decide how many children's hats to stock in each possible size. Should she stock the same number of hats in each size? Or should she stock more hats in some sizes and fewer in others?

Help Ms. Woods decide. Pretend that she has asked each class in your school to collect and organize data about students' head sizes. She plans to combine the data and then use it to figure out how many hats of each size to stock.

As a class, collect and organize data about one another's head sizes.

1. Ask your partner to help you measure the distance around your head.
   - Wrap the tape measure once around your head.
   - See where the tape touches the end tip of the tape measure.
   - Read the mark where the tape touches the end tip.
   - Read this length to the nearest $\frac{1}{2}$ centimeter.

   Answers vary.

   Record your head size. About ______ cm
2. What is the median head size for the class? About ______ cm
3. Find the following landmarks for the head-size data shown in the bar graph on journal page 47.

   Minimum: ______ Maximum: ______ Range: ______

   Mode: ______ Median: ______
4. How would the landmarks above help Ms. Woods, a clothing store owner, decide how many baseball caps of each size to stock?

   Sample answer: Ms. Woods will want to stock a lot more baseball caps in the median and mode sizes than in any other size. She will also want to be sure not to stock many baseball caps that are smaller than the minimum size and larger than the maximum size.

Math Journal 1, p. 46

Adjusting the Activity

Ask students to discuss whether the mean is a useful data landmark in this situation.

AUDITORY ◆ KINESTHETIC ◆ TACTILE ◆ VISUAL

NOTE If graphing software is available, have students use it to create bar graphs. Consider using the bar grapher at http://illuminations.nctm.org/ActivityDetail.aspx?id=63. Then have the class compare these with the graphs students made on journal page 47.

NOTE The median head size for fourth graders is about 52 centimeters. Of all fourth graders, 95 percent have head sizes between 49 and 55 centimeters.

Men's and women's hats are sized in different ways. The size of a woman's hat — 22, for example — is approximately the distance around the head in inches. To understand a man's hat size — 6 $\frac{7}{8}$, for example, imagine taking a sweatband inside the hat and forming it into a circle. The size is the diameter of the circle to the nearest $\frac{1}{8}$ inch. This system began centuries ago, when new hats were round. Men used a device called a *hat screw* to force their hats into a more comfortable oval shape.

Finding the Median Head Size

Have students record their head sizes on stick-on notes and line up in order from smallest to largest head size. Send students to the line, one at a time, and have each one compare the measurement he or she wrote on the stick-on note with those of students who are already in line. If two students have the same head size, they should stand next to each other.

Ask for suggestions for identifying the person in the middle of the line. Suggest one of the following methods, or encourage students to make up one of their own:

- ▷ Count off from one end of the line to the other (1, 2, 3, and so on). Find the person (or people) whose number is halfway between 1 and the number of the last person in line.
- ▷ Count off from both ends of the line (1, 1, 2, 2, 3, 3, and so on). The highest number identifies the middle person (or people).
- ▷ Have the person at each end of the line sit down. Repeat until one or two people are left standing.

Remind students that the median head size is the head size of the person in the middle. If there are two people, it is the measurement halfway between the two middle head sizes. Have students record the median in Problem 2 on journal page 46.

Making a Bar Graph of the Data

You can follow these steps to make a **bar graph** of the data.

1. On the board, draw a horizontal and vertical axis, and write 0 next to the point where the two axes meet.
2. Draw additional points, about 4 inches apart, on the horizontal axis, and label the first point with the smallest measurement. Label the rest of the points in half-centimeter increments. Write "Head Sizes to the Nearest $\frac{1}{2}$ cm" under the horizontal axis.
3. Have students attach their stick-on notes in the appropriate places above the horizontal axis. Each note should just touch the one below it.
4. Label the points on the vertical axis. Write "Number of Students" next to the vertical axis. Write an appropriate title for the graph at the top.

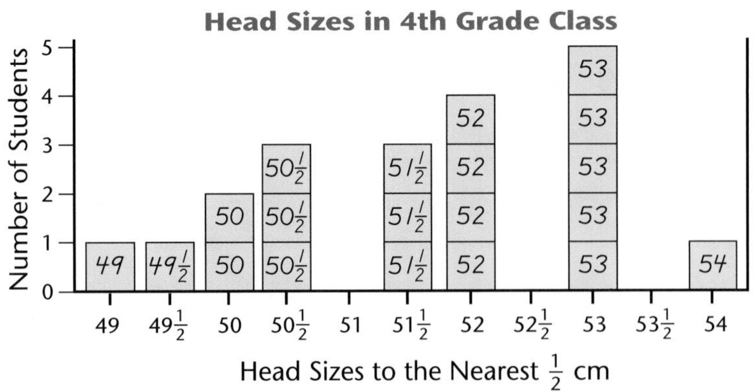

5. Ask students to copy the bar graph onto journal page 47. Have them mark and label the axes and color the bars to represent the stick-on notes. Each column of stick-on notes represents one of the bars in the bar graph. Remind students to copy the title of the graph.

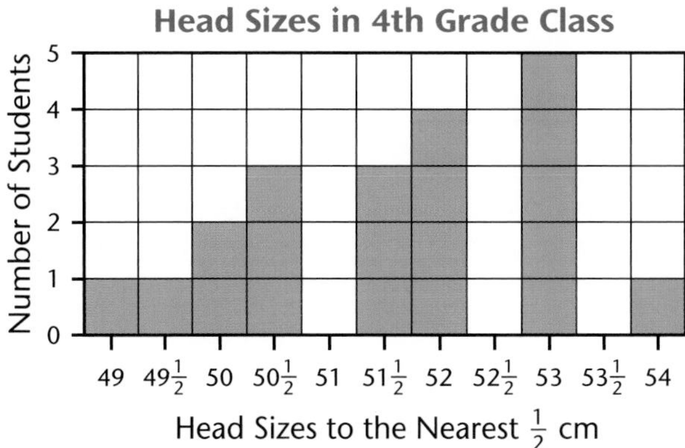

Adjusting the Activity

Ask volunteers to pose questions to the class regarding the data displayed. *For example:*

- Are the bars bunched together?
- Are there any isolated or way-out bars?
- Are there more _____ or more _____?
- How many _____ and _____ are there in all?

AUDITORY • KINESTHETIC • TACTILE • VISUAL

Making a Line Plot of the Data

Direct students to the essay on *Student Reference Book,* page 71, "Organizing Data." Discuss features of line plots. Ask students to use the information in the original bar graph to create a line plot on journal page 47B. Have them label the axes and use an X to replace each stick-on note. Remind students to write the title of the graph.

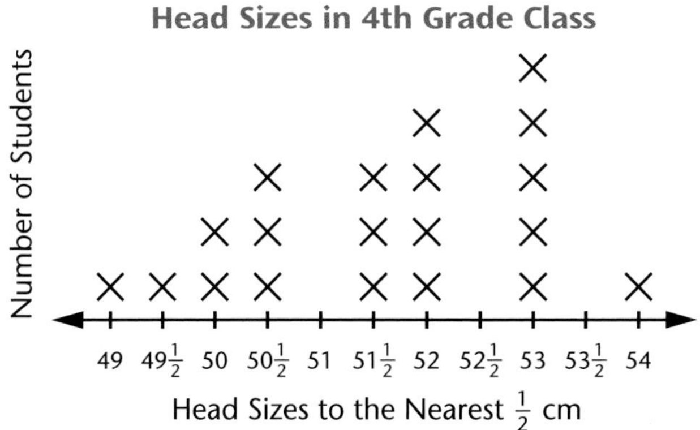

After students complete the line plot, have them answer the questions on journal page 47A.

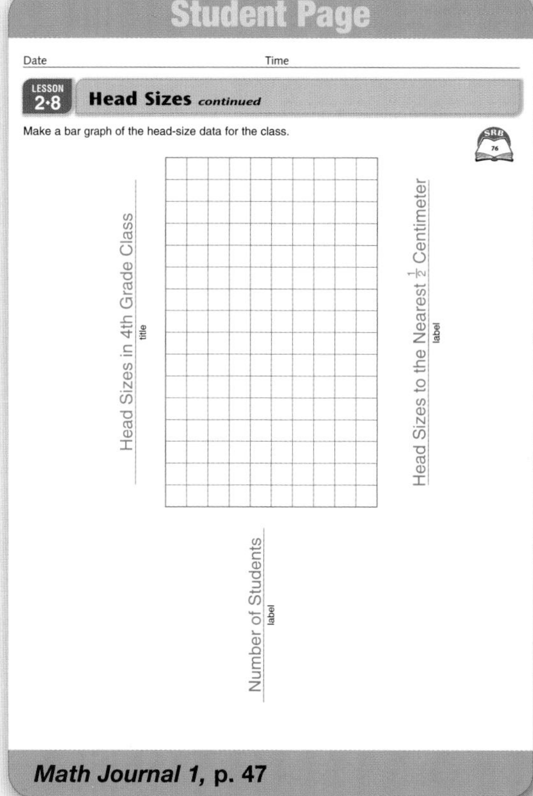

Student Page

Date Time

LESSON 2·8 **Head Sizes** *continued*

Make a bar graph of the head-size data for the class.

Head Sizes in 4th Grade Class (title)

Head Sizes to the Nearest $\frac{1}{2}$ Centimeter (label)

Number of Students (label)

Math Journal 1, p. 47

NOTE Stem-and-leaf plots are covered in Grade 5. If your curriculum requires that this concept be covered in Grade 4, see www.everydaymathonline.com.

Student Page

Date Time

LESSON 2·8 **Head Sizes** *continued*

1. Count the Xs in the line plot you created on journal page 47B to answer the questions below. Answers vary.
   a. What is the largest head size? _____
   b. What is the smallest head size? _____
   c. What is the difference between the largest and the smallest head size? Write a number model to show how you found your answer.
   d. What is the mode of the head-size data? _____
   e. What is the difference between your head size and the mode? Write a number model to show how you found your answer.
2. Did anything about the data surprise you? Did you expect the head sizes to be close together or spread out?
   Sample answer: I expected the head sizes to be clumped together because everyone in the class is close in age.
3. The average head size for an infant at birth is 35 cm. Use a number model to show how your head size compares to that of an infant.
   Answers vary.
4. Imagine that you measured the head sizes of a room full of newborn babies and created a line plot. What would you expect the graph to look like? Explain your answer.
   Sample answer: I would expect the middle of the data to be around 35 cm. There might be some way-out numbers because babies can be many different sizes when they are born.

Math Journal 1, p. 47A

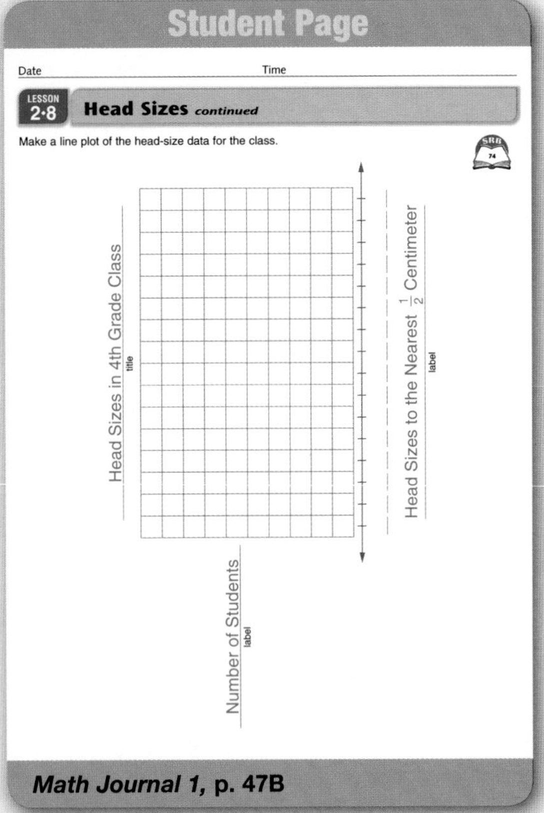
Student Page

Date Time

LESSON 2·8 **Head Sizes** *continued*

Make a line plot of the head-size data for the class.

Math Journal 1, **p. 47B**

▶ Analyzing Head-Size Data

INDEPENDENT ACTIVITY

(*Math Journal 1,* pp. 46 and 47)

Have students complete Problems 3 and 4 on journal page 46 on their own.

Ongoing Assessment: Recognizing Student Achievement

Journal page 46 Problem 4

Use **journal page 46, Problem 4** to assess students' ability to use data landmarks and a bar graph to draw conclusions about a data set. Students are making adequate progress if their responses include ideas such as the following:

- ▷ The smallest and largest sizes suggest the range of sizes Ms. Woods should have in her inventory.
- ▷ The most frequently reported size and the median would suggest the sizes for which Ms. Woods should have the largest inventory.

Some students may be able to explain why the mean would not be a useful data landmark in this situation.

[Data and Chance Goal 2]

2 Ongoing Learning & Practice

▶ Constructing a Kite

(*Math Journal 1,* p. 48)

Students use a compass and a straightedge to construct a kite. Ask students to explain how they know the polygon is a kite.

▶ Math Boxes 2·8

(*Math Journal 1,* p. 45)

Mixed Practice Math Boxes in this lesson are paired with Math Boxes in Lesson 2-6. The skills in Problems 5 and 6 preview Unit 3 content.

Writing/Reasoning Have students write a response for the following: *Describe the patterns in the number sentences in Problem 1.* Sample answer: The numbers in the second problem of each set are 10 times the numbers in the first problem. The numbers in the third problem of each set are 10 times the numbers in the second problem and 100 times the numbers in the first problem.

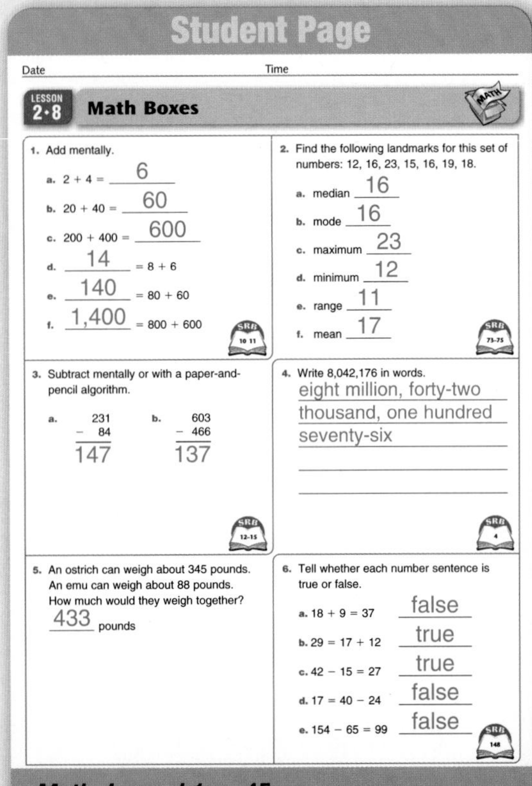
Student Page

Date Time

LESSON 2·8 **Math Boxes**

1. Add mentally.
   a. 2 + 4 = 6
   b. 20 + 40 = 60
   c. 200 + 400 = 600
   d. 14 = 8 + 6
   e. 140 = 80 + 60
   f. 1,400 = 800 + 600

2. Find the following landmarks for this set of numbers: 12, 16, 23, 15, 16, 19, 18.
   a. median 16
   b. mode 16
   c. maximum 23
   d. minimum 12
   e. range 11
   f. mean 17

3. Subtract mentally or with a paper-and-pencil algorithm.
   a. 231 − 84 = 147
   b. 603 − 466 = 137

4. Write 8,042,176 in words.
   eight million, forty-two thousand, one hundred seventy-six

5. An ostrich can weigh about 345 pounds. An emu can weigh about 88 pounds. How much would they weigh together?
   433 pounds

6. Tell whether each number sentence is true or false.
   a. 18 + 9 = 37 false
   b. 29 = 17 + 12 true
   c. 42 − 15 = 27 true
   d. 17 = 40 − 24 false
   e. 154 − 65 = 99 false

Math Journal 1, **p. 45**

▶ Study Link 2·8

(*Math Masters,* p. 61)

Home Connection Students answer questions based on gestation-period data for selected animals.

3 Differentiation Options

READINESS

PARTNER ACTIVITY

15–30 Min

Constructing a "Real Graph"

(*Math Masters,* pp. 62 and 406)

To provide experience with a bar graph using a concrete model, have students use pattern blocks (4 hexagons, 8 trapezoids, 2 triangles, 4 squares, 6 blue rhombi, and 3 tan rhombi) to construct a "real graph" and answer questions based on their display. When students have completed the graph, discuss an appropriate title and labels.

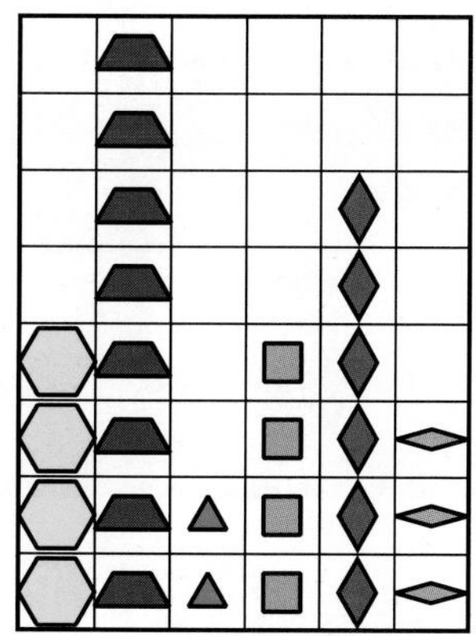

ENRICHMENT

PARTNER ACTIVITY

5–15 Min

Determining the Validity of the "One Size Fits All" Claim

(*Math Journal 1,* pp. 46 and 47; *Math Masters,* p. 63)

Consumer Link To investigate the application of data, have students determine whether an adjustable cap will fit all students in the class.

Teaching Master

Name Date Time

LESSON 2·8 "One Size Fits All" Claim

Makers of adjustable baseball caps claim that "one size fits all." Do you think this is a true statement? Use the head-size data you collected on journal pages 46 and 47 to help you decide.

Answers vary.

1. Select a baseball cap and adjust the headband to the smallest size. Measure and record the distance around the inside of the baseball cap to the nearest half centimeter.

   Smallest size: ______ cm

2. Now adjust the headband to the largest size. Measure and record.

   Largest size: ______ cm

3. Compare the measurements above with the head-size data you and your class collected. Could this baseball cap be worn by everyone in the class? Explain your answer.

4. Do you think you have enough information to decide whether or not the claim "one size fits all" is true? ______ Explain.

Math Masters, p. 63

Study Link Master

Name Date Time

STUDY LINK 2·8 Gestation Period

SRB 73

The period between the time an animal becomes pregnant and the time its baby is born is called the **gestation period.** The table below shows the number of days in the average gestation period for some animals.

Average Gestation Period (in days)

Animal	Number of Days
dog	61
giraffe	457
goat	151
human	266
Asian elephant	645
mouse	19
squirrel	44
rhinoceros	480
rabbit	31

Source: World Almanac

1. For the gestation periods listed in the table ...
   a. what is the maximum number of days? 645 days
   b. what is the minimum number of days? 19 days
   c. what is the range (the difference between the maximum and the minimum)? 626 days
   d. what is the median (middle) number of days? 151 days
2. Which animals have an average gestation period that is longer than 1 year? giraffe, Asian elephant, and rhinoceros
3. How much longer is the average gestation period for a goat than for a dog? 90 days
4. Which animal has an average gestation period that is about twice as long as a rabbit's? dog
5. Which animal has an average gestation period that is about half as long as a squirrel's? mouse

Practice

6. 56 + 33 = 89
7. 263 = 167 + 96
8. 46 = 78 − 32
9. 271 − 89 = 182

Math Masters, p. 61

NOTE For practice with pictographs, see www.everydaymathonline.com.

Teaching Master

Name Date Time

LESSON 2·8 Construct a "Real" Graph

SRB 76

Do this activity with a partner.

Materials ☐ set of pattern blocks from your teacher

☐ graph mat (4 copies of *Math Masters,* page 406 taped together)

1. Display the pattern blocks on the graph mat so that you can easily count and compare the number of hexagons, trapezoids, triangles, squares, blue rhombi, and tan rhombi.

   hexagon, trapezoid, triangle, square, blue rhombus, tan rhombus

2. Use your display to answer the following questions.
   a. Which pattern block appears the most? trapezoid The least? triangle
   b. How many hexagons and triangles are there altogether? 6
   c. How many more trapezoids are there than squares? 4
3. Use your display to complete the following statements. Sample answers:
   a. There are fewer squares than trapezoids.
   b. There are more blue rhombi than triangles.
   c. There is the same number of hexagons as squares.
4. Write a question that can be answered by looking at your display. Answer your question.
   a. Question How many rhombi are there altogether?
   b. Answer 9

Try This

5. How many more quadrangles are there than nonquadrangles? 15

Math Masters, p. 62

2•9 Subtraction of Multidigit Numbers

Objectives To review the trade-first and counting-up methods, and to introduce the partial-differences method of solving multidigit subtraction problems; and to provide practice estimating differences for multidigit subtraction problems.

Technology Resources www.everydaymathonline.com

ePresentations

eToolkit

Algorithms Practice

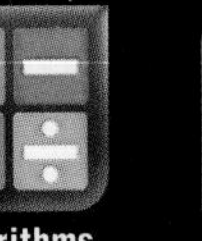
EM Facts Workshop Game™

Family Letters

Assessment Management

Common Core State Standards

Curriculum Focal Points

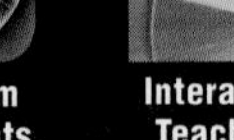
Interactive Teacher's Lesson Guide

1 Teaching the Lesson

Key Concepts and Skills

- Identify places in whole numbers and the values of the digits in those places. [Number and Numeration Goal 1]
- Apply extended subtraction facts. [Operations and Computation Goal 1]
- Use the trade-first and partial-differences algorithms to solve multidigit subtraction problems; choose an appropriate paper-and-pencil algorithm to solve multidigit subtraction problems. [Operations and Computation Goal 2]
- Make ballpark estimates for multidigit subtraction problems. [Operations and Computation Goal 6]

Key Activities

Students use the trade-first and partial-differences methods for subtraction.

Ongoing Assessment: Recognizing Student Achievement
Use journal page 49.
[Operations and Computation Goal 2]

Key Vocabulary

trade-first method ◆ partial-differences method

Materials

Math Journal 1, pp. 49 and 50
Student Reference Book, pp. 12 and 15
Study Link 2•8
Math Masters, p. 403 or 404 (optional)
slate ◆ quarter-sheet of paper ◆ base-10 blocks (optional)

2 Ongoing Learning & Practice

Playing *Subtraction Target Practice*
Student Reference Book, p. 262
Math Masters, p. 504
calculator ◆ 4 each of number cards 0–9 (from the Everything Math Deck, if available)
Students practice place-value and subtraction skills.

Math Boxes 2•9
Math Journal 1, p. 51
Students practice and maintain skills through Math Box problems.

Study Link 2•9
Math Masters, pp. 64 and 65
Students practice and maintain skills through Study Link activities.

3 Differentiation Options

READINESS

Subtracting by Counting Up
Student Reference Book, p. 14
Math Masters, p. 66
Students explore visual models for solving subtraction problems.

ENRICHMENT

Solving Number-Tile Problems
Math Masters, p. 67
scissors
Students find missing digits in addition and subtraction problems.

ENRICHMENT

Writing Subtraction Number Stories
Students write and solve subtraction number stories.

Advance Preparation

Plan to spend two days on this lesson. Place quarter-sheets of paper near the Math Message. If students need computation grids in Part 1, make copies of *Math Masters,* page 403 or 404.

***Teacher's Reference Manual,* Grades 4–6** pp. 122–126, 260, 261

Getting Started

Mental Math and Reflexes

Pose subtraction problems such as the following. Have students estimate the differences.

Level	Problem	Estimate	Estimate
●○○	43 − 26	40 − 20 = 20;	40 − 30 = 10
	67 − 52	60 − 50 = 10;	70 − 50 = 20
	84 − 39	80 − 40 = 40;	90 − 40 = 50
●●○	126 − 81	130 − 80 = 50;	120 − 80 = 40
	392 − 47	400 − 50 = 350;	390 − 50 = 340
	643 − 98	650 − 100 = 550;	600 − 100 = 500
●●●	245 − 199	250 − 200 = 50;	240 − 200 = 40
	563 − 370	560 − 400 = 160;	600 − 400 = 200
	808 − 257	800 − 300 = 500;	800 − 250 = 550

Math Message

Solve the problems on a quarter-sheet of paper. Show your work.

$$\begin{array}{r} 90 \\ -\ 37 \\ \hline 53 \end{array} \qquad \begin{array}{r} 239 \\ -\ 157 \\ \hline 82 \end{array}$$

Study Link 2·8 Follow-Up

Have students compare answers. Ask volunteers to share number models for Problems 4 and 5.

1 Teaching the Lesson

Math Message Follow-Up

WHOLE-CLASS ACTIVITY

COMPUTATION PRACTICE

Have students share their solution strategies. Tell the class that in this lesson they will review the **trade-first method** and explore the **partial-differences method.** Some students may have used these algorithms to solve the Math Message problems.

Discussing and Practicing the Trade-First Method for Subtraction

WHOLE-CLASS ACTIVITY

COMPUTATION PRACTICE

(*Math Journal 1,* p. 49; *Student Reference Book,* p. 12)

Students used the trade-first method in *Third Grade Everyday Mathematics*. Discuss the example on page 12 of the *Student Reference Book* and point out the following:

- ▷ The problem is written vertically.
- ▷ If each digit of the larger (top) number is greater than or equal to the digit directly below it, no adjustments are required before subtracting.
- ▷ Subtraction is performed column by column.
- ▷ If one (or more) digit of the top number is less than the digit directly below it, then the top number is adjusted by "trading" before any subtracting is done. For example, we might need to trade one of the tens for 10 ones or one of the hundreds for 10 tens.
- ▷ All adjustments are made from right to left.

Links to the Future

In Unit 4 of *Fourth Grade Everyday Mathematics* students apply these subtraction algorithms to decimal numbers.

Algorithm Project The focus of this lesson is the trade-first and partial-differences algorithms for subtraction. To teach U.S. traditional subtraction, see Algorithm Project 3 on page A10.

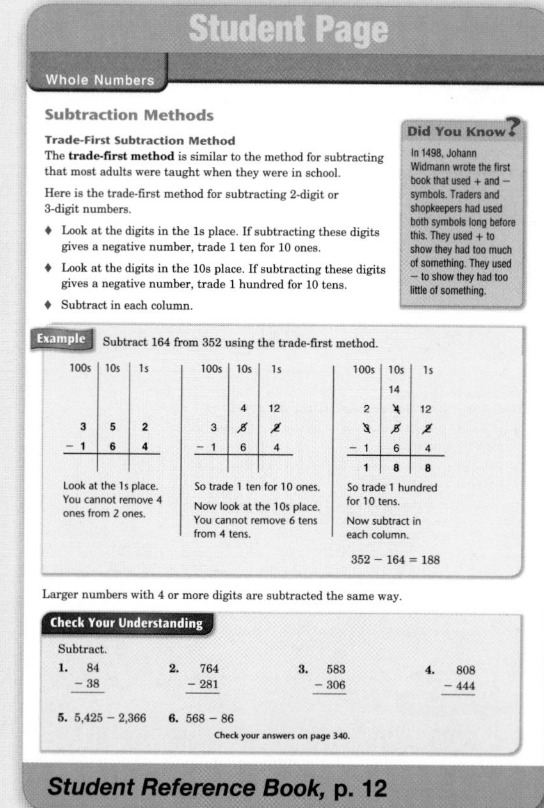

Student Page

Whole Numbers

Subtraction Methods

Trade-First Subtraction Method

The **trade-first method** is similar to the method for subtracting that most adults were taught when they were in school.

Here is the trade-first method for subtracting 2-digit or 3-digit numbers.

- ♦ Look at the digits in the 1s place. If subtracting these digits gives a negative number, trade 1 ten for 10 ones.
- ♦ Look at the digits in the 10s place. If subtracting these digits gives a negative number, trade 1 hundred for 10 tens.
- ♦ Subtract in each column.

Did You Know? In 1498, Johann Widmann wrote the first book that used + and − symbols. Traders and shopkeepers had used both symbols long before this. They used + to show they had too much of something. They used − to show they had too little of something.

Example Subtract 164 from 352 using the trade-first method.

100s	10s	1s
3	5	2
− 1	6	4

Look at the 1s place. You cannot remove 4 ones from 2 ones.

100s	10s	1s
	4	12
3	~~5~~	~~2~~
− 1	6	4

So trade 1 ten for 10 ones.

Now look at the 10s place. You cannot remove 6 tens from 4 tens.

100s	10s	1s
	14	
2	~~4~~	12
~~3~~	~~5~~	~~2~~
− 1	6	4
1	8	8

So trade 1 hundred for 10 tens.

Now subtract in each column.

352 − 164 = 188

Larger numbers with 4 or more digits are subtracted the same way.

Check Your Understanding

Subtract.

1. 84 − 38
2. 764 − 281
3. 583 − 306
4. 808 − 444
5. 5,425 − 2,366
6. 568 − 86

Check your answers on page 340.

Student Reference Book, p. 12

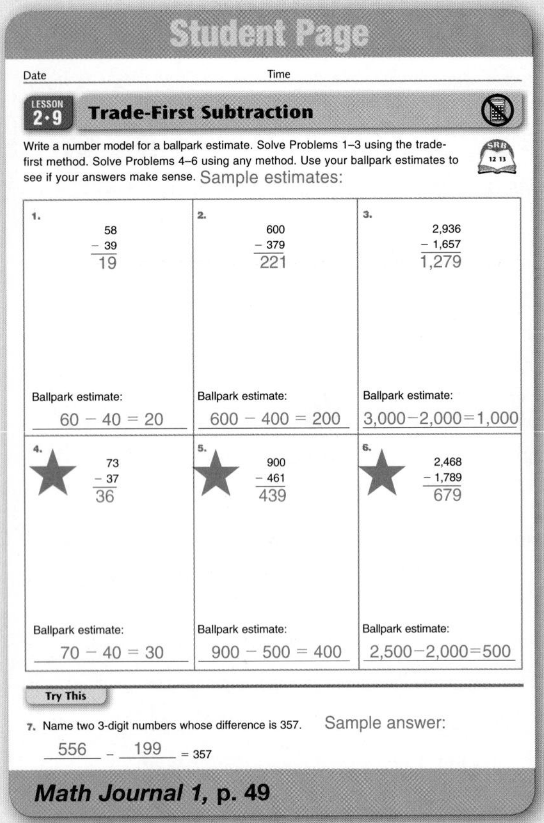

Student Page

Date Time

LESSON 2·9 **Trade-First Subtraction**

Write a number model for a ballpark estimate. Solve Problems 1–3 using the trade-first method. Solve Problems 4–6 using any method. Use your ballpark estimates to see if your answers make sense. Sample estimates:

1. 58 − 39 = 19	2. 600 − 379 = 221	3. 2,936 − 1,657 = 1,279
Ballpark estimate: 60 − 40 = 20	Ballpark estimate: 600 − 400 = 200	Ballpark estimate: 3,000−2,000=1,000
4. 73 − 37 = 36	5. 900 − 461 = 439	6. 2,468 − 1,789 = 679
Ballpark estimate: 70 − 40 = 30	Ballpark estimate: 900 − 500 = 400	Ballpark estimate: 2,500−2,000=500

Try This

7. Name two 3-digit numbers whose difference is 357. Sample answer: 556 − 199 = 357

Math Journal 1, p. 49

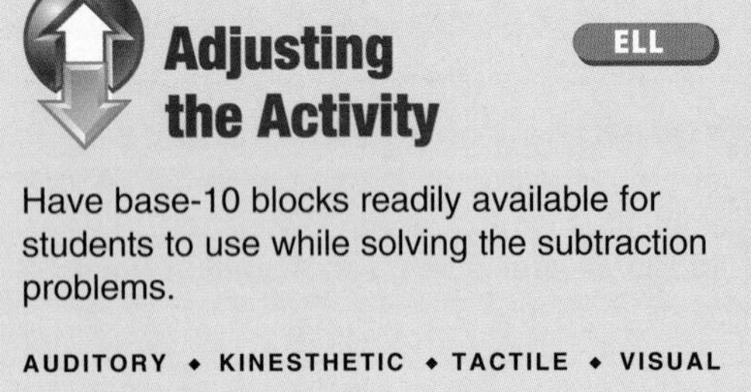

Adjusting the Activity ELL

Have base-10 blocks readily available for students to use while solving the subtraction problems.

AUDITORY ◆ KINESTHETIC ◆ TACTILE ◆ VISUAL

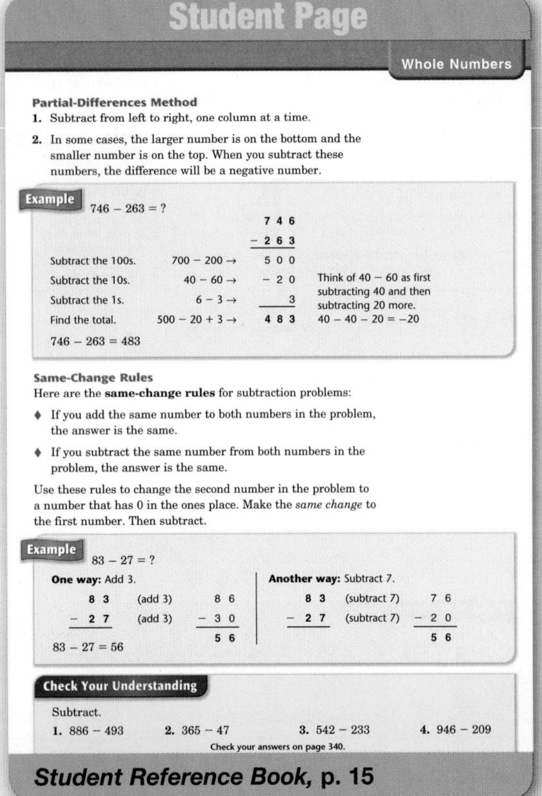

Student Page

Whole Numbers

Partial-Differences Method

1. Subtract from left to right, one column at a time.
2. In some cases, the larger number is on the bottom and the smaller number is on the top. When you subtract these numbers, the difference will be a negative number.

Example 746 − 263 = ?

		746 − 263	
Subtract the 100s.	700 − 200 →	500	
Subtract the 10s.	40 − 60 →	− 20	Think of 40 − 60 as first subtracting 40 and then subtracting 20 more. 40 − 40 − 20 = −20
Subtract the 1s.	6 − 3 →	3	
Find the total.	500 − 20 + 3 →	483	

746 − 263 = 483

Same-Change Rules

Here are the **same-change rules** for subtraction problems:

- If you add the same number to both numbers in the problem, the answer is the same.
- If you subtract the same number from both numbers in the problem, the answer is the same.

Use these rules to change the second number in the problem to a number that has 0 in the ones place. Make the *same change* to the first number. Then subtract.

Example 83 − 27 = ?

One way: Add 3.
83 (add 3) 86
− 27 (add 3) − 30
56
83 − 27 = 56

Another way: Subtract 7.
83 (subtract 7) 76
− 27 (subtract 7) − 20
56

Check Your Understanding

Subtract.

1. 886 − 493 2. 365 − 47 3. 542 − 233 4. 946 − 209

Check your answers on page 340.

Student Reference Book, p. 15

Pose the following subtraction problem:

$$\begin{array}{r} 512 \\ -\ 364 \\ \hline \end{array}$$

Ask students to make a ballpark estimate. Sample answers: 500 − 300 = 200; 500 − 350 = 150 Encourage students to use terms such as *closer to, between,* and *a little more than* to refine their estimates.

Have students examine the columns of digits from right to left.

▷ 2 is less than 4.

▷ 1 is less than 6.

▷ 5 is greater than 3.

So the top number (512) must be adjusted *before* subtracting.

Trade 1 ten for 10 ones:

100s	10s	1s
	0	12
5	~~1~~	~~2~~
− 3	6	4

Trade 1 hundred for 10 tens:

Now subtract separately in each column:

100s	10s	1s
	10	
4	~~0~~	12
~~5~~	~~1~~	~~2~~
− 3	6	4
1	4	8

Ask volunteers to write several 2-digit and 3-digit subtraction problems on the board. Have them use and describe the trade-first method to solve the problems. Ask for and record ballpark estimates for each problem before solving.

Keep the following points in mind as students write and solve the subtraction problems on the board:

▷ Make sure that the numbers students write are properly aligned in columns.

▷ Have students draw lines separating the digits into columns to help them keep the digits aligned or provide computation grids.

▷ Tell struggling students to write place-value reminders (100s, 10s, and 1s) above the columns.

▷ Although it is convenient to adjust the larger number from right to left, do not expect that all students will do it that way. What is important is that a student trades correctly and that the final adjusted number has each digit greater than or equal to the digit directly below it.

Assign Problems 1–7 on journal page 49. Have computation grids available (*Math Masters,* page 403 or 404) for those students who prefer to use them to help keep digits in the proper columns. Ask students to share their solutions to Problem 7 and indicate thumbs-up if they agree with an answer.

Ongoing Assessment: Recognizing Student Achievement

Journal page 49 Problems 4–6 ★

Use **journal page 49, Problems 4–6** to assess students' ability to solve multidigit subtraction problems. Students are making adequate progress if they are able to use a paper-and-pencil algorithm to calculate the correct differences. Some students may be able to use more than one method to solve the problems or demonstrate how the relationship between – and + can be used to check their answers.

[Operations and Computation Goal 2]

▶ Discussing and Practicing the Partial-Differences Method for Subtraction

WHOLE-CLASS ACTIVITY

(*Math Journal 1,* p. 50; *Student Reference Book,* p. 15)

The partial-differences method is another way to subtract numbers. This method avoids renaming, which is the major pitfall for many students when using the standard subtraction algorithm. Discuss the example on page 15 of the *Student Reference Book* and point out the following:

- ▷ In the partial-differences method, subtraction is performed from left to right. For example, when subtracting 3-digit numbers, the difference of hundreds is calculated first, then the difference of tens, then the difference of ones.
- ▷ Each difference is written on a separate line beneath the problem.
- ▷ After all the differences have been found, the numbers are added to find the total difference.

Pose the following subtraction problem:

$$\begin{array}{r} 528 \\ -\ 263 \\ \hline \end{array}$$

Ask students to make a ballpark estimate. Sample answers: 500 – 300 = 200; 530 – 260 = 270

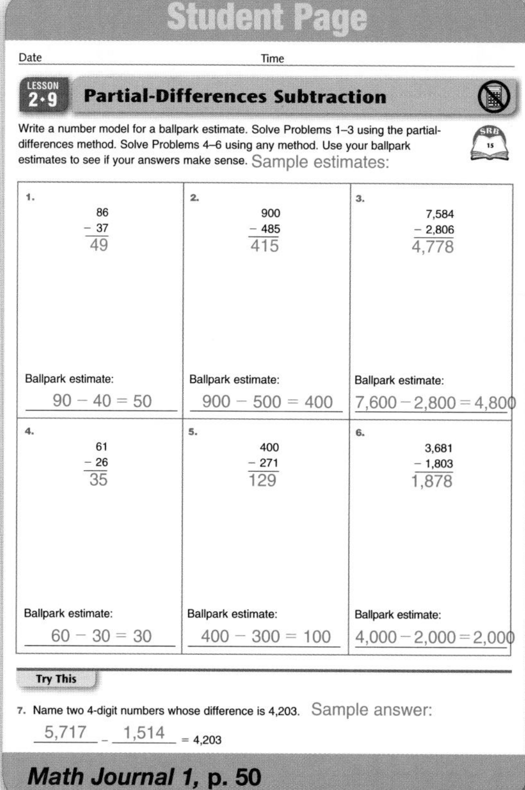

Student Page

Date Time

LESSON 2·9 **Partial-Differences Subtraction**

Write a number model for a ballpark estimate. Solve Problems 1–3 using the partial-differences method. Solve Problems 4–6 using any method. Use your ballpark estimates to see if your answers make sense. Sample estimates:

1.	2.	3.
86 − 37 = 49	900 − 485 = 415	7,584 − 2,806 = 4,778
Ballpark estimate: 90 − 40 = 50	Ballpark estimate: 900 − 500 = 400	Ballpark estimate: 7,600 − 2,800 = 4,800
4.	**5.**	**6.**
61 − 26 = 35	400 − 271 = 129	3,681 − 1,803 = 1,878
Ballpark estimate: 60 − 30 = 30	Ballpark estimate: 400 − 300 = 100	Ballpark estimate: 4,000 − 2,000 = 2,000

Try This

7. Name two 4-digit numbers whose difference is 4,203. Sample answer: 5,717 – 1,514 = 4,203

Math Journal 1, p. 50

Student Page

Date Time

LESSON 2·9 **Math Boxes**

1. A number has
6 in the tens place,
9 in the millions place,
4 in the thousands place,
3 in the ten-thousands place,
2 in the hundred-thousands place,
0 in the ones place, and
8 in the hundreds place.
Write the number. 9, 2 3 4, 8 6 0

2. Write five names for 1,000. Sample answers:

1,000
999 + 1
1,010 − 10
10 × 10 × 10
432 + 568
10,000 ÷ 10

3. Which number sentence is true? Fill in the circle next to the best answer.
Ⓐ 34 − 4 = 31
Ⓑ 812 < 218
Ⓒ 423 + 20 > 443
● 123 + 5 + 5 = 113 + 20

4. Draw a polygon that has no parallel sides.
Sample answer:

5. Measure these line segments to the nearest $\frac{1}{2}$ centimeter.
a. About 2.5 cm
b. About 5 cm

6. Multiply mentally.
a. 20 = 5 × 4
b. 5 × 6 = 30
c. 9 × 3 = 27
d. 4 × 6 = 24
e. 6 × 8 = 48

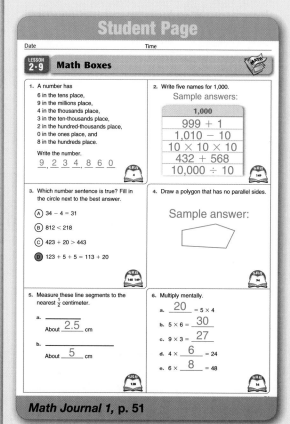

Math Journal 1, p. 51

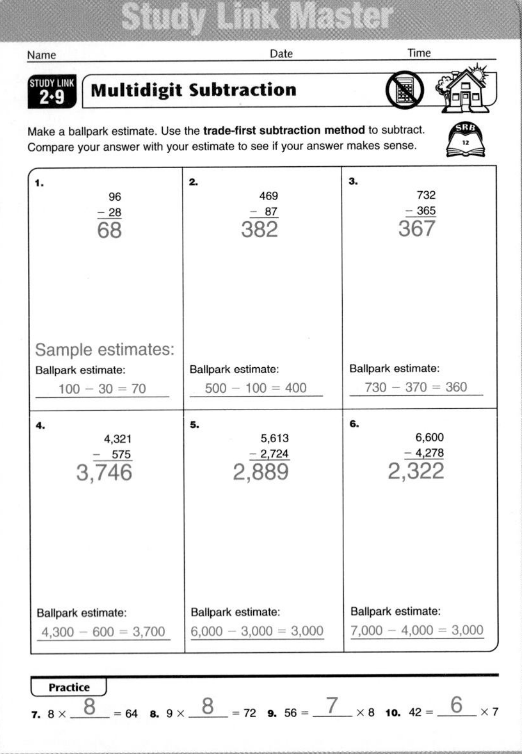
Study Link Master

Name Date Time

STUDY LINK 2·9 **Multidigit Subtraction**

Make a ballpark estimate. Use the **trade-first subtraction method** to subtract. Compare your answer with your estimate to see if your answer makes sense.

1.	2.	3.
96 − 28 = 68	469 − 87 = 382	732 − 365 = 367
Sample estimates: Ballpark estimate: 100 − 30 = 70	Ballpark estimate: 500 − 100 = 400	Ballpark estimate: 730 − 370 = 360
4. 4,321 − 575 = 3,746	**5.** 5,613 − 2,724 = 2,889	**6.** 6,600 − 4,278 = 2,322
Ballpark estimate: 4,300 − 600 = 3,700	Ballpark estimate: 6,000 − 3,000 = 3,000	Ballpark estimate: 7,000 − 4,000 = 3,000

Practice

7. 8 × 8 = 64 8. 9 × 8 = 72 9. 56 = 7 × 8 10. 42 = 6 × 7

Math Masters, p. 64

Adjusting the Activity

ELL

Use a number line to model 3 − 8 versus 8 − 3. Record several of these pairs on the board and discuss the patterns students see.

AUDITORY ♦ KINESTHETIC ♦ TACTILE ♦ VISUAL

Study Link Master

Name Date Time

STUDY LINK 2·9 **Multidigit Subtraction** *continued*

Make a ballpark estimate. Use the **partial-differences method** to subtract. Compare your answer with your estimate to see if your answer makes sense.

11.	12.	13.
84 − 55 = 29	136 − 79 = 57	573 − 167 = 406
Sample estimates: Ballpark estimate: 80 − 50 = 30	Ballpark estimate: 140 − 80 = 60	Ballpark estimate: 600 − 200 = 400
14. 506 − 282 = 224	**15.** 5,673 − 1,194 = 4,479	**16.** 3,601 − 1,063 = 2,538
Ballpark estimate: 500 − 300 = 200	Ballpark estimate: 5,700 − 1,200 = 4,500	Ballpark estimate: 3,600 − 1,100 = 2,500

Practice

17. 77, 66, 55, 44, 33, 22 Rule: −11

18. 36, 45, 54, 63, 72, 81 Rule: +9

Math Masters, p. 65

Have students solve the problem using the partial-differences method.

		528
		− 263
Subtract the 100s:	500 − 200 →	+ 300
Subtract the 10s:	20 − 60 →	− 40
Subtract the 1s:	8 − 3 →	+ 5
Add the partial differences:	300 + (−40) + 5 →	265

Have volunteers write several 2-digit and 3-digit subtraction problems on the board. Ask students to use and describe the partial-differences method to solve these problems. Before student solve each problem, ask for and record ballpark estimates.

Assign Problems 1–7 on journal page 50. Bring small groups of students together to share solutions.

2 Ongoing Learning & Practice

▶ Playing *Subtraction Target Practice*

PARTNER ACTIVITY

(*Student Reference Book,* p. 262; *Math Masters,* p. 504)

Students play *Subtraction Target Practice* to practice place-value and subtraction skills.

▶ Math Boxes 2·9

INDEPENDENT ACTIVITY

(*Math Journal 1,* p. 51)

Mixed Practice Math Boxes in this lesson are linked with Math Boxes in Lessons 2-5 and 2-7. The skill in Problem 6 previews Unit 3 content.

Writing/Reasoning Have students write a response to the following: *Marisa looked at the multiplication equation she wrote for Problem 6b and said, "I know that 30 is 5 times as many as 6. I also know that 30 is 6 times as many as 5." Write similar statements for the multiplication equation in Problem 6e.* Sample answer: I know that 48 is 6 times as many as 8. I also know that 48 is 8 times as many as 6.

▶ Study Link 2·9

INDEPENDENT ACTIVITY

(*Math Masters,* pp. 64 and 65)

Home Connection Students solve subtraction problems and show someone at home how to use the subtraction methods they practiced in this lesson.

3 Differentiation Options

READINESS

COMPUTATION PRACTICE

PARTNER ACTIVITY

Subtracting by Counting Up

15–30 Min

(*Student Reference Book*, p. 14; *Math Masters*, p. 66)

To explore visual models for solving subtraction problems using a counting-up method, have students perform counting-up subtraction on number lines. This method was reviewed in Mental Math and Reflexes in Lesson 2-6.

ENRICHMENT

PARTNER ACTIVITY

Solving Number-Tile Problems

15–30 Min

(*Math Masters*, p. 67)

To apply computation and estimation skills, have students cut out and use number tiles to find missing numbers in addition and subtraction problems.

ENRICHMENT

PARTNER ACTIVITY

Writing Subtraction Number Stories

15–30 Min

To apply students' understanding of subtraction algorithms, have them write and solve multistep subtraction number stories. Then have them record a number model using a letter for the unknown. Stories may look similar to the following:

▷ Ginny bought a 50-foot coil of rope from the store. She used 27 feet of rope to tie her boat to the dock, and another 12 feet to make a rope swing. How many feet of rope are left in on the coil? Answer: 11 feet; Number model: $50 - 27 - 12 = r$

Some students may be interested in writing and solving problems that involve distances, intervals of time, liquid volumes, masses of objects, or money. Stories may look similar to the following:

▷ The delivery truck began the day with 1,550 lb of dog food. At the first animal shelter they delivered 879 lb of dog food, and at the second animal shelter they delivered 342 lb of dog food. How many ounces are left after the two stops? Answer: 5,264 ounces; Number models: $1{,}550 - 879 - 342 = 329$ and $329 \times 16 = f$

Provide opportunities for students to revise and share their writing. Then have partners solve each other's problems.

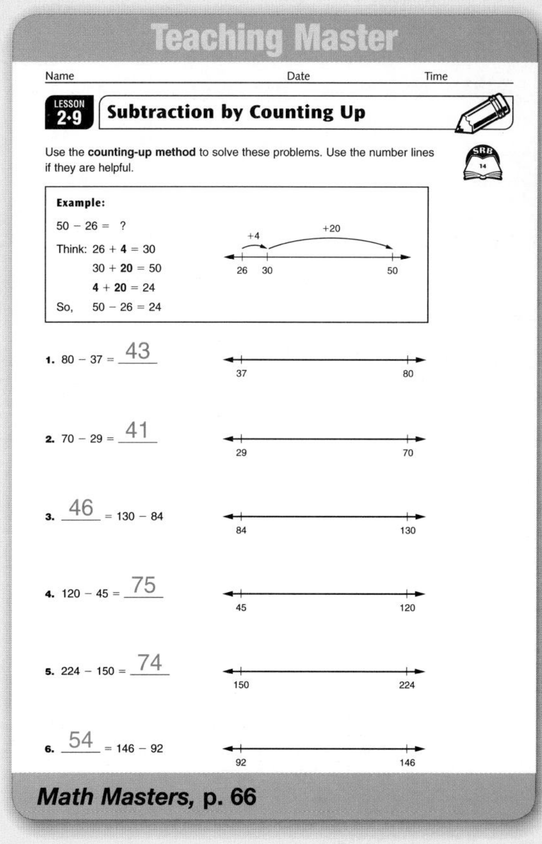

Teaching Master

Name Date Time

LESSON 2·9 **Subtraction by Counting Up**

Use the **counting-up method** to solve these problems. Use the number lines if they are helpful.

SRB 14

Example:

50 − 26 = ?

Think: 26 + **4** = 30

30 + **20** = 50

4 + **20** = 24

So, 50 − 26 = 24

(number line: 26, 30, 50; +4, +20)

1. 80 − 37 = 43 (number line: 37, 80)

2. 70 − 29 = 41 (number line: 29, 70)

3. 46 = 130 − 84 (number line: 84, 130)

4. 120 − 45 = 75 (number line: 45, 120)

5. 224 − 150 = 74 (number line: 150, 224)

6. 54 = 146 − 92 (number line: 92, 146)

Math Masters, p. 66

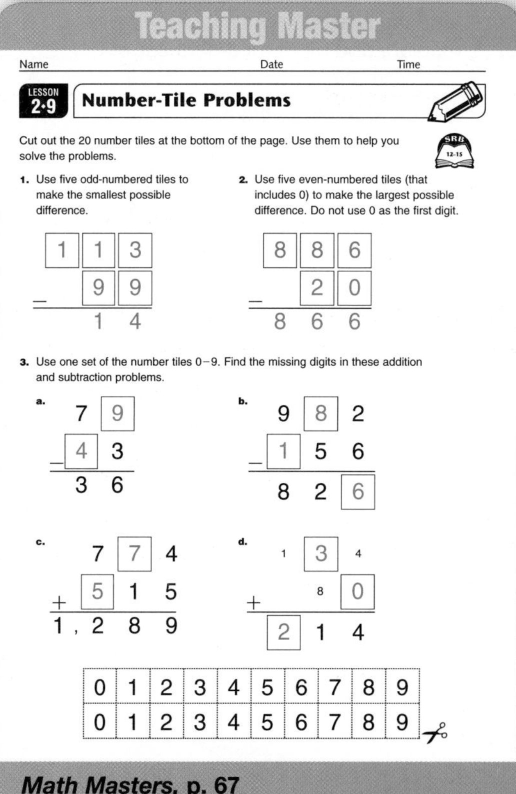
Teaching Master

Name Date Time

LESSON 2·9 **Number-Tile Problems**

Cut out the 20 number tiles at the bottom of the page. Use them to help you solve the problems.

SRB 12-15

1. Use five odd-numbered tiles to make the smallest possible difference.

113 − 99 = 14

2. Use five even-numbered tiles (that includes 0) to make the largest possible difference. Do not use 0 as the first digit.

886 − 20 = 866

3. Use one set of the number tiles 0–9. Find the missing digits in these addition and subtraction problems.

a. 79 − 43 = 36

b. 982 − 156 = 826

c. 774 + 515 = 1,289

d. 134 + 80 = 214

0	1	2	3	4	5	6	7	8	9
0	1	2	3	4	5	6	7	8	9

Math Masters, p. 67

Objective To assess students' progress on mathematical content through the end of Unit 2.

1 Looking Back: Cumulative Assessment

Input student data from Progress Check 2 into the **Assessment Management Spreadsheets**.

Materials

- Study Link 2•9
- *Assessment Handbook,* pp. 60–67, 159–163, 217, and 250–253
- slate; Geometry Template

CONTENT ASSESSED	LESSON(S)	ASSESSMENT ITEMS				
		SELF	ORAL/SLATE	WRITTEN PART A	WRITTEN PART B	OPEN RESPONSE
Read and write whole numbers up to 1,000,000,000; identify places in such numbers and the values of the digits in those places. [Number and Numeration Goal 1]	2•3, 2•4, 2•7	1	1, 3			
Use numerical expressions to give equivalent names for whole numbers. [Number and Numeration Goal 4]	2•2, 2•5, 2•7, 2•9	2			16	
Solve problems involving the addition and subtraction of whole numbers. [Operations and Computation Goal 2]	2•1–2•9	3, 4		1–6	19	
Make reasonable estimates for whole-number addition and subtraction problems. [Operations and Computation Goal 6]	2•7, 2•9	5			19, 20	
Use a tally chart; create a bar graph. [Data and Chance Goal 1]	2•5, 2•6 2•8	6		9–13, 15		✓
Find the maximum, minimum, range, median, and mode of a data set. [Data and Chance Goal 2]	2•5, 2•6 2•8	7	2	9–14		✓
Measure length to the nearest $\frac{1}{2}$ centimeter. [Measurement and Reference Frames Goal 1]	2•5, 2•7–2•9				17, 18	
Describe and classify plane figures. [Geometry Goal 2]	2•1–2•3 2•8, 2•9		4	7, 8		

2 Looking Ahead: Preparing for Unit 3

Math Boxes 2•10

Study Link 2•10: Unit 3 Family Letter

Materials

- *Math Journal 1,* p. 52
- *Math Masters,* pp. 68–71

Getting Started

Math Message • Self Assessment

Complete the Self Assessment (Assessment Handbook, *page 159*).

Study Link 2·9 Follow-Up

Have partners compare answers.

1 Looking Back: Cumulative Assessment

Math Message Follow-Up

INDEPENDENT ACTIVITY

(Self Assessment, *Assessment Handbook,* p. 159)

The Self Assessment offers students the opportunity to reflect upon their progress.

Oral and Slate Assessments

WHOLE-CLASS ACTIVITY

Problems 1–3 provide summative information and can be used for grading purposes. Problem 4 provides formative information that can be useful in planning future instruction.

Oral Assessment

1. Write numbers such as the following on the board. Ask students to read them and identify the values of digits in specified places. *Suggestions:*

4,327	34,872	325,004	1,000,295
8,093	96,005	409,667	1,567,380

2. Have students explain how to find the mode, median, and range of a data set.

Slate Assessment

3. Read numbers such as the following. Students write each number on their slates. Ask them to identify places in the numbers and the value of the digits in those places. *Suggestions:*

2,978	25,893	947,040	3,678,100
9,060	75,002	236,799	9,678,452

4. Have students draw geometric shapes to match descriptions. *Suggestions:*
   - A polygon
   - A shape that is not a polygon
   - A trapezoid
   - A parallelogram
   - A parallelogram with at least one right angle
   - A rhombus that is not a square

Assessment Master

Name Date Time

LESSON 2·10 **Self Assessment** Progress Check 2

Think about each skill listed below. Assess your own progress by checking the most appropriate box.

Skills	I can do this on my own and explain how to do it.	I can do this on my own.	I can do this if I get help or look at an example.
1. Read and write large numbers.			
2. Fill in name-collection boxes.			
3. Add multidigit numbers.			
4. Subtract multidigit numbers.			
5. Make ballpark estimates for addition and subtraction problems.			
6. Create and read a bar graph.			
7. Find the minimum, maximum, range, median, and mode of a data set.			

***Assessment Handbook,* p. 159**

Assessment Master

Name Date Time

LESSON 2·10 **Written Assessment** Progress Check 2

Part A

Add or subtract with a paper-and-pencil algorithm.

1. 129 + 462 = 591	2. 507 + 1,829 = 2,336	3. 4,326 + 2,974 = 7,300
4. 924 − 648 = 276	5. 208 − 72 = 136	6. 4,361 − 2,498 = 1,863

7. Draw a polygon with at least one right angle. Mark the right angle(s) with a square corner symbol. Sample answer

8. Is the polygon you drew a parallelogram? ____ Explain. Answers vary.

***Assessment Handbook,* p. 160**

Assessment Master

Name ____ Date ____ Time ____

LESSON 2•10 **Written Assessment** *continued*

The students in Ivan's class are selling rolls of wrapping paper to raise money for their school. Use Ivan's chart to answer the following questions:

Number of Rolls Sold	Number of Students
20	////
21	//
22	~~////~~
23	//
24	///
25	~~////~~ /
26	
27	/
28	/

9. How many students sold 22 rolls of wrapping paper? 5 students
10. What is the maximum number of rolls sold? 28
11. What is the range of the number of rolls sold? 8
12. What is the mode (most frequent number) of rolls sold? 25
13. What is the median (or typical number) of rolls sold by the students? 23
14. Explain how you found the median. Sample answer: When the data are listed in order, the two middle numbers are both 23.
15. Make a bar graph of the data.

Assessment Handbook, **p. 161**

NOTE For Problem 16, you may find it useful to make a qualitative evaluation of students' responses rather than simply marking them correct or incorrect. A clever response combining several operations and a variety of numbers might be a better indication of a student's understanding of numbers and operations than one that uses simple numbers in a routine way.

Assessment Master

Name ____ Date ____ Time ____

LESSON 2•10 **Written Assessment** *continued*

Part B

16. Su Lin wanted to show the number 27 on her calculator. The 7-key on her calculator was broken, so this is what she did:

3 ⊗ 8 ⊕ 3 (Enter) 27 — Sample answers:

Show two other ways to show 27 without using the 7-key. Try to use different numbers and operations.

a. $(5 \times 6) - 3$ b. $54 \div 2$

17. Measure the line segments to the nearest $\frac{1}{2}$ centimeter.

a. ________ About 10 cm

b. ________ About 7.5 cm

18. Draw a line segment 12.5 centimeters long.

19. Solve *only* those problems with a sum or difference *greater than* 2,500.

a. 1,859 + 2,098 = 3,957 b. 1,132 + 1,246 c. 3,127 − 1,989 d. 6,800 − 3,229 = 3,571

20. Explain the estimation strategy you used to decide which problems to solve. Sample answer: I rounded the numbers and added or subtracted to see if the sum or difference was greater than 2,500.

Assessment Handbook, **p. 162**

▶ Written Assessment

INDEPENDENT ACTIVITY

(*Assessment Handbook,* pp. 160–162)

Part A Recognizing Student Achievement

Problems 1–15 provide summative information and may be used for grading purposes.

Problem(s)	Description
1–6	Add and subtract multidigit numbers.
7	Draw a polygon. Mark the right angles.
8	Explain whether or not a given polygon is a parallelogram.
9–14	Interpret a tally chart and find the maximum, range, mode, and median for a set of data.
15	Construct a bar graph.

Part B Informing Instruction

Problems 16–20 provide formative information that can be useful in planning future instruction.

Problem(s)	Description
16	Write equivalent names for numbers.
17	Measure line segments to the nearest half-centimeter.
18	Draw a line segment to the nearest half-centimeter.
19	Estimate sums and differences; solve multidigit addition and subtraction problems.
20	Describe a strategy for estimating sums and differences.

Use the checklists on pages 251 and 253 of the *Assessment Handbook* to record results. Then input the data into the **Assessment Management Spreadsheets** to keep an ongoing record of students' progress toward Grade-Level Goals.

▶ Open Response

INDEPENDENT ACTIVITY

(*Assessment Handbook,* p. 163)

Jelly Bean Data

The open-response item requires students to apply concepts and skills from Unit 2 to solve a multistep problem. See *Assessment Handbook,* pages 63–67 for rubrics and students' work samples for this problem.

2 Looking Ahead: Preparing for Unit 3

Math Boxes 2•10

INDEPENDENT ACTIVITY

(*Math Journal 1,* p. 52)

Mixed Practice This Math Boxes page previews Unit 3 content.

Study Link 2•10: Unit 3 Family Letter

INDEPENDENT ACTIVITY

(*Math Masters,* pp. 68–71)

Home Connection The Unit 3 Family Letter provides parents and guardians with information and activities related to Unit 3 topics.

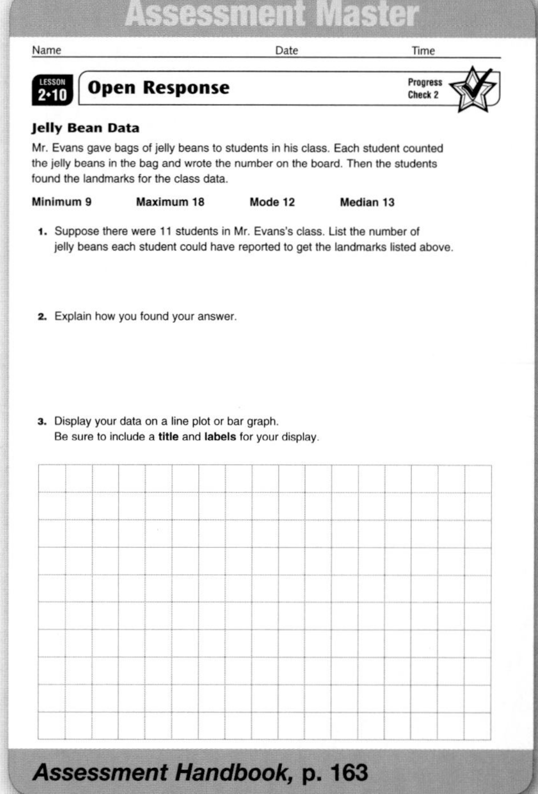

Assessment Master

Name Date Time

LESSON 2•10 **Open Response** Progress Check 2

Jelly Bean Data

Mr. Evans gave bags of jelly beans to students in his class. Each student counted the jelly beans in the bag and wrote the number on the board. Then the students found the landmarks for the class data.

Minimum 9 **Maximum 18** **Mode 12** **Median 13**

1. Suppose there were 11 students in Mr. Evans's class. List the number of jelly beans each student could have reported to get the landmarks listed above.

2. Explain how you found your answer.

3. Display your data on a line plot or bar graph. Be sure to include a **title** and **labels** for your display.

Assessment Handbook, p. 163

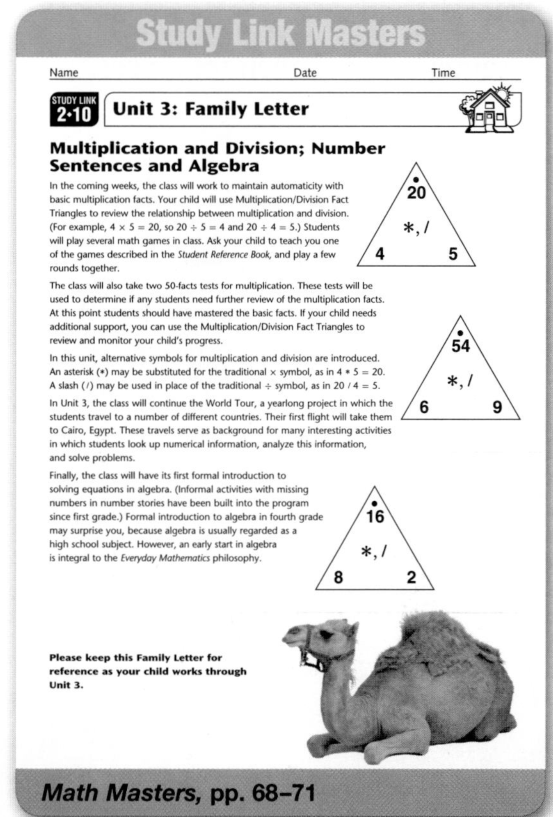

Study Link Masters

Name Date Time

STUDY LINK 2•10 **Unit 3: Family Letter**

Multiplication and Division; Number Sentences and Algebra

In the coming weeks, the class will work to maintain automaticity with basic multiplication facts. Your child will use Multiplication/Division Fact Triangles to review the relationship between multiplication and division. (For example, 4 × 5 = 20, so 20 ÷ 5 = 4 and 20 ÷ 4 = 5.) Students will play several math games in class. Ask your child to teach you one of the games described in the *Student Reference Book,* and play a few rounds together.

The class will also take two 50-facts tests for multiplication. These tests will be used to determine if any students need further review of the multiplication facts. At this point students should have mastered the basic facts. If your child needs additional support, you can use the Multiplication/Division Fact Triangles to review and monitor your child's progress.

In this unit, alternative symbols for multiplication and division are introduced. An asterisk (*) may be substituted for the traditional × symbol, as in 4 * 5 = 20. A slash (/) may be used in place of the traditional ÷ symbol, as in 20 / 4 = 5.

In Unit 3, the class will continue the World Tour, a yearlong project in which the students travel to a number of different countries. Their first flight will take them to Cairo, Egypt. These travels serve as background for many interesting activities in which students look up numerical information, analyze this information, and solve problems.

Finally, the class will have its first formal introduction to solving equations in algebra. (Informal activities with missing numbers in number stories have been built into the program since first grade.) Formal introduction to algebra in fourth grade may surprise you, because algebra is usually regarded as a high school subject. However, an early start in algebra is integral to the *Everyday Mathematics* philosophy.

Please keep this Family Letter for reference as your child works through Unit 3.

Math Masters, pp. 68–71

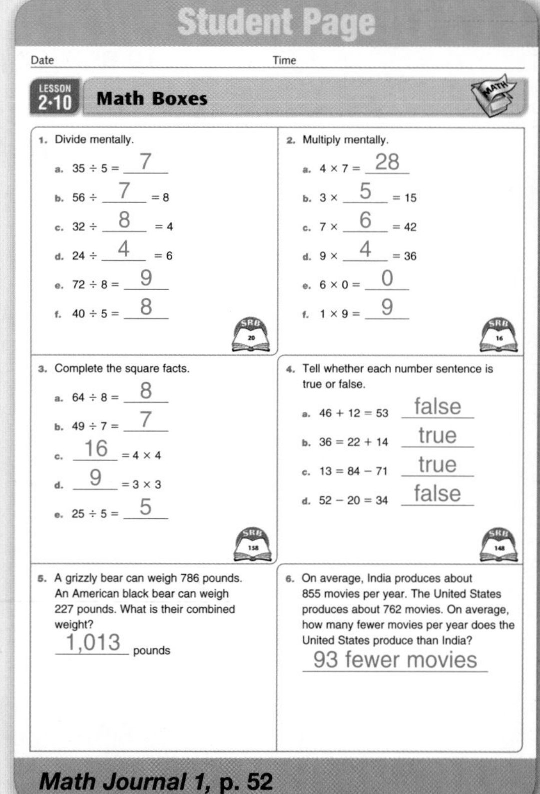

Student Page

Date Time

LESSON 2•10 **Math Boxes**

1. Divide mentally.
   a. 35 ÷ 5 = 7
   b. 56 ÷ 7 = 8
   c. 32 ÷ 8 = 4
   d. 24 ÷ 4 = 6
   e. 72 ÷ 8 = 9
   f. 40 ÷ 5 = 8

2. Multiply mentally.
   a. 4 × 7 = 28
   b. 3 × 5 = 15
   c. 7 × 6 = 42
   d. 9 × 4 = 36
   e. 6 × 0 = 0
   f. 1 × 9 = 9

3. Complete the square facts.
   a. 64 ÷ 8 = 8
   b. 49 ÷ 7 = 7
   c. 16 = 4 × 4
   d. 9 = 3 × 3
   e. 25 ÷ 5 = 5

4. Tell whether each number sentence is true or false.
   a. 46 + 12 = 53 false
   b. 36 = 22 + 14 true
   c. 13 = 84 – 71 true
   d. 52 – 20 = 34 false

5. A grizzly bear can weigh 786 pounds. An American black bear can weigh 227 pounds. What is their combined weight?
   1,013 pounds

6. On average, India produces about 855 movies per year. The United States produces about 762 movies. On average, how many fewer movies per year does the United States produce than India?
   93 fewer movies

Math Journal 1, p. 52

Unit 3 Organizer

Multiplication and Division; Number Sentences and Algebra

Overview

Unit 3 is divided into four main sections. The first section gives students an opportunity to review and practice basic multiplication facts. Next, a routine is established for the World Tour Project. Students are then taught a general problem-solving scheme that will help them solve number stories and find mathematical models for more complicated problems. Finally, some algebra concepts and skills that students have previously learned are extended. Unit 3 has four main areas of focus:

- To review strategies for solving multiplication facts; and to help students maintain automaticity with multiplication facts,
- To provide practice interpreting data, measuring length, and using a map scale through the World Tour Project,
- To introduce a simplified approach to solving number stories; and to provide practice solving number stories, and
- To provide practice with number sentences and open sentences.

Linking to the Common Core State Standards

The content of Unit 3 addresses the Common Core State Standards for Mathematics in *Operations and Algebraic Thinking.* The correlation of the Common Core State Standards to the *Everyday Mathematics* Grade 4 lessons begins on page CS1.

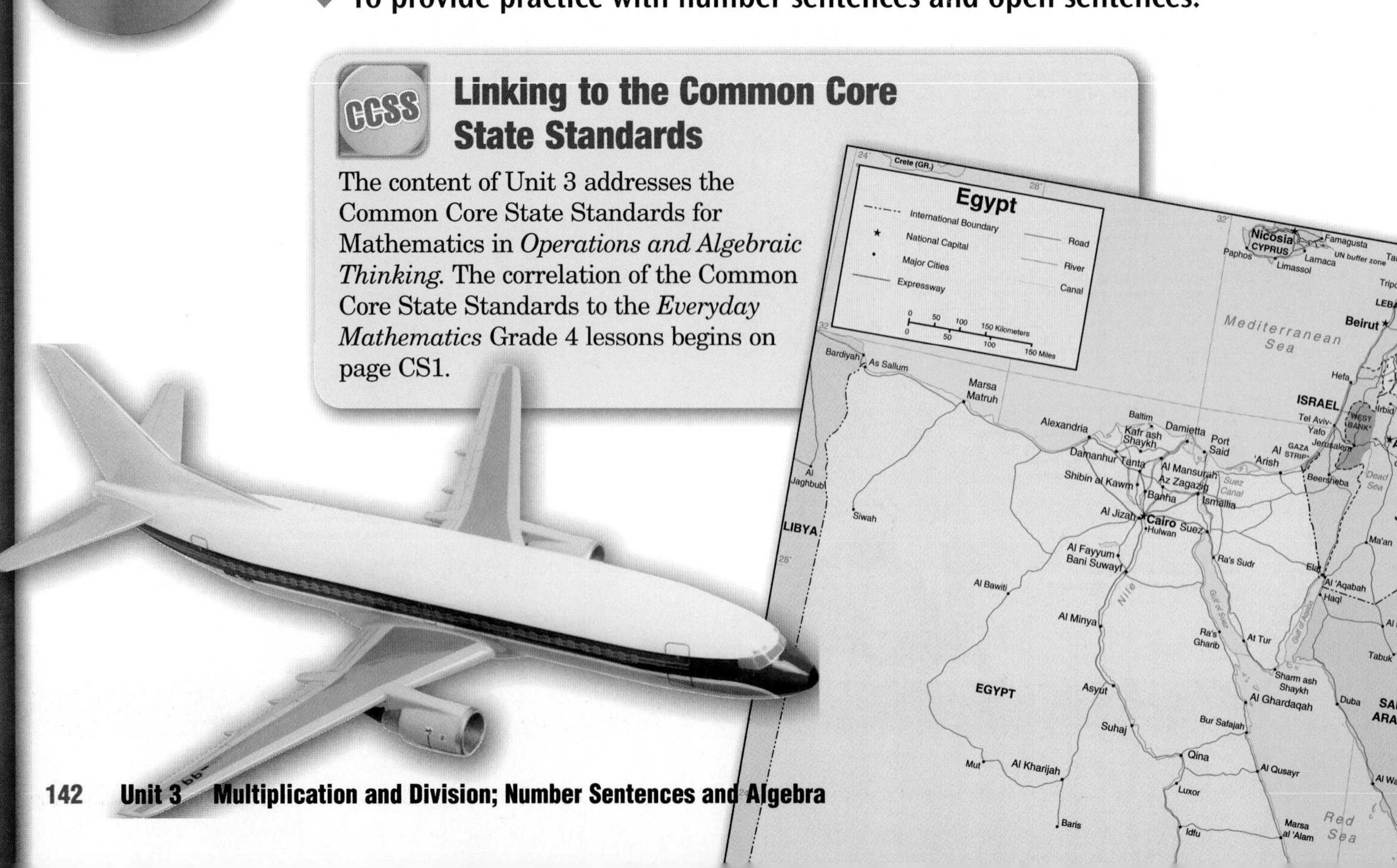

Contents

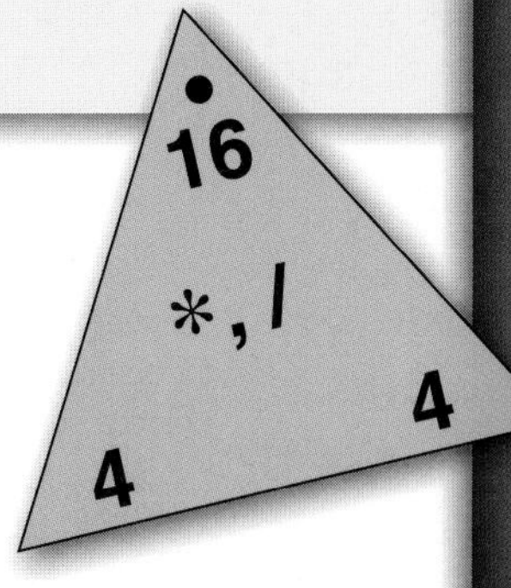

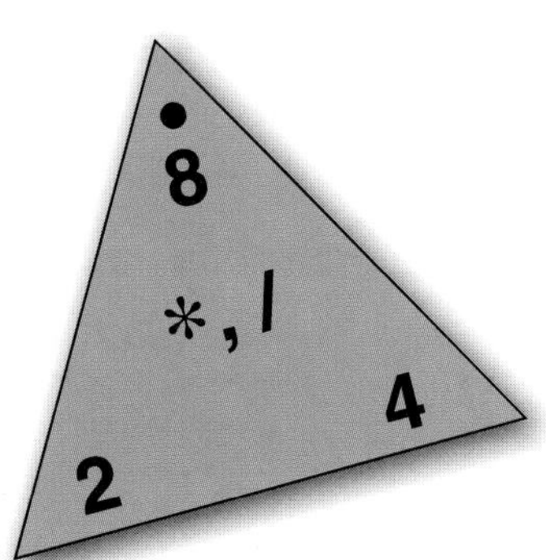

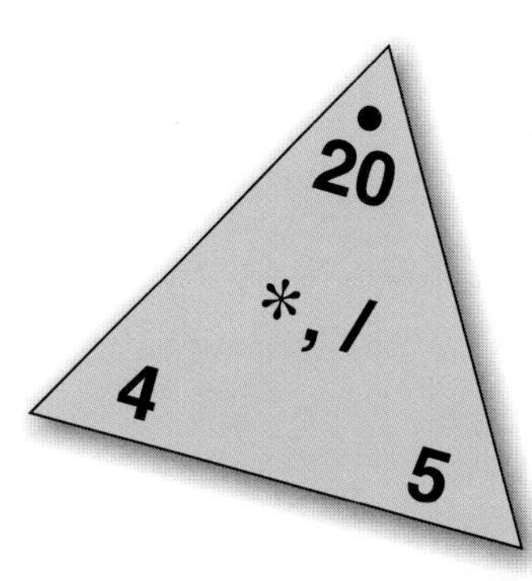

Learning In Perspective

	Lesson Objectives	Links to the Past	Links to the Future
3·1	To review "What's My Rule?" problems.	Grades 1–3: Use "What's My Rule?" tables and function machine routines.	Grades 4–6: Applications and maintenance.
3·2	To review strategies for solving multiplication facts; to help students maintain automaticity with multiplication facts; and to introduce prime and composite numbers.	Grade 3: Use Fact Triangles and the Facts Table to explore the relationship between * and ÷; play games that promote recall of multiplication and division facts.	Grade 5: Find the prime factorization of a number.
3·3	To introduce the 50-facts test; and to provide practice with multiplication facts.	Grade 3: Use Fact Triangles and the Facts Table to explore the relationship between * and ÷; play games that promote recall of multiplication and division facts.	Grades 4–6: Applications and maintenance through games and routines.
3·4	To give a 50-facts test and record the results; and to provide practice with multiplication facts.	Grade 3: Use Fact Triangles and the Facts Table to explore the relationship between * and ÷; play games that promote recall of multiplication and division facts.	Grades 4–6: Applications and maintenance through games and routines.
3·5	To guide exploration of the relationship between multiplication and division; and to provide practice with division facts.	Grade 3: Use Fact Triangles and the Facts Table to explore the relationship between * and ÷; play games that promote recall of multiplication and division facts.	Grade 5: Find the prime factorization of a number; use a divisibility test to determine if a number is divisible by another number.
3·6	To provide practice interpreting data through the World Tour Project.	Grades 1–3: Collect, organize and analyze data in projects and Explorations.	Grades 4 and 5: Applications and maintenance. Grade 6: Investigate how graphs may be used to propagandize or mislead.
3·7	To provide practice measuring length and using a map scale.	Grade 3: Use a map scale to estimate the direct distance between two places.	Grade 4: Estimate the lengths of non-linear paths drawn on square grids that include scale bars; make scale drawings. Grades 4–6: Applications and maintenance.
3·8	To introduce a simplified approach to solving number stories; and to provide practice solving number stories.	Grades 1 and 2: Use parts-and-total, change, and comparison diagrams to model and solve problems. Grade 3: Introduce and use a Guide to Solving Number Stories.	Grades 5 and 6: Solve number stories by modeling them with open sentences and then solving the open sentences.
3·9	To review the meanings of number sentences; and to provide practice determining whether number sentences are true or false.	Grades 1–3: Complete number sentences by inserting relation symbols (=, >, <) to make them true.	Grades 4–6: Applications and maintenance, with increasing complexity of number sentences.
3·10	To review the use of parentheses in number sentences.	Grade 3: Use parentheses to specify which operation to do first in a number sentence; insert parentheses to make a number sentence true.	Grades 5 and 6: Introduce the order of operations; introduce nested parentheses; match number stories to appropriate expressions.
3·11	To introduce vocabulary and notation for open sentences; and to provide practice solving open sentences.	Grades 1–3: Introduce the relation symbols (=, >, <); solve open sentences in which the missing numbers are shown by a question mark, blank, or box.	Grades 5 and 6: Use formulas to solve problems by substitution and by trial-and-error; introduce a pan-balance approach for solving equations.

	Key Concepts and Skills	Grade 4 Goals*
3·1	Solve addition and subtraction problems.	Operations and Computation Goals 1 and 2
	Solve multiplication and division problems.	Operations and Computation Goals 3 and 4
	Use rules to complete "What's My Rule?" tables.	Patterns, Functions, and Algebra Goal 1
	Use words and symbols to describe and write rules for functions.	Patterns, Functions, and Algebra Goal 1
3·2	Find factors and multiples of numbers.	Number and Numeration Goal 3
	Identify prime and composite numbers.	Number and Numeration Goal 3
	Identify square numbers.	Number and Numeration Goal 4
	Solve multiplication facts.	Operations and Computation Goal 3
	Identify and use patterns in the Multiplication/Division Facts Table.	Patterns, Functions, and Algebra Goal 1
3·3	Rename a fraction as an equivalent fraction and as a percent.	Number and Numeration Goal 5
	Solve multiplication facts.	Operations and Computation Goal 3
	Identify and use patterns in the Multiplication/Division Facts Table.	Patterns, Functions, and Algebra Goal 1
3·4	Rename a fraction as an equivalent fraction and as a percent.	Number and Numeration Goal 5
	Solve multiplication facts.	Operations and Computation Goal 3
	Use data to create a line graph.	Data and Chance Goal 1
	Find the median and mean of a data set.	Data and Chance Goal 2
3·5	Solve multiplication facts.	Operations and Computation Goal 3
	Use multiplication facts to generate related division facts.	Operations and Computation Goal 3
	Apply multiplication and division facts and extended facts to solve problems.	Operations and Computation Goal 3
	Write multiplication and division number sentences.	Patterns, Functions, and Algebra Goal 2
3·6	Read and write large numbers.	Number and Numeration Goal 1
	Calculate relative time across time zones.	Operations and Computation Goal 2
	Judge the reasonableness of counts; describe the difference between a count and an estimate.	Operations and Computation Goal 6
	Use a table of climate data and a time zones map.	Data and Chance Goal 2
3·7	Solve multiplication problems.	Operations and Computation Goal 4
	Use a map scale.	Operations and Computation Goal 7
	Measure to the nearest $\frac{1}{2}$ inch.	Measurement and Reference Frames Goal 1
3·8	Solve addition and subtraction number stories.	Operations and Computation Goal 2
	Explain strategies for solving addition and subtraction number stories.	Operations and Computation Goal 2
	Use a table of air distance data.	Data and Chance Goal 2
	Write number models to represent addition and subtraction number stories.	Patterns, Functions, and Algebra Goal 2
3·9	Compare whole numbers.	Number and Numeration Goal 6
	Add, subtract, multiply, and divide to solve expressions.	Operations and Computation Goals 1–4
	Use conventional notation to write number sentences.	Patterns, Functions, and Algebra Goal 2
	Determine whether a number sentence is true or false.	Patterns, Functions, and Algebra Goal 2
3·10	Add, subtract, multiply, and divide to solve expressions.	Operations and Computation Goals 1–4
	Determine whether number sentences are true or false.	Patterns, Functions, and Algebra Goal 2
	Evaluate expressions containing parentheses.	Patterns, Functions, and Algebra Goal 3
	Insert parentheses to make true number sentences.	Patterns, Functions, and Algebra Goal 3
3·11	Add, subtract, multiply, and divide to solve open sentences.	Operations and Computation Goals 1–4
	Use a "guess-and-check" strategy to make reasonable estimates for open sentences.	Operations and Computation Goal 6
	Identify the solution of an open sentence.	Patterns, Functions, and Algebra Goal 2
	Determine whether number sentences are true or false.	Patterns, Functions, and Algebra Goal 2

*See the Appendix for a complete list of Grade 4 Goals.

A Balanced Curriculum

Ongoing Practice

Everyday Mathematics provides numerous opportunities for ongoing practice. These activities are embedded throughout the lessons:

Mental Math and Reflexes activities promote speed and accuracy in mental computation.

Math Boxes offer mixed practice and are paired across lessons as shown in the brackets below. This makes them useful as assessment tools. The last one or two boxes on each page preview the next unit's content.

Mixed practice	[3•1, 3•3, 3•5], [3•2, 3•4], [3•6, 3•8], [3•7, 3•9], [3•10, 3•11]
Mixed practice with multiple choice	3•2, 3•5, 3•6, 3•8, 3•9, 3•10, 3•12
Mixed practice with writing/reasoning opportunity	3•1, 3•3, 3•4, 3•6, 3•7, 3•8, 3•10, 3•11

Study Links are daily homework assignments that review the content of the lesson and often contain ongoing facts practice or computation practice.

5-Minute Math problems are offered for additional practice in Lessons 3•7 and 3•10.

EM Facts Workshop Game provides online practice of basic facts and computation.

EXTRA PRACTICE **Extra Practice** activities are included in Lessons 3•1, 3•2, 3•3, 3•5, 3•7, 3•10, and 3•11.

Practice through Games

Games are an essential component of practice in the *Everyday Mathematics* program. Games offer skills practice and promote strategic thinking. See the *Differentiation Handbook* for ways to adapt games to meet students' needs.

Lesson	Game	Skill Practiced
3•2, 3•10	*Name That Number*	Representing numbers in different ways [NN Goal 4]
3•2	*Buzz* and *Bizz-Buzz*	Naming multiples [NN Goal 3]
3•3	*Baseball Multiplication*	Solving multiplication facts [OC Goal 3]
3•3, 3•6	*Multiplication Top-It*	Solving multiplication facts [OC Goal 3]
3•5	*Beat the Calculator*	Solving multiplication facts [OC Goal 3]
3•5	*Division Arrays*	Exploring the relationship between multiplication and division [OC Goal 7]
3•6	*Seega*	Exploring mathematical connections with Egypt [PFA Goal 1]
3•7	*Polygon Pair-Up*	Identifying properties of polygons [GEO Goal 2]
3•8	*High-Number Toss*	Identifying place-value and comparing numbers [NN Goals 1 and 6]

[NN] Number and Numeration
[MRF] Measurement and Reference Frames
[OC] Operations and Computation
[GEO] Geometry
[DC] Data and Chance
[PFA] Patterns, Functions, and Algebra

Problem Solving 

Experts at problem solving and mathematical modeling generally do these things:

- Identify the problem.
- Decide what information is needed to solve the problem.
- Play with and study the data to find patterns and meaning.
- Identify and use mathematical procedures to solve the problem.
- Decide whether the solution makes sense and whether it can be applied to other problems.

The table below lists some of the opportunities in this unit for students to practice these strategies.

Lesson	Activity
3•3	Find patterns in the 9s, 5s, and other multiplication facts.
3•7	Find the air distances between cities.
3•8	Solve addition and subtraction number stories involving a variety of data.
3•10	Use three numbers to name a target number when playing *Name That Number.*
3•11	Solve Broken Calculator problems.

Lessons that teach *through* problem solving, not just *about* problem solving

See Chapter 18: Problem Solving in the *Teacher's Reference Manual* for more information.

The Language of Mathematics

Everyday Mathematics provides lesson-specific suggestions to help all students acquire, process, and express mathematical ideas. Throughout Unit 3, there are lesson-specific language development notes that address the needs of English language learners, indicated by ELL.

ELL SUPPORT Activities to support English language learners are in Part 3 of Lessons 3•2, 3•5, 3•8, and 3•9.

The *English Learners Handbook* and the *Differentiation Handbook* have suggestions for promoting language development and acquisition of mathematics vocabulary. See Unit 3 in each handbook.

Literacy Connection

Each Orange Had 8 Slices: A Counting Book, by Paul Giganti, Jr., Greenwillow Books, 1999

My Full Moon Is Square, by Elinor J. Pinczes, Houghton Mifflin, 2002

Sea Squares, by Joy N. Hulme, Hyperion Books for Children, 1999

Lesson 3•6 *Nine O'Clock Lullaby,* by Marilyn Singer, HarperCollins, 1993

Safari Park, by Stuart J. Murphy, HarperCollins Publishers, 2002

For more literacy connections, see the *Home Connection Handbook,* Grades 4–6.

Unit 3 Vocabulary

composite number
dividend
divisor
fact family
factor pair
factors
false number sentence
function machine
input
multiples
multiplication facts
number sentence
open sentence
output
parentheses
percent
prime number
products
quotient
remainder
rule
solution
solve
square numbers
true number sentence
turn-around facts
variable
"What's My Rule?"

Cross-Curricular Links 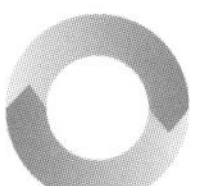

Social Studies – Lessons 3•6, 3•8, 3•11 **Literature** – Lesson 3•6

Balanced Assessment

Daily Assessments

- **Recognizing Student Achievement** – A daily assessment that is included in every lesson to evaluate students' progress toward the Grade 4 Grade-Level Goals.
- **Informing Instruction** – Notes that appear throughout the unit to help anticipate students' common errors and suggest appropriate problem-solving strategies.

Lesson	Recognizing Student Achievement	Informing Instruction
3•1	Complete "What's My Rule?" tables. [PFA Goal 1]	
3•2	Use numerical expressions involving arithmetic operations to give equivalent names for whole numbers. [NN Goal 4]	
3•3	Estimate reasonable solutions for whole-number addition and subtraction problems. [OC Goal 6]	
3•4	Demonstrate automaticity with multiplication facts. [OC Goal 3]	
3•5	Use conventional notation to write multiplication and division number sentences. [PFA Goal 2]	
3•6	Solve multidigit addition and subtraction problems. [OC Goal 2]	Understand vocabulary used in Country Notes.
3•7	Use a map scale to estimate distances. [OC Goal 7]	Differentiate between distances traveled and travel time.
3•8	Use and explain a strategy for solving an addition number story. [OC Goal 2]	
3•9	Determine whether number sentences are true or false. [PFA Goal 2]	Represent a word sentence as a number sentence correctly.
3•10	Demonstrate proficiency with basic division facts. [OC Goal 3]	Understand the reason for parentheses placement.
3•11	Use and explain a strategy for solving open number sentences. [PFA Goal 2]	Calculate correctly when variables are placed in different positions.

[NN] Number and Numeration
[MRF] Measurement and Reference Frames
[OC] Operations and Computation
[GEO] Geometry
[DC] Data and Chance
[PFA] Patterns, Functions, and Algebra

Portfolio Opportunities

The following lessons provide opportunities to gather samples of students' mathematical writings, drawings, and creations to add balance to the assessment process: Lessons 3•1, 3•2, 3•3, 3•4, 3•6, 3•7, 3•8, 3•10, and 3•12.

See pages 16 and 17 in the *Assessment Handbook* for more information about portfolios and how to use them.

Unit Assessment

Progress Check 3 – A cumulative assessment of concepts and skills taught in Unit 3 and in previous units, providing information for evaluating students' progress and planning for future instruction. These assessments include oral/slate, written, and open-response activities, as shown below in the sample Progress Check lesson opener.

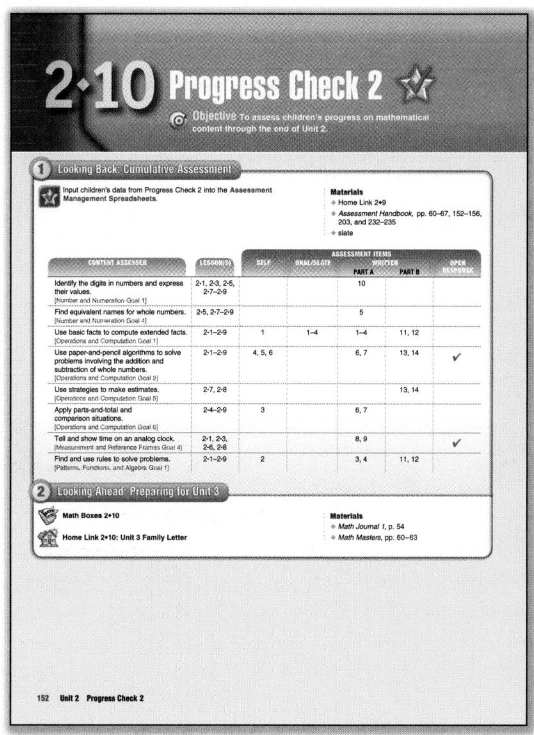

2·10 Progress Check 2

Objective To assess children's progress on mathematical content through the end of Unit 2.

1 Looking Back: Cumulative Assessment

Input children's data from Progress Check 2 into the Assessment Management Spreadsheets.

Materials
- Home Link 2•9
- *Assessment Handbook*, pp. 60–67, 152–156, 203, and 232–235
- slate

Content Assessed	Lesson(s)	Assessment Items: Self	Oral/Slate	Written: Part A	Written: Part B	Open Response
Identify the digits in numbers and express their values. [Number and Numeration Goal 1]	2·1, 2·3, 2·5, 2·7–2·9			10		
Find equivalent names for whole numbers. [Number and Numeration Goal 4]	2·5, 2·7–2·9			5		
Use basic facts to compute extended facts. [Operations and Computation Goal 1]	2·1–2·9	1	1–4	1–4	11, 12	
Use paper-and-pencil algorithms to solve problems involving the addition and subtraction of whole numbers. [Operations and Computation Goal 2]	2·1–2·9	4, 5, 6		6, 7	13, 14	✓
Use strategies to make estimates. [Operations and Computation Goal 5]	2·7, 2·8				13, 14	
Apply parts-and-total and comparison situations. [Operations and Computation Goal 6]	2·4–2·9	3		6, 7		
Tell and show time on an analog clock. [Measurement and Reference Frames Goal 4]	2·1, 2·3, 2·6, 2·8			8, 9		✓
Find and use rules to solve problems. [Patterns, Functions, and Algebra Goal 1]	2·1–2·9	2		3, 4	11, 12	

2 Looking Ahead: Preparing for Unit 3

Math Boxes 2•10

Home Link 2•10: Unit 3 Family Letter

Materials
- *Math Journal 1*, p. 54
- *Math Masters*, pp. 60–63

152 Unit 2 Progress Check 2

Core Assessment Resources

Assessment Handbook

- **Unit 3 Assessment Overview,** pages 68–75
- **Unit 3 Assessment Masters,** pages 164–168
- **Unit 3 Individual Profiles of Progress,** pages 254, 255, and 302
- **Unit 3 Class Checklists,** pages 256, 257, and 303
- **Quarterly Checklist: Quarter 1,** pages 294 and 295
- **Math Logs,** pages 306–308
- **Exit Slip,** page 311
- **Other Student Assessment Forms,** pages 304, 305, 309, and 310

Assessment Management Spreadsheets

The Assessment Management Spreadsheets consist of the Digital Class Checklists and Individual Profile of Progress Checklists. Use them to monitor, record, and report student progress.

Addressing All Needs

Differentiated Instruction

Adjusting the Activity – suggests adaptations that target advanced learners, English language learners, or learners who need additional instructional support.

ELL SUPPORT / ELL – provides lesson-specific suggestions to help English language learners understand and process the mathematical content.

READINESS – accesses students' prior knowledge or previews content that prepares students to engage in the lesson's Part 1 activities.

EXTRA PRACTICE – provides additional opportunities to apply the mathematical content of the lesson.

ENRICHMENT – enables students to apply or further explore the mathematical content of the lesson.

Lesson	Adjusting the Activity	ELL Support/ ELL	Readiness	Extra Practice	Enrichment
3•1	•	•	•	•	•
3•2	•	•	•	•	
3•3	•	•	•	•	•
3•4		•	•		•
3•5	•	•	•	•	•
3•6		•	•		•
3•7	•		•	•	•
3•8	•	•	•		•
3•9	•	•	•		•
3•10	•	•		•	•
3•11	•		•	•	•

Additional Resources

Differentiation Handbook
Provides ideas and strategies for differentiating instruction.
Pages 62–68

English Learners Handbook
Contains lesson-specific comprehension strategies.
Pages 18–28

Multilingual Handbook
Previews concepts and vocabulary. It is written in six languages.
Pages 35–56

Planning Tips

Multiage Classroom

Companion Lessons from Grades 3 and 5 can help you meet instructional needs of a multiage classroom. The full Scope and Sequence can be found in the Appendix.

Grade 3	2•3	4•1, 4•5, 4•6, 4•8	4•1, 4•5, 4•6	4•1, 4•5, 4•6, 4•8	4•1, 4•4	4•9	4•9	2•4, 2•6, 4•1, 4•2		7•4, 7•5	
Grade 4	**3•1**	**3•2**	**3•3**	**3•4**	**3•5**	**3•6**	**3•7**	**3•8**	**3•9**	**3•10**	**3•11**
Grade 5	10•4, 10•6	2•8, 2•9	2•8, 2•9	2•8, 2•9	8•7, 8•8, 8•12	4•1	2•1, 4•3	2•4, 12•5	7•4	7•4	2•4, 7•5

Pacing for Success

Pacing depends on a number of factors, such as students' individual needs and how long your school has been using *Everyday Mathematics*. At the beginning of Unit 3, you may want to use tools available at www.everydaymathonline.com to help you set your pace.

Home Support

Unit 3 Family Letter (English/Spanish) provides families with an overview, Do-Anytime Activities, Building Skills through Games, a list of vocabulary, and answers to the daily homework (Study Links). Family Letters in English, Spanish, and seven other languages are also available online.

Study Links are the daily homework assignments. They consist of active projects and ongoing review problems.

Home Support Resources

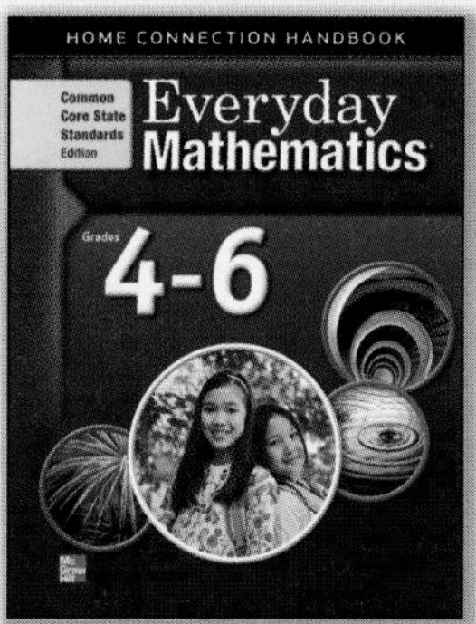

Home Connection Handbook
Offers ideas and reproducible masters for communicating with families. See Table of Contents for unit information.

Student Reference Book
Provides a resource for students and parents.

Pages 8, 151, 175, 178, 178A, 178B, 231–234, 240, 252, 254, 258, 264, 276, 277, 279–283, 293, 297, 302–305, 309

Technology Resources

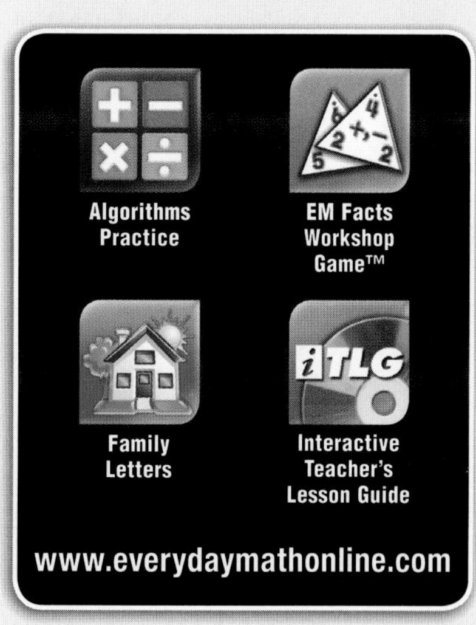

Materials

ePresentations

eToolkit

Algorithms Practice

EM Facts Workshop Game™

Family Letters

Assessment Management

Common Core State Standards

Curriculum Focal Points

Interactive Teacher's Lesson Guide

Lesson	Masters	Manipulative Kit	Other Items
3•1	Transparency of *Math Masters,* p. 407 Study Link Master, p. 72 Teaching Masters, pp. 73 and 74 Teaching Aid Master, p. 407	slate; pattern blocks (triangles, squares, hexagons)	straightedge; calculator
3•2	Transparencies of *Math Masters,* pp. 408* and 409*; Study Link Master, p. 75 Game Master, p. 489 Teaching Master, p. 76 *Differentiation Handbook,* p. 140	deck of number cards; 4 each of number cards 1–10; centimeter cubes	paper clips; envelopes or resealable plastic bags; scissors; counters*; calculator
3•3	Teaching Aid Masters, pp. 403 and 410 Study Link Master, p. 78 Game Masters, pp. 460 and 506 Transparency of *Math Masters,* p. 460* Teaching Masters, pp. 77, 79, and 80	slate; base-10 blocks*; 4 each of number cards 1–10; per partnership: 2 six-sided dice	pen or colored pencil; highlighter, colored pencil, or crayon; per partnership: 4 pennies or other markers, counters*, calculator
3•4	Teaching Masters, pp. 81, 83, and 84 Teaching Aid Masters, pp. 411, 414, 415, 416*, and 417* Transparency of *Math Masters,* p. 414* Study Link Master, p. 82	slate	chart paper; pen or colored pencil; calculator; centimeter cubes
3•5	Transparencies of *Math Masters,* pp. 408* and 409* Study Link Master, p. 85 Game Masters, pp. 461 and 470 Teaching Master, p. 86 Teaching Aid Master, p. 418	slate; 4 each of number cards 1–10; 1 each of number cards 6–18; 1 six-sided die	∗, / Fact Triangles; 18 counters; grid paper*; calculator; colored pencils, markers, or crayons
3•6	Teaching Aid Masters, pp. 419–421* Study Link Master, p. 87 Game Masters, pp. 503 and 506*	slate; 4 each of number cards 1–10	globe; classroom world map; 6 counters (3 each of 2 colors); *Nine O'Clock Lullaby;* demonstration clock*, calculator*
3•7	Study Link Master, p. 88 *Math Masters,* pp. 496 and 497 Teaching Masters, pp. 89 and 90	slate; per partnership: cloth tape measure	classroom world map; globes; ruler; calculator
3•8	Teaching Aid Masters, pp. 388 or 389, 422*, and 423*; Transparency of *Math Masters,* p. 422*; Study Link Master, p. 91; Game Master, p. 487; Teaching Masters, pp. 92 and 93	per partnership: 1 six-sided die	chart paper
3•9	Study Link Master, p. 94 Teaching Masters, pp. 95 and 96 *Differentiation Handbook,* p. 141	slate	scissors; tape; calculator*
3•10	Study Link Master, p. 97; Game Master, p. 489*; Teaching Master, p. 98; Teaching Aid Masters, pp. 412, 414, and 416*	slate; deck of number cards	pen or colored pencil
3•11	Teaching Aid Masters, pp. 388 or 389 and 424 Transparency of *Math Masters,* p. 425* Study Link Master, p. 99 Teaching Masters, pp. 100 and 101	slate	overhead calculator*; ruler; ∗, / Fact Triangles; calculator*
3•12	Assessment Masters, pp. 164–168 Study Link Masters, pp. 102–105		

*Denotes optional materials

Mathematical Background

The discussion below highlights the major content ideas presented in Unit 3 and helps establish instructional priorities.

"What's My Rule?" (Lesson 3•1)

In the first four grades, *Everyday Mathematics* uses function machines and tables of values to study functions. Function machines help students visualize how a rule associates each input value with an output value. A principal activity for developing this concept further is called "What's My Rule?"

For more information about the "What's My Rule?" routine, see Section 1.3.7 in the *Teacher's Reference Manual.*

Instant Recall of Basic Multiplication Facts (Lessons 3•2–3•5)

The authors believe that most students should learn the basic facts for addition and multiplication to the point of instant recall. Mastery of the basic facts will give students surprising power in making quick estimates and operating with larger numbers.

Most of your fourth-grade students will already have rapid recall of addition facts. The majority of students will also have rapid recall of multiplication facts. A 50-facts test, introduced in Lessons 3-3 and 3-4, can be used as one type of screening tool for determining automaticity with multiplication facts. An opportunity to administer this test will occur approximately once per unit as a Part 3 Extra Practice activity. These tests should help students who need additional support to develop speed and accuracy with the multiplication facts. Fact Triangles are another screening tool that can be used to assess automaticity. The games introduced in Lessons 3-3, 3-5, and 3-6 are a means of maintaining automaticity and developing reflex multiplication skills.

Recall of division facts is an important skill, but instant recall is not an objective of *Everyday Mathematics.* Real understanding of the link between multiplication and division is crucial, however. Students who have instant recall of the multiplication facts will, with a few seconds' pause, always produce the related division facts.

Notice that the basic Multiplication/Division Facts Table does not include the 0s facts, because they may cause difficulty in using the table as a division facts table. The 10s facts are included; these are useful and easy.

See Section 16.3 in the *Teacher's Reference Manual* for more about multiplication and division fact recall.

Note

A few students may find it difficult, if not impossible, to achieve instant recall of addition and multiplication facts. Those few should be encouraged to move on by various means, and not to feel bad about what amounts to a minor handicap. They may, for example, rely on using Facts Tables or devise other strategies rather than always relying on memory.

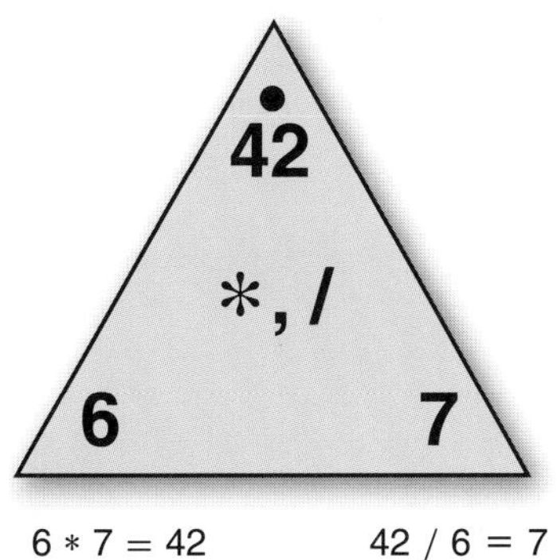

6 * 7 = 42 42 / 6 = 7

7 * 6 = 42 42 / 7 = 6

Students use Fact Triangles to practice multiplication and division facts.

World Tour Project (Lessons 3•6 and 3•7)

In Lesson 2-1, students began the World Tour by visiting Washington, D.C. Now it is time to leave the United States and fly to the first of five regions they will visit—the continent of Africa.

Lesson 3-6 is critical because it establishes the World Tour routine that students will follow throughout the year:

- Students travel as a class to one country in each of five regions of the world.
- For each country they visit, they look up specified information in the World Tour section of the *Student Reference Book* and record it on the Country Notes pages in their journals.

Optional Extension of the World Tour: Many teachers have expanded the World Tour for their classrooms by having students form small groups that travel to one or more additional countries within each region visited. If this is your routine, have students complete Country Notes pages for each additional country they visit, using *Math Masters,* pages 419 and 420.

The World Tour section contains information about 10 countries in each of the five world regions. If you plan to follow the optional extension of the World Tour, students should limit their additional travel to the 10 countries highlighted within each region.

The World Tour section also contains a time-zone map, maps for each of the world regions, and representative games from each of the regions. The games provide opportunities for developing thinking skills.

Above all, the authors want students to experience the many ways in which numerical data affect people's lives, in their own immediate environment as well as in other parts of the world.

Problem-Solving Strategies (Lesson 3◆8)

Most elementary school mathematics texts display a list of "steps in problem solving." This is usually a brief recipe for finding answers to arithmetic word problems. These guides may be helpful in doing textbook word problems, but they are usually oversimplified and often not useful in coping with even relatively simple problems that arise in everyday life.

Lesson 3-8 contains a more extensive and more useful "Guide for Solving Number Stories," which students discuss and apply as they solve problems.

In many cases, a student will "see" a solution right away and decide immediately what math to use to solve the problem and compute an answer. In some cases, a student may play with the data first by drawing a picture or diagram, and then use some math to solve the problem by writing a number model. Other examples that illustrate this problem-solving approach appear in Lesson 3-8.

For more on problem-solving strategies, see the *Teacher's Reference Manual,* Section 18.4.

Diagrams for Representing Addition and Subtraction (Lesson 3◆8)

In *Second* and *Third Grade Everyday Mathematics,* students were introduced to number-story diagrams to help them solve number stories involving addition and subtraction. The purpose of these diagrams is to help students organize the information given in the story, to identify the missing information, and to determine whether to add or subtract to solve the story. A review of number-story diagrams is an optional Readiness activity in Lesson 3-8, based on material in the *Student Reference Book* and on a page of number stories. Most uses of addition and subtraction in solving problems fall into three large categories. A diagram can illustrate each category.

Parts-and-total diagrams are used to represent problems in which two or more quantities (parts) are combined to find a total quantity.

Example: 35 children are riding on the bus. 20 of these children are boys. How many are girls? See the parts-and-total diagram in the margin.

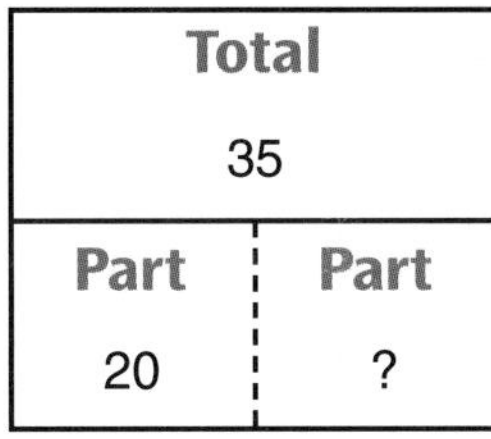

Parts-and-total diagram

Change diagrams are used to represent problems in which a given (start) quantity is increased or decreased.

Example: 25 children are riding on the bus. At the next stop, 5 more children get on. How many children are on the bus now? See the top change diagram in the margin.

Example: A bus leaves school with 35 children. At the first stop, 6 children get off. How many children are left on the bus? See the bottom change diagram in the margin.

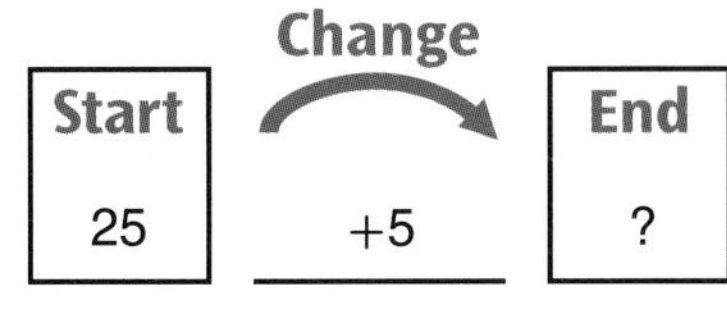

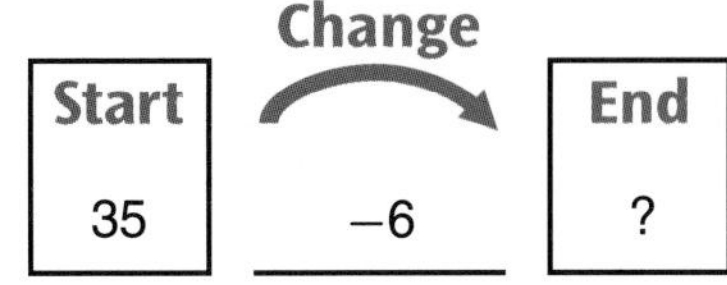

Change diagrams

Comparison diagrams are used to represent problems in which two quantities are given, and you are to find how much more or how much less one quantity is than the other (the difference).

Example: On the bus, there are 12 fourth graders and 8 third graders. How many more fourth graders are there than third graders? See the comparison diagram below.

Quantity	
12	

Quantity	Difference
8	?

Comparison diagram

Note

While a diagram may be useful in solving a particular number story, there are usually many ways of thinking about a problem. It is important for students to understand that problem solving is a creative activity that requires ingenuity and cannot be performed according to a preset prescription.

Extending Algebra Concepts and Skills (Lessons 3◆9–3◆11)

The ideas introduced in these three lessons are very powerful. They are also fairly easy to understand, if presented carefully and with clarity. These ideas will be reviewed, extended, and practiced often during the rest of the year—in Mental Math and Reflexes, in Math Boxes, and in Study Links.

In Lesson 3-9, students review **number sentences** as shorthand notation for word sentences. A number sentence can be true ($5 + 8 = 13$) or false ($12 \div 6 = 4$). In this lesson, students examine a variety of number sentences and determine whether they are true or false.

Lesson 3-10 reviews the use of parentheses in number sentences that involve more than one operation. Students determine whether number sentences containing parentheses are true or false. They practice using parentheses by inserting them in proper places in number sentences.

Lesson 3-11 considers number sentences in which a number is missing. A letter or other symbol, called a **variable,** can represent the missing number. Number sentences that contain variables are called **open sentences.** (In the algebra you studied, they may have been called "equations" or "linear equations.")

To solve an open sentence, students learn to replace the variable with a number that will make the sentence true. For example, if students replace the variable x in $8 + x = 12$ with the number 4, they obtain the true sentence $8 + 4 = 12$. The number 4 is called the solution of the open sentence $8 + x = 12$. If they replace the variable x with the number 6, the number sentence becomes $8 + 6 = 12$. This sentence is false; therefore, 6 is not a solution of the open sentence $8 + x = 12$. These ideas are summarized on page 148 of the *Student Reference Book.*

Everyday Mathematics has used open sentences informally since first grade. Missing numbers have been shown by a question mark, a blank, or a box. From now on, the program uses letters for variables in open sentences to reflect the more convenient and "grown-up" notation used in later grades and everywhere outside schools.

Note

An open sentence can have more than one solution; for example, 1, 2, and 3 are all solutions of the *inequality* $x < 4$. However, most open sentences in this unit contain an = sign and have only one solution.

$3 + x = 13$

$5 = 12 - x$

$25 - x = 15$

Calculator Usage (Lesson 3◆1 and following)

Calculators are used in this unit for games such as *Beat the Calculator* and activities such as Broken Calculator. In *Beat the Calculator,* students quickly realize that their brains are much more efficient than their calculators when finding a product such as 7 * 3. In Broken Calculator, students pretend, for example, that the minus keys on their calculators are broken and then devise strategies to solve such problems as $2{,}421 - 874 = n$. Calculator usage is also encouraged as students work on the World Tour Project.

However, the no-calculator icon (see margin) does appear on some journal pages, including those in which the intention is to encourage practice with algorithms for adding and subtracting numbers. Alert students to watch for the icon.

 **Objective** To review "What's My Rule?" problems.

Technology Resources www.everydaymathonline.com

ePresentations

eToolkit

Algorithms Practice

EM Facts Workshop Game™

Family Letters

Assessment Management

Common Core State Standards

Curriculum Focal Points

Interactive Teacher's Lesson Guide

1 Teaching the Lesson

Key Concepts and Skills

- Solve addition and subtraction problems. [Operations and Computation Goals 1 and 2]
- Solve multiplication and division problems. [Operations and Computation Goals 3 and 4]
- Use rules to complete "What's My Rule?" tables. [Patterns, Functions, and Algebra Goal 1]
- Use words and symbols to describe and write rules for functions. [Patterns, Functions, and Algebra Goal 1]

Key Activities

Students discuss problems in which one quantity depends on another. They illustrate this kind of relationship between pairs of numbers with a function machine and a "What's My Rule?" table. They solve "What's My Rule?" problems.

Ongoing Assessment: Recognizing Student Achievement
Use journal page 53.
[Patterns, Functions, and Algebra Goal 1]

Key Vocabulary

function machine ◆ input ◆ output ◆ rule ◆ "What's My Rule?"

Materials

Math Journal 1, p. 53
transparency of *Math Masters,* p. 407 ◆ slate ◆ calculator (optional)

2 Ongoing Learning & Practice

Identifying Polygon Properties
Math Journal 1, p. 54
straightedge
Students design polygon letters.

Math Boxes 3·1
Math Journal 1, p. 55
Students practice and maintain skills through Math Box problems.

Study Link 3·1
Math Masters, p. 72
Students practice and maintain skills through Study Link activities.

3 Differentiation Options

READINESS

Modeling Functional Relationships with Pattern Blocks
Math Masters, p. 73
pattern blocks (triangles, squares)
Students use pattern blocks to investigate and describe functional relationships.

ENRICHMENT

Solving a Perimeter Problem
Math Masters, p. 74
pattern blocks (squares, hexagons)
Students apply the "What's My Rule?" concept to solve a perimeter problem.

EXTRA PRACTICE

Completing "What's My Rule?" Tables
Math Masters, p. 407
calculator
Students practice using words and symbols to describe and write rules for functions.

Advance Preparation

 ***Teacher's Reference Manual,* Grades 4–6** pp. 19, 278–284

Getting Started

Mental Math and Reflexes

Pose multidigit addition and subtraction problems. *Suggestions:*

●○○	30 + 50 = 80	60 + 40 = 100
	90 − 20 = 70	80 − 40 = 40
●●○	42 + 20 = 62	53 + 30 = 83
	56 − 10 = 46	75 − 20 = 55
●●●	32 + 62 = 94	98 + 22 = 120
	66 − 41 = 25	76 − 25 = 51

Math Message

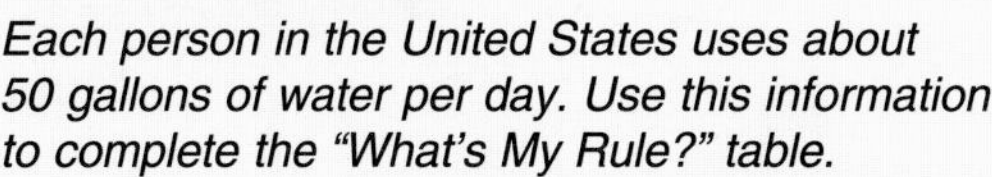

Each person in the United States uses about 50 gallons of water per day. Use this information to complete the "What's My Rule?" table.

in (days)	out (gallons)
2	100
6	300
10	500
30	1,500
365	18,250

1 Teaching the Lesson

Interactive whiteboard-ready **ePresentations** are available at www.everydaymathonline.com to help you teach the lesson.

Math Message Follow-Up

(*Math Masters,* p. 407)

Algebraic Thinking Have students compare their completed tables.

Display the function machine on the transparency of *Math Masters,* page 407. Remind students how a **function machine** works:

▷ A number (the **input**) is dropped into the machine.

▷ The machine changes the number according to a rule.

▷ A new number (the **output**) comes out the other end.

The **rule** for the Math Message problem is *multiply by 50.* Write "× 50" in the function machine. To support English language learners, discuss that the word *rule* has an everyday usage, such as a classroom *rule,* and a mathematical usage.

Point out the **"What's My Rule?"** table in the Math Message problem. Ask:

- What do the numbers in the *in* column represent? Number of days
- What do the numbers in the *out* column represent? Average number of gallons of water used by one person in that many days
- How are the 2 in the *in* column and the 100 in the *out* column related? $2 \times 50 = 100$

Tell students that in this lesson they will review variations of function machines.

Adjusting the Activity

Have volunteers pose questions. *For example:*

- If 8 is dropped into the function machine, which number will come out? 400
- If 600 comes out of the function machine, which number was dropped in? 12

AUDITORY ♦ KINESTHETIC ♦ TACTILE ♦ VISUAL

Type 1

Rule
Subtract 15

in	out
30	15
90	75
65	50
110	95

Type 2

Rule
Add 100

in	out
250	350
20	120
565	665
321	421

Type 3

Rule
Multiply by 7

in	out
7	49
2	14
9	63
600	4,200

Type 4

Rule
Divide by 6

in	out
54	9
42	7
24	4
600	100

Rule
A pound of nuts costs $3.75

pounds	cost
1	$3.75
2	$7.50
5	$18.75
11	$41.25

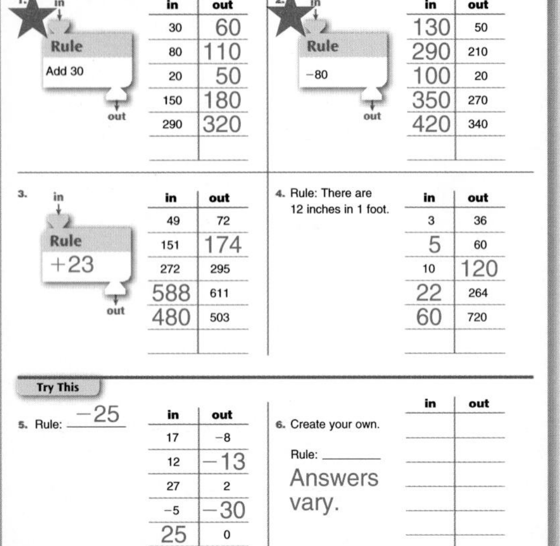

Student Page

Date Time

LESSON 3·1 **"What's My Rule?"** SRB 162-166

Complete the "What's My Rule?" tables and state the rules.

1. Rule: Add 30

in	out
30	60
80	110
20	50
150	180
290	320

2. Rule: −80

in	out
130	50
290	210
100	20
350	270
420	340

3. Rule: +23

in	out
49	72
151	174
272	295
588	611
480	503

4. Rule: There are 12 inches in 1 foot.

in	out
3	36
5	60
10	120
22	264
60	720

Try This

5. Rule: −25

in	out
17	−8
12	−13
27	2
−5	−30
25	0

6. Create your own.

Rule: ______

Answers vary.

in	out

Math Journal 1, p. 53

▶ Reviewing Variations of the "What's My Rule?" Routine

WHOLE-CLASS ACTIVITY

(*Math Masters,* p. 407)

Algebraic Thinking Demonstrate each type of "What's My Rule?" table (*see margin*) on the transparency of *Math Masters,* page 407.

- ▷ In Type 1, as in the Math Message problem, the rule and sample inputs are known, and the outputs must be determined.
- ▷ In Type 2, the rule and sample outputs are known, and the inputs must be determined.
- ▷ In Type 3, the inputs and outputs are known, and the rule must be determined.
- ▷ In Type 4, some inputs and outputs are known, and the missing numbers and the rule must be determined.

To find the rule, students should use the pairs in which both the *in* and *out* numbers are given. Then students can use the rule to fill in the missing *in* and *out* numbers. Also discuss any other patterns not stated in the rule. For example, the Type 3 table in the margin shows that when an even number is multiplied by an odd number, the result is an even number, and when an odd number is multiplied by an odd number, the result is an odd number.

Pose problems like Type 4 to the class. Rules may be stated as simple statements, such as "Subtract 15," or rules may be stated in a context like the problem in the margin (A pound of nuts costs $3.75) or as in the Math Message (50 gallons per day). Encourage students to supply both types of rules. Supplying a context for a rule will be more difficult.

▶ Completing "What's My Rule?" Tables

PARTNER ACTIVITY

(*Math Journal 1,* p. 53)

Students complete Problems 1 and 2 on their own. They work in partnerships to complete the remainder of the page. Have calculators on hand for students to use as necessary while solving the "What's My Rule?" problems.

Ongoing Assessment: Recognizing Student Achievement

Journal page 53 Problems 1 and 2

Use **journal page 53, Problems 1 and 2** to assess students' ability to use rules to complete "What's My Rule?" tables. Students are making adequate progress if they are able to correctly identify the *in* and *out* numbers when given the rule. Some students may be able to identify the rules in Problems 3 and 5 and use these rules to complete the tables.

[Patterns, Functions, and Algebra Goal 1]

2 Ongoing Learning & Practice

Identifying Polygon Properties

INDEPENDENT ACTIVITY

(*Math Journal 1,* p. 54)

Students design polygon letters.

Math Boxes 3·1

INDEPENDENT ACTIVITY

(*Math Journal 1,* p. 55)

Mixed Practice Math Boxes in this lesson are linked with Math Boxes in Lessons 3-3 and 3-5. The skill in Problem 6 previews Unit 4 content.

Writing/Reasoning Have students write a response to the following: *Explain how you found the* range *of the data set in Problem 2.* Sample answer: I subtracted the smallest number (16) from the largest number (25) to find the range (9).

Study Link 3·1

INDEPENDENT ACTIVITY

(*Math Masters,* p. 72)

Home Connection Students complete several types of "What's My Rule?" problems.

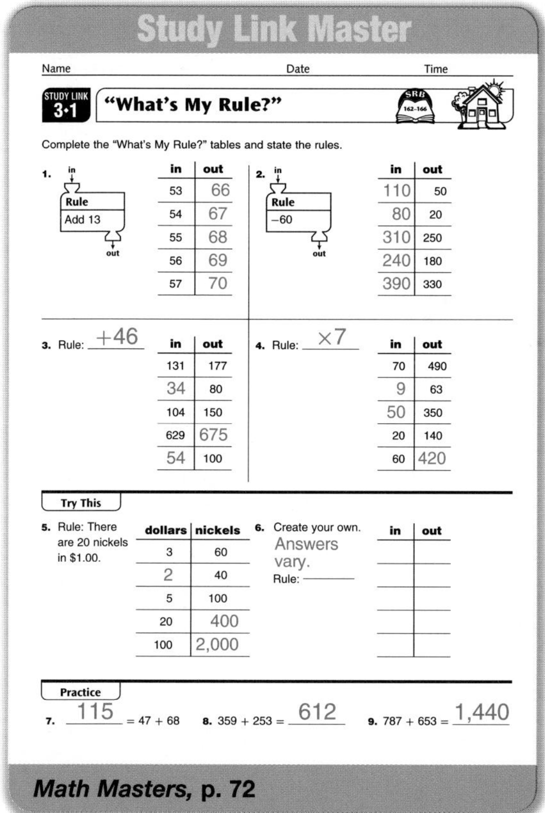

Study Link Master

Name　　Date　　Time

STUDY LINK 3·1 **"What's My Rule?"** SRB 162–166

Complete the "What's My Rule?" tables and state the rules.

1. Rule: Add 13

in	out
53	66
54	67
55	68
56	69
57	70

2. Rule: −60

in	out
110	50
80	20
310	250
240	180
390	330

3. Rule: +46

in	out
131	177
34	80
104	150
629	675
54	100

4. Rule: ×7

in	out
70	490
9	63
50	350
20	140
60	420

Try This

5. Rule: There are 20 nickels in $1.00.

dollars	nickels
3	60
2	40
5	100
20	400
100	2,000

6. Create your own. Answers vary. Rule: ______

in	out

Practice

7. 115 = 47 + 68　8. 359 + 253 = 612　9. 787 + 653 = 1,440

Math Masters, p. 72

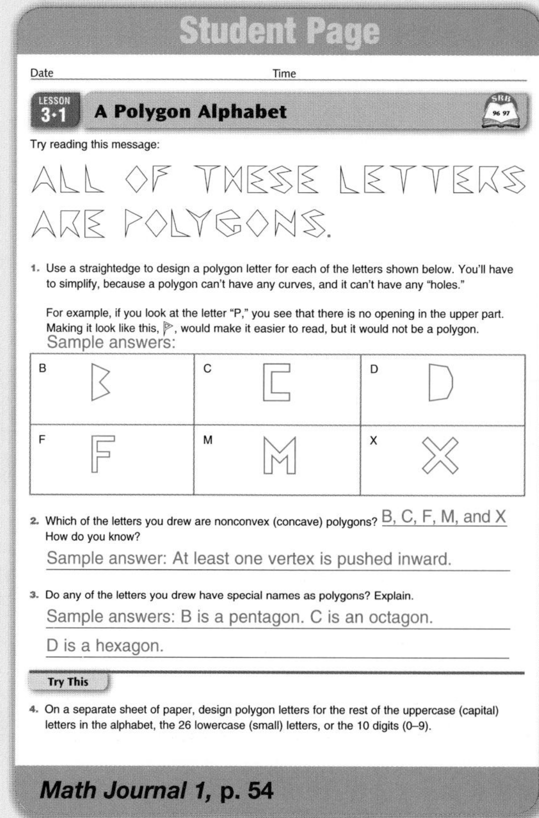

Student Page

Date　　Time

LESSON 3·1 **A Polygon Alphabet** SRB 96 97

Try reading this message:

ALL OF THESE LETTERS ARE POLYGONS.

1. Use a straightedge to design a polygon letter for each of the letters shown below. You'll have to simplify, because a polygon can't have any curves, and it can't have any "holes."

For example, if you look at the letter "P," you see that there is no opening in the upper part. Making it look like this, P, would make it easier to read, but it would not be a polygon.

Sample answers:

B	C	D
F	M	X

2. Which of the letters you drew are nonconvex (concave) polygons? B, C, F, M, and X
How do you know?
Sample answer: At least one vertex is pushed inward.

3. Do any of the letters you drew have special names as polygons? Explain.
Sample answers: B is a pentagon. C is an octagon.
D is a hexagon.

Try This

4. On a separate sheet of paper, design polygon letters for the rest of the uppercase (capital) letters in the alphabet, the 26 lowercase (small) letters, or the 10 digits (0–9).

Math Journal 1, p. 54

NOTE To further explore function rules, see www.everydaymathonline.com.

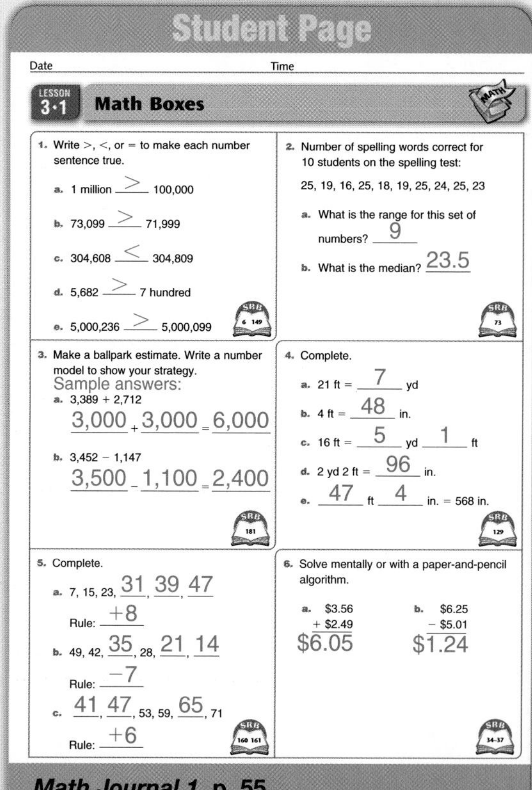

Student Page

Date　　Time

LESSON 3·1 **Math Boxes**

1. Write >, <, or = to make each number sentence true.
a. 1 million > 100,000
b. 73,099 > 71,999
c. 304,608 < 304,809
d. 5,682 > 7 hundred
e. 5,000,236 > 5,000,099
SRB 6 149

2. Number of spelling words correct for 10 students on the spelling test:
25, 19, 16, 25, 18, 19, 25, 24, 25, 23
a. What is the range for this set of numbers? 9
b. What is the median? 23.5
SRB 73

3. Make a ballpark estimate. Write a number model to show your strategy.
Sample answers:
a. 3,389 + 2,712
3,000 + 3,000 = 6,000
b. 3,452 − 1,147
3,500 − 1,100 = 2,400
SRB 181

4. Complete.
a. 21 ft = 7 yd
b. 4 ft = 48 in.
c. 16 ft = 5 yd 1 ft
d. 2 yd 2 ft = 96 in.
e. 47 ft 4 in. = 568 in.
SRB 129

5. Complete.
a. 7, 15, 23, 31, 39, 47
Rule: +8
b. 49, 42, 35, 28, 21, 14
Rule: −7
c. 41, 47, 53, 59, 65, 71
Rule: +6
SRB 160 161

6. Solve mentally or with a paper-and-pencil algorithm.
a. $3.56 + $2.49 = $6.05
b. $6.25 − $5.01 = $1.24
SRB 34–37

Math Journal 1, p. 55

Teaching Master

Name Date Time

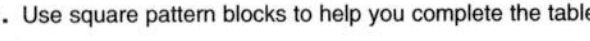

LESSON 3·1 **"What's My Rule?" Polygon Sides**

1. Use square pattern blocks to help you complete the table.

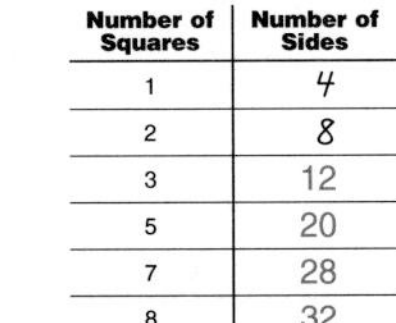

Number of Squares	Number of Sides
1	4
2	8
3	12
5	20
7	28
8	32

2. Suppose there are 12 squares. Explain how to find the number of sides without counting.
Sample answer: Multiply 12 squares by 4 sides. This equals 48 sides. $(12 \times 4 = 48)$

3. Use triangle pattern blocks to help you complete the table.

Number of Triangles	Number of Sides
1	3
2	6
5	15
4	12
3	9
6	18

4. Suppose there are 30 sides. Explain how to find the number of triangles without counting.
Sample answer: Divide 30 sides by 3. This equals 10 triangles. $(30 \div 3 = 10)$

Math Masters, p. 73

Teaching Master

Name Date Time

LESSON 3·1 **"What's My Rule?" Perimeter**

The distance around a shape is called its **perimeter.** The perimeter of a square pattern block is 4 inches.

1 in. / 1 in. / 1 in. / 1 in.

1 + 1 + 1 + 1 = 4

1. Place 2 square pattern blocks side by side. What is the perimeter of the shape? 6 inches

2. Complete the "What's My Rule?" table. Use square pattern blocks to create the shapes.

3. Explain the rule for finding the perimeter of the shapes.
Sample answer: Multiply the number of squares by 2, then add 2.

Number of Square Pattern Blocks	Perimeter of Shape (inches)
1	4
2	6
3	8
4	10
5	12
6	14
7	16
8	18

4. Use your rule to complete the following: 214 square pattern blocks are placed side by side. What is the perimeter of the shape? 430 inches

Try This

5. Use words or symbols to explain the rule for finding the perimeter of shapes made by placing hexagon pattern blocks side by side.
Sample answer: Multiply the number of hexagons by 4, then add 2. $(h \times 4) + 2$

Math Masters, p. 74

3 Differentiation Options

READINESS

PARTNER ACTIVITY

5–15 Min

▶ Modeling Functional Relationships with Pattern Blocks

(*Math Masters,* p. 73)

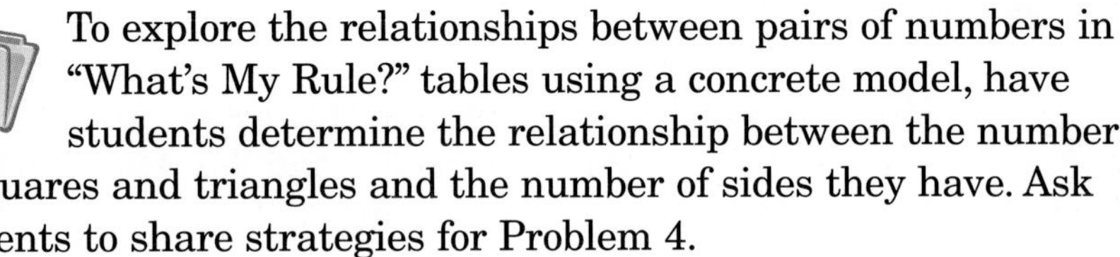

To explore the relationships between pairs of numbers in "What's My Rule?" tables using a concrete model, have students determine the relationship between the number of squares and triangles and the number of sides they have. Ask students to share strategies for Problem 4.

ENRICHMENT

PARTNER ACTIVITY

5–15 Min

▶ Solving a Perimeter Problem

(*Math Masters,* p. 74)

To apply students' understanding of functional relationships, have them explore the perimeter of shapes created by placing square pattern blocks side by side. Students record their data in a table and use the relationships between pairs of numbers to generate a rule for finding the perimeter of any shape made by n number of squares placed side by side.

Problem 5 challenges students to explain the rule for finding the perimeter of shapes created by placing hexagon pattern blocks side by side.

NOTE *Perimeter* is defined as the distance around a closed 2-dimensional shape. Square and hexagon pattern blocks are prisms, not 2-dimensional polygons, as the names imply. For this activity, have students consider only the square or hexagonal bases of the pattern blocks.

EXTRA PRACTICE

INDEPENDENT ACTIVITY

5–15 Min

▶ Completing "What's My Rule?" Tables

(*Math Masters,* p. 407)

Algebraic Thinking To practice using words and symbols to describe and write rules for functions, have students solve "What's My Rule?" problems. Use *Math Masters,* page 407 to create problems to meet the needs of individual students, or have students create and solve their own problems. Afterward, discuss any patterns that were not part of the rule.

3·2 Multiplication Facts

Objectives To review strategies for solving multiplication facts; to help students maintain automaticity with multiplication facts; and to introduce prime and composite numbers.

www.everydaymathonline.com

ePresentations

eToolkit

Algorithms Practice

EM Facts Workshop Game™

Family Letters

Assessment Management

Common Core State Standards

Curriculum Focal Points

Interactive Teacher's Lesson Guide

1 Teaching the Lesson

Key Concepts and Skills

- Find factors and multiples of numbers. [Number and Numeration Goal 3]
- Identify prime and composite numbers. [Number and Numeration Goal 3]
- Identify square numbers. [Number and Numeration Goal 4]
- Solve multiplication facts. [Operations and Computation Goal 3]
- Identify and use patterns in the Multiplication/Division Facts Table. [Patterns, Functions, and Algebra Goal 1]

Key Activities

Students cut out Multiplication/Division Fact Triangles. They discuss the Multiplication/Division Facts Table, symbols, and vocabulary for multiplication. Students identify prime and composite numbers. They use Fact Triangles to maintain automaticity with multiplication facts.

Key Vocabulary

multiplication facts ◆ factors ◆ products ◆ factor pair ◆ multiples ◆ square numbers ◆ turn-around facts ◆ prime number ◆ composite number

Materials

Math Journal 1, inside front cover; p. 56; Activity Sheets 1–4 ◆ *Student Reference Book,* pp. 8, 178A, and 178B ◆ Study Link 3•1 transparencies of *Math Masters,* pp. 408 and 409 (optional) ◆ paper clips ◆ envelopes or resealable plastic bags ◆ scissors ◆ calculator ◆ counters (optional)

2 Ongoing Learning & Practice

Playing *Name That Number*

Student Reference Book, p. 254
Math Masters, p. 489
deck of number cards (the Everything Math Deck, if available)
Students practice representing numbers in different ways.

Ongoing Assessment: Recognizing Student Achievement

Use *Math Masters,* page 489.
[Number and Numeration Goal 4]

Math Boxes 3·2

Math Journal 1, p. 57
Students practice and maintain skills through Math Box problems.

Study Link 3·2

Math Masters, p. 75
Students practice and maintain skills through Study Link activities.

3 Differentiation Options

READINESS

Making Rectangular Arrays

Math Masters, p. 76
centimeter cubes ◆ 4 each of number cards 1–10 (from the Everything Math Deck, if available)
Students practice multiplication facts using a concrete model.

EXTRA PRACTICE

Playing *Buzz* and *Bizz-Buzz*

Student Reference Book, p. 234
Students practice naming multiples.

ELL SUPPORT

Building a Math Word Bank

Differentiation Handbook, p. 140
Students add the term *square numbers* to their Math Word Banks.

Advance Preparation

For Part 1, have plastic bags or envelopes available for storing the Fact Triangles. Think about how to pair students for this activity so they will be at similar skill levels.

***Teacher's Reference Manual,* Grades 4–6** pp. 16, 79, 80, 267–269

Getting Started

Mental Math and Reflexes

In preparation for discussing multiples, pose calculator skip-counting problems, starting with 0. *Suggestions:*

●○○ 20s 0, 20, 40, 60, 80, 100, ...
50s 0, 50, 100, 150, 200, 250, ...

●●○ 6s 0, 6, 12, 18, 24, 30, ...
8s 0, 8, 16, 24, 32, 40, ...

●●● Back by 4s 0, –4, –8, –12, –16, –20, ...
Back by 7s 0, –7, –14, –21, –28, –35, ...

Math Message

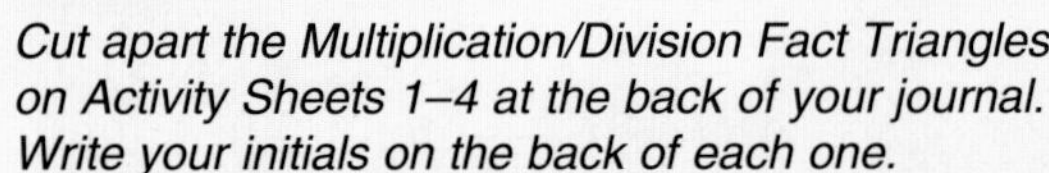

Cut apart the Multiplication/Division Fact Triangles on Activity Sheets 1–4 at the back of your journal. Write your initials on the back of each one.

Put the Fact Triangles and two paper clips into a plastic bag or envelope.

Study Link 3·1 Follow-Up

Have partners discuss the pattern in Problem 1 and explain why the numbers will always change from odd to even or even to odd when moving from the in column to the out column.

NOTE For Multiplication/ Division Fact Triangles and a Facts Table with facts through 12 ∗ 12, see www.everydaymathonline.com.

1 Teaching the Lesson

▶ Math Message Follow-Up

Tell the class they will use Fact Triangles to practice multiplication facts and another tool, the Multiplication/Division Facts Table, to discuss the terms *factor, product,* and *multiple.*

▶ Reviewing the Multiplication/ Division Facts Table

(*Math Journal 1,* inside front cover; *Math Masters,* p. 408)

Introducing the Symbols ∗ and /

Ask students to look at the inside front cover of *Math Journal 1.* Display an overhead transparency of *Math Masters,* page 408. Remind students of the following:

▷ The table shows the **multiplication facts.**

▷ The 0s facts have been omitted to avoid confusion about division by 0 (which is not possible).

▷ The 10s facts are included.

Point out the ∗ and / symbols in the upper left-hand corner of the table. Explain that in Grades 4, 5, and 6 of *Everyday Mathematics*, an asterisk (∗) is usually used to indicate multiplication. A slash (/) is often used to indicate division, but the ÷ and the $\overline{)\ \ }$ symbols are also used.

NOTE The symbols ∗ and / are used for multiplication and division on computer keyboards. The asterisk helps avoid confusion between the × symbol and the variable *x* in algebra. Using the slash for division clearly relates division to fractions. 1 / 2, $\frac{1}{2}$, 1 ÷ 2, and $2\overline{)1}$ all represent the same number.

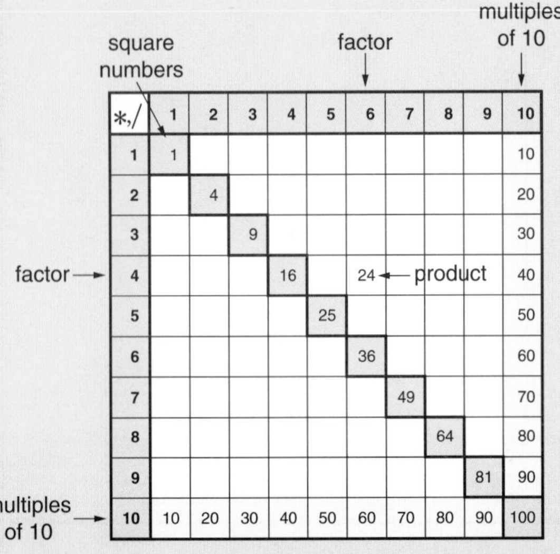

∗,/	1	2	3	4	5	6	7	8	9	10
1	1									10
2		4								20
3			9							30
4				16		24				40
5					25					50
6						36				60
7							49			70
8								64		80
9									81	90
10	10	20	30	40	50	60	70	80	90	100

Multiplication/Division Facts Table from the inside front cover of *Math Journal 1* and *Math Masters,* page 408

Reviewing the Meaning of Factors, Products, and Multiples

Remind students that the numbers in the shaded row and shaded column in the table are called **factors,** and the rest of the numbers are called **products.** For example, in 4 * 6 = 24, 4 and 6 are factors of 24, and 24 is the product of 4 and 6. 4 and 6 are a **factor pair** of 24. A number may have more than one factor pair. For example, the factor pairs for 24 are 1 and 24, 2 and 12, 3 and 8, and 4 and 6. To support English language learners, label and identify the factors and products on the transparency of *Math Masters,* page 408 as students do so on the inside front cover of *Math Journal 1.*

Direct students to look across a row or down a column to find the **multiples** of a number. The multiples of 10, for example, are 10, 20, 30, 40, and so on. Point out that a whole number is a multiple of each of its factors.

Reviewing Square Numbers

Next point out the shaded products on the diagonal. Remind students that these products are called **square numbers.** Each square number is the product of a counting number multiplied by itself. For example, 9 is a square number, because 3 * 3 = 9.

Reviewing Turn-Around Facts

Point out that the products above the diagonal of square numbers are "mirror images" of the products below the diagonal. For example, 6 * 3 and 3 * 6 both equal 18. These are called **turn-around facts.** If you know a fact, you also know its turn-around fact. To support English language learners, ask: *Why do you think these facts are called turn-around facts?*

Reviewing Other Multiplication Shortcuts

Ask students if they know any other multiplication shortcuts. *For example:*

▷ 0 times any number equals 0.

▷ 1 times any number equals the number.

▷ To find 2 times a number, double the number.

▷ To find 10 times a number, write 0 after the number.

Factors Pairs of Prime Numbers

WHOLE-CLASS ACTIVITY

(*Student Reference Book,* p. 8; *Math Journal 1,* p. 56; *Math Masters,* p. 409)

On the board, draw the Fact Triangle in the margin, or fill in the numbers on a transparency of *Math Masters,* page 409.

Have students identify the product and the factors. Product: 2. Factors: 1, 2. Point out that every Fact Triangle illustrates a factor pair of the product. For example, the Fact Triangle in the margin shows that 1 and 2 make up a factor pair of the product, 2.

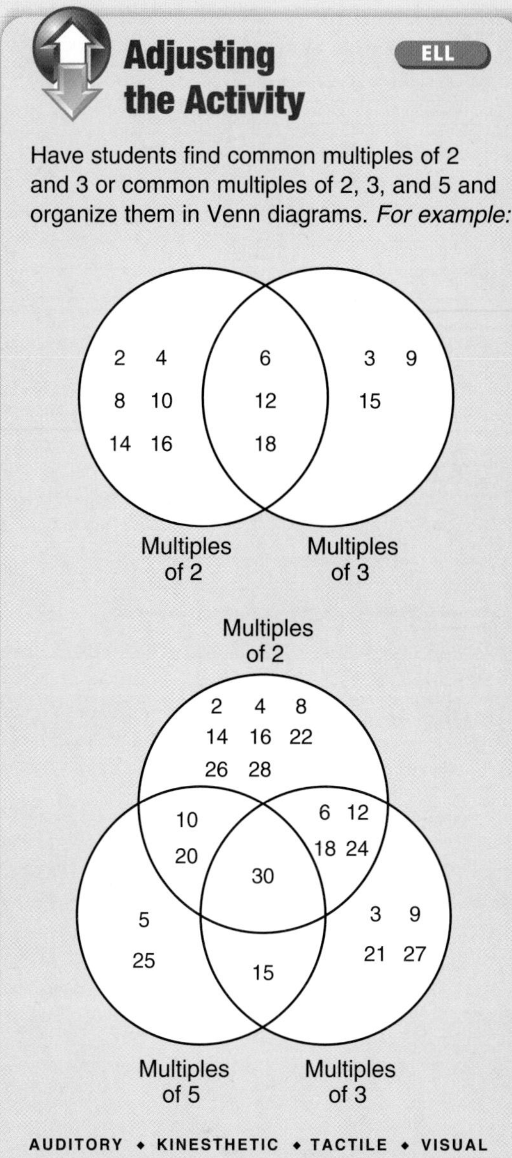

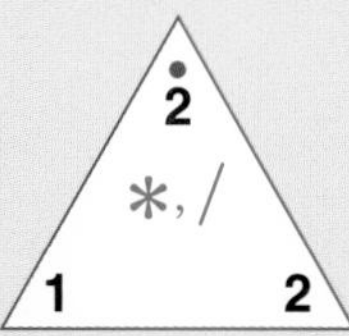

1. In the table below, list all the factor pairs of each number.

Number	Factor Pairs
2	1 and 2
3	1 and 3
4	1 and 4; 2 and 2
5	1 and 5
6	1 and 6 2 and 3
7	1 and 7
8	1 and 8; 2 and 4
9	1 and 9; 3 and 3
10	1 and 10; 2 and 5
11	1 and 11
12	1 and 12; 2 and 6; 3 and 4

2. Name a number in the table above that is not a prime number. Explain how you know it is not prime.
Sample answer: 12; it has three factor pairs: 1 and 12, 2 and 6, and 3 and 4. A prime number has only one factor pair.

3. Name at least three prime numbers that are not in the table above.
Sample answers: 13, 17, 19

4. Choose one of your answers from Problem 3. Explain how you know it is a prime number.
Sample answer: 13 is a prime number because its only factor pair is 1 and 13.

Math Journal 1, **p. 56**

Table. Ask students to name the numbers in the table that have only one factor pair. 2, 3, 5, 7, and 11 Explain that there is a nam for numbers that have only one factor pair. Ask: *Does anyone kno what these numbers are called?* **Prime numbers** List the prime numbers on the board along with their factor pairs:

Prime Number	Factor Pair
2	1 and 2
3	1 and 3
5	1 and 5
7	1 and 7
11	1 and 11

Ask students if they notice anything about the factor pairs of the prime numbers. If no one suggests it, point out that each factor pair consists of 1 and the original number. Explain that a counting number is a prime number if it has exactly two factors: 1 and itself.

Next, ask students to name the numbers that are *not* prime. 4, 6, 8, 9, 10, and 12 Tell students that these are called composite numbers. A **composite number** is a counting number with more than two factors. Composite numbers have at least two factor pairs.

For more information about prime and composite numbers, students can refer to *Student Reference Book,* page 8. Ask studen to complete journal page 56.

▶ Reviewing the Models of Multiplication

(*Student Reference Book,* pp. 178A and 178B)

Tell students that thinking about what a multiplication fact means can help them figure out facts they can't remember. For example, a student who could not remember the answer to 7 * 6 could think about this fact in several ways:

▷ *Equal groups:* How many objects are in 7 groups of 6?

▷ *Arrays or area:* How many objects are in an array with 7 rows and 6 objects in each row?

▷ *Multiplicative comparison:* What number is 7 times as many as 6

These interpretations are described on *Student Reference Book,* pages 178A and 178B.

Suggest additional facts and have students record the corresponding questions on their slates. *For example:*

- 8 * 7
- 9 * 4
- 6 *

Sorting Fact Triangles

(*Math Journal 1,* inside front cover; *Math Masters,* p. 409)

PARTNER ACTIVITY

Ask students to count the Fact Triangles they stored—there should be 36.

Draw a large Multiplication/Division Fact Triangle on the board, or display a transparency of *Math Masters,* page 409, with numbers inserted. Remind students that the numbers in the bottom corners of the triangle are factors and that the number under the dot is the product of the two factors. Demonstrate how to use the Fact Triangle by covering the product.

Divide the class into partnerships. As students practice their facts, remind them to sort the Fact Triangles into two piles—"OK" and "Try Again"—as they did with the +, – Fact Triangles in Unit 1.

Use this Fact Triangle session to screen the class to determine which students are proficient with the basic multiplication facts. Students with triangles in the "Try Again" pile will need additional support. Games and Fact Triangles are available to provide opportunities for students to practice these facts. See the *Teacher's Reference Manual* for ideas on establishing a game routine in your classroom. Students identified in this initial screening as needing additional support should participate in the 50-Facts Test routine throughout the year. See Lesson 3-3 for more information.

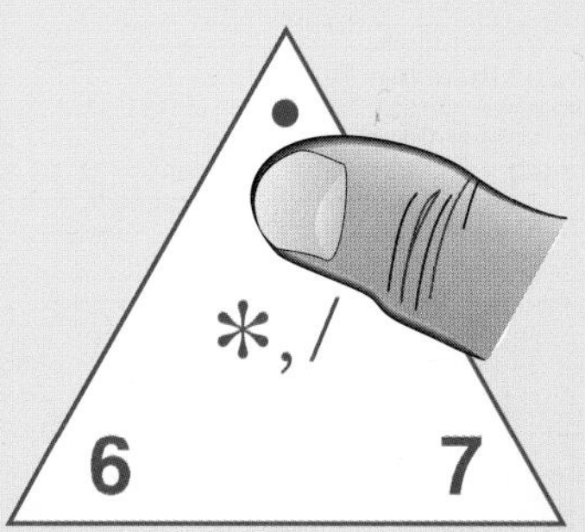

"6 times 7 equals what number?" or "What number is 6 times as many as 7?"

Adjusting the Activity

ELL

Encourage the use of tools and strategies, such as:

- counters or pictures to illustrate facts,
- calculators for skip counting to find products, and
- the Multiplication/Division Facts Table to find products.

AUDITORY ◆ KINESTHETIC ◆ TACTILE ◆ VISUAL

2 Ongoing Learning & Practice

Playing *Name That Number*

PARTNER ACTIVITY

(*Student Reference Book,* p. 254; *Math Masters,* p. 489)

Students play *Name That Number* to practice representing numbers in different ways. See Lesson 2-2 for additional information.

Ongoing Assessment: Recognizing Student Achievement

***Math Masters* Page 489**

Use ***Math Masters,* page 489** to assess students' ability to use numerical expressions involving one or more of the basic four arithmetic operations to give equivalent names for whole numbers. Students are making adequate progress if they are able to create numerical expressions to name the target number for two rounds of play. Some students may write numerical expressions that include parentheses or exponents.

[Number and Numeration Goal 4]

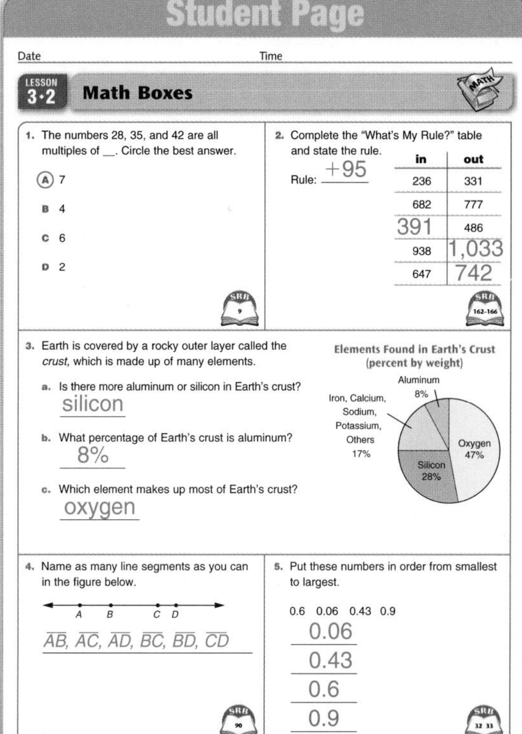

Student Page

Date Time

LESSON 3·2 **Math Boxes**

1. The numbers 28, 35, and 42 are all multiples of __. Circle the best answer.
   (A) 7
   B 4
   C 6
   D 2

2. Complete the "What's My Rule?" table and state the rule.
   Rule: +95

in	out
236	331
682	777
391	486
938	1,033
647	742

3. Earth is covered by a rocky outer layer called the *crust,* which is made up of many elements.
   a. Is there more aluminum or silicon in Earth's crust? silicon
   b. What percentage of Earth's crust is aluminum? 8%
   c. Which element makes up most of Earth's crust? oxygen

4. Name as many line segments as you can in the figure below.
   A B C D
   $\overline{AB}$, $\overline{AC}$, $\overline{AD}$, $\overline{BC}$, $\overline{BD}$, $\overline{CD}$

5. Put these numbers in order from smallest to largest.
   0.6 0.06 0.43 0.9
   0.06
   0.43
   0.6
   0.9

Math Journal 1, p. 57

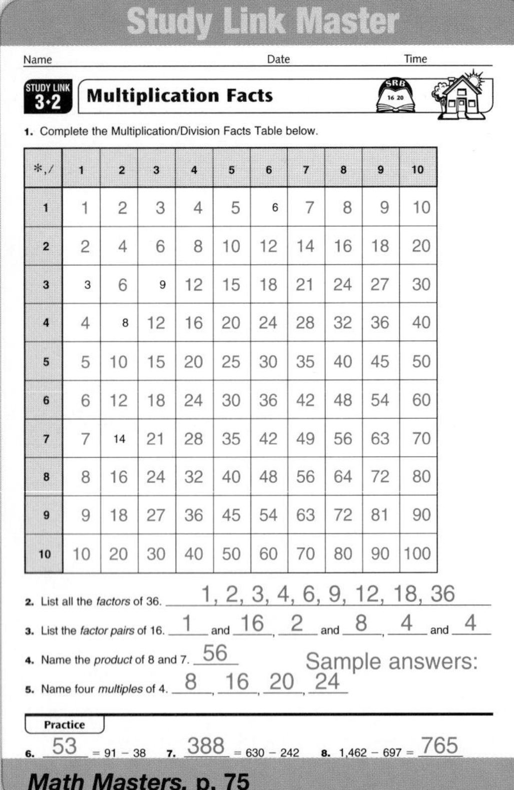
Study Link Master

Name Date Time

STUDY LINK 3•2 **Multiplication Facts**

1. Complete the Multiplication/Division Facts Table below.

*,/	1	2	3	4	5	6	7	8	9	10
1	1	2	3	4	5	6	7	8	9	10
2	2	4	6	8	10	12	14	16	18	20
3	3	6	9	12	15	18	21	24	27	30
4	4	8	12	16	20	24	28	32	36	40
5	5	10	15	20	25	30	35	40	45	50
6	6	12	18	24	30	36	42	48	54	60
7	7	14	21	28	35	42	49	56	63	70
8	8	16	24	32	40	48	56	64	72	80
9	9	18	27	36	45	54	63	72	81	90
10	10	20	30	40	50	60	70	80	90	100

2. List all the *factors* of 36. 1, 2, 3, 4, 6, 9, 12, 18, 36
3. List the *factor pairs* of 16. 1 and 16, 2 and 8, 4 and 4
4. Name the *product* of 8 and 7. 56
5. Name four *multiples* of 4. 8, 16, 20, 24 Sample answers:

Practice

6. 53 = 91 − 38 7. 388 = 630 − 242 8. 1,462 − 697 = 765

Math Masters, p. 75

▶ Math Boxes 3•2

INDEPENDENT ACTIVITY

(*Math Journal 1,* p. 57)

Mixed Practice Math Boxes in this lesson are paired with Math Boxes in Lesson 3-4. The skill in Problem 5 previews Unit 4 content.

▶ Study Link 3•2

INDEPENDENT ACTIVITY

(*Math Masters,* p. 75)

Home Connection Students complete a Multiplication/Division Facts Table and name factors, products, and multiples of numbers.

NOTE For practice with facts through 12 * 12, have students use the Online Master at www.everydaymathonline.com in place of Study Link 3•2.

3 Differentiation Options

READINESS

PARTNER ACTIVITY

▶ Making Rectangular Arrays

5–15 Min

(*Math Masters,* p. 76)

To provide experience with multiplication facts using a concrete model, have students make rectangular arrays with centimeter cubes and record a number model for each array.

EXTRA PRACTICE

SMALL-GROUP ACTIVITY

▶ Playing *Buzz* and *Bizz-Buzz*

5–15 Min

(*Student Reference Book,* p. 234)

To practice naming multiples, have students play *Buzz* and *Bizz-Buzz.* Before playing the game, remind students that a whole number is a multiple of each of its factors.

ELL SUPPORT

SMALL-GROUP ACTIVITY

▶ Building a Math Word Bank

5–15 Min

(*Differentiation Handbook,* p. 140)

To provide language support for multiplication, have students use the Word Bank Template found on *Differentiation Handbook,* page 140. Ask students to write the term *square numbers,* draw pictures relating to the term, and write other related words. See the *Differentiation Handbook* for more information.

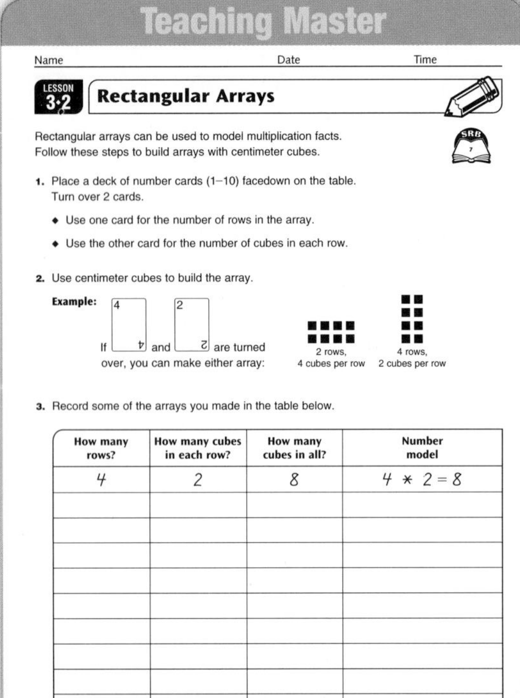
Teaching Master

Name Date Time

LESSON 3•2 **Rectangular Arrays**

Rectangular arrays can be used to model multiplication facts. Follow these steps to build arrays with centimeter cubes.

1. Place a deck of number cards (1–10) facedown on the table. Turn over 2 cards.
   - Use one card for the number of rows in the array.
   - Use the other card for the number of cubes in each row.
2. Use centimeter cubes to build the array.

Example: If 4 and 2 are turned over, you can make either array: 2 rows, 4 cubes per row; 4 rows, 2 cubes per row

3. Record some of the arrays you made in the table below.

How many rows?	How many cubes in each row?	How many cubes in all?	Number model
4	2	8	4 * 2 = 8

Math Masters, p. 76

3·3 Multiplication Facts Practice

Objectives To introduce the 50-facts test; and to provide practice with multiplication facts.

Technology Resources www.everydaymathonline.com

Presentations

eToolkit

Algorithms Practice

EM Facts Workshop Game™

Family Letters

Assessment Management

Common Core State Standards

Curriculum Focal Points

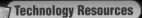

Interactive Teacher's Lesson Guide

1 Teaching the Lesson

Key Concepts and Skills

- Rename a fraction as an equivalent fraction and as a percent. [Number and Numeration Goal 5]
- Solve multiplication facts. [Operations and Computation Goal 3]
- Identify and use patterns in the Multiplication/Division Facts Table. [Patterns, Functions, and Algebra Goal 1]

Key Activities

Students look for patterns in multiplication facts. A 50-facts test for assessing students' automaticity with multiplication facts is given.

Key Vocabulary

percent

Materials

Math Journal 1, p. 58 and inside front cover
Study Link 3•2
Math Masters, p. 410
slate ◆ pen or colored pencil ◆
base-10 blocks (optional)

2 Ongoing Learning & Practice

Playing *Baseball Multiplication*
Student Reference Book, pp. 231 and 232
Math Masters, p. 460
per partnership: 4 pennies or other markers, 2 six-sided dice, calculator, counters (optional) ◆ transparency of *Math Masters,* p. 460 (optional)
Students practice multiplication facts.

Math Boxes 3·3
Math Journal 1, p. 59
Students practice and maintain skills through Math Box problems.

Ongoing Assessment: Recognizing Student Achievement
Use Math Boxes, Problem 3.
[Operations and Computation Goal 6]

Study Link 3·3
Math Masters, p. 78
Students practice and maintain skills through Study Link activities.

3 Differentiation Options

READINESS

Exploring Skip-Count Patterns on the Hundreds Grid
Math Masters, p. 79
highlighter, colored pencil, or crayon
Students skip count on a hundreds grid to identify patterns.

ENRICHMENT

Calculating Combinations
Math Masters, p. 80
Students apply multiplication facts and patterns to solve a combinations problem.

EXTRA PRACTICE

Exploring Prime and Composite Numbers
Math Masters, pp. 77 and 403
Students use rectangular arrays to investigate prime and composite numbers.

EXTRA PRACTICE

Playing *Multiplication Top-It*
Student Reference Book, p. 264
Math Masters, p. 506
4 each of number cards 1–10 (from the Everything Math Deck, if available)
Students practice multiplication facts.

Additional Information

Students take and score a practice 50-facts test. They will take a real test in Lesson 3•4. After that, the test will be offered as an optional Part 3 Extra Practice activity about once per unit. Four versions of the test are supplied on *Math Masters,* pages 410–413.

***Teacher's Reference Manual,* Grades 4–6** pp. 269–271

Getting Started

Mental Math and Reflexes

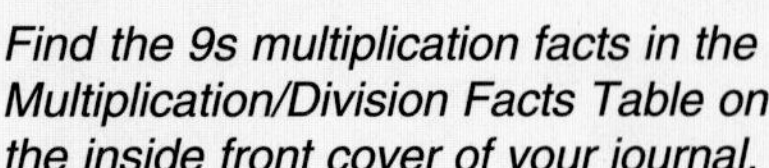

Pose multiplication facts and extended facts.
Suggestions:

●○○	●●○	●●●
3 * 2 = 6	7 * 5 = 35	40 * 6 = 240
5 * 4 = 20	8 * 4 = 32	9 * 50 = 450
4 * 3 = 12	9 * 6 = 54	40 * 70 = 2,800
6 * 6 = 36	8 * 7 = 56	80 * 50 = 4,000

Math Message

Find the 9s multiplication facts in the Multiplication/Division Facts Table on the inside front cover of your journal.

What patterns do you see? Write about them at the top of journal page 58.

Study Link 3·2 Follow-Up

Have students determine which factors of 36 are prime.

NOTE For Facts Practice Tests with facts through 12 * 12, see www.everydaymathonline.com.

1 Teaching the Lesson

▶ Math Message Follow-Up

(*Math Journal 1,* p. 58; inside front cover)

WHOLE-CLASS DISCUSSION

Have students share their observations about the 9s multiplication facts. These might include the following:

▷ The sum of the two digits in a 9s product is 9. For example, 9 * 7 = 63 and 6 + 3 = 9.

▷ As you review the 9s facts in order, the 10s digit increases by 1, and the 1s digit decreases by 1.

▷ To find 9 times a number, find 10 times the number, and then subtract the original number from the result. For example, to find 9 * 8, think 10 * 8 = 80 and 80 − 8 = 72.

Have students complete journal page 58 and discuss their findings.

▶ Administering a Multiplication Facts Practice Test

(*Math Masters,* p. 410)

WHOLE-CLASS ACTIVITY

Discuss with students the importance of memorizing multiplication facts:

▷ It allows you to solve problems you encounter in everyday life. For example, to determine how many cupcakes are in 6 packages with 6 cupcakes per package, you use multiplication to solve the problem.

▷ It makes doing math much easier. If you have to stop and think what 7 * 8 is when you are solving a problem, it slows you down. You are more likely to make a mistake or lose track of what you are doing.

Student Page

Date Time

LESSON 3·3 **Patterns in Multiplication Facts**

Math Message

Look at the Multiplication/Division Facts Table on the inside front cover of your journal.

1. Find a pattern in the 9s multiplication facts. Describe the pattern.
Sample answers: When you add the digits of the product together, the sum is always 9. Halfway down the column, the ones and tens digits switch places. The ones digit decreases by one each time you move down, and the tens digit increases by one.

2. Find a pattern in the 5s multiplication facts. Describe the pattern.
Sample answers: The last digit in the product is always either 0 or 5. The tens digit is repeated twice as you move down, then increases by one and repeats twice again.

3. What other patterns can you find in the multiplication facts? Write about some of them.
Sample answers: The multiples of 3 always have digits that add up to 3, 6, or 9. The chart is symmetrical on either side of the square numbers. Multiples of 10 have zero in the ones place. For the 2s facts, the digit in the ones place of the product is an even number.

Math Journal 1, p. 58

Tell students:

- Today you will practice taking a timed test on the multiplication facts.
- This test will help you measure your automaticity with the facts.
- In the next lesson, you will take a real test.
- Now take out a pencil and a pen or colored pencil.
- The tests will be passed out facedown.
- Do not turn the tests over until I give the signal to begin.

Next explain the procedure for the test.

One-Minute Start

- On my signal, turn the tests over and work for one minute in pencil, answering as many facts as possible. Do not skip any facts.
- Begin at the top of the first (left-most) column, work down that column, and continue at the top of the next column.

Two-Minute Finish

- After one minute, I will give another signal. At this signal, switch from pencil to pen or colored pencil. You will have two more minutes to complete as many facts as possible. Now you may skip facts.

Stop

- At the end of three minutes, I will say "Stop." You must immediately put down your pen or colored pencil.
- Then you can use your pencil to fill in your name and the date.

Scoring

- In the one-minute part of the test, correct answers will be counted only up to the first fact missed. Answers that come after the first missed fact will not be counted. Therefore, do not skip any problems in this part of the test.
- The three-minute score will include all correct answers, which I will explain later.

Give each student a copy of 50-Facts Test 1 (*Math Masters,* page 410) facedown. Give the signal to begin, and follow the procedure described above.

NOTE This test will be administered as a whole-class activity in this lesson and in Lesson 3-4. It should be used as a screening tool to help identify any students who have not yet memorized the multiplication facts. This test then becomes an optional Part 3 Extra Practice activity that can be used with students who have been identified in the initial screening. The 50-Facts Test routine can be used to show students' progress over time.

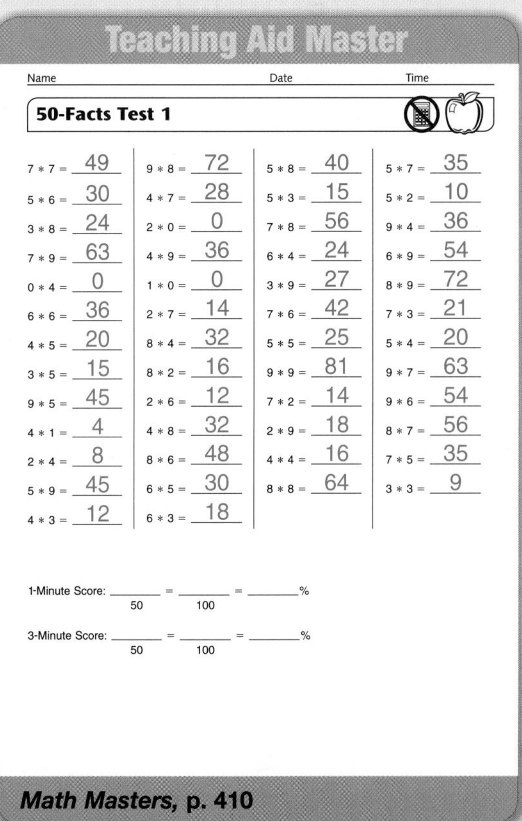

Teaching Aid Master

Name Date Time

50-Facts Test 1

7 * 7 = 49	9 * 8 = 72	5 * 8 = 40	5 * 7 = 35
5 * 6 = 30	4 * 7 = 28	5 * 3 = 15	5 * 2 = 10
3 * 8 = 24	2 * 0 = 0	7 * 8 = 56	9 * 4 = 36
7 * 9 = 63	4 * 9 = 36	6 * 4 = 24	6 * 9 = 54
0 * 4 = 0	1 * 0 = 0	3 * 9 = 27	8 * 9 = 72
6 * 6 = 36	2 * 7 = 14	7 * 6 = 42	7 * 3 = 21
4 * 5 = 20	8 * 4 = 32	5 * 5 = 25	5 * 4 = 20
3 * 5 = 15	8 * 2 = 16	9 * 9 = 81	9 * 7 = 63
9 * 5 = 45	2 * 6 = 12	7 * 2 = 14	9 * 6 = 54
4 * 1 = 4	4 * 8 = 32	2 * 9 = 18	8 * 7 = 56
2 * 4 = 8	8 * 6 = 48	4 * 4 = 16	7 * 5 = 35
5 * 9 = 45	6 * 5 = 30	8 * 8 = 64	3 * 3 = 9
4 * 3 = 12	6 * 3 = 18		

1-Minute Score: ____/50 = ____/100 = ____%

3-Minute Score: ____/50 = ____/100 = ____%

Math Masters, p. 410

NOTE The one-minute scoring criterion is tough, but recall should be fast and error free. If students are allowed to skip around, then they can avoid harder facts, thus appearing to know the facts better than they really do.

▶ Scoring the Practice Test

WHOLE-CLASS ACTIVITY

(*Math Masters,* p. 410)

Students will calculate two scores for the test: a one-minute score and a three-minute score. The one-minute score includes only correct answers in pencil up to the first fact answered incorrectly or skipped. The three-minute score includes all correct answers.

Read the facts and answers so that students can correct their work. In the pencil part of the test, they should draw a line above the first fact they answered incorrectly or skipped. In this first part, a skipped fact counts as incorrect.

Have students record the number of correct answers in one minute (the number of problems above the line drawn), and the total number of correct answers in three minutes, at the bottom of the test. Scores are first recorded as a fraction of the 50 facts—for example, 40 correct would be $\frac{40}{50}$.

Next show students how to rename each score as a percent. Remind them that **percent** means "per hundred," so they must rename the first fraction as a fraction whose denominator is 100. For example, the fraction $\frac{40}{50}$ can be renamed as $\frac{80}{100}$ which means that getting 40 correct answers out of 50 is equivalent to getting 80 correct answers out of 100—which is 80 percent (80%).

$$\frac{40}{50} = \frac{80}{100} = 80\%$$

Do a few sample conversions with the class. Then have students convert their own scores, writing the score as a fraction with a denominator of 100 and then as a percent.

Adjusting the Activity

ELL

Have students use base-10 blocks to illustrate 80 out of 100, or 80%. Students cover a flat with 8 longs or 80 cubes.

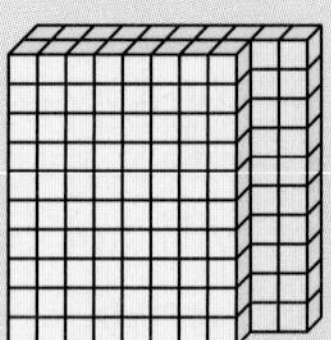

AUDITORY • KINESTHETIC • TACTILE • VISUAL

Student Page

Date Time

LESSON 3·3 **Math Boxes**

1. Write >, <, or = to make each number sentence true.
   a. 45,699 > 45,609
   b. 67,749 > 66,749
   c. 208,775 < 200 million
   d. 1,000,000 > 858,192
   e. 2 million < 20,000,000

2. Number of days it took 10 students to complete their science projects:
   6, 4, 10, 11, 8, 6, 14, 9, 3, 12
   a. What is the range for this set of numbers? 11
   b. What is the median? 8.5

3. Make a ballpark estimate. Write a number model to show your strategy.
   Sample answers:
   a. 1,459 + 291
   1,500 + 300 = 1,800
   b. 1,381 − 646
   1,400 − 650 = 750

4. Complete.
   a. 3 yd = 9 ft
   b. 4 ft = 48 in.
   c. 54 in. = 4 ft 6 in.
   d. $\frac{1}{2}$ yd = 1 ft 6 in.
   e. $17\frac{1}{2}$ yd = 630 in.

5. Complete.
   a. 20, 35, 50, 65, 80, 95
   Rule: +15
   b. 55, 68, 81, 94, 107, 120
   Rule: +13
   c. 58, 46, 34, 22, 10, −2
   Rule: −12

6. Solve mentally or with a paper-and-pencil algorithm.
   a. $10.97 + $15.60 = $26.57
   b. $4.56 − $2.07 = $2.49

Math Journal 1, p. 59

2 Ongoing Learning & Practice

▶ Playing *Baseball Multiplication*

PARTNER ACTIVITY

(*Student Reference Book,* pp. 231 and 232; *Math Masters,* p. 460)

Students play *Baseball Multiplication* to maintain automaticity with multiplication facts.

Adjusting the Activity

Have Multiplication/Division Facts Tables, counters to make arrays, and calculators for skip counting readily available. Refer students to game variations in the *Student Reference Book,* page 232.

AUDITORY ◆ KINESTHETIC ◆ TACTILE ◆ VISUAL

▶ Math Boxes 3◆3

INDEPENDENT ACTIVITY

(*Math Journal 1,* p. 59)

Mixed Practice Math Boxes in this lesson are linked with Math Boxes in Lessons 3-1 and 3-5. The skill in Problem 6 previews Unit 4 content.

Writing/Reasoning Have students write a response to the following: *Suppose the measurements given in Problems 4a–4d represent the lengths of four pieces of fabric Suma purchased at a craft store. What is the total number of feet of fabric she purchased?* 19 feet *What is the total number of inches?* 228 inches

Ongoing Assessment: Recognizing Student Achievement

Math Boxes Problem 3 

Use **Math Boxes, Problem 3** to assess students' ability to estimate reasonable solutions for whole-number addition and subtraction problems. Students are making adequate progress if the number models for their ballpark estimates include "close-but-easier" numbers. Some students may be able to show more than one possible solution.

[Operations and Computation Goal 6]

▶ Study Link 3◆3

INDEPENDENT ACTIVITY

(*Math Masters,* p. 78)

Home Connection Students complete Multiplication/Division Fact Triangles. Each Fact Triangle gives the factors; students find each product. Students will also solve multiplicative comparison problems.

Study Link Master

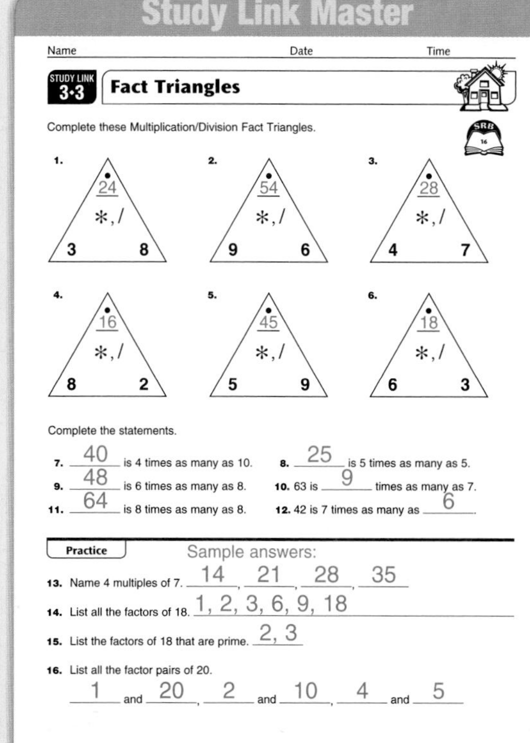

Name Date Time

STUDY LINK 3◆3 **Fact Triangles**

Complete these Multiplication/Division Fact Triangles.

1. 24; ∗,/; 3, 8
2. 54; ∗,/; 9, 6
3. 28; ∗,/; 4, 7
4. 16; ∗,/; 8, 2
5. 45; ∗,/; 5, 9
6. 18; ∗,/; 6, 3

Complete the statements.

7. 40 is 4 times as many as 10.
8. 25 is 5 times as many as 5.
9. 48 is 6 times as many as 8.
10. 63 is 9 times as many as 7.
11. 64 is 8 times as many as 8.
12. 42 is 7 times as many as 6.

Practice

Sample answers:

13. Name 4 multiples of 7. 14, 21, 28, 35
14. List all the factors of 18. 1, 2, 3, 6, 9, 18
15. List the factors of 18 that are prime. 2, 3
16. List all the factor pairs of 20. 1 and 20, 2 and 10, 4 and 5

Math Masters, p. 78

Teaching Master

Name Date Time

LESSON 3◆3 **Skip-Count Patterns**

1. Start at 0. Skip count by 2s. Record the pattern.

0

1	2	3	4	5	6	7	8	9	10
11	12	13	14	15	16	17	18	19	20
21	22	23	24	25	26	27	28	29	30
31	32	33	34	35	36	37	38	39	40
41	42	43	44	45	46	47	48	49	50
51	52	53	54	55	56	57	58	59	60
61	62	63	64	65	66	67	68	69	70
71	72	73	74	75	76	77	78	79	80
81	82	83	84	85	86	87	88	89	90
91	92	93	94	95	96	97	98	99	100

2. Start at 0. Skip count by 3s. Record the pattern.

0

1	2	3	4	5	6	7	8	9	10
11	12	13	14	15	16	17	18	19	20
21	22	23	24	25	26	27	28	29	30
31	32	33	34	35	36	37	38	39	40
41	42	43	44	45	46	47	48	49	50
51	52	53	54	55	56	57	58	59	60
61	62	63	64	65	66	67	68	69	70
71	72	73	74	75	76	77	78	79	80
81	82	83	84	85	86	87	88	89	90
91	92	93	94	95	96	97	98	99	100

3. Start at 0. Skip count by 4s. Record the pattern.

0

1	2	3	4	5	6	7	8	9	10
11	12	13	14	15	16	17	18	19	20
21	22	23	24	25	26	27	28	29	30
31	32	33	34	35	36	37	38	39	40
41	42	43	44	45	46	47	48	49	50
51	52	53	54	55	56	57	58	59	60
61	62	63	64	65	66	67	68	69	70
71	72	73	74	75	76	77	78	79	80
81	82	83	84	85	86	87	88	89	90
91	92	93	94	95	96	97	98	99	100

4. Start at 0. Skip count by 6s. Record the pattern.

0

1	2	3	4	5	6	7	8	9	10
11	12	13	14	15	16	17	18	19	20
21	22	23	24	25	26	27	28	29	30
31	32	33	34	35	36	37	38	39	40
41	42	43	44	45	46	47	48	49	50
51	52	53	54	55	56	57	58	59	60
61	62	63	64	65	66	67	68	69	70
71	72	73	74	75	76	77	78	79	80
81	82	83	84	85	86	87	88	89	90
91	92	93	94	95	96	97	98	99	100

5. On the back of this page, write about the skip-count patterns you see in each grid.

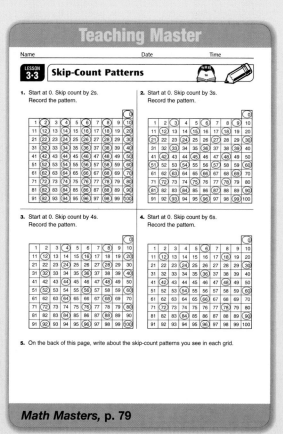

Math Masters, p. 79

Teaching Master

Name Date Time

LESSON 3·3 **Calculating Combinations**

Super Sweet sells ice-cream sundaes. Each sundae comes with one scoop of ice cream and one topping.

Ice-Cream Flavors	Toppings
chocolate	hot fudge
vanilla	whipped cream
strawberry	sprinkles
cookie dough	nuts
fudge swirl	

1. How many *different* sundaes that have one scoop of ice cream and one topping can Super Sweet sell? 20 sundaes

   Use an organized list, table, or picture to solve the problem. Show your work.
   Sample answer:

	hot fudge	whipped cream	sprinkles	nuts
chocolate	✓	✓	✓	✓
vanilla	✓	✓	✓	✓
strawberry	✓	✓	✓	✓
cookie dough	✓	✓	✓	✓
fudge swirl	✓	✓	✓	✓

2. Super Sweet has decided to add butterscotch to the list of available toppings. How many *different* sundaes can Super Sweet sell now? 25 sundaes

   Explain how you found your answer.
   Sample answer: I added another column to my table.

3. Explain how you might use multiplication to solve a problem like this.
   Sample answer: Multiply the number of ice-cream flavors by the number of toppings.

Math Masters, p. 80

NOTE For additional information about solving combination problems, see www.everydaymathonline.com.

Teaching Master

Name Date Time

LESSON 3·3 **Prime and Composite Numbers**

You can use arrays to help you determine whether a counting number is prime or composite. If there is only one array for a number, the number has only two factors, so it is a prime number. If two or more arrays can be made for a number, then it is a composite number.

Example: Two different arrays can be made for 8.
1, 2, 4, and 8 are factors of 8.
8 is a composite number.

Example: Only one array can be made for 5.
1 and 5 are factors of 5.
5 is a prime number.

1 ∗ 8 = 8 8 ∗ 1 = 8 1 ∗ 5 = 5 5 ∗ 1 = 5
4 ∗ 2 = 8
2 ∗ 4 = 8

1. On centimeter grid paper, draw as many arrays as you can for each of the following numbers: 2, 3, 4, 6, 7, 11, 12, 15, 16.
   Label each array with a number model and its turn-around fact, as shown in the examples above.
2. Use the arrays to decide if each number is prime or composite. Write the numbers on the appropriate line below.
   Prime numbers: 2, 3, 7, 11
   Composite numbers: 4, 6, 12, 15, 16
3. There are 20 prime numbers that are greater than 11, but less than 100. List them below.
   13, 17, 19, 23, 29, 31, 37, 41, 43, 47, 53, 59, 61, 67, 71, 73, 79, 83, 89, 97

Math Masters, p. 77

3 Differentiation Options

READINESS

▶ Exploring Skip-Count Patterns on the Hundreds Grid

(*Math Masters,* p. 79)

To provide a visual model for understanding multiplication facts, have students color skip-count patterns on the number grid. They then write about the patterns they see in the rows and columns.

Encourage students to think about how they might use skip-count patterns to solve multiplication facts.

ENRICHMENT

INDEPENDENT ACTIVITY

 5–15 Min

▶ Calculating Combinations

(*Math Masters,* p. 80)

To apply students' understanding of multiplication, have them find all possible sundaes that can be made by combining one scoop of ice cream and one topping from a variety of choices.

When solving a combination problem such as this, students count the number of pairs that can be made from two or more groups of objects. Multiplication can be used to solve such problems. The *factors* are the number of objects in each group; the *product* is the number of combinations that is possible.

EXTRA PRACTICE

▶ Exploring Prime and Composite Numbers

(*Math Masters,* pp. 77 and 403)

To extend students' work with factors, have them construct arrays for various numbers to determine if they are prime or composite.

EXTRA PRACTICE

▶ Playing *Multiplication Top-It*

(*Student Reference Book,* p. 264; *Math Masters,* p. 506)

5–15 Min

To maintain automaticity with multiplication facts, have students play *Multiplication Top-It.* See Lesson 3-6 for additional information.

NOTE For facts practice through 12 ∗ 12, have students include number cards 11 and 12 when playing *Multiplication Top-It.*

3•4 More Multiplication Facts Practice

Objectives To give a 50-facts test and record the results; and to provide practice with multiplication facts.

Technology Resources www.everydaymathonline.com

ePresentations

eToolkit

Algorithms Practice

EM Facts Workshop Game™

Family Letters

Assessment Management

Common Core State Standards

Curriculum Focal Points

Interactive Teacher's Lesson Guide

1 Teaching the Lesson

Key Concepts and Skills

- Rename a fraction as an equivalent fraction and as a percent.
  [Number and Numeration Goal 5]
- Solve multiplication facts.
  [Operations and Computation Goal 3]
- Use data to create a line graph.
  [Data and Chance Goal 1]
- Find the median and mean of a data set.
  [Data and Chance Goal 2]

Key Activities

Students take their first 50-facts test of record. They graph individual and optional class scores.

Ongoing Assessment: Recognizing Student Achievement
Use Mental Math and Reflexes.
[Operations and Computation Goal 3]

Materials

Study Link 3•3
Math Masters, pp. 81, 411, 414, and 415; pp. 416 and 417 (optional)
transparency of *Math Masters,* p. 414 (optional) ◆ slate ◆ chart paper ◆ calculator ◆ pen or colored pencil

2 Ongoing Learning & Practice

Math Boxes 3•4
Math Journal 1, p. 60
Students practice and maintain skills through Math Box problems.

Study Link 3•4
Math Masters, p. 82
Students practice and maintain skills through Study Link activities.

3 Differentiation Options

READINESS

Finding the Mean
Math Masters, p. 83
centimeter cubes
Students "even out" stacks of cubes to find the mean of a data set.

ENRICHMENT

Comparing the Mean and Median
Math Masters, p. 84
calculator
Students apply the concepts of mean and median to analyze baseball players' salaries.

Advance Preparation

If you choose to do the optional Part 1 activity of graphing class results, use *Math Masters,* pages 416 and 417 as a model to draw a classroom graph on a large sheet of chart paper. Alternately, tape copies of these masters together to make a smaller version of the graph. Copy *Math Masters,* page 414 for each student. Copy and cut apart *Math Masters,* page 81 so each student has one answer sheet for the Math Message.

***Teacher's Reference Manual,* Grades 4–6** p. 271

Getting Started

Mental Math and Reflexes

Pose multiplication facts and extended facts.
Suggestions:

●○○	●●○	●●●
$4 * 4 = 16$	$6 * 7 = 42$	$30 * 9 = 270$
$6 * 5 = 30$	$5 * 7 = 35$	$60 * 7 = 420$
$7 * 3 = 21$	$9 * 8 = 72$	$90 * 90 = 8{,}100$
$8 * 3 = 24$	$8 * 6 = 48$	$60 * 50 = 3{,}000$

Math Message

Take an answer sheet (Math Masters, *page 81*) *and complete it.*

Study Link 3·3 Follow-Up

Students describe how they completed the multiplicative comparison statements in Problems 7–12.

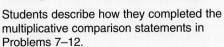

Ongoing Assessment: Recognizing Student Achievement

Mental Math and Reflexes ★

Use **Mental Math and Reflexes** to assess students' automaticity with multiplication facts. Students are making adequate progress if they demonstrate automaticity with the ●○○ and ●●○ problems. Some students may demonstrate automaticity with the extended facts in the ●●● problems.

[Operations and Computation Goal 3]

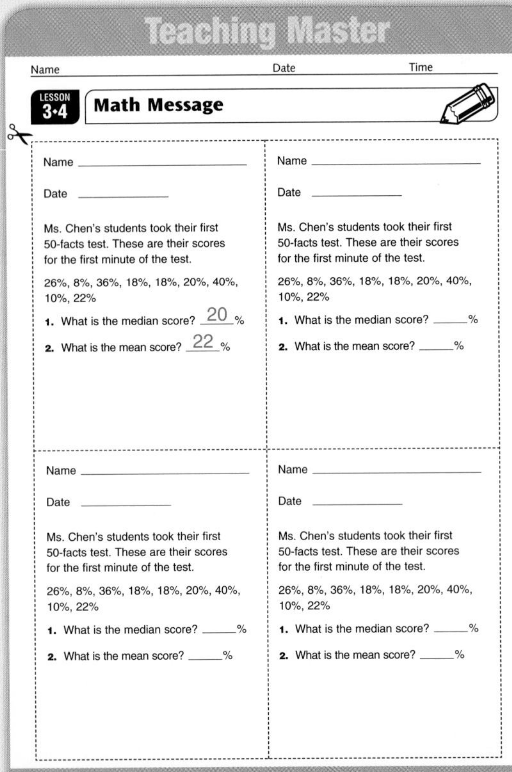

Teaching Master

Name ______ Date ______ Time ______

LESSON 3·4 **Math Message**

Name ______
Date ______

Ms. Chen's students took their first 50-facts test. These are their scores for the first minute of the test.

26%, 8%, 36%, 18%, 18%, 20%, 40%, 10%, 22%

1. What is the median score? 20 %
2. What is the mean score? 22 %

Name ______
Date ______

Ms. Chen's students took their first 50-facts test. These are their scores for the first minute of the test.

26%, 8%, 36%, 18%, 18%, 20%, 40%, 10%, 22%

1. What is the median score? ______%
2. What is the mean score? ______%

Name ______
Date ______

Ms. Chen's students took their first 50-facts test. These are their scores for the first minute of the test.

26%, 8%, 36%, 18%, 18%, 20%, 40%, 10%, 22%

1. What is the median score? ______%
2. What is the mean score? ______%

Name ______
Date ______

Ms. Chen's students took their first 50-facts test. These are their scores for the first minute of the test.

26%, 8%, 36%, 18%, 18%, 20%, 40%, 10%, 22%

1. What is the median score? ______%
2. What is the mean score? ______%

Math Masters, p. 81

1 Teaching the Lesson

▶ Math Message Follow-Up

(*Math Masters,* p. 81)

Ask students to help you find the "typical" or median test score. Have them order the test scores from least to greatest and find th middle number. 20

Ask students to calculate another typical score, the mean.

1. Find the total of all the scores.
2. Count the number of scores that make up the sum.
3. Divide the sum of the scores by the number of scores. 22

The result is the mean test score. Ask: *Are the median and mean test scores fairly close to each other?* yes As indicators of typical values, the median and mean of a data set are often close but may be skewed differently by extreme values.

To support English language learners, discuss the everyday and mathematical meanings of the words *mean* and *average.*

Administering a 50-Facts Test

WHOLE-CLASS ACTIVITY

FACTS PRACTICE

(*Math Masters,* p. 411)

Briefly review the procedure for taking the test as described on page 171. After reviewing the procedure, pass out 50-Facts Test 2 and begin.

NOTE The 50-facts test should not be used for grading purposes. These tests are one type of screening tool. They will help identify any students who have not yet memorized the multiplication facts. You can revisit these tests in the optional Part 3 Extra Practice activities in Lessons 3-10, 4-10, 5-10, 6-10, 7-8, 8-2, 9-6, 11-3, and 12-6. The 50-Facts Test routine can be used to show students' progress over time.

Recording and Graphing Individual Test Results

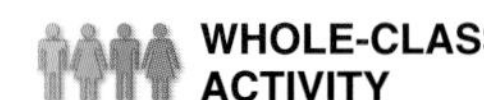

WHOLE-CLASS ACTIVITY

(*Math Masters,* pp. 414 and 415)

Have students correct their tests and record the one-minute and three-minute scores on their test sheets.

Review the graph on *Math Masters,* page 414, using a transparency if available.

▷ Discuss the title and how the axes are labeled.

▷ Show students how to enter the date and how to graph their scores with dots, using pencil for the one-minute scores and pen or colored pencil for the three-minute scores.

If students take another 50-facts test, they will mark the results on the graph and draw line segments to connect the points on their grids, using pencil for the one-minute scores and pen or colored pencil for the three-minute scores. When this master is filled up, a copy of *Math Masters,* page 415 can be taped to it. This way, students can keep track of their progress throughout the school year if they continue taking 50-facts tests.

Recording Individual One-Minute Test Results on the Class Graph (Optional)

WHOLE-CLASS ACTIVITY

(*Math Masters,* pp. 416 and 417)

From this point on, the 50-facts tests will appear only in Part 3 as Extra Practice opportunities. You may choose to use them for your whole class, or only for those students who need additional practice with basic multiplication facts. If you expect that only a few students will continue taking the tests, you may choose to skip this optional activity of graphing the class results.

Teaching Aid Master

Name ______ Date ______ Time ______

50-Facts Test 2

6 * 6 = 36	4 * 7 = 28	8 * 3 = 24	7 * 7 = 49
5 * 0 = 0	4 * 2 = 8	6 * 5 = 30	6 * 9 = 54
4 * 4 = 16	5 * 8 = 40	5 * 5 = 25	4 * 6 = 24
6 * 3 = 18	5 * 9 = 45	9 * 8 = 72	3 * 6 = 18
8 * 7 = 56	2 * 5 = 10	8 * 2 = 16	9 * 5 = 45
2 * 7 = 14	8 * 8 = 64	7 * 8 = 56	9 * 9 = 81
4 * 9 = 36	4 * 8 = 32	8 * 6 = 48	8 * 5 = 40
5 * 3 = 15	6 * 8 = 48	9 * 7 = 63	7 * 6 = 42
8 * 1 = 8	7 * 3 = 21	3 * 3 = 9	5 * 4 = 20
3 * 8 = 24	9 * 6 = 54	7 * 5 = 35	3 * 7 = 21
7 * 9 = 63	7 * 4 = 28	9 * 4 = 36	9 * 2 = 18
6 * 7 = 42	4 * 3 = 12	4 * 5 = 20	8 * 9 = 72
3 * 5 = 15	9 * 3 = 27		

1-Minute Score: ______ / 50 = ______ / 100 = ______

3-Minute Score: ______ / 50 = ______ / 100 = ______

Math Masters, p. 411

Individual student's test scores (*Math Masters,* pages 414 and 415)

Teaching Aid Master

Name ______ Date ______ Time ______

My 50-Facts Test Scores

Write the date on the bottom line. Using a pencil, make a dot above each date to record your 1-minute score. Using a pen, make a dot above each date to record your 3-minute score. Connect the pencil dots. Then connect the pen dots.

Score

100% 50, 90% 45, 80% 40, 70% 35, 60% 30, 50% 25, 40% 20, 30% 15, 20% 10, 10% 5, 0% 0

Sample student answer:

(3-minute scores)

(1-minute scores)

Date 10/5 10/15

Math Masters, p. 414

Teaching Aid Master

Name Date Time

Class 50-Facts Test Scores

Write the date on the bottom line. Make a dot above each date to record each student's 1-minute score. On the gridline above each date, mark "M" for the class median score and "A" for the class mean, or average, score.

Score: 100% 50, 90% 45, 80% 40, 70% 35, 60% 30, 50% 25, 40% 20, 30% 15, 20% 10, 10% 5, 0% 0

Sample class answers for 1-minute scores:

Date 10/5 10/15

Math Masters, **p. 416**

Class's test scores (optional)
(*Math Masters,* pages 416 and 417)

Use a large copy of *Math Masters,* pages 416 and 417 to record the one-minute scores, preserving the anonymity of students. Here are some ways to collect and graph the class results:

- Ask students to write raw and percent scores for the *one-minute part* on slips of paper and pass them in. Then you call out the numbers, and students plot the scores on the class graph. This allows you to point out any errors in converting raw scores to percent scores.
- Have students turn in their papers, and you plot the scores yourself after class.

After plotting the class scores, have students find the median and calculate the mean for the day's scores. Mark "M" for median and "A" for mean, or average, on the appropriate vertical scale. Later you can compare these landmarks with those of previous tests. To monitor the progress of the entire class, use different colors to connect the median and mean scores for each test administration.

2 Ongoing Learning & Practice

▶ Math Boxes 3•4

(*Math Journal 1,* p. 60)

Mixed Practice Math Boxes in this lesson are paired with Math Boxes in Lesson 3-2. The skill in Problem 5 previews Unit 4 content.

Writing/Reasoning Have students write a response to the following: *Explain how you solved Problem 3c.* Sample answer: The part of the circle graph that represents apples is bigger than the part that represents peaches.

Student Page

Date Time

LESSON 3•4 **Math Boxes**

1. Complete. Sample answers:
   a. Name four multiples of 5. 5, 10, 15, 20
   b. Name four multiples of 9. 9, 18, 27, 36

2. Complete the "What's My Rule?" table and state the rule.
   Rule: −156

in	out
502	346
1,238	1,082
1,083	927
871	715
1,600	1,444

3. Mr. Rosario's fourth graders collected data about their favorite fruits.
   a. Which kind of fruit do most students prefer? bananas
   b. Which kind is preferred least? grapes
   c. Do more people prefer apples or peaches? apples
   d. About $\frac{1}{4}$ of the students prefer apples.

   Favorite Fruits: peaches, grapes, bananas, apples

4. Name as many line segments as you can in the figure below.
   E F G H
   $\overline{EF}$, $\overline{EG}$, $\overline{EH}$, $\overline{FG}$, $\overline{FH}$, $\overline{GH}$

5. Put these numbers in order from smallest to largest.
   0.7 0.007 0.5 0.63
   0.007
   0.5
   0.63
   0.7

Math Journal 1, **p. 60**

▶ Study Link 3•4

(*Math Masters,* p. 82)

Home Connection Students find missing factors in multiplication facts. They also write their own mystery-number problem involving multiplication facts and solve multiplicative comparison problems.

3 Differentiation Options

READINESS

INDEPENDENT ACTIVITY

5–15 Min

Finding the Mean

(*Math Masters,* p. 83)

To explore finding the mean using a concrete model, have students use centimeter cubes to build a bar graph of a data set and "even out" the centimeter cubes to find the mean of the data set.

In this activity, there are 21 books in all $(5 + 2 + 6 + 4 + 0 + 1 + 3 = 21)$. Students even out the centimeter cubes by sharing them equally among the 7 students' backpacks. After moving the cubes, they end up with 21 / 7, or 3 books in each student's backpack. The number model for finding the mean of the data set is $21 / 7 = 3$.

Have students describe the process they used to find the mean.

ENRICHMENT

INDEPENDENT ACTIVITY

5–15 Min

Comparing the Mean and Median

(*Math Masters,* p. 84)

To apply students' understanding of mean and median, have them examine and compare baseball salaries based on these data landmarks.

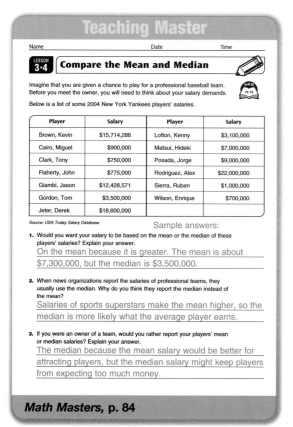

Teaching Master

Name Date Time

LESSON 3·4 **Compare the Mean and Median**

Imagine that you are given a chance to play for a professional baseball team. Before you meet the owner, you will need to think about your salary demands.

Below is a list of some 2004 New York Yankees players' salaries.

Player	Salary	Player	Salary
Brown, Kevin	$15,714,286	Lofton, Kenny	$3,100,000
Cairo, Miguel	$900,000	Matsui, Hideki	$7,000,000
Clark, Tony	$750,000	Posada, Jorge	$9,000,000
Flaherty, John	$775,000	Rodriguez, Alex	$22,000,000
Giambi, Jason	$12,428,571	Sierra, Ruben	$1,000,000
Gordon, Tom	$3,500,000	Wilson, Enrique	$700,000
Jeter, Derek	$18,600,000		

Source: USA Today Salary Database

Sample answers:

1. Would you want your salary to be based on the mean or the median of these players' salaries? Explain your answer.
On the mean because it is greater. The mean is about $7,300,000, but the median is $3,500,000.

2. When news organizations report the salaries of professional teams, they usually use the median. Why do you think they report the median instead of the mean?
Salaries of sports superstars make the mean higher, so the median is more likely what the average player earns.

3. If you were an owner of a team, would you rather report your players' mean or median salaries? Explain your answer.
The median because the mean salary would be better for attracting players, but the median salary might keep players from expecting too much money.

Math Masters, p. 84

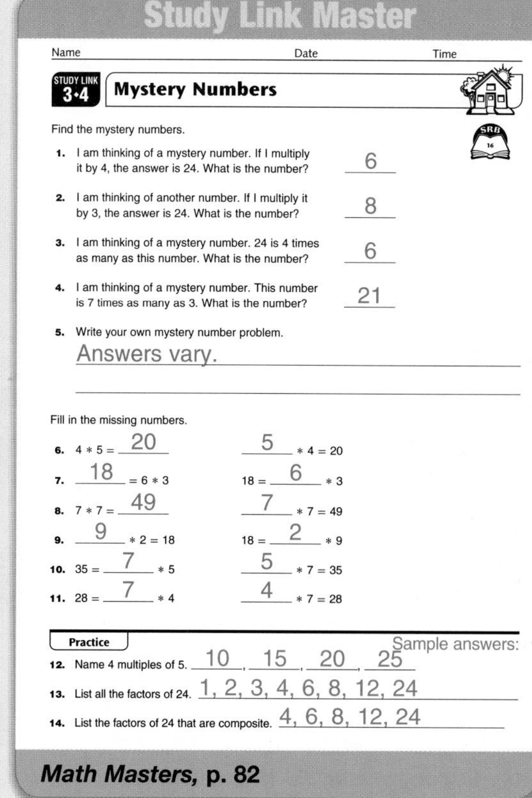

Study Link Master

Name Date Time

STUDY LINK 3·4 **Mystery Numbers**

Find the mystery numbers.

1. I am thinking of a mystery number. If I multiply it by 4, the answer is 24. What is the number? 6
2. I am thinking of another number. If I multiply it by 3, the answer is 24. What is the number? 8
3. I am thinking of a mystery number. 24 is 4 times as many as this number. What is the number? 6
4. I am thinking of a mystery number. This number is 7 times as many as 3. What is the number? 21
5. Write your own mystery number problem.
Answers vary.

Fill in the missing numbers.

6. 4 * 5 = 20   5 * 4 = 20
7. 18 = 6 * 3   18 = 6 * 3
8. 7 * 7 = 49   7 * 7 = 49
9. 9 * 2 = 18   18 = 2 * 9
10. 35 = 7 * 5   5 * 7 = 35
11. 28 = 7 * 4   4 * 7 = 28

Practice

Sample answers:

12. Name 4 multiples of 5. 10, 15, 20, 25
13. List all the factors of 24. 1, 2, 3, 4, 6, 8, 12, 24
14. List the factors of 24 that are composite. 4, 6, 8, 12, 24

Math Masters, p. 82

NOTE For practice with pictographs, see www.everydaymathonline.com.

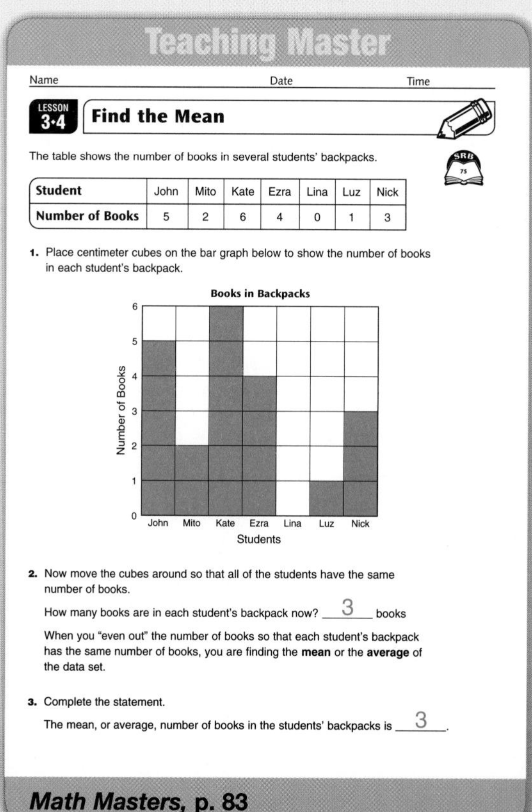

Teaching Master

Name Date Time

LESSON 3·4 **Find the Mean**

The table shows the number of books in several students' backpacks.

Student	John	Mito	Kate	Ezra	Lina	Luz	Nick
Number of Books	5	2	6	4	0	1	3

1. Place centimeter cubes on the bar graph below to show the number of books in each student's backpack.

2. Now move the cubes around so that all of the students have the same number of books.
How many books are in each student's backpack now? 3 books
When you "even out" the number of books so that each student's backpack has the same number of books, you are finding the **mean** or the **average** of the data set.

3. Complete the statement.
The mean, or average, number of books in the students' backpacks is 3.

Math Masters, p. 83

3•5 Multiplication and Division

Objectives To guide exploration of the relationship between multiplication and division; and to provide practice with division facts.

Technology Resources www.everydaymathonline.com

ePresentations

eToolkit

Algorithms Practice

EM Facts Workshop Game™

Family Letters

Assessment Management

Common Core State Standards

Curriculum Focal Points

Interactive Teacher's Lesson Guide

1 Teaching the Lesson

Key Concepts and Skills

- Solve multiplication facts. [Operations and Computation Goal 3]
- Use multiplication facts to generate related division facts. [Operations and Computation Goal 3]
- Apply multiplication and division facts and extended facts to solve problems. [Operations and Computation Goal 3]
- Write multiplication and division number sentences. [Patterns, Functions, and Algebra Goal 2]

Key Activities

Students explore the relationships between multiplication and division. They use the Multiplication/Division Facts Table to solve division facts, and they use Multiplication/Division Fact Triangles to generate fact families and to practice division facts.

Ongoing Assessment: Recognizing Student Achievement
Use journal page 61.
[Patterns, Functions, and Algebra Goal 2]

Key Vocabulary

dividend ◆ divisor ◆ quotient ◆ remainder ◆ fact family

Materials

Math Journal 1, p. 61
Student Reference Book, pp. 178A and 178B
Study Link 3•4
transparencies of *Math Masters,* pp. 408 and 409 (optional) ◆ *, / Fact Triangles ◆ slate

2 Ongoing Learning & Practice

Playing *Beat the Calculator*
Student Reference Book, p. 233
Math Masters, p. 461
calculator ◆ 4 each of number cards 1–10 (from the Everything Math Deck, if available)
Students practice multiplication facts.

Math Boxes 3•5
Math Journal 1, p. 62
Students practice and maintain skills through Math Box problems.

Study Link 3•5
Math Masters, p. 85
Students practice and maintain skills through Study Link activities.

3 Differentiation Options

READINESS
Playing *Division Arrays*
Student Reference Book, p. 240
Math Masters, p. 470
number cards 6–18 (from the Everything Math Deck, if available) ◆ 1 six-sided die ◆ 18 counters ◆ grid paper (optional)
Students explore the connections between multiplication and division using a concrete model.

ENRICHMENT
Exploring the Relationship between Division and Fractions
Math Masters, p. 86
Students use division facts to solve a fraction problem.

EXTRA PRACTICE
Practicing with Fact Families
Math Masters, p. 418
Students complete Fact Triangles and write the related fact families.

ELL SUPPORT
Creating a Poster
colored pencils, markers, or crayons
Students create a poster for the terms *dividend, divisor, quotient,* and *remainder.*

Getting Started

Mental Math and Reflexes

Have students name the next three numbers in each pattern. *Suggestions:*

●○○
10, 12, 14, 16, 18, 20
12, 16, 20, 24, 28, 32
30, 25, 20, 15, 10, 5
18, 15, 12, 9, 6, 3

●●○
18, 27, 36, 45, 54, 63
24, 30, 36, 42, 48, 54
49, 42, 35, 28, 21, 14
40, 32, 24, 16, 8, 0

●●●
24, 28, 32, 36, 40, 44
24, 36, 48, 60, 72, 84
63, 56, 49, 42, 35, 28
72, 64, 56, 48, 40, 32

Math Message

How many bags of oranges, with 5 oranges in each bag, can be made with 35 oranges? How many can be made with 42 oranges?

Study Link 3·4 Follow-Up

Have students represent the multiplication equations in Problems 6–11 with multiplicative comparison statements. For example, "20 is 4 times as many as 5 and 20 is 5 times as many as 4."

1 Teaching the Lesson

▶ Math Message Follow-Up

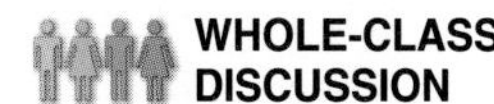

WHOLE-CLASS DISCUSSION

(*Student Reference Book,* pp. 178A and 178B)

As you and the students discuss the first problem, use alternative statements such as these:

▷ *How many 5s in 35?* This is an equal-groups interpretation of the problem.

▷ *35 is 5 times as many as what number?* This is a comparison interpretation of the problem.

▷ *What number multiplied by 5 gives 35?* This suggests an area interpretation and points out the inverse relationship between multiplication and division.

These interpretations are described on *Student Reference Book,* pages 178A and 178B.

Point out that in the division fact 35 / 5 = 7, the number 35 is the **dividend,** 5 is the **divisor,** and 7 is the **quotient.**

In the second problem, there will still be 2 oranges left over after making 8 bags with 5 oranges in each bag. Remind students that 2 is called the **remainder.**

Adjusting the Activity

ELL

To help students keep the terms *dividend* and *divisor* straight, point out that the suffix *-or* indicates someone or something doing the action—doctor, senator, tailor, generator, and so on. So the divisor is the number that is doing the dividing. The dividend is the number that is being divided.

AUDITORY ◆ KINESTHETIC ◆ TACTILE ◆ VISUAL

Student Page

Date Time

LESSON 3·5 **Multiplication and Division**

Equivalents			
3 * 4	12 / 3	12 ÷ 3	3 < 5 (< means "is less than")
3 × 4	$\frac{12}{3}$	3)‾12	5 > 3 (> means "is greater than")

1. Choose 3 Fact Triangles. Write the fact family for each. Answers vary.

___ * ___ = ___	___ × ___ = ___	___ * ___ = ___
___ * ___ = ___	___ × ___ = ___	___ * ___ = ___
___ / ___ = ___	___ / ___ = ___	___ ÷ ___ = ___
___ / ___ = ___	___ / ___ = ___	___ ÷ ___ = ___

2. Solve each division fact.
   a. 27 / 3 = 9 Think: How many 3s in 27?
   b. 9 = 45 / 5 Think: 45 is 5 times as many as what number?
   c. 36 ÷ 6 = 6 Think: 6 times what number equals 36?
   d. 24 / 8 = 3 Think: 24 is 8 times as many as what number?

Try This

3. A cashier has 5 rolls of quarters and 6 rolls of dimes in the cash register. Each roll of quarters is worth $10, and each roll of dimes is worth $5.
   a. How much are the rolls of quarters and dimes worth in all? $ 80
   b. How many quarters are in 1 roll? 40 quarters
   c. How many quarters are in the 5 rolls? 200 quarters
   d. How many dimes are in 1 roll? 50 dimes
   e. How many dimes are in the 6 rolls? 300 dimes
   f. There is also $7.50 worth of half-dollars in the cash register. How many half-dollars is that? 15 half-dollars

Math Journal 1, **p. 61**

Adjusting the Activity

Use a piece of paper to track across and up. For example, to solve 56 / 7, line up the bottom of a piece of paper along the top of the 7s row. Scan across the 7s row to find 56. Line up the right edge of the paper with the left side of the column containing 56. Then scan up that column to find the answer, 8, at the top.

								8	9	10
								8	9	10
								16	18	20
								24	27	30
								32	36	40
								40	45	50
								48	54	60
7	7	14	21	28	35	42	49	56	63	70
8	8	16	24	32	40	48	56	64	72	80
9	9	18	27	36	45	54	63	72	81	90
10	10	20	30	40	50	60	70	80	90	100

AUDITORY ◆ KINESTHETIC ◆ TACTILE ◆ VISUAL

▶ Exploring the Relationship between Multiplication and Division

WHOLE-CLASS DISCUSSION

(*Math Journal 1,* p. 61; *Math Masters,* p. 409)

On the board, draw the ∗, / Fact Triangle shown below, or use a transparency of *Math Masters,* page 409.

Remind students of the following symbols: ∗ or × for multiplication, and ÷ or / for division. Then show them how to use the Fact Triangle to generate a multiplication/division **fact family:**

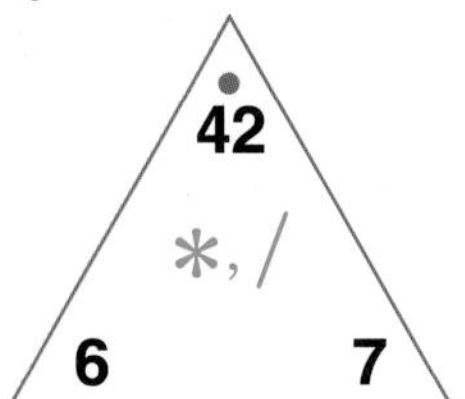

6 ∗ 7 = 42

7 ∗ 6 = 42

42 / 6 = 7

42 / 7 = 6

Do several more examples with the class. Then have students choose three of their Fact Triangles and record the fact families for those triangles in Problem 1 on journal page 61.

Ongoing Assessment: Recognizing Student Achievement

Journal page 61 Problem 1

Use **journal page 61, Problem 1** to assess students' ability to use conventional notation to write multiplication and division number sentences. Students are making adequate progress if they are able to record the appropriate fact families. Some students may use factors greater than 10.

[Patterns, Functions, and Algebra Goal 2]

▶ Using the Multiplication/Division Facts Table for Division

WHOLE-CLASS ACTIVITY

(*Math Journal 1,* p. 61; *Math Masters,* p. 408)

You may want to use an overhead transparency of the Multiplication/Division Facts Table (*Math Masters,* page 408) to remind students how to use it for division. For example, to find the answer to 24 / 3, move across the 3s row to the cell containing 24. Then move up the column containing 24 to find the answer, 8, at the top. Tell students that the arrow (see below) from the 3 to the 24 can represent the question "How many 3s in 24?"

∗,/	1	2	3	4	5	6	7	8	9	10
1	1									10
2		4								20
3			9					(24)		30
4				16						40

Have students complete Problems 2 and 3 on journal page 61 on their own or with a partner.

Practicing Division Facts with Fact Triangles

PARTNER ACTIVITY

Demonstrate the following procedure:

1. Student A takes the top triangle from his or her OK pile and asks Student B a division fact from the triangle, such as "42 divided by 6 is equal to what number?"
2. Partners help each other. If Student B is not sure of the answer, Student A gives a clue. For example, if the fact is 42 divided by 6, Student A can help Student B by asking, "What number times 6 is equal to 42?" or "How many 6s in 42?" or "42 is 6 times as many as what number?" If Student B still is not sure, Student A reads the answer.
3. Partners take turns asking and answering until they have gone through the triangles in both their OK and Try Again piles, or as long as time permits.

Student Page

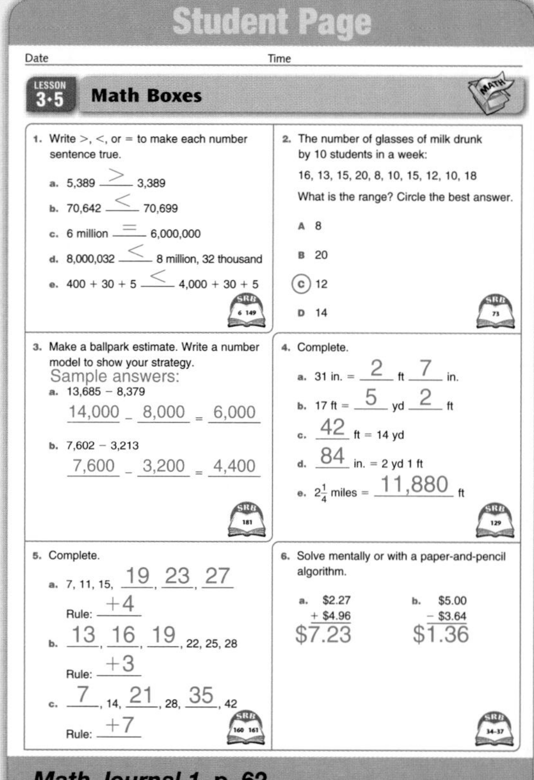

Date Time

LESSON 3·5 **Math Boxes**

1. Write >, <, or = to make each number sentence true.
 a. 5,389 __>__ 3,389
 b. 70,642 __<__ 70,699
 c. 6 million __=__ 6,000,000
 d. 8,000,032 __<__ 8 million, 32 thousand
 e. 400 + 30 + 5 __<__ 4,000 + 30 + 5

SRB 6 149

2. The number of glasses of milk drunk by 10 students in a week:
 16, 13, 15, 20, 8, 10, 15, 12, 10, 18
 What is the range? Circle the best answer.
 A 8
 B 20
 (C) 12
 D 14

SRB 73

3. Make a ballpark estimate. Write a number model to show your strategy.
 Sample answers:
 a. 13,685 − 8,379
 __14,000__ − __8,000__ = __6,000__
 b. 7,602 − 3,213
 __7,600__ − __3,200__ = __4,400__

SRB 181

4. Complete.
 a. 31 in. = __2__ ft __7__ in.
 b. 17 ft = __5__ yd __2__ ft
 c. __42__ ft = 14 yd
 d. __84__ in. = 2 yd 1 ft
 e. $2\frac{1}{4}$ miles = __11,880__ ft

SRB 129

5. Complete.
 a. 7, 11, 15, __19__, __23__, __27__
 Rule: __+4__
 b. __13__, __16__, __19__, 22, 25, 28
 Rule: __+3__
 c. __7__, 14, __21__, 28, __35__, 42
 Rule: __+7__

SRB 160 161

6. Solve mentally or with a paper-and-pencil algorithm.
 a. $2.27 + $4.96 = $7.23
 b. $5.00 − $3.64 = $1.36

SRB 34-37

Math Journal 1, p. 62

2 Ongoing Learning & Practice

Playing *Beat the Calculator*

SMALL-GROUP ACTIVITY

(*Student Reference Book*, p. 233; *Math Masters*, p. 461)

Students play *Beat the Calculator* to maintain automaticity with multiplication facts.

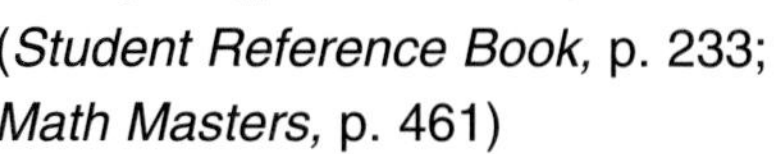

NOTE For practice with facts through 12 ∗ 12, have students use the Online Master available at www.everydaymathonline.com in place of Study Link 3•5.

Adjusting the Activity

Have students play the extended-facts version of the game described on *Student Reference Book*, page 233.

AUDITORY • KINESTHETIC • TACTILE • VISUAL

Math Boxes 3·5

INDEPENDENT ACTIVITY

(*Math Journal 1*, p. 62)

Mixed Practice Math Boxes in this lesson are linked with Math Boxes in Lessons 3-1 and 3-3. The skill in Problem 6 previews Unit 4 content.

Study Link 3·5

INDEPENDENT ACTIVITY

(*Math Masters*, p. 85)

Home Connection Students fill in the missing numbers in multiplication and division facts.

Study Link Master

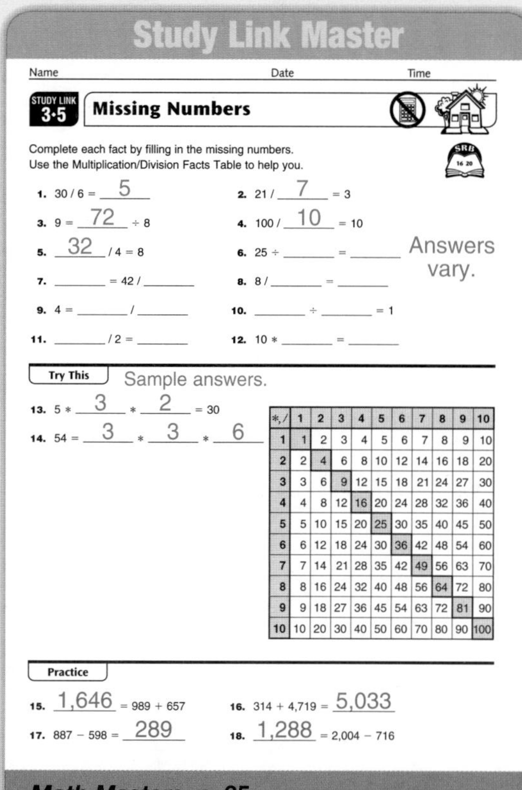

Name Date Time

STUDY LINK 3·5 **Missing Numbers**

Complete each fact by filling in the missing numbers.
Use the Multiplication/Division Facts Table to help you.

SRB 16 20

1. 30 / 6 = __5__
2. 21 / __7__ = 3
3. 9 = __72__ ÷ 8
4. 100 / __10__ = 10
5. __32__ / 4 = 8
6. 25 ÷ ____ = ____
7. ____ = 42 / ____
8. 8 / ____ = ____
9. 4 = ____ / ____
10. ____ ÷ ____ = 1
11. ____ / 2 = ____
12. 10 ∗ ____ = ____

Answers vary.

Try This Sample answers.

13. 5 ∗ __3__ ∗ __2__ = 30
14. 54 = __3__ ∗ __3__ ∗ __6__

∗,/	1	2	3	4	5	6	7	8	9	10
1	1	2	3	4	5	6	7	8	9	10
2	2	4	6	8	10	12	14	16	18	20
3	3	6	9	12	15	18	21	24	27	30
4	4	8	12	16	20	24	28	32	36	40
5	5	10	15	20	25	30	35	40	45	50
6	6	12	18	24	30	36	42	48	54	60
7	7	14	21	28	35	42	49	56	63	70
8	8	16	24	32	40	48	56	64	72	80
9	9	18	27	36	45	54	63	72	81	90
10	10	20	30	40	50	60	70	80	90	100

Practice

15. __1,646__ = 989 + 657
16. 314 + 4,719 = __5,033__
17. 887 − 598 = __289__
18. __1,288__ = 2,004 − 716

Math Masters, p. 85

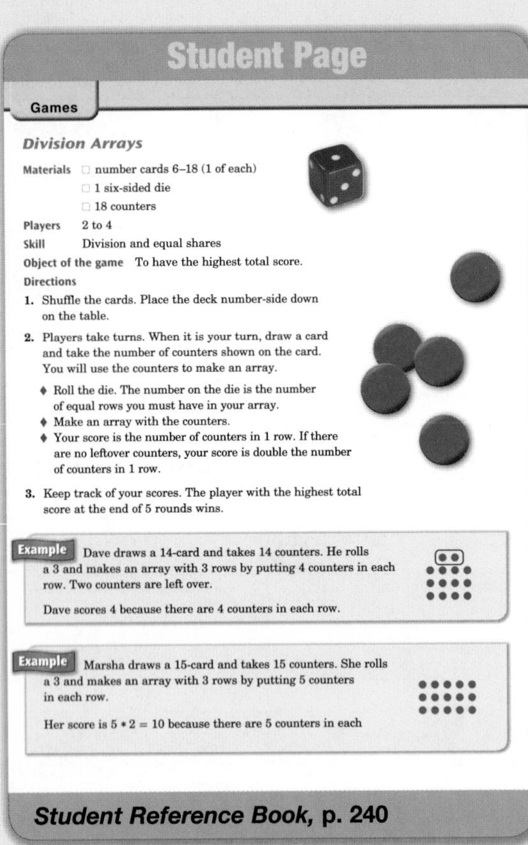
Student Page

Games

Division Arrays

Materials □ number cards 6–18 (1 of each)
□ 1 six-sided die
□ 18 counters

Players 2 to 4

Skill Division and equal shares

Object of the game To have the highest total score.

Directions

1. Shuffle the cards. Place the deck number-side down on the table.
2. Players take turns. When it is your turn, draw a card and take the number of counters shown on the card. You will use the counters to make an array.
   - Roll the die. The number on the die is the number of equal rows you must have in your array.
   - Make an array with the counters.
   - Your score is the number of counters in 1 row. If there are no leftover counters, your score is double the number of counters in 1 row.
3. Keep track of your scores. The player with the highest total score at the end of 5 rounds wins.

Example Dave draws a 14-card and takes 14 counters. He rolls a 3 and makes an array with 3 rows by putting 4 counters in each row. Two counters are left over.

Dave scores 4 because there are 4 counters in each row.

Example Marsha draws a 15-card and takes 15 counters. She rolls a 3 and makes an array with 3 rows by putting 5 counters in each row.

Her score is 5 * 2 = 10 because there are 5 counters in each

Student Reference Book, p. 240

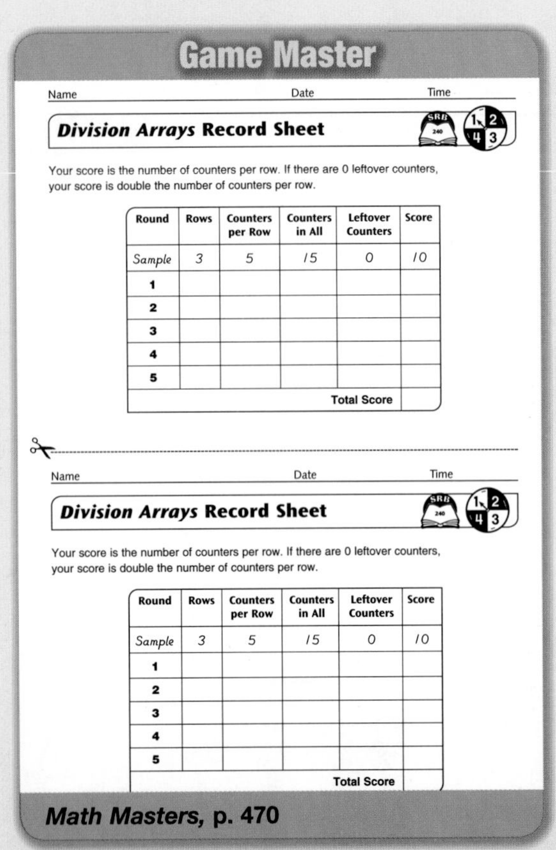
Game Master

Name Date Time

***Division Arrays* Record Sheet**

Your score is the number of counters per row. If there are 0 leftover counters, your score is double the number of counters per row.

Round	Rows	Counters per Row	Counters in All	Leftover Counters	Score
Sample	*3*	*5*	*15*	*0*	*10*
1					
2					
3					
4					
5					
				Total Score	

Name Date Time

***Division Arrays* Record Sheet**

Your score is the number of counters per row. If there are 0 leftover counters, your score is double the number of counters per row.

Round	Rows	Counters per Row	Counters in All	Leftover Counters	Score
Sample	*3*	*5*	*15*	*0*	*10*
1					
2					
3					
4					
5					
				Total Score	

Math Masters, p. 470

3 Differentiation Options

READINESS

PARTNER ACTIVITY

▶ Playing *Division Arrays*

15–30 Min

(*Student Reference Book*, p. 240; *Math Masters*, p. 470)

To explore the connections between multiplication and division using a concrete model, have students play *Division Arrays* and record their work on *Math Masters*, page 470. Some students may find it helpful to organize the counters on grid paper.

ENRICHMENT

PARTNER ACTIVITY

▶ Exploring the Relationship between Division and Fractions

5–15 Min

(*Math Masters*, p. 86)

To apply students' understanding of division, have them use division facts to solve a fraction problem. Both fractions and division involve sharing something equally or forming equal groups. Fraction notation is one way to write a division problem.

Some students may solve the pizza problem by dividing each pizza into 4 equal pieces. Each person gets 1 piece, or $\frac{1}{4}$, of *each* pizza. So one person's share of the 3 pizzas is three-fourths, or $\frac{3}{4}$ of *one* pizza.

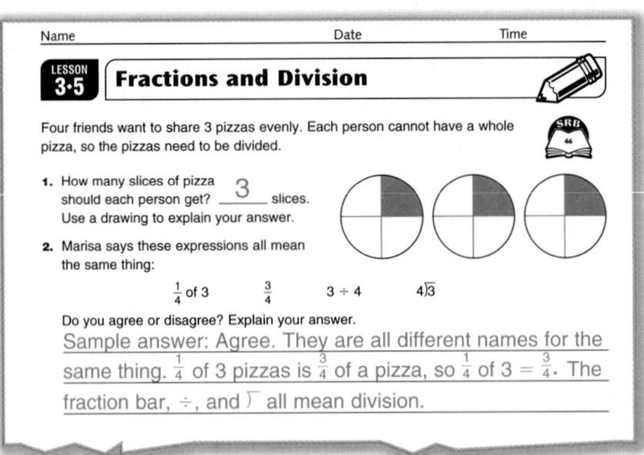
Name Date Time

LESSON 3·5 **Fractions and Division**

Four friends want to share 3 pizzas evenly. Each person cannot have a whole pizza, so the pizzas need to be divided.

1. How many slices of pizza should each person get? 3 slices. Use a drawing to explain your answer.
2. Marisa says these expressions all mean the same thing:

$\frac{1}{4}$ of 3 $\frac{3}{4}$ $3 \div 4$ $4\overline{)3}$

Do you agree or disagree? Explain your answer.

Sample answer: Agree. They are all different names for the same thing. $\frac{1}{4}$ of 3 pizzas is $\frac{3}{4}$ of a pizza, so $\frac{1}{4}$ of 3 = $\frac{3}{4}$. The fraction bar, ÷, and $\overline{)}$ all mean division.

Math Masters, page 86

EXTRA PRACTICE

INDEPENDENT ACTIVITY

Practicing with Fact Families

5–15 Min

FACTS PRACTICE

(*Math Masters,* p. 418)

To practice the connection between multiplication and division, have students complete Fact Triangles and related fact families.

ELL SUPPORT

SMALL-GROUP ACTIVITY

Creating a Poster

5–15 Min

To provide language support for division, have students create a poster representing the terms *dividend, divisor, quotient,* and *remainder.* Ask them to write a division number sentence and label all of the parts. Students can color code the number sentence so that each part is drawn in the same color as the label.

Planning Ahead

Lesson 3-6 provides a detailed introduction to the World Tour. Read through the lesson well in advance, along with the related pages in the World Tour section of the *Student Reference Book.* In addition to a globe and a large map of the world, try to collect as many reference materials as possible for a World Tour Corner. The authors recommend several copies of an almanac, such as the *World Almanac,* a full-sized atlas, and several student atlases similar to the *National Geographic World Atlas for Young Explorers* (National Geographic Society, 2007).

Ask students to bring country guide books to school. Begin a collection of travel information, including airline schedules and fares, travel articles, weather reports, and currency exchange rates from the local newspaper or the Internet.

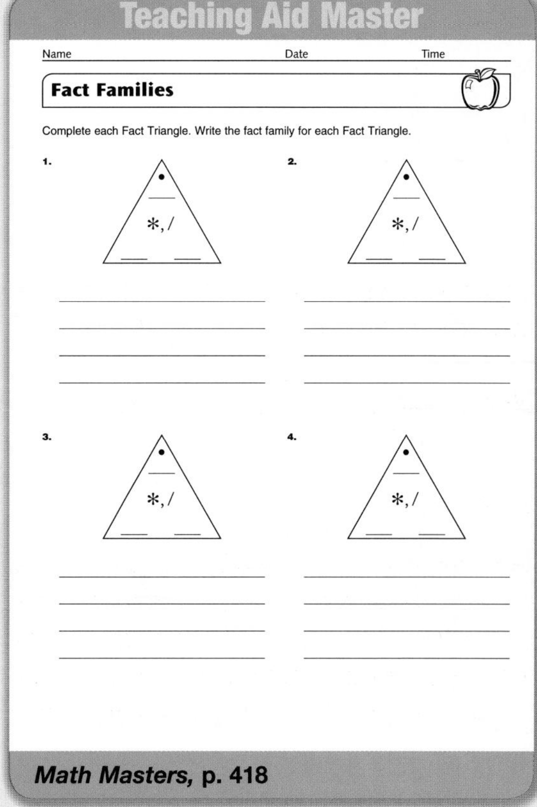
Teaching Aid Master

Name Date Time

Fact Families

Complete each Fact Triangle. Write the fact family for each Fact Triangle.

1. • *, /

2. • *, /

3. • *, /

4. • *, /

Math Masters, p. 418

3•6 World Tour: Flying to Africa

Objective To provide practice interpreting data through the World Tour Project.

Technology Resources www.everydaymathonline.com

ePresentations

eToolkit

Algorithms Practice

EM Facts Workshop Game™

Family Letters

Assessment Management

Common Core State Standards

Curriculum Focal Points

Interactive Teacher's Lesson Guide

1 Teaching the Lesson

Key Concepts and Skills

- Read and write large numbers. [Number and Numeration Goal 1]
- Calculate relative time across time zones. [Operations and Computation Goal 2]
- Judge the reasonableness of counts; describe the difference between a count and an estimate. [Operations and Computation Goal 6]
- Use a table of climate data and a time zones map. [Data and Chance Goal 2]

Key Activities

Students travel to Cairo, Egypt, on the World Tour, which was introduced in Lesson 2•1.

Ongoing Assessment: Informing Instruction See page 188.

Materials

Math Journal 1, p. 171 (optional); pp. 172–175
Student Reference Book, pp. 276, 277, 279–283, 297, and 302–305
Study Link 3•5
Math Masters, pp. 419–421 (optional)
slate ◆ globe ◆ classroom world map

2 Ongoing Learning & Practice

Playing *Multiplication Top-It*
Student Reference Book, p. 264
Math Masters, p. 506 (optional)
4 each of number cards 1–10 (from the Everything Math Deck, if available)
Students practice multiplication facts.

Solving Elapsed-Time Problems
Math Journal 1, pp. 63A and 63B
demonstration clock (optional) ◆ calculator (optional)
Students solve elapsed-time problems.

Math Boxes 3•6
Math Journal 1, p. 63
Students practice and maintain skills through Math Box problems.

Ongoing Assessment: Recognizing Student Achievement
Use Math Boxes, Problem 4. [Operations and Computation Goal 2]

Study Link 3•6
Math Masters, p. 87
Students practice and maintain skills through Study Link activities.

3 Differentiation Options

READINESS

Exploring Time Zones
Student Reference Book, pp. 276 and 277
Students read *Nine O'Clock Lullaby* as an introduction to time zones.

ENRICHMENT

Playing *Seega*
Student Reference Book, p. 309
Math Masters, p. 503
6 counters (3 each of 2 colors)
Students play a traditional Egyptian game.

Additional Information

Students travel as a class to Egypt. In future units, they travel to other countries and gather and record information about the country on the Country Notes pages.

For Part 1, collect reference materials, especially atlases and almanacs. See page 185. For the optional Readiness activity in Part 3, obtain a copy of ***Nine O'Clock Lullaby*** by Marilyn Singer (HarperCollins Children's Books, 1993).

Getting Started

Mental Math and Reflexes

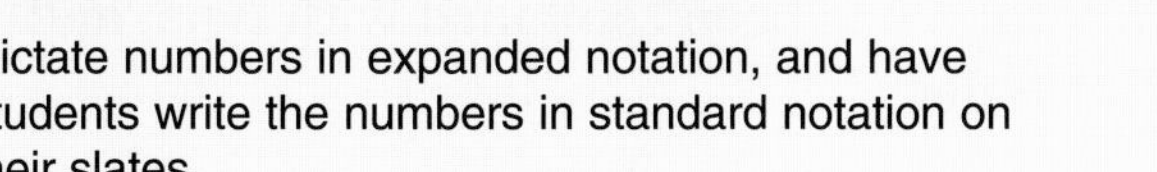
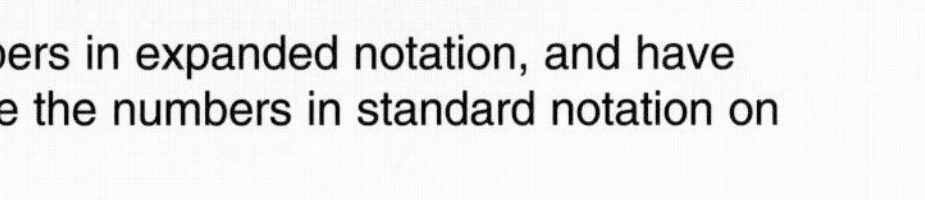

Dictate numbers in expanded notation, and have students write the numbers in standard notation on their slates.

●○○ 7,000 + 800 + 40 + 2 7,842
3,000 + 400 + 90 + 1 3,491
9,000 + 100 + 3 9,103

●●○ 20,000 + 8,000 + 500 + 70 + 6 28,576
80,000 + 300 + 70 + 4 80,374
60,000 + 900 + 50 60,950

●●● 5,000,000 + 300,000 + 20,000 + 8,000 + 500 + 90 + 4 5,328,594
4,000,000 + 90,000 + 7,000 + 80 + 5 4,097,085
1,000,000 + 80,000 + 300 + 2 1,080,302

Math Message

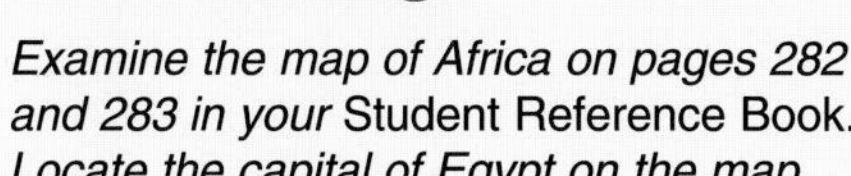

Examine the map of Africa on pages 282 and 283 in your Student Reference Book. *Locate the capital of Egypt on the map.*

Study Link 3·5 Follow-Up

Students compare answers. Problems 6–14 have more than one correct answer.

1 Teaching the Lesson

Math Message Follow-Up

WHOLE-CLASS ACTIVITY

(*Student Reference Book,* pp. 282 and 283)

Ask students to point to Cairo, Egypt, on the map. Tell students that in this lesson they will make their first World Tour excursion outside the United States when they travel to Cairo, Egypt, on the African continent. This trip establishes routines for the yearlong activity.

Examining the List of Countries and Regions

WHOLE-CLASS DISCUSSION

ELL

(*Student Reference Book,* pp. 279–281)

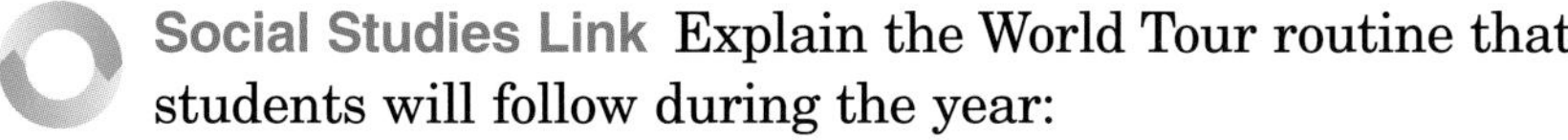

Social Studies Link Explain the World Tour routine that students will follow during the year:

▷ Students travel to various regions as a class, visiting one country within each region.

▷ When students visit a country, they look up information about it in the World Tour section of the *Student Reference Book* and record that information on the Country Notes pages found at the back of the journal or on *Math Masters,* pages 419 and 420. They record their progress on the Route Map (journal pages 172 and 173).

Tell students to turn to the Country Profiles on pages 279–281 in the *Student Reference Book.* To support English language learners, explain the meaning of the word *profile* in this context. Ask students to name a country for which there is not a profile.

Have students guess how many profiles there would be if there were one for every country in the world. If you have a world almanac, show the flag pages. There are now nearly 200 countries.

NOTE You may expand the World Tour for your class by having students form small groups that travel to additional countries within each region visited. See Lesson 4-7.

Ask students to name the seven continents. North America, South America, Europe, Africa, Asia, Australia, and Antarctica Write them on the board. Point out that the Country Profiles are organized into five regions. Most of the regions are single continents, but Australia has been combined with Asia, and Antarctica is not included.

NOTE If you are using the Route Log on *Math Journal 1,* page 171 or on *Math Masters,* page 421, direct students to enter today's date next to the name of the country they are visiting (Egypt) and its capital (Cairo). Air distance will be recorded in the next lesson.

Completing the Route Map and Country Notes for Egypt

(*Math Journal 1,* pp. 171–175; *Student Reference Book,* pp. 276, 277, 279, 282, 283, 297, and 302–305; *Math Masters,* pp. 419–421, optional)

Divide the class into partnerships. Ask students to turn to the Route Map on journal pages 172 and 173; draw the direct route from Washington, D.C., to Cairo; and put an arrowhead at the destination.

Ask students to record information about Egypt in the Country Notes on journal pages 174 and 175 or on *Math Masters,* pages 419 and 420. Remind them that the World Tour section of the *Student Reference Book* serves as their major source for filling in the Country Notes.

Ongoing Assessment: Informing Instruction

Watch for students who are having difficulty completing the Country Notes due to a lack of understanding of vocabulary, such as *border, country, capital, monetary unit,* and *exchange rate,* rather than an inability to locate the information in the *Student Reference Book.* Discuss the terms and provide examples.

Be sure to include the following in your discussion of the Country Notes.

Facts about the Country

▷ Egypt's population is more than 76 million. Its area is about 387,000 square miles.

- Have students discuss these figures in rounded as well as in exact terms.
- Have students examine the population figures for other countries. The population figures for all countries are rounded to the nearest thousand. Ask students why this makes more sense than reporting unrounded figures, such as 76,117,437.

▷ Arabic, English, and French are spoken in Egypt.

- The language printed in boldface type in each Country Profile is the primary language spoken in that country, but the other languages listed are spoken by significant numbers of people.

Student Page

Date Time

My Route Log

Date	Country	Capital	Air distance from last capital	Total distance traveled so far
	1 U.S.A.	Washington, D.C.		
	2 Egypt	Cairo		
	3			
	4			
	5			
	6			
	7			
	8			
	9			
	10			
	11			
	12			
	13			
	14			
	15			
	16			
	17			
	18			
	19			
	20			

Math Journal 1, p. 171

▷ The monetary unit in Egypt is the Egyptian pound.

- Entry of the exchange rate is optional, because this rate changes constantly. Current exchange rates are given in the *Wall Street Journal* and in Sunday editions of major newspapers. The Web site www.oanda.com/convert/classic also provides exchange rates.
- The exchange rate may be quoted in different ways.
  For example:
  \$1 U.S. = 6.2102 Egyptian pounds
  1 Egyptian pound = \$0.1610 U.S. (16.10 cents U.S.)

Facts about the Capital of the Country

▷ The capital of Egypt is Cairo.

- Have students look at the population figures for Cairo and other capitals.

▷ The time in Cairo in relation to the time at your school will vary based on the location of your school.

- Have students use the time zones map on *Student Reference Book* pages 276 and 277 to check answers to Problem B1.

▷ Discuss the climate data in the table on page 297 of the *Student Reference Book.* Average temperatures are in degrees Fahrenheit, and average rainfall is in inches. The temperature data in each column consists of two numbers. The first number is the average high temperature; the second number is the average low temperature. Each figure was obtained by adding the average figures for each of the three months, dividing the result by 3, and rounding the resulting average. In Cairo from September to November, the average high temperature is about 83°F; the average low temperature is about 64°F. There is usually no measurable rainfall.

- Students should use these data to decide what kinds of clothes to pack.

▷ The Country Notes provide space for students to record interesting facts about the countries they are visiting. Encourage students to use classroom and library resources to find such facts. Have students check Fascinating Facts on pages 302–305 of the *Student Reference Book.*

- Remind students that they may record any fact that is intriguing to them about Egypt or about a country bordering Egypt.
- Students may use other reference books to find country information. Country information in other reference books often includes other number facts. Egyptian civilization developed along the Nile Valley about 4000 B.C., or about 6,000 years ago. The Aswan Dam, completed in 1971, helps in the irrigation of about 1,500 square miles. The Suez Canal, which links the Mediterranean and Red Seas, is 103 miles long.

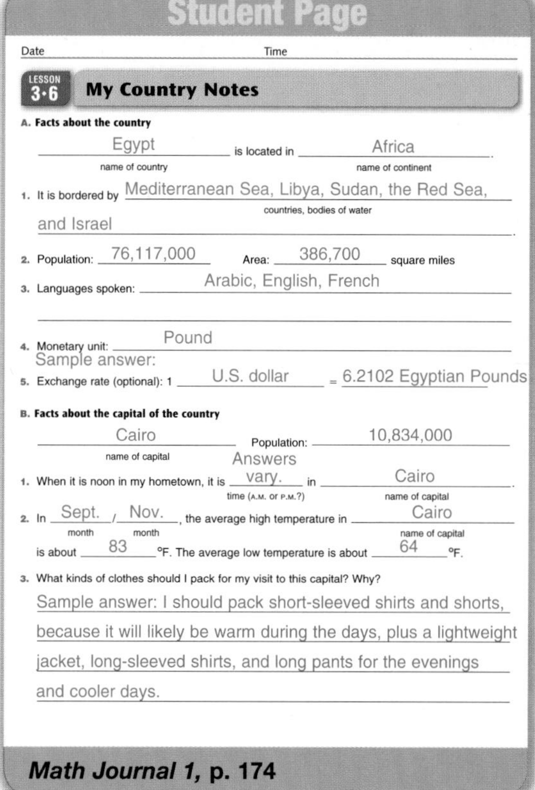

Student Page

Date Time

LESSON 3·6 **My Country Notes**

A. Facts about the country

Egypt (name of country) is located in Africa (name of continent).

1. It is bordered by Mediterranean Sea, Libya, Sudan, the Red Sea, and Israel (countries, bodies of water).
2. Population: 76,117,000 Area: 386,700 square miles
3. Languages spoken: Arabic, English, French
4. Monetary unit: Pound
5. Exchange rate (optional): 1 U.S. dollar = 6.2102 Egyptian Pounds (Sample answer:)

B. Facts about the capital of the country

Cairo (name of capital) Population: 10,834,000

1. When it is noon in my hometown, it is Answers vary. (time (A.M. or P.M.?)) in Cairo (name of capital).
2. In Sept. / Nov. (month, month), the average high temperature in Cairo (name of capital) is about 83 °F. The average low temperature is about 64 °F.
3. What kinds of clothes should I pack for my visit to this capital? Why?
   Sample answer: I should pack short-sleeved shirts and shorts, because it will likely be warm during the days, plus a lightweight jacket, long-sleeved shirts, and long pants for the evenings and cooler days.

Math Journal 1, p. 174

NOTE For practice reading and comparing Fahrenheit temperatures, see www.everydaymathonline.com.

Student Page

Date Time

LESSON 3·6 **My Country Notes** *continued*

4. Turn to the Route Map found on journal pages 172 and 173. Draw a line from the last city you visited to the capital of this country.
5. If your class is using the Route Log, record the information on journal page 171 or *Math Masters,* page 421.
6. Can you find any facts on pages 302–305 in your *Student Reference Book* that apply to this country? For example, is one of the 10 tallest mountains in the world located in this country? List all the facts you can find. Sample answers:
   Egypt is bordered by the world's fourth-largest sea—the Mediterranean. The world's longest river—the Nile—runs through the country. Part of Egypt lies in the world's largest desert—the Sahara.

C. My impressions about the country

Do you know anyone who has visited or lived in this country? If so, ask that person for an interview. Read about the country's customs and about interesting places to visit there. Use encyclopedias, travel books, the travel section of a newspaper, or library books. Try to get brochures from a travel agent. Then describe below some interesting things you have learned about this country.

Answers vary.

Math Journal 1, p. 175

Student Page

Date Time

LESSON 3·6 **Flying to London**

Suppose you are flying from Charleston, South Carolina, to London, England. You have a connecting flight in Washington, D.C.

1. Your flight to Washington, D.C., leaves Charleston at 7:05 A.M. It lands in Washington at 8:34 A.M. How long was the flight?
   1 hr, 29 min
2. Your flight from Washington, D.C., to London is scheduled to leave at 12:02 P.M. The flight time is 7 hours and 19 minutes. At what time does the flight land (in Washington, D.C., time)?
   7:21 P.M.
3. There is a 5-hour time difference between Washington, D.C., and London. What time does your flight land, London time?
   12:21 A.M.
4. Your return flight from London arrives in Washington, D.C., at 4:46 P.M. Your flight to Charleston is scheduled to leave Washington, D.C., 3 hours and 12 minutes later. What time does your flight to Charleston leave?
   7:58 P.M.

Math Journal 1, **p. 63A**

NOTE Open number lines are useful for representing relationships between the quantities in a problem situation. Open number lines are not usually drawn to scale, or at best, are only drawn approximately to scale, so they are not standard number lines.

Student Page

Date Time

LESSON 3·6 **Flying to London** *continued*

5. Your flight to Charleston is delayed because of stormy weather. It finally leaves at 8:57 P.M. and lands in Charleston 1 hour and 44 minutes later. What time does it land in Charleston?
   10:41 P.M.
6. A friend who traveled with you lives in New York City. She took a direct flight from London to New York that left at 9:20 A.M., New York time. The flight was 7 hours, 36 minutes long. What time did it land?
   4:56 P.M.
7. You go to bed at 11:15 P.M. and wake up at 8:37 A.M. How long did you sleep?
   9 hr, 22 min
8. The next day, you spend 45 minutes looking at all the photos you took on your trip. If you finish at 10:25 A.M., what time did you start?
   9:40 A.M.

Math Journal 1, **p. 63B**

2 Ongoing Learning & Practice

▶ Playing *Multiplication Top-It*

(*Student Reference Book,* p. 264;
Math Masters, p. 506)

Students play *Multiplication Top-It* to maintain automaticity with multiplication facts.

NOTE For facts practice through 12 ∗ 12, have students include number cards 11 and 12 when playing *Multiplication Top-It.*

▶ Solving Elapsed-Time Problems

(*Math Journal 1,* pp. 63A and 63B)

Students solve elapsed-time problems. Students may use the demonstration clock, calculators, or anything else that may help. Some students may find it helpful to use an open number line to illustrate the strategy of counting up in hours and minutes. For example, in Problem 1, students might draw a diagram like the one below. Students mark off the starting time and count up in hours and then in minutes, while recording the actual and elapsed time.

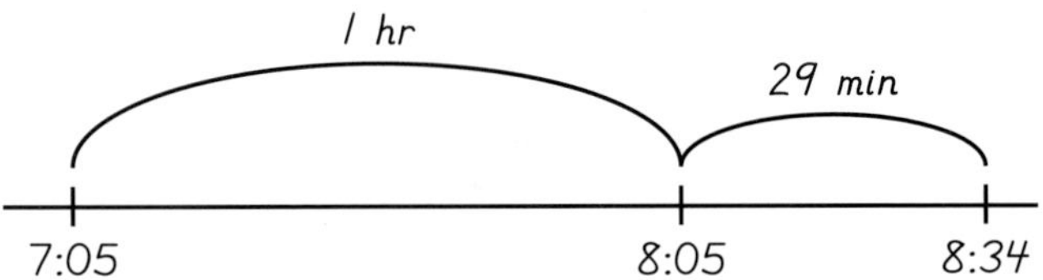

Encourage students to share their strategies.

▶ Math Boxes 3·6

INDEPENDENT ACTIVITY

(*Math Journal 1,* p. 63)

Mixed Practice Math Boxes in this lesson are paired with Math Boxes in Lesson 3-8. The skill in Problem 5 previews Unit 4 content.

Writing/Reasoning Have students write a response to the following: *For Problem 5, suppose Riley wanted to estimate the height of the classroom ceiling in centimeters and millimeters instead of meters. Give the new measurements.* 300 centimeters and 3,000 millimeters *Which unit of measurement (meters, centimeters, or millimeters) do you think makes the most sense for Riley's estimate?* meters *Why?* Sample answer: Larger units are better to use when estimating long distances. Centimeters and millimeters make more sense when estimating the length of something small.

Ongoing Assessment: Recognizing Student Achievement

Math Boxes Problem 4 

Use **Math Boxes, Problem 4** to assess students' ability to solve multidigit addition and subtraction problems. Students are making adequate progress if they are able to use a paper-and-pencil algorithm to calculate the correct sum and difference. Some students may be able to use more than one method to solve the problems or demonstrate how the relationship between + and – can be used to check their answers.

[Operations and Computation Goal 2]

Study Link 3·6

INDEPENDENT ACTIVITY

(*Math Masters,* p. 87)

Home Connection Students solve number stories related to Egypt. The problems offer practice in subtraction, multiplication, estimation, and comparing numbers. Point out that some problems ask students to write a number model to show how they solved the problem.

3 Differentiation Options

READINESS

SMALL-GROUP ACTIVITY

Exploring Time Zones

5–15 Min

(*Student Reference Book,* pp. 276 and 277)

Literature Link To provide students with an introduction to time zones, read ***Nine O'Clock Lullaby*** by Marilyn Singer (HarperCollins Children's Books, 1993). Have students locate each of the places mentioned in the book on the Time Zones of the World map on *Student Reference Book,* pages 276 and 277.

ENRICHMENT

PARTNER ACTIVITY

Playing *Seega*

5–15 Min

(*Student Reference Book,* p. 309; *Math Masters,* p. 503)

To further explore mathematical connections with Egypt, have students play *Seega,* a traditional Egyptian game popular among young Egyptians today. Players use strategic moves to transfer three counters on a game board to a new straight line.

Planning Ahead

Gather as many globes as possible for the activities in the next lesson on measuring air distances. You will need a cloth tape measure for each partnership.

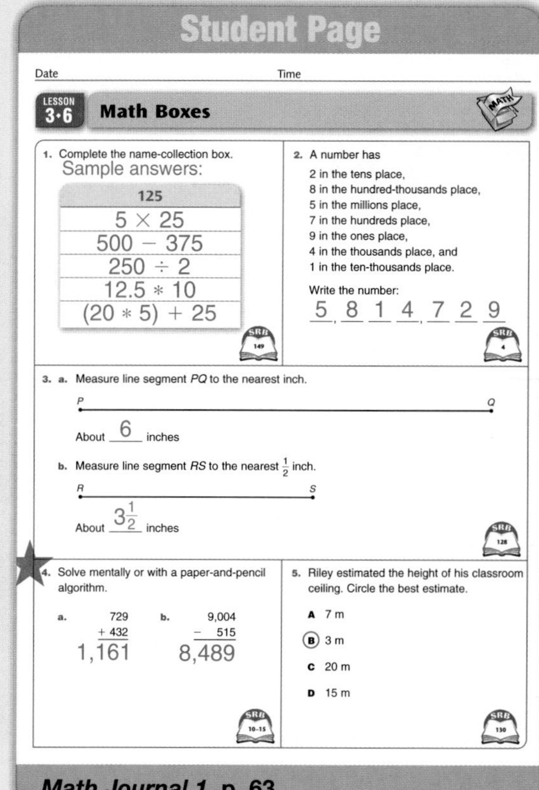

Student Page

Date Time

LESSON 3·6 **Math Boxes**

1. Complete the name-collection box. Sample answers:

125
5×25
$500 - 375$
$250 \div 2$
$12.5 * 10$
$(20 * 5) + 25$

SRB 149

2. A number has
2 in the tens place,
8 in the hundred-thousands place,
5 in the millions place,
7 in the hundreds place,
9 in the ones place,
4 in the thousands place, and
1 in the ten-thousands place.

Write the number: 5 8 1 4 7 2 9

SRB 4

3. a. Measure line segment *PQ* to the nearest inch.

About 6 inches

b. Measure line segment *RS* to the nearest $\frac{1}{2}$ inch.

About $3\frac{1}{2}$ inches

SRB 128

4. Solve mentally or with a paper-and-pencil algorithm.

a. 729 + 432 = 1,161

b. 9,004 − 515 = 8,489

SRB 10-15

5. Riley estimated the height of his classroom ceiling. Circle the best estimate.

A 7 m
(B) 3 m
C 20 m
D 15 m

SRB 130

Math Journal 1, p. 63

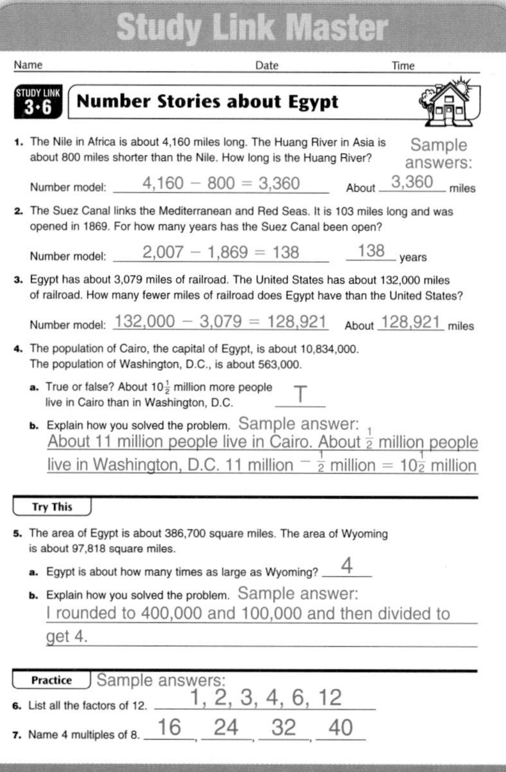

Study Link Master

Name Date Time

STUDY LINK 3·6 **Number Stories about Egypt**

1. The Nile in Africa is about 4,160 miles long. The Huang River in Asia is about 800 miles shorter than the Nile. How long is the Huang River? Sample answers:

Number model: 4,160 − 800 = 3,360 About 3,360 miles

2. The Suez Canal links the Mediterranean and Red Seas. It is 103 miles long and was opened in 1869. For how many years has the Suez Canal been open?

Number model: 2,007 − 1,869 = 138 138 years

3. Egypt has about 3,079 miles of railroad. The United States has about 132,000 miles of railroad. How many fewer miles of railroad does Egypt have than the United States?

Number model: 132,000 − 3,079 = 128,921 About 128,921 miles

4. The population of Cairo, the capital of Egypt, is about 10,834,000. The population of Washington, D.C., is about 563,000.

a. True or false? About $10\frac{1}{2}$ million more people live in Cairo than in Washington, D.C. T

b. Explain how you solved the problem. Sample answer: About 11 million people live in Cairo. About $\frac{1}{2}$ million people live in Washington, D.C. 11 million − $\frac{1}{2}$ million = $10\frac{1}{2}$ million

Try This

5. The area of Egypt is about 386,700 square miles. The area of Wyoming is about 97,818 square miles.

a. Egypt is about how many times as large as Wyoming? 4

b. Explain how you solved the problem. Sample answer: I rounded to 400,000 and 100,000 and then divided to get 4.

Practice Sample answers:

6. List all the factors of 12. 1, 2, 3, 4, 6, 12

7. Name 4 multiples of 8. 16, 24, 32, 40

Math Masters, p. 87

3•7 Finding Air Distances

Objective To provide practice measuring length and using a map scale.

Technology Resources www.everydaymathonline.com

ePresentations

eToolkit

Algorithms Practice

EM Facts Workshop Game™

Family Letters

Assessment Management

Common Core State Standards

Curriculum Focal Points

Interactive Teacher's Lesson Guide

1 Teaching the Lesson

Key Concepts and Skills

- Solve multiplication problems. [Operations and Computation Goal 4]
- Use a map scale. [Operations and Computation Goal 7]
- Measure to the nearest $\frac{1}{2}$ inch. [Measurement and Reference Frames Goal 1]

Key Activities

Students measure the shortest distances between international locations on a globe. Then students use a map scale to convert these measurements to actual air distances.

Ongoing Assessment: Informing Instruction See page 193.

Ongoing Assessment: Recognizing Student Achievement Use journal page 64. [Operations and Computation Goal 7]

Materials

Math Journal 1, p. 64
Study Link 3•6
slate ◆ classroom world map ◆ globes ◆ per partnership: cloth tape measure ◆ calculator

2 Ongoing Learning & Practice

Playing *Polygon Pair-Up*
Student Reference Book, p. 258
Polygon Pair-Up Property Cards and Polygon Cards (*Math Masters,* pp. 496 and 497)
Students practice naming properties of polygons.

Math Boxes 3•7
Math Journal 1, p. 65
Students practice and maintain skills through Math Box problems.

Study Link 3•7
Math Masters, p. 88
Students practice and maintain skills through Study Link activities.

3 Differentiation Options

READINESS

Measuring to the Nearest $\frac{1}{2}$ Inch
Math Masters, p. 89
ruler
Students measure line segments to the nearest $\frac{1}{2}$ inch.

ENRICHMENT

Comparing Map Scales
Student Reference Book, pp. 282–293
Math Masters, p. 90
ruler ◆ globe ◆ cloth tape measure
Students investigate whether changing a map scale changes actual distances.

EXTRA PRACTICE

5-Minute Math
5-Minute Math™, pp. 54, 55, and 60
Students practice using a scale to determine actual measurements.

Advance Preparation

For Part 1, obtain as many globes as possible.

***Teacher's Reference Manual,* Grades 4–6** p. 252

Getting Started

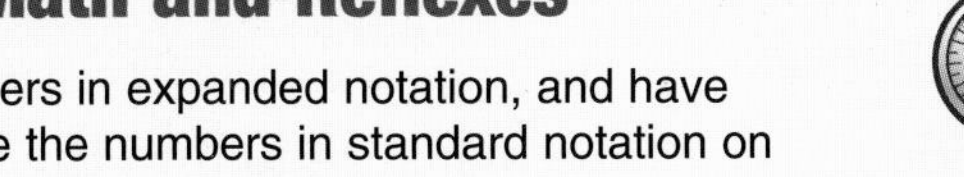

Mental Math and Reflexes

Dictate numbers in expanded notation, and have students write the numbers in standard notation on their slates.

●○○ 2,000 + 600 + 30 + 8 2,638
4,000 + 500 + 40 4,540
7,000 + 20 + 5 7,025

●●○ 80,000 + 7,000 + 400 + 30 + 2 87,432
50,000 + 2,000 + 600 + 4 52,604
60,000 + 900 + 50 60,950

●●● 4,000,000 + 800,000 + 50,000 + 3,000 + 700 + 30 + 9 4,853,739
1,000,000 + 700,000 + 2,000 + 60 + 8 1,702,068
3,000,000 + 4,000 + 10 3,004,010

Math Message

Vanessa and Marcus traveled from Chicago to Washington, D.C. Vanessa flew and Marcus drove. Who do you think traveled the greater number of miles?

Study Link 3•6 Follow-Up

Have small groups compare answers.

1 Teaching the Lesson

▶ Math Message Follow-Up

WHOLE-CLASS DISCUSSION

Most likely, a car would take a less direct route than a plane and therefore travel more miles. Some students may mention that a flight sometimes stops in a connecting city or is detoured because of bad weather, so the air route is not necessarily shorter than the driving distance.

Tell students that in this lesson they will use a map scale to calculate the flying distance between Washington, D.C., and different cities in the world.

Ongoing Assessment: Informing Instruction

As students explain their answers, watch for those who confuse the distance traveled with the time it takes to travel that distance. Encourage them to consider the unit associated with each number.

▶ Finding the Air Distances between Cities

WHOLE-CLASS ACTIVITY

Pose the following problem:

Pretend that you are flying from Chicago to Beijing, China. If you took the shortest route, about how many miles would you travel?

Ask students how to find the shortest distance on a globe. Most will probably agree on the following strategy:

▷ Find and measure the shortest route between the two cities on the globe.

▷ Using the scale of miles for the globe, calculate the actual distance between the two cities.

Because the globe is not flat, it would be difficult to measure the distance on it using a rigid ruler. Demonstrate how to take the measurement using a cloth tape measure. Be sure to show students how to begin measurements at the 0-mark. Then carry out the following steps:

1. Have a student use a tape measure to find the distance between Chicago and Beijing on the globe. Alert students to look for the shortest route between the two cities. The tape measure should pass over the top of the globe near the North Pole.
2. Record the measurement, to the nearest $\frac{1}{2}$ inch, on the board.
3. Review how to use the globe scale to find estimated distances. For example, if 1 inch on the globe represents about 660 miles, then 2 inches represent twice that distance (2 * 660 miles = 1,320 miles); $\frac{1}{2}$ inch represents half of 660, or 330 miles; and so on.

NOTE The distance around Earth at the equator is about 25,000 miles. The circumference of a globe with a 12-inch diameter is about 12 inches * 3.14, or about 37.7 inches. To find the approximate number of miles per inch, divide 25,000 miles by 37.7 inches; the answer is about 660 miles per inch.

Then have students use their calculators to compute the actual air distance from Chicago to Beijing. If the distance between the two cities is about 10 inches, and 1 inch on the globe represents about 660 miles, the actual air distance is about 6,600 miles (10 inches * 660 miles per inch = 6,600 miles).

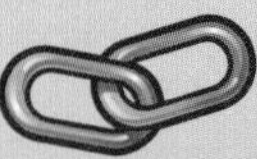

Links to the Future

Students will have additional opportunities to explore scale in Unit 8 of *Fourth Grade Everyday Mathematics.* They will use measurements and given scales to create scale drawings.

▶ Finding More Air Distances between Cities

(*Math Journal 1,* p. 64)

Ask students to guess which city listed on journal page 64 is the closest to and which is the farthest from Washington, D.C. Then have them check their guesses, using a cloth tape measure to measure the distance between Washington, D.C., and each city on the list. Students should measure to the nearest $\frac{1}{2}$ inch and then use the scale to calculate the air distance.

Adjusting the Activity

Encourage students to use a calculator to create a reference tool for use while completing journal page 64. *For example:*

1 inch → 660 miles

$1\frac{1}{2}$ inches → 990 miles

2 inches → 1,320 miles

$2\frac{1}{2}$ inches → 1,650 miles

AUDITORY ♦ KINESTHETIC ♦ TACTILE ♦ VISUAL

How best to carry out this activity depends on how many globes are available.

▷ If you have only one globe, you can have students go up to the globe in pairs to measure the air distance from Washington, D.C., to one of the other cities. The rest of the students can then calculate the actual air distance and record it in their journals. Or, assign a city to each partnership and have each pair come up to the globe while the rest of the class plays *Polygon Pair-Up* in Part 2 of the lesson. When everyone has had a turn, have the class share results.

▷ If you have several globes, divide the class into small groups and assign each group to a globe. Each group then finds the air distances for all the cities. Ask students to compare results.

Ongoing Assessment: Recognizing Student Achievement

Journal page 64 Problem 4

Use **journal page 64, Problem 4** to assess students' ability to use a map scale to estimate distances. Students are making adequate progress if their explanations include the actual measurement on the globe and how they used the map scale to convert it to an estimated air distance. Some students may be able to explain how they solved problems involving measurements on the globe that include $\frac{1}{2}$ inches.

[Operations and Computation Goal 7]

NOTE If you are using the Route Log, have students record the air distance from Washington, D.C., to Cairo, and calculate the distance they have traveled so far.

Student Page

Date Time

LESSON 3•7 **Measuring Air Distances**

1. Estimate which city listed below is the closest to Washington, D.C. Mexico City
2. Estimate which city is the farthest. Sydney
3. Measure the shortest distance between Washington, D.C., and each of the cities shown in the table below. Use the globe scale to convert these measurements to approximate air distances.
   a. Record the globe scale. 1 inch → 660 miles
   b. Complete the table.

Distance from Washington, D.C., to	Measurement on Globe (to the nearest $\frac{1}{2}$ inch)	Air Distance (estimated number of miles)
Cairo, Egypt	9	5,940
Mexico City, Mexico	3	1,980
Stockholm, Sweden	$6\frac{1}{2}$	4,290
Moscow, Russia	$7\frac{1}{2}$	4,950
Tokyo, Japan	$10\frac{1}{2}$	6,930
Shanghai, China	$11\frac{1}{2}$	7,590
Sydney, Australia	$15\frac{1}{2}$	10,230
Warsaw, Poland	7	4,620
Cape Town, South Africa	12	7,920
Rio de Janeiro, Brazil	7	4,620
Choose a city. ______	Answers vary.	Answers vary.

4. Explain how you used the globe scale to estimate the air distance between Washington, D.C., and Mexico City, Mexico.

★ Sample answer: I measured the distance from Washington, D.C., to Mexico City in inches. Then I multiplied that distance by 660, because 1 in. represents 660 miles. $3 * 660 = 1,980$

Math Journal 1, p. 64

Student Page

Games

Polygon Pair-Up

Materials
- 1 *Polygon Pair-Up* Polygon Deck (*Math Masters,* p. 496)
- 1 *Polygon Pair-Up* Property Deck (*Math Masters,* p. 497)
- paper and pencils for sketching

Players 2, or two teams of 2

Skill Properties of polygons

Object of the game To collect more cards by matching polygons with their properties.

Directions

1. Shuffle the deck of Polygon cards. Then shuffle the deck of Property cards. Place the decks side by side and facedown.
2. Players take turns. When it is your turn:
   - Turn over one Polygon card and one Property card. Place these cards faceup and below the card decks.
   - If you are able to match a Polygon card with a Property card, say "Match!" and take those two cards. Your turn is over. (You may make only one match and take two cards per turn.)
   - If you are not able to match a Polygon card with a Property card, say "Done!" Your turn is over. All the cards that were faceup remain faceup for the next player's turn.
3. When you are ready to begin your turn, you may notice a Polygon card and Property card that match. If you say "Steal!" you make take those matching cards. Then continue with your regular turn (see Step 2).
4. You may use a WILD card to make a match during any turn.
   - To use a WILD PROPERTY card, pick any faceup Polygon card. If you name a property to match that Polygon card, you take both cards.
   - To use a WILD POLYGON card, pick any faceup Property card. If you sketch a polygon that matches that Property card, you take both cards.
5. The game is over when all the cards have been turned over and no more matches can be made. The player with the most cards wins.

WILD Polygon Card: Pick a faceup Property card and draw a polygon to match that card.

Examples of Polygon Cards

There is only 1 pair of parallel sides. | There are only 4 sides. | Pairs of sides next to each other have the same length. There are no parallel sides. | WILD Property Card: Pick a faceup Polygon card and name a property to match that card.

Examples of Property Cards

There are only three vertices.

a Polygon card and a Property card that match

Student Reference Book, p. 258

2 Ongoing Learning & Practice

▶ Playing *Polygon Pair-Up*

(*Student Reference Book,* p. 258; *Math Masters,* pp. 496 and 497)

Students practice identifying properties of polygons by playing *Polygon Pair-Up*. See Lesson 1-6 for additional information.

▶ Math Boxes 3•7

(*Math Journal 1,* p. 65)

Mixed Practice Math Boxes in this lesson are paired with Math Boxes in Lesson 3-9. The skills in Problems 5 and 6 preview Unit 4 content.

Writing/Reasoning Have students write a response to the following: *Is the polygon in Problem 4 a regular polygon? Explain why or why not.* Sample answer: No. The kite does not have four equal sides and angles, so it is not a regular polygon.

▶ Study Link 3•7

(*Math Masters,* p. 88)

Home Connection Students use a map of South Africa and a map scale to determine distances.

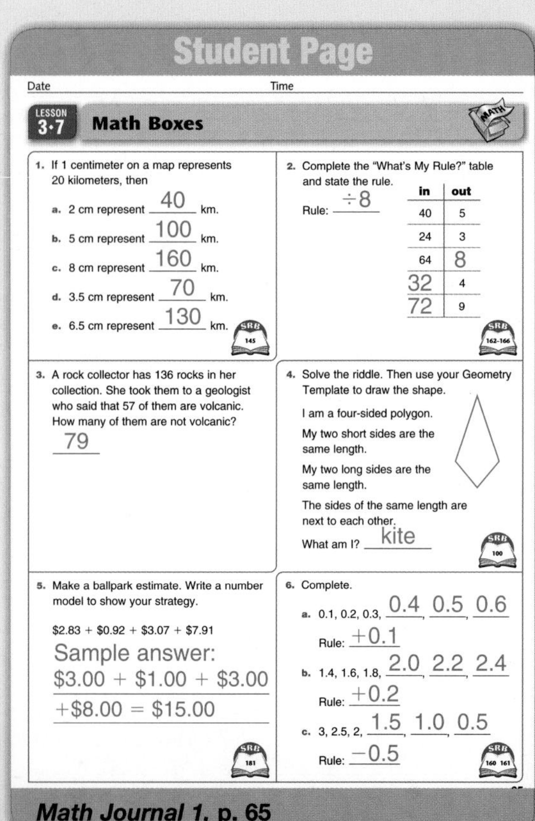

Student Page

Date Time

LESSON 3•7 **Math Boxes**

1. If 1 centimeter on a map represents 20 kilometers, then
   a. 2 cm represent 40 km.
   b. 5 cm represent 100 km.
   c. 8 cm represent 160 km.
   d. 3.5 cm represent 70 km.
   e. 6.5 cm represent 130 km.

2. Complete the "What's My Rule?" table and state the rule.

Rule: ÷8

in	out
40	5
24	3
64	8
32	4
72	9

3. A rock collector has 136 rocks in her collection. She took them to a geologist who said that 57 of them are volcanic. How many of them are not volcanic? 79

4. Solve the riddle. Then use your Geometry Template to draw the shape.
   I am a four-sided polygon.
   My two short sides are the same length.
   My two long sides are the same length.
   The sides of the same length are next to each other.
   What am I? kite

5. Make a ballpark estimate. Write a number model to show your strategy.
   $2.83 + $0.92 + $3.07 + $7.91
   Sample answer: $3.00 + $1.00 + $3.00 + $8.00 = $15.00

6. Complete.
   a. 0.1, 0.2, 0.3, 0.4, 0.5, 0.6 Rule: +0.1
   b. 1.4, 1.6, 1.8, 2.0, 2.2, 2.4 Rule: +0.2
   c. 3, 2.5, 2, 1.5, 1.0, 0.5 Rule: −0.5

Math Journal 1, p. 65

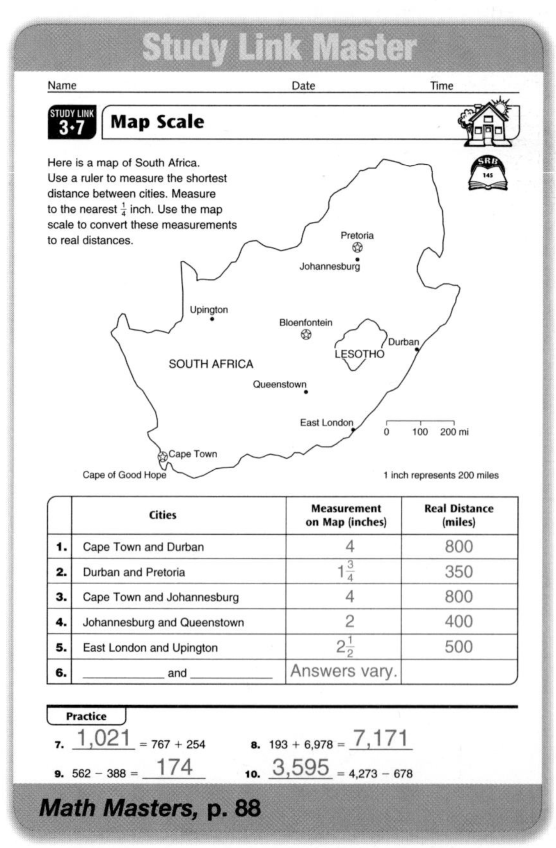

Study Link Master

Name Date Time

STUDY LINK 3•7 **Map Scale**

Here is a map of South Africa. Use a ruler to measure the shortest distance between cities. Measure to the nearest $\frac{1}{4}$ inch. Use the map scale to convert these measurements to real distances.

	Cities	Measurement on Map (inches)	Real Distance (miles)
1.	Cape Town and Durban	4	800
2.	Durban and Pretoria	$1\frac{3}{4}$	350
3.	Cape Town and Johannesburg	4	800
4.	Johannesburg and Queenstown	2	400
5.	East London and Upington	$2\frac{1}{2}$	500
6.	_____ and _____	Answers vary.	

Practice

7. 1,021 = 767 + 254
8. 193 + 6,978 = 7,171
9. 562 − 388 = 174
10. 3,595 = 4,273 − 678

Math Masters, p. 88

3 Differentiation Options

READINESS

INDEPENDENT ACTIVITY

5–15 Min

Measuring to the Nearest $\frac{1}{2}$ Inch

(*Math Masters,* p. 89)

To provide experience with measuring to the nearest $\frac{1}{2}$ inch, have students measure line segments using a ruler marked at $\frac{1}{4}$ inches. Make sure students are lining up one end of the line segment with the 0-mark on the ruler.

ENRICHMENT

PARTNER ACTIVITY

15–30 Min

Comparing Map Scales

(*Student Reference Book,* pp. 282–293; *Math Masters,* p. 90)

To apply students' understanding of map scale, have them use and compare map scales in the *Student Reference Book* to determine whether changing the scale on a map affects the actual distance represented by the map.

EXTRA PRACTICE

SMALL-GROUP ACTIVITY

5–15 Min

5-Minute Math

To offer students more experience with scale, see *5-Minute Math,* pages 54, 55, and 60.

Teaching Master

Name Date Time

LESSON 3·7 **Measure Line Segments**

Sometimes you do not need an exact measurement. Measuring to the nearest $\frac{1}{2}$ inch might be good enough.

Cut out the ruler at the bottom of the page. Use it to measure the line segments to the nearest $\frac{1}{2}$ inch. Record your measurements.

1. ______

Think: Is the measure of the line segment closer to 4 inches or $4\frac{1}{2}$ inches?

About $4\frac{1}{2}$ in.

2. ______

Think: Is the measure of the line segment closer to 2 inches or $2\frac{1}{2}$ inches?

About 2 in.

3. ______

Think: Is the measure of the line segment closer to $3\frac{1}{2}$ inches or 4 inches?

About 4 in.

4. Allison and Marta measured the line segment below to the nearest $\frac{1}{2}$ inch. Allison said, "The line segment measures about $5\frac{1}{2}$ inches." Marta said, "I think it measures about 6 inches." Who do you agree with? Explain your answer.

Sample answer: Both are correct. It is right between $5\frac{1}{2}$ and 6 inches. Depending on the situation, it might make more sense to round up or down.

5. On the back of this page, draw several line segments. Use your ruler to measure them to the nearest $\frac{1}{2}$ inch. Record your measurements. Answers vary.

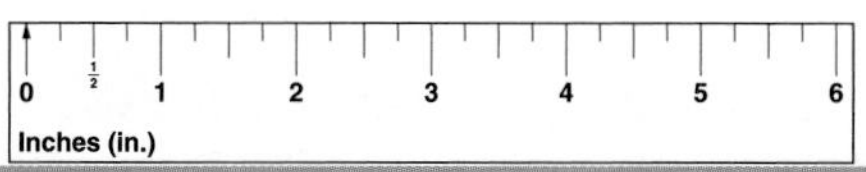

Math Masters, p. 89

Teaching Master

Name Date Time

LESSON 3·7 **Compare Map Scales**

Different maps use different scales. On one map, 1 inch might represent 10 actual miles, but on another map, 1 inch might represent 100 miles.

1. Record the globe scale you used in Lesson 3-7. 1 inch → 660 miles

2. Locate the maps on pages *282–293* in your *Student Reference Book.* Record the map scale for each region.
   a. Region 1: Africa 1 in. → 550 miles
   b. Region 2: Europe 1 in. → 300 miles
   c. Region 3: South America 1 in. → 400 miles
   d. Region 4: Asia 1 in. → 750 miles

3. Do you think changing a map scale changes actual distances? Explain your answer.
   Sample answer: No. Map scales show how the distance on the map and the actual distance are related. Changing the scale changes the size of the map.

4. Complete the table below to justify your answer to Problem 3. Measure to the nearest $\frac{1}{2}$ inch.

Distance Between	Measurement on Globe (inches)	Air Distance (miles)	Measurement on Region 3 Map (inches)	Air Distance (miles)
Bogotá, Colombia, and Brasilia, Brazil	$3\frac{1}{2}$	2,310	$5\frac{1}{2}$	2,200
Quito, Ecuador, and Sucre, Bolivia	$2\frac{1}{2}$	1,650	4	1,600

Try This

5. A **cartographer** is a person who makes maps. Sample answers:
   a. Give an example of a map scale that would show very little detail. 1 cm → 1,000 miles
   b. Explain your answer.
   As the actual distance gets larger compared with the distance on the map, the room for details gets smaller.

Math Masters, p. 90

3•8 A Guide for Solving Number Stories

Objectives To introduce a simplified approach to solving number stories; and to provide practice solving number stories.

Technology Resources www.everydaymathonline.com

ePresentations

eToolkit

Algorithms Practice

EM Facts Workshop Game™

Family Letters

Assessment Management

Common Core State Standards

Curriculum Focal Points

Interactive Teacher's Lesson Guide

1 Teaching the Lesson

Key Concepts and Skills

- Solve addition and subtraction number stories.
  [Operations and Computation Goal 2]
- Explain strategies for solving addition and subtraction number stories.
  [Operations and Computation Goal 2]
- Use a table of air distance data.
  [Data and Chance Goal 2]
- Write number models to represent addition and subtraction number stories.
  [Patterns, Functions, and Algebra Goal 2]

Key Activities

Students learn and apply a four-step approach that can be used to solve number stories. They focus on addition and subtraction number stories.

Ongoing Assessment: Recognizing Student Achievement Use a Math Log or Exit Slip (*Math Masters,* page 388 or 389).
[Operations and Computation Goal 2]

Materials

Math Journal 1, pp. 66 and 67
Student Reference Book, p. 175
Study Link 3•7
Math Masters, p. 388 or 389 (optional); pp. 422 and 423 (optional)
transparency of *Math Masters,* p. 422 (optional)

2 Ongoing Learning & Practice

Playing *High-Number Toss*
Student Reference Book, p. 252
Math Masters, p. 487
per partnership: 1 six-sided die
Students practice place-value skills and compare numbers.

Math Boxes 3•8
Math Journal 1, p. 68
Students practice and maintain skills through Math Box problems.

Study Link 3•8
Math Masters, p. 91
Students practice and maintain skills through Study Link activities.

3 Differentiation Options

READINESS

Reviewing Situation Diagrams
Student Reference Book, p. 178
Math Masters, p. 92
Students explore situation diagrams as visual organizers for solving number stories.

ENRICHMENT

Writing Number Stories
Math Masters, p. 93
Students solve a number story and write an additional one.

ELL SUPPORT

Building Vocabulary
chart paper
Students generate a list of words commonly used in number stories that may indicate an operation.

Advance Preparation

For Part 1, read page 175 of the *Student Reference Book* before class. You can enlarge *Math Masters,* page 422 to use as a poster of "A Guide for Solving Number Stories."

***Teacher's Reference Manual,* Grades 4–6** pp. 19, 104–107, 298–309

Getting Started

Mental Math and Reflexes

Pose number stories. *Suggestions:*

●○○ Anthony has saved $7 toward a ticket to a theme park. Tickets are $12. How much more does he need? $5

Michael, Meredith, and 3 of their friends are going to the aquarium. Tickets cost $2 each. What is the total cost? $10

●●○ Ben and Wilson built a model airplane. Wilson spent $3.50 for supplies, and Ben spent $6.50. How much did all the supplies cost? $10

Alyssa runs 3 miles every day. About how many miles does she run in a month? About 90 miles

●●● Nander's farm has three silos. One silo holds 28 bushels of corn, another holds 34 bushels, and the third holds 36 bushels. How many bushels of corn can Nander store on his farm? 98 bushels

Hannah has $400. She spent $175 on groceries and $50 on clothes. How much money does she have left? $175

Math Message

J.T. traveled from Colorado to Maine. He traveled 586 miles on Monday, 487 miles on Tuesday, 630 miles on Wednesday, and 373 miles on Thursday. How many total miles did he travel? 2,076 miles

Study Link 3·7 Follow-Up

Partners compare answers. Note that an incorrect real distance may be due to an initial measurement error rather than an error in the conversion.

1 Teaching the Lesson

Math Message Follow-Up

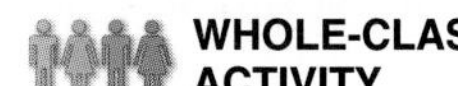

WHOLE-CLASS ACTIVITY

(*Student Reference Book,* p. 175; *Math Masters,* p. 422)

Briefly discuss "A Guide for Solving Number Stories" on *Student Reference Book,* page 175. You may want to show a transparency or a poster of *Math Masters,* page 422.

Use the problem in the Math Message to illustrate the steps.

1. **Understand the problem.**
   - ▷ Ask students to explain what J.T. is doing. Taking a trip
   - ▷ Ask what the question in the problem is. How far did he travel?
   - ▷ Ask what details are given about J.T.'s trip. Amounts he traveled each day: 586, 487, 630, and 373
2. **Plan what to do.**
   - ▷ Ask for suggestions on how to solve the problem. Make a table, draw a picture, make a list, make a diagram, and so on.
   - ▷ Ask for an estimate of the answer.
3. **Carry out the plan.**
   - ▷ Tell students to use an approach that makes sense to them to solve the problem. Give them a few minutes to work.

Student Page

Problem Solving

A Guide for Solving Number Stories

Learning to solve problems is the main reason for studying mathematics. One way you learn to solve problems is by solving number stories. A **number story** is a story with a problem that can be solved with arithmetic.

1. Understand the problem.
- ♦ Read the problem. Can you retell it in your own words?
- ♦ What do you want to find out?
- ♦ What do you know?
- ♦ Do you have all the information needed to solve the problem?

2. Plan what to do.
- ♦ Is the problem like one that you solved before?
- ♦ Is there a pattern you can use?
- ♦ Can you draw a picture or a diagram?
- ♦ Can you write a number model or make a table?
- ♦ Can you use counters, base-10 blocks, or some other tool?
- ♦ Can you estimate the answer and check if you are right?

3. Carry out the plan.
- ♦ After you decide what to do, do it. Be careful.
- ♦ Make a written record of what you do.
- ♦ Answer the question.

4. Look back.
- ♦ Does your answer make sense?
- ♦ Does your answer agree with your estimate?
- ♦ Can you write a number model for the problem?
- ♦ Can you solve the problem in another way?

A Guide for Number Stories
1. Understand the problem.
2. Plan what to do.
3. Carry out the plan.
4. Look back.

Note
Understanding the problem is a very important step. Good problem solvers take time to make sure they really understand the problem.

Note
Sometimes it's easy to know what to do. Other times you need to be creative.

Check Your Understanding

Use the *Guide for Solving Number Stories* to help you solve the following problems. Explain your thinking at each step. Also explain your answer(s).

1. Mr. Cline walked 2 miles per day for 2 days in a row, 3 miles per day for the next 3 days, and so on, until he walked 6 miles per day. On which day did he first walk 6 miles?
2. Lisa cut a rectangle with a perimeter of 24 inches into two squares. What were the length and width of the original rectangle?

Check your answers on page 346.

Student Reference Book, p. 175

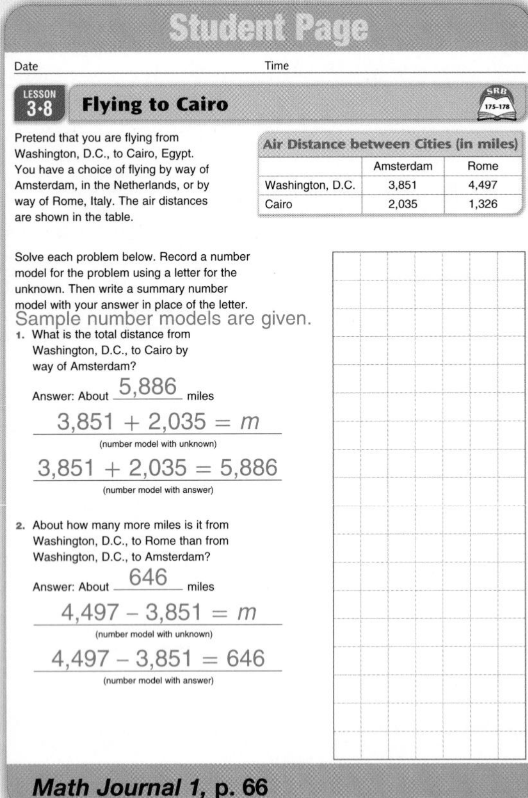

Student Page

Date Time

LESSON 3·8 **Flying to Cairo**

Pretend that you are flying from Washington, D.C., to Cairo, Egypt. You have a choice of flying by way of Amsterdam, in the Netherlands, or by way of Rome, Italy. The air distances are shown in the table.

Air Distance between Cities (in miles)

	Amsterdam	Rome
Washington, D.C.	3,851	4,497
Cairo	2,035	1,326

Solve each problem below. Record a number model for the problem using a letter for the unknown. Then write a summary number model with your answer in place of the letter.
Sample number models are given.

1. What is the total distance from Washington, D.C., to Cairo by way of Amsterdam?

   Answer: About 5,886 miles

   $3,851 + 2,035 = m$
   (number model with unknown)

   $3,851 + 2,035 = 5,886$
   (number model with answer)

2. About how many more miles is it from Washington, D.C., to Rome than from Washington, D.C., to Amsterdam?

   Answer: About 646 miles

   $4,497 - 3,851 = m$
   (number model with unknown)

   $4,497 - 3,851 = 646$
   (number model with answer)

Math Journal 1, p. 66

Student Page

Date Time

LESSON 3·8 **Flying to Cairo** *continued*

3. What is the total distance from Washington, D.C., to Cairo by way of Rome?

   Answer: About 5,823 miles

   $4,497 + 1,326 = m$
   (number model with unknown)

   $4,497 + 1,326 = 5,823$
   (number model with answer)

4. About how many fewer miles will you fly if you go by way of Rome rather than Amsterdam?

   Answer: About 63 miles

   $5,886 - 5,823 = m$
   (number model with unknown)

   $5,886 - 5,823 = 63$
   (number model with answer)

Try This

5. If you fly first class, your ticket will cost $9,250. If you fly economy class, you will save $6,500. You bought 2 first class tickets and 4 economy tickets. What is the total cost?

   Answer: $29,500

   $9,250 – $6,500 = $2,750;
   $9,250 ∗ 2 + $2,750 ∗ 4 = *t*
   (number model(s) with unknown)

   $9,250 – $6,500 = $2,750;
   $9,250 ∗ 2 + $2,750 ∗ 4 = $29,500
   (number model(s) with answer)

Math Journal 1, p. 67

4. **Look back.**

   ▷ Ask students if their answers agree with their estimates.

   ▷ Compare different approaches, being sure to emphasize that the answers obtained from using different approaches should agree. J.T. traveled 2,076 miles.

   ▷ Ask students if their answers make sense. Ask how they can tell. Sample answer: Yes. The total number of miles traveled is more than any one day.

   ▷ Ask students how to write a number model for the problem that uses a letter for the unknown information. This will symbolically represent the number story. Sample answer: $586 + 487 + 630 + 373 = m$

   ▷ Ask students if their answers make the number model true.

Write a summary number model on the board with the answer, 2,076, in place of m: $586 + 487 + 630 + 373 = 2,076$.

Pose another problem to the class: *Amelia's goal is to run 30 miles every week. So far this week, she has gone for a 6-mile run, a 4-mile run, a 7-mile run, and a 5-mile run. How much more does she need to run to meet her goal?*

Have students solve the problem in small groups. Ask:

- What is the answer? 8 miles Have students share their solution strategies.
- Does the answer make sense? yes How can you tell? Sample answer: I can estimate that she has run more than 20 miles, so the answer should be less than 10.

Have volunteers suggest number models for the number story that use a letter for the unknown.
Sample answer: $6 + 4 + 7 + 5 + m = 30$

NOTE Some students may suggest $30 - 6 + 4 + 7 + 5 = m$. Although students will not work with parentheses until Lesson 3-10, acknowledge this number model with the unknown and write it with parentheses: $30 - (6 + 4 + 7 + 5) = m$. Explain that the numbers inside the parentheses are added first, then the sum is subtracted from 30 to find the missing part. Other students may suggest two separate number models: $6 + 4 + 7 + 5 = 22$, then $22 + m = 30$. This is acceptable.

Ask students if their answers make the number model true.

Write a summary number model on the board with the answer, 8, in place of m: $6 + 4 + 7 + 5 + 8 = 30$.

Solving Number Stories about Air Distances

PARTNER ACTIVITY

(*Math Journal 1,* pp. 66 and 67; *Math Masters,* p. 423)

Encourage students to refer to "A Guide for Solving Number Stories" as they work on journal pages 66 and 67. When most students have finished, discuss their strategies.

Ongoing Assessment: Recognizing Student Achievement

Math Log or Exit Slip

Use a **Math Log** or an **Exit Slip** (*Math Masters,* page 388 or 389) to assess students' ability to use and explain a strategy for solving an addition number story. Have students explain how they used the table of air distances to solve Problem 3 on journal page 67. Students are making adequate progress if their explanations involve adding the distance between Washington, D.C., and Rome to the distance between Rome and Cairo. Some students may demonstrate how subtraction can be used to check their answers.

[Operations and Computation Goal 2]

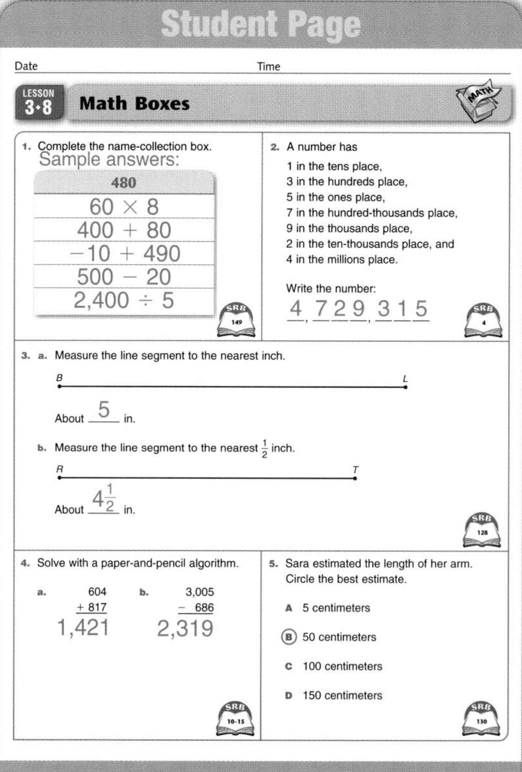

Student Page

Date Time

LESSON 3•8 **Math Boxes**

1. Complete the name-collection box.
Sample answers:

480
60 × 8
400 + 80
−10 + 490
500 − 20
2,400 ÷ 5

SRB 149

2. A number has
1 in the tens place,
3 in the hundreds place,
5 in the ones place,
7 in the hundred-thousands place,
9 in the thousands place,
2 in the ten-thousands place, and
4 in the millions place.

Write the number: 4,729,315

SRB 4

3. a. Measure the line segment to the nearest inch.

B ———— L

About 5 in.

b. Measure the line segment to the nearest $\frac{1}{2}$ inch.

R ———— T

About $4\frac{1}{2}$ in.

SRB 128

4. Solve with a paper-and-pencil algorithm.

a. 604 + 817 = 1,421

b. 3,005 − 686 = 2,319

SRB 10-15

5. Sara estimated the length of her arm. Circle the best estimate.

A 5 centimeters

(B) 50 centimeters

C 100 centimeters

D 150 centimeters

SRB 130

Math Journal 1, p. 68

2 Ongoing Learning & Practice

Playing *High-Number Toss*

PARTNER ACTIVITY

(*Student Reference Book,* p. 252; *Math Masters,* p. 487)

Students play *High-Number Toss* to practice place-value skills and comparing large numbers. See Lesson 2-7 for additional information.

Adjusting the Activity

Have situation diagrams (*Math Masters,* page 423) available for student use.

AUDITORY ◆ KINESTHETIC ◆ TACTILE ◆ VISUAL

Math Boxes 3•8

INDEPENDENT ACTIVITY

(*Math Journal 1,* p. 68)

Mixed Practice Math Boxes in this lesson are paired with Math Boxes in Lesson 3-6. The skill in Problem 5 previews Unit 4 content.

Writing/Reasoning Have students write a response to the following: *Explain why you chose the measurement for Problem 5.* Sample answer: Five centimeters is about the length of my little finger. 100 centimeters is as long as a meterstick. So I picked 50 centimeters because my arm is close to half a meterstick in length.

Study Link 3•8

INDEPENDENT ACTIVITY

(*Math Masters,* p. 91)

Home Connection Students solve addition and subtraction number stories. Students write a number model with an unknown and a summary number model.

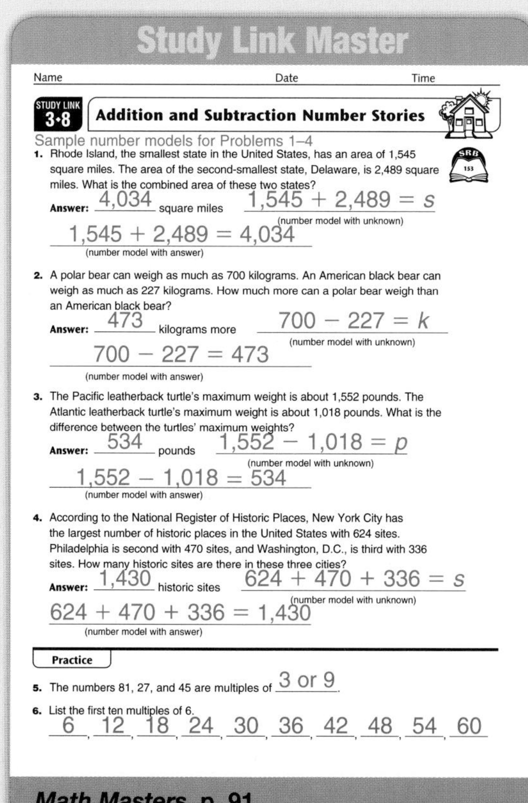

Study Link Master

Name Date Time

STUDY LINK 3•8 **Addition and Subtraction Number Stories**

Sample number models for Problems 1–4

1. Rhode Island, the smallest state in the United States, has an area of 1,545 square miles. The area of the second-smallest state, Delaware, is 2,489 square miles. What is the combined area of these two states? SRB 133

Answer: 4,034 square miles 1,545 + 2,489 = *s* (number model with unknown)

1,545 + 2,489 = 4,034 (number model with answer)

2. A polar bear can weigh as much as 700 kilograms. An American black bear can weigh as much as 227 kilograms. How much more can a polar bear weigh than an American black bear?

Answer: 473 kilograms more 700 − 227 = *k* (number model with unknown)

700 − 227 = 473 (number model with answer)

3. The Pacific leatherback turtle's maximum weight is about 1,552 pounds. The Atlantic leatherback turtle's maximum weight is about 1,018 pounds. What is the difference between the turtles' maximum weights?

Answer: 534 pounds 1,552 − 1,018 = *p* (number model with unknown)

1,552 − 1,018 = 534 (number model with answer)

4. According to the National Register of Historic Places, New York City has the largest number of historic places in the United States with 624 sites. Philadelphia is second with 470 sites, and Washington, D.C., is third with 336 sites. How many historic sites are there in these three cities?

Answer: 1,430 historic sites 624 + 470 + 336 = *s* (number model with unknown)

624 + 470 + 336 = 1,430 (number model with answer)

Practice

5. The numbers 81, 27, and 45 are multiples of 3 or 9

6. List the first ten multiples of 6.
6, 12, 18, 24, 30, 36, 42, 48, 54, 60

Math Masters, p. 91

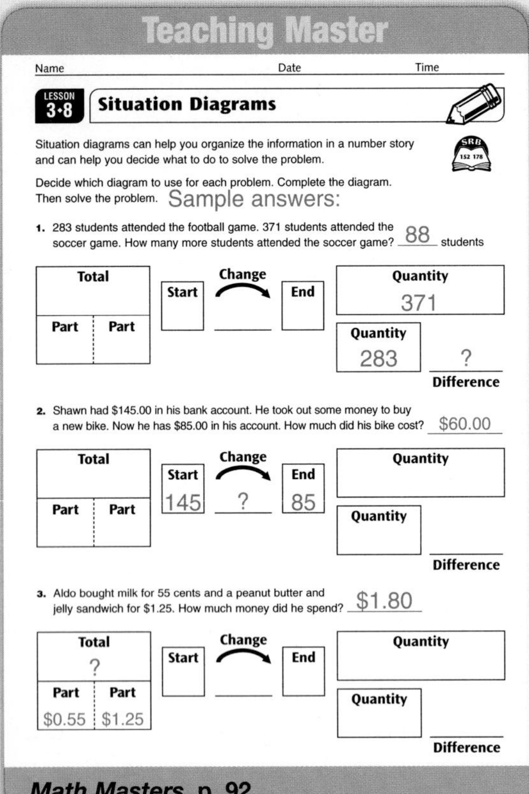

Teaching Master

Name Date Time

LESSON 3·8 **Situation Diagrams**

Situation diagrams can help you organize the information in a number story and can help you decide what to do to solve the problem.

SRB 152 178

Decide which diagram to use for each problem. Complete the diagram. Then solve the problem. Sample answers:

1. 283 students attended the football game. 371 students attended the soccer game. How many more students attended the soccer game? 88 students

Total / Part / Part; Start / Change / End; Quantity 371 / Quantity 283 / ? Difference

2. Shawn had $145.00 in his bank account. He took out some money to buy a new bike. Now he has $85.00 in his account. How much did his bike cost? $60.00

Total / Part / Part; Start 145 / Change ? / End 85; Quantity / Quantity / Difference

3. Aldo bought milk for 55 cents and a peanut butter and jelly sandwich for $1.25. How much money did he spend? $1.80

Total ? / Part $0.55 / Part $1.25; Start / Change / End; Quantity / Quantity / Difference

Math Masters, p. 92

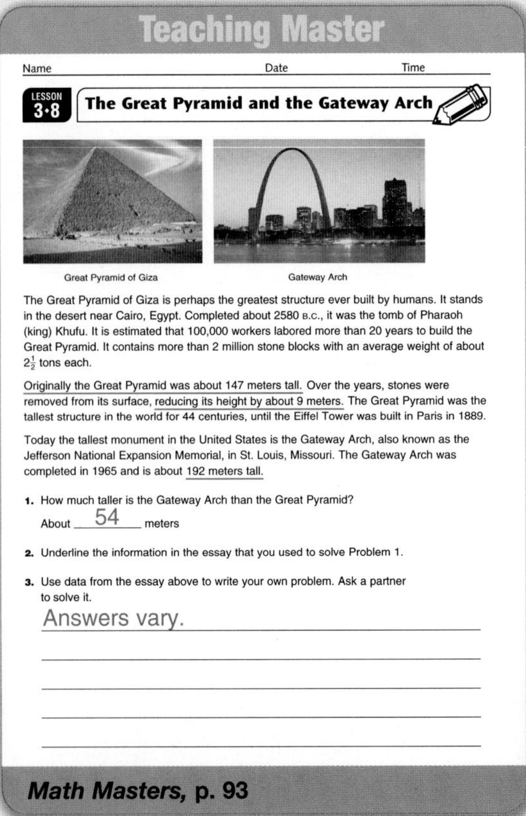

Teaching Master

Name Date Time

LESSON 3·8 **The Great Pyramid and the Gateway Arch**

Great Pyramid of Giza

Gateway Arch

The Great Pyramid of Giza is perhaps the greatest structure ever built by humans. It stands in the desert near Cairo, Egypt. Completed about 2580 B.C., it was the tomb of Pharaoh (king) Khufu. It is estimated that 100,000 workers labored more than 20 years to build the Great Pyramid. It contains more than 2 million stone blocks with an average weight of about $2\frac{1}{2}$ tons each.

Originally the Great Pyramid was about 147 meters tall. Over the years, stones were removed from its surface, reducing its height by about 9 meters. The Great Pyramid was the tallest structure in the world for 44 centuries, until the Eiffel Tower was built in Paris in 1889.

Today the tallest monument in the United States is the Gateway Arch, also known as the Jefferson National Expansion Memorial, in St. Louis, Missouri. The Gateway Arch was completed in 1965 and is about 192 meters tall.

1. How much taller is the Gateway Arch than the Great Pyramid? About 54 meters
2. Underline the information in the essay that you used to solve Problem 1.
3. Use data from the essay above to write your own problem. Ask a partner to solve it. Answers vary.

Math Masters, p. 93

3 Differentiation Options

READINESS

INDEPENDENT ACTIVITY

5–15 Min

▶ Reviewing Situation Diagrams

(*Student Reference Book,* p. 178; *Math Masters,* p. 92)

To explore solving number stories using a visual organizer, have students use situation diagrams to model number stories. Some students will like the diagrams and use them often. Other students will approach problems in other ways. Encourage students to use a question mark to represent the missing information.

ENRICHMENT

INDEPENDENT ACTIVITY

15–30 Min

ELL

▶ Writing Number Stories

(*Math Masters,* p. 93)

Social Studies Link To apply students' understanding of solving number stories, have them read a short essay and solve and write a number story based on data in the essay. Remind students that often more information is provided than is necessary to solve a problem.

To support English language learners, provide an opportunity for students to share and revise their writing. *For example:*

- ▷ Read problems aloud or have students read their own problems aloud.
- ▷ Have students read and comment on each other's drafts.

ELL SUPPORT

SMALL-GROUP ACTIVITY

5–15 Min

▶ Building Vocabulary

To provide language support for number stories, have students make and display a poster like the one shown below. With the students, generate words and phrases that may help determine which operation to use when solving a number story.

Operations

+ Addition	− Subtraction	* Multiplication	÷ Division
• altogether • added • got • total • in all • sum	• left • more or less • difference • lost • shorter or longer	• some number of equal groups • each has • times • by (with dimensions)	• share • How many in each group? • How many groups? • divide

3•9 True or False Number Sentences

Objectives To review the meanings of number sentences; and to provide practice determining whether number sentences are true or false.

Technology Resources www.everydaymathonline.com

ePresentations

eToolkit

Algorithms Practice

EM Facts Workshop Game™

Family Letters

Assessment Management

Common Core State Standards

Curriculum Focal Points

Interactive Teacher's Lesson Guide

1 Teaching the Lesson

Key Concepts and Skills

- Compare whole numbers.
  [Number and Numeration Goal 6]
- Add, subtract, multiply, and divide to solve expressions.
  [Operations and Computation Goals 1–4]
- Use conventional notation to write number sentences.
  [Patterns, Functions, and Algebra Goal 2]
- Determine whether a number sentence is true or false.
  [Patterns, Functions, and Algebra Goal 2]

Key Activities

Students review the meanings of number sentences and determine, whenever possible, whether number sentences are true or false.

Ongoing Assessment: Informing Instruction See page 205.

Ongoing Assessment: Recognizing Student Achievement Use journal page 69.
[Patterns, Functions, and Algebra Goal 2]

Key Vocabulary

number sentence ◆ true number sentence ◆ false number sentence

Materials

Math Journal 1, p. 69
Study Link 3•8
calculator (optional) ◆ slate

2 Ongoing Learning & Practice

Math Boxes 3•9
Math Journal 1, p. 70
Students practice and maintain skills through Math Box problems.

Study Link 3•9
Math Masters, p. 94
Students practice and maintain skills through Study Link activities.

3 Differentiation Options

READINESS

Reviewing > and < Symbols
Math Masters, p. 95
Students practice using relation symbols.

ENRICHMENT

Solving a Puzzle
Math Masters, p. 96
scissors ◆ tape
Students apply their understanding of a true number sentence to solve a number-sentence puzzle.

ELL SUPPORT

Building a Math Word Bank
Differentiation Handbook, p. 141
Students add the terms *number sentence, true,* and *false* to their Math Word Banks.

Advance Preparation

***Teacher's Reference Manual,* Grades 4–6** pp. 98–103

Getting Started

Mental Math and Reflexes

Dictate numbers in expanded notation, and have students write the numbers in standard notation on their slates.

●○○ 1,736 1,000 + 700 + 30 + 6
9,891 9,000 + 800 + 90 + 1
6,023 6,000 + 20 + 3

●●○ 29,456 20,000 + 9,000 + 400 + 50 + 6
58,203 50,000 + 8,000 + 200 + 3
33,700 30,000 + 3,000 + 700

●●● 410,619 400,000 + 10,000 + 600 + 10 + 9
762,040 700,000 + 60,000 + 2,000 + 40
8,760,900 8,000,000 + 700,000 + 60,000 + 900

Math Message

Write a sentence that is true. Write a sentence that is false.

Study Link 3·8 Follow-Up

Students compare answers and number models.

1 Teaching the Lesson

▶ Math Message Follow-Up

WHOLE-CLASS DISCUSSION

Have a student read a sentence without saying whether it is true or false. Ask the class to indicate thumbs-up if the sentence is true. Repeat the procedure for other sentences. Some of these sentences may be opinions that are neither true nor false, so you may need to discuss fact versus opinion.

Tell students that in this lesson the class will discuss number sentences. Number sentences, like word sentences, can also be true or false.

▶ Exploring the Meaning of *Number Sentence*

WHOLE-CLASS DISCUSSION

Write the following sentence on the board:

The sum of five and eight is equal to thirteen.

Ask whether there is another way to write this sentence. If no one suggests it, write $5 + 8 = 13$ under the sentence.

Now write $5 < 7$ on the board, and ask someone to read it. Then write the sentence in words. Five is less than seven.

Repeat with $25 - 15 > 3$. Twenty-five minus fifteen is greater than three.

Point out that number models or **number sentences,** such as $5 + 8 = 13$, $5 < 7$, and $25 - 15 > 3$, are shorthand for sentences written in words. Words are replaced by mathematical symbols: numerals consisting of the digits 0 through 9; operation symbols such as +, –, ∗ (or ×), and / (or ÷); and other symbols such as the relation symbols =, >, and <. Mathematical symbols are easier to write and can be easier to understand than words.

ELL

Ongoing Assessment: Informing Instruction

Watch for English language learners who have difficulty representing a word sentence as a number sentence due to how phrases or words are translated from one language to another. Some English words translate into a single word in another language. *Less* and *minus* are examples of such words. Keep in mind that English language learners may, for example, hear "1 less than 570" and write "1 – 570."

Determining Whether a Number Sentence Is True or False

WHOLE-CLASS ACTIVITY

Write the number sentence $4 * 5 = 20$ on the board, and ask whether this sentence is correct. yes Tell the class that another way to talk about the number sentence is to say that $4 * 5 = 20$ is a **true number sentence.** Write the word *true* next to $4 * 5 = 20$. Point out that multiplying the expression $4 * 5$ on the left side of the equals sign and the number 20 on the right side of the equals sign by the *same* number will result in another true number sentence. For example, $(4 * 5) * \mathbf{8} = 20 * \mathbf{8}$ is also a true number sentence. Note that this will work for *any true* number sentence involving an equal sign. Have students summarize by stating that if you multiply equals by equals you get equal quantities. Similarly, if you add equals to equals you get equal quantities. For example, $(4 * 5) + \mathbf{10} = 20 + \mathbf{10}$ is also a true number sentence.

Now write the number sentence $12 / 4 = 4$ on the board, and ask whether this sentence is correct. no $12 / 4 = 4$ is an example of a **false number sentence.** Write the word *false* next to $12 / 4 = 4$.

To reinforce this idea, lead the class in the following slate routine: Write a number sentence on the board. Have students write T on their slates if they think the sentence is true, F if they think it is false, and ? if they can't tell. Discuss their answers. Repeat with other examples (not all number sentences) such as the following:

▷ $15 + 13 = 28$ T

▷ $8 = 5 * 3$ F

▷ $42 - 12 = 20$ F

▷ $17 < 27$ T

▷ $3 = 18 / 6$ T

▷ $716 - 487 = 616 - 487$ F Ask: *Can you tell whether it is true or false before doing the subtractions?*

▷ $4{,}684 + 182 > 4{,}694 + 482$ F Ask: *Can you tell whether it is true or false before doing the additions?*

▷ $42 + \_\_\_ = 50$? (can't tell) Ask: *Why can't you tell? How would you change this to make it into a true sentence? A false sentence?*

▷ $8 * 6$? (can't tell) It is not a number sentence. Ask: *How would you change this to make it into a true number sentence? A false number sentence?*

NOTE A number sentence has three parts: the left side, the relation symbol, and the right side. In $5 > 10 + 3$, for example, the left side is 5, the relation symbol is >, and the right side is $10 + 3$. (Note that the sentence $5 > 10 + 3$ is false.) Numbers and operation symbols (+, –, ∗, /, and so on) can appear on either side of the relation symbol.

NOTE Additional information about solving inequalities can be found at www.everydaymathonline.com.

Adjusting the Activity

The focus of this activity is to determine whether a number sentence is true or false. Encourage students to use calculators as appropriate.

AUDITORY ◆ KINESTHETIC ◆ TACTILE ◆ VISUAL

Student Page

Date ______ Time ______

LESSON 3•9 Number Sentences

Tell whether each number sentence below is true or false. Write T for true or F for false. If it is not possible to tell, write ? on the answer blank.

1. 7 < 3 + 1 ____F____
2. 6 = 36 ÷ 6 ____T____
3. 80 − ? = 40 ____?____
4. 28 − 16 = 12 ____T____
5. 0 = 4 / 4 ____F____
6. 2 ∗ 7 ____?____
7. 14 × 3 < 19 × 2 ____F____
8. 144 + 76 = 880 ÷ 4 ____T____

9. Make up two true number sentences and two false number sentences. Answers vary.
   a. true ______
   b. true ______
   c. false ______
   d. false ______

10. Make up three true number sentences and three false number sentences. Mix them up. Ask your partner to write whether each sentence is true or false. Answers vary.

Example: 4 ∗ 7 = 34 − 6 ____T____

a. ______ ______
b. ______ ______
c. ______ ______
d. ______ ______
e. ______ ______
f. ______ ______

***Math Journal 1,* p. 69**

Student Page

Date ______ Time ______

LESSON 3•9 Math Boxes

1. If 1 inch on a map represents 30 miles, what would 3 inches represent? Circle the best answer.
   A 10 miles
   B 60 miles
   (C) 90 miles
   D 300 miles

2. Complete the "What's My Rule?" table and state the rule.

Rule: ÷ 9

in	out
45	5
81	9
27	3
36	4
72	8

3. The Statue of Chief Crazy Horse in South Dakota is 563 feet tall. The Statue of Liberty is 151 feet tall. What is the difference in height of the two statues?
   412 feet

4. Solve the riddle. Then use your Geometry Template to trace the shape.
   I am a polygon.
   All my angles have the same measure.
   Each of my 5 sides has the same measure.
   What am I? regular pentagon

5. Make a ballpark estimate. Write a number model to show your strategy.
   \$2.50 + \$0.75 + \$3.85 + \$12.70
   Sample answer: \$2.50 + \$1 + \$4 + \$13 = \$20.50

6. Complete.
   a. 5.05, 5.06, 5.07, 5.08, 5.09, 5.10
      Rule: +0.01
   b. 4, 3.8, 3.6, 3.4, 3.2, 3.0
      Rule: −0.2
   c. 2.7, 3.2, 3.7, 4.2, 4.7, 5.2
      Rule: +0.5

***Math Journal 1,* p. 70**

▶ Practicing with Number Sentences

PARTNER ACTIVITY

(*Math Journal 1,* p. 69)

Partners identify number sentences in Problems 1–8 as true, false, or "can't tell." Then have students work independently to complete Problems 9 and 10. When they are finished, have students ask their partners to decide which number sentences in Problem 10 are true.

Ongoing Assessment: Recognizing Student Achievement

Journal page 69 Problem 9

Use **journal page 69, Problem 9** to assess students' ability to determine whether number sentences are true or false. Students are making adequate progress if they are able to use conventional notation to write appropriate number sentences. They may write simple number sentences involving an equals symbol, one operation symbol, and 1-digit whole numbers. Some students may write more elaborate number sentences with several operations, large numbers, fractions or decimals, parentheses, and the relation symbol < or >.

[Patterns, Functions, and Algebra Goal 2]

2 Ongoing Learning & Practice

▶ Math Boxes 3•9

INDEPENDENT ACTIVITY

(*Math Journal 1,* p. 70)

Mixed Practice Math Boxes in this lesson are paired with Math Boxes in Lesson 3-7. The skills in Problems 5 and 6 preview Unit 4 content.

▶ Study Link 3•9

INDEPENDENT ACTIVITY

(*Math Masters,* p. 94)

Home Connection Students tell whether sentences are true or false. They write a question mark if it is not possible to tell. Then they write true and false number sentences and explain why a given expression is not a number sentence.

3 Differentiation Options

READINESS

SMALL-GROUP ACTIVITY

5–15 Min

Reviewing > and < Symbols

(*Math Masters,* p. 95)

To provide experience using relation symbols, have students solve comparison problems using analogies and mnemonic devices.

ENRICHMENT

INDEPENDENT ACTIVITY

5–15 Min

Solving a Puzzle

(*Math Masters,* p. 96)

To apply students' understanding of true number sentences, have them arrange digits in a puzzle grid to make three number sentences. Students may not repeat a digit in any row or column.

ELL SUPPORT

SMALL-GROUP ACTIVITY

5–15 Min

Building a Math Word Bank

(*Differentiation Handbook,* p. 141)

To provide language support for number sentences, have students use the Word Bank template found on *Differentiation Handbook,* page 141. Ask students to write the terms *number sentence, true,* and *false,* draw pictures relating to each term, and write other related words. See the *Differentiation Handbook* for more information.

Study Link Master

Name Date Time

STUDY LINK 3·9 Number Sentences

Next to each number sentence, write T if it is true, F if it is false, or ? if you can't tell.

SRB 148

1. 20 − 12 = 8 ∗ 3 F
2. 7 = 14 ∗ 2 F
3. 497 < 500 T
4. 16 / 4 = 4 T
5. 15 + 10 = 5 F
6. 24 > 11 + 11 T
7. 100 − 5 = 95 T
8. 33 − 4 ?
9. Write two true number sentences. Answers vary.
10. Write two false number sentences. Answers vary.
11. a. Explain why 7 ∗ 8 is not a number sentence.
    Sample answer: There is not a relation symbol, such as =, >, or <.
    b. How could you change 7 ∗ 8 to make a true number sentence?
    Sample answers: 7 ∗ 8 = 56; 24 < 7 ∗ 8; 9 ∗ 9 > 7 ∗ 8
    c. How could you change 7 ∗ 8 to make a false number sentence?
    Sample answers: 7 ∗ 8 = 13; 65 < 7 ∗ 8; 2^2 > 7 ∗ 8

Practice

12. 24, 36, 48, 60, 72, 84 Rule: +12
13. 54, 108, 162, 216, 270, 324 Rule: +54

Math Masters, p. 94

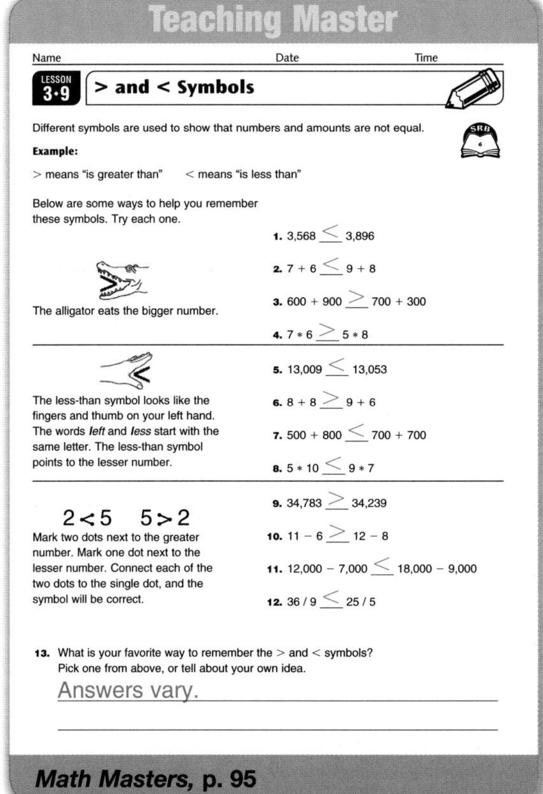

Teaching Master

Name Date Time

LESSON 3·9 > and < Symbols

Different symbols are used to show that numbers and amounts are not equal.

SRB 6

Example:

> means "is greater than" < means "is less than"

Below are some ways to help you remember these symbols. Try each one.

The alligator eats the bigger number.

1. 3,568 < 3,896
2. 7 + 6 < 9 + 8
3. 600 + 900 > 700 + 300
4. 7 ∗ 6 > 5 ∗ 8

The less-than symbol looks like the fingers and thumb on your left hand. The words *left* and *less* start with the same letter. The less-than symbol points to the lesser number.

5. 13,009 < 13,053
6. 8 + 8 > 9 + 6
7. 500 + 800 < 700 + 700
8. 5 ∗ 10 < 9 ∗ 7

2 < 5 5 > 2

Mark two dots next to the greater number. Mark one dot next to the lesser number. Connect each of the two dots to the single dot, and the symbol will be correct.

9. 34,783 > 34,239
10. 11 − 6 > 12 − 8
11. 12,000 − 7,000 < 18,000 − 9,000
12. 36 / 9 < 25 / 5
13. What is your favorite way to remember the > and < symbols? Pick one from above, or tell about your own idea.
    Answers vary.

Math Masters, p. 95

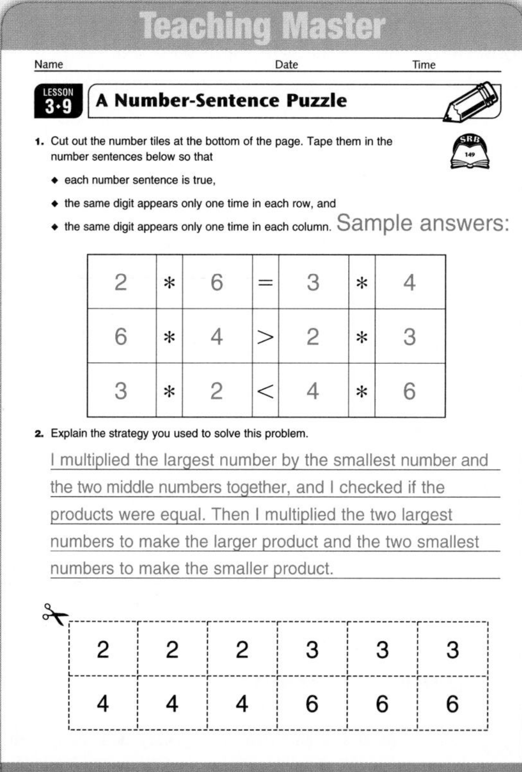

Teaching Master

Name Date Time

LESSON 3·9 A Number-Sentence Puzzle

SRB 149

1. Cut out the number tiles at the bottom of the page. Tape them in the number sentences below so that
   - each number sentence is true,
   - the same digit appears only one time in each row, and
   - the same digit appears only one time in each column. Sample answers:

2	∗	6	=	3	∗	4
6	∗	4	>	2	∗	3
3	∗	2	<	4	∗	6

2. Explain the strategy you used to solve this problem.
   I multiplied the largest number by the smallest number and the two middle numbers together, and I checked if the products were equal. Then I multiplied the two largest numbers to make the larger product and the two smallest numbers to make the smaller product.

2	2	2	3	3	3
4	4	4	6	6	6

Math Masters, p. 96

3•10 Parentheses in Number Sentences

Objective To review the use of parentheses in number sentences.

www.everydaymathonline.com

ePresentations

eToolkit

Algorithms Practice

EM Facts Workshop Game™

Family Letters

Assessment Management

Common Core State Standards

Curriculum Focal Points

Interactive Teacher's Lesson Guide

1 Teaching the Lesson

Key Concepts and Skills

- Add, subtract, multiply, and divide to solve expressions.
  [Operations and Computation Goals 1–4]
- Determine whether number sentences are true or false.
  [Patterns, Functions, and Algebra Goal 2]
- Evaluate expressions containing parentheses.
  [Patterns, Functions, and Algebra Goal 3]
- Insert parentheses to make true number sentences.
  [Patterns, Functions, and Algebra Goal 3]

Key Activities

Students review the use of parentheses in number sentences that involve more than one operation. They determine whether number sentences containing parentheses are true or false, and they insert parentheses to make true number sentences.

Ongoing Assessment: Recognizing Student Achievement Use Mental Math and Reflexes.
[Operations and Computation Goal 3]

Ongoing Assessment: Informing Instruction See page 211.

Key Vocabulary

parentheses

Materials

Math Journal 1, p. 71
Student Reference Book, p. 151 (optional)
Study Link 3•9
slate

2 Ongoing Learning & Practice

Playing *Name That Number*

Student Reference Book, p. 254
Math Masters, p. 489 (optional)
deck of number cards (the Everything Math Deck, if available)
Students practice representing numbers in different ways and inserting parentheses to make true number sentences.

Math Boxes 3•10

Math Journal 1, p. 72
Students practice and maintain skills through Math Box problems.

Study Link 3•10

Math Masters, p. 97
Students practice and maintain skills through Study Link activities.

3 Differentiation Options

ENRICHMENT

Writing Number Models with Parentheses

Math Masters, p. 98
Students use parentheses to solve a number story.

EXTRA PRACTICE

Taking a 50-Facts Test

Math Masters, pp. 412 and 414; p. 416 (optional)
pen or colored pencil
Students take a 50-facts test. They use a line graph to record individual and optional class scores.

EXTRA PRACTICE

5-Minute Math

5-Minute Math™, pp. 77 and 78
Students solve number stories with parentheses.

Advance Preparation

***Teacher's Reference Manual,* Grades 4–6** pp. 98, 99, 102

Getting Started

Mental Math and Reflexes ★

Pose division and extended division facts.
Suggestions:

FACTS PRACTICE

●○○	●●○	●●●
12 ÷ 2 = 6	25 ÷ 5 = 5	240 ÷ 6 = 40
10 ÷ 10 = 1	18 ÷ 6 = 3	720 ÷ 9 = 80
20 ÷ 4 = 5	49 ÷ 7 = 7	4,800 ÷ 8 = 600
18 ÷ 2 = 9	48 ÷ 8 = 6	3,600 ÷ 4 = 900
30 ÷ 10 = 3	32 ÷ 4 = 8	4,200 ÷ 60 = 70
35 ÷ 5 = 7	27 ÷ 3 = 9	8,100 ÷ 90 = 90

Math Message

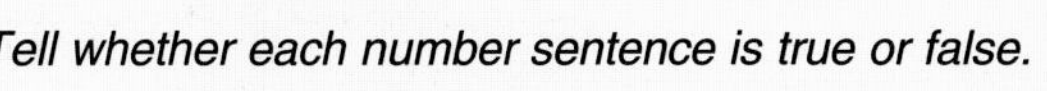

Tell whether each number sentence is true or false.

28 – 6 + 9 = 31
28 – 6 + 9 = 13

Be ready to defend your answer.

Study Link 3·9 Follow-Up

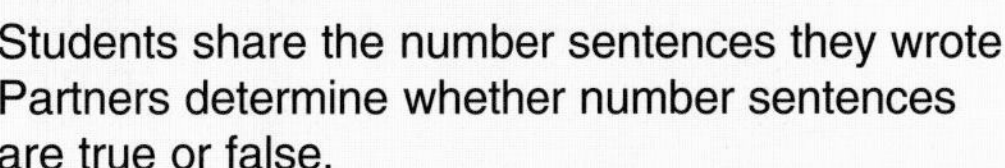

Students share the number sentences they wrote. Partners determine whether number sentences are true or false.

Ongoing Assessment: Recognizing Student Achievement

Mental Math and Reflexes ★

Use **Mental Math and Reflexes** to assess students' proficiency with basic division facts. Students are making adequate progress if they are able to solve the ●○○ and ●●○ problems. Some students may be able to solve the ●●● problems, which involve extended division facts.

[Operations and Computation Goal 3]

1 Teaching the Lesson

▶ Math Message Follow-Up

WHOLE-CLASS DISCUSSION

Most students probably worked the problem from left to right and indicated that the first number sentence is true. 28 – 6 = 22; 22 + 9 = 31 If no one chose the second number sentence, discuss how this sentence could also be true. Add 6 + 9 first; then subtract the result from 28: 6 + 9 = 15; 28 – 15 = 13. Commend students who said that both sentences could be true, depending on what you do first.

Adjusting the Activity

In the absence of parentheses, the convention is to add and subtract in order from left to right. 28 – 6 + 9 = 31 would be considered true and 28 – 6 + 9 = 13 false. Order of operations is discussed on page 151 of the *Student Reference Book.* Some students might be interested in learning more about this topic.

AUDITORY ◆ KINESTHETIC ◆ TACTILE ◆ VISUAL

Write the word **parentheses** on the board. Remind the class that parentheses are used in a number sentence to show which operation to do first.

Write the two number sentences on the board. Ask students to insert parentheses around the part in each sentence that was done first:

(28 – 6) + 9 = 31

28 – (6 + 9) = 13

Show how to work through these sentences step by step. One way is to rewrite the sentence below the original one with the term in parentheses simplified.

(28 – 6) + 9 = ___	28 – (6 + 9) = ___
↓	↓
22 + 9 = 31	28 – 15 = 13

Work through another example, asking students to insert parentheses to make each sentence true. *Suggestion:*

(10 – 3) ∗ 2 = 14

10 – (3 ∗ 2) = 4

NOTE Additional information about solving simple equations and inequalities can be found at www.everydaymathonline.com.

Adjusting the Activity

In discussing these problems, you might demonstrate the following approach:

Is 15 + (2 ∗ 5) = 25 true or false?

↓

15 + 10 = 25

25 = 25 It is true.

Is (4 ∗ 8) – 4 = 16 true or false?

↓

32 – 4 = 16

28 = 16 It is false.

AUDITORY ♦ KINESTHETIC ♦ TACTILE ♦ VISUAL

▶ Determining Whether Number Sentences Containing Parentheses Are True or False

Lead the class in the following slate routine: Write number sentences containing parentheses on the board. Students write T for true or F for false on their slates and discuss answers after each problem. To support English language learners, encourage them to write out *true* and *false* in their entirety. *Suggestions:*

- ▷ 15 + (2 ∗ 5) = 25 T
- ▷ (4 ∗ 8) – 4 = 16 F
- ▷ 12 = (24 / 6) ∗ 3 T
- ▷ (36 / 6) / 2 < 12 T
- ▷ 20 < 40 – (9 + 11) F
- ▷ 4 ∗ 9 > (6 ∗ 6) – 5 T

▶ Using Parentheses in Number Sentences

PARTNER ACTIVITY

(*Math Journal 1,* p. 71)

Algebraic Thinking Journal page 71 is divided into three parts, each consisting of a set of problems involving parentheses. In Part 1, students fill in the missing numbers to make the sentences true. In Part 2, students insert parentheses to make the sentences true. In Part 3, multiple numbers and a target number are given in each problem. Students use these numbers to write true number sentences containing parentheses.

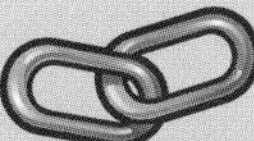

Links to the Future

Problem 8 on journal page 71 requires students to insert *nested parentheses* to make a true number sentence. Evaluating expressions containing nested parentheses and inserting nested parentheses to make true number sentences is a Grade 5 Goal.

Do one sample of each type of problem with the class (see below). Then divide the class into partnerships. Students complete the journal page on their own and then compare their answers with their partner's.

Part 1 Sample Problem: Make a true sentence by filling in the missing number.

Write the following sample problem on the board:

12 + (4 / 4) = ____

- What operation should you do first? 4 / 4 = 1
  Why? The operation inside the parentheses is done first.
- What should you do next? 12 + 1 = 13

Part 2 Sample Problem: Make a true sentence by inserting parentheses.

Write the following number sentence on the board:

15 − 7 ∗ 2 = 16

The result of these operations is 16.

- What was done first? 15 − 7 = 8
  What was done next? 8 ∗ 2 = 16
- Show where you would insert the parentheses.
  (15 − 7) ∗ 2 = 16

Ongoing Assessment: Informing Instruction

Watch for students who insert parentheses but are unable to explain why they chose the particular placement. Suggest that students write intermediate calculations above the parentheses as a record of their reasoning. *For example:*

$(15 \overset{8}{-} 7) * 2 = 16$

Part 3 Sample Problem: Given three numbers and a target number, write a true number sentence containing parentheses.

Write the following problem on the board:

Use: 5, 5, 20   Target number: 3

Tell students to pretend that they are playing a game of *Name That Number* in which they use three numbers to name the target number. They make a true sentence containing parentheses, using the three numbers and the target number. (20 − 5) / 5 = 3

Student Page

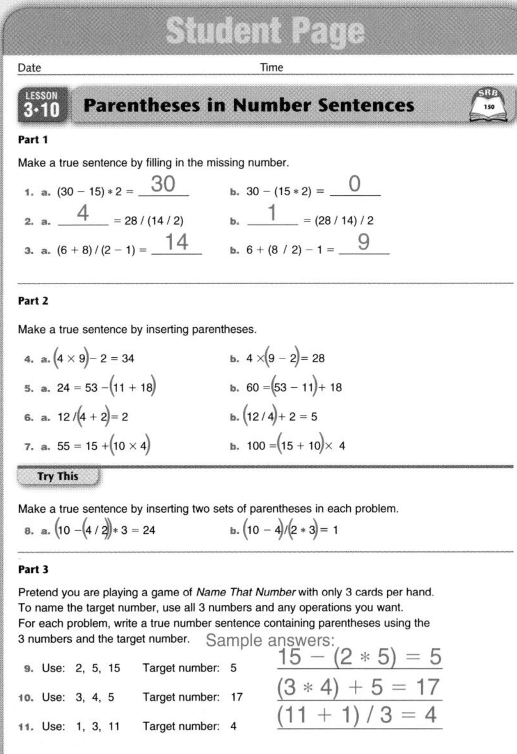

Date   Time

LESSON 3·10 **Parentheses in Number Sentences**

Part 1

Make a true sentence by filling in the missing number.

1. a. (30 − 15) ∗ 2 = 30   b. 30 − (15 ∗ 2) = 0
2. a. 4 = 28 / (14 / 2)   b. 1 = (28 / 14) / 2
3. a. (6 + 8) / (2 − 1) = 14   b. 6 + (8 / 2) − 1 = 9

Part 2

Make a true sentence by inserting parentheses.

4. a. (4 × 9) − 2 = 34   b. 4 × (9 − 2) = 28
5. a. 24 = 53 − (11 + 18)   b. 60 = (53 − 11) + 18
6. a. 12 / (4 + 2) = 2   b. (12 / 4) + 2 = 5
7. a. 55 = 15 + (10 × 4)   b. 100 = (15 + 10) × 4

Try This

Make a true sentence by inserting two sets of parentheses in each problem.

8. a. (10 − (4 / 2)) ∗ 3 = 24   b. (10 − 4) / (2 ∗ 3) = 1

Part 3

Pretend you are playing a game of *Name That Number* with only 3 cards per hand. To name the target number, use all 3 numbers and any operations you want. For each problem, write a true number sentence containing parentheses using the 3 numbers and the target number. Sample answers:

9. Use: 2, 5, 15 Target number: 5 15 − (2 ∗ 5) = 5
10. Use: 3, 4, 5 Target number: 17 (3 ∗ 4) + 5 = 17
11. Use: 1, 3, 11 Target number: 4 (11 + 1) / 3 = 4

Math Journal 1, p. 71

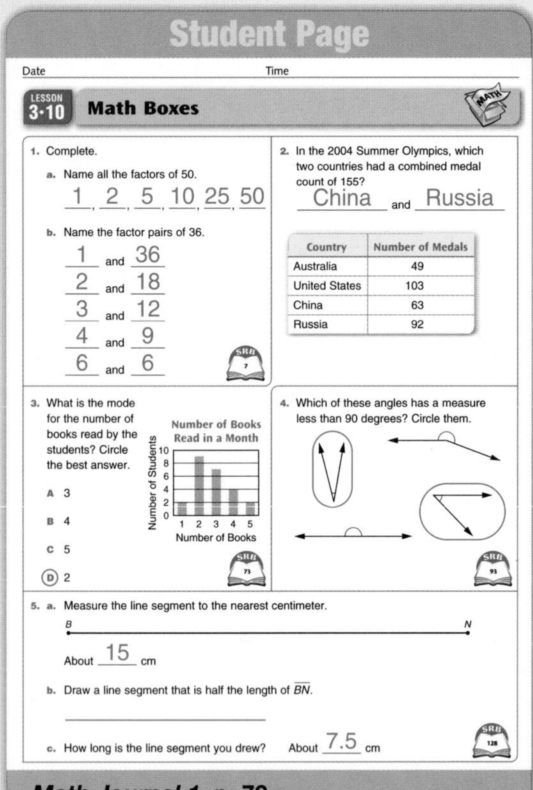
Student Page

Date Time

LESSON 3·10 **Math Boxes**

1. Complete.
   a. Name all the factors of 50.
   1, 2, 5, 10, 25, 50
   b. Name the factor pairs of 36.
   1 and 36
   2 and 18
   3 and 12
   4 and 9
   6 and 6

2. In the 2004 Summer Olympics, which two countries had a combined medal count of 155?
   China and Russia

Country	Number of Medals
Australia	49
United States	103
China	63
Russia	92

3. What is the mode for the number of books read by the students? Circle the best answer.
   A 3
   B 4
   C 5
   (D) 2

4. Which of these angles has a measure less than 90 degrees? Circle them.

5. a. Measure the line segment to the nearest centimeter.
   About 15 cm
   b. Draw a line segment that is half the length of $\overline{BN}$.
   c. How long is the line segment you drew? About 7.5 cm

Math Journal 1, p. 72

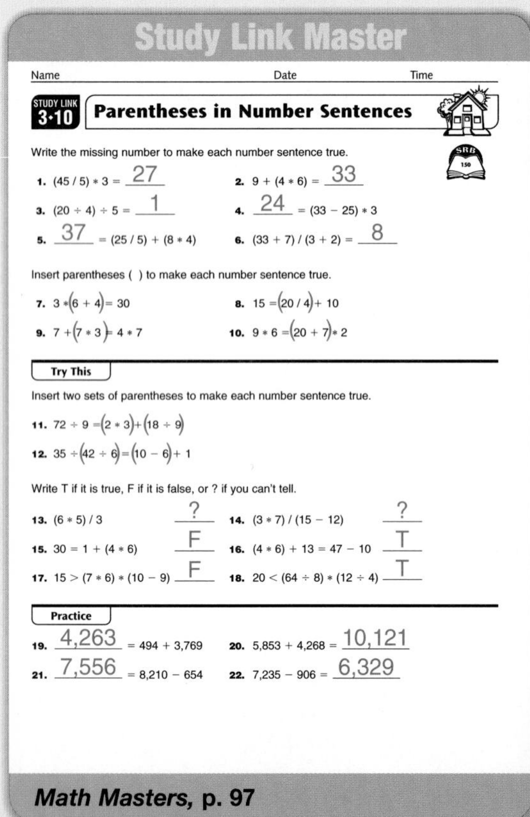
Study Link Master

Name Date Time

STUDY LINK 3·10 **Parentheses in Number Sentences**

Write the missing number to make each number sentence true.

1. (45 / 5) ∗ 3 = 27
2. 9 + (4 ∗ 6) = 33
3. (20 ÷ 4) ÷ 5 = 1
4. 24 = (33 − 25) ∗ 3
5. 37 = (25 / 5) + (8 ∗ 4)
6. (33 + 7) / (3 + 2) = 8

Insert parentheses ( ) to make each number sentence true.

7. 3 ∗ (6 + 4) = 30
8. 15 = (20 / 4) + 10
9. 7 + (7 ∗ 3) = 4 ∗ 7
10. 9 ∗ 6 = (20 + 7) ∗ 2

Try This

Insert two sets of parentheses to make each number sentence true.

11. 72 ÷ 9 = (2 ∗ 3) + (18 ÷ 9)
12. 35 ÷ (42 ÷ 6) = (10 − 6) + 1

Write T if it is true, F if it is false, or ? if you can't tell.

13. (6 ∗ 5) / 3 ?
14. (3 ∗ 7) / (15 − 12) ?
15. 30 = 1 + (4 ∗ 6) F
16. (4 ∗ 6) + 13 = 47 − 10 T
17. 15 > (7 ∗ 6) ∗ (10 − 9) F
18. 20 < (64 ÷ 8) ∗ (12 ÷ 4) T

Practice

19. 4,263 = 494 + 3,769
20. 5,853 + 4,268 = 10,121
21. 7,556 = 8,210 − 654
22. 7,235 − 906 = 6,329

Math Masters, p. 97

2 Ongoing Learning & Practice

▶ Playing *Name That Number*

PARTNER ACTIVITY

(*Student Reference Book,* p. 254; *Math Masters,* p. 489)

Students play *Name That Number* to practice representing numbers in different ways. See Lesson 2-2 for additional information. Encourage students to use parentheses in their number sentences.

▶ Math Boxes 3·10

INDEPENDENT ACTIVITY

(*Math Journal 1,* p. 72)

Mixed Practice Math Boxes in this lesson are paired with Math Boxes in Lesson 3-11. The skill in Problem 5 previews Unit 4 content.

Writing/Reasoning Have students write a response to the following: *Explain how you could use the bar graph in Problem 3 to find the total number of books read by the students.* Sample answer: For each bar on the graph, I multiplied the number of students by the number of books they each read. Then I added the numbers. (2 + 18 + 21 + 16 + 10 = 67 books)

▶ Study Link 3·10

INDEPENDENT ACTIVITY

(*Math Masters,* p. 97)

Home Connection Students solve problems with parentheses and insert parentheses to make true number sentences.

3 Differentiation Options

ENRICHMENT

Writing Number Models with Parentheses

5–15 Min

(*Math Masters,* p. 98)

Algebraic Thinking To apply students' understanding of parentheses, have them explain how the context of a problem is important when deciding where to place parentheses in a number model.

EXTRA PRACTICE

Taking a 50-Facts Test

5–15 Min

(*Math Masters,* pp. 412, 414, and 416)

See Lesson 3-4 for details regarding the administration of the 50-facts test and the recording and graphing of individual and optional class results.

EXTRA PRACTICE

5-Minute Math

5–15 Min

Algebraic Thinking To offer students more experience with parentheses in number sentences, see *5-Minute Math,* pages 77 and 78.

Teaching Master

Name ______ Date ______ Time ______

LESSON 3·10 **Number Models with Parentheses**

Joel and his parents were buying treats for his birthday party. He asked his mother and father, "How much is 6 plus 6 times 3?" His mother said "36," and his father said "24."

1. How did his mother get 36? His mom added 6 to 6 first, then multiplied by 3; (6 + 6) ∗ 3 = 36.
2. How did his father get 24? His dad multiplied 6 by 3 first, then added 6; 6 + (6 ∗ 3) = 24.

Joel's parents both thought their answers were correct. Finally Joel said, "I want to buy 1 six-pack of vanilla cupcakes and 3 six-packs of chocolate cupcakes." Then Joel's parents knew whose answer made more sense.

3. Which answer, 36 or 24, makes more sense in this situation? Explain. 24, because he needs 1 six-pack of vanilla (6) plus 3 six-packs (6 ∗ 3) of chocolate

Name ______ Date ______ Time ______

LESSON 3·10 **Number Models with Parentheses**

Joel and his parents were buying treats for his birthday party. He asked his mother and father, "How much is 6 plus 6 times 3?" His mother said "36," and his father said "24."

1. How did his mother get 36? ______
2. How did his father get 24? ______

Joel's parents both thought their answers were correct. Finally Joel said, "I want to buy 1 six-pack of vanilla cupcakes and 3 six-packs of chocolate cupcakes." Then Joel's parents knew whose answer made more sense.

3. Which answer, 36 or 24, makes more sense in this situation? Explain. ______

Math Masters, p. 98

3•11 Open Sentences

Objectives To introduce vocabulary and notation for open sentences; and to provide practice solving open sentences.

Technology Resources www.everydaymathonline.com

ePresentations

eToolkit

Algorithms Practice

EM Facts Workshop Game™

Family Letters

Assessment Management

Common Core State Standards

Curriculum Focal Points

Interactive Teacher's Lesson Guide

1 Teaching the Lesson

Key Concepts and Skills

- Add, subtract, multiply, and divide to solve open sentences. [Operations and Computation Goals 1–4]
- Use a "guess-and-check" strategy to make reasonable estimates for open sentences. [Operations and Computation Goal 6]
- Identify the solution of an open sentence. [Patterns, Functions, and Algebra Goal 2]
- Determine whether number sentences are true or false. [Patterns, Functions, and Algebra Goal 2]

Key Activities

Students learn about open sentences and their solutions. They participate in the Broken Calculator activity to reinforce the concept of open sentences and to practice estimation.

Ongoing Assessment: Informing Instruction See page 215.

Ongoing Assessment: Recognizing Student Achievement Use a Math Log or Exit Slip. [Patterns, Functions, and Algebra Goal 2]

Key Vocabulary

variable ◆ open sentence ◆ solve ◆ solution

Materials

Math Journal 1, pp. 73 and 74
Study Link 3•10
Math Masters, p. 388 or 389; p. 424
transparency of *Math Masters,* p. 425 (optional) ◆ slate ◆ calculator ◆ overhead calculator (optional)

2 Ongoing Learning & Practice

Using a Map Scale

Math Journal 1, p. 75
ruler
Students use a map scale to convert measurements to actual distances.

Math Boxes 3•11

Math Journal 1, p. 76
Students practice and maintain skills through Math Box problems.

Study Link 3•11

Math Masters, p. 99
Students practice and maintain skills through Study Link activities.

3 Differentiation Options

READINESS

Using Fact Triangles to Solve Open Sentences

Math Masters, p. 100
∗, / Fact Triangles
Students explore the concept of open number sentences.

ENRICHMENT

Solving Open Sentences

Math Masters, p. 101
Students find missing values for letters.

EXTRA PRACTICE

Solving Broken-Calculator Problems

Math Masters, p. 424
Students practice solving open sentences.

Additional Information

An open sentence is a number sentence that contains one or more variables, such as $3 + x = 5$. When the variable x is replaced by a number in $3 + x = 5$, the sentence becomes either true or false: $3 + 2 = 5$ is true, but $3 + 4 = 5$ is false.

***Teacher's Reference Manual,* Grades 4–6** pp. 284–297

Getting Started

Mental Math and Reflexes

Students solve addition and subtraction problems mentally and share their strategies. *Suggestions:*

●○○	●●○	●●●
16 + 5 = 21	70 + 40 = 110	92 + 59 = 151
8 + 14 = 22	180 + 50 = 230	76 + 25 = 101
25 − 8 = 17	190 − 60 = 130	92 − 48 = 44
28 − 9 = 19	210 − 30 = 180	184 − 126 = 58

Math Message

Is this sentence true or false? The sum of 10 and some number is 15. Be ready to explain your thinking.

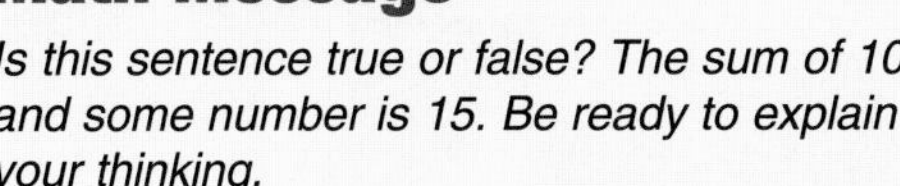

Study Link 3·10 Follow-Up

Partners compare answers. Ask students to rewrite Problem 14 so that it is a false number sentence and Problem 13 so that it is a true number sentence.

1 Teaching the Lesson

Math Message Follow-Up

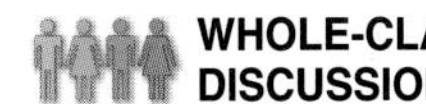

The Math Message is likely to cause some confusion. Students should conclude that they can't tell because some information is missing, but some students may make good arguments for other conclusions.

Tell students that in this lesson they will explore number sentences with missing information and learn to solve them.

Exploring the Meaning of Open Sentences

Algebraic Thinking Now write the same sentence with math symbols:

$10 + x = 15$

In this sentence, the letter x stands for the missing number. A different letter could also be used; for example, $10 + n = 15$. Any letter or other symbol that is not a number will do. A letter or symbol that stands for a missing number is called a **variable.**

Now ask students what number they would write in place of x to change $10 + x = 15$ into a true number sentence. 5, because $10 + 5$ is equal to 15.

A sentence that has a variable in it, such as $10 + x = 15$, is called an **open sentence.** To **solve** an open sentence, replace the variable with a number that makes the sentence true. The number that makes the number sentence true is called the **solution.** The solution of $10 + x = 15$ is the number 5.

Ongoing Assessment: Informing Instruction

Watch for students who have difficulty with variables when they are positioned in different places. For example, a student may have little difficulty with a problem such as $15 - x = 9$ but struggle with a problem such as $x - 6 = 9$. Suggest that students write the number sentence with their solution to see if it makes sense.

Example:

Teacher: $10 + x = 15$

Student: $10 + (5) = 15$

NOTE The Broken Calculator activity is a good way to reinforce the idea that the solution of an open sentence is a number that makes the sentence true. It is an activity you can do with students from time to time to remind them of this basic idea. Broken Calculator is also an excellent routine for practicing estimation.

Algebraic Thinking Use a procedure like the following. (See margin

- ▷ Write an open sentence on the board.
- ▷ Students solve the open sentence.
- ▷ On their slates, students write the number sentence with the solution in place of the variable. They circle the solution.
- ▷ If students disagree on the solution, they check their solutions on their calculators.

Begin with problems like the following:

▷ $12 + x = 55$ $12 + (43) = 55$	▷ $36 / p = 9$ $36 / (4) = 9$
▷ $2 * x = 18$ $2 * (9) = 18$	▷ $17 = z - 8$ $17 = (25) - 8$
▷ $21 - 8 = n$ $21 - 8 = (13)$	▷ $k / 6 = 10$ $(60) / 6 = 10$
▷ $14 = t - 9$ $14 = (23) - 9$	▷ $m / 25 = 4$ $(100) / 25 = 4$

Adjusting the Activity

Have students restate the open sentences in words. For example, for $12 + x = 55$, ask: *What number added to 12 will equal 55?* For $2 * x = 18$, ask: *18 is 2 times as many as what number?*

AUDITORY ◆ KINESTHETIC ◆ TACTILE ◆ VISUAL

▶ Introducing the Broken Calculator Activity

WHOLE-CLASS ACTIVITY

(*Math Masters,* pp. 424 and 425)

Algebraic Thinking Ask students to pretend that the minus key on their calculator is broken. Write the following open sentence on the board, and ask students to solve it using their calculators but without using the minus key:

$452 + x = 735$

Have the class share solution strategies. Use an overhead calculator, if available. Students who are very skilled in mental computation may have subtracted 452 from 735 in their heads. Others probably replaced the variable x with various numbers until they found a true number sentence. This guess-and-check strategy can be organized in a table like the one shown in the margin.

Broken Key: [–]	
To Solve: 452 + x = 735	
452 + **300** = 752	too much
452 + **250** = 702	too little
452 + **280** = 732	very close
452 + **283** = 735	Got it!

The solution of $452 + x = 735$ is 283, because $452 + 283 = 735$ is true.

Pose a few more problems like the following on a transparency of *Math Masters*, page 425. Have students record their work on *Math Masters*, page 424.

Open Sentence	Broken Key	Solution
$75 + x = 415$	[–]	340
$y + 128 = 563$	[–]	435
$r - 156 = 954$	[+]	1,110
$p / 34 = 27$	[X]	918
$y / 29 = 52$	[X]	1,508
$19 * t = 1,330$	[÷]	70

Solving Broken Calculator Problems

(*Math Journal 1,* p. 73)

The journal page contains five Broken Calculator problems and a blank table on which students write problems for their partners to solve.

Ongoing Assessment: Recognizing Student Achievement

Math Log or Exit Slip

Use a **Math Log** or an **Exit Slip** (*Math Masters,* page 388 or 389) to assess students' ability to use and explain a strategy for solving open number sentences. Have students explain the strategy they used to solve Problem 1, 2, 3, or 4 on journal page 73. Students are making adequate progress if their strategy involves using estimation to close in on the solution to the open sentence. Some students may be able to explain how they solved Problem 5, which involves estimating the product of two 2-digit numbers.

[Patterns, Functions, and Algebra Goal 2]

Solving Open Sentences

(*Math Journal 1,* p. 74)

Have students solve open sentences and rewrite each sentence with the solution in place of the variable.

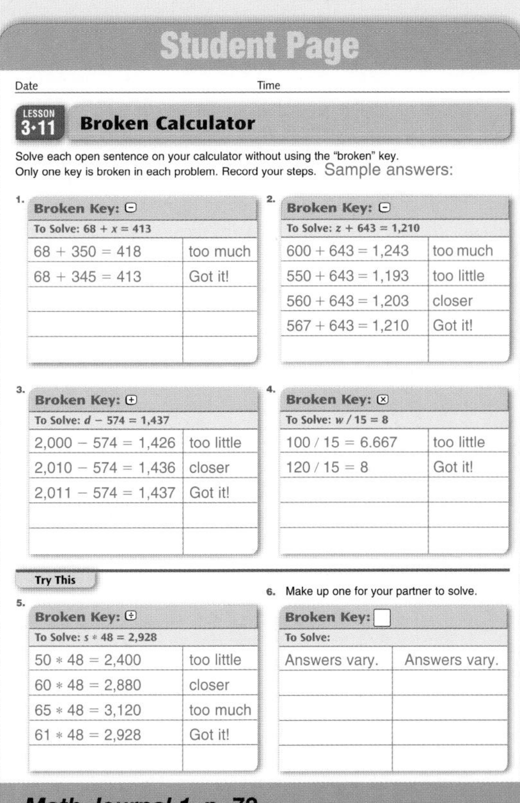
Student Page

Date Time

LESSON 3•11 **Broken Calculator**

Solve each open sentence on your calculator without using the "broken" key. Only one key is broken in each problem. Record your steps. Sample answers:

1.

Broken Key: [–]	
To Solve: $68 + x = 413$	
68 + 350 = 418	too much
68 + 345 = 413	Got it!

2.

Broken Key: [–]	
To Solve: $z + 643 = 1,210$	
600 + 643 = 1,243	too much
550 + 643 = 1,193	too little
560 + 643 = 1,203	closer
567 + 643 = 1,210	Got it!

3.

Broken Key: [+]	
To Solve: $d - 574 = 1,437$	
2,000 – 574 = 1,426	too little
2,010 – 574 = 1,436	closer
2,011 – 574 = 1,437	Got it!

4.

Broken Key: [X]	
To Solve: $w / 15 = 8$	
100 / 15 = 6.667	too little
120 / 15 = 8	Got it!

Try This

5.

Broken Key: [÷]	
To Solve: $s * 48 = 2,928$	
50 * 48 = 2,400	too little
60 * 48 = 2,880	closer
65 * 48 = 3,120	too much
61 * 48 = 2,928	Got it!

6. Make up one for your partner to solve.

Broken Key: [ ]	
To Solve:	
Answers vary.	Answers vary.

Math Journal 1, p. 73

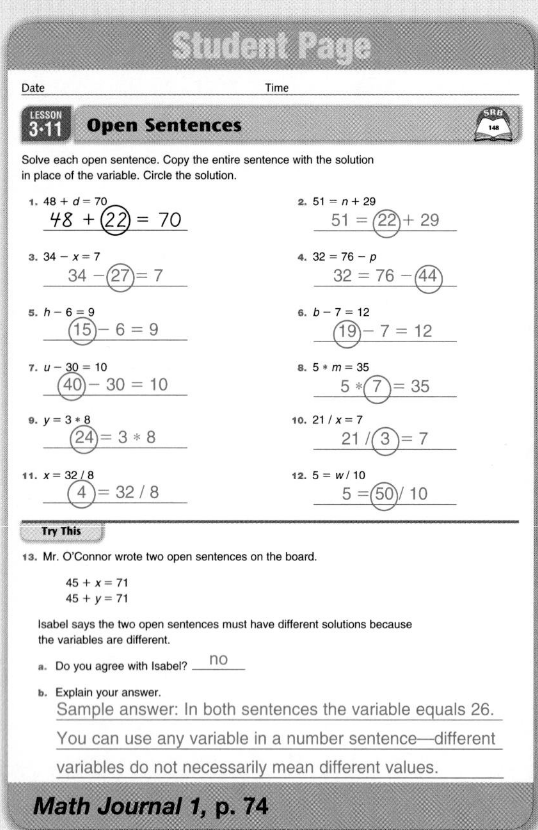
Student Page

Date Time

LESSON 3·11 **Open Sentences** SRB 148

Solve each open sentence. Copy the entire sentence with the solution in place of the variable. Circle the solution.

1. $48 + d = 70$ — 48 + (22) = 70
2. $51 = n + 29$ — 51 = (22) + 29
3. $34 - x = 7$ — 34 − (27) = 7
4. $32 = 76 - p$ — 32 = 76 − (44)
5. $h - 6 = 9$ — (15) − 6 = 9
6. $b - 7 = 12$ — (19) − 7 = 12
7. $u - 30 = 10$ — (40) − 30 = 10
8. $5 * m = 35$ — 5 * (7) = 35
9. $y = 3 * 8$ — (24) = 3 * 8
10. $21 / x = 7$ — 21 / (3) = 7
11. $x = 32 / 8$ — (4) = 32 / 8
12. $5 = w / 10$ — 5 = (50) / 10

Try This

13. Mr. O'Connor wrote two open sentences on the board.

$45 + x = 71$
$45 + y = 71$

Isabel says the two open sentences must have different solutions because the variables are different.

a. Do you agree with Isabel? no

b. Explain your answer.
Sample answer: In both sentences the variable equals 26. You can use any variable in a number sentence—different variables do not necessarily mean different values.

Math Journal 1, p. 74

2 Ongoing Learning & Practice

Using a Map Scale

INDEPENDENT ACTIVITY

(*Math Journal 1*, p. 75)

Social Studies Link Students measure the distances between locations on a map of Egypt. They use the map scale to convert the measurements to actual distances.

Math Boxes 3·11

INDEPENDENT ACTIVITY

(*Math Journal 1*, p. 76)

Mixed Practice Math Boxes in this lesson are paired with Math Boxes in Lesson 3-10. The skill in Problem 5 previews Unit 4 content.

Writing/Reasoning Have students write a response to the following: *In Problem 1b, you wrote the factor pairs of 16. Is 16 a prime number or a composite number? Explain how you know.* Sample answer: Composite. Composite numbers have more than one factor pair and prime numbers have only one factor pair. The number 16 has 3 factor pairs.

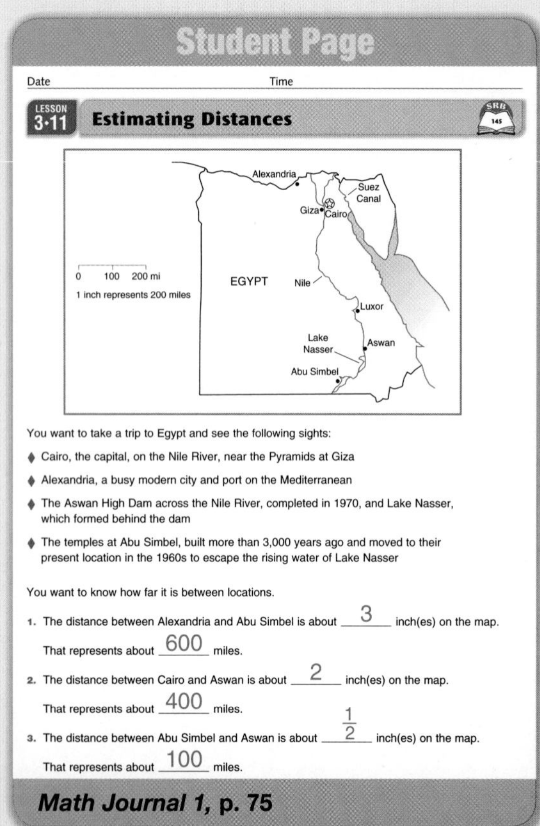
Student Page

Date Time

LESSON 3·11 **Estimating Distances** SRB 145

You want to take a trip to Egypt and see the following sights:

- Cairo, the capital, on the Nile River, near the Pyramids at Giza
- Alexandria, a busy modern city and port on the Mediterranean
- The Aswan High Dam across the Nile River, completed in 1970, and Lake Nasser, which formed behind the dam
- The temples at Abu Simbel, built more than 3,000 years ago and moved to their present location in the 1960s to escape the rising water of Lake Nasser

You want to know how far it is between locations.

1. The distance between Alexandria and Abu Simbel is about 3 inch(es) on the map. That represents about 600 miles.
2. The distance between Cairo and Aswan is about 2 inch(es) on the map. That represents about 400 miles.
3. The distance between Abu Simbel and Aswan is about $\frac{1}{2}$ inch(es) on the map. That represents about 100 miles.

Math Journal 1, p. 75

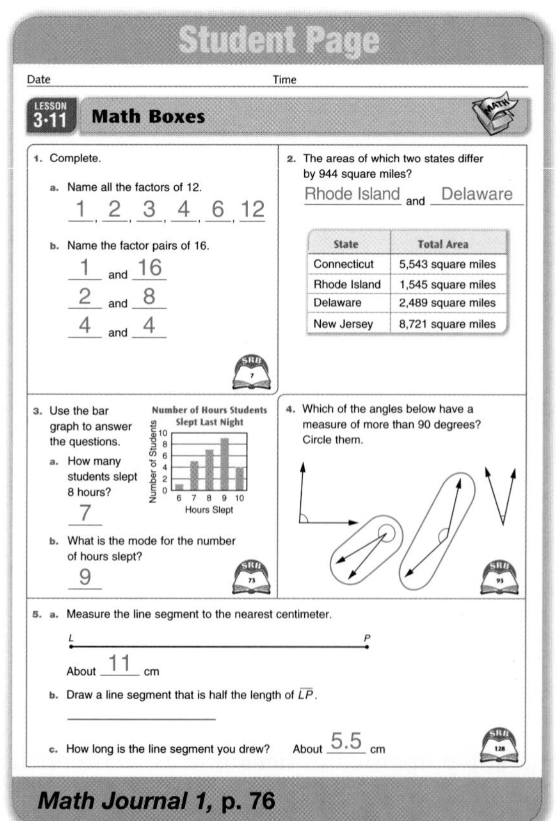
Student Page

Date Time

LESSON 3·11 **Math Boxes**

1. Complete.

a. Name all the factors of 12.
1, 2, 3, 4, 6, 12

b. Name the factor pairs of 16.
1 and 16
2 and 8
4 and 4

SRB 7

2. The areas of which two states differ by 944 square miles?
Rhode Island and Delaware

State	Total Area
Connecticut	5,543 square miles
Rhode Island	1,545 square miles
Delaware	2,489 square miles
New Jersey	8,721 square miles

3. Use the bar graph to answer the questions.

a. How many students slept 8 hours? 7

b. What is the mode for the number of hours slept? 9

SRB 73

4. Which of the angles below have a measure of more than 90 degrees? Circle them.

SRB 95

5. a. Measure the line segment to the nearest centimeter.

L P

About 11 cm

b. Draw a line segment that is half the length of $\overline{LP}$.

c. How long is the line segment you drew? About 5.5 cm

SRB 128

Math Journal 1, p. 76

Study Link 3•11

INDEPENDENT ACTIVITY

(*Math Masters,* p. 99)

Home Connection Students tell whether number sentences are true or false, make true number sentences by filling in missing numbers and inserting parentheses, and find solutions for open sentences.

3 Differentiation Options

READINESS

PARTNER ACTIVITY

5–15 Min

Using Fact Triangles to Solve Open Sentences

(*Math Masters,* p. 100)

To explore the concept of open number sentences, have students use Multiplication/Division Fact Triangles to write and solve open sentences. *For example:*

Cole picked up a Fact Triangle and asked, "3 times what number equals 15?"

He wrote $3 * ? = 15; ? = 5$

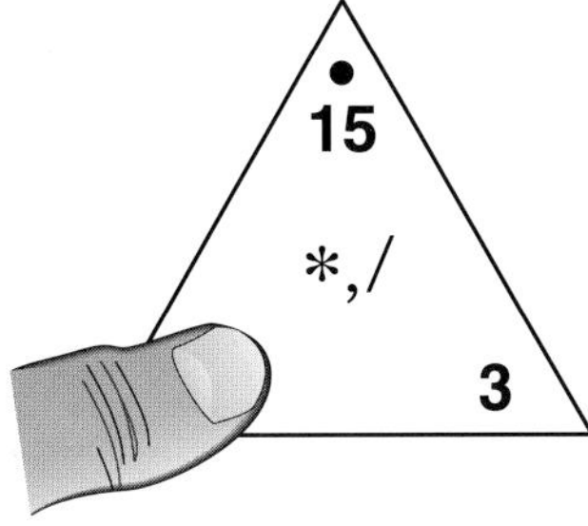

ENRICHMENT

INDEPENDENT ACTIVITY

15–30 Min

Solving Open Sentences

(*Math Masters,* p. 101)

To apply students' understanding of open sentences, have them determine the unknown values of letters in animal names.

EXTRA PRACTICE

INDEPENDENT ACTIVITY

5–15 Min

Solving Broken-Calculator Problems

(*Math Masters,* p. 424)

To provide practice solving open sentences, have students complete Broken Calculator problems. Use *Math Masters,* page 424 to create problems to meet the needs of individual students, or have students create and solve their own problems.

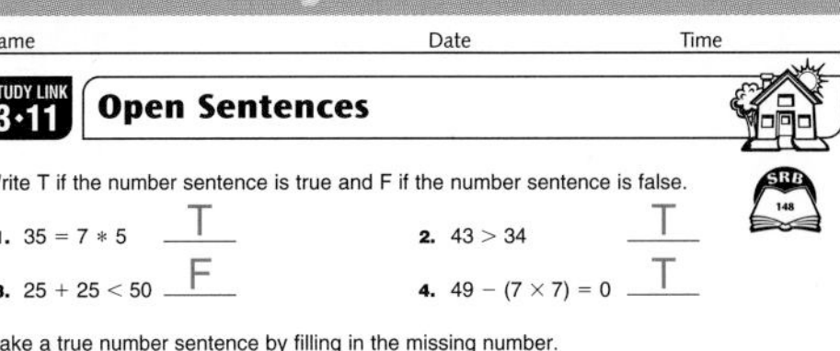

Study Link Master

Name Date Time

STUDY LINK 3•11 **Open Sentences**

Write T if the number sentence is true and F if the number sentence is false.

1. $35 = 7 * 5$ T
2. $43 > 34$ T
3. $25 + 25 < 50$ F
4. $49 - (7 \times 7) = 0$ T

Make a true number sentence by filling in the missing number.

5. 2 $= 12 / (3 + 3)$
6. $(60 - 28) / 4 =$ 8
7. $(3 \times 8) \div 6 =$ 4
8. $30 - (4 + 6) =$ 20

Make a true number sentence by inserting parentheses.

9. $(4 * 2) + 10 = 18$
10. $16 = (16 - 8) * 2$
11. $(27 / 9) / 3 = 1$
12. $27 / (9 / 3) = 9$

Find the solution of each open sentence below. Write a number sentence with the solution in place of the variable. Check to see whether the number sentence is true.

Example: $6 + x = 14$ **Solution:** 8 **Number sentence:** $6 + 8 = 14$

	Open sentence	Solution	Number sentence
13.	$12 + x = 32$	20	$12 + 20 = 32$
14.	$s = 200 - 3$	197	$197 = 200 - 3$
15.	$5 * y = 40$	8	$5 * 8 = 40$
16.	$7 = x / 4$	28	$7 = 28 / 4$

Practice

17. $366 + 7{,}565 =$ 7,931
18. $3{,}238 + 9{,}784 =$ 13,022
19. $9{,}325 - 756 =$ 8,569
20. $4{,}805 - 2{,}927 =$ 1,878

Math Masters, **p. 99**

NOTE For practice solving simple inequalities, see www.everydaymathonline.com.

Teaching Master

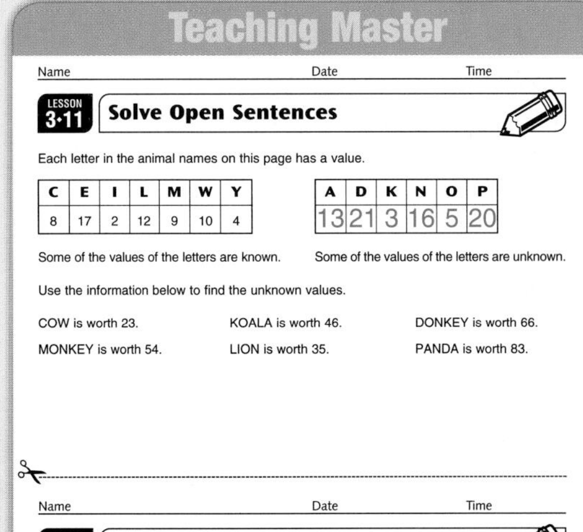

Name Date Time

LESSON 3•11 **Solve Open Sentences**

Each letter in the animal names on this page has a value.

C	E	I	L	M	W	Y
8	17	2	12	9	10	4

Some of the values of the letters are known.

A	D	K	N	O	P
13	21	3	16	5	20

Some of the values of the letters are unknown.

Use the information below to find the unknown values.

COW is worth 23. KOALA is worth 46. DONKEY is worth 66.

MONKEY is worth 54. LION is worth 35. PANDA is worth 83.

Name Date Time

LESSON 3•11 **Solve Open Sentences**

Each letter in the animal names on this page has a value.

C	E	I	L	M	W	Y
8	17	2	12	9	10	4

Some of the values of the letters are known.

A	D	K	N	O	P

Some of the values of the letters are unknown.

Use the information below to find the unknown values.

COW is worth 23. KOALA is worth 46. DONKEY is worth 66.

MONKEY is worth 54. LION is worth 35. PANDA is worth 83.

Math Masters, **p. 101**

3•12 Progress Check 3

Objective To assess students' progress on mathematical content through the end of Unit 3.

1 Looking Back: Cumulative Assessment

Input student data from Progress Check 3 into the **Assessment Management Spreadsheets.**

Materials
- Study Link 3•11
- *Assessment Handbook,* pp. 68–75, 164–168, 218, and 254–257

CONTENT ASSESSED	LESSON(S)	ASSESSMENT ITEMS				
		SELF	ORAL/SLATE	WRITTEN PART A	WRITTEN PART B	OPEN RESPONSE
Find multiples and factors. [Number and Numeration Goal 3]	3•2–3•6, 3•8, 3•10, 3•11	1	1	22	31	
Give equivalent names for whole numbers. [Number and Numeration Goal 4]	3•2					✓
Solve addition and subtraction number stories. [Operations and Computation Goal 2]	3•1, 3•6–3•11	2		19, 20		
Know multiplication and division facts. [Operations and Computation Goal 3]	3•1–3•6, 3•9, 3•11	3, 4	3	1–13, 17, 21	24, 25, 26, 28	
Use a map scale. [Operations and Computation Goal 7]	3•7, 3•9, 3•11	5	4		29, 30	
Interpret a bar graph. [Data and Chance Goal 2]	3•4, 3•6, 3•8, 3•10, 3•11			18		
Estimate and measure the length of line segments. [Measurement and Reference Frames Goal 1]	3•6–3•8, 3•10, 3•11, 3•12				29, 30	
Solve "What's My Rule?" problems. [Patterns, Functions, and Algebra Goal 1]	3•1, 3•5, 3•7, 3•9, 3•12	6		21		
Use conventional notation to write expressions and number sentences. [Patterns, Functions, and Algebra Goal 2]	3•5, 3•8, 3•9					✓
Determine whether a number sentence is true or false. [Patterns, Functions, and Algebra Goal 2]	3•9, 3•10		2	4–9, 14–17		
Solve open sentences. [Patterns, Functions, and Algebra Goal 2]	3•5, 3•8–3•11	7		1–3, 10–13	23–28	
Use parentheses. [Patterns, Functions, and Algebra Goal 3]	3•10, 3•11	8		8–17		✓

2 Looking Ahead: Preparing for Unit 4

Math Boxes 3•12

Study Link 3•12: Unit 4 Family Letter

Materials
- *Math Journal 1,* p. 77
- *Math Masters,* pp. 102–105

Getting Started

Math Message • Self Assessment

Complete the Self Assessment
(Assessment Handbook, *page 164*).

Study Link 3·11 Follow-Up

Students compare answers.

1 Looking Back: Cumulative Assessment

Math Message Follow-Up

(Self Assessment, *Assessment Handbook,* p. 164)

The Self Assessment offers students the opportunity to reflect upon their progress.

Oral and Slate Assessments

Problems 1 and 2 provide summative information and can be used for grading purposes. Problems 3 and 4 provide formative information that can be useful in planning future instruction.

Oral Assessment

1. Ask students to explain the meaning of *factor, multiple,* and *product.* Ask students to give examples of each. Sample answers: A factor is one of at least two numbers that is multiplied to get a product; for example, 2 and 3 are factors of 6 ($2 * 3 = 6$). A multiple is a number found by multiplying a number times a whole number; for example, 16 and 24 are multiples of 8 ($2 * 8 = 16$ and $3 * 8 = 24$). A product is the answer you get when at least two numbers are multiplied; for example, 12 is the product of 3 and 4 ($3 * 4 = 12$).
2. Ask students to explain why "18 divided by 6" (18 / 6) is not a number sentence. Ask: *How could you make it into a true number sentence?* Sample answer: Add "equals 3" to it. *A false number sentence?* Sample answer: Add "is greater than 5" to it.

Slate Assessment

3. Have students solve multiplication and division facts. *Suggestions:*
   - $9 * 7 = 63$
   - $4 * 9 = 36$
   - $72 / 8 = 9$
   - $42 / 6 = 7$
   - $8 * 6 = 48$
   - $7 * 8 = 56$
   - $54 / 9 = 6$
   - $32 / 4 = 8$
4. Write "Map Scale: 1 inch represents 100 miles" on the board. For each measurement, students write the distance it represents. *Suggestions:*
   - 2 inches 200 miles
   - $4\frac{1}{2}$ inches 450 miles
   - $\frac{1}{2}$ inch 50 miles
   - $1\frac{3}{4}$ inches 175 miles

Assessment Master

Name Date Time

LESSON 3·12 **Self Assessment** Progress Check 3

Think about each skill listed below. Assess your own progress by checking the most appropriate box.

Skills	I can do this on my own and explain how to do it.	I can do this on my own.	I can do this if I get help or look at an example.
1. Find multiples and factors.			
2. Solve addition and subtraction number stories.			
3. Know multiplication facts.			
4. Know division facts.			
5. Use a map scale.			
6. Solve "What's My Rule?" problems.			
7. Solve open sentences.			
8. Use parentheses.			

Assessment Handbook, p. 164

Assessment Master

Name Date Time

LESSON 3·12 **Written Assessment** Progress Check 3

Part A

Fill in the missing number in each Fact Triangle.

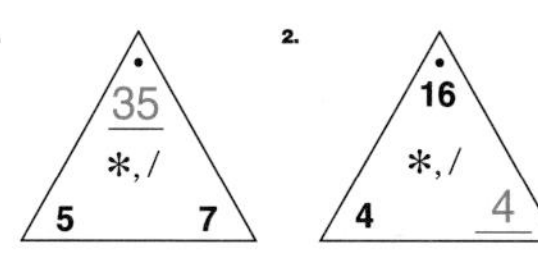

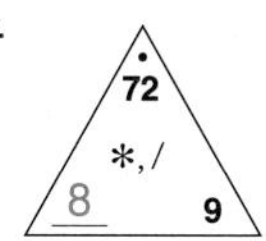

Write T if the number sentence is true, F if it is false, or ? if you can't tell.

4. $6 * 8 = 48$ T
5. $9 * 6$?
6. $3 * 3 = 45 / 5$ T
7. $4 * 6 < 30$ T
8. $3 * (4 + 5) = 17$ F
9. $(7 * 4) \div 2 > 3 * 7$ F

Make a true sentence by filling in the missing number.

10. $85 = (8 * 9) + 13$
11. $35 = (12 - 5) * 5$
12. $(14 - 6) + (32 / 8) = 12$
13. $(12 \div 4) * (24 \div 4) = 18$

Make a true sentence by inserting parentheses.

14. $30 - (15 + 2) = 13$
15. $56 / (8 + 48) = 1$
16. $26 - (3 + 13) = 10$
17. $(6 * 4) + 57 = 81$

Assessment Handbook, p. 165

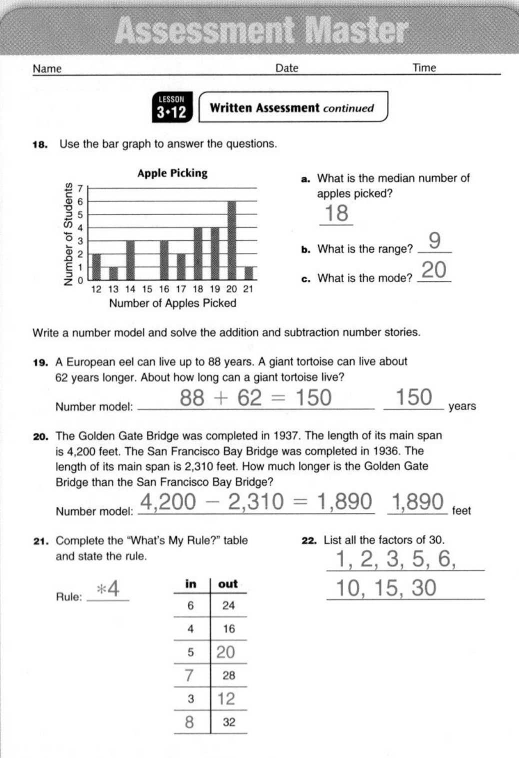

Assessment Master

Name Date Time

LESSON 3•12 Written Assessment *continued*

18. Use the bar graph to answer the questions.

a. What is the median number of apples picked? 18

b. What is the range? 9

c. What is the mode? 20

Write a number model and solve the addition and subtraction number stories.

19. A European eel can live up to 88 years. A giant tortoise can live about 62 years longer. About how long can a giant tortoise live?

Number model: 88 + 62 = 150 150 years

20. The Golden Gate Bridge was completed in 1937. The length of its main span is 4,200 feet. The San Francisco Bay Bridge was completed in 1936. The length of its main span is 2,310 feet. How much longer is the Golden Gate Bridge than the San Francisco Bay Bridge?

Number model: 4,200 − 2,310 = 1,890 1,890 feet

21. Complete the "What's My Rule?" table and state the rule.

Rule: *4

in	out
6	24
4	16
5	20
7	28
3	12
8	32

22. List all the factors of 30.

1, 2, 3, 5, 6, 10, 15, 30

Assessment Handbook, p. 166

▶ Written Assessment

INDEPENDENT ACTIVITY

(*Assessment Handbook,* pp. 165–167)

Part A Recognizing Student Achievement

Problems 1–22 provide summative information and may be used for grading purposes.

Problem(s)	Description
1–3	Fill in missing Fact Triangle numbers.
4–9	Tell whether a number sentence is true, false, or "can't tell."
10–13	Make a true sentence by filling in a missing number.
14–17	Make a true sentence by inserting parentheses.
18	Use a bar graph to find the median, range, and mode of a data set.
19, 20	Solve addition and subtraction number stories.
21	Solve "What's My Rule?" problems.
22	Name factors of 30.

Part B Informing Instruction

Problems 23–31 provide formative information that can be useful in planning future instruction.

Problem(s)	Description
23–28	Solve an open sentence.
29, 30	Use a map and map scale.
31	Complete a Venn diagram with multiples.

Use the checklists on pages 255 and 257 of the *Assessment Handbook* to record results. Then input the data into the **Assessment Management Spreadsheets** to keep an ongoing record of students' progress toward Grade-Level Goals.

Assessment Master

Name Date Time

LESSON 3•12 Written Assessment *continued*

Part B

Solve the open sentences.

23. 19 = 12 + x Solution: 7

24. 4 ∗ n = 16 Solution: 4

25. z / 3 = 6 Solution: 18

26. x / 6 = 5 Solution: 30

27. 17 − x = 8 Solution: 9

28. 4 ∗ 5 = 30 − t Solution: 10

Use the map and map scale to answer the following questions.

29. The distance between Mombasa and Wajir is about 2 inches on the map.

That represents about 400 miles.

30. The distance between Nairobi and Lodwar is about $1\frac{1}{2}$ inches on the map.

That represents about 300 miles.

31. Complete the Venn diagram. Use at least 10 numbers.

Sample answers:

Assessment Handbook, p. 167

▶ Open Response

INDEPENDENT ACTIVITY

(*Assessment Handbook,* p. 168)

Name That Number

The open-response item requires students to apply concepts and skills from Unit 3 to solve a multistep problem. See *Assessment Handbook,* pages 71–75 for rubrics and students' work samples for this problem.

2 Looking Ahead: Preparing for Unit 4

Math Boxes 3·12

(*Math Journal 1*, p. 77)

Mixed Practice This Math Boxes page previews Unit 4 content.

Study Link 3·12: Unit 4 Family Letter

(*Math Masters*, pp. 102–105)

Home Connection The Unit 4 Family Letter provides parents and guardians with information and activities related to Unit 4 topics.

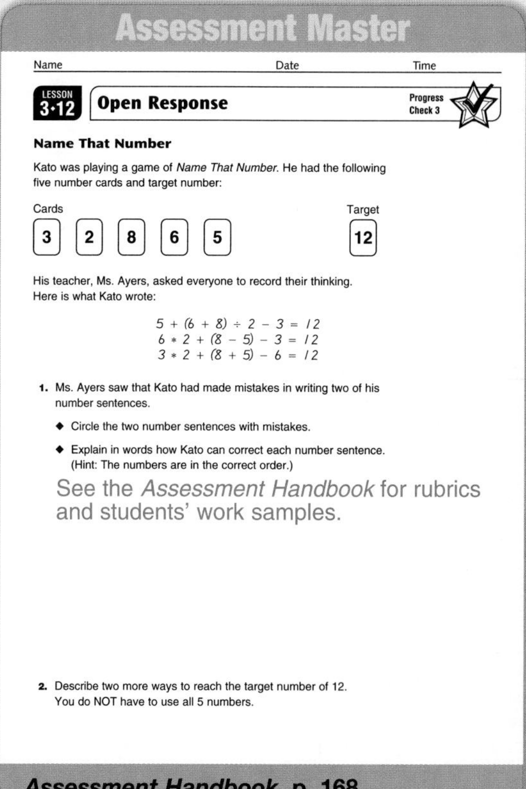

Assessment Master

Name Date Time

LESSON 3·12 **Open Response** Progress Check 3

Name That Number

Kato was playing a game of *Name That Number*. He had the following five number cards and target number:

Cards: 3 2 8 6 5 Target: 12

His teacher, Ms. Ayers, asked everyone to record their thinking. Here is what Kato wrote:

5 + (6 + 8) ÷ 2 − 3 = 12
6 ∗ 2 + (8 − 5) − 3 = 12
3 ∗ 2 + (8 + 5) − 6 = 12

1. Ms. Ayers saw that Kato had made mistakes in writing two of his number sentences.
   - Circle the two number sentences with mistakes.
   - Explain in words how Kato can correct each number sentence. (Hint: The numbers are in the correct order.)

See the *Assessment Handbook* for rubrics and students' work samples.

2. Describe two more ways to reach the target number of 12. You do NOT have to use all 5 numbers.

***Assessment Handbook*, p. 168**

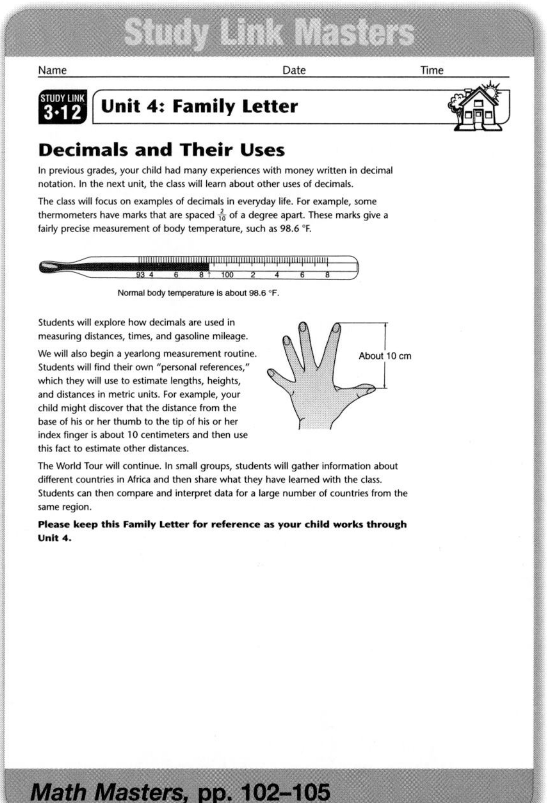

Study Link Masters

Name Date Time

STUDY LINK 3·12 **Unit 4: Family Letter**

Decimals and Their Uses

In previous grades, your child had many experiences with money written in decimal notation. In the next unit, the class will learn about other uses of decimals.

The class will focus on examples of decimals in everyday life. For example, some thermometers have marks that are spaced $\frac{2}{10}$ of a degree apart. These marks give a fairly precise measurement of body temperature, such as 98.6 °F.

Normal body temperature is about 98.6 °F.

Students will explore how decimals are used in measuring distances, times, and gasoline mileage.

We will also begin a yearlong measurement routine. Students will find their own "personal references," which they will use to estimate lengths, heights, and distances in metric units. For example, your child might discover that the distance from the base of his or her thumb to the tip of his or her index finger is about 10 centimeters and then use this fact to estimate other distances.

About 10 cm

The World Tour will continue. In small groups, students will gather information about different countries in Africa and then share what they have learned with the class. Students can then compare and interpret data for a large number of countries from the same region.

Please keep this Family Letter for reference as your child works through Unit 4.

***Math Masters*, pp. 102–105**

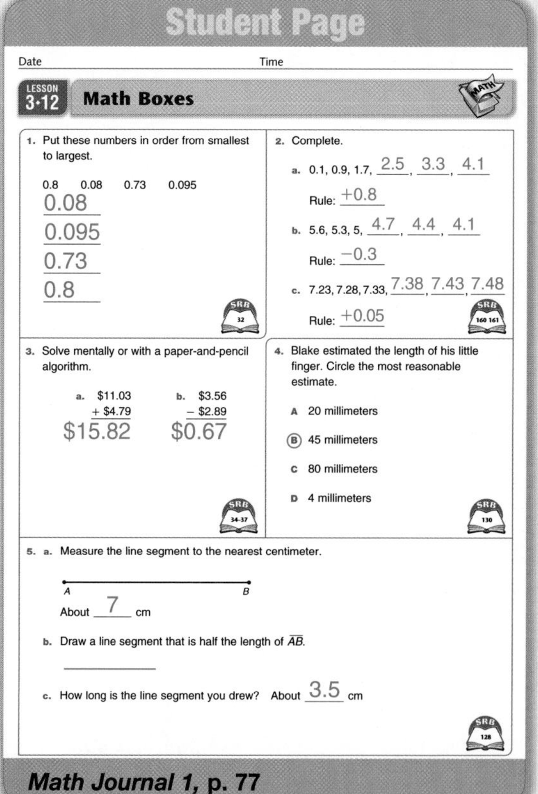

Student Page

Date Time

LESSON 3·12 **Math Boxes**

1. Put these numbers in order from smallest to largest.
   0.8 0.08 0.73 0.095
   0.08, 0.095, 0.73, 0.8

2. Complete.
   a. 0.1, 0.9, 1.7, 2.5, 3.3, 4.1 Rule: +0.8
   b. 5.6, 5.3, 5, 4.7, 4.4, 4.1 Rule: −0.3
   c. 7.23, 7.28, 7.33, 7.38, 7.43, 7.48 Rule: +0.05

3. Solve mentally or with a paper-and-pencil algorithm.
   a. $11.03 + $4.79 = $15.82
   b. $3.56 − $2.89 = $0.67

4. Blake estimated the length of his little finger. Circle the most reasonable estimate.
   A 20 millimeters
   (B) 45 millimeters
   C 80 millimeters
   D 4 millimeters

5. a. Measure the line segment to the nearest centimeter.
   A ——— B
   About 7 cm
   b. Draw a line segment that is half the length of $\overline{AB}$.
   c. How long is the line segment you drew? About 3.5 cm

***Math Journal 1*, p. 77**

Unit 4 Organizer

Decimals and Their Uses

Overview

Unit 4 begins the more formal study of decimals through thousandths. Metric units of length, including conversions, are also studied. Unit 4 has four main areas of focus:

- To extend the base-ten place-value system to decimals,
- To review and extend basic concepts, notation, and applications for decimals,
- To extend whole-number methods of addition and subtraction to decimals, and
- To review relationships among metric units of length, and guide students as they use them.

Linking to the Common Core State Standards

The content of Unit 4 addresses the Common Core State Standards for Mathematics in *Number and Operations in Base Ten.* The correlation of the Common Core State Standards to the *Everyday Mathematics* Grade 4 lessons begins on page CS1.

Contents

Learning In Perspective

	Lesson Objectives	Links to the Past	Links to the Future
4•1	To extend the base-ten place-value system to decimals.	Grades 1–3: Use dollars and cents notation. Grade 3: Model decimals with base-10 blocks.	Grades 4–6: Applications and maintenance.
4•2	To review basic concepts and notation for decimals through hundredths.	Grade 3: Read and write 1-digit and 2-digit decimals.	Grade 5: Extend decimal notation through thousandths.
4•3	To guide students as they compare and order decimals in tenths and hundredths.	Grade 3: Compare metric measurements in decimal notation. Compare decimals through hundredths directly or by coloring 10-by-10 grids.	Grades 5 and 6: Compare fractions by renaming them as equivalent decimals.
4•4	To explain why decimals are useful; and to guide estimation of sums and differences of decimals.	Grade 3: Relate decimals to metric measures.	Grades 4–6: Applications and maintenance.
4•5	To extend methods for whole-number addition and subtraction to decimals.	Grades 1–3: Invent, share, and discuss paper-and-pencil methods for adding and subtracting multidigit whole numbers. Use money to model decimal addition and subtraction.	Grades 5 and 6: Extend addition and subtraction methods to decimal places beyond the hundredths.
4•6	To provide practice adding and subtracting decimals to compute balances in a savings account.	Grades 1–3: Use dollars-and-cents notation to represent money amounts; act out purchasing and change-making situations to practice adding and subtracting money amounts.	Grades 4–6: Applications and maintenance; in particular, money amounts are continually used to exemplify and practice algorithms for operations with decimals.
4•7	To extend basic concepts and notation for decimals through thousandths.	Grades 1 and 2: Model decimals through hundredths. Grade 3: Display decimals through thousandths.	Grades 5 and 6: Read, write, compare, and calculate with decimals to thousandths; practice place-value skills to thousandths.
4•8	To review the relationships among metric units of length; and to guide students as they work with metric measurements.	Grades K–2: Introduce and use linear metric measures. Use decimals for money, with rulers, and on number lines. Grade 3: Express metric measurements in decimal notation.	Grades 5 and 6: Applications and maintenance.
4•9	To assist students as they establish personal references for metric units of length.	Grades 1 and 2: Introduce nonstandard linear measures, such as hand and arm spans and foot lengths; introduce linear metric measures. Grade 3: Use personal references.	Grades 5 and 6: Applications and maintenance.
4•10	To guide students as they measure lengths to the nearest millimeter; and to provide practice converting measurements between millimeters and centimeters.	Grades 1–3: Choose and use appropriate measuring tools; refer to tables of equivalent units of metric measure.	Grades 4–6: Applications and maintenance, including repeated opportunities to measure in metric units.

	Key Concepts and Skills	Grade 4 Goals*
4•1	Identify the values of digits in decimals.	Number and Numeration Goal 1
	Read and write decimals through thousandths.	Number and Numeration Goal 1
	Order decimals through thousandths on a number line.	Number and Numeration Goal 6
	Use extended division facts to expand the place-value chart to decimals.	Operations and Computation Goal 3
	Describe numeric patterns in number lines.	Patterns, Functions, and Algebra Goal 1
4•2	Read and write decimals through hundredths.	Number and Numeration Goal 1
	Model decimals through hundredths with base-10 blocks.	Number and Numeration Goal 1
	Name the fractional part of the ONE represented by a base-10 block.	Number and Numeration Goal 2
	Rename fractions with 10 and 100 in the denominator as decimals.	Number and Numeration Goal 5
4•3	Model decimals through hundredths with base-10 blocks.	Number and Numeration Goal 1
	Read and write decimals through hundredths.	Number and Numeration Goal 1
	Rename fractions with 100 in the denominator as decimals.	Number and Numeration Goal 5
	Compare and order decimals through hundredths.	Number and Numeration Goal 6
4•4	Read and interpret decimals through tenths.	Number and Numeration Goal 1
	Compare whole numbers and decimals.	Number and Numeration Goal 6
	Estimate sums and differences of decimals; explain the strategies used.	Operations and Computation Goal 6
	Use a table of data to answer questions.	Data and Chance Goal 2
4•5	Model decimals through hundredths with base-10 blocks.	Number and Numeration Goal 1
	Express the values of digits in decimals.	Number and Numeration Goal 1
	Add and subtract decimals to the hundredths place.	Operations and Computation Goal 2
	Judge the reasonableness of solutions to decimal addition and subtraction problems.	Operations and Computation Goal 6
4•6	Read and write decimals through hundredths in the context of money.	Number and Numeration Goal 1
	Add and subtract decimals through hundredths in the context of money.	Operations and Computation Goal 2
	Estimate reasonable solutions for decimal addition and subtraction problems.	Operations and Computation Goal 6
	Complete a table of deposits and withdrawals.	Data and Chance Goal 1
4•7	Read, write, and model (with base-10 blocks) decimals through thousandths.	Number and Numeration Goal 1
	Name the fractional part of the ONE represented by each base-10 block.	Number and Numeration Goal 2
	Rename fractions with 10, 100, and 1,000 in the denominator as decimals.	Number and Numeration Goal 5
	Compare and order decimals through thousandths.	Number and Numeration Goal 6
4•8	Read and write decimals through hundredths.	Number and Numeration Goal 1
	Use extended multiplication facts to convert between metric measurements.	Operations and Computation Goal 3
	Measure objects or distances to the nearest centimeter.	Measurement and Reference Frames Goal 1
	Describe relationships among metric units of length.	Measurement and Reference Frames Goal 3
4•9	Identify personal references for metric units of length.	Measurement and Reference Frames Goal 1
	Estimate, without tools, the length of objects or distances in centimeters, decimeters, and meters.	Measurement and Reference Frames Goal 1
	Measure the length of objects or distances in centimeters, decimeters, and meters.	Measurement and Reference Frames Goal 1
4•10	Use extended multiplication facts to convert between metric measurements.	Operations and Computation Goal 3
	Use a scale to determine actual size.	Operations and Computation Goal 7
	Measure lengths to the nearest millimeter.	Measurement and Reference Frames Goal 1
	Describe the relationship among metric units of length.	Measurement and Reference Frames Goal 3

*See the Appendix for a complete list of Grade 4 Goals.

A Balanced Curriculum

Ongoing Practice

Everyday Mathematics provides numerous opportunities for ongoing practice. These activities are embedded throughout the lessons:

Mental Math and Reflexes activities promote speed and accuracy in mental computation.

Math Boxes offer mixed practice and are paired across lessons as shown in the brackets below. This makes them useful as assessment tools. The last one or two boxes on each page preview the next unit's content.

Mixed practice	[4•1, 4•3], [4•2, 4•4], [4•5, 4•7], [4•6, 4•9], [4•8, 4•10]
Mixed practice with multiple choice	4•1, 4•4 , 4•6
Mixed practice with writing/reasoning opportunity	4•2, 4•3, 4•5, 4•6, 4•8, 4•9

Study Links are daily homework assignments that review the content of the lesson and often contain ongoing facts practice or computation practice.

5-Minute Math problems are offered for additional practice in Lessons 4•3 and 4•9.

EM Facts Workshop Game provides online practice of basic facts and computation.

EXTRA PRACTICE **Extra Practice** activities are included in Lessons 4•1, 4•3, 4•7, 4•9, and 4•10.

Practice through Games

Games are an essential component of practice in the *Everyday Mathematics* program. Games offer skills practice and promote strategic thinking. See the *Differentiation Handbook* for ways to adapt games to meet students' needs.

Lesson	Game	Skill Practiced
4•1	*Polygon Pair-Up*	Identifying properties of polygons [GEO Goal 2]
4•2	*Baseball Multiplication*	Solving multiplication facts [OC Goal 3]
4•2, 4•7	*Base-10 Exchange*	Exploring relationships in decimal place values [NN Goal 1]
4•3	*Product Pile-Up*	Solving multiplication facts [OC Goal 3]
4•3	*Coin Top-It*	Comparing decimals in a money context [NN Goal 6]
4•4, 4•9	*Number Top-It* (Decimals)	Comparing and ordering sets of decimals [NN Goal 6]
4•6	*Name That Number*	Representing numbers in different ways [NN Goal 4]
4•8	*Fishing for Digits*	Expressing values of digits in whole numbers [NN Goal 1]

[NN] Number and Numeration
[MRF] Measurement and Reference Frames
[OC] Operations and Computation
[GEO] Geometry
[DC] Data and Chance
[PFA] Patterns, Functions, and Algebra

Problem Solving 

Experts at problem solving and mathematical modeling generally do these things:

- Identify the problem.
- Decide what information is needed to solve the problem.
- Play with and study the data to find patterns and meaning.
- Identify and use mathematical procedures to solve the problem.
- Decide whether the solution makes sense and whether it can be applied to other problems.

The table below lists some of the opportunities in this unit for students to practice these strategies.

Lessons that teach *through* problem solving, not just *about* problem solving

Lesson	Activity
4•3	Compare and order decimals using place value.
4•4	Use estimation to solve number stories.
4•5, 4•6	Apply place-value concepts to solve decimal addition and subtraction problems.
4•8	Measure in centimeters and compare measurements.
4•9	Estimate lengths with personal references.
4•10	Measure land invertebrates and convert between metric units.

See Chapter 18: Problem Solving in the *Teacher's Reference Manual* for more information.

The Language of Mathematics

Everyday Mathematics provides lesson-specific suggestions to help all students acquire, process, and express mathematical ideas. Throughout Unit 4, there are lesson-specific language development notes that address the needs of English language learners, indicated by ELL.

ELL SUPPORT Activities to support English language learners are in Part 3 of Lessons 4•3, 4•6, and 4•8.

The *English Learners Handbook* and the *Differentiation Handbook* have suggestions for promoting language development and acquisition of mathematics vocabulary. See Unit 4 in each handbook.

Unit 4 Vocabulary

balance
centimeter (cm)
decimal
decimeter (dm)
deposit
hundredth
interest
meter (m)
millimeter (mm)
ONE
personal measurement reference
speedometer
tenth
thousandth
trip meter
unit
whole
withdrawal

Literacy Connection

Lesson 4•3 *The Everything Kids' Joke Book: Side-Splitting, Rib-Tickling Fun,* by Michael Dahl, Adams Media Corporation, 2002

Lesson 4•3 *Kids' Funniest Jokes,* edited by Sheila Anne Barry, Sterling Publishing Co., 1994

Lesson 4•10 *If You Hopped Like a Frog,* by David M. Schwartz, Scholastic Inc., 1999

Millions to Measure, by David M. Schwartz, HarperCollins, 2006

For more literacy connections, see the *Home Connection Handbook,* Grades 4–6.

Cross-Curricular Links 

Literature – Lessons 4•3, 4•10
Social Studies – Lesson 4•7
Science – Lesson 4•10

Balanced Assessment

Daily Assessments

- **Recognizing Student Achievement** – A daily assessment that is included in every lesson to evaluate students' progress toward the Grade 4 Grade-Level Goals.
- **Informing Instruction** – Notes that appear throughout the unit to help anticipate students' common errors and suggest appropriate problem-solving strategies.

Lesson	Recognizing Student Achievement	Informing Instruction
4•1	Identify values of digits in whole numbers. [NN Goal 1]	
4•2	Identify values of decimal digits. [NN Goal 1]	Use base-10 blocks to model fractions.
4•3	Compare decimals through hundredths. [NN Goal 6]	Express values of decimal digits.
4•4	Estimate sums of decimals and explain strategy. [OC Goal 6]	Use a number line to reinforce the concept of decimal value.
4•5	Identify values of decimal digits. [NN Goal 1]	Align digits correctly in decimal sums and differences.
4•6	Identify data landmarks. [DC Goal 2]	
4•7	Write decimals through hundredths. [NN Goal 1]	Use base-10 blocks to model thousandths.
4•8	Measure line segments to the nearest centimeter. [MRF Goal 1]	Convert metric units of length.
4•9	Compare decimals through thousandths. [NN Goal 6]	
4•10	Demonstrate automaticity with multiplication facts. [OC Goal 3]	

[NN] Number and Numeration
[MRF] Measurement and Reference Frames
[OC] Operations and Computation
[GEO] Geometry
[DC] Data and Chance
[PFA] Patterns, Functions, and Algebra

Portfolio Opportunities

The following lessons provide opportunities to gather samples of students' mathematical writings, drawings, and creations to add balance to the assessment process: Lessons 4•1, 4•2, 4•3, 4•5, 4•6, 4•9, and 4•11.

See pages 16 and 17 in the *Assessment Handbook* for more information about portfolios and how to use them.

Unit Assessment

Progress Check 4 – A cumulative assessment of concepts and skills taught in Unit 4 and in previous units, providing information for evaluating students' progress and planning for future instruction. These assessments include oral/slate, written, and open-response activities, as shown below in the sample Progress Check lesson opener.

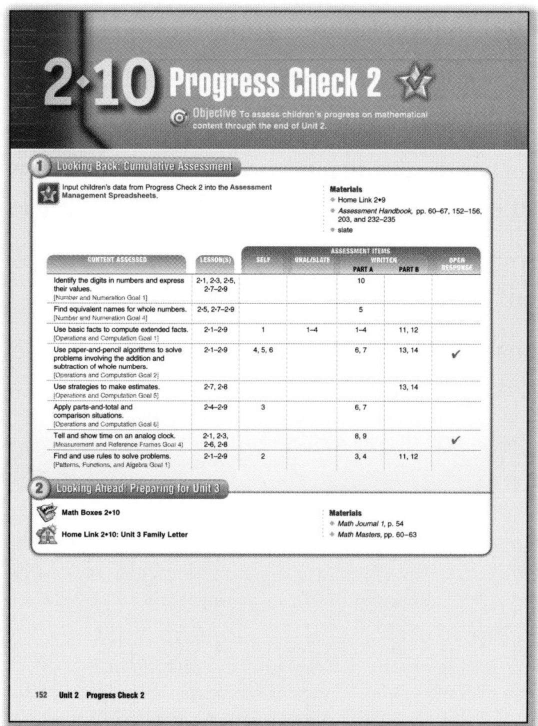

2·10 Progress Check 2

Objective To assess children's progress on mathematical content through the end of Unit 2.

1 Looking Back: Cumulative Assessment

Input children's data from Progress Check 2 into the Assessment Management Spreadsheets.

Materials
- Home Link 2•9
- *Assessment Handbook*, pp. 60–67, 152–156, 203, and 232–235
- slate

Content Assessed	Lesson(s)	Assessment Items: Self	Oral/Slate	Written: Part A	Written: Part B	Open Response
Identify the digits in numbers and express their values. [Number and Numeration Goal 1]	2·1, 2·3, 2·5, 2·7–2·9			10		
Find equivalent names for whole numbers. [Number and Numeration Goal 4]	2·5, 2·7–2·9			5		
Use basic facts to compute extended facts. [Operations and Computation Goal 1]	2·1–2·9	1	1–4	1–4	11, 12	
Use paper-and-pencil algorithms to solve problems involving the addition and subtraction of whole numbers. [Operations and Computation Goal 2]	2·1–2·9	4, 5, 6		6, 7	13, 14	✔
Use strategies to make estimates. [Operations and Computation Goal 5]	2·7, 2·8				13, 14	
Apply parts-and-total and comparison situations. [Operations and Computation Goal 6]	2·4–2·9	3		6, 7		
Tell and show time on an analog clock. [Measurement and Reference Frames Goal 4]	2·1, 2·3, 2·6, 2·8			8, 9		✔
Find and use rules to solve problems. [Patterns, Functions, and Algebra Goal 1]	2·1–2·9	2		3, 4	11, 12	

2 Looking Ahead: Preparing for Unit 3

Math Boxes 2•10

Home Link 2•10: Unit 3 Family Letter

Materials
- *Math Journal 1*, p. 54
- *Math Masters*, pp. 60–63

152 Unit 2 Progress Check 2

Core Assessment Resources

Assessment Handbook

- **Unit 4 Assessment Overview,** pages 76–83
- **Unit 4 Assessment Masters,** pages 169–173
- **Unit 4 Individual Profiles of Progress,** pages 258, 259, and 302
- **Unit 4 Class Checklists,** pages 260, 261, and 303
- **Math Logs,** pages 306–308
- **Exit Slip,** page 311
- **Other Student Assessment Forms,** pages 304, 305, 309, and 310

Assessment Management Spreadsheets

The Assessment Management Spreadsheets consist of the Digital Class Checklists and Individual Profile of Progress Checklists. Use them to monitor, record, and report student progress.

Addressing All Needs

Differentiated Instruction

Adjusting the Activity – suggests adaptations that target advanced learners, English language learners, or learners who need additional instructional support.

ELL SUPPORT / ELL – provides lesson-specific suggestions to help English language learners understand and process the mathematical content.

READINESS – accesses students' prior knowledge or previews content that prepares students to engage in the lesson's Part 1 activities.

EXTRA PRACTICE – provides additional opportunities to apply the mathematical content of the lesson.

ENRICHMENT – enables students to apply or further explore the mathematical content of the lesson.

Lesson	Adjusting the Activity	ELL Support/ ELL	Readiness	Extra Practice	Enrichment
4•1	•		•	•	•
4•2	•	•	•		•
4•3	•	•	•	•	•
4•4	•	•	•		•
4•5	•	•	•		•
4•6	•	•	•		•
4•7	•	•	•	•	•
4•8	•	•	•		•
4•9	•	•	•	•	•
4•10	•	•	•	•	•

Additional Resources

Differentiation Handbook
Provides ideas and strategies for differentiating instruction.
Pages 69–75

English Learners Handbook
Contains lesson-specific comprehension strategies.
Pages 29–38

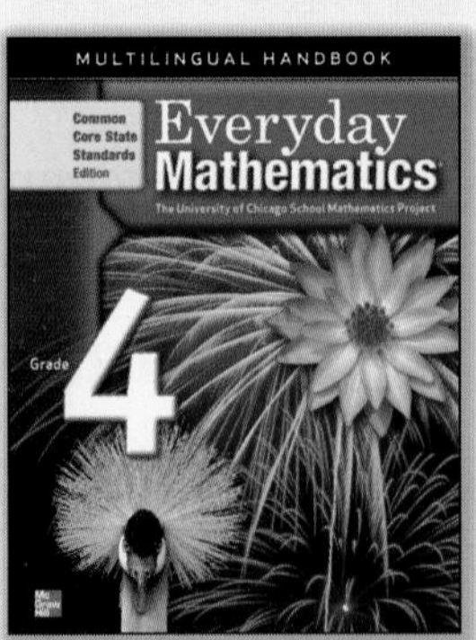

Multilingual Handbook
Previews concepts and vocabulary. It is written in six languages.
Pages 57–76

Planning Tips

Multiage Classroom

Companion Lessons from Grades 3 and 5 can help you meet instructional needs of a multiage classroom. The full Scope and Sequence can be found in the Appendix.

Grade 3	5•11	1•1, 5•1, 5•7, 6•10	1•5, 5•2	1•9, 7•7	2•1, 2•2	1•10, 1•11	5•5, 5•8, 5•11	3•1, 3•3, 5•9	1•4, 3•1, 10•1	3•1, 3•3, 10•1
Grade 4	**4•1**	**4•2**	**4•3**	**4•4**	**4•5**	**4•6**	**4•7**	**4•8**	**4•9**	**4•10**
Grade 5	2•7	5•5	5•3, 5•6	5•7	2•2, 2•3		4•1		6•2, 6•3	

Pacing for Success

Pacing depends on a number of factors, such as students' individual needs and how long your school has been using *Everyday Mathematics*. At the beginning of Unit 4, you may want to use tools available at www.everydaymathonline.com to help you set your pace.

Home Support

Unit 4 Family Letter (English/Spanish) provides families with an overview, Do-Anytime Activities, Building Skills through Games, a list of vocabulary, and answers to the daily homework (Study Links). Family Letters in English, Spanish, and seven other languages are also available online.

Study Links are the daily homework assignments. They consist of active projects and ongoing review problems.

▸ Home Support Resources

Home Connection Handbook
Offers ideas and reproducible masters for communicating with families. See Table of Contents for unit information.

Student Reference Book
Provides a resource for students and parents.

Pages 26, 130, 178–178B, 231, 232, 242, 254, 256, 258, 259, 276, 277, 279, 282, 283, 296–305

Technology Resources

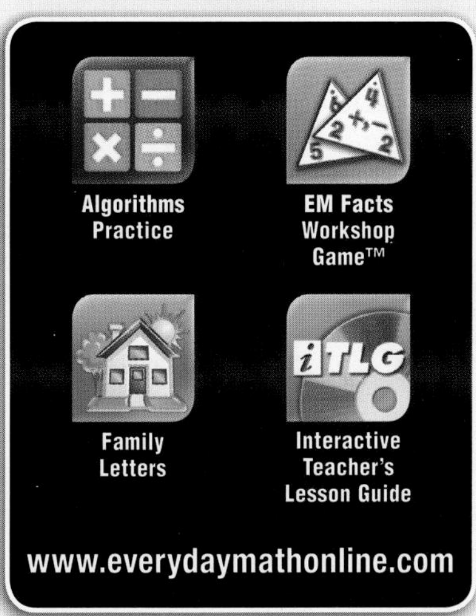

Lesson	Masters	Manipulative Kit	Other Items
4•1	Transparencies of *Math Masters,* pp. 106* and 107* Study Link Master, p. 108 Game Masters, pp. 496 and 497 Teaching Master, p. 109 Teaching Aid Masters, pp. 399–402 and 428	slate; dimes and pennies	overhead calculator*; scissors; calculator
4•2	Teaching Aid Masters, pp. 388* or 389* and 426 Transparency of *Math Masters,* p. 426* Study Link Master, p. 110 Game Masters, pp. 458 and 460 Teaching Master, p. 111	base-10 blocks; slate; per partnership: 2 six-sided dice, 4 pennies	per partnership: ∗ , / Facts Table*, calculator*
4•3	Study Link Master, p. 112 Game Masters, pp. 467 and 506	base-10 blocks; 8 each of number cards 1–10; coins	scissors; *The Everything Kids' Joke Book: Side-Splitting, Rib-Tickling Fun; Kids' Funniest Jokes*
4•4	Study Link Master, p. 113 Game Masters, pp. 490, 491*, and 506* Teaching Masters, pp. 114–117 Teaching Aid Master, p. 428	per partnership: 4 each of number cards 0–9; slate; quarters; dimes	
4•5	Teaching Masters, pp. 118, 120, and 121 Teaching Aid Masters, pp. 427 and 428* Study Link Master, p. 119	base-10 blocks; slate; Number-Grid Poster; quarters*; nickels*; dimes*; pennies*	
4•6	Teaching Masters, pp. 114 and 124 Teaching Aid Masters, pp. 427* and 428 Transparency of *Math Masters,* p. 122 Study Link Master, p. 123 Game Master, p. 489 *Differentiation Handbook,* p. 141	slate; base-10 blocks*; deck of number cards; coins	money*; scissors; calculator
4•7	Transparency of *Math Masters,* p. 125* Study Link Master, p. 126 Teaching Aid Masters, pp. 419–421* Teaching Master, p. 127 Game Master, p. 459	per partnership: 3 six-sided dice; base-10 blocks; slate	calculator
4•8	Study Link Master, p. 128 Game Master, p. 472* Teaching Masters, pp. 129 and 130 *Differentiation Handbook,* p. 141	slate; meterstick; tape measure; centimeter ruler; base-10 cubes and longs	chart paper; calculator
4•9	Study Link Master, p. 131 Game Masters, pp. 491 and 506 Teaching Master, p. 132	slate; tape measure; meterstick; 4 each of number cards 0–9	ruler
4•10	Teaching Aid Masters, pp. 413, 414, 416*, and 429 Study Link Master, p. 133 Teaching Master, p. 134	centimeter ruler; slate	scissors; highlighter; ruler; *If You Hopped Like a Frog;* pen or colored pencil
4•11	Assessment Masters, pp. 169–173 Study Link Masters, pp. 135–138	slate	

*Denotes optional materials

Mathematical Background

The discussion below highlights the major content ideas presented in Unit 4 and helps establish instructional priorities.

Decimal Concepts, Notation, and Applications (Lessons 4◆1–4◆10)

Numbers that are used to count are usually expressed as whole numbers. But numbers that are measures frequently fall between two whole numbers. In ancient times people realized this and long ago began inventing ways to express those in-between numbers. Some of these ancient inventions are what mathematicians now call fractions, and some are what they now call decimals. The focus of Unit 4 is on decimals; fractions will be covered in detail in Unit 7.

The first six lessons of Unit 4 review basic concepts and notation for tenths and hundredths with the help of base-10 blocks and money applications. These concepts are extended to thousandths, beginning in Lesson 4-7, again using base-10 blocks to represent decimals and with metric linear measure applications.

As your class studies decimals in Unit 4, there are several important ideas to keep in mind.

- Decimal notation is a natural and fairly easy extension of "place-value" notation for whole numbers, which by now is very familiar to students. The trading rules are exactly the same—each move of one place to the left increases the value by a factor of ten, and each move to the right decreases the value by a factor of one-tenth.

Note

In our modern world, decimals are often used to express extremely precise measures. Two hundred years ago, the most precise timepieces available were the chronometers used by the British navy. These instruments kept accurate time merely to seconds. But today, Olympic sports events are frequently timed to thousandths of a second. Atomic clocks, used by scientists, are able to measure time to trillionths of a second (picoseconds).

$\div 10$ $\div 10$ $\div 10$ $\div 10$ $\div 10$ $\div 10$

1,000s	100s	10s	1s		0.1s	0.01s	0.001s
Thousands	Hundreds	Tens	Ones	.	Tenths	Hundredths	Thousandths

- Procedures for all operations with decimals are exactly like the corresponding procedures with whole numbers, whether students compute answers using calculators or paper-and-pencil algorithms. For addition and subtraction, it is necessary to keep track of where the decimal points are so that the digits stay in the correct place-value columns. (For an example, see Lessons 4-5 and 4-6.) For multiplication and division, the computation is performed as if all numbers were whole numbers, and then the decimal point is placed by estimating the size of the answer. (See Lessons 9-8 and 9-9.)

Project Note

To teach U.S. traditional addition and subtraction of decimals, see Algorithm Projects 2 and 4.

Unit 4 Organizer

- Since first grade, the *Everyday Mathematics* program has placed a strong emphasis on decimal notation for uses of money, including calculations with decimal money notation in response to number stories. Furthermore, teachers have reported that students often can do fairly difficult calculations—even with 4- and 5-digit numbers—if they think of the numbers as money. Additionally, by fourth grade, students have done much work with metric measures, sometimes expressed in decimal notation.

- The natural notation for a calculator world is decimal notation. All calculators work in decimal notation, even the special calculators that also handle fraction notation.
- All of the problems and examples are presented in real-world contexts. This special emphasis on the uses of decimals is consistent with the general intention of *Everyday Mathematics* to tie mathematics closely to its uses.

The odometer above shows 12,963. This tells us that the car has traveled at least 12,963 miles but less than 12,964 miles. The trip meter shows 45.6. This means that the car traveled at least 45.6 miles but less than 45.7 miles, after the trip meter was reset to 0.

Decimal notation has become indispensable in science and industry. In particular, decimal notation linked to "scientific notation" is useful in expressing both very small and very large numbers. (Scientific notation will be introduced in Grade 5.)

For additional information about decimal concepts, notation, and applications, see Section 9.3 of the *Teacher's Reference Manual.*

World Tour Follow-Up (Lesson 4◆7)

In Lesson 4-7, the class will divide into small tour groups. Each group will select and visit another country in Africa. In Unit 5, the entire class will travel to another region.

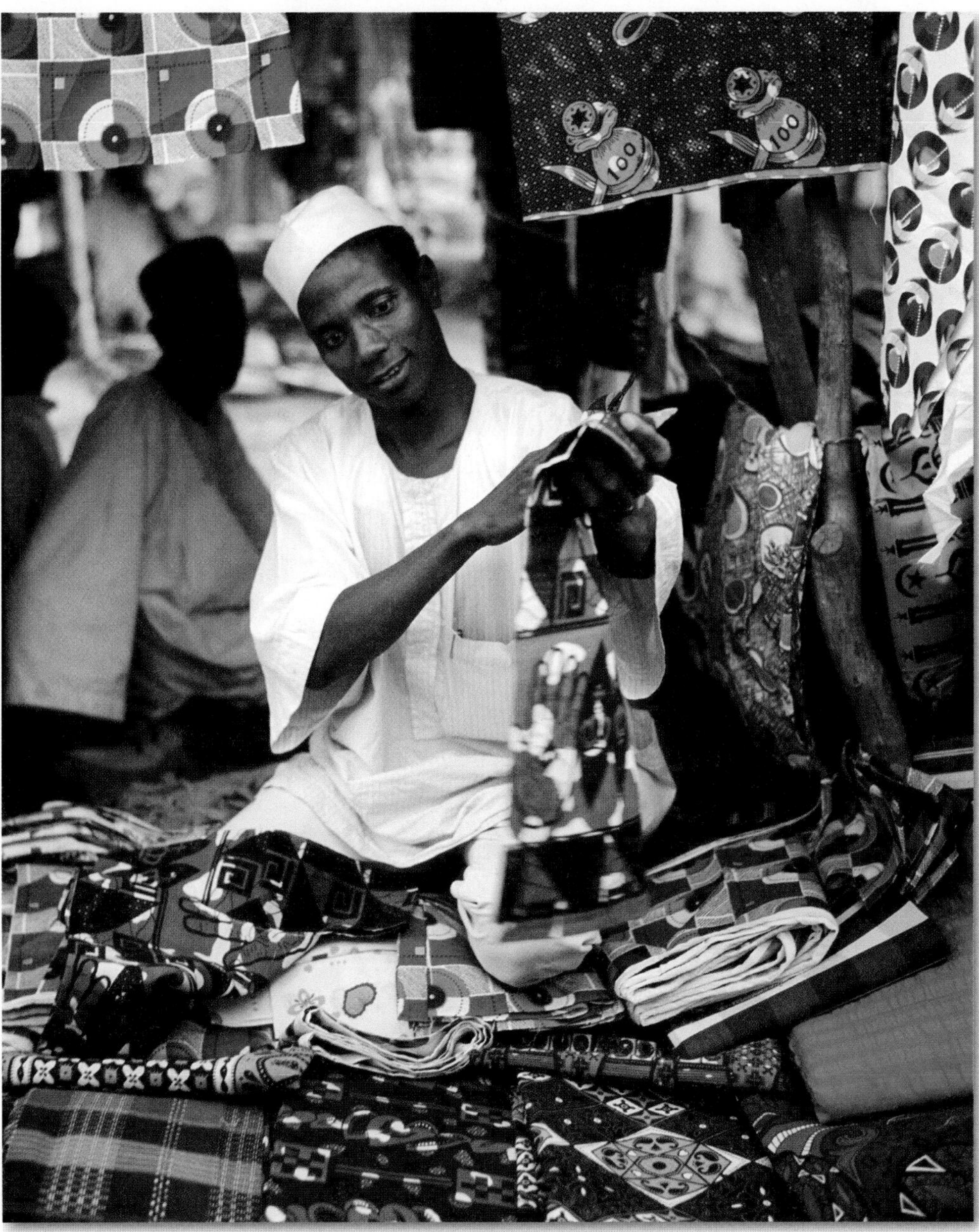

Personal References (Lesson 4◆9)

Lesson 4-9 introduces a new routine that focuses on measures. Students are asked to find their own personal references for common units of measure. They record the names of familiar objects that happen to be good estimates for different metric lengths. A finger width, for example, may be about a centimeter; the thickness of a dime or paper clip, about a millimeter. Students' personal references will be used throughout the year to help estimate lengths of many objects, with the results recorded on *Math Journal 1,* page 99.

Section 14.1 of the *Teacher's Reference Manual* provides additional information about personal references for common units of measure.

4•1 Decimal Place Value

 **Objective** To extend the base-ten place-value system to decimals.

Technology Resources www.everydaymathonline.com

ePresentations

eToolkit

Algorithms Practice

EM Facts Workshop Game™

Family Letters

Assessment Management

Common Core State Standards

Curriculum Focal Points

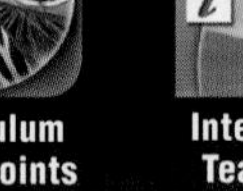

Interactive Teacher's Lesson Guide

1 Teaching the Lesson

Key Concepts and Skills

- Identify the values of digits in decimals. [Number and Numeration Goal 1]
- Read and write decimals through thousandths. [Number and Numeration Goal 1]
- Order decimals through thousandths on a number line. [Number and Numeration Goal 6]
- Use extended division facts to expand the place-value chart to decimals. [Operations and Computation Goal 3]
- Describe numeric patterns in number lines. [Patterns, Functions, and Algebra Goal 1]

Key Activities

Students use number lines to visualize the relationship between successive places in decimals. They review the place-value chart for whole numbers and extend it to decimals. They practice identifying places in decimals and the values of the digits in those places.

Materials

Math Journal 1, p. 78
transparencies of *Math Masters,* pp. 106 and 107 (optional) ◆ calculator ◆ overhead calculator (optional) ◆ slate

2 Ongoing Learning & Practice

Playing *Polygon Pair-Up*
Student Reference Book, p. 258
Math Masters, pp. 496 and 497
Students practice naming properties of polygons.

Math Boxes 4•1
Math Journal 1, p. 79
Students practice and maintain skills through Math Box problems.

Ongoing Assessment: Recognizing Student Achievement
Use Math Boxes, Problems 3a–3d.
[Number and Numeration Goal 1]

Study Link 4•1
Math Masters, p. 108
Students practice and maintain skills through Study Link activities.

3 Differentiation Options

READINESS

Using Money to Explore Decimals
Math Masters, pp. 109 and 428
scissors ◆ dimes and pennies
Students use bills and coins to explore decimals to hundredths.

ENRICHMENT

Writing and Solving Place-Value Puzzles
Students make up and solve place-value puzzles.

EXTRA PRACTICE

Making and Using a Place-Value Tool
Math Masters, pp. 399–402
Students construct and use a Place-Value Flip Book.

Advance Preparation

 ***Teacher's Reference Manual,* Grades 4–6** pp. 37–39, 62, 63

Getting Started

Mental Math and Reflexes

Write whole numbers through millions on the board. Ask students to identify the digits in each place and the values of the digits. *Suggestions:*

Write 5,972,681 on the board.

●○○ Which digit is in the thousands place? 2 How much is that digit worth? 2,000

●●○ Which digit is in the ten-thousands place? 7 How much is that digit worth? 70,000

●●● Which digit is in the millions place? 5 How much is that digit worth? 5,000,000

Math Message

Complete Problem 1 on journal page 78.

1 Teaching the Lesson

▶ Math Message Follow-Up

WHOLE-CLASS ACTIVITY

(*Math Journal 1,* p. 78; *Math Masters,* p. 106)

Have students skip count on their calculators to check their answers to Problem 1. Model the keystrokes on an overhead calculator, if available.

Remind the class to reset the calculator (clear all settings and memory) before each problem. For the TI-15 calculator, students press [On/Off] and [Clear] at the same time. For the *fx*-55 calculator, students press [AC].

For the TI-15 calculator, they enter the following keystrokes:

[Op1] [+] 1 [Op1] 0 [Op1] [Op1] ...

For the Casio *fx*-55 calculator, they enter the following keystrokes:

1 [+] [+] [=] [=] ...

You may want to use a transparency of *Math Masters,* page 106 to discuss the relationships between and among the number lines. Remind students that a number line goes on infinitely in both directions and that it is not possible to draw the entire number line.

Ask students to imagine that they are looking at the interval from 0 to 1 on the first number line under a magnifying glass—here, they would see the second number line. Or, to put it another way, the second number line shows the segment from 0 to 1 in greater detail than the first number line. Similarly, if students looked at the interval from 0 to 0.1 on the second number line under a magnifying glass, they would see the third number line.

Interactive whiteboard-ready ePresentations are available at www.everydaymathonline.com to help you teach the lesson.

NOTE *Math Masters,* page 106 is identical to *Math Journal 1,* page 78 and may be used to make a transparency.

Student Page

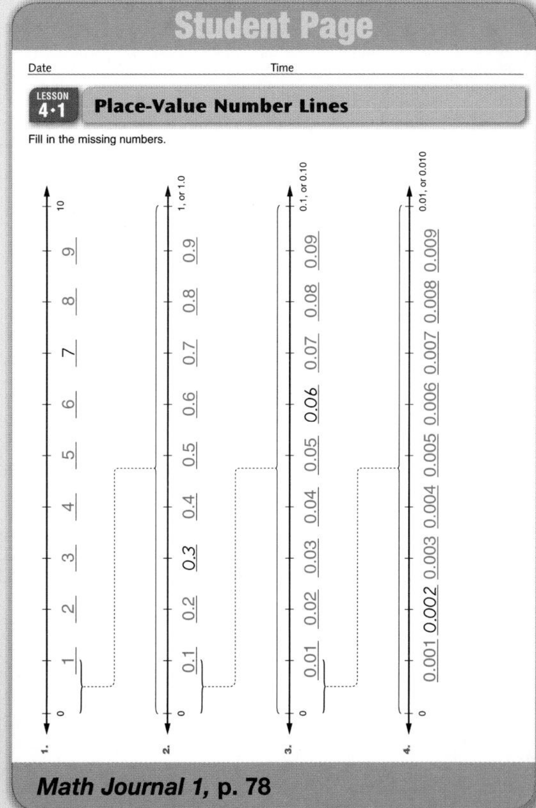

Date Time

LESSON 4·1 **Place-Value Number Lines**

Fill in the missing numbers.

1. 0, 1, 2, 3, 4, 5, 6, 7, 8, 9, 10

2. 0, 0.1, 0.2, 0.3, 0.4, 0.5, 0.6, 0.7, 0.8, 0.9, 1, or 1.0

3. 0, 0.01, 0.02, 0.03, 0.04, 0.05, 0.06, 0.07, 0.08, 0.09, 0.1, or 0.10

4. 0, 0.001, 0.002, 0.003, 0.004, 0.005, 0.006, 0.007, 0.008, 0.009, 0.01, or 0.010

Math Journal 1, p. 78

Have students skip count on their calculators to complete the remaining number lines.

For the TI-15:

Problem 2: [Op1] [+] 0.1 [Op1] 0 [Op1] [Op1] ...

Problem 3: [Op1] [+] 0.01 [Op1] 0 [Op1] [Op1] ...

Problem 4: [Op1] [+] 0.001 [Op1] 0 [Op1] [Op1] ...

For the Casio *fx*-55:

Problem 2: 0.1 [+] [+] [=] [=] ...

Problem 3: 0.01 [+] [+] [=] [=] ...

Problem 4: 0.001 [+] [+] [=] [=] ...

From this activity and discussion, some students may realize, or at least grasp intuitively, that 1 is ten times as much as 0.1, that 0.1 is ten times as much as 0.01, and so on. This idea leads naturally to the extension of place value in the remainder of this lesson.

▶ Reviewing the Place-Value Chart for Whole Numbers and Extending It to Decimals

WHOLE-CLASS ACTIVITY

(*Math Masters,* p. 107)

Use the place-value chart on *Math Masters,* page 107 to review the headings for whole-number places. Remind students how to use the chart to determine the value of each digit in the number 5,709:

- ▷ The digit 5 is in the thousands place—its value is 5 thousands, or 5,000.
- ▷ The digit 7 is in the hundreds place—its value is 7 hundreds, or 700; and so on.

Write each digit in the chart as you review its value.

Point out that each place has a value that is 10 times the value of the place to its right: 1,000 is 10 times 100; 100 is 10 times 10; and so on. Stated another way, each place has a value that is one-tenth the value of the place to its left: 1 is one-tenth of 10; 10 is one-tenth of 100; and so on.

÷10 ÷10 ÷10

1,000s	100s	10s	1s				
Thousands	Hundreds	Tens	Ones	.			
5	7	0	9				

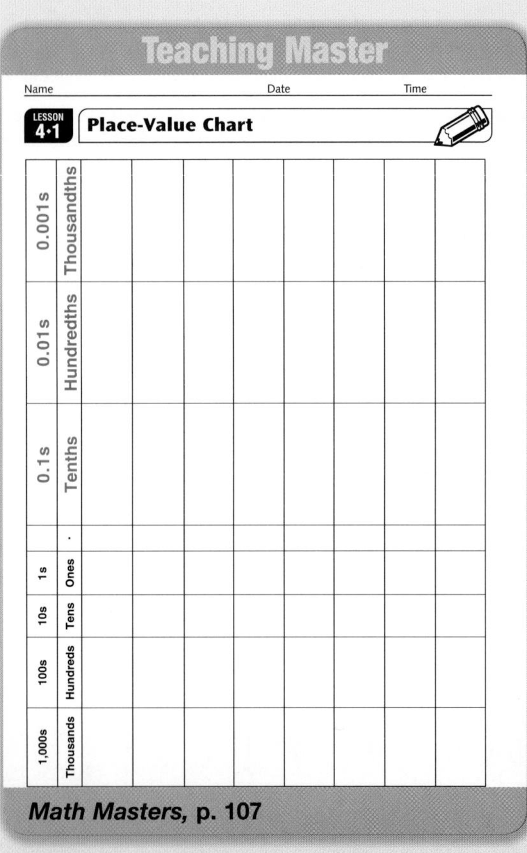

Teaching Master

Name Date Time

LESSON 4·1 Place-Value Chart

1,000s	100s	10s	1s		0.1s	0.01s	0.001s
Thousands	Hundreds	Tens	Ones	.	Tenths	Hundredths	Thousandths

Math Masters, p. 107

Demonstrate how to use a calculator to derive the headings for the place-value chart: Ask students to enter 1000 (÷) 10 (Enter). The display shows the next heading to the right, 100. Enter (÷) 10 (Enter). 10, for the tens place Then enter (÷) 10 (Enter) again. 1, for the ones place STOP!

- What would the calculator display show if you divided by 10 again? 0.1, for the tenths place Why? 0.1 is one-tenth of 1.

Enter the headings 0.1s and Tenths in the next column of your chart.

- What if you divided by 10 again? 0.01, for the hundredths place One more time? 0.001, for the thousandths place

Complete the headings in the chart.

1,000s	100s	10s	1s		0.1s	0.01s	0.001s
Thousands	Hundreds	Tens	Ones	.	Tenths	Hundredths	Thousandths
5	7	0	9				

Call students' attention to the spellings of the headings: The headings for the decimal places end in *-ths*. Students must be careful not to confuse *tens* with *tenths, hundreds* with *hundredths,* and so on.

Adjusting the Activity

Have students speculate about the names of the places to the right of the thousandths place. Ten-thousandths, hundred-thousandths, millionths, and so on

AUDITORY ♦ KINESTHETIC ♦ TACTILE ♦ VISUAL

Identifying Digits and the Values of Digits in Decimals

WHOLE-CLASS ACTIVITY

Write a decimal, such as 7.386, in the place-value chart. Discuss why the decimal point is necessary.

Discuss the value of each digit:

▷ The digit 7 is in the ones place—its value is 7.

▷ The digit 3 is in the tenths place—its value is 3 tenths; and so on.

Write other decimals in the place-value chart. As a slate activity, have students identify the digits in each place and their values.

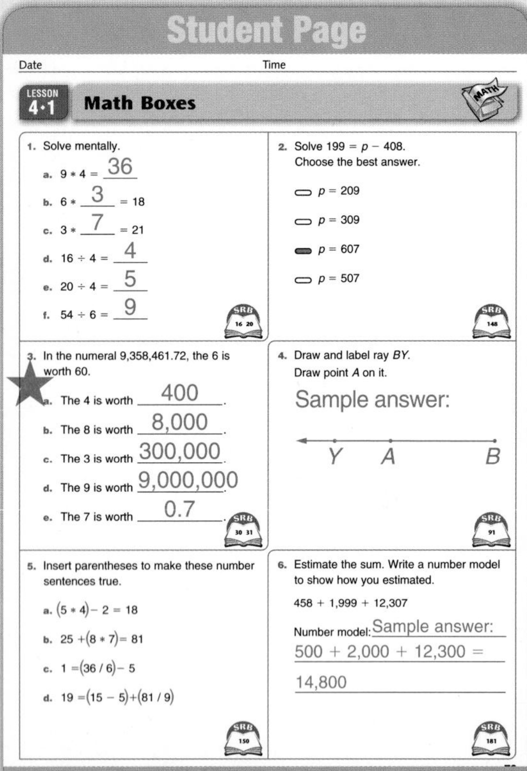

Student Page

Date Time

LESSON 4•1 **Math Boxes**

1. Solve mentally.
   a. 9 ∗ 4 = 36
   b. 6 ∗ 3 = 18
   c. 3 ∗ 7 = 21
   d. 16 ÷ 4 = 4
   e. 20 ÷ 4 = 5
   f. 54 ÷ 6 = 9

2. Solve 199 = p − 408. Choose the best answer.
   - p = 209
   - p = 309
   - p = 607 (filled)
   - p = 507

3. In the numeral 9,358,461.72, the 6 is worth 60.
   a. The 4 is worth 400.
   b. The 8 is worth 8,000.
   c. The 3 is worth 300,000.
   d. The 9 is worth 9,000,000.
   e. The 7 is worth 0.7.

4. Draw and label ray BY. Draw point A on it.
   Sample answer: Y A B

5. Insert parentheses to make these number sentences true.
   a. (5 ∗ 4) − 2 = 18
   b. 25 + (8 ∗ 7) = 81
   c. 1 = (36 / 6) − 5
   d. 19 = (15 − 5) + (81 / 9)

6. Estimate the sum. Write a number model to show how you estimated.
   458 + 1,999 + 12,307
   Number model: Sample answer: 500 + 2,000 + 12,300 = 14,800

Math Journal 1, p. 79

2 Ongoing Learning & Practice

▶ Playing *Polygon Pair-Up*

PARTNER ACTIVITY

(*Student Reference Book,* p. 258; *Math Masters,* pp. 496 and 497)

Students play *Polygon Pair-Up* to practice identifying properties of polygons. See Lesson 1-6 for additional information.

▶ Math Boxes 4•1

INDEPENDENT ACTIVITY

(*Math Journal 1,* p. 79)

Mixed Practice Math Boxes in this lesson are paired with Math Boxes in Lesson 4-3. The skill in Problem 6 previews Unit 5 content.

Ongoing Assessment: Recognizing Student Achievement

Math Boxes Problems 3a–3d ★

Use **Math Boxes, Problems 3a–3d** to assess students' ability to identify the values of digits in whole numbers. Students are making adequate progress if they correctly identify the values of digits through millions. Some students may be able to identify the values of digits in the tenths and hundredths places.

[Number and Numeration Goal 1]

▶ Study Link 4•1

INDEPENDENT ACTIVITY

(*Math Masters,* p. 108)

Home Connection Students solve place-value puzzles.

Study Link Master

Name Date Time

STUDY LINK 4•1 **Place-Value Puzzles**

Use the clues to write the digits in the boxes and find each number.

1. ◆ Write 5 in the tens place.
   ◆ Find $\frac{1}{2}$ of 24. Subtract 4. Write the result in the hundreds place.
   ◆ Add 7 to the digit in the tens place. Divide by 2. Write the result in the thousands place.
   ◆ In the ones place, write an even number greater than 2 that has not been used yet.

1,000s	100s	10s	1s
6	8	5	4

2. ◆ Divide 15 by 3. Write the result in the hundredths place.
   ◆ Multiply 2 by 10. Divide by 10. Write the result in the ones place.
   ◆ Write a digit in the tenths place that is 4 more than the digit in the hundredths place.
   ◆ Add 7 to the digit in the ones place. Write the result in the thousandths place.

100s	10s	1s	.	0.1s	0.01s	0.001s
		2	.	9	5	9

3. ◆ Write the result of 6 ∗ 9 divided by 18 in the ones place.
   ◆ Double 8. Divide by 4. Write the result in the thousandths place.
   ◆ Add 3 to the digit in the thousandths place. Write the result in the tens place.
   ◆ Write the same digit in the tenths and hundredths place so that the sum of all the digits is 14.

10s	1s	.	0.1s	0.01s	0.001s
7	3	.	0	0	4

Practice

Write true or false.

4. 6 ∗ 5 = 15 + 15 true
5. 15 + 7 < 13 − 8 false
6. 72 / 9 > 9 false

Math Masters, p. 108

3 Differentiation Options

READINESS

PARTNER ACTIVITY

5–15 Min

Using Money to Explore Decimals

(*Math Masters,* pp. 109 and 428)

To explore decimals to the hundredths place using a concrete model, have students make bill and coin combinations for given amounts. Upon completion of the table, have students discuss patterns. Sample answer: The number of pennies is always written in the place farthest to the right (the hundredths place), dimes in the tenths place, and dollars in the ones place.

ENRICHMENT

Writing and Solving Place-Value Puzzles

Portfolio Ideas

To apply students' understanding of place value, have them create place-value puzzles. They write puzzles similar to those on Study Link 4-1 and ask a partner to solve them. Encourage students to use multiplication and division facts in their clues.

EXTRA PRACTICE

Making and Using a Place-Value Tool

(*Math Masters,* pp. 399–402)

To practice decimal place value, have students adapt the flip book they made in Lesson 2-4 to use with decimals. On page 12 of the flip book, there are decimal points in each place, so a wide range of numbers can be displayed. *Suggestions:*

▷ Dictate a number. Have students display the number with their books. Ask them to display and read the number that is 0.1 more (and less); 0.01 more (and less); and so on.

▷ Direct students to display certain digits in the places you specify. Have students read the resulting number.

▷ Have students count in unison as they turn over the digits in the books. Count by 1s, starting at 1; by 0.1s, starting at 0.1; by 0.01s, starting at 0.01; and by 0.001s, starting at 0.001.

Teaching Master

Name Date Time

LESSON 4•1 **Money and Decimals**

Use only $1 bills, dimes, and pennies.

1. Use as few bills and coins as possible to show each amount below. Record your work.

Amount	$1 bills	Dimes	Pennies
$1.26	1	2	6
$1.11	1	1	1
$2.35	2	3	5
$3.40	3	4	0
$2.06	2	0	6
$0.96	0	9	6
$0.70	0	7	0
$0.03	0	0	3

2. Describe any patterns you see in the table.
Sample answer: The ones place shows dollars, the tenths place shows dimes, and the hundredths place shows pennies.

3. You can use $1 bills, dimes, and pennies to make any amount of money. Why do you think we have nickels, quarters, and half-dollars?
Sample answer: Having nickels, quarters, and half-dollars lets us make change using fewer coins.

Math Masters, p. 109

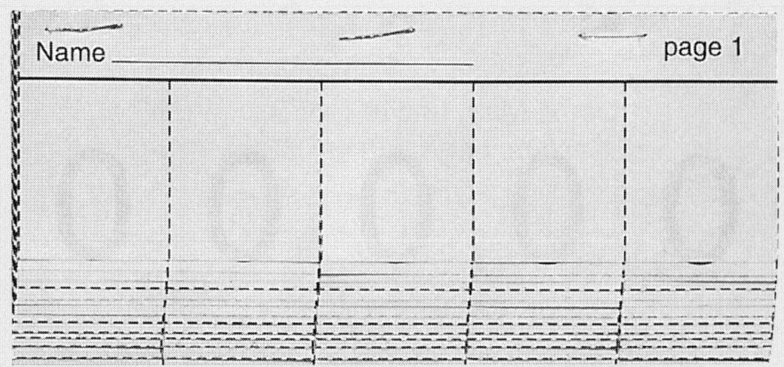

Students fold back the last page of the Place-Value Flip Book for use with decimals.

4•2 Review of Basic Decimal Concepts

Objective To review basic concepts and notation for decimals through hundredths.

www.everydaymathonline.com

ePresentations

eToolkit

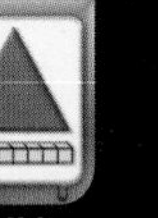
Algorithms Practice

EM Facts Workshop Game™

Family Letters

Assessment Management

Common Core State Standards

Curriculum Focal Points

Interactive Teacher's Lesson Guide

1 Teaching the Lesson

Key Concepts and Skills

- Read and write decimals through hundredths.
 [Number and Numeration Goal 1]
- Model decimals through hundredths with base-10 blocks.
 [Number and Numeration Goal 1]
- Name the fractional part of the ONE represented by a base-10 block.
 [Number and Numeration Goal 2]
- Rename fractions with 10 and 100 in the denominator as decimals.
 [Number and Numeration Goal 5]

Key Activities

Students review basic concepts and notation for decimals for tenths and hundredths.

Ongoing Assessment: Informing Instruction See page 246.

Ongoing Assessment: Recognizing Student Achievement Use a Math Log or Exit Slip (*Math Masters,* page 388 or 389).
[Number and Numeration Goal 1]

Key Vocabulary

ONE ◆ whole ◆ unit ◆ tenth ◆ hundredth

Materials

Math Journal 1, p. 80
Study Link 4•1
Math Masters, p. 388 or 389 (optional); p. 426
transparency of *Math Masters,* p. 426 (optional) ◆ base-10 blocks ◆ slate

2 Ongoing Learning & Practice

Playing *Baseball Multiplication*
Student Reference Book, pp. 231 and 232
Math Masters, p. 460
per partnership: 2 six-sided dice and 4 pennies, calculator or *, / Facts Table (optional)
Students practice multiplication facts.

Math Boxes 4•2
Math Journal 1, p. 81
Students practice and maintain skills through Math Box problems.

Study Link 4•2
Math Masters, p. 110
Students practice and maintain skills through Study Link activities.

3 Differentiation Options

READINESS

Playing *Base-10 Exchange*
Math Masters, p. 458
per partnership: base-10 blocks (1 flat, 20 longs, 20 cubes), 2 six-sided dice
Students explore the relationships among hundredths, tenths, and ones.

ENRICHMENT

Exploring the ONE
Math Masters, p. 111
base-10 blocks
Students explore the concept of the whole, or the ONE, using a concrete model.

Advance Preparation

Place a flat, a long, and a cube near the Math Message. Write *flat, long,* and *cube* on slips of paper and use them to label the base-10 blocks.

***Teacher's Reference Manual,* Grades 4–6** pp. 37–39, 62, 63, 84

Getting Started

Mental Math and Reflexes

Practice counting decimal amounts. Use base-10 blocks on the overhead to model the following:

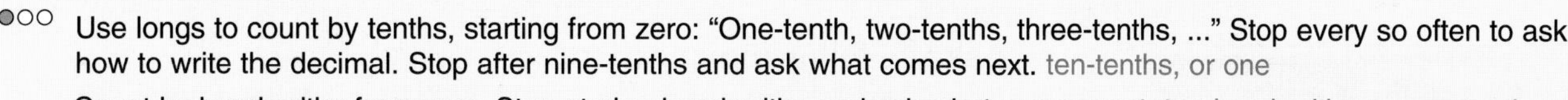

●○○ Use longs to count by tenths, starting from zero: "One-tenth, two-tenths, three-tenths, ..." Stop every so often to ask how to write the decimal. Stop after nine-tenths and ask what comes next. ten-tenths, or one

Count by hundredths from zero. Stop at nine-hundredths and ask what comes next. ten-hundredths, or one-tenth

●●○ Use cubes to count by tenths from other numbers (0.8, 1.5, and so on), again stopping occasionally to write the numbers or ask what comes next. Focus on counting through landmarks like 1.0 or 2.0.

Count by hundredths from other numbers.

●●● Count backward by tenths and hundredths, focusing on counting through landmarks.

Math Message

Write the answers.

1 flat = 10 longs   1 flat = 100 cubes

1 long = 10 cubes

Study Link 4·1 Follow-Up

Have partners compare answers. Note that for each problem, some answers depend on previous answers. On the back of the page have students use words to write the numbers they found in Problems 1–3.

1 Teaching the Lesson

Math Message Follow-Up

WHOLE-CLASS ACTIVITY

(*Math Masters,* p. 426)

Have students share their answers. Review relationships among the base-10 blocks.

▷ To demonstrate that 1 flat = 10 longs, show a copy or an overhead transparency of *Math Masters,* page 426, and cover the 10-by-10 square with longs.

▷ To demonstrate that 1 long = 10 cubes, cover one of the 10-strips with cubes.

▷ Explain that because 1 long = 10 cubes, 1 flat must have 10 times as many cubes, or 100 cubes.

In this lesson students revisit the connection between decimals and fractions, and the relationship of both to the ONE.

Understanding Fraction Concepts

WHOLE-CLASS ACTIVITY

ELL

Remind students that a fraction is always a fraction of something, such as $\frac{1}{2}$ of an apple, $\frac{1}{5}$ of the crayons in a box, or $\frac{3}{4}$ of a yard. We refer to this "something" as the **ONE,** or the **whole;** for measures, "something" refers to the **unit.** To support English language learners, write the word *whole* on the board and explain its meaning in this context. Clarify the difference between *whole* and *hole*.

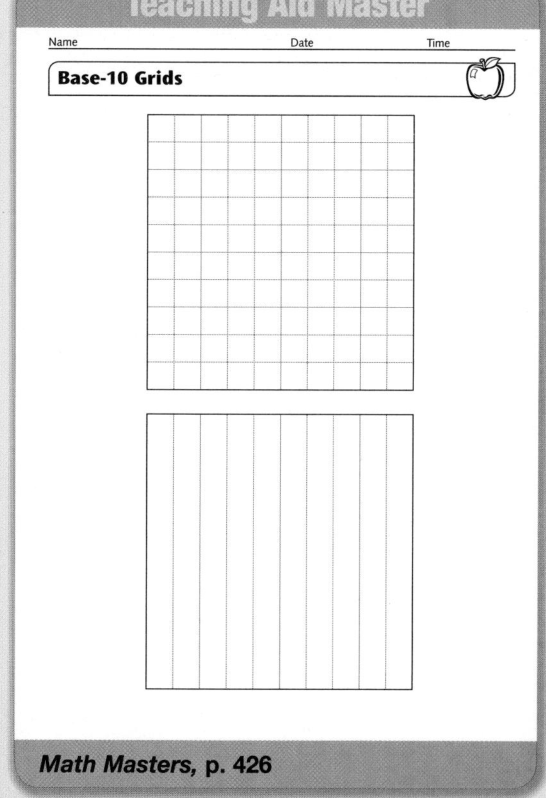

Teaching Aid Master

Name | Date | Time

Base-10 Grids

***Math Masters*, p. 426**

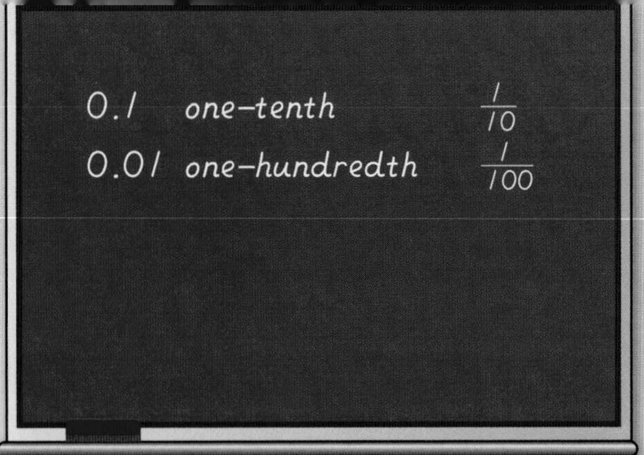

0.1 one-tenth 1/10
0.01 one-hundredth 1/100

Ask the following questions:

- If we think of a flat as the ONE, what fraction of a flat is a long? $\frac{1}{10}$ because 10 longs = 1 flat (Write 0.1 on the board. Remind students that this is another way of writing $\frac{1}{10}$; 0.1 is read as "one-tenth." Next to 0.1, write "one-tenth" and "$\frac{1}{10}$")
- If we think of a flat as the ONE, what fraction of a flat is a cube? $\frac{1}{100}$ because 100 cubes = 1 flat (Write 0.01 on the board. Remind students that this is another way of writing $\frac{1}{100}$; 0.01 is read as "one-hundredth." Next to 0.01, write "one-hundredth" and "$\frac{1}{100}$.")

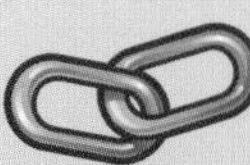

Links to the Future

In Unit 7 of *Fourth Grade Everyday Mathematics* students will continue to explore the *whole* as they use pattern blocks and counters to find the ONE for given fractions of sets and regions.

▶ Modeling Decimals with Base-10 Blocks

(*Math Masters,* p. 426)

Use the following steps to review decimal notation for **tenths** and **hundredths.**

Modeling fractions with base-10 blocks

Students use base-10 blocks to model numbers containing tenths and hundredths on copies of *Math Masters,* page 426 while you do so on the transparency.

Ask: If the flat is ONE, then what are

- 3 longs? $\frac{3}{10}$
- 5 longs? $\frac{5}{10}$, or $\frac{1}{2}$
- 13 cubes? $\frac{13}{100}$
- 4 longs and 2 cubes? $\frac{42}{100}$
- 2 flats, 3 longs, and 4 cubes? $2\frac{34}{100}$
- 1 flat and 6 cubes? $1\frac{6}{100}$

Ongoing Assessment: Informing Instruction

When base-10 blocks were used in Unit 2 to model whole numbers, the cube was the ONE, the long was 10, the flat was 100, and the big cube was 1,000. Watch for students who may not have made the transition to using base-10 blocks to model fractions with the flat as the new ONE. Draw a sketch of a flat on the board and label it ONE. Throughout the lesson, draw and label sketches to support students' transition to the new ONE.

Representing numbers with base-10 blocks

Have students use as few base-10 blocks as possible to show numbers. If base-10 blocks are not available, students can draw the blocks to record their answers. See their symbols on journal page 80. *Suggestions:*

- ▷ $\frac{2}{10}$ 2 longs
- ▷ $\frac{7}{10}$ 7 longs
- ▷ $\frac{3}{100}$ 3 cubes
- ▷ $\frac{35}{100}$ 3 longs and 5 cubes
- ▷ $2\frac{1}{10}$ 2 flats and 1 long
- ▷ $3\frac{24}{100}$ 3 flats, 2 longs, and 4 cubes
- ▷ $5\frac{3}{10}$ 5 flats and 3 longs

Reviewing decimal notation

Have students write numbers in decimal notation. *Suggestions:*

- ▷ $\frac{3}{10}$ 0.3
- ▷ $\frac{4}{100}$ 0.04
- ▷ $\frac{6}{10}$ 0.6
- ▷ $2\frac{8}{10}$ 2.8
- ▷ $\frac{27}{100}$ 0.27
- ▷ $7\frac{59}{100}$ 7.59
- ▷ $\frac{4}{10}$ 0.4
- ▷ $3\frac{2}{100}$ 3.02

Compare the decimals for $\frac{4}{10}$ and $\frac{4}{100}$ Emphasize the need for the second 0 in 0.04 to name $\frac{4}{100}$. Without this zero, the value of the decimal would be $\frac{4}{10}$.

Adjusting the Activity

Have students think of tenths and hundredths in terms of dollars-and-cents notation when asked to compare decimals such as 0.4 and 0.04. In dollars-and-cents notation, the first digit to the right of the decimal point stands for dimes, or tenths of a dollar, and the second digit stands for pennies, or hundredths of a dollar.

- How many dimes are in $1.00? 10 What fraction of a dollar is 1 dime? $\frac{1}{10}$ How would you write 4 dimes in dollars-and-cents notation? $0.40
- How many pennies are in $1.00? 100 What fraction of a dollar is 1 penny? $\frac{1}{100}$ How would you write 4 pennies in dollars-and-cents notation? $0.04

AUDITORY ◆ KINESTHETIC ◆ TACTILE ◆ VISUAL

Reviewing reading decimals for tenths and hundredths

Remind students that decimals are read the same way as their fraction equivalents: 0.3 is read as 3 *tenths,* 0.27 as 27 *hundredths,* and 0.04 as 4 *hundredths.*

Students should read numbers like 4.78 as *four and seventy-eight hundredths* rather than *four point seven eight.* While the second reading is correct and is commonly used, especially for longer decimals, students can benefit from the more formal reading at this stage in their learning.

Adjusting the Activity

ELL

Have students adjust their voice to be louder or lower to emphasize the *-th* in the decimal names.

AUDITORY ◆ KINESTHETIC ◆ TACTILE ◆ VISUAL

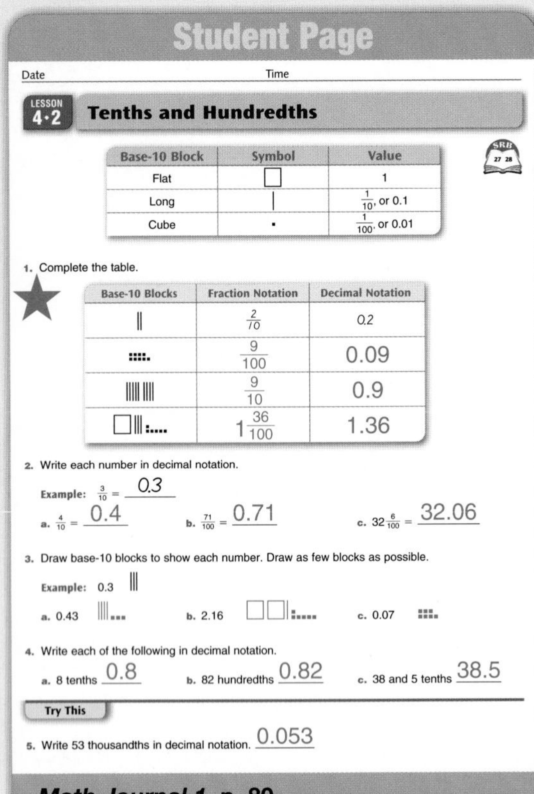
Student Page

Date Time

LESSON 4·2 **Tenths and Hundredths**

Base-10 Block	Symbol	Value
Flat	□	1
Long	|	$\frac{1}{10}$, or 0.1
Cube	·	$\frac{1}{100}$, or 0.01

1. Complete the table.

Base-10 Blocks	Fraction Notation	Decimal Notation
||	$\frac{2}{10}$	0.2
::::.	$\frac{9}{100}$	0.09
|||||||||	$\frac{9}{10}$	0.9
□|||:....	$1\frac{36}{100}$	1.36

2. Write each number in decimal notation.

Example: $\frac{3}{10}$ = 0.3

a. $\frac{4}{10}$ = 0.4 b. $\frac{71}{100}$ = 0.71 c. $32\frac{6}{100}$ = 32.06

3. Draw base-10 blocks to show each number. Draw as few blocks as possible.

Example: 0.3 |||

a. 0.43 ||||... b. 2.16 □□|:..... c. 0.07 :::.

4. Write each of the following in decimal notation.

a. 8 tenths 0.8 b. 82 hundredths 0.82 c. 38 and 5 tenths 38.5

Try This

5. Write 53 thousandths in decimal notation. 0.053

Math Journal 1, p. 80

▶ Practicing with Tenths and Hundredths

INDEPENDENT ACTIVITY

(*Math Journal 1,* p. 80)

Students solve problems involving the representation of numbers with base-10 blocks, fractions, and decimals.

Ongoing Assessment: Recognizing Student Achievement

Math Log or Exit Slip

Portfolio Ideas

Use a **Math Log** or an **Exit Slip** (*Math Masters,* page 388 or 389) to assess students' understanding of the values of decimal digits. Ask students to explain the difference between 0.9 and 0.09 on journal page 80, Problem 1. Students are making adequate progress if their responses make reference to the value of the 9 in 0.9 9 tenths and the value of the 9 in 0.09 9 hundredths. Some students may support their explanations by referring to the pictures on journal page 80 or by stating the decimals in terms of money amounts.

[Number and Numeration Goal 1]

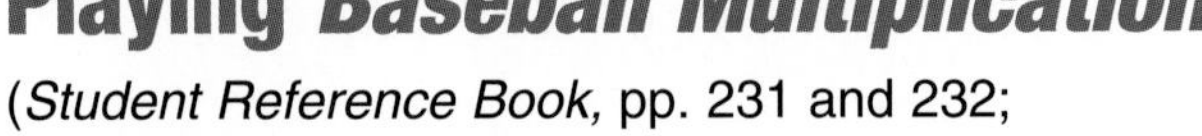

2 Ongoing Learning & Practice

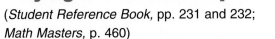

▶ Playing *Baseball Multiplication*

PARTNER ACTIVITY

(*Student Reference Book,* pp. 231 and 232; *Math Masters,* p. 460)

Students play *Baseball Multiplication* to maintain automaticity with multiplication facts. See Lesson 3-3 for additional information.

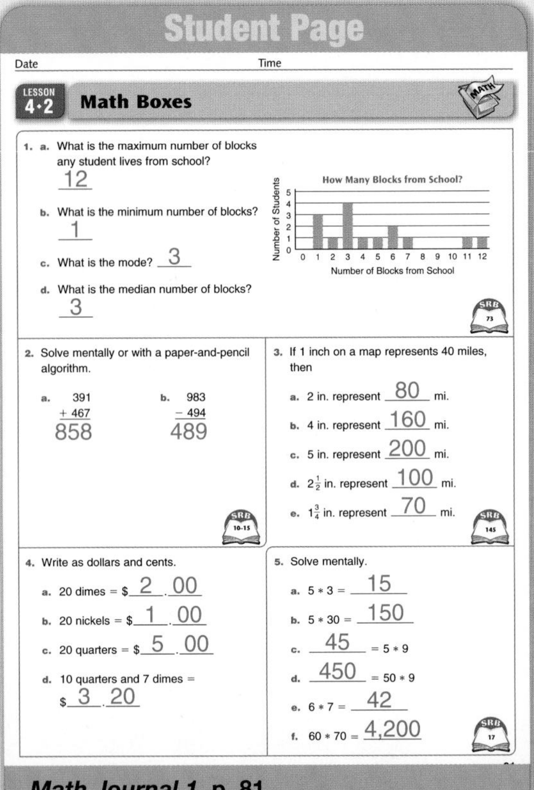
Student Page

Date Time

LESSON 4·2 **Math Boxes**

1. a. What is the maximum number of blocks any student lives from school? 12

b. What is the minimum number of blocks? 1

c. What is the mode? 3

d. What is the median number of blocks? 3

How Many Blocks from School? (Number of Students; Number of Blocks from School)

2. Solve mentally or with a paper-and-pencil algorithm.

a. 391 + 467 = 858

b. 983 − 494 = 489

3. If 1 inch on a map represents 40 miles, then

a. 2 in. represent 80 mi.

b. 4 in. represent 160 mi.

c. 5 in. represent 200 mi.

d. $2\frac{1}{2}$ in. represent 100 mi.

e. $1\frac{3}{4}$ in. represent 70 mi.

4. Write as dollars and cents.

a. 20 dimes = $2.00

b. 20 nickels = $1.00

c. 20 quarters = $5.00

d. 10 quarters and 7 dimes = $3.20

5. Solve mentally.

a. 5 * 3 = 15

b. 5 * 30 = 150

c. 45 = 5 * 9

d. 450 = 50 * 9

e. 6 * 7 = 42

f. 60 * 70 = 4,200

Math Journal 1, p. 81

▶ Math Boxes 4·2

INDEPENDENT ACTIVITY

(*Math Journal 1,* p. 81)

Mixed Practice Math Boxes in this lesson are paired with Math Boxes in Lesson 4-4. The skill in Problem 5 previews Unit 5 content.

Writing/Reasoning Have students write a response to the following: *Explain the strategy you used in Problem 4d to convert 10 quarters and 7 dimes into dollars and cents.* Sample answer: 10 * 25 cents = 250 cents, and 7 * 10 cents = 70 cents. Total: 250 cents + 70 cents = 320 cents, or 3 dollars and 20 cents.

▶ Study Link 4·2

INDEPENDENT ACTIVITY

(*Math Masters,* p. 110)

Home Connection Students collect examples of decimals.

3 Differentiation Options

READINESS

PARTNER ACTIVITY

Playing *Base-10 Exchange*

5–15 Min

(*Math Masters,* p. 458)

To explore the relationship among hundredths, tenths, and ones using a concrete model, have students play *Base-10 Exchange.* The object of the game is to be the first player to make an exchange for a flat (1).

1. The bank starts with 1 flat, 20 longs, and 20 cubes.
2. Players take turns. A player rolls two dice, announces the total, takes that number of cubes (hundredths) from the bank, and places them on the mat.
3. Whenever possible, a player exchanges 10 cubes (hundredths) for a long (tenth) from the bank.
4. The first player to exchange 10 longs (tenths) for 1 flat (1) wins.

Have students describe the exchanges they make. For example, "I have 12 cubes, so I exchange 10 of them for 1 long. Now I have 1 long and 2 cubes."

ENRICHMENT

INDEPENDENT ACTIVITY

Exploring the ONE

5–15 Min

(*Math Masters,* p. 111)

To apply students' understanding of the whole or ONE using a concrete model, have them identify the value of base-10 blocks when different combinations are designated as ONE. They are also asked to find the whole, or ONE, when a fraction is given.

Have students review their answers to Problem 1. Ask: *What would $\frac{1}{100}$ look like?* Sample answer: It would be very small. You would need to cut a cube into 10 equal pieces. One piece is $\frac{1}{100}$. Ask: *What would $\frac{1}{1,000}$ look like?* Sample answer: Cut a cube into 100 equal parts. Each part is $\frac{1}{1,000}$.

Study Link Master

Name Date Time

STUDY LINK 4·2 **Decimals All Around**

Find examples of decimals in newspapers, in magazines, in books, or on food packages. Ask people in your family for examples.

SRB 26

Write your numbers below or, if an adult says you may, cut them out and tape them on this page. Be sure to write what the numbers mean. For example, "The body temperature of a hibernating dormouse may go down to 35.6°F."

Answers vary.

Practice

Write true or false.

1. 286 + 286 = 462 false
2. 907 − 709 = 200 false
3. 641 + 359 = 359 + 641 true
4. 2,345 − 198 = 2,969 − 822 true

Math Masters, p. 110

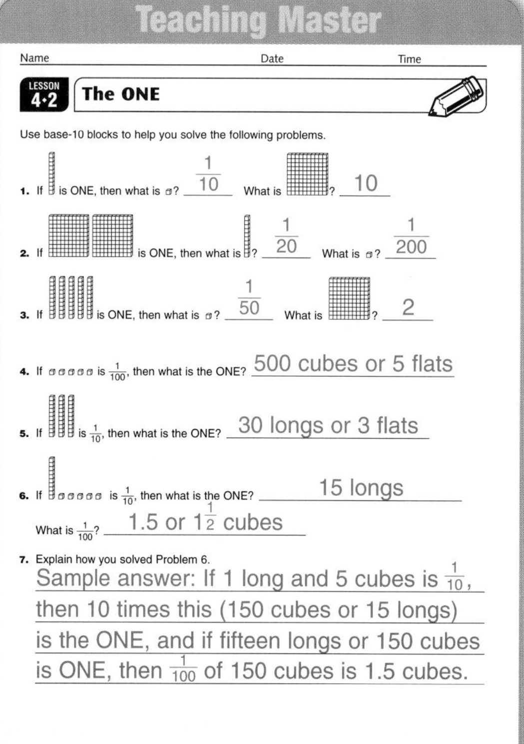

Teaching Master

Name Date Time

LESSON 4·2 **The ONE**

Use base-10 blocks to help you solve the following problems.

1. If [long] is ONE, then what is [cube]? $\frac{1}{10}$ What is [flat]? 10
2. If [2 flats] is ONE, then what is [long]? $\frac{1}{20}$ What is [cube]? $\frac{1}{200}$
3. If [5 longs] is ONE, then what is [cube]? $\frac{1}{50}$ What is [flat]? 2
4. If [5 cubes] is $\frac{1}{100}$, then what is the ONE? 500 cubes or 5 flats
5. If [3 longs] is $\frac{1}{10}$, then what is the ONE? 30 longs or 3 flats
6. If [1 long and 5 cubes] is $\frac{1}{10}$, then what is the ONE? 15 longs
   What is $\frac{1}{100}$? 1.5 or $1\frac{1}{2}$ cubes
7. Explain how you solved Problem 6.
   Sample answer: If 1 long and 5 cubes is $\frac{1}{10}$, then 10 times this (150 cubes or 15 longs) is the ONE, and if fifteen longs or 150 cubes is ONE, then $\frac{1}{100}$ of 150 cubes is 1.5 cubes.

Math Masters, p. 111

4•3 Comparing and Ordering Decimals

Objective To guide students as they compare and order decimals in tenths and hundredths.

Technology Resources www.everydaymathonline.com

ePresentations

eToolkit

Algorithms Practice

EM Facts Workshop Game™

Family Letters

Assessment Management

Common Core State Standards

Curriculum Focal Points

Interactive Teacher's Lesson Guide

1 Teaching the Lesson

Key Concepts and Skills

- Model decimals through hundredths with base-10 blocks.
  [Number and Numeration Goal 1]
- Read and write decimals through hundredths.
  [Number and Numeration Goal 1]
- Rename fractions with 100 in the denominator as decimals.
  [Number and Numeration Goal 5]
- Compare and order decimals through hundredths.
  [Number and Numeration Goal 6]

Key Activities

Students compare decimals using base-10 blocks. They append zeros to decimals in order to compare them. Then they put sets of decimals in sequential order.

Ongoing Assessment: Informing Instruction See page 251.

Ongoing Assessment: Recognizing Student Achievement Use journal page 83.
[Number and Numeration Goal 6]

Key Vocabulary

decimal

Materials

Math Journal 1, pp. 82 and 83
Study Link 4•2
base-10 blocks

2 Ongoing Learning & Practice

Playing *Product Pile-Up*
Student Reference Book, p. 259
8 each of number cards 1–10 (from the Everything Math Deck, if available)
Students practice multiplication facts.

Math Boxes 4•3
Math Journal 1, p. 84
Students practice and maintain skills through Math Box problems.

Study Link 4•3
Math Masters, p. 112
Students practice and maintain skills through Study Link activities.

3 Differentiation Options

READINESS

Playing *Coin Top-It*
Math Masters, pp. 467 and 506
scissors ◆ coins
Students practice comparing decimals in a money context.

ENRICHMENT

Writing Decimal Riddles
The Everything Kids' Joke Book: Side-Splitting, Rib-Tickling Fun ◆ *Kids' Funniest Jokes*
Students create riddles and order decimals to solve them.

EXTRA PRACTICE

5-Minute Math
5-Minute Math™, pp. 14, 89, and 94
Students solve problems involving decimals.

ELL SUPPORT

Creating a Decimals All Around Museum
Differentiation Handbook
Students create a Decimals All Around Museum.

Advance Preparation

For the optional Enrichment activity in Part 3, obtain the books ***The Everything Kids' Joke Book: Side-Splitting, Rib-Tickling Fun*** by Michael Dahl (Adams Media Corporation, 2002) and ***Kids' Funniest Jokes*** edited by Sheila Anne Barry (Sterling Publishing Co., 1994).

***Teacher's Reference Manual,* Grades 4–6** pp. 13, 37–39, 62, 63, 84

Getting Started

Mental Math and Reflexes

Write decimals on the board and ask students to read them. *Suggestions:*

●○○	0.5	●●○	34.12	●●●	0.984
	0.76		9.03		0.733
	0.14		465.81		0.804

Math Message

Solve Problem 1 on journal page 82.

Study Link 4·2 Follow-Up

Have students share examples of decimals they brought from home. Discuss their meanings and values. Use such language as, *The label on a package of chicken reads "2.89 pounds." 2.89 pounds is between 2 and 3 pounds. It is almost 3 pounds.* Encourage students to continue bringing examples of decimals to display in a Decimals All Around Museum. See the optional ELL Support activity in Part 3 for details.

1 Teaching the Lesson

Math Message Follow-Up

WHOLE-CLASS DISCUSSION

(*Math Journal 1,* p. 82)

Discuss ways to show that 0.3 > 0.15. Be sure to include the following two methods:

▷ Model **decimals** with base-10 blocks. If a flat is ONE, then 0.3 is $\frac{3}{10}$ of the flat, or 3 longs, and 0.15 is $\frac{15}{100}$ of the flat, or 15 cubes. Because 3 longs are more than 15 cubes, 0.3 > 0.15.

▷ Rename one of the decimals so that both decimals have the same number of digits to the right of the decimal point. Do so by appending zeros to the decimal having fewer digits after the decimal point. In this problem, show that 0.3 = 0.30 by trading 3 longs for 30 cubes. Because 30 cubes are more than 15 cubes, 0.30 > 0.15. Therefore, 0.3 > 0.15.

Have students use base-10 blocks to complete Problem 2 on journal page 82.

Ongoing Assessment: Informing Instruction

Watch for students who think 0.3 is less than 0.15 because 3 is less than 15. Modeling the problems with base-10 blocks and then trading longs for cubes can help students understand why zeros can be appended to a decimal without changing its value.

Writing a zero at the end of a decimal corresponds to thinking about the number in terms of the next smaller place. For example, 30 hundredths, 0.30, or 30 cubes is greater than 15 hundredths, 0.15, or 15 cubes. Note how this differs from the situation with whole numbers: With whole numbers, the number with more digits is always greater.

Student Page

Date Time

LESSON 4·3 **Comparing Decimals**

Math Message

1. Arjun thought that 0.3 was less than 0.15. Explain or draw pictures to help Arjun see that 0.3 is more than 0.15.

Sample answer: Model the decimals with base-10 blocks. Model 0.3 using 3 longs and model 0.15 using 1 long and 5 cubes. 3 longs is greater than 1 long and 5 cubes, so 0.3 > 0.15.

2. Use base-10 blocks to complete the following table.

"<" means "is less than."
">" means "is greater than."

Base-10 Blocks	Decimal	>, <, or =	Decimal	Base-10 Blocks
	0.2	>	0.12	
	0.05	<	0.1	
	0.13	<	0.31	
	0.33	>	0.3	
	1.2	<	2.1	
	0.47	>	0.39	
	2.3	=	2.3	

Math Journal 1, p. 82

Student Page

Date Time

LESSON 4·3 **Ordering Decimals**

1. Write < or >.

   a. 0.24 > 0.18 b. 0.05 < 0.1 c. 0.2 < 0.35

   d. 1.03 > 0.30 e. 3.2 < 6.59 f. 25.9 > 25.72

2. Write your own decimals to make true number sentences. Sample answers:

   a. 0.9 > 0.2 b. 1.06 < 1.07 c. −1.5 < 0.003

3. Put these numbers in order from smallest to largest.

   a. 0.05, 0.5, 0.55, 5.5 — 0.05 (smallest), 0.5, 0.55, 5.5 (largest)

   b. 0.99, 0.27, 1.8, 2.01 — 0.27 (smallest), 0.99, 1.8, 2.01 (largest)

   c. 2.1, 2.01, 20.1, 20.01 — 2.01 (smallest), 2.1, 20.01, 20.1 (largest)

   d. 0.01, 0.10, 0.11, 0.09 — 0.01 (smallest), 0.09, 0.10, 0.11 (largest)

4. Write your own decimals in order from smallest to largest. Sample answer:

   0.03 (smallest), 0.08, 0.3, 0.33 (largest)

5. "What's green inside, white outside, and hops?"
   To find the answer, put the numbers in order from smallest to largest.

0.66	1	0.2	1.05	0.90	0.01	0.75	0.35	$\frac{25}{100}$	$\frac{50}{100}$	0.05	0.09	5.5
N	I	O	C	W	A	D	S	G	A	F	R	H

Write your answers in the following table. The first answer is done for you.

0.01	0.05	0.09	0.2	$\frac{25}{100}$	0.35	$\frac{50}{100}$	0.66	0.75	0.90	1	1.05	5.5
A	F	R	O	G	S	A	N	D	W	I	C	H

***Math Journal 1,* p. 83**

Student Page

Games

Product Pile-Up

Materials ☐ number cards 1–10 (8 of each)

Players 3 to 5

Skill Multiplication facts 1 to 10

Object of the game To play all of your cards and have none left.

Directions

1. Shuffle the cards and deal 12 cards to each player. Place the rest of the deck number-side down on the table.
2. The player to the left of the dealer begins. This player selects 2 of their cards, places them number-side up on the table, multiplies the numbers, and gives the product.
3. Play continues with each player selecting and playing 2 cards with a product that is *greater than* the product of the last 2 cards played.

Example Joe plays 3 and 6 and says, "3 times 6 equals 18."

The next player, Rachel, looks at her hand to find 2 cards with a product higher than 18. She plays 5 and 4 and says, "5 times 4 equals 20."

4. If a player is not able to play 2 cards with a greater product, the player must draw 2 cards from the deck. These 2 cards are added to the player's hand. If the player is now able to make a greater product, the 2 cards are played, and play continues.
5. If after drawing the 2 cards a player still cannot make a play, the player says "Pass." If all the other players say "Pass," the last player who was able to lay down 2 cards starts play again. That player may select any 2 cards to make *any* product and play continues.
6. If a player states an incorrect product, he or she must take back the 2 cards, draw 2 cards from the deck, and say "Pass." Play moves to the next person.
7. The winner is the first player to run out of cards, or the player with the fewest cards when there are no more cards to draw.

***Student Reference Book,* p. 259**

▶ Ordering Decimals

(*Math Journal 1,* p. 83)

PARTNER ACTIVITY

ELL

Students compare and order decimals. Base-10 blocks should be available. English language learners may struggle with understanding the answer to the riddle in Problem 5.

Ongoing Assessment: Recognizing Student Achievement

Journal page 83 Problem 1 ★

Use **journal page 83, Problem 1** to assess students' ability to compare decimals through hundredths. Students are making adequate progress if they are able to solve Problems 1a–1f correctly. In Problem 2, some students may demonstrate the ability to compare decimals beyond hundredths or decimals less than 0.

[Number and Numeration Goal 6]

2 Ongoing Learning & Practice

▶ Playing *Product Pile-Up*

(*Student Reference Book,* p. 259)

Students play *Product Pile-Up* to maintain automaticity with multiplication facts. Consider playing against three or four students to model the game.

Adjusting the Activity

Have Multiplication/Division Facts Tables, counters to make arrays, and calculators for skip counting available.

Have students describe the strategies they use to decide which cards to play.

AUDITORY ♦ KINESTHETIC ♦ TACTILE ♦ VISUAL

▶ Math Boxes 4·3

(*Math Journal 1,* p. 84)

Mixed Practice Math Boxes in this lesson are paired with Math Boxes in Lesson 4-1. The skill in Problem 6 previews Unit 5 content.

Portfolio Ideas

Writing/Reasoning Have students write a response to the following: *In Problem 4, is* $\overrightarrow{TC}$ *another name for* $\overrightarrow{CT}$*? Explain why or why not.*

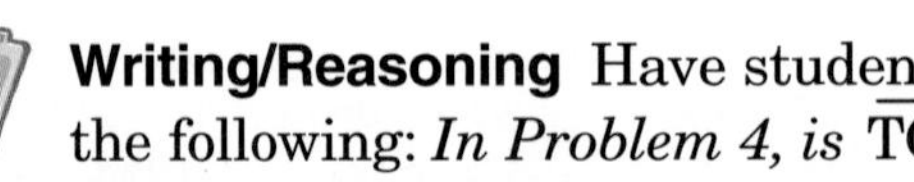

No. Sample answer: The endpoint of ray *CT* is point *C*, so ray *TC* is not the same as ray *CT*. The first letter in the name of a ray is the ray's endpoint.

Study Link 4·3

INDEPENDENT ACTIVITY

(*Math Masters,* p. 112)

Home Connection Students order decimals on a number line and find decimals between two given amounts.

3 Differentiation Options

READINESS

PARTNER ACTIVITY

Playing *Coin Top-It*

5–15 Min

(*Math Masters,* pp. 467 and 506)

To provide experience comparing decimals in a money context, have students play *Coin Top-It.* Ask them to model the amounts shown on the cards with actual coins and record play on *Math Masters,* page 506.

1. Each player cuts apart a copy of *Math Masters,* page 467. Players shuffle the cards and place them facedown.
2. Each player draws one card and says the total amount of the coins. The player with the greater amount keeps both cards. In case of a tie, each player takes another card. The player with the larger amount takes all of the cards.
3. The game ends when no cards are left. The player who collects more cards wins.

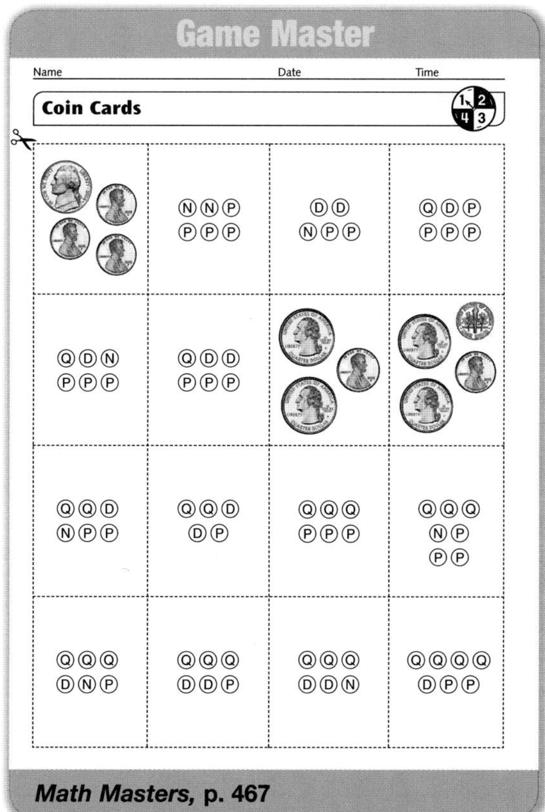

Game Master

Name Date Time

Coin Cards

	Ⓝ Ⓝ Ⓟ Ⓟ Ⓟ Ⓟ	Ⓓ Ⓓ Ⓝ Ⓟ Ⓟ	Ⓠ Ⓓ Ⓟ Ⓟ Ⓟ Ⓟ
Ⓠ Ⓓ Ⓝ Ⓟ Ⓟ Ⓟ	Ⓠ Ⓓ Ⓓ Ⓟ Ⓟ Ⓟ		
Ⓠ Ⓠ Ⓓ Ⓝ Ⓟ Ⓟ	Ⓠ Ⓠ Ⓓ Ⓓ Ⓟ	Ⓠ Ⓠ Ⓠ Ⓟ Ⓟ Ⓟ	Ⓠ Ⓠ Ⓠ Ⓝ Ⓟ Ⓟ Ⓟ
Ⓠ Ⓠ Ⓠ Ⓓ Ⓝ Ⓟ	Ⓠ Ⓠ Ⓠ Ⓓ Ⓓ Ⓟ	Ⓠ Ⓠ Ⓠ Ⓓ Ⓓ Ⓝ	Ⓠ Ⓠ Ⓠ Ⓠ Ⓓ Ⓟ Ⓟ

Math Masters, p. 467

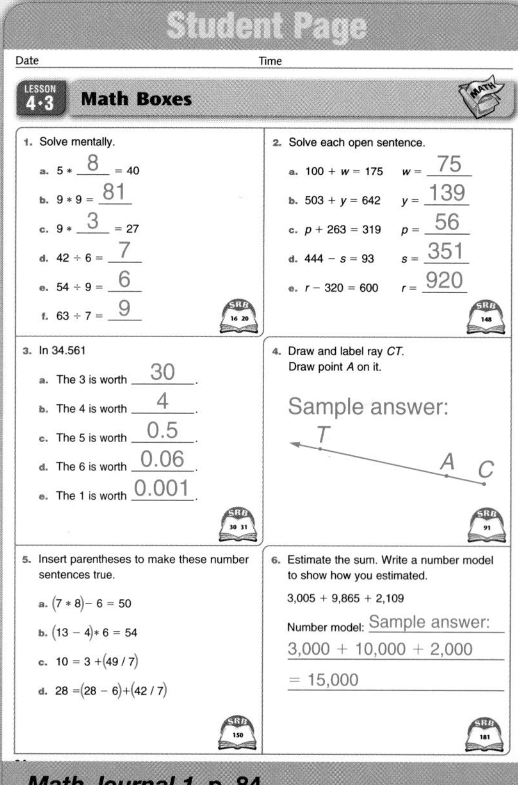

Student Page

Date Time

LESSON 4·3 **Math Boxes**

1. Solve mentally.
   a. 5 ∗ 8 = 40
   b. 9 ∗ 9 = 81
   c. 9 ∗ 3 = 27
   d. 42 ÷ 6 = 7
   e. 54 ÷ 9 = 6
   f. 63 ÷ 7 = 9

2. Solve each open sentence.
   a. 100 + *w* = 175 *w* = 75
   b. 503 + *y* = 642 *y* = 139
   c. *p* + 263 = 319 *p* = 56
   d. 444 − *s* = 93 *s* = 351
   e. *r* − 320 = 600 *r* = 920

3. In 34.561
   a. The 3 is worth 30.
   b. The 4 is worth 4.
   c. The 5 is worth 0.5.
   d. The 6 is worth 0.06.
   e. The 1 is worth 0.001.

4. Draw and label ray *CT.* Draw point *A* on it.
   Sample answer: T A C

5. Insert parentheses to make these number sentences true.
   a. (7 ∗ 8) − 6 = 50
   b. (13 − 4) ∗ 6 = 54
   c. 10 = 3 + (49 / 7)
   d. 28 = (28 − 6) + (42 / 7)

6. Estimate the sum. Write a number model to show how you estimated.
   3,005 + 9,865 + 2,109
   Number model: Sample answer: 3,000 + 10,000 + 2,000 = 15,000

Math Journal 1, p. 84

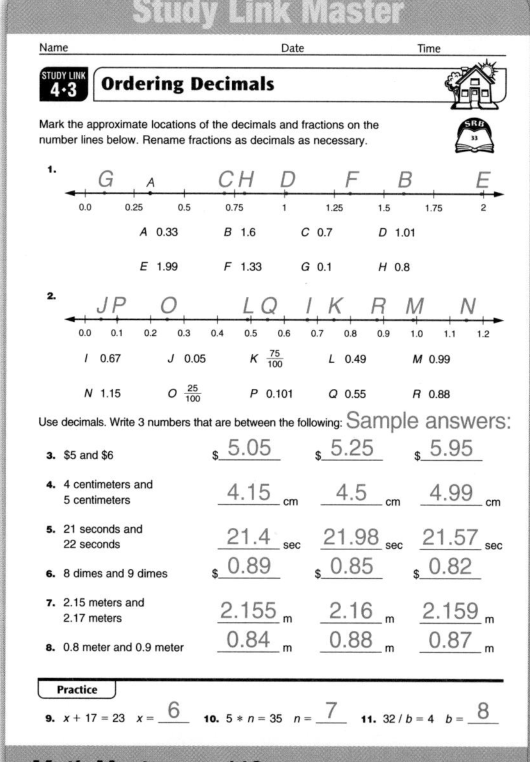

Study Link Master

Name Date Time

STUDY LINK 4·3 **Ordering Decimals**

Mark the approximate locations of the decimals and fractions on the number lines below. Rename fractions as decimals as necessary.

1. Number line 0.0 to 2 (0.0, 0.25, 0.5, 0.75, 1, 1.25, 1.5, 1.75, 2): G A C H D F B E
   A 0.33 B 1.6 C 0.7 D 1.01
   E 1.99 F 1.33 G 0.1 H 0.8

2. Number line 0.0 to 1.2 (0.0, 0.1, 0.2, 0.3, 0.4, 0.5, 0.6, 0.7, 0.8, 0.9, 1.0, 1.1, 1.2): J P O L Q I K R M N
   I 0.67 J 0.05 K $\frac{75}{100}$ L 0.49 M 0.99
   N 1.15 O $\frac{25}{100}$ P 0.101 Q 0.55 R 0.88

Use decimals. Write 3 numbers that are between the following: Sample answers:

3. $5 and $6	$5.05	$5.25	$5.95
4. 4 centimeters and 5 centimeters	4.15 cm	4.5 cm	4.99 cm
5. 21 seconds and 22 seconds	21.4 sec	21.98 sec	21.57 sec
6. 8 dimes and 9 dimes	$0.89	$0.85	$0.82
7. 2.15 meters and 2.17 meters	2.155 m	2.16 m	2.159 m
8. 0.8 meter and 0.9 meter	0.84 m	0.88 m	0.87 m

Practice

9. *x* + 17 = 23 *x* = 6 10. 5 ∗ *n* = 35 *n* = 7 11. 32 / *b* = 4 *b* = 8

Math Masters, p. 112

ENRICHMENT

▶ Writing Decimal Riddles

Literature Link To apply students' understanding of decimal concepts, have them write and solve decimal riddles similar to the one on journal page 83. The following books are good sources for riddles:

- ***The Everything Kids' Joke Book: Side-Splitting, Rib-Tickling Fun*** (Everything Kids Series) by Michael Dahl (Adams Media Corporation, 2002)
- ***Kids' Funniest Jokes,*** edited by Sheila Anne Barry (Sterling Publishing Co., 1994)

EXTRA PRACTICE

SMALL-GROUP ACTIVITY

▶ *5-Minute Math*

To offer students more experience with decimals, see *5-Minute Math,* pages 14, 89, and 94.

ELL SUPPORT

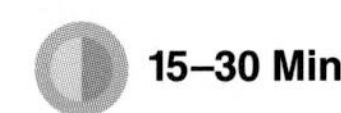

▶ Creating a Decimals All Around Museum

15–30 Min

(*Differentiation Handbook*)

To provide language support for decimals, have students create a Decimals All Around Museum. See the *Differentiation Handbook* for additional information.

Ask students to read the numbers and describe some of the ways that decimals are used in the museum; for example, what the numbers mean, the different categories of uses, or the units attached to the decimals.

4•4 Estimating with Decimals

 **Objectives** To explain why decimals are useful; and to guide estimation of sums and differences of decimals.

Technology Resources www.everydaymathonline.com

ePresentations

eToolkit

Algorithms Practice

EM Facts Workshop Game™

Family Letters

Assessment Management

Common Core State Standards

Curriculum Focal Points

Interactive Teacher's Lesson Guide

1 Teaching the Lesson

Key Concepts and Skills

- Read and interpret decimals through tenths. [Number and Numeration Goal 1]
- Compare whole numbers and decimals. [Number and Numeration Goal 6]
- Estimate sums and differences of decimals; explain the strategies used. [Operations and Computation Goal 6]
- Use a table of data to answer questions. [Data and Chance Goal 2]

Key Activities

Students list examples of decimals used in everyday life and sort them into categories. They estimate sums and differences of decimals to answer questions about a bicycle trip.

 **Ongoing Assessment: Informing Instruction** See page 257.

 **Ongoing Assessment: Recognizing Student Achievement** Use journal page 85. [Operations and Computation Goal 6]

Key Vocabulary

trip meter ◆ speedometer

Materials

Math Journal 1, p. 85
Student Reference Book, p. 26
Study Link 4•3
slate

2 Ongoing Learning & Practice

Playing *Number Top-It* (Decimals)
Student Reference Book, p. 256
Math Masters, p. 490; pp. 491 and 506 (optional)
per partnership: 4 each of number cards 0–9 (from the Everything Math Deck, if available)
Students practice comparing and ordering decimals.

Math Boxes 4•4
Math Journal 1, p. 86
Students practice and maintain skills through Math Box problems.

Study Link 4•4
Math Masters, p. 113
Students practice and maintain skills through Study Link activities.

3 Differentiation Options

READINESS

Estimating Cost of Purchase
Math Masters, pp. 114, 115, and 428
quarters ◆ dimes
Students estimate decimal sums in a money context.

ENRICHMENT

Solving Gasoline Mileage Problems
Math Masters, p. 116
Students use estimation to solve problems involving mileage.

ENRICHMENT

Solving a Decimal Magic Square Puzzle
Math Masters, p. 117
Students use estimation to solve a decimal magic square puzzle.

Advance Preparation

 ***Teacher's Reference Manual,* Grades 4–6** pp. 256–259

Getting Started

Mental Math and Reflexes

Have students give a whole-number estimate for decimal addition and subtraction problems. *Suggestions:* Sample answers:

●○○		●●○		●●●	
3.8 + 9.9	14	3.6 + 4.5	8	25.5 + 11.9	38
2.7 + 8.1	11	8.8 + 8.9	18	48.7 + 20.3	69
10.5 − 6.6	4	16.8 − 9.9	7	26.2 − 10.8	15
12.6 − 9.8	3	23.7 − 8.8	15	62.6 − 50.8	12

Math Message

Describe two examples in which decimals are used in real-life situations.

Study Link 4·3 Follow-Up

Have students compare answers and decide whether partners have found appropriate numbers for Problems 3–8.

1 Teaching the Lesson

▶ Math Message Follow-Up

Discuss students' answers. Sort the uses they suggest into three categories: measurements, money, and other. The majority of responses are likely to be measurements.

Tell students that in this lesson they will explore some uses of decimals.

▶ Discussing Why Decimals Are Useful

(*Student Reference Book,* p. 26)

Have students read page 26 in the *Student Reference Book*. Guide students as they read by asking them to share one thing they learned after each paragraph.

Most students have seen a **trip meter** on the **speedometer** of a car. Discuss the purposes of this instrument. The numbers that represent *whole* numbers of miles traveled are usually in one color, and the numbers that represent *tenths* of miles are in another color.

Discuss what information you would get if a trip meter showed only whole numbers of miles traveled.

- If the trip meter showed 45 miles, what would this tell you about the distance you have traveled so far? It would show that you have traveled at least 45 miles but less than 46 miles.

Student Page

Decimals and Percents

Decimals

Mathematics in everyday life involves more than just **whole numbers.** We also use **decimals** and **fractions** to name numbers that are between whole numbers.

Both decimals and fractions are used to name a part of a whole thing or a part of a collection. Decimals and fractions are also used to make more precise measurements than can be made using only whole numbers.

Fractional parts of a dollar are almost always written as decimals. The receipt at the right shows that lunch cost between 25 dollars and 26 dollars. The "64" in the cost names a part of a dollar.

THE QUAY KEY WEST

TOTAL: 25.64

COME BACK SOON!

You probably see many other uses of decimals every day.

Weather reports give rainfall amounts in decimals. The average annual rainfall in New Orleans, Louisiana, is 66.28 inches.

Digital scales in supermarkets show the weight of fruits, vegetables, and meat with decimals.

Winners of many Olympic events are often decided by times measured to hundredths, and sometimes even thousandths, of a second. Florence Griffith-Joyner's winning time for the 100-meter run in 1988 was 10.54 seconds.

Many sports statistics use decimals. In 1993, basketball player Michael Jordan averaged 32.6 points per game. In 1901, baseball player Napoleon Lajoie had a batting average of .426.

Cars have instruments called odometers that measure distance. The word *odometer* comes from the Greek words *odos,* which means road, and *metron,* which means measure. The odometer at the right shows 12,963, which means the car has traveled at least 12,963 miles. The trip meter above it is more precise and shows tenths of a mile traveled. The trip meter at the right shows the car has traveled at least 45.6 miles since it was last reset to 0.

Decimals use the same base-ten place-value system that whole numbers use. The way you compute with decimals is very similar to the way you compute with whole numbers.

***Student Reference Book,* p. 26**

Decimals make it possible to make more precise measurements. For example, on a trip meter that shows tenths of a mile, a reading of 45.6 miles tells you that the car has traveled at least 45.6 miles but less than 45.7 miles.

Ongoing Assessment: Informing Instruction

Watch for students who do not think of decimals as numbers with a value between two consecutive whole numbers. You can reinforce this concept by asking such questions as "20.964 is between which two consecutive whole numbers?" and by asking students to fill in missing numbers on a number line. Write the word *consecutive* on the board with an example.

Estimating Decimal Sums

(*Math Journal 1,* p. 85)

Read the first part of "A Bicycle Trip" on journal page 85 aloud, and discuss what is meant by *estimation*. Have partnerships finish the page. Emphasize that they are to answer the questions by using estimation, not by computing exact answers.

Adjusting the Activity

Direct students to the table on journal page 85. For each day, have students draw a circle around the *before lunch* and *after lunch* distances to emphasize that students need to consider both numbers when determining the total distance traveled each day.

Travel Log		
	Distance Traveled	
Timetable	Before lunch	After lunch
Day 1	27.0 mi	31.3 mi

AUDITORY ◆ KINESTHETIC ◆ TACTILE ◆ VISUAL

Allow time for students to share solution strategies.

▷ One approach to Problem 3 is to estimate the sum of the distances traveled before and after lunch and then compare the totals. Another possibility: Diego and Alex traveled about 4 more miles after lunch on Day 1 and about 1 more mile on Day 3. However, they traveled so many more miles before lunch on Day 2 that this more than offsets the results for Days 1 and 3.

▷ For Problem 7, a good strategy is to count up from 25.8 to 26.0 (0.2 more) and then from 26.0 to 27.0 (1.0 more) for a total of 1.2 miles.

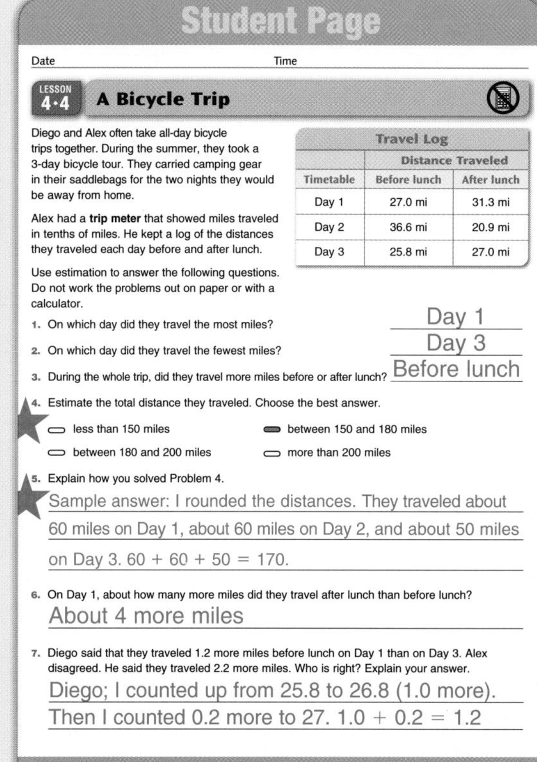

Student Page

Date Time

LESSON 4•4 **A Bicycle Trip**

Diego and Alex often take all-day bicycle trips together. During the summer, they took a 3-day bicycle tour. They carried camping gear in their saddlebags for the two nights they would be away from home.

Alex had a **trip meter** that showed miles traveled in tenths of miles. He kept a log of the distances they traveled each day before and after lunch.

Travel Log		
	Distance Traveled	
Timetable	Before lunch	After lunch
Day 1	27.0 mi	31.3 mi
Day 2	36.6 mi	20.9 mi
Day 3	25.8 mi	27.0 mi

Use estimation to answer the following questions. Do not work the problems out on paper or with a calculator.

1. On which day did they travel the most miles? Day 1
2. On which day did they travel the fewest miles? Day 3
3. During the whole trip, did they travel more miles before or after lunch? Before lunch
4. Estimate the total distance they traveled. Choose the best answer.
   - less than 150 miles
   - between 150 and 180 miles (filled)
   - between 180 and 200 miles
   - more than 200 miles
5. Explain how you solved Problem 4.
   Sample answer: I rounded the distances. They traveled about 60 miles on Day 1, about 60 miles on Day 2, and about 50 miles on Day 3. 60 + 60 + 50 = 170.
6. On Day 1, about how many more miles did they travel after lunch than before lunch?
   About 4 more miles
7. Diego said that they traveled 1.2 more miles before lunch on Day 1 than on Day 3. Alex disagreed. He said they traveled 2.2 more miles. Who is right? Explain your answer.
   Diego; I counted up from 25.8 to 26.8 (1.0 more). Then I counted 0.2 more to 27. 1.0 + 0.2 = 1.2

Math Journal 1, p. 85

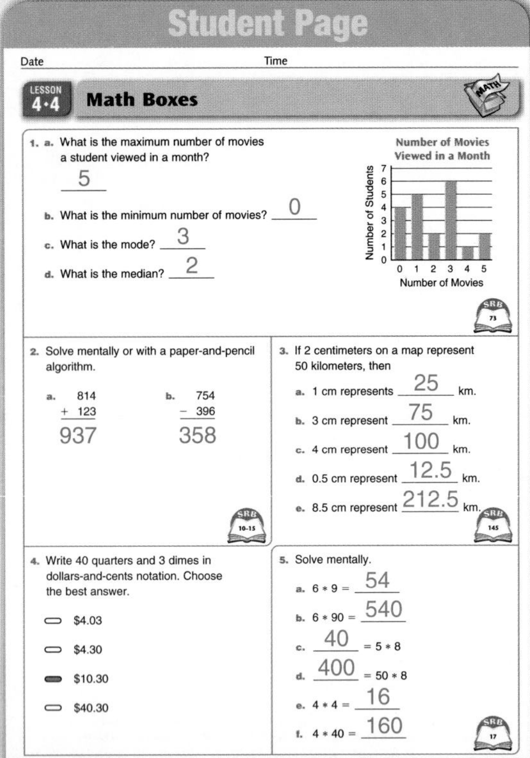
Student Page

Date Time

LESSON 4·4 **Math Boxes**

1. a. What is the maximum number of movies a student viewed in a month? 5
   b. What is the minimum number of movies? 0
   c. What is the mode? 3
   d. What is the median? 2

2. Solve mentally or with a paper-and-pencil algorithm.
   a. 814 + 123 = 937
   b. 754 − 396 = 358

3. If 2 centimeters on a map represent 50 kilometers, then
   a. 1 cm represents 25 km.
   b. 3 cm represent 75 km.
   c. 4 cm represent 100 km.
   d. 0.5 cm represent 12.5 km.
   e. 8.5 cm represent 212.5 km.

4. Write 40 quarters and 3 dimes in dollars-and-cents notation. Choose the best answer.
   - $4.03
   - $4.30
   - $10.30 (filled)
   - $40.30

5. Solve mentally.
   a. 6 ∗ 9 = 54
   b. 6 ∗ 90 = 540
   c. 40 = 5 ∗ 8
   d. 400 = 50 ∗ 8
   e. 4 ∗ 4 = 16
   f. 4 ∗ 40 = 160

Math Journal 1, p. 86

Ongoing Assessment: Recognizing Student Achievement

Journal page 85 Problems 4 and 5

Use **journal page 85, Problems 4 and 5** to assess students' ability to estimate sums of decimals and explain their estimation strategy. Students are making adequate progress if they are able to describe a strategy that involves "close-but-easier" numbers. Some students may estimate the total distance traveled on each of the three days (about 58, 57, and 53 miles) and then estimate the sum of these totals. Others may round each distance to the nearest ten and find the sum (30 + 30 + 40 + 20 + 30 + 30 = 180).

[Operations and Computation Goal 6]

2 Ongoing Learning & Practice

Playing *Number Top-It* (Decimals)

PARTNER ACTIVITY

(*Student Reference Book,* p. 256; *Math Masters,* pp. 490 and 506)

Students play *Number Top-It* (Decimals) to practice comparing 2-place decimals. The version for more than 2 players provides students with practice ordering sets of decimals. Consider having students record a few rounds of play on *Math Masters,* page 506.

Adjusting the Activity

Have students use *Math Masters,* page 491 to play a 3-place-decimal version of the game.

AUDITORY ◆ KINESTHETIC ◆ TACTILE ◆ VISUAL

Math Boxes 4·4

INDEPENDENT ACTIVITY

(*Math Journal 1,* p. 86)

Mixed Practice Math Boxes in this lesson are paired with Math Boxes in Lesson 4-2. The skill in Problem 5 previews Unit 5 content.

Study Link 4·4

INDEPENDENT ACTIVITY

ELL

(*Math Masters,* p. 113)

Home Connection Students estimate sums and differences of lengths of the world's longest railroad tunnels. To support English language learners, discuss the meaning of the word *tunnel*.

Study Link Master

Name Date Time

STUDY LINK 4·4 **Railroad Tunnel Lengths**

The table below shows the five longest railroad tunnels in the world.

Tunnel	Location	Year Completed	Length in Miles
Seikan	Japan	1988	33.46
Channel	France/England	1994	31.35
Moscow Metro	Russia	1979	19.07
London Underground	United Kingdom	1939	17.30
Dai-Shimizu	Japan	1982	13.98

Use estimation to answer the following questions.

1. Which two tunnels have a combined length of about 60 miles? Seikan Tunnel and Channel Tunnel
2. Which of the following is closest to the combined length of all five tunnels? Choose the best answer.
   - Less than 90 miles
   - Between 90 and 130 miles (filled)
   - Between 130 and 160 miles
   - More than 160 miles
3. Explain how you solved Problem 2. Sample answer: I rounded the tunnel lengths to "close-but-easier" numbers and added 35 + 30 + 20 + 15 + 15 = 115 to find the total length.
4. About how many miles longer is the Channel Tunnel than the Moscow Metro Tunnel? About 12 miles

Try This

5. The Cascade Tunnel in Washington State is the longest railroad tunnel in the United States. It is about $\frac{1}{4}$ the length of the Seikan. About how long is the Cascade Tunnel? About 8 miles

Practice

6. 190 + *b* = 200 *b* = 10
7. *g* − 500 = 225 *g* = 725

Math Masters, p. 113

3 Differentiation Options

READINESS

PARTNER ACTIVITY

Estimating Cost of Purchase

5–15 Min

(*Math Masters,* pp. 114, 115, and 428)

To explore estimation using decimals, have students estimate the total cost of items. Students cut apart the item slips on *Math Masters,* page 114. Ask them to place the slips facedown. At each turn, a student flips over three slips, estimates the total cost of the items, and records a number model for their estimate on *Math Masters,* page 115. Provide bills (*Math Masters,* page 428), quarters, and dimes so that students can model amounts that are close to the cost of the items and combine these to find the total.

NOTE The item slips from *Math Masters,* page 114 are used again in Lesson 4-6 in an optional Readiness activity. Store them for use in that lesson.

ENRICHMENT

INDEPENDENT ACTIVITY

Solving Gasoline Mileage Problems

5–15 Min

(*Math Masters,* p. 116)

To apply students' understanding of estimating with decimals, have them use estimation and mental arithmetic strategies to solve mileage problems. Emphasize that the data on *Math Masters,* page 116 are approximations:

- ▷ The numbers on the map are not exact distances: they have been rounded to the nearest 10 miles.
- ▷ The number of miles a car travels on 1 gallon of gasoline (called gas mileage) varies, depending on driving conditions.

ENRICHMENT

INDEPENDENT ACTIVITY

Solving a Decimal Magic Square Puzzle

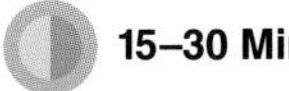

15–30 Min

(*Math Masters,* p. 117)

To apply students' understanding of place value and addition of decimals, have students complete a magic square. Students use estimation to place decimals so that the sum of the numbers in each row, column, and diagonal of the magic square is equal to 6.5. Have students describe how they decided to place the decimal points; for example, "I knew that on the diagonal, the 80 had to be 0.80 because the sum is 6.5, and 8 and 80 are each greater than 6.5."

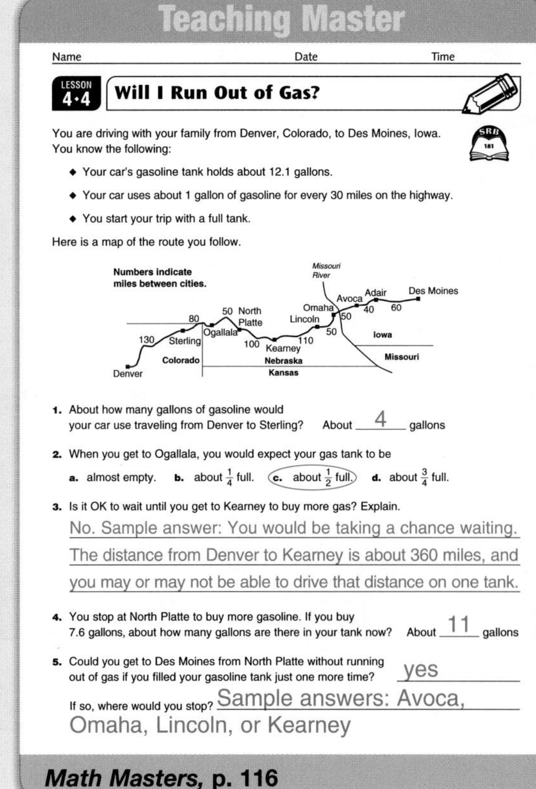

Teaching Master

Name Date Time

LESSON 4•4 **Will I Run Out of Gas?**

You are driving with your family from Denver, Colorado, to Des Moines, Iowa. You know the following:

- Your car's gasoline tank holds about 12.1 gallons.
- Your car uses about 1 gallon of gasoline for every 30 miles on the highway.
- You start your trip with a full tank.

Here is a map of the route you follow.

1. About how many gallons of gasoline would your car use traveling from Denver to Sterling? About 4 gallons
2. When you get to Ogallala, you would expect your gas tank to be
   a. almost empty. b. about $\frac{1}{4}$ full. (c. about $\frac{1}{2}$ full.) d. about $\frac{3}{4}$ full.
3. Is it OK to wait until you get to Kearney to buy more gas? Explain.
   No. Sample answer: You would be taking a chance waiting. The distance from Denver to Kearney is about 360 miles, and you may or may not be able to drive that distance on one tank.
4. You stop at North Platte to buy more gasoline. If you buy 7.6 gallons, about how many gallons are there in your tank now? About 11 gallons
5. Could you get to Des Moines from North Platte without running out of gas if you filled your gasoline tank just one more time? yes
   If so, where would you stop? Sample answers: Avoca, Omaha, Lincoln, or Kearney

Math Masters, p. 116

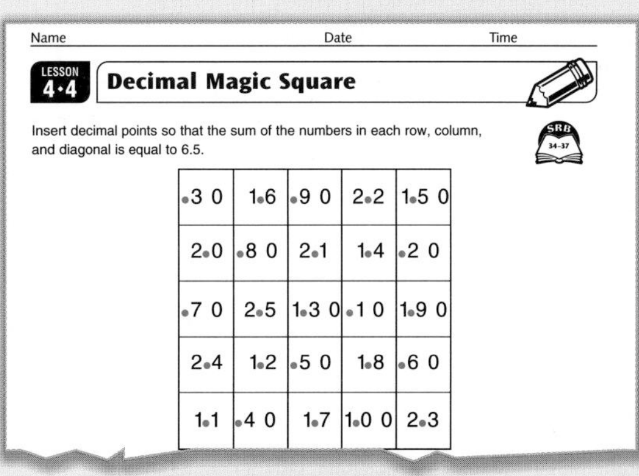

Name Date Time

LESSON 4•4 **Decimal Magic Square**

Insert decimal points so that the sum of the numbers in each row, column, and diagonal is equal to 6.5.

.30	1.6	.90	2.2	1.50
2.0	.80	2.1	1.4	.20
.70	2.5	1.30	.10	1.90
2.4	1.2	.50	1.8	.60
1.1	.40	1.7	1.00	2.3

Math Masters, page 117

4•5 Decimal Addition and Subtraction

Objective To extend methods for whole-number addition and subtraction to decimals.

Technology Resources www.everydaymathonline.com

ePresentations

eToolkit

Algorithms Practice

EM Facts Workshop Game™

Family Letters

Assessment Management

Common Core State Standards

Curriculum Focal Points

Interactive Teacher's Lesson Guide

1 Teaching the Lesson

Key Concepts and Skills

- Model decimals through hundredths with base-10 blocks. [Number and Numeration Goal 1]
- Express the values of digits in decimals. [Number and Numeration Goal 1]
- Add and subtract decimals to the hundredths place. [Operations and Computation Goal 2]
- Judge the reasonableness of solutions to decimal addition and subtraction problems. [Operations and Computation Goal 6]

Key Activities

Students discuss different methods in which to add and subtract decimals, including modeling with base-10 blocks and using algorithms.

Ongoing Assessment: Recognizing Student Achievement Use *Math Masters,* page 118. [Number and Numeration Goal 1]

Ongoing Assessment: Informing Instruction See page 263.

Materials

Math Journal 1, p. 87
Student Reference Book, pp. 178–178B
Study Link 4•4
Math Masters, p. 118; pp. 427 and 428 (optional)
base-10 blocks ◆ quarters, nickels, dimes, pennies (optional) ◆ slate

2 Ongoing Learning & Practice

Analyzing Circle Graphs
Math Journal 1, p. 88
Students compare population data presented in circle graphs.

Math Boxes 4•5
Math Journal 1, p. 89
Students practice and maintain skills through Math Box problems.

Study Link 4•5
Math Masters, p. 119
Students practice and maintain skills through Study Link activities.

3 Differentiation Options

READINESS

Investigating a Decimal Version of the Number Grid
Math Masters, p. 427
Number-Grid Poster
Students use a decimal version of the number grid to model decimal addition and subtraction.

ENRICHMENT

Solving Hiking Trail Problems
Math Masters, pp. 120 and 121
Students compute various distances on a hiking trail.

Advance Preparation

For Part 1, copy and cut apart *Math Masters,* page 118 so that each student has one answer sheet for the Math Message. Place these sheets near the Math Message.

***Teacher's Reference Manual,* Grades 4–6** pp. 119–126

Getting Started

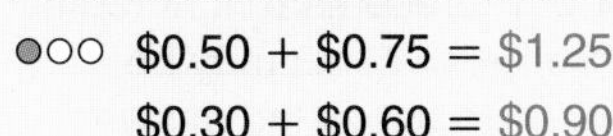

Mental Math and Reflexes

Pose decimal addition and subtraction problems within a money context. *Suggestions:*

●○○	●●○	●●●
$0.50 + $0.75 = $1.25	$1.20 + $0.25 = $1.45	$1.39 + $0.46 = $1.85
$0.30 + $0.60 = $0.90	$1.18 + $0.10 = $1.28	$2.40 + $0.63 = $3.03
$1.00 − $0.70 = $0.30	$1.75 − $1.25 = $0.50	$0.64 − $0.33 = $0.31
$0.80 − $0.40 = $0.40	$1.41 − $0.30 = $1.11	$0.45 − $0.28 = $0.17

Math Message ★

Take an answer sheet (Math Masters, *page 118*) *and complete it.*

Study Link 4·4 Follow-Up

Draw students' attention to Problems 4 and 5. Problem 4 describes what should be added to the length of one tunnel to get the length of another. This is an example of a comparison situation involving addition. Problem 5 describes what one tunnel length should be multiplied by to get another tunnel length. This is an example of a comparison situation involving multiplication.

Descriptions of these problem types are on *Student Reference Book,* pages 178–178B. Refer to these pages as you lead a discussion about the difference between these two types of comparisons. You might suggest that students sketch a situation diagram for each problem.

1 Teaching the Lesson

Math Message Follow-Up

(*Math Masters,* p. 118)

Have students discuss why the answer to the problem is incorrect. There are many ways to explain the mistake. Mention the following, if no one brings them up:

▷ Model the problem with base-10 blocks or pictures of base-10 blocks. (*See margin.*) This gives a total of 9 longs and 6 cubes, or 0.96.

▷ Write the problem in dollars-and-cents notation.

0.76 = $0.76 and 0.2 = $0.20. Think of the 7 in $0.76 as 7 dimes and the 6 as 6 pennies. Think of the 2 in $0.20 as 2 dimes and the 0 as no pennies. This gives a total of 9 dimes and 6 pennies, or $0.96.

▷ Think in terms of place value.

0.76 = 7 tenths and 6 hundredths, and 0.2 = 2 tenths. This gives a total of 9 tenths and 6 hundredths, or 0.96.

▷ Rename 0.2 as 0.20 so that both addends name hundredths. Then use an addition algorithm.

$$\begin{array}{r} 0.76 \\ +\ 0.2 \\ \hline \end{array} \quad \begin{array}{c} \rightarrow \\ \rightarrow \end{array} \quad \begin{array}{r} 0.76 \\ +\ 0.20 \\ \hline 0.96 \end{array} \quad (0.2 = 0.20)$$

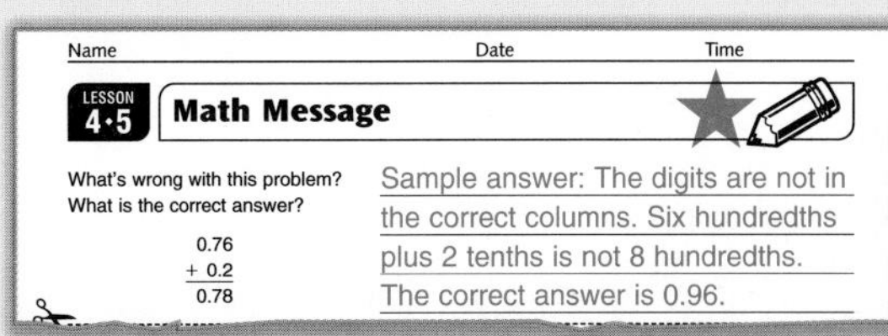

Name | Date | Time

LESSON 4·5 **Math Message** ★

What's wrong with this problem? What is the correct answer?

  0.76
+ 0.2
  0.78

Sample answer: The digits are not in the correct columns. Six hundredths plus 2 tenths is not 8 hundredths. The correct answer is 0.96.

Math Masters, p. 118

Ongoing Assessment: Recognizing Student Achievement

Math Message

Use the **Math Message** to assess students' understanding of the values of decimal digits. Students are making adequate progress if their responses indicate that the digit 6 stands for or represents 6 hundredths and the digit 2 stands for or represents 2 tenths. Some students may be able to describe how a ballpark estimate can be used to check the answer to the problem.

[Number and Numeration Goal 1]

Algorithm Project In this lesson, students use various methods to add and subtract decimals. To teach U.S. traditional addition and subtraction of decimals, see Algorithm Projects 2 and 4 on pages A5 and A15.

▶ Adding and Subtracting Decimals Using an Algorithm

Ask: *Is it possible to use the same methods for adding and subtracting decimals that you use for whole numbers?* yes As with whole numbers, all digits of a given place value must be lined up correctly.

One way to make sure the digits align correctly is to rename the numbers so that each has the same number of digits after the decimal point. For example, if adding or subtracting decimals in tenths and hundredths, rename the tenths as hundredths by adding a zero to the end of the numbers. When the digits are aligned correctly, the decimal points will also align.

Pose several decimal addition and subtraction problems. Ask students to model their answers with base-10 blocks (or symbols).

Suggestions:

$2.63 + 3.5 = ?$ $\quad 17 + 5.1 = ?$

$8.1 - 4.72 = ?$ $\quad 9 - 0.09 = ?$

The zeros in boldface have been appended so both numbers have the same number of digits after the decimal point.

$$\begin{array}{r} 2.63 \\ +\,3.5\mathbf{0} \\ \hline 6.13 \end{array} \qquad \begin{array}{r} 17.\mathbf{0} \\ +\;\;5.1 \\ \hline 22.1 \end{array} \qquad \begin{array}{r} 8.1\mathbf{0} \\ -\,4.72 \\ \hline 3.38 \end{array} \qquad \begin{array}{r} 9.\mathbf{00} \\ -\,0.09 \\ \hline 8.91 \end{array}$$

Links to the Future

Do not be concerned if students use manipulatives such as base-10 blocks or bills and coins to add and subtract decimals. Students will be expected to do so without the use of manipulatives in Grade 5.

Practicing Decimal Addition and Subtraction

INDEPENDENT ACTIVITY

(*Math Journal 1,* p. 87)

Students solve decimal addition and subtraction problems.

Adjusting the Activity

ELL

Have base-10 blocks, coins and bills (*Math Masters*, page 428), and a decimal number grid (*Math Masters*, page 427) available. Encourage students to think in terms of the partial-sums algorithm.

			2.05
			+ 1.83
Add the 1s:	2 + 1	→	3.00
Add the 0.1s:	0.0 + 0.8	→	0.80
Add the 0.01s:	0.05 + 0.03	→	+ 0.08
Find the total:	3 + 0.8 + 0.08	→	3.88

AUDITORY • KINESTHETIC • TACTILE • VISUAL

Ongoing Assessment: Informing Instruction

Watch for students who do not correctly align the digits when adding and subtracting. All digits of a given place value must be written in the same column. Encourage students to use computation grid paper and record the place-value heading above each column.

2 Ongoing Learning & Practice

Analyzing Circle Graphs

INDEPENDENT ACTIVITY

(*Math Journal 1,* p. 88)

Students compare population data presented in circle graphs. To support English language learners, discuss the terms *population, urban,* and *rural.*

Links to the Future

Creating and interpreting circle graphs are Grade 5 and Grade 6 Goals.

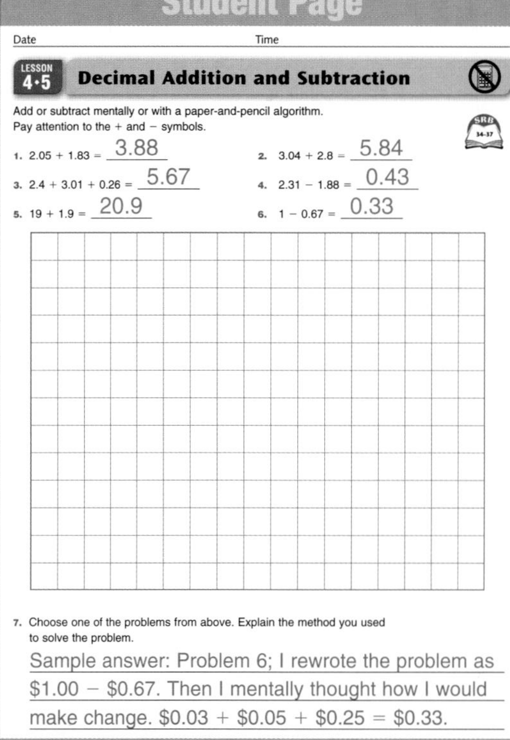

Student Page

Date Time

LESSON 4•5 **Decimal Addition and Subtraction**

Add or subtract mentally or with a paper-and-pencil algorithm.
Pay attention to the + and − symbols.

1. 2.05 + 1.83 = 3.88
2. 3.04 + 2.8 = 5.84
3. 2.4 + 3.01 + 0.26 = 5.67
4. 2.31 − 1.88 = 0.43
5. 19 + 1.9 = 20.9
6. 1 − 0.67 = 0.33

7. Choose one of the problems from above. Explain the method you used to solve the problem.

Sample answer: Problem 6; I rewrote the problem as $1.00 − $0.67. Then I mentally thought how I would make change. $0.03 + $0.05 + $0.25 = $0.33.

Math Journal 1, p. 87

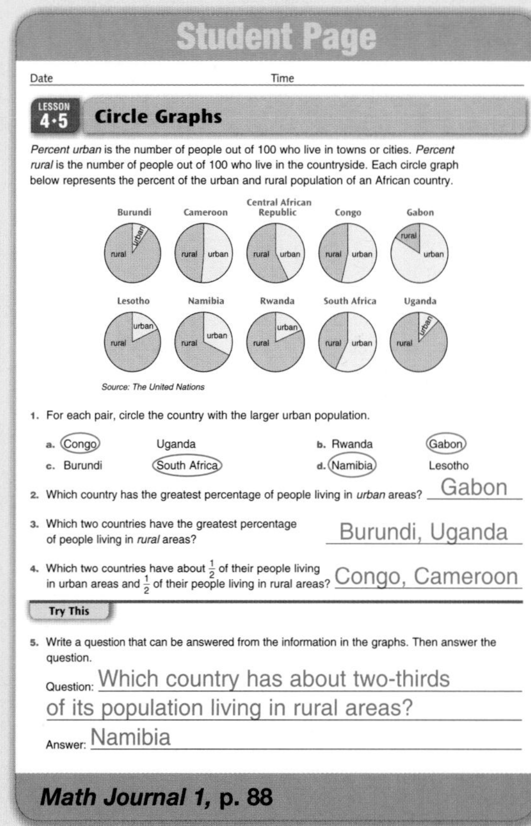

Student Page

Date Time

LESSON 4•5 **Circle Graphs**

Percent urban is the number of people out of 100 who live in towns or cities. *Percent rural* is the number of people out of 100 who live in the countryside. Each circle graph below represents the percent of the urban and rural population of an African country.

Source: The United Nations

1. For each pair, circle the country with the larger urban population.
   a. (Congo) Uganda
   b. Rwanda (Gabon)
   c. Burundi (South Africa)
   d. (Namibia) Lesotho
2. Which country has the greatest percentage of people living in *urban* areas? Gabon
3. Which two countries have the greatest percentage of people living in *rural* areas? Burundi, Uganda
4. Which two countries have about $\frac{1}{2}$ of their people living in urban areas and $\frac{1}{2}$ of their people living in rural areas? Congo, Cameroon

Try This

5. Write a question that can be answered from the information in the graphs. Then answer the question.

Question: Which country has about two-thirds of its population living in rural areas?

Answer: Namibia

Math Journal 1, p. 88

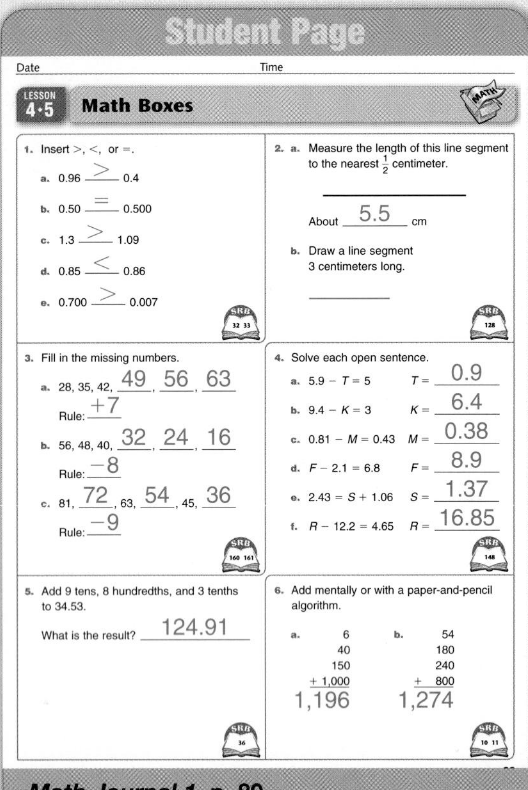

Student Page

Date Time

LESSON 4·5 **Math Boxes**

1. Insert >, <, or =.
   a. 0.96 > 0.4
   b. 0.50 = 0.500
   c. 1.3 > 1.09
   d. 0.85 < 0.86
   e. 0.700 > 0.007

SRB 32 33

2. a. Measure the length of this line segment to the nearest $\frac{1}{2}$ centimeter.

   About 5.5 cm

   b. Draw a line segment 3 centimeters long.

SRB 128

3. Fill in the missing numbers.
   a. 28, 35, 42, 49, 56, 63
      Rule: +7
   b. 56, 48, 40, 32, 24, 16
      Rule: −8
   c. 81, 72, 63, 54, 45, 36
      Rule: −9

SRB 160 161

4. Solve each open sentence.
   a. 5.9 − T = 5   T = 0.9
   b. 9.4 − K = 3   K = 6.4
   c. 0.81 − M = 0.43   M = 0.38
   d. F − 2.1 = 6.8   F = 8.9
   e. 2.43 = S + 1.06   S = 1.37
   f. R − 12.2 = 4.65   R = 16.85

SRB 148

5. Add 9 tens, 8 hundredths, and 3 tenths to 34.53.

   What is the result? 124.91

SRB 36

6. Add mentally or with a paper-and-pencil algorithm.

a.	b.
6	54
40	180
150	240
+ 1,000	+ 800
1,196	1,274

SRB 10 11

Math Journal 1, p. 89

▶ Math Boxes 4·5

INDEPENDENT ACTIVITY

(*Math Journal 1,* p. 89)

Mixed Practice Math Boxes in this lesson are paired with Math Boxes in Lesson 4-7. The skill in Problem 6 previews Unit 5 content.

Writing/Reasoning Have students write a response to the following: *Explain how you found the value of* S *in Problem 4e.* Sample answer: Since I knew the whole (2.43) and one of the parts (1.06), I subtracted 1.06 from 2.43 to find the value of *S*.

▶ Study Link 4·5

(*Math Masters,* p. 119)

Home Connection Students add and subtract decimals. They also write <, >, or = symbols to make true number sentences.

Encourage students to continue bringing examples of decimals to display in the Decimals All Around Museum.

3 Differentiation Options

READINESS

▶ Investigating a Decimal Version of the Number Grid

(*Math Masters,* p. 427)

To explore the use of a visual organizer for understanding the base-ten place-value system for decimals, have students use a decimal version of the number grid.

Have students compare the Number-Grid Poster with the decimal version. Ask: *What are some similarities and differences?* Possible answers: Patterns in the digits are similar in that the hundredths digit stays the same as you move down a column, and the tenths digit stays the same as you move across a row. The numbers increase by 0.01 as you move a step to the right; the numbers increase by 0.1 as you move a step down.

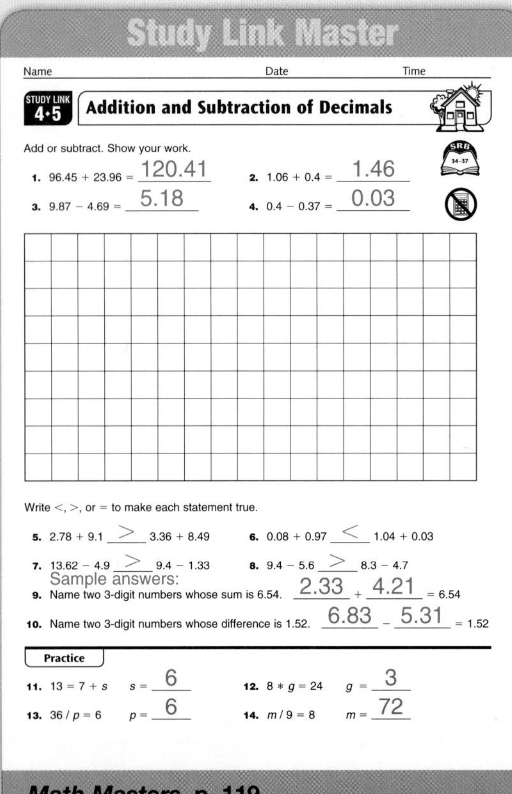

Study Link Master

Name Date Time

STUDY LINK 4·5 **Addition and Subtraction of Decimals**

Add or subtract. Show your work.

SRB 34-37

1. 96.45 + 23.96 = 120.41
2. 1.06 + 0.4 = 1.46
3. 9.87 − 4.69 = 5.18
4. 0.4 − 0.37 = 0.03

Write <, >, or = to make each statement true.

5. 2.78 + 9.1 > 3.36 + 8.49
6. 0.08 + 0.97 < 1.04 + 0.03
7. 13.62 − 4.9 > 9.4 − 1.33
8. 9.4 − 5.6 > 8.3 − 4.7

Sample answers:

9. Name two 3-digit numbers whose sum is 6.54. 2.33 + 4.21 = 6.54
10. Name two 3-digit numbers whose difference is 1.52. 6.83 − 5.31 = 1.52

Practice

11. 13 = 7 + s   s = 6
12. 8 ∗ g = 24   g = 3
13. 36 / p = 6   p = 6
14. m / 9 = 8   m = 72

Math Masters, p. 119

Ask students to solve addition or subtraction problems by counting on the grid.

Examples:

▷ Write 0.02 + 0.07 on the board.

Have students put their fingers on 0.02 and count by hundredths as they move their fingers 7 steps to the right—one step for each hundredth. 0.09

▷ Write 0.14 + 0.10 on the board.

Have students put their fingers on 0.14 and count by hundredths as they move their fingers 10 steps to the right—one for each hundredth. Or, move down one row for each tenth. 0.24

Teaching Aid Master

Name Date Time

Number Grid (Decimal Version)

									0
0.01	0.02	0.03	0.04	0.05	0.06	0.07	0.08	0.09	0.10
0.11	0.12	0.13	0.14	0.15	0.16	0.17	0.18	0.19	0.20
0.21	0.22	0.23	0.24	0.25	0.26	0.27	0.28	0.29	0.30
0.31	0.32	0.33	0.34	0.35	0.36	0.37	0.38	0.39	0.40
0.41	0.42	0.43	0.44	0.45	0.46	0.47	0.48	0.49	0.50
0.51	0.52	0.53	0.54	0.55	0.56	0.57	0.58	0.59	0.60
0.61	0.62	0.63	0.64	0.65	0.66	0.67	0.68	0.69	0.70
0.71	0.72	0.73	0.74	0.75	0.76	0.77	0.78	0.79	0.80
0.81	0.82	0.83	0.84	0.85	0.86	0.87	0.88	0.89	0.90
0.91	0.92	0.93	0.94	0.95	0.96	0.97	0.98	0.99	1.00

Math Masters, p. 427

ENRICHMENT

COMPUTATION PRACTICE

PARTNER ACTIVITY

5–15 Min

Solving Hiking Trail Problems

(*Math Masters*, pp. 120 and 121)

To apply students' understanding of computation with decimals to the hundredths place, have them find distances on a hiking map.

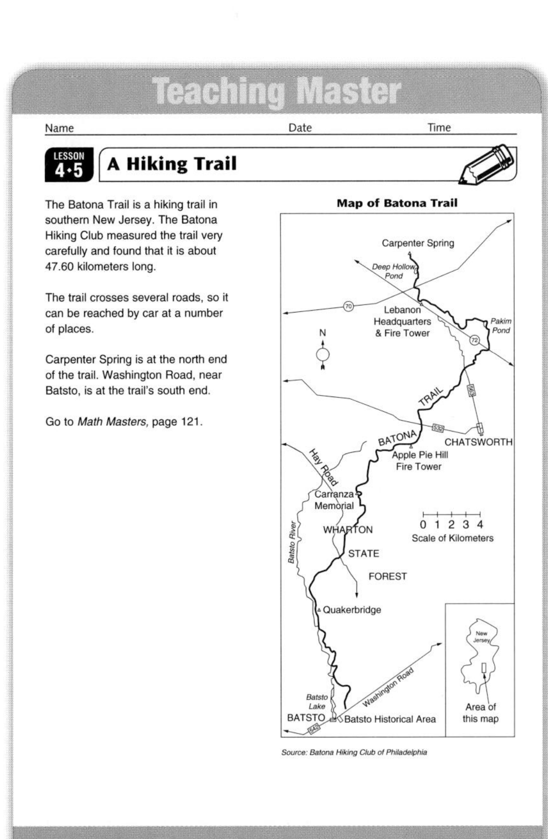

Teaching Master

Name Date Time

LESSON 4•5 **A Hiking Trail**

The Batona Trail is a hiking trail in southern New Jersey. The Batona Hiking Club measured the trail very carefully and found that it is about 47.60 kilometers long.

The trail crosses several roads, so it can be reached by car at a number of places.

Carpenter Spring is at the north end of the trail. Washington Road, near Batsto, is at the trail's south end.

Go to *Math Masters*, page 121.

Map of Batona Trail

Source: Batona Hiking Club of Philadelphia

Math Masters, p. 120

Teaching Master

Name Date Time

LESSON 4•5 **A Hiking Trail** *continued*

The following table shows distances from several points of interest from the north to the south end of the trail. Fill in the missing distances.

SRB 34–37

Batona Trail

Point of Interest	Distance from Carpenter Spring (km)	Distance from Washington Road (km)
Carpenter Spring	0	47.60
Deep Hollow Pond	1.91	45.69
Route 70	3.37	44.23
Lebanon Headquarters	4.66	42.94
Pakim Pond	9.91	37.69
Route 72	12.10	35.50
Route 563	14.04	33.56
Route 532	19.53	28.07
Apple Pie Hill Fire Tower	21.31	26.29
Carranza Memorial	27.80	19.80
Hay Road	33.05	14.55
Quakerbridge	37.92	9.68
Washington Road	47.60	0

How can you check your answers?

Sample answer: Finding the sum of the two entries on each line should give you the distance of the whole trail: 47.60 km.

Math Masters, p. 121

4•6 Decimals in Money

Objective To provide practice adding and subtracting decimals to compute balances in a savings account.

Technology Resources www.everydaymathonline.com

ePresentations

eToolkit

Algorithms Practice

EM Facts Workshop Game™

Family Letters

Assessment Management

Common Core State Standards

Curriculum Focal Points

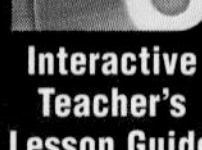

Interactive Teacher's Lesson Guide

1 Teaching the Lesson

Key Concepts and Skills

- Read and write decimals through hundredths in the context of money. [Number and Numeration Goal 1]
- Add and subtract decimals through hundredths in the context of money. [Operations and Computation Goal 2]
- Estimate reasonable solutions for decimal addition and subtraction problems. [Operations and Computation Goal 6]
- Complete a table of deposits and withdrawals. [Data and Chance Goal 1]

Key Activities

Students read about deposits and withdrawals in savings accounts and about interest earned. They use estimation, mental arithmetic, and paper-and-pencil algorithms to find account balances.

Key Vocabulary

deposit ◆ withdrawal ◆ balance ◆ interest

Materials

Math Journal 1, pp. 90 and 91
Study Link 4•5
Math Masters, pp. 427 and 428 (optional)
transparency of *Math Masters,* p. 122 ◆ base-10 blocks (optional) ◆ money (optional) ◆ slate

2 Ongoing Learning & Practice

Playing *Name That Number*
Student Reference Book, p. 254
Math Masters, p. 489
deck of number cards (the Everything Math Deck, if available)
Students practice representing numbers in different ways.

Math Boxes 4•6
Math Journal 1, p. 92
Students practice and maintain skills through Math Box problems.

Ongoing Assessment: Recognizing Student Achievement
Use Math Boxes, Problem 4.
[Data and Chance Goal 2]

Study Link 4•6
Math Masters, p. 123
Students practice and maintain skills through Study Link activities.

3 Differentiation Options

READINESS

Finding Totals and Making Change
Math Masters, pp. 114 and 428
coins ◆ calculator ◆ scissors
Students role-play being salesclerks and customers using money.

ENRICHMENT

Solving "Goodie Bag" Problems
Math Masters, p. 124
Students apply decimal computation skills to solve problems involving the contents and cost of "goodie bags."

ELL SUPPORT

Building a Math Word Bank
Differentiation Handbook, p. 141
Students add the terms *deposit, withdrawal,* and *balance* to their Math Word Banks.

Advance Preparation

***Teacher's Reference Manual,* Grades 4–6** pp. 119–126

Getting Started

Mental Math and Reflexes

FACTS PRACTICE

Pose multiplication facts and extended facts.
Suggestions:

●○○ 4 ∗ 5 = 20
7 ∗ 4 = 28
5 ∗ 5 = 25
3 ∗ 6 = 18

●●○ 6 ∗ 9 = 54
7 ∗ 5 = 35
8 ∗ 8 = 64
7 ∗ 9 = 63

●●● 9 ∗ 50 = 450
70 ∗ 8 = 560
60 ∗ 70 = 4,200
50 ∗ 50 = 2,500

Math Message

Solve Problems 1 and 2 on journal page 90.

Study Link 4·5 Follow-Up

Have partners compare answers. Ask if students used computation or estimation to solve Problems 5–8. Have students indicate thumbs-up if they agree with the answers given by students for Problems 9 and 10.

1 Teaching the Lesson

▶ Math Message Follow-Up

WHOLE-CLASS ACTIVITY

(*Math Journal 1,* p. 90)

Have students share the strategies they used to solve the addition and subtraction problems. Some students may have modeled the problems with money or base-10 blocks. Other students may have used algorithms similar to the ones they use for whole-number addition and subtraction.

Tell students that in this lesson they will solve more problems involving the addition and subtraction of money amounts.

▶ Introducing Bank Accounts

WHOLE-CLASS ACTIVITY
ELL

(*Math Journal 1,* pp. 90 and 91)

Ask students to tell what they know about savings accounts. Have them read the introduction to "Keeping a Bank Balance" on journal page 90 and examine the table on page 91. Discuss the uses of savings accounts. Be sure students understand the terms **deposit, withdrawal, balance,** and **interest.** To support English language learners, write these terms on the board along with examples as they are introduced.

▷ Money is put into (deposited into) an account. It can be taken out of (withdrawn from) the account.

▷ The bank holds onto the money (the balance) in the account and keeps track of it.

▷ At regular intervals, the bank adds money to the account (interest) to pay for the use of the money. The amount of interest earned depends on the amount of money in the account—the greater the balance, the more interest earned.

Student Page

Date Time

LESSON 4·6 **Keeping a Bank Balance** SRB 34-37

Math Message

Solve. Show your work on the grid.

1. Cleo went to the store to buy school supplies. She bought a notebook for $2.39, a pen for $0.99, and a set of markers for $3.99. How much money did she spend in all?
$7.37

2. Nicholas went to the store with a $20 bill. His groceries cost $13.52. How much change did he get?
$6.48

On January 2, Kate's aunt opened a bank account for Kate. Her aunt deposited $100.00 in the account.

Over the next several months, Kate made regular deposits into her account. She deposited part of her allowance and most of the money she made babysitting.

Kate also made a few withdrawals—to buy a radio and some new clothes.

Think about the answers to the following questions:

- When you **withdraw** money, do you take money out or put money in?
- When you **deposit** money, do you take money out or put money in?
- When your money earns **interest,** does this add money to your account or take money away?

The table on the next page shows the transactions (deposits and withdrawals) that Kate made during the first 4 months of the year and the interest she earned.

Bank of Centerville

***Math Journal 1,* p. 90**

To support English language learners, also discuss the meanings of the terms *allowance* and *regular deposits*. Summarize by posing the questions at the bottom of journal page 90.

▶ Practicing Mental Arithmetic

(*Math Journal 1,* p. 91)

Ask students to solve Problems 3 and 4 on journal page 91 using mental arithmetic. Discuss their solution strategies. One possible line of reasoning for Problem 3:

- ▷ No money was withdrawn in January.
- ▷ Two withdrawals of \$16.50 each were made in February for a total of \$33. (Double \$16 = \$32. Double 50¢ = \$1. \$32 + \$1 = \$33.) This is less than the amount deposited that month.
- ▷ April deposit: One deposit of \$70.60
- ▷ April withdrawals: Add the dollar amounts: \$45 + \$27 = \$72, which is more than \$70.60. So Kate withdrew more than she deposited.

Point out how our monetary system uses place value. An amount like \$27.91 can be thought of as 2 ten-dollar bills, 7 one-dollar bills, 9 dimes, and 1 penny. If \$1 is the ONE, then a ten-dollar bill is ten dollars, a dime is one-tenth of a dollar, and a penny is one-hundredth of a dollar.

▶ Maintaining a Savings Account

(*Math Journal 1,* p. 91; *Math Masters,* p. 122)

Using a transparency of *Math Masters,* page 122, compute the balance for the first two or three transactions with the class. Students may suggest several different ways of doing these computations. They can complete the rest of the table on their own and check their answers with partners.

Adjusting the Activity

Provide one or two intermediate balances and the final balance on journal page 91. Have base-10 blocks, coins and bills (*Math Masters,* page 428), and a decimal version of the number grid (*Math Masters,* page 427) available for students to use.

AUDITORY ◆ KINESTHETIC ◆ TACTILE ◆ VISUAL

Student Page

Date Time

LESSON 4·6 **Keeping a Bank Balance** *continued*

3. In March, Kate took more money out of her bank account than she put in. In which other month did she withdraw more money than she deposited? April

4. Estimate whether Kate will have more or less than \$100.00 at the end of April. Less than \$100

5. Complete the table. Remember to add if Kate makes a deposit or earns interest and to subtract if she makes a withdrawal.

Date	Transaction		Current Balance
January 2	Deposit	\$100.00	\$ 100.00
January 14	Deposit	\$14.23	+ \$ 14.23 \$ 114.23
February 4	Withdrawal	\$16.50	− \$ 16.50 \$ 97.73
February 11	Deposit	\$33.75	+ \$ 33.75 \$ 131.48
February 14	Withdrawal	\$16.50	− \$ 16.50 \$ 114.98
March 19	Deposit	\$62.00	+ \$ 62.00 \$ 176.98
March 30	Withdrawal	\$104.26	− \$ 104.26 \$ 72.72
March 31	Interest	\$0.78	+ \$ 0.78 \$ 73.50
April 1	Deposit	\$70.60	+ \$ 70.60 \$ 144.10
April 3	Withdrawal	\$45.52	− \$ 45.52 \$ 98.58
April 28	Withdrawal	\$27.91	− \$ 27.91 \$ 70.67

Math Journal 1, p. 91

2 Ongoing Learning & Practice

Playing *Name That Number*

(*Student Reference Book,* p. 254; *Math Masters,* p. 489)

Students play *Name That Number* to practice representing numbers in different ways. See Lesson 2-2 for additional information.

Math Boxes 4•6

(*Math Journal 1,* p. 92)

Mixed Practice Math Boxes in this lesson are paired with Math Boxes in Lesson 4-9. The skill in Problem 5 previews Unit 5 content.

Writing/Reasoning Have students write a response to the following: *For Problem 3, how many grams heavier is the trumpeter swan than the Manchurian crane?* 1,900 grams *Explain what you did to find your answer.* Sample answer: I know that there are 1,000 grams in 1 kilogram. 1.9 ∗ 1,000 = 1,900

Ongoing Assessment: Recognizing Student Achievement

Math Boxes Problem 4

Use **Math Boxes, Problem 4** to assess students' understanding of data landmarks. Students are making adequate progress if they can determine the maximum, minimum, range, mode, and median of the data set. Some students may be able to calculate the mean.

[Data and Chance Goal 2]

Study Link 4•6

(*Math Masters,* p. 123)

Home Connection Students solve addition and subtraction problems that involve grocery prices from the year 2000 and predicted prices for the year 2025. They compare prices, compute change, and find total costs.

To support English language learners, discuss the meaning of the term *change* in this context.

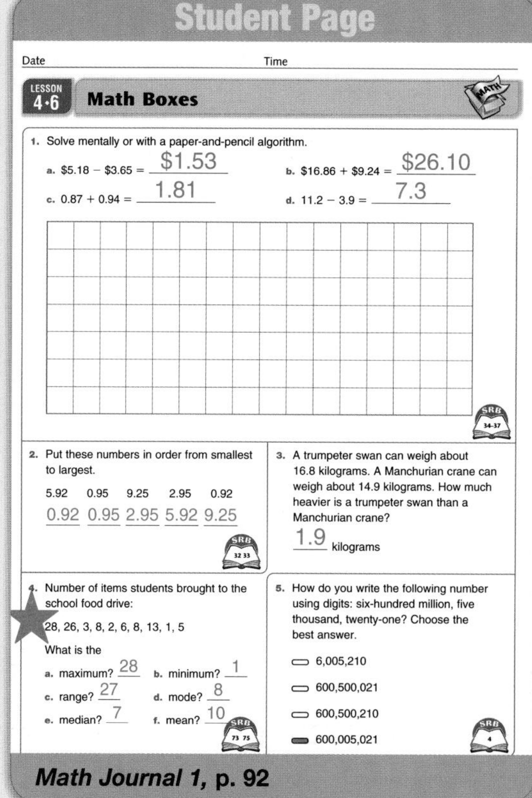

Student Page

Date Time

LESSON 4•6 **Math Boxes**

1. Solve mentally or with a paper-and-pencil algorithm.

a. $5.18 − $3.65 = $1.53
b. $16.86 + $9.24 = $26.10
c. 0.87 + 0.94 = 1.81
d. 11.2 − 3.9 = 7.3

2. Put these numbers in order from smallest to largest.

5.92 0.95 9.25 2.95 0.92

0.92 0.95 2.95 5.92 9.25

3. A trumpeter swan can weigh about 16.8 kilograms. A Manchurian crane can weigh about 14.9 kilograms. How much heavier is a trumpeter swan than a Manchurian crane?

1.9 kilograms

4. Number of items students brought to the school food drive:

28, 26, 3, 8, 2, 6, 8, 13, 1, 5

What is the

a. maximum? 28
b. minimum? 1
c. range? 27
d. mode? 8
e. median? 7
f. mean? 10

5. How do you write the following number using digits: six-hundred million, five thousand, twenty-one? Choose the best answer.

- 6,005,210
- 600,500,021
- 600,500,210
- 600,005,021 (filled)

Math Journal 1, p. 92

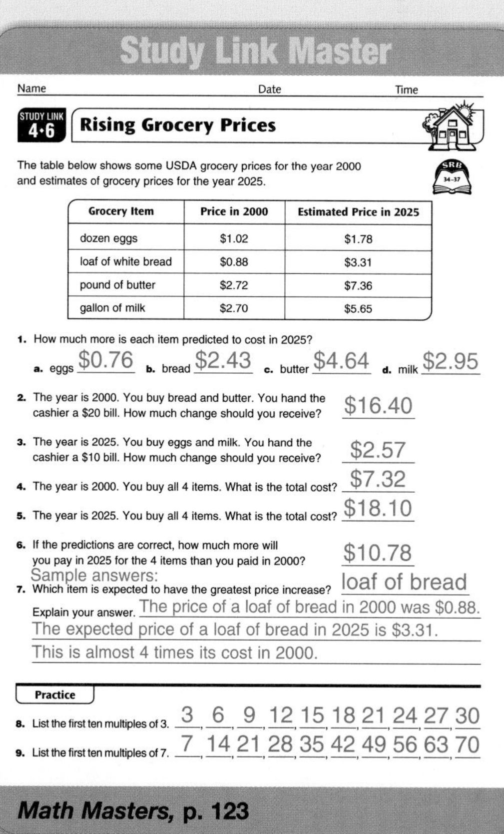

Study Link Master

Name Date Time

STUDY LINK 4•6 **Rising Grocery Prices**

The table below shows some USDA grocery prices for the year 2000 and estimates of grocery prices for the year 2025.

Grocery Item	Price in 2000	Estimated Price in 2025
dozen eggs	$1.02	$1.78
loaf of white bread	$0.88	$3.31
pound of butter	$2.72	$7.36
gallon of milk	$2.70	$5.65

1. How much more is each item predicted to cost in 2025?

a. eggs $0.76 b. bread $2.43 c. butter $4.64 d. milk $2.95

2. The year is 2000. You buy bread and butter. You hand the cashier a $20 bill. How much change should you receive? $16.40

3. The year is 2025. You buy eggs and milk. You hand the cashier a $10 bill. How much change should you receive? $2.57

4. The year is 2000. You buy all 4 items. What is the total cost? $7.32

5. The year is 2025. You buy all 4 items. What is the total cost? $18.10

6. If the predictions are correct, how much more will you pay in 2025 for the 4 items than you paid in 2000? $10.78

7. Which item is expected to have the greatest price increase? Sample answers: loaf of bread

Explain your answer. The price of a loaf of bread in 2000 was $0.88. The expected price of a loaf of bread in 2025 is $3.31. This is almost 4 times its cost in 2000.

Practice

8. List the first ten multiples of 3. 3 6 9 12 15 18 21 24 27 30

9. List the first ten multiples of 7. 7 14 21 28 35 42 49 56 63 70

Math Masters, p. 123

Teaching Master

Name Date Time

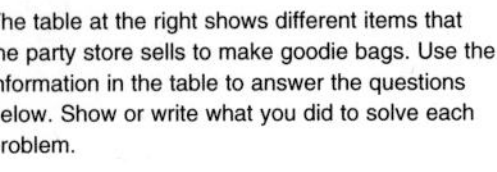

LESSON 4·6 "Goodie Bags"

The table at the right shows different items that the party store sells to make goodie bags. Use the information in the table to answer the questions below. Show or write what you did to solve each problem.

Item	Price
erasers	\$0.16 each
clay	2 cans for \$1.22
key chains	\$0.59 each
rubber balls	3 for \$0.51
markers	4 packs for \$5.60
stickers	\$1.39 per pack
whistles	\$0.18 each
marbles	\$1.41 per bag
gum	3 packs for \$1.86

1. Kareem put a pack of stickers, a rubber ball, and a pack of gum in each of his goodie bags. What is the cost of each bag? \$2.18

   rubber ball: \$0.51 ÷ 3 = \$0.17; gum: \$1.86 ÷ 3 = \$0.62;
   \$1.39 + \$0.17 + \$0.62 = \$2.18

2. Ella created a bag that cost the same amount as Kareem's bag but was not filled with the same things. What did Ella put in her bag?

   Sample answer: stickers, clay, and a whistle
   clay: \$1.22 ÷ 2 = \$0.61;
   \$1.39 + \$0.61 + \$0.18 = \$2.18

3. Create your own goodie bag. You must place 5 different items in your bag and the total cost must be between \$3.25 and \$3.50. Tell what is in your bag and how much you spent.

   Sample answer: eraser, rubber ball, whistle, marbles, and stickers; \$3.31
   rubber ball: \$0.51 ÷ 3 = \$0.17;
   \$0.16 + \$0.17 + \$0.18 + \$1.41 + \$1.39 = \$3.31

***Math Masters,* p. 124**

3 Differentiation Options

READINESS

PARTNER ACTIVITY

5–15 Min

▶ Finding Totals and Making Change

(*Math Masters,* pp. 114 and 428)

To explore adding and subtracting decimals using a concrete model, have students use money to find totals and make change. Partners cut apart the item slips and the bills from *Math Masters,* pages 114 and 428.

They place the slips facedown in a pile and take turns being "customer" and "salesclerk." At each turn:

1. The customer draws two slips and turns them over. These are the items to be purchased. The customer computes the cost of the items without using a calculator.
2. The salesclerk uses a calculator like a cash register to find the total cost.
3. Then the customer gives the salesclerk a \$10 bill. The salesclerk gives the customer the correct change.

ENRICHMENT

INDEPENDENT ACTIVITY

30+ Min

▶ Solving "Goodie Bag" Problems

(*Math Masters,* p. 124)

To apply students' decimal computation skills, have them solve problems involving the contents and cost of goodie bags.

ELL SUPPORT

PARTNER ACTIVITY

5–15 Min

▶ Building a Math Word Bank

(*Differentiation Handbook,* p. 141)

To provide language support for monetary transactions, have students use the Word Bank template found on *Differentiation Handbook,* page 141. Ask students to write the terms *deposit, withdrawal,* and *balance;* draw pictures relating to each term; and write other related words. See the *Differentiation Handbook* for more information.

4•7 Thousandths

Objective To extend basic concepts and notation for decimals through thousandths.

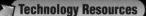

www.everydaymathonline.com

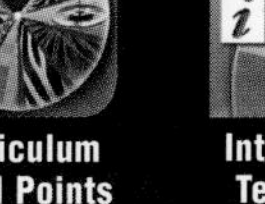

1 Teaching the Lesson

Key Concepts and Skills

- Read, write, and model (with base-10 blocks) decimals through thousandths. [Number and Numeration Goal 1]
- Name the fractional part of the ONE represented by each base-10 block. [Number and Numeration Goal 2]
- Rename fractions with 10, 100, and 1,000 in the denominator as decimals. [Number and Numeration Goal 5]
- Compare and order decimals through thousandths. [Number and Numeration Goal 6]

Key Activities

Students review the relationships among base-10 blocks. They name collections of base-10 blocks as fractions and decimals to thousandths. They read, write, and compare decimals through thousandths.

Ongoing Assessment: Recognizing Student Achievement Use Mental Math and Reflexes. [Number and Numeration Goal 1]

Ongoing Assessment: Informing Instruction See page 273.

Key Vocabulary

thousandth

Materials

Math Journal 1, pp. 94 and 95
Study Link 4•6
transparency of *Math Masters,* p. 125 (optional) ◆ base-10 blocks ◆ slate

2 Ongoing Learning & Practice

World Tour Option: Visiting Africa

Math Journal 1, pp. 171–173, 176, and 177
Student Reference Book, pp. 276, 277, 279, 282, 283, and 296–305
Math Masters, pp. 419–421 (optional)
Students resume the World Tour by traveling to a second country in Africa.

Math Boxes 4•7

Math Journal 1, p. 93
Students practice and maintain skills through Math Box problems.

Study Link 4•7

Math Masters, p. 126
Students practice and maintain skills through Study Link activities.

3 Differentiation Options

READINESS

Counting by Thousandths

calculator
Students use calculators to skip count by thousandths.

ENRICHMENT

Analyzing Softball Batting Averages

Math Masters, p. 127
Students apply their knowledge of decimals in the thousandths.

EXTRA PRACTICE

Playing *Base-10 Exchange*

Math Masters, p. 459
per partnership: base-10 blocks, 3 six-sided dice
Students practice exchanging tenths, hundredths, and thousandths.

Advance Preparation

Place a big cube, a flat, a long, and a cube near the Math Message. Write *big cube, flat, long,* and *cube* on slips of paper. Use them to label these base-10 blocks.

***Teacher's Reference Manual,* Grades 4–6** pp. 62, 63

Getting Started

Mental Math and Reflexes 

Dictate decimals and ask students to write them on their slates. *Suggestions:*

●○○ 5 tenths 0.5
6 tenths 0.6
2 and 3 tenths 2.3

●●○ 7 hundredths 0.07
86 hundredths 0.86
4 and 13 hundredths 4.13

●●● 2 thousandths 0.002
35 thousandths 0.035
563 thousandths 0.563

Math Message 

Complete Problems 1–3 on journal page 94.

Study Link 4·6 Follow-Up

Have partners compare answers. Discuss Problem 7 as a class. Some students may choose butter because the price increases by $4.64 in 2025. Others may argue for bread, noting that the price of bread in 2025 is almost 4 times the price in 2000, while the price of butter in 2025 is less than 3 times the price in 2000.

Ongoing Assessment: Recognizing Student Achievement

Mental Math and Reflexes 

Use **Mental Math and Reflexes** to assess students' ability to write decimals through hundredths. Students are making adequate progress if they are able to write the decimals in the ●○○ and ●●○ problems correctly. Some students may be able to write decimals through thousandths in the ●●● problems.

[Number and Numeration Goal 1]

1 Teaching the Lesson

▶ Math Message Follow-Up

WHOLE-CLASS ACTIVITY

(*Math Journal 1,* p. 94)

Review answers.

▷ To demonstrate that 1 big cube = 10 flats, have students make a stack of 10 flats to form a big cube. Since 1 big cube = 10 flats, 1 flat is $\frac{1}{10}$ of a big cube.

▷ Since 1 flat = 10 longs, 1 big cube must have 10 times as many longs; that is, 100 longs. Since 1 big cube = 100 longs, 1 long is $\frac{1}{100}$ of a big cube.

▷ Since 1 big cube = 100 longs, and 1 long = 10 cubes, 1 big cube must have 10 * 100 cubes; that is, 1,000 cubes. Since 1 big cube = 1,000 cubes, 1 cube is $\frac{1}{1,000}$ of a big cube.

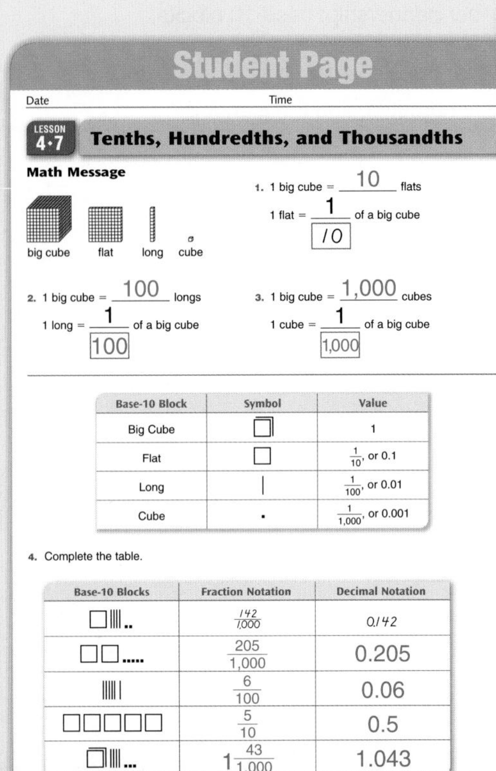

Student Page

Date Time

LESSON 4·7 **Tenths, Hundredths, and Thousandths**

Math Message

big cube flat long cube

1. 1 big cube = 10 flats
1 flat = $\frac{1}{10}$ of a big cube

2. 1 big cube = 100 longs
1 long = $\frac{1}{100}$ of a big cube

3. 1 big cube = 1,000 cubes
1 cube = $\frac{1}{1,000}$ of a big cube

Base-10 Block	Symbol	Value
Big Cube	◻	1
Flat	□	$\frac{1}{10}$, or 0.1
Long	|	$\frac{1}{100}$, or 0.01
Cube	•	$\frac{1}{1,000}$, or 0.001

4. Complete the table.

Base-10 Blocks	Fraction Notation	Decimal Notation
□||||..	$\frac{142}{1000}$	0.142
□□.....	$\frac{205}{1,000}$	0.205
||||||	$\frac{6}{100}$	0.06
□□□□□	$\frac{5}{10}$	0.5
◻||||...	$1\frac{43}{1,000}$	1.043

Math Journal 1, p. 94

Modeling Decimals with Base-10 Blocks

(*Math Masters,* p. 125)

To introduce decimals in **thousandths,** ask students to think of the big cube as ONE.

Have students imagine that they are going to trade 235 cubes for flats and longs so that they have as few base-10 blocks as possible.

- How many flats would we have? 2 flats How many longs? 3 longs How many cubes would be left? 5 cubes

Stack flats, longs, and cubes to demonstrate the result.

If the big cube is ONE, then 235 cubes can be represented by the fraction $\frac{235}{1{,}000}$ or by the decimal 0.235. The decimal 0.235 is read as "235 thousandths." Although it can also be read as "point two three five," students can benefit from the more formal reading at this stage in their learning.

Point out that the digit before the decimal point (0) names the number of big cubes, the first digit after the decimal point (2) names the number of flats, the second digit (3) names the number of longs, and the third digit (5) names the number of cubes.

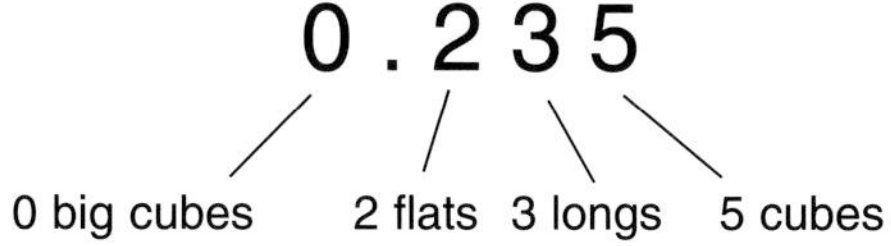

Use a transparency of *Math Masters,* page 125, or draw the table on the board. Complete the table as a class. Ask volunteers to show each decimal with the fewest base-10 blocks and to read each decimal.

Ask students why the decimal for a fraction like $\frac{64}{1{,}000}$ must have a zero after the decimal point. The decimal 0.64 is equivalent to $\frac{64}{100}$, not $\frac{64}{1{,}000}$. Similarly, ask why the decimal for $\frac{8}{1{,}000}$ must have two zeros after the decimal point. The decimal 0.8 is equivalent to $\frac{8}{10}$, and the decimal 0.08 is equivalent to $\frac{8}{100}$. Two zeros are needed to make $\frac{8}{1{,}000}$.

Ask: *If there are fewer than 1,000 cubes, is the fraction (and the equivalent decimal) less than or greater than 1?* Less than *How many cubes are needed to show a number that is at least 1?* 1,000 or more cubes So 1,843 cubes show the decimal 1.843. This decimal is read as "1 and 843 thousandths."

Ongoing Assessment: Informing Instruction

When base-10 blocks were used in Lesson 4-2 to model tenths and hundredths, the flat was the ONE. Watch for students who may not have made the transition to using base-10 blocks to model thousandths with the big cube as the new ONE.

Draw a sketch of the big cube on the board and label it ONE. Throughout the lesson, draw and label sketches to support students' transition to the new ONE.

Teaching Master

Name Date Time

LESSON 4•7 **Modeling Decimals**

Base-10 Blocks					Fraction	Decimal
Total Cubes	Big Cubes	Flats	Longs	Cubes		
235	0	2	3	5	$\frac{235}{1{,}000}$	0.235
832	0	8	3	2	$\frac{832}{1{,}000}$	0.832
408	0	4	0	8	$\frac{408}{1{,}000}$	0.408
790	0	7	9	0	$\frac{790}{1{,}000}$	0.790
64	0	0	6	4	$\frac{64}{1{,}000}$	0.064
8	0	0	0	8	$\frac{8}{1{,}000}$	0.008
200	0	2	0	0	$\frac{200}{1{,}000}, \frac{20}{100}, \frac{2}{10}$	0.200, 0.20, 0.2
20	0	0	2	0	$\frac{20}{1{,}000}, \frac{2}{100}$	0.020, 0.02
2	0	0	0	2	$\frac{2}{1{,}000}$	0.002
1,843	1	8	4	3	$1\frac{843}{1{,}000}$	1.843
27,051	27	0	5	1	$27\frac{51}{1{,}000}$	27.051

Math Masters, p. 125

▶ Practicing Reading and Writing Decimals

Write decimals and ask students to read them aloud. *Suggestions:*

- ▷ 0.581 581 thousandths
- ▷ 0.072 72 thousandths
- ▷ 0.006 6 thousandths
- ▷ 3.703 3 and 703 thousandths
- ▷ 15.024 15 and 24 thousandths
- ▷ 15.24 15 and 24 hundredths
- ▷ 34.09 34 and 9 hundredths

Adjusting the Activity

ELL

Encourage the following method for reading decimals:

1. Read the whole-number part.
2. Say "and."
3. Read the digits after the decimal point as though they are a whole number.
4. Say "tenths," "hundredths," or "thousandths" as appropriate.

AUDITORY ◆ KINESTHETIC ◆ TACTILE ◆ VISUAL

Reverse the procedure. Name decimals and ask students to write them on their slates. *Suggestions:*

- 367 thousandths 0.367
- 51 thousandths 0.051
- 9 and 634 thousandths 9.634
- 3 thousandths 0.003
- 5 and 79 hundredths 5.79
- 7 and 8 tenths 7.8

▶ Practicing with Tenths, Hundredths, and Thousandths

(*Math Journal 1,* pp. 94 and 95)

Students solve problems involving the representation of numbers with base-10 blocks, with fractions, and with decimals. They compare decimals. For Problem 6, remind students to use the base-10 block symbols shown on journal page 94.

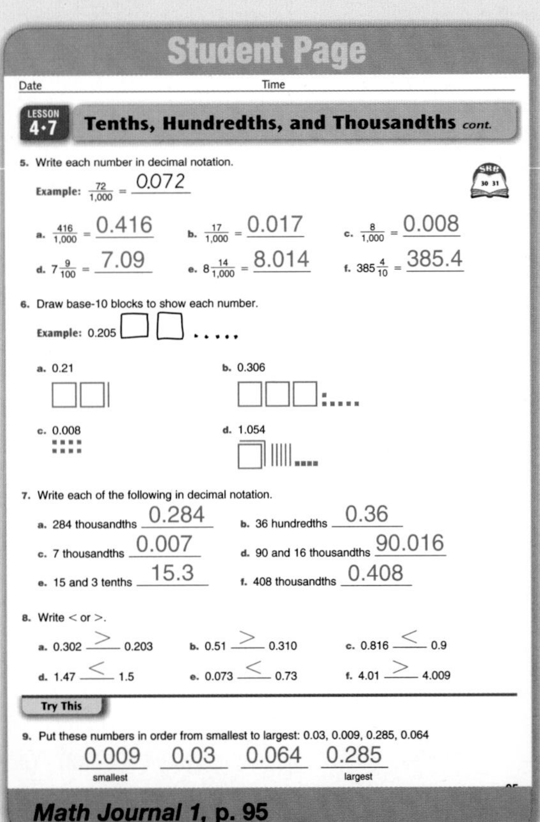

Student Page

Date Time

LESSON 4•7 **Tenths, Hundredths, and Thousandths** *cont.*

5. Write each number in decimal notation.

Example: $\frac{72}{1,000}$ = 0.072

a. $\frac{416}{1,000}$ = 0.416 b. $\frac{17}{1,000}$ = 0.017 c. $\frac{8}{1,000}$ = 0.008

d. $7\frac{9}{100}$ = 7.09 e. $8\frac{14}{1,000}$ = 8.014 f. $385\frac{4}{10}$ = 385.4

6. Draw base-10 blocks to show each number.

Example: 0.205

a. 0.21 b. 0.306

c. 0.008 d. 1.054

7. Write each of the following in decimal notation.

a. 284 thousandths 0.284 b. 36 hundredths 0.36

c. 7 thousandths 0.007 d. 90 and 16 thousandths 90.016

e. 15 and 3 tenths 15.3 f. 408 thousandths 0.408

8. Write < or >.

a. 0.302 > 0.203 b. 0.51 > 0.310 c. 0.816 < 0.9

d. 1.47 < 1.5 e. 0.073 < 0.73 f. 4.01 > 4.009

Try This

9. Put these numbers in order from smallest to largest: 0.03, 0.009, 0.285, 0.064

0.009 (smallest), 0.03, 0.064, 0.285 (largest)

Math Journal 1, p. 95

2 Ongoing Learning & Practice

World Tour Option: Visiting Africa

SMALL-GROUP ACTIVITY

(*Math Journal 1,* pp. 171–173, 176, and 177; *Student Reference Book,* pp. 276, 277, 279, 282, 283, and 296–305; *Math Masters,* pp. 419–421)

Social Studies Link Divide the class into groups of 4 or 5. Ask groups to look at the data for the remaining countries in Africa in the World Tour section of the *Student Reference Book.* Refer them to the map of Africa, the Country Profiles, the tables on pages 296–301, and the Fascinating Facts pages.

On the basis of this information, any prior knowledge, and/or interest in countries in Africa, each group selects a country they want to visit. Have each student complete Country Notes pages for the country he or she visits. If you are using the Route Log (*Math Journal 1,* page 171 or *Math Masters,* page 421), students should update it.

Math Boxes 4•7

INDEPENDENT ACTIVITY

(*Math Journal 1,* p. 93)

Mixed Practice Math Boxes in this lesson are paired with Math Boxes in Lesson 4-5. The skill in Problem 6 previews Unit 5 content.

Study Link 4•7

INDEPENDENT ACTIVITY

(*Math Masters,* p. 126)

Home Connection Students complete decimal problems similar to the ones on journal pages 94 and 95.

Encourage students to continue bringing examples of decimals to display in the Decimals All Around Museum.

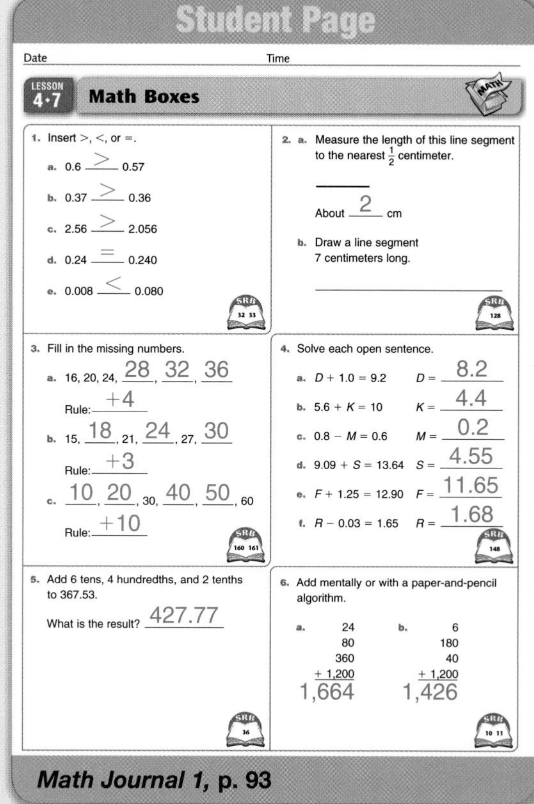

Student Page

Date Time

LESSON 4•7 **Math Boxes**

1. Insert >, <, or =.
   a. 0.6 > 0.57
   b. 0.37 > 0.36
   c. 2.56 > 2.056
   d. 0.24 = 0.240
   e. 0.008 < 0.080

2. a. Measure the length of this line segment to the nearest $\frac{1}{2}$ centimeter.
   About 2 cm
   b. Draw a line segment 7 centimeters long.

3. Fill in the missing numbers.
   a. 16, 20, 24, 28, 32, 36
   Rule: +4
   b. 15, 18, 21, 24, 27, 30
   Rule: +3
   c. 10, 20, 30, 40, 50, 60
   Rule: +10

4. Solve each open sentence.
   a. $D + 1.0 = 9.2$ $D =$ 8.2
   b. $5.6 + K = 10$ $K =$ 4.4
   c. $0.8 - M = 0.6$ $M =$ 0.2
   d. $9.09 + S = 13.64$ $S =$ 4.55
   e. $F + 1.25 = 12.90$ $F =$ 11.65
   f. $R - 0.03 = 1.65$ $R =$ 1.68

5. Add 6 tens, 4 hundredths, and 2 tenths to 367.53.
   What is the result? 427.77

6. Add mentally or with a paper-and-pencil algorithm.
   a. 24 + 80 + 360 + 1,200 = 1,664
   b. 6 + 180 + 40 + 1,200 = 1,426

Math Journal 1, p. 93

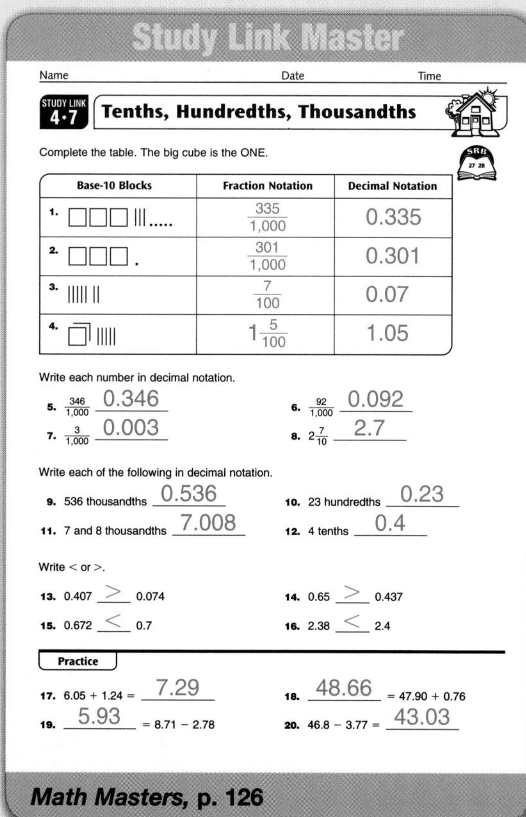

Study Link Master

Name Date Time

STUDY LINK 4•7 **Tenths, Hundredths, Thousandths**

Complete the table. The big cube is the ONE.

	Base-10 Blocks	Fraction Notation	Decimal Notation
1.	□□□ ǀǀǀ	$\frac{335}{1,000}$	0.335
2.	□□□ .	$\frac{301}{1,000}$	0.301
3.	ǀǀǀǀǀ ǀǀ	$\frac{7}{100}$	0.07
4.	▢ ǀǀǀǀǀ	$1\frac{5}{100}$	1.05

Write each number in decimal notation.

5. $\frac{346}{1,000}$ 0.346
6. $\frac{92}{1,000}$ 0.092
7. $\frac{3}{1,000}$ 0.003
8. $2\frac{7}{10}$ 2.7

Write each of the following in decimal notation.

9. 536 thousandths 0.536
10. 23 hundredths 0.23
11. 7 and 8 thousandths 7.008
12. 4 tenths 0.4

Write < or >.

13. 0.407 > 0.074
14. 0.65 > 0.437
15. 0.672 < 0.7
16. 2.38 < 2.4

Practice

17. $6.05 + 1.24 =$ 7.29
18. 48.66 $= 47.90 + 0.76$
19. 5.93 $= 8.71 - 2.78$
20. $46.8 - 3.77 =$ 43.03

Math Masters, p. 126

Teaching Master

Name Date Time

LESSON 4·7 Batting Averages

The women listed in this table were members of the 2004 U.S. Olympic Softball Team. These are their batting statistics after the 2004 Olympics in Athens, Greece.

Player	At Bats (AB)	Hits (H)	Batting Average $\left(\frac{H}{AB}\right)$
Berg, Laura	19	7	0.368
Bustos, Crystl	26	9	0.346
Fernandez, Lisa	22	12	0.545
Freed, Amanda	6	1	0.167
Jung, Lovieanne	20	6	0.300
Mendoza, Jessica	20	5	0.250
Nuveman, Stacey	16	5	0.313
O'Brien Amico, Leah	25	5	0.200
Topping, Jenny	6	4	0.667
Watley, Natasha	30	12	0.400

Source: U.S. Softball Official Web site

1. Which players have a better batting average than Crystl Bustos?
   Berg, Fernandez, Topping, and Watley
2. If the coaches need a strong hitter to bat first, which player should they choose? Why?
   Sample answer: Fernandez; high batting average and a lot of experience at bat
3. Some players were up at bat more times than others. If a player is up at bat more times, does this mean she will have a higher batting average? Explain.
   No. Sample answer: The batting average is calculated by the hits at bat divided by the number of times at bat. Batting more times does not give a player a higher batting average.
4. **a.** Based on her batting average, if Mendoza went to bat 1,000 times, about how many hits should she get? 250 hits
   b. 100 times? 25 hits **c.** 10 times? 2 or 3 hits

***Math Masters,* p. 127**

Game Master

Name Date Time

***Base-10 Exchange* (Thousandths)**

one-thousandth $\frac{1}{1,000}$ 0.001	
one-hundredth $\frac{1}{100}$ 0.01	
one-tenth $\frac{1}{10}$ 0.1	
ONE $\frac{1}{1}$ 1	

***Math Masters,* p. 459**

3 Differentiation Options

READINESS

SMALL-GROUP ACTIVITY

5–15 Min

▶ Counting by Thousandths

To explore extending the place value system to thousandths, have students skip count by thousandths on their calculators. Follow these steps:

- ▷ Clear the calculator.
- ▷ Enter 1,000.
- ▷ Divide by 10 and read the new display. 100
- ▷ Divide by 10 again and read the new display. 10
- ▷ Repeat until the display shows 0.001.

Now have students program their calculator to count by 0.001s. (*See Lesson 4-1.*) Then count together with each keystroke. Ask them to predict how many counts are needed to reach 0.01 and 0.1. 10, 100

ENRICHMENT

PARTNER ACTIVITY

5–15 Min

▶ Analyzing Softball Batting Averages

(*Math Masters,* p. 127)

To apply students' knowledge of decimals in the thousandths, have them analyze batting averages. To find a batting average, the number of "Hits" is divided by the number of "At Bats" and then rounded to the nearest thousandth.

EXTRA PRACTICE

PARTNER ACTIVITY

5–15 Min

▶ Playing *Base-10 Exchange*

(*Math Masters,* p. 459)

To practice exchanging tenths, hundredths, and thousandths, have students play *Base-10 Exchange.*

The object of the game is to be the first player to make an exchange for a big cube (1).

1. The bank starts with 1 big cube, 20 flats, 20 longs, and 20 cubes.
2. Players take turns. A player rolls three dice, announces the sum, takes that number of cubes (thousandths) from the bank, and places them on the mat.
3. Whenever possible, a player exchanges 10 cubes (thousandths) for a long (hundredth) or 10 longs (hundredths) for a flat (tenth) from the bank.
4. The first player to exchange 10 flats for a big cube wins.

4•8 Metric Units of Length

Objectives To review the relationships among metric units of length; and to guide students as they work with metric measurements.

www.everydaymathonline.com

ePresentations

eToolkit

Algorithms Practice

EM Facts Workshop Game™

Family Letters

Assessment Management

Common Core State Standards

Curriculum Focal Points

Interactive Teacher's Lesson Guide

1 Teaching the Lesson

Key Concepts and Skills

- Read and write decimals through hundredths. [Number and Numeration Goal 1]
- Use extended multiplication facts to convert between metric measurements. [Operations and Computation Goal 3]
- Measure objects or distances to the nearest centimeter. [Measurement and Reference Frames Goal 1]
- Describe relationships among metric units of length. [Measurement and Reference Frames Goal 3]

Key Activities

Students review the relationships among metric units and practice converting measurements. They measure objects or distances to the nearest centimeter and convert their measurements to meters.

Ongoing Assessment: Informing Instruction See page 279.

Ongoing Assessment: Recognizing Student Achievement Use journal page 96. [Measurement and Reference Frames Goal 1]

Key Vocabulary

centimeter (cm) ◆ meter (m) ◆ millimeter (mm) ◆ decimeter (dm)

Materials

Math Journal 1, p. 96
Student Reference Book
Study Link 4•7
slate ◆ meterstick ◆ tape measure ◆ centimeter ruler ◆ chart paper

2 Ongoing Learning & Practice

Playing *Fishing for Digits*
Student Reference Book, p. 242
Math Masters, p. 472 (optional)
calculator
Students practice identifying digits in whole numbers and expressing their values.

Math Boxes 4•8
Math Journal 1, p. 97
Students practice and maintain skills through Math Box problems.

Study Link 4•8
Math Masters, p. 128
Students practice and maintain skills through Study Link activities.

3 Differentiation Options

READINESS

Exploring the Relationship between Metric Units
Math Masters, p. 129
base-10 cubes and longs ◆ metersticks
Students use base-10 cubes and longs to demonstrate the relationships between metric units of linear measure.

ENRICHMENT

Exploring the Use of Prefixes in Metric Units
Math Masters, p. 130
Students explore the use of prefixes in metric units.

ELL SUPPORT

Building a Math Word Bank
Differentiation Handbook, p. 141
Students add the terms *millimeter, centimeter,* and *meter* to their Math Word Banks.

Advance Preparation

For Part 1, choose five objects or distances for students to measure.

***Teacher's Reference Manual,* Grades 4–6** pp. 44–46, 216, 217, 233, 234, 236

Getting Started

Mental Math and Reflexes

Write decimals on the board and ask students to read them. *Suggestions:*

●○○ 0.3; 0.7; 1.6; 2.5

●●○ 0.05; 0.14; 7.02; 3.28

●●● 0.136; 0.049; 4.006; 3.102

Math Message

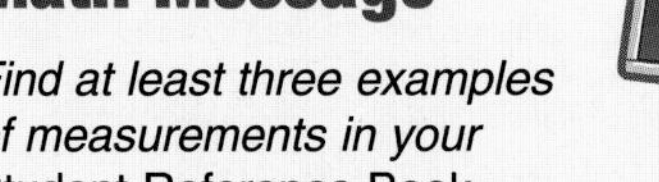

Find at least three examples of measurements in your Student Reference Book.

Study Link 4·7 Follow-Up

Have partners compare answers. Ask volunteers to explain how they were able to complete Problems 13–16.

1 Teaching the Lesson

▶ Math Message Follow-Up

(*Student Reference Book*)

Write *U.S. customary units* and *metric units* on the board. As volunteers share their measurement examples, write them in the appropriate columns. After several examples are recorded, tell students that this lesson will focus on using metric units to measure length.

Discuss why it is important to learn about metric units, even though U.S. customary units, such as the foot, mile, and pound, are commonly used in this country. Ask students where they have seen metric units used in their daily lives.

▷ Manufacturers increasingly use metric measures. (Most automobile parts are measured in metric units.)

▷ Scientists use the metric system almost exclusively.

▷ Most countries of the world use the metric system exclusively.

▷ Many sports statistics are measured in metric units. For example, at the Olympics, distance, weight, and speed are measured in metric units.

▶ Reviewing Metric Units of Linear Measures

Ask students to examine their centimeter rulers. To support English language learners, use a transparent ruler on the overhead.

- What do the numbers stand for? centimeters
- What do the smallest marks stand for? millimeters

NOTE Point out that the ruler on the overhead is larger than real life.

Display a meterstick and point out the numbered marks.

- How many **centimeters** are there in 1 **meter**? 100
- How many **millimeters** are there in 1 centimeter? 10
- How many millimeters are there in 1 meter? 1,000
- How many centimeters are there in 1 **decimeter**? 10
- How many decimeters are there in 1 meter? 10

Conclusion: Each metric unit is 10 times greater than the next-smaller standard unit. A centimeter is 10 times longer than a millimeter. A decimeter is 10 times longer than a centimeter. A meter is 10 times longer than a decimeter. Thus, a meter is 100 times longer than a centimeter and 1,000 times longer than a millimeter.

Discuss these relationships and record them on chart paper.

1 centimeter = 10 millimeters

1 decimeter = 10 centimeters

1 meter = 10 decimeters

Discuss the symbols for metric units and record them on chart paper:

mm	millimeter(s)
cm	centimeter(s)
dm	decimeter(s)
m	meter(s)

Practicing Conversions among Metric Units

WHOLE-CLASS ACTIVITY

Pose the following types of conversion problems and have students record their answers on their slates. *Suggestions:*

▷ Meters to decimeters
Ask: *How many decimeters are there in 5 meters?* 50 dm

▷ Meters to centimeters
Ask: *How many centimeters are there in 3 meters?* 300 cm

▷ Decimeters to centimeters
Ask: *How many centimeters are there in 8 decimeters?* 80 cm

Ongoing Assessment: Informing Instruction

Watch for students who think that 3 meters and 300 centimeters are measures for different distances because the numbers and units are different. Have these students line up three metersticks and count by 100s to 300 cm.

NOTE Review that when working with money, the dollar may be designated as ONE, the dime as $\frac{1}{10}$ and the penny as $\frac{1}{100}$. When working with base-10 blocks, the big cube may be designated as ONE, the flat as $\frac{1}{10}$, the long as $\frac{1}{100}$, and the cube as $\frac{1}{1,000}$. Similarly, when working with metric units, the meter may be designated as ONE, the decimeter as $\frac{1}{10}$, the centimeter as $\frac{1}{100}$, and the millimeter as $\frac{1}{1,000}$.

Links to the Future

Millimeters are introduced in this lesson but are covered in greater detail in Lesson 4-10.

Adjusting the Activity

Encourage students who are not using a mental strategy to solve the conversion problems to use metersticks.

AUDITORY ♦ KINESTHETIC ♦ TACTILE ♦ VISUAL

1. Your teacher will choose several objects or distances to measure. Measure each to the nearest centimeter. Then compare your measurements with your partner's. If you do not agree, work together to measure the objects again. Record the results in the table. Answers vary.

Object or Distance	My Measurement	Partner's Measurement	Agreed Measurement
	About ___ cm	About ___ cm	About ___ cm
	About ___ cm	About ___ cm	About ___ cm
	About ___ cm	About ___ cm	About ___ cm
	About ___ cm	About ___ cm	About ___ cm
	About ___ cm	About ___ cm	About ___ cm

2. Measure these line segments to the nearest centimeter.

a. ___

About 9 centimeters

b. ___

About 12 centimeters

3. Measure these line segments to the nearest $\frac{1}{2}$ centimeter.

a. ___

About 10 centimeters

b. ___

About 13.5 centimeters

Math Journal 1, p. 96

Object or Distance	Measurement
height of a picture frame	37 cm = 0.37 m
width of a calculator	5 cm = 0.05 m
height of a person	168 cm = 1.68 m

(*Math Journal 1*, p. 96)

Choose five objects or distances for students to measure.

▷ One object should be less than 15 centimeters long; for example, the length of the side of a calculator.

▷ Another item should be fairly substantial in size, but shorter than 1 meter; for example, the height of a desk.

▷ One distance should be something that must be measured with a tape measure, such as the distance around a partner's wrist or neck.

▷ Still another distance should be greater than 1 meter, such as the length of the classroom.

▷ You might also want to include a measurement that calls for some ingenuity, such as the shortest distance from the North Pole to the South Pole on a globe, going through the center of the globe.

Have each student measure the objects and distances to the nearest centimeter and record the measurements on journal page 96. Ask partners to compare their measurements. If there is a discrepancy, they should measure the object again and record a measurement on which they agree.

Have the class compare results. Record students' measurements in centimeters and in meters using decimals. (*See margin.*) For example, 37 centimeters = $\frac{37}{100}$ of a meter, so it can be renamed as 0.37 meter; 5 centimeters can be renamed as 0.05 meter, and 168 centimeters as 1.68 meters.

Ask students to complete Problems 2 and 3 on journal page 96 independently.

Ongoing Assessment: Recognizing Student Achievement

Journal page 96 Problem 2

Use **journal page 96, Problem 2** to assess students' ability to measure line segments to the nearest centimeter. Students are making adequate progress if their measurements are accurate. Some students may be able to measure the line segments in Problem 3 to the nearest millimeter or $\frac{1}{2}$ centimeter.

[Measurement and Reference Frames Goal 1]

2 Ongoing Learning & Practice

Playing *Fishing for Digits*

PARTNER ACTIVITY

(*Student Reference Book,* p. 242; *Math Masters,* p. 472)

Students play *Fishing for Digits* to practice identifying digits in whole numbers and expressing their values. See Lesson 2-4 for additional information.

Math Boxes 4•8

INDEPENDENT ACTIVITY

(*Math Journal 1,* p. 97)

Mixed Practice Math Boxes in this lesson are paired with Math Boxes in Lesson 4-10. The skill in Problem 6 previews Unit 5 content.

Writing/Reasoning Have students write a response to the following: *In Problem 6a, explain how you knew which number was closer to 47.* Sample answer: 47 is closer to 50 because it is greater than 45, which is halfway between 40 and 50.

Study Link 4•8

(*Math Masters,* p. 128)

Home Connection Students measure line segments to the nearest centimeter. They record the measurements in both centimeters and meters.

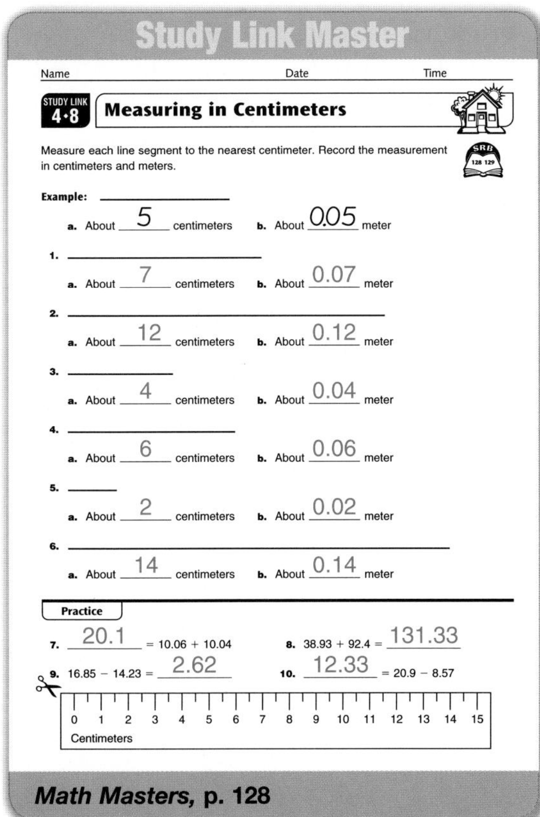

Study Link Master

Name Date Time

STUDY LINK 4•8 **Measuring in Centimeters**

Measure each line segment to the nearest centimeter. Record the measurement in centimeters and meters. SRB 128 129

Example:

a. About 5 centimeters b. About 0.05 meter

1. a. About 7 centimeters b. About 0.07 meter

2. a. About 12 centimeters b. About 0.12 meter

3. a. About 4 centimeters b. About 0.04 meter

4. a. About 6 centimeters b. About 0.06 meter

5. a. About 2 centimeters b. About 0.02 meter

6. a. About 14 centimeters b. About 0.14 meter

Practice

7. 20.1 = 10.06 + 10.04
8. 38.93 + 92.4 = 131.33
9. 16.85 − 14.23 = 2.62
10. 12.33 = 20.9 − 8.57

0 1 2 3 4 5 6 7 8 9 10 11 12 13 14 15
Centimeters

Math Masters, p. 128

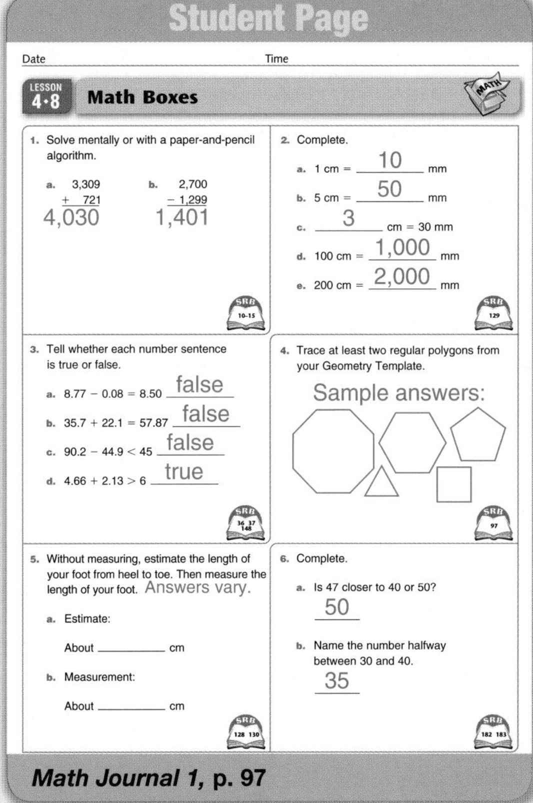

Student Page

Date Time

LESSON 4•8 **Math Boxes**

1. Solve mentally or with a paper-and-pencil algorithm.
a. 3,309 + 721 = 4,030
b. 2,700 − 1,299 = 1,401
SRB 10-15

2. Complete.
a. 1 cm = 10 mm
b. 5 cm = 50 mm
c. 3 cm = 30 mm
d. 100 cm = 1,000 mm
e. 200 cm = 2,000 mm
SRB 129

3. Tell whether each number sentence is true or false.
a. 8.77 − 0.08 = 8.50 false
b. 35.7 + 22.1 = 57.87 false
c. 90.2 − 44.9 < 45 false
d. 4.66 + 2.13 > 6 true
SRB 36 37 148

4. Trace at least two regular polygons from your Geometry Template.
Sample answers:
SRB 97

5. Without measuring, estimate the length of your foot from heel to toe. Then measure the length of your foot. Answers vary.
a. Estimate: About ______ cm
b. Measurement: About ______ cm
SRB 128 130

6. Complete.
a. Is 47 closer to 40 or 50? 50
b. Name the number halfway between 30 and 40. 35
SRB 182 183

Math Journal 1, p. 97

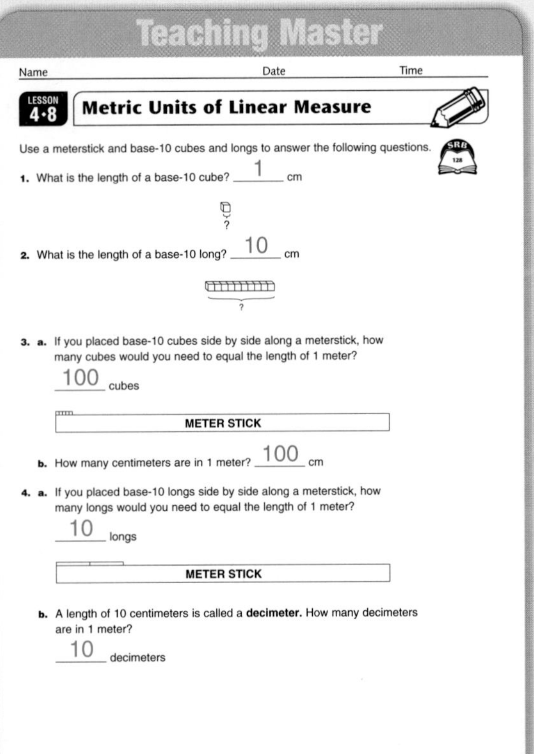
Teaching Master

Name Date Time

LESSON 4·8 **Metric Units of Linear Measure**

Use a meterstick and base-10 cubes and longs to answer the following questions. SRB 128

1. What is the length of a base-10 cube? 1 cm

2. What is the length of a base-10 long? 10 cm

3. a. If you placed base-10 cubes side by side along a meterstick, how many cubes would you need to equal the length of 1 meter?
100 cubes

METER STICK

b. How many centimeters are in 1 meter? 100 cm

4. a. If you placed base-10 longs side by side along a meterstick, how many longs would you need to equal the length of 1 meter?
10 longs

METER STICK

b. A length of 10 centimeters is called a **decimeter.** How many decimeters are in 1 meter?
10 decimeters

***Math Masters,* p. 129**

Teaching Master

Name Date Time

LESSON 4·8 **Metric Prefixes**

1. Research metric units of length and record your results in the table below.

Unit	Prefix	Number of Meters
terameter	tera–	1,000,000,000,000
gigameter	giga-	1,000,000,000
megameter	mega-	1,000,000
kilometer	kilo-	1,000
hectometer	hecto-	100
decameter	deka-	10
meter		1
decimeter	deci-	$\frac{1}{10}$
centimeter	centi-	$\frac{1}{100}$
millimeter	milli–	$\frac{1}{1000}$
micrometer	micro-	$\frac{1}{1,000,000}$
nanometer	nano-	$\frac{1}{1,000,000,000}$
picometer	pico-	$\frac{1}{1,000,000,000,000}$

2. Describe any patterns you see in the table.
Sample answer: In the Number of Meters column, there's a pattern around 1: decameter is 10 and decimeter is $\frac{1}{10}$; hectometer is 100 and centimeter is $\frac{1}{100}$; and so on.

***Math Masters,* p. 130**

3 Differentiation Options

READINESS

SMALL-GROUP ACTIVITY

▶ Exploring the Relationship between Metric Units

5–15 Min

(*Math Masters,* p. 129)

To explore the relationship between metric units of linear measure using a concrete model, have students use base-10 cubes and longs to complete *Math Masters,* page 129.

ENRICHMENT

INDEPENDENT ACTIVITY

▶ Exploring the Use of Prefixes in Metric Units

15–30 Min

(*Math Masters,* p. 130)

To further explore metric units, have students research the metric units used to measure length and identify the prefixes used. Students find the number of meters or fraction of a meter each prefix represents and record the results in a table.

ELL SUPPORT

PARTNER ACTIVITY

▶ Building a Math Word Bank

5–15 Min

(*Differentiation Handbook*, p. 141)

To provide language support for measurement, have students use the Word Bank template found on *Differentiation Handbook,* page 141. Ask students to write the terms *millimeter, centimeter,* and *meter;* draw pictures relating to each term; and write other related words. Some students may also draw a picture showing how the units are related, such as the following:

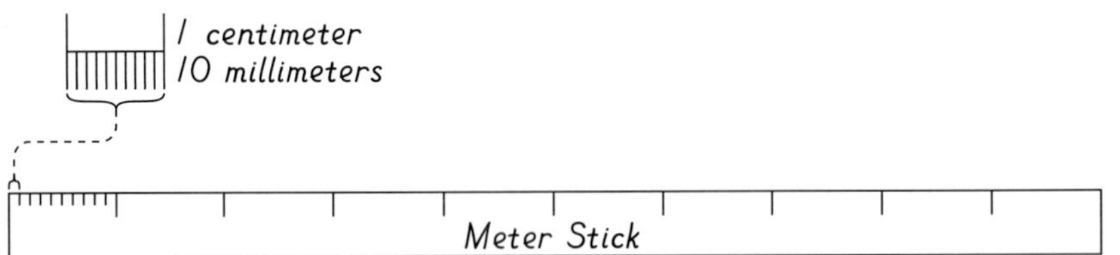

See the *Differentiation Handbook* for more information.

4•9 Personal References for Metric Length

Objective To assist students as they establish personal references for metric units of length.

www.everydaymathonline.com

ePresentations

eToolkit

Algorithms Practice

EM Facts Workshop Game™

Family Letters

Assessment Management

Common Core State Standards

Curriculum Focal Points

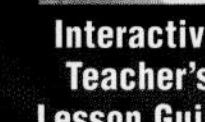
Interactive Teacher's Lesson Guide

1 Teaching the Lesson

Key Concepts and Skills

- Identify personal references for metric units of length. [Measurement and Reference Frames Goal 1]
- Estimate, without tools, the length of objects or distances in centimeters, decimeters, and meters. [Measurement and Reference Frames Goal 1]
- Measure the length of objects or distances in centimeters, decimeters, and meters. [Measurement and Reference Frames Goal 1]

Key Activities

Students find personal references (parts of their bodies or other objects) to help them estimate lengths of 1 centimeter, 10 centimeters, and 1 meter.

Key Vocabulary

personal measurement reference

Materials

Math Journal 1, pp. 98 and 99
Student Reference Book, p. 130
Study Link 4•8
tape measure ◆ ruler ◆ meterstick ◆ slate

2 Ongoing Learning & Practice

Playing *Number Top-It* (Decimals)
Student Reference Book, p. 256
Math Masters, pp. 491 and 506
4 each of number cards 0–9 (from the Everything Math Deck, if available)
Students practice comparing and ordering decimals.

Ongoing Assessment: Recognizing Student Achievement
Use *Math Masters,* page 506.
[Number and Numeration Goal 6]

Math Boxes 4•9
Math Journal 1, p. 100
Students practice and maintain skills through Math Box problems.

Study Link 4•9
Math Masters, p. 131
Students practice and maintain skills through Study Link activities.

3 Differentiation Options

READINESS

Matching Metric Units
Math Masters, p. 132
Students explore relative sizes of metric units.

ENRICHMENT

Designing a Measurement Scavenger Hunt
tape measure ◆ ruler ◆ meterstick
Students make up clues for a measurement scavenger hunt.

EXTRA PRACTICE

5-Minute Math
5-Minute Math™, pp. 48 and 49
Students solve problems involving metric measurements.

Advance Preparation

For the Math Message, choose something in the classroom that measures between 30 and 60 centimeters in length or height. Measure the object, rounding to the nearest 10 centimeters. Use the measurement to complete the Math Message.

***Teacher's Reference Manual,* Grades 4–6** pp. 214–216

Getting Started

Mental Math and Reflexes

Pose multiplication facts and extended facts. *Suggestions:*

FACTS PRACTICE

●○○ 4 ∗ 2 = 8
6 ∗ 3 = 18
5 ∗ 7 = 35
6 ∗ 5 = 30

●●○ 7 ∗ 8 = 56
9 ∗ 7 = 63
6 ∗ 7 = 42
9 ∗ 8 = 72

●●● 80 ∗ 4 = 320
7 ∗ 40 = 280
50 ∗ 90 = 4,500
60 ∗ 80 = 4,800

Math Message

Without measuring, try to find something in the classroom whose length or height is about (fill in the measurement of the object you chose) *centimeters. Be ready to explain how you made your choice.*

Study Link 4·8 Follow-Up

Briefly go over the answers. If there is disagreement, have students measure the line segments again.

Adjusting the Activity

Have students solve problems that involve more than one measurement. For example: *I'm thinking of an object that is about* x *centimeters high and about* y *centimeters long. What object might I be thinking of?*

AUDITORY ◆ KINESTHETIC ◆ TACTILE ◆ VISUAL

1 Teaching the Lesson

▶ Math Message Follow-Up

SMALL-GROUP ACTIVITY

Working in small groups, have students name the objects they chose and share how they made their decisions. Now, or at some later time, they should measure the objects to see how close their estimates are. Ask: *Did anyone choose the same object you chose?*

▶ Introducing Personal Measurement References

WHOLE-CLASS ACTIVITY

(*Student Reference Book,* p. 130)

Read page 130 in the *Student Reference Book* as a class. Discuss why **personal measurement references** might be useful. Reasons might include the following:

▷ It is hard to remember how long a centimeter or a foot is, how much area a square yard takes up, or how heavy a pound feels. Relating measures to common objects makes it easier to remember their relative sizes.

▷ Sometimes we need to measure something but don't have a tool. Personal measurement references can be used to estimate the unknown measurement.

Tell students that in this lesson they will look for personal references for 1 centimeter, 10 centimeters (1 decimeter), and 1 meter. Students will use their personal references to estimate the measurements of various objects.

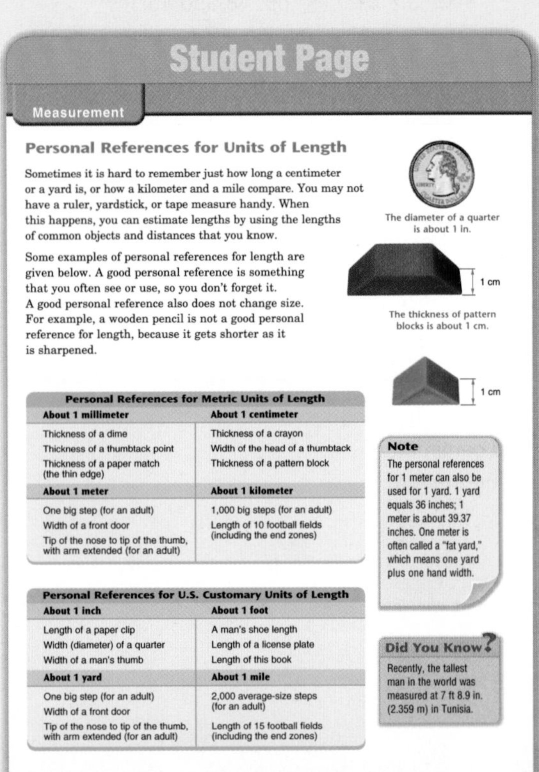

Student Page

Measurement

Personal References for Units of Length

Sometimes it is hard to remember just how long a centimeter or a yard is, or how a kilometer and a mile compare. You may not have a ruler, yardstick, or tape measure handy. When this happens, you can estimate lengths by using the lengths of common objects and distances that you know.

Some examples of personal references for length are given below. A good personal reference is something that you often see or use, so you don't forget it. A good personal reference also does not change size. For example, a wooden pencil is not a good personal reference for length, because it gets shorter as it is sharpened.

The diameter of a quarter is about 1 in.

1 cm

The thickness of pattern blocks is about 1 cm.

1 cm

Personal References for Metric Units of Length

About 1 millimeter	About 1 centimeter
Thickness of a dime Thickness of a thumbtack point Thickness of a paper match (the thin edge)	Thickness of a crayon Width of the head of a thumbtack Thickness of a pattern block
About 1 meter	**About 1 kilometer**
One big step (for an adult) Width of a front door Tip of the nose to tip of the thumb, with arm extended (for an adult)	1,000 big steps (for an adult) Length of 10 football fields (including the end zones)

Note

The personal references for 1 meter can also be used for 1 yard. 1 yard equals 36 inches; 1 meter is about 39.37 inches. One meter is often called a "fat yard," which means one yard plus one hand width.

Personal References for U.S. Customary Units of Length

About 1 inch	About 1 foot
Length of a paper clip Width (diameter) of a quarter Width of a man's thumb	A man's shoe length Length of a license plate Length of this book
About 1 yard	**About 1 mile**
One big step (for an adult) Width of a front door Tip of the nose to tip of the thumb, with arm extended (for an adult)	2,000 average-size steps (for an adult) Length of 15 football fields (including the end zones)

Did You Know?

Recently, the tallest man in the world was measured at 7 ft 8.9 in. (2.359 m) in Tunisia.

Student Reference Book, p. 130

Adjusting the Activity

ELL

Discuss the mathematical and everyday meanings of the term *reference.* For example:

▷ The class uses a *Student Reference Book.*

▷ Today students will find personal measurement references.

AUDITORY ◆ KINESTHETIC ◆ TACTILE ◆ VISUAL

▸ Finding Personal References for Metric Units of Length

PARTNER ACTIVITY

(*Math Journal 1,* p. 98)

Determining personal references for 1 centimeter and 10 centimeters

Students use metric rulers or tape measures to find common objects that are about 1 centimeter and 10 centimeters in length. Have them select one or two objects and record them in the Personal References Table on the top half of journal page 98. (The table for U.S. customary units of length on the bottom half of the page will be completed in Lesson 5-1.)

Encourage each student to find his or her own objects so that the references will be personal. Stress that students should look for objects that are easy to find and that are available when needed. Body parts are ideal, although these references will change over time. The idea is to use objects that can help students develop a sense of the sizes of the units and that can help students estimate lengths in metric units when a ruler is not available.

Point out that the objects students choose as personal references must maintain their lengths. Therefore, a pencil would not be a good choice since it will be shorter after it has been sharpened. Have students share their choices.

Determining personal references for 1 meter

This may be more difficult than it appears. Many items commonly used in the United States, such as furniture and building materials, are manufactured to specifications in inches and feet. As a result, few objects end up being exactly 1 meter in length. Thus, students may have to settle for objects that are a little more or less than 1 meter.

Two approaches are recommended:

▷ If you have enough metersticks or metric tape measures, have students explore the classroom with their partners, looking for objects or spaces that are about 1 meter in length. Have students record and share their results.

▷ Alternatively, have students propose possible objects or spaces while seated. Ask students if they think the proposed object or space is more or less than 1 meter in length. Then measure the object or space yourself.

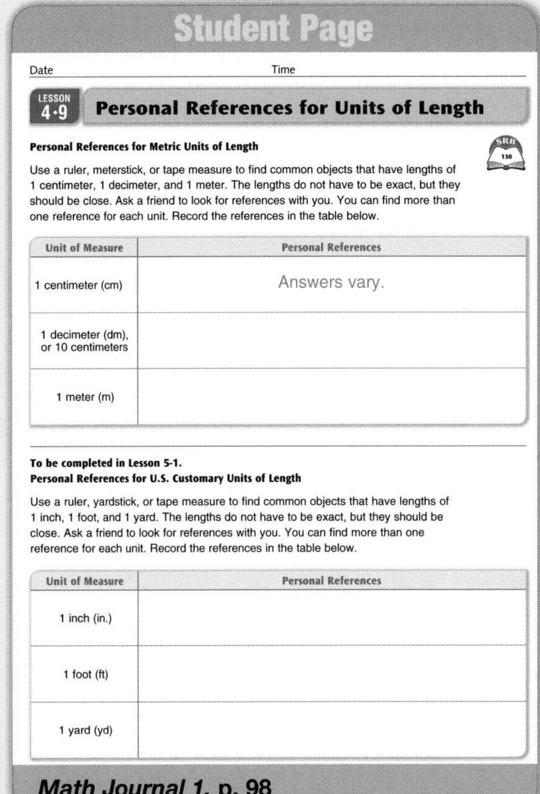

Student Page

Date Time

LESSON 4·9 **Personal References for Units of Length**

Personal References for Metric Units of Length

SRB 130

Use a ruler, meterstick, or tape measure to find common objects that have lengths of 1 centimeter, 1 decimeter, and 1 meter. The lengths do not have to be exact, but they should be close. Ask a friend to look for references with you. You can find more than one reference for each unit. Record the references in the table below.

Unit of Measure	Personal References
1 centimeter (cm)	Answers vary.
1 decimeter (dm), or 10 centimeters	
1 meter (m)	

To be completed in Lesson 5-1.
Personal References for U.S. Customary Units of Length

Use a ruler, yardstick, or tape measure to find common objects that have lengths of 1 inch, 1 foot, and 1 yard. The lengths do not have to be exact, but they should be close. Ask a friend to look for references with you. You can find more than one reference for each unit. Record the references in the table below.

Unit of Measure	Personal References
1 inch (in.)	
1 foot (ft)	
1 yard (yd)	

Math Journal 1, p. 98

NOTE If students have difficulty finding objects, here are some possibilities:

1 cm width of a fingertip
width of the stem of a house key

10 cm height of a crayon box
length of a paper clip (straightened out)

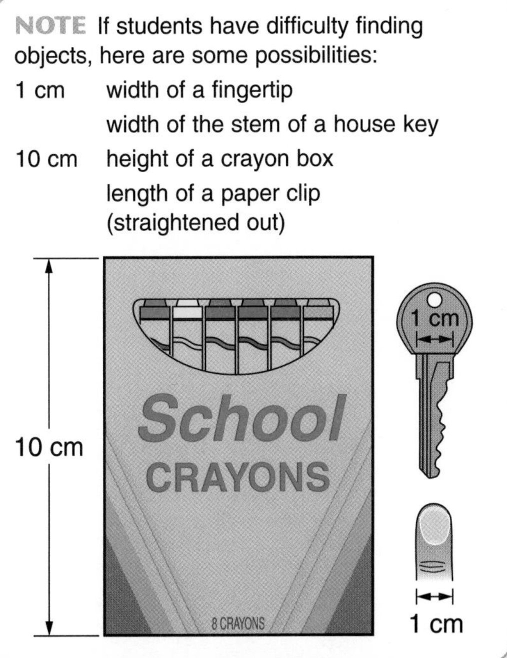

▶ Estimating Lengths with Personal References

Have students put away their metric rulers and tape measures. Then ask them to use their personal references to estimate the lengths of several objects. *Suggestions:*

▷ length and width of their journal

▷ diameter of a penny or quarter

▷ length and width of a calculator

Record students' estimates on the board. Then have students measure their objects with a metric ruler to check the accuracy of their estimates.

Next, select several longer objects in the room. Ask the class to judge the length of each in meters: *Is it closer to 1 meter, half a meter, or a meter and a half?* Check students' estimates with a meterstick.

▶ Practicing Estimating Lengths

(*Math Journal 1,* p. 99)

Students use their personal references to estimate a distance or the length or height of an object in centimeters, decimeters, or meters. Then they measure the object or distance to check their estimates.

NOTE As students fill in the table on journal page 99, you may wish to assign several objects or distances that all students must estimate and measure. This will allow for easier assessment of student work.

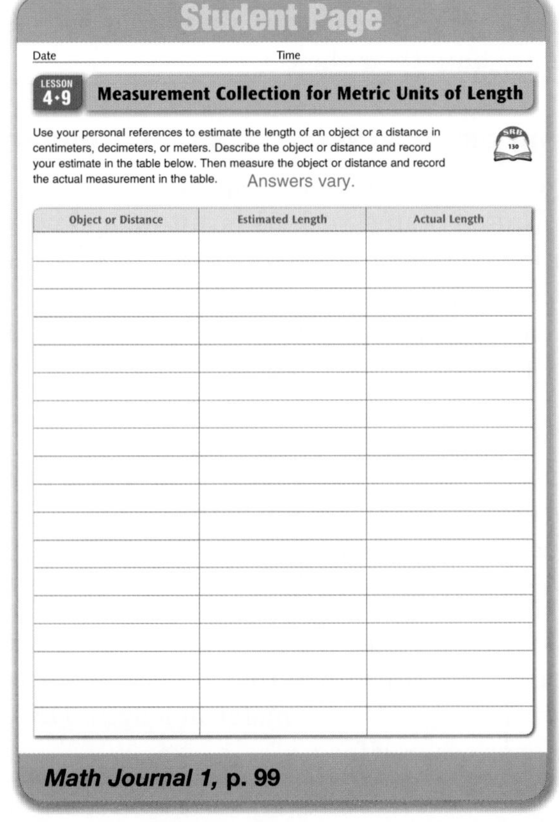

Student Page

Date Time

LESSON 4·9 **Measurement Collection for Metric Units of Length**

Use your personal references to estimate the length of an object or a distance in centimeters, decimeters, or meters. Describe the object or distance and record your estimate in the table below. Then measure the object or distance and record the actual measurement in the table. Answers vary.

Object or Distance	Estimated Length	Actual Length

Math Journal 1, p. 99

2 Ongoing Learning & Practice

Playing *Number Top-It* (Decimals)

(*Student Reference Book,* p. 256; *Math Masters,* pp. 491 and 506)

Students play *Number Top-It* (Decimals) to practice comparing and ordering decimals. See Lesson 4-4 for additional information.

Ongoing Assessment: Recognizing Student Achievement

Math Masters, Page 506

Use the ***Number Top-It*** **(Decimals) Record Sheet** (*Math Masters,* page 506) to assess students' ability to compare decimals through thousandths. Students are making adequate progress if they are able to record rounds *of Number Top-It* (Decimals) with number sentences using > and < correctly. Some students may be able to order decimals to thousandths.

[Number and Numeration Goal 6]

Math Boxes 4•9

(*Math Journal 1,* p. 100)

Mixed Practice Math Boxes in this lesson are paired with Math Boxes in Lesson 4-6. The skill in Problem 5 previews Unit 5 content.

Writing/Reasoning Have students write a response to the following: *Explain the strategy you used to order the decimals in Problem 2.* Sample answer: First I wrote the four decimals vertically and aligned them by the decimal points. Then I checked the values of the digits in the ones place, tenths place, and hundredths place of each number to write the decimals from smallest to largest.

Study Link 4•9

(*Math Masters,* p. 131)

Home Connection Students use personal references to estimate the lengths of objects, and then they measure each object. Students convert between metric measures.

Encourage students to continue bringing examples of decimals to display in the Decimals All Around Museum.

Student Page

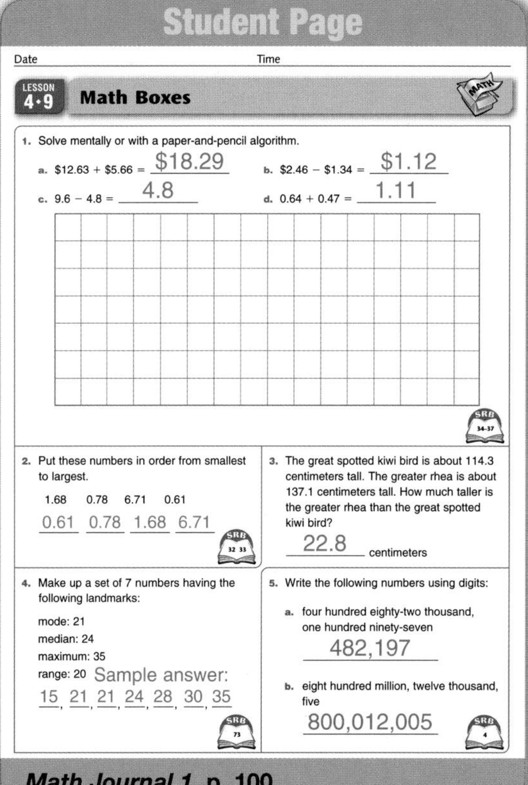

Date Time

LESSON 4•9 **Math Boxes**

1. Solve mentally or with a paper-and-pencil algorithm.
   a. $12.63 + $5.66 = $18.29
   b. $2.46 − $1.34 = $1.12
   c. 9.6 − 4.8 = 4.8
   d. 0.64 + 0.47 = 1.11

2. Put these numbers in order from smallest to largest.
   1.68 0.78 6.71 0.61
   0.61, 0.78, 1.68, 6.71

3. The great spotted kiwi bird is about 114.3 centimeters tall. The greater rhea is about 137.1 centimeters tall. How much taller is the greater rhea than the great spotted kiwi bird?
   22.8 centimeters

4. Make up a set of 7 numbers having the following landmarks:
   mode: 21
   median: 24
   maximum: 35
   range: 20 Sample answer:
   15, 21, 21, 24, 28, 30, 35

5. Write the following numbers using digits:
   a. four hundred eighty-two thousand, one hundred ninety-seven
   482,197
   b. eight hundred million, twelve thousand, five
   800,012,005

Math Journal 1, p. 100

Study Link Master

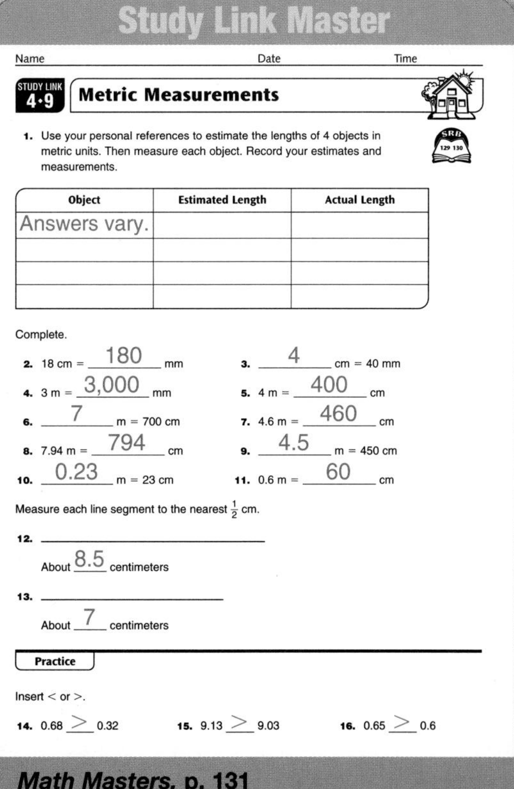

Name Date Time

STUDY LINK 4•9 **Metric Measurements**

1. Use your personal references to estimate the lengths of 4 objects in metric units. Then measure each object. Record your estimates and measurements.

Object	Estimated Length	Actual Length
Answers vary.		

Complete.

2. 18 cm = 180 mm
3. 4 cm = 40 mm
4. 3 m = 3,000 mm
5. 4 m = 400 cm
6. 7 m = 700 cm
7. 4.6 m = 460 cm
8. 7.94 m = 794 cm
9. 4.5 m = 450 cm
10. 0.23 m = 23 cm
11. 0.6 m = 60 cm

Measure each line segment to the nearest $\frac{1}{2}$ cm.

12. About 8.5 centimeters

13. About 7 centimeters

Practice

Insert < or >.

14. 0.68 > 0.32
15. 9.13 > 9.03
16. 0.65 > 0.6

Math Masters, p. 131

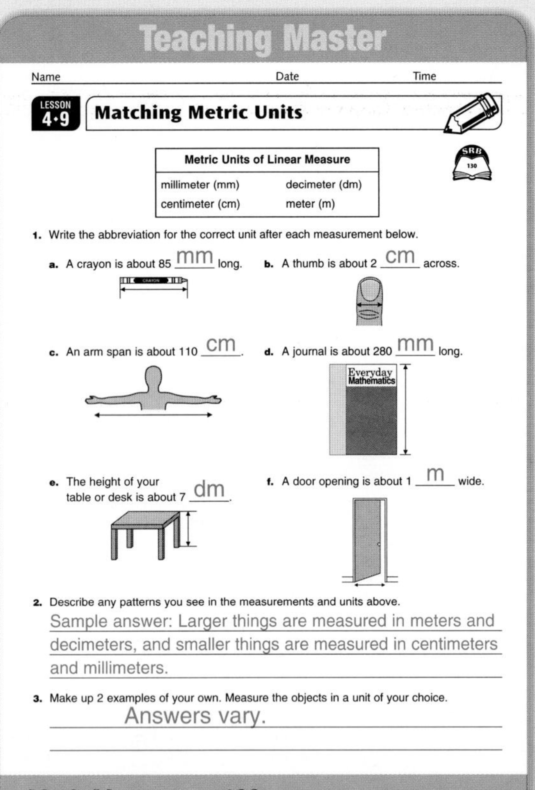
Teaching Master

Name Date Time

LESSON 4·9 **Matching Metric Units**

Metric Units of Linear Measure	
millimeter (mm)	decimeter (dm)
centimeter (cm)	meter (m)

1. Write the abbreviation for the correct unit after each measurement below.
   a. A crayon is about 85 mm long.
   b. A thumb is about 2 cm across.
   c. An arm span is about 110 cm.
   d. A journal is about 280 mm long.
   e. The height of your table or desk is about 7 dm.
   f. A door opening is about 1 m wide.
2. Describe any patterns you see in the measurements and units above.
   Sample answer: Larger things are measured in meters and decimeters, and smaller things are measured in centimeters and millimeters.
3. Make up 2 examples of your own. Measure the objects in a unit of your choice.
   Answers vary.

Math Masters, p. 132

3 Differentiation Options

READINESS

▶ Matching Metric Units

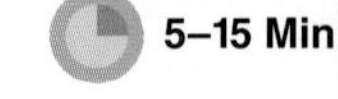

(*Math Masters,* p. 132)

To explore relative sizes of metric units, have students match units to measurements. Ask them to refer to the actual objects listed on *Math Masters,* page 132 so students can measure them to decide which unit should be used.

ENRICHMENT

▶ Designing a Measurement Scavenger Hunt

To apply students' understanding of metric units of linear measure, have them create a scavenger hunt for other students or another class. You might suggest the following procedure:

1. Begin by using personal references to estimate the size of objects.
2. Use a meterstick to check estimates.
3. Write the measure of each object as the first clue.
4. Then write a second clue—something that will help limit the possible choices. *For example:*
   - ▷ This object is about 2 meters high. You wouldn't be able to get into the classroom without it. door
   - ▷ This object is about 15 centimeters long. It is useful to have around when solving problems with large numbers. calculator

Have students read their clues aloud.

EXTRA PRACTICE

▶ *5-Minute Math*

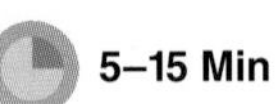

To offer students more experience with metric measurements, see *5-Minute Math,* pages 48 and 49.

4·10 Measuring in Millimeters

Objectives To guide students as they measure lengths to the nearest millimeter; and to provide practice converting measurements between millimeters and centimeters.

Technology Resources www.everydaymathonline.com

ePresentations

eToolkit

Algorithms Practice

EM Facts Workshop Game™

Family Letters

Assessment Management

Common Core State Standards

Curriculum Focal Points

Interactive Teacher's Lesson Guide

1 Teaching the Lesson

Key Concepts and Skills

- Use extended multiplication facts to convert between metric measurements.
  [Operations and Computation Goal 3]
- Use a scale to determine actual size.
  [Operations and Computation Goal 7]
- Measure lengths to the nearest millimeter.
  [Measurement and Reference Frames Goal 1]
- Describe the relationship among metric units of length.
  [Measurement and Reference Frames Goal 3]

Key Activities

Students examine the millimeter marks on their centimeter rulers. They measure line segments in millimeters and centimeters. Then they measure illustrations of various invertebrates in millimeters and convert their measurements to centimeters.

Ongoing Assessment: Recognizing Student Achievement
Use Mental Math and Reflexes.
[Operations and Computation Goal 3]

Materials

Math Journal 1, pp. 101–103
Study Link 4•9
Math Masters, p. 429
centimeter ruler ◆ slate ◆ scissors ◆ highlighter

2 Ongoing Learning & Practice

Math Boxes 4•10
Math Journal 1, p. 104
Students practice and maintain skills through Math Box problems.

Study Link 4•10
Math Masters, p. 133
Students practice and maintain skills through Study Link activities.

3 Differentiation Options

READINESS

Exploring the Need for Millimeters
Math Masters, p. 134
scissors ◆ ruler
Students explore the need for a metric unit of measure smaller than a centimeter.

ENRICHMENT

Investigating Ratios
If You Hopped Like a Frog
Students explore the concept of scale by comparing what humans could do if they had bodies like different animals.

EXTRA PRACTICE

Measuring to the Nearest Millimeter
ruler
Students draw line segments and measure them to the nearest millimeter.

EXTRA PRACTICE

Taking a 50-Facts Test
Math Masters, pp. 413 and 414;
p. 416 (optional)
pen or colored pencil
Students take a 50-facts test. They use a line graph to record individual and optional class scores.

Advance Preparation

For Part 1, make one copy of *Math Masters,* page 429 per four students. Cut the sections apart along the dashed lines.

For the optional Enrichment activity in Part 3, obtain the book ***If You Hopped Like a Frog*** by David M. Schwartz (Scholastic Inc., 1999).

***Teacher's Reference Manual,* Grades 4–6** pp. 217, 218

Getting Started

Mental Math and Reflexes

Pose multiplication facts and extended facts.
Suggestions:

●○○	0 ∗ 6 = 0	●●○	6 ∗ 6 = 36	●●●	40 ∗ 5 = 200
	9 ∗ 1 = 9		3 ∗ 4 = 12		300 ∗ 6 = 1,800
	2 ∗ 7 = 14		7 ∗ 7 = 49		70 ∗ 80 = 5,600
	5 ∗ 8 = 40		4 ∗ 6 = 24		40 ∗ 90 = 3,600
	10 ∗ 3 = 30		6 ∗ 3 = 18		500 ∗ 30 = 15,000

Math Message

Complete Problems 1–4 on journal page 101.

Study Link 4·9 Follow-Up

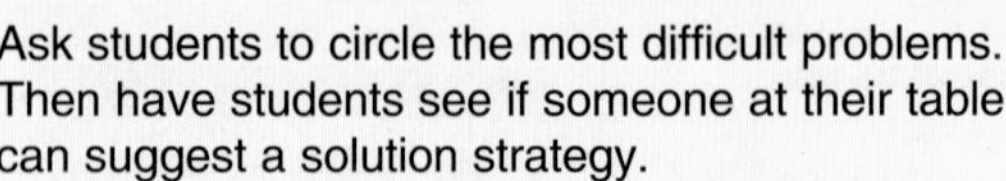

Ask students to circle the most difficult problems. Then have students see if someone at their table can suggest a solution strategy.

Ongoing Assessment: Recognizing Student Achievement

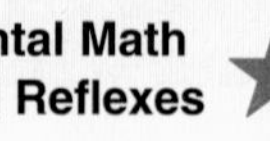

Use **Mental Math and Reflexes** to assess students' automaticity with multiplication facts. Students are making adequate progress if they demonstrate automaticity with the ●○○ and ●●○ problems. Some students may demonstrate automaticity with the ●●● problems.

[Operations and Computation Goal 3]

1 Teaching the Lesson

▶ Math Message Follow-Up

(*Math Journal 1,* p. 101)

If students have difficulty naming things that measure about 1 millimeter, suggest these possibilities: the thickness of the wire in a paper clip; the width of a pencil point; or the edge of a dime.

Students should conclude that both line segments they drew are the same length. Thus, 8 centimeters = 80 millimeters.

In this lesson students use millimeters to measure very small invertebrates. They also practice converting millimeters to centimeters.

Student Page

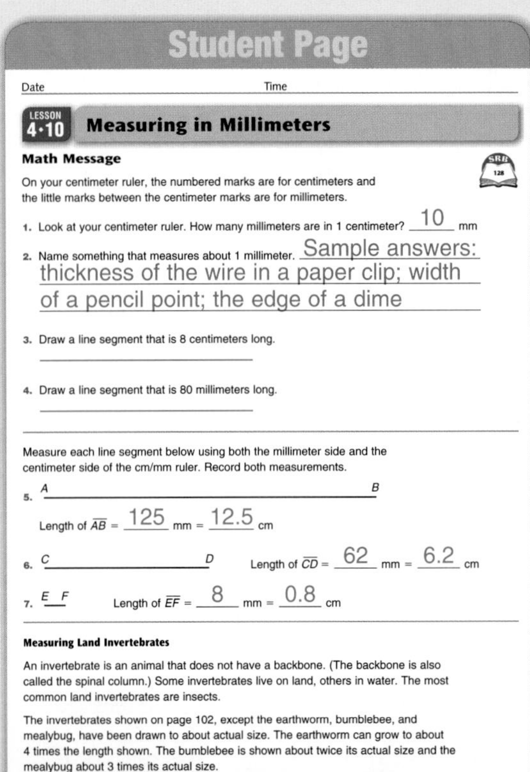

Date Time

LESSON 4·10 **Measuring in Millimeters**

Math Message

On your centimeter ruler, the numbered marks are for centimeters and the little marks between the centimeter marks are for millimeters.

1. Look at your centimeter ruler. How many millimeters are in 1 centimeter? 10 mm
2. Name something that measures about 1 millimeter. Sample answers: thickness of the wire in a paper clip; width of a pencil point; the edge of a dime
3. Draw a line segment that is 8 centimeters long.
4. Draw a line segment that is 80 millimeters long.

Measure each line segment below using both the millimeter side and the centimeter side of the cm/mm ruler. Record both measurements.

5. A ________ B
   Length of $\overline{AB}$ = 125 mm = 12.5 cm
6. C ________ D   Length of $\overline{CD}$ = 62 mm = 6.2 cm
7. E _ F   Length of $\overline{EF}$ = 8 mm = 0.8 cm

Measuring Land Invertebrates

An invertebrate is an animal that does not have a backbone. (The backbone is also called the spinal column.) Some invertebrates live on land, others in water. The most common land invertebrates are insects.

The invertebrates shown on page 102, except the earthworm, bumblebee, and mealybug, have been drawn to about actual size. The earthworm can grow to about 4 times the length shown. The bumblebee is shown about twice its actual size and the mealybug about 3 times its actual size.

Math Journal 1, p. 101

Measuring Lengths in Millimeters and Centimeters

WHOLE-CLASS ACTIVITY

(*Math Journal 1,* p. 101; *Math Masters,* p. 429)

Pass out the quarter-sheets of *Math Masters,* page 429 and have students cut out the cm/mm rulers. Then have them fold the rulers carefully along the center line. Encourage students to use a highlighter to mark *mm* and *cm* on the ruler so that the units are emphasized.

Demonstrate how to use the centimeter side of the ruler by having students measure the line segment they drew in Math Message Problem 3. Instruct students to place the centimeter side of the folded ruler above the line segment with 0 aligned with the left end of the segment. Then demonstrate how to use the millimeter side of the ruler by having students measure the line segment they drew in Problem 4. Instruct students to place the millimeter side of the folded ruler under the line segment with 0 aligned with the left end of the segment.

Now ask students to measure line segments *AB, CD,* and *EF* (Problems 5–7) using both sides of the cm/mm ruler. Record their measurements on the board: 125 mm = 12.5 cm; 62 mm = 6.2 cm; 8 mm = 0.8 cm.

NOTE When converting between millimeters and centimeters, tell students to think of the centimeter as the ONE, or the *unit,* and the millimeter as $\frac{1}{10}$.

Adjusting the Activity

Some students may note that the measurements of each line segment on journal page 101 vary slightly. Ask students to explain why they think this might happen. Possible response: "The spaces between millimeter marks are so small. A measurement is never exact—it is only an approximation."

AUDITORY ◆ KINESTHETIC ◆ TACTILE ◆ VISUAL

Write several millimeter/centimeter conversion problems on the board. Ask students to write their answers on their slates. *Suggestions:*

1 cm = 10 mm	4 cm = 40 mm	2.3 cm = 23 mm
10 mm = 1 cm	130 mm = 13 cm	42 mm = 4.2 cm
1 mm = 0.1 cm	4 mm = 0.4 cm	8 mm = 0.8 cm

Adjusting the Activity

Have students use their cm/mm rulers as concrete models for conversions between metric units. Pose millimeter/meter conversions to students.

AUDITORY ◆ KINESTHETIC ◆ TACTILE ◆ VISUAL

Teaching Aid Master

Name Date Time

A cm/mm Ruler

cm 0 0.5 1 1.5 2 2.5 3 3.5 4 4.5 5 5.5 6 6.5 7 7.5 8 8.5 9 9.5 10 10.5 11 11.5 12 12.5 13 13.5 14 14.5 15 15.5 16

Fold

mm 0 5 10 15 20 25 30 35 40 45 50 55 60 65 70 75 80 85 90 95 100 105 110 115 120 125 130 135 140 145 150 155 160

Math Masters, p. 429

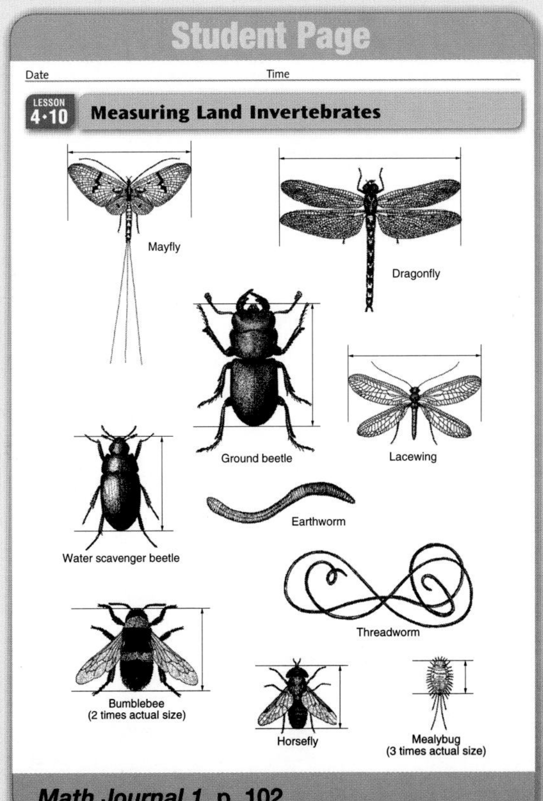

Math Journal 1, p. 102

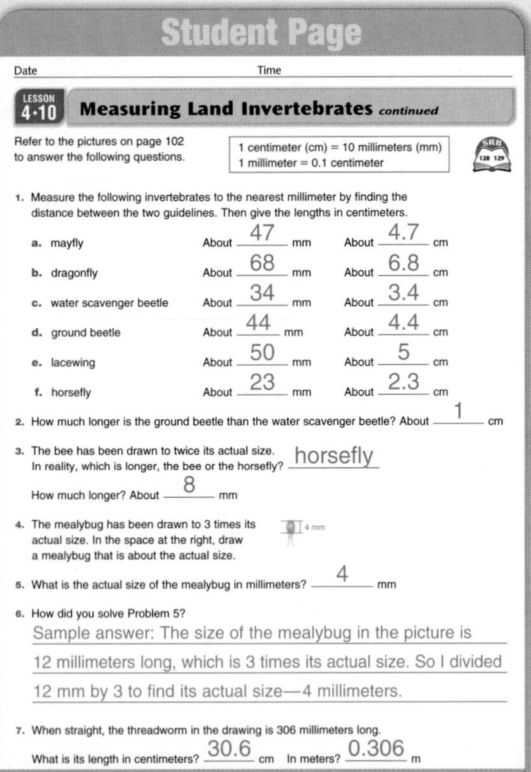
Student Page

Date Time

LESSON 4·10 **Measuring Land Invertebrates** *continued*

Refer to the pictures on page 102 to answer the following questions.

1 centimeter (cm) = 10 millimeters (mm)
1 millimeter = 0.1 centimeter

SRB 128 129

1. Measure the following invertebrates to the nearest millimeter by finding the distance between the two guidelines. Then give the lengths in centimeters.

a. mayfly	About 47 mm	About 4.7 cm
b. dragonfly	About 68 mm	About 6.8 cm
c. water scavenger beetle	About 34 mm	About 3.4 cm
d. ground beetle	About 44 mm	About 4.4 cm
e. lacewing	About 50 mm	About 5 cm
f. horsefly	About 23 mm	About 2.3 cm

2. How much longer is the ground beetle than the water scavenger beetle? About 1 cm

3. The bee has been drawn to twice its actual size. In reality, which is longer, the bee or the horsefly? horsefly
How much longer? About 8 mm

4. The mealybug has been drawn to 3 times its actual size. In the space at the right, draw a mealybug that is about the actual size. 4 mm

5. What is the actual size of the mealybug in millimeters? 4 mm

6. How did you solve Problem 5?
Sample answer: The size of the mealybug in the picture is 12 millimeters long, which is 3 times its actual size. So I divided 12 mm by 3 to find its actual size—4 millimeters.

7. When straight, the threadworm in the drawing is 306 millimeters long.
What is its length in centimeters? 30.6 cm In meters? 0.306 m

Math Journal 1, **p. 103**

Measuring Invertebrates in Metric Units

PARTNER ACTIVITY

PROBLEM SOLVING

(*Math Journal 1,* pp. 101–103)

Science Link Ask students to read about measuring land invertebrates on journal page 101 and to examine the illustrations of land invertebrates on page 102. Explain how to measure the length or wingspan of the invertebrates by measuring the distance between the guidelines. Students should use their regular centimeter ruler to measure in millimeters (not the paper cm/mm ruler) and then convert the measurements to centimeters.

Links to the Future

Drawing and measuring line segments to the nearest millimeter is a Grade 5 Goal. In Unit 8 of *Fourth Grade Everyday Mathematics* students use measurements to create scale drawings and use scale drawings to find area.

When students have finished journal page 103, have them look at the picture they drew for Problem 4. Ask them to use "times-as-many" language to compare the length of their drawing to the length of the mealybug picture on journal page 102. Sample answer: The picture is 3 times as long as my drawing. Then ask them to use a multiplication equation to represent this comparison $4 * 3 = 12$

Student Page

Date Time

LESSON 4·10 **Math Boxes**

1. Solve mentally or with a paper-and-pencil algorithm.
a. 4,647 + 3,228 = 7,875
b. 2,500 − 1,398 = 1,102
SRB 10-15

2. Complete.
a. 7 cm = 70 mm
b. 15 cm = 150 mm
c. 500 cm = 5 m
d. 4 cm = 40 mm
e. 800 cm = 8 m
SRB 129

3. Tell whether each number sentence is true or false.
a. 2.34 − 0.09 = 2.25 true
b. 89.6 + 21.7 = 111.3 true
c. 56.4 − 23.8 < 33 true
d. 5.17 + 3.86 > 10 false
SRB 36 37 148

4. Name two properties of a regular polygon.
a. The sides are the same length.
b. The angles have the same measure.
Sample answers.
SRB 97

5. Without measuring, estimate the height of your chair. Then measure it.
Answers vary.
a. Estimate:
About ______ cm
b. Measurement:
About ______ cm
SRB 128 130

6. Complete.
a. Is 326 closer to 300 or 400? 300
b. Name the number halfway between 500 and 800. 650
SRB 182 183

Math Journal 1, **p. 104**

2 Ongoing Learning & Practice

Math Boxes 4·10

INDEPENDENT ACTIVITY

(*Math Journal 1,* p. 104)

Mixed Practice Math Boxes in this lesson are paired with Math Boxes in Lesson 4-8. The skill in Problem 6 previews Unit 5 content.

Study Link 4·10

INDEPENDENT ACTIVITY

(*Math Masters,* p. 133)

Home Connection Students convert between metric units.

3 Differentiation Options

READINESS

PARTNER ACTIVITY

5–15 Min

Exploring the Need for Millimeters

(*Math Masters,* p. 134)

To explore the need for standard units of measure, have students cut out the ruler at the bottom of *Math Masters,* page 134, and use it to measure the pencils in Problem 1. Discuss the need for a unit of metric measure that is smaller than a centimeter.

ENRICHMENT

PARTNER ACTIVITY

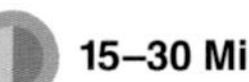

15–30 Min

Investigating Ratios

Literature Link To further explore the concept of scale, have students read ***If You Hopped Like a Frog*** by David M. Schwartz (Scholastic Inc., 1999). This book compares what humans could do if they had bodies like different animals. After students have read the book, have them answer the questions posed at the back of the book.

EXTRA PRACTICE

PARTNER ACTIVITY

5–15 Min

Measuring to the Nearest Millimeter

To practice measuring to the nearest millimeter, have students draw line segments, measure them to the nearest millimeter, and record the measurements in millimeters and centimeters. Partners measure each other's line segments and compare answers.

EXTRA PRACTICE

SMALL-GROUP ACTIVITY

5–15 Min

Taking a 50-Facts Test

(*Math Masters,* pp. 413, 414, and 416)

See Lesson 3-4 for details regarding the administration of the 50-facts test and the recording and graphing of individual and optional class results.

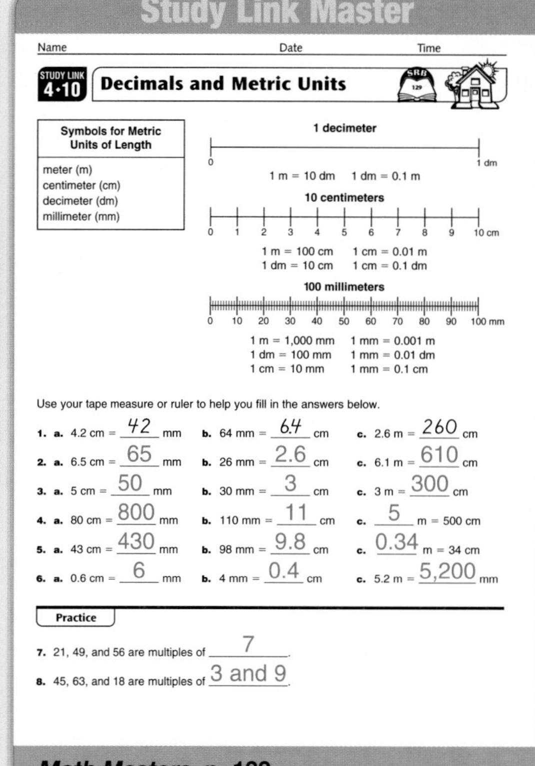

Study Link Master

Name Date Time

STUDY LINK 4•10 **Decimals and Metric Units**

Symbols for Metric Units of Length
meter (m)
centimeter (cm)
decimeter (dm)
millimeter (mm)

1 decimeter

1 m = 10 dm 1 dm = 0.1 m

10 centimeters

1 m = 100 cm 1 cm = 0.01 m
1 dm = 10 cm 1 cm = 0.1 dm

100 millimeters

1 m = 1,000 mm 1 mm = 0.001 m
1 dm = 100 mm 1 mm = 0.01 dm
1 cm = 10 mm 1 mm = 0.1 cm

Use your tape measure or ruler to help you fill in the answers below.

1. a. 4.2 cm = 42 mm b. 64 mm = 6.4 cm c. 2.6 m = 260 cm
2. a. 6.5 cm = 65 mm b. 26 mm = 2.6 cm c. 6.1 m = 610 cm
3. a. 5 cm = 50 mm b. 30 mm = 3 cm c. 3 m = 300 cm
4. a. 80 cm = 800 mm b. 110 mm = 11 cm c. 5 m = 500 cm
5. a. 43 cm = 430 mm b. 98 mm = 9.8 cm c. 0.34 m = 34 cm
6. a. 0.6 cm = 6 mm b. 4 mm = 0.4 cm c. 5.2 m = 5,200 mm

Practice

7. 21, 49, and 56 are multiples of 7.
8. 45, 63, and 18 are multiples of 3 and 9.

Math Masters, p. 133

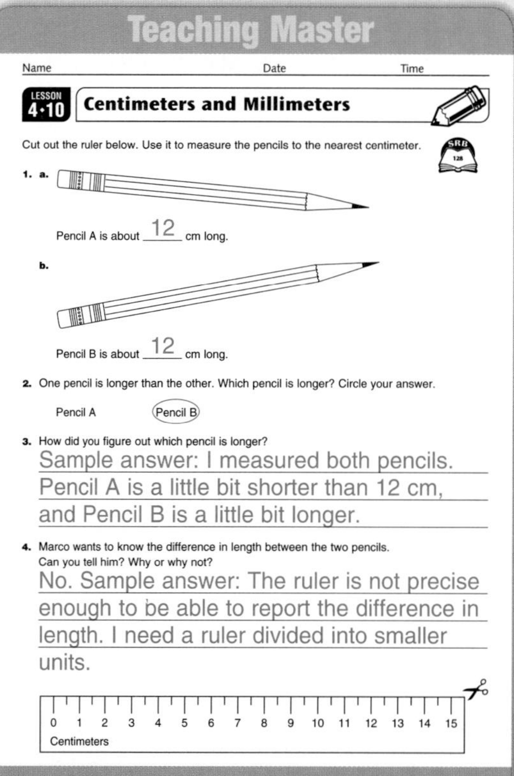

Teaching Master

Name Date Time

LESSON 4•10 **Centimeters and Millimeters**

Cut out the ruler below. Use it to measure the pencils to the nearest centimeter.

1. a. Pencil A is about 12 cm long.
   b. Pencil B is about 12 cm long.
2. One pencil is longer than the other. Which pencil is longer? Circle your answer.
   Pencil A (Pencil B)
3. How did you figure out which pencil is longer?
   Sample answer: I measured both pencils. Pencil A is a little bit shorter than 12 cm, and Pencil B is a little bit longer.
4. Marco wants to know the difference in length between the two pencils. Can you tell him? Why or why not?
   No. Sample answer: The ruler is not precise enough to be able to report the difference in length. I need a ruler divided into smaller units.

Math Masters, p. 134

4•11 Progress Check 4

Objective To assess students' progress on mathematical content through the end of Unit 4.

1 Looking Back: Cumulative Assessment

Input student data from Progress Check 3 into the **Assessment Management Spreadsheets**.

Materials

- Study Link 4◆10
- *Assessment Handbook,* pp. 76–83, 169–173, 219, and 258–261
- slate

CONTENT ASSESSED	LESSON(S)	ASSESSMENT ITEMS				
		SELF	ORAL/SLATE	WRITTEN PART A	WRITTEN PART B	OPEN RESPONSE
Read, write, and represent decimals through thousandths; identify digits and express their values in such numbers. [Number and Numeration Goal 1]	4•1–4•8	1, 2	1, 3		29	
Find multiples of numbers less than 10; find factors of numbers; identify prime and composite numbers. [Number and Numeration Goal 3]	4•5, 4•7			11, 12		
Convert "easy" fractions to decimals. [Number and Numeration Goal 5]	4•1–4•3, 4•7				23–25	
Compare and order decimals through thousandths. [Number and Numeration Goal 6]	4•3, 4•4, 4•6, 4•7, 4•9	3		1–7		✔
Add and subtract decimals to hundredths. [Operations and Computation Goal 2]	4•5–4•10	4, 5		3, 4, 13–18	28	
Estimate sums and differences of decimals. [Operations and Computation Goal 6]	4•4–4•6		2			✔
Measure to the nearest centimeter. [Measurement and Reference Frames Goal 1]	4•5, 4•8–4•10	6, 7		8–10	26, 27	
Describe relationships among metric units of length. [Measurement and Reference Frames Goal 3]	4•8–4•10		4		26, 27	
Solve open number sentences. [Patterns, Functions, and Algebra Goal 2]	4•1, 4•3–4•5, 4•7			1–4, 19–22		

2 Looking Ahead: Preparing for Unit 5

Math Boxes 4◆11

Study Link 4◆11: Unit 5 Family Letter

Materials

- *Math Journal 1,* p. 105
- *Math Masters,* pp. 135–138

Getting Started

Math Message • Self Assessment

Complete the Self Assessment (Assessment Handbook, *page 169*).

Study Link 4•10 Follow-Up

Have partners compare answers. Encourage students to use a meterstick to check answers as necessary.

1 Looking Back: Cumulative Assessment

Math Message Follow-Up

(Self Assessment, *Assessment Handbook,* p. 169)

The Self Assessment offers students the opportunity to reflect upon their progress.

Oral and Slate Assessments

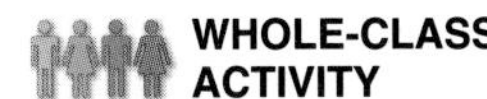

Problems 1 and 3 provide summative information and can be used for grading purposes. Problems 2 and 4 provide formative information that can be useful in planning future instruction.

Oral Assessment

1. Write 1-, 2-, and 3-place decimals on the board. Have students read them aloud. *Suggestions:*
   - 0.4
   - 0.503
   - 1.37
   - 23.7
   - 2.006
   - 1.062
2. Pose decimal addition and subtraction problems. Have students describe the strategy they used to estimate the answer to each problem. *Suggestions:* Sample answers:
   - 17.6 – 12.1 6
   - 13.8 – 9.2 5
   - 22.4 + 14.9 37
   - 25.01 + 25.3 50

Slate Assessment

3. Read 1-, 2-, and 3-place decimals aloud. Have students write them on their slates. *Suggestions:*
   - 1.5
   - 0.23
   - 6.05
   - 0.003
4. Pose problems involving converting metric measurements to other metric units. *Suggestions:*
   - 2 m = 200 cm
   - 146 cm = 1.46 m
   - 36 mm = 3.6 cm
   - 12 cm = 120 mm

Assessment Master

Name Date Time

LESSON 4•11 **Self Assessment** Progress Check 4

Think about each skill listed below. Assess your own progress by checking the most appropriate box.

Skills	I can do this on my own and explain how to do it.	I can do this on my own.	I can do this if I get help or look at an example.
1. Read decimals through thousandths.			
2. Write decimals through thousandths.			
3. Compare and order decimals through thousandths.			
4. Add decimals like these: \$23.62 + \$7.95 15.8 + 2.23			
5. Subtract decimals like these: \$14.35 – \$6.27 5.9 – 4.61			
6. Measure objects to the nearest centimeter.			
7. Measure objects to the nearest $\frac{1}{2}$ centimeter.			

Assessment Handbook, **p. 169**

Assessment Master

Name Date Time

LESSON 4•11 **Written Assessment** Progress Check 4

Part A

Write > or < to make a true number sentence.

1. 5.46 < 5.9
2. 0.45 < 0.7
3. 4.8 + 6.9 > 3.4 + 7.7
4. 3.85 – 3.46 < 9.1 – 6.2
5. Write the following numbers in order from smallest to largest.
   0.001, 4.3, 4.05, 0.6, 0.06, 0.1
   0.001, 0.06, 0.1, 0.6, 4.05, 4.3
   smallest largest
6. Write 2 numbers between 0 and 1. Use decimals. Sample answers: 0.6 0.8
7. Write 2 numbers between 1 and 2. Use decimals. Sample answers: 1.48 1.79
8. Use your ruler to measure the line segment to the nearest centimeter.
   About 10 cm
9. Use your ruler to measure the line segment to the nearest $\frac{1}{2}$ centimeter.
   About 8.5 cm
10. Draw a line segment that is 12.5 centimeters long.
11. a. List the first six multiples of 8. 8, 16, 24, 32, 40, 48
    b. Is 8 a prime number or a composite number? composite number
12. a. List the factor pairs of 28.
    1 and 28 2 and 14 4 and 7
    b. Is 28 a prime number or a composite number? composite number

Assessment Handbook, **p. 170**

Assessment Master

Name Date Time

LESSON 4•11 **Written Assessment** *continued*

Add or subtract mentally or with a paper-and-pencil algorithm.

13. $12.34 + $7.45 = $19.79

14. 10.4 = 9.6 + 0.8

15. 41.12 + 6.9 = 48.02

16. $15.46 − $9.23 = $6.23

17. 9.9 = 12.8 − 2.9

18. 34.3 − 26.51 = 7.79

Solve each open sentence.

19. $r + 129 = 254$ $r =$ 125

20. $93 - p = 37$ $p =$ 56

21. $w * 6 = 54$ $w =$ 9

22. $56 / g = 7$ $g =$ 8

Assessment Handbook, p. 171

Assessment Master

Name Date Time

LESSON 4•11 **Written Assessment** *continued*

Part B

Write each decimal as a fraction.

23. 0.4 = $\frac{4}{10}$

24. 0.34 = $\frac{34}{100}$

25. 0.674 = $\frac{674}{1,000}$

Use your ruler to measure and record the length of the line segments below to the nearest millimeter. Then write your answers in centimeters.

26. A ——— B 82 mm 8.2 cm

27. C ——— D 58 mm 5.8 cm

28. Mrs. Austin had $98.37 in her savings account. She withdrew $42.50. A week later, she deposited $38.25. What is the new balance in her savings account? $94.12

Write what you did to find the answer.

Sample answer: I subtracted $42.50 from $98.37 because she withdrew $42.50 from her account, and I got $55.87. Then I added $38.25 to $55.87 because she deposited $38.25 to her account, and I got $94.12.

29. Teneil was working with base-10 blocks. She was using the big cube as the ONE. The flats were tenths. Teneil counted 12 flats—

"one-tenth, two-tenths, three-tenths, four-tenths, five-tenths, six-tenths, seven-tenths, eight-tenths, nine-tenths, ten-tenths, eleven-tenths, twelve-tenths"

She wrote 0.12 to show what the blocks were worth. Is Teneil right? Explain.

No. Sample answers: 12 tenths is the same as 10 tenths (1) plus 2 more tenths (0.2); 1 + 0.2 = 1.2. 0.12 is 12 hundredths, which isn't the same as 12 tenths. She should have written 1.2.

Assessment Handbook, p. 172

▶ Written Assessment

(*Assessment Handbook,* pp. 170–172)

Part A Recognizing Student Achievement

Problems 1–22 provide summative information and may be used for grading purposes.

Problem(s)	Description
1–4	Insert > or < to make true number sentences.
5	Order decimals.
6, 7	Write numbers between 2 whole numbers.
8	Measure line segments to the nearest centimeter.
9, 10	Measure and draw line segments to the nearest $\frac{1}{2}$ centimeter.
11, 12	Write factors and multiples; identify prime and composite numbers.
13–18	Add and subtract decimals.
19–22	Solve open sentences.

Part B Informing Instruction

Problems 23–29 provide formative information that can be useful in planning future instruction.

Problem(s)	Description
23–25	Rename decimals as fractions with 10, 100, and 1,000 in the denominator.
26, 27	Measure line segments to the nearest millimeter.
28	Solve a decimal addition and subtraction number story.
29	Identify decimal digits and express their value.

Use the checklists on pages 259 and 261 of the *Assessment Handbook* to record results. Then input the data into the **Assessment Management Spreadsheets** to keep an ongoing record of students' progress toward Grade-Level Goals.

▶ Open Response

(*Assessment Handbook,* p. 173)

Forming a Relay Team

The open-response item requires students to apply concepts and skills from Unit 4 to solve a multistep problem. See *Assessment Handbook,* pages 79–83 for rubrics and students' work samples for this problem.

2 Looking Ahead: Preparing for Unit 5

▶ Math Boxes 4•11

INDEPENDENT ACTIVITY

(*Math Journal 1,* p. 105)

Mixed Practice This Math Boxes page previews Unit 5 content.

▶ Study Link 4•11: Unit 5 Family Letter

INDEPENDENT ACTIVITY

(*Math Masters,* pp. 135–138)

Home Connection The Unit 5 Family Letter provides parents and guardians with information and activities related to Unit 5 topics.

Study Link Masters

Name Date Time

STUDY LINK 4•11 **Unit 5: Family Letter**

Big Numbers, Estimation, and Computation

In this unit, your child will begin to multiply 1- and 2-digit numbers using what we call the **partial-products method.** In preparation for this, students will learn to play the game *Multiplication Wrestling.* Ask your child to explain the rules to you and play an occasional game together. While students are expected to learn the partial-products method, they will also investigate the **lattice multiplication method,** which students have often enjoyed in the past.

If your child is having trouble with multiplication facts, give short (five-minute) reviews at home, concentrating on the facts he or she finds difficult.

Another important focus in this unit is on reading and writing big numbers. Students will use big numbers to solve problems and make reasonable estimates. Help your child locate big numbers in newspapers and other sources, and ask your child to read them to you. Or, you can read the numbers and have your child write them.

Sometimes it is helpful to write big numbers in an abbreviated form so that they are easier to work with. One way is to use **exponents,** which tell how many times a number, called the base, is used as a factor. For example, 100,000 is equal to 10 * 10 * 10 * 10 * 10. So 100,000 can be written as 10^5. The small raised 5 is called an exponent, and 10^5 is read as "10 to the fifth power." This will be most students' first experience with exponents, which will be studied in depth during fifth and sixth grades.

The class is well into the World Tour. Students are beginning to see how numerical information about a country helps them get a better understanding of the country—its size, climate, location, and population distribution—and how these characteristics affect the way people live. The next stop on the World Tour will be Budapest, Hungary, the starting point for an exploration of European countries. Encourage your child to bring to school materials about Europe, such as articles in the travel section of your newspaper, magazine articles, and travel brochures.

Please keep this Family Letter for reference as your child works through Unit 5.

Math Masters, pp. 135–138

Assessment Master

Name Date Time

LESSON 4•11 **Open Response** Progress Check 4

Forming a Relay Team

Mrs. Wong, the gym teacher, wants to form 3 teams for a 200-yard relay race. There will be 4 students on each team. Each student will run 50 yards.

The table at the right shows how long it took some fourth-grade students to run 50 yards the last time they had a race. They were timed to the nearest tenth of a second.

Runner	Time (seconds)
Art	6.3
Bruce	7.0
Jamal	7.4
Doug	7.9
Al	8.3
Will	8.8
Linda	6.2
Sue	7.6
Pat	7.7
Mary	8.1
Alba	8.4
Joyce	8.5

1. Help Mrs. Wong create 3 teams that will be fairly evenly matched. She will use their times from the last race to predict about how fast they will run in the relay race.

Write the names of the four students that you think should be on each team.

Estimate about how long you think it will take each team to complete the race.

Names of 4 Students on Each Team	Estimated Team Time
Team 1: ______	About: ___.___ seconds
Team 2: ______	About: ___.___ seconds
Team 3: ______	About: ___.___ seconds

2. Explain how you made your teams so that they would be fairly matched.

See the *Assessment Handbook* for rubrics and students' work samples.

Assessment Handbook, p. 173

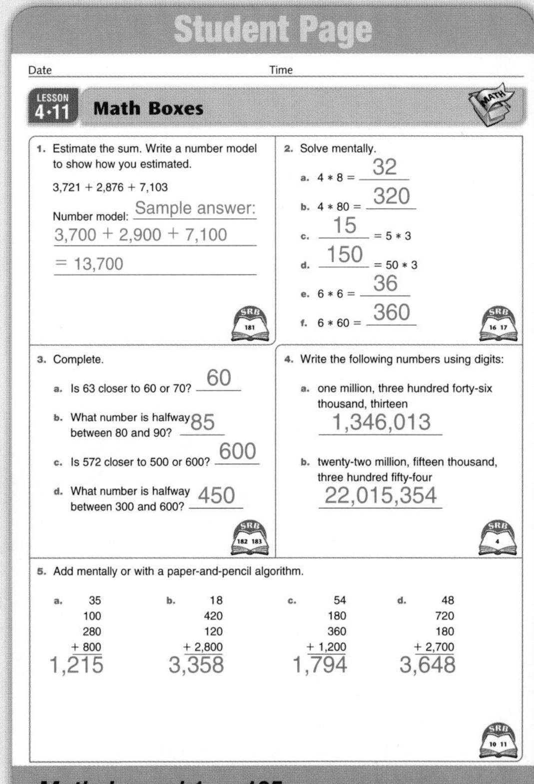

Student Page

Date Time

LESSON 4•11 **Math Boxes**

1. Estimate the sum. Write a number model to show how you estimated.

3,721 + 2,876 + 7,103

Number model: Sample answer: 3,700 + 2,900 + 7,100 = 13,700

SRB 181

2. Solve mentally.

a. 4 * 8 = 32
b. 4 * 80 = 320
c. 15 = 5 * 3
d. 150 = 50 * 3
e. 6 * 6 = 36
f. 6 * 60 = 360

SRB 16 17

3. Complete.

a. Is 63 closer to 60 or 70? 60
b. What number is halfway between 80 and 90? 85
c. Is 572 closer to 500 or 600? 600
d. What number is halfway between 300 and 600? 450

SRB 182 183

4. Write the following numbers using digits:

a. one million, three hundred forty-six thousand, thirteen 1,346,013
b. twenty-two million, fifteen thousand, three hundred fifty-four 22,015,354

SRB 4

5. Add mentally or with a paper-and-pencil algorithm.

a.	b.	c.	d.
35	18	54	48
100	420	180	720
280	120	360	180
+ 800	+ 2,800	+ 1,200	+ 2,700
1,215	3,358	1,794	3,648

SRB 10 11

Math Journal 1, p. 105

Unit 5 Organizer

Big Numbers, Estimation, and Computation

Overview

Unit 5 begins with two lessons that focus on extending multiplication skills, in preparation for the introduction of the partial-products algorithm for multiplication. The lattice algorithm is also introduced as an alternative to the partial-products algorithm. Unit 5 also emphasizes reading, writing, and using large numbers, including the use of powers of 10 to represent large numbers. Unit 5 has four main areas of focus:

- To extend basic multiplication facts and to review the basic principles of multiplication of multidigit numbers,
- To provide practice estimating and deciding when estimation is appropriate,
- To review and provide practice with the partial-products algorithm and the lattice method for multiplication, and
- To provide practice reading, writing, and comparing large numbers using patterns in the base-ten place-value system.

Linking to the Common Core State Standards

The content of Unit 5 addresses the Common Core State Standards for Mathematics in *Operations and Algebraic Thinking* and *Number and Operations in Base Ten.* The correlation of the Common Core State Standards to the *Everyday Mathematics* Grade 4 lessons begins on page CS1.

Contents

Learning In Perspective

	Lesson Objectives	Links to the Past	Links to the Future
5·1	To extend basic multiplication facts to products of ones and tens and products of tens and tens.	Grade 3: Use mental strategies to calculate products of 1-digit and multidigit numbers, and of 2-digit numbers and powers of 10.	Grades 4–6: Applications and maintenance, including extensions to solve related division facts.
5·2	To provide practice with extended multiplication facts; and to introduce the basic principles of multiplication with multidigit numbers.	Grade 3: Use mental strategies to calculate products of 1-digit and multidigit numbers, and of 2-digit numbers and powers of 10.	Grades 4–6: Applications and maintenance, including extensions to solve related division facts.
5·3	To provide practice deciding whether estimation is appropriate in a given situation; and to provide practice estimating sums.	Grades 1-3: Use estimates to check the reasonableness of answers. Grades 2 and 3: Use terms such as *about, a little more than, almost,* and *in between.*	Grades 4–6: Round numbers and then use magnitude estimates to locate the decimal point when multiplying and dividing decimals.
5·4	To provide practice estimating whether a product is in the tens, hundreds, thousands, or more.	Grades 1–3: Solve number-story problems using estimation and use estimates to check the reasonableness of answers. Grades 2 and 3: List situations that call for estimates; use terms such as *about, a little more than, almost,* and *in between.*	Grades 4–6: Round numbers and then use magnitude estimates to locate the decimal point when multiplying and dividing decimals.
5·5	To review and provide practice with the partial-products algorithm for 1-digit multipliers.	Grade 3: Use arrays and base-10 blocks to model a partial-products method for finding products of 2-digit numbers.	Grade 4: Extend the partial-products method to multiplication of decimals; use multiplication and division to calculate rates and unit rates (Units 6, 9, 12). Grades 5 and 6: Applications and maintenance.
5·6	To introduce and provide practice with the partial-products algorithm for 2-digit multipliers.	Grade 3: Use arrays and base-10 blocks to model a partial-products method for finding products of 2-digit numbers.	Grade 4: Extend the partial-products method to multiplication of decimals; use multiplication and division to calculate rates and unit rates (Units 6, 9, 12).
5·7	To review and provide practice with the lattice method for multiplication.	Grade 3: Introduce the lattice method for multidigit multiplication.	Grade 4: Extend the lattice method to multiplication of decimals; use multiplication and division to calculate rates and unit rates (Units 9, 12).
5·8	To provide practice reading, writing, and comparing large numbers using patterns in the base-ten place-value system.	Grades 1 and 2: Explore place value through base-10 blocks, place-value books, and games; read and write numbers less than 100,000. Grade 3: Extend place value to millions.	Grade 5: Extend place-value facility to trillions and to thousandths; use exponential notation and scientific notation to represent both large and small numbers.
5·9	To introduce exponential notation for powers of 10 as a way of naming the values of places in our base-ten system.	Grades 2 and 3: Model square numbers with arrays.	Grades 5 and 6: Compare numbers written in exponential and scientific notation.
5·10	To discuss sensible ways of reporting a count when a large number of items has been counted; and to practice rounding numbers.	Grade 3: Estimate to solve number-story problems and to check the reasonableness of answers; use a slate routine to practice rounding to multiples of 10.	Grades 5 and 6: Applications and extensions, including rounding to decimal place values.
5·11	To guide students as they look up and compare numerical data, including geographical measurements.	Grades 2 and 3: Use relation symbols (=, >, <) to compare numbers.	Grades 4–6: Applications and maintenance.

Lesson	Key Concepts and Skills	Grade 4 Goals*
5•1	Solve basic multiplication facts.	Operations and Computation Goal 3
	Use basic multiplication facts to compute fact extensions.	Operations and Computation Goal 3
	Use repeated addition and arrays to model multiplication.	Operations and Computation Goal 7
	Describe rules to solve problems involving products of ones and tens and products of tens and tens.	Patterns, Functions, and Algebra Goal 1
5•2	Write numbers in expanded notation.	Number and Numeration Goal 4
	Add multidigit numbers.	Operations and Computation Goal 2
	Use basic facts to compute extended facts.	Operations and Computation Goal 3
	Solve multidigit multiplication problems.	Operations and Computation Goal 4
	Evaluate numeric expressions containing parentheses.	Patterns, Functions, and Algebra Goal 3
	Use the Distributive Property of Multiplication over Addition.	Patterns, Functions, and Algebra Goal 4
5•3	Estimate sums.	Operations and Computation Goal 6
	Compare appropriate situations for the use of exact answers and estimates.	Operations and Computation Goal 6
	Use a travel map to find driving distance and driving time.	Data and Chance Goal 2
5•4	Solve problems involving products where factors are multiples of 10, 100, 1,000, and so on.	Operations and Computation Goal 3
	Estimate whether a product is in the tens, hundreds, thousands, or more.	Operations and Computation Goal 6
	Explore meanings of *average*.	Data and Chance Goal 2
5•5	Write numbers in expanded notation.	Number and Numeration Goal 4
	Add multidigit numbers.	Operations and Computation Goal 2
	Use basic facts to compute extended facts.	Operations and Computation Goal 3
	Use the partial-products algorithm to solve multiplication problems with 1-digit multipliers.	Operations and Computation Goal 4
	Estimate whether a product is in the tens, hundreds, thousands, or more.	Operations and Computation Goal 6
	Apply the Distributive Property of Multiplication over Addition.	Patterns, Functions, and Algebra Goal 4
5•6	Write numbers in expanded notation.	Number and Numeration Goal 4
	Use the partial-products algorithm to solve multiplication problems with 2-digit multipliers.	Operations and Computation Goal 4
	Estimate whether a product is in the tens, hundreds, thousands, or more.	Operations and Computation Goal 6
	Apply the Distributive Property of Multiplication over Addition.	Patterns, Functions, and Algebra Goal 4
5•7	Add single-digit numbers.	Operations and Computation Goal 2
	Solve basic multiplication facts.	Operations and Computation Goal 3
	Use the lattice method to solve multiplication problems with 1- and 2-digit multipliers.	Operations and Computation Goal 4
5•8	Read and write whole numbers to hundred billions.	Number and Numeration Goal 1
	Identify digits and their values in whole numbers to hundred billions.	Number and Numeration Goal 1
	Use multiplication to solve a multistep problem.	Operations and Computation Goals 3 and 4
	Make reasonable estimates.	Operations and Computation Goal 6
5•9	Read and write large numbers; identify the digits and their values.	Number and Numeration Goal 1
	Use exponential notation to represent powers of 10.	Number and Numeration Goal 4
	Use expanded notation to represent powers of 10.	Number and Numeration Goal 4
	Identify and describe patterns in a place-value table.	Patterns, Functions, and Algebra Goal 1
5•10	Read and write whole numbers; identify digits and their values.	Number and Numeration Goal 1
	Describe differences between estimates and exact counts.	Operations and Computation Goal 6
	Round numbers to a given place.	Operations and Computation Goal 6
	Use data presented in a table.	Data and Chance Goal 2
5•11	Read and write large numbers.	Number and Numeration Goal 1
	Develop the meaning of percent as per 100.	Number and Numeration Goal 5
	Compare large numbers.	Number and Numeration Goal 6
	Use a table of information.	Data and Chance Goal 2

*See the Appendix for a complete list of Grade 4 Goals.

A Balanced Curriculum

Ongoing Practice

Everyday Mathematics provides numerous opportunities for ongoing practice. These activities are embedded throughout the lessons:

Mental Math and Reflexes activities promote speed and accuracy in mental computation.

Math Boxes offer mixed practice and are paired across lessons as shown in the brackets below. This makes them useful as assessment tools. The last one or two boxes on each page preview the next unit's content.

Mixed practice	[5•1, 5•3], [5•2, 5•4], [5•5, 5•7], [5•6, 5•8, 5•10], [5•9, 5•11]
Mixed practice with multiple choice	5•3, 5•4, 5•5, 5•8, 5•9, 5•10
Mixed practice with writing/reasoning opportunity	5•1, 5•3, 5•4, 5•5, 5•6, 5•7, 5•8, 5•9

Study Links are daily homework assignments that review the content of the lesson and often contain ongoing facts practice or computation practice.

5-Minute Math problems are offered for additional practice in Lessons 5•4, 5•9, and 5•10.

EM Facts Workshop Game provides online practice of basic facts and computation.

EXTRA PRACTICE **Extra Practice** activities are included in Lessons 5•1, 5•3, 5•4, 5•9, 5•10, and 5•11.

Practice through Games

Games are an essential component of practice in the *Everyday Mathematics* program. Games offer skills practice and promote strategic thinking. See the *Differentiation Handbook* for ways to adapt games to meet students' needs.

Lesson	Game	Skill Practiced
5•1	*Beat the Calculator*	Solving extended multiplication facts [OC Goal 3]
5•1, 5•7	*Multiplication Top-It*	Maintaining automaticity with multiplication facts [OC Goal 3]
5•2, 5•4	*Multiplication Wrestling*	Calculating and finding the sum of partial products [OC Goal 4 and PFA Goal 4]
5•3	*Product Pile-Up*	Maintaining automaticity with multiplication facts [OC Goal 3]
5•6	*Name That Number*	Representing numbers in different ways [NN Goal 4]
5•8, 5•11	*High-Number Toss*	Identifying values of digits and comparing large numbers [NN Goals 1 and 6]
5•9	*Polygon Pair-Up*	Identifying properties of polygons [GEO Goal 2]
5•11	*Number Top-It*	Comparing large numbers [NN Goal 6]

[NN] Number and Numeration
[MRF] Measurement and Reference Frames
[OC] Operations and Computation
[GEO] Geometry
[DC] Data and Chance
[PFA] Patterns, Functions, and Algebra

Problem Solving 

Experts at problem solving and mathematical modeling generally do these things:

- Identify the problem.
- Decide what information is needed to solve the problem.
- Play with and study the data to find patterns and meaning.
- Identify and use mathematical procedures to solve the problem.
- Decide whether the solution makes sense and whether it can be applied to other problems.

The table below lists some of the opportunities in this unit for students to practice these strategies.

Lessons that teach *through* problem solving, not just *about* problem solving

Lesson	Activity
5•1, 5•5	Write and solve number stories involving multiplication.
5•3	Plan a driving trip to four cities by using a travel map to estimate distance and time.
5•4	Compare a student's weekly and yearly consumption of food and beverages to that of the "average" American.
5•8	Find how many dots are in a 50 by 40 array on one page, then on multiple pages and on multiple reams.
5•9	Find the largest number in the World Tour section of the *Student Reference Book.*
5•11	Identify minimum/maximum values and compare data in population, area, and climate tables.

See Chapter 18: Problem Solving in the *Teacher's Reference Manual* for more information.

The Language of Mathematics

Everyday Mathematics provides lesson-specific suggestions to help all students acquire, process, and express mathematical ideas. Throughout Unit 5, there are lesson-specific language development notes that address the needs of English language learners, indicated by ELL.

ELL SUPPORT Activities to support English language learners are in Part 3 of Lessons 5•1, 5•3, 5•7, and 5•9.

The *English Learners Handbook* and the *Differentiation Handbook* have suggestions for promoting language development and acquisition of mathematics vocabulary. See Unit 5 in each handbook.

Unit 5 Vocabulary

billion
estimation
extended multiplication facts
exponent
lattice
lattice method (for multiplication)
magnitude estimate
million
partial product
partial-products method
powers of 10
quadrillion
quintillion
rough estimate
round
rounding (to a certain place)
scientific notation
sextillion
trillion

Literacy Connection

Ten Times Better, by Richard Michelson, Marshall Cavendish Children's Books, 2000

Moira's Birthday, by Robert Munsch, Annick Press, 1992

Lesson 5•8 *How Much Is a Million?,* by David M. Schwartz, Mulberry Books, 1993

For more literacy connections, see the *Home Connection Handbook,* Grades 4–6.

Cross-Curricular Links 

Social Studies – Lessons 5•2, 5•3, 5•8, 5•11

Literature – Lesson 5•8

Balanced Assessment

Daily Assessments

- **Recognizing Student Achievement** – A daily assessment that is included in every lesson to evaluate students' progress toward the Grade 4 Grade-Level Goals.
- **Informing Instruction** – Notes that appear throughout the unit to help anticipate students' common errors and suggest appropriate problem-solving strategies.

Lesson	Recognizing Student Achievement	Informing Instruction
5•1	Use basic facts to compute fact extensions. [OC Goal 3]	Understand equivalence when multiplying ones and tens.
5•2	Determine whether a number sentence is true or false. [PFA Goal 2]	Align partial products according to values of digits. Interpret a data table.
5•3	Explain use of estimation to solve addition problems. [OC Goal 6]	Plan an extended trip.
5•4	Use the Distributive Property of Multiplication over Addition in the context of the partial-products algorithm. [PFA Goal 4]	
5•5	Use the partial-products algorithm. [OC Goal 4]	Express the value of a digit.
5•6	Estimate reasonable solutions to whole-number multiplication problems. [OC Goal 6]	Consider the value of each digit.
5•7	Demonstrate automaticity with multiplication facts. [OC Goal 3]	
5•8	Use extended multiplication facts in a problem-solving situation. [OC Goal 3]	Understand appropriateness of estimation or exact answers.
5•9	Describe numeric patterns. [PFA Goal 1]	
5•10	Demonstrate automaticity with multiplication facts. [OC Goal 3]	
5•11	Compare numbers up to 1 billion. [NN Goal 6]	

[NN] Number and Numeration
[MRF] Measurement and Reference Frames
[OC] Operations and Computation
[GEO] Geometry
[DC] Data and Chance
[PFA] Patterns, Functions, and Algebra

Portfolio Opportunities

The following lessons provide opportunities to gather samples of students' mathematical writings, drawings, and creations to add balance to the assessment process: Lessons 5•2, 5•3, 5•4, 5•5, 5•8, 5•9, and 5•12.

See pages 16 and 17 in the *Assessment Handbook* for more information about portfolios and how to use them.

Unit Assessment

Progress Check 5 – A cumulative assessment of concepts and skills taught in Unit 5 and in previous units, providing information for evaluating students' progress and planning for future instruction. These assessments include oral/slate, written, and open-response activities, as shown below in the sample Progress Check lesson opener.

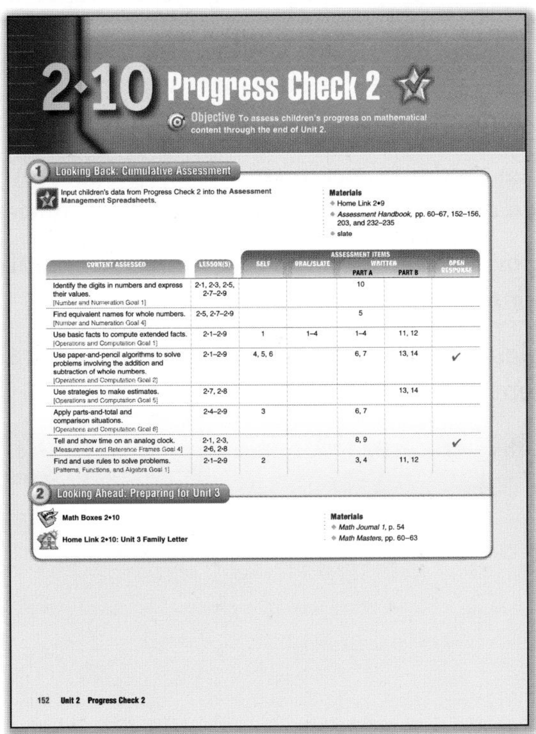

2·10 Progress Check 2

Objective To assess children's progress on mathematical content through the end of Unit 2.

1 Looking Back: Cumulative Assessment

Input children's data from Progress Check 2 into the Assessment Management Spreadsheets.

Materials
- Home Link 2•9
- *Assessment Handbook*, pp. 60–67, 152–156, 203, and 232–235
- slate

CONTENT ASSESSED	LESSON(S)	ASSESSMENT ITEMS				
		SELF	ORAL/SLATE	WRITTEN PART A	WRITTEN PART B	OPEN RESPONSE
Identify the digits in numbers and express their values. [Number and Numeration Goal 1]	2·1, 2·3, 2·5, 2·7–2·9			10		
Find equivalent names for whole numbers. [Number and Numeration Goal 4]	2·5, 2·7–2·9			5		
Use basic facts to compute extended facts. [Operations and Computation Goal 1]	2·1–2·9	1	1–4	1–4	11, 12	
Use paper-and-pencil algorithms to solve problems involving the addition and subtraction of whole numbers. [Operations and Computation Goal 2]	2·1–2·9	4, 5, 6		6, 7	13, 14	✓
Use strategies to make estimates. [Operations and Computation Goal 5]	2·7, 2·8				13, 14	
Apply parts-and-total and comparison situations. [Operations and Computation Goal 6]	2·4–2·9	3		6, 7		
Tell and show time on an analog clock. [Measurement and Reference Frames Goal 4]	2·1, 2·3, 2·6, 2·8			8, 9		✓
Find and use rules to solve problems. [Patterns, Functions, and Algebra Goal 1]	2·1–2·9	2		3, 4	11, 12	

2 Looking Ahead: Preparing for Unit 3

Math Boxes 2•10

Home Link 2•10: Unit 3 Family Letter

Materials
- *Math Journal 1*, p. 54
- *Math Masters*, pp. 60–63

152 Unit 2 Progress Check 2

Core Assessment Resources

Assessment Handbook

- **Unit 5 Assessment Overview,** pages 84–91
- **Unit 5 Assessment Masters,** pages 174–178
- **Unit 5 Individual Profiles of Progress,** pages 262, 263, and 302
- **Unit 5 Class Checklists,** pages 264, 265, and 303
- **Math Logs,** pages 306–308
- **Exit Slip,** page 311
- **Other Student Assessment Forms,** pages 304, 305, 309, and 310

Assessment Management Spreadsheets

The Assessment Management Spreadsheets consist of the Digital Class Checklists and Individual Profile of Progress Checklists. Use them to monitor, record, and report student progress.

Addressing All Needs

Differentiated Instruction

Adjusting the Activity – suggests adaptations that target advanced learners, English language learners, or learners who need additional instructional support.

ELL SUPPORT / **ELL** – provides lesson-specific suggestions to help English language learners understand and process the mathematical content.

READINESS – accesses students' prior knowledge or previews content that prepares students to engage in the lesson's Part 1 activities.

EXTRA PRACTICE – provides additional opportunities to apply the mathematical content of the lesson.

ENRICHMENT – enables students to apply or further explore the mathematical content of the lesson.

Lesson	Adjusting the Activity	ELL Support/ ELL	Readiness	Extra Practice	Enrichment
5•1	•	•	•	•	
5•2	•	•	•		•
5•3	•	•	•	•	•
5•4	•		•	•	•
5•5	•		•		•
5•6	•		•		•
5•7	•	•	•		•
5•8			•		•
5•9	•	•		•	•
5•10	•	•	•	•	•
5•11	•	•	•	•	

Additional Resources

Differentiation Handbook
Provides ideas and strategies for differentiating instruction.
Pages 76–82

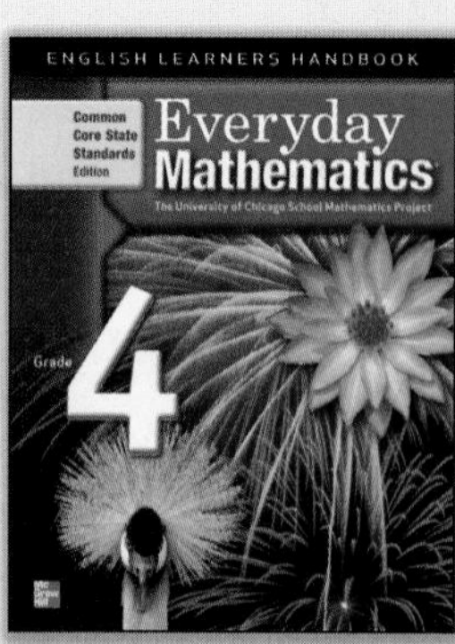

English Learners Handbook
Contains lesson-specific comprehension strategies.
Pages 39–49

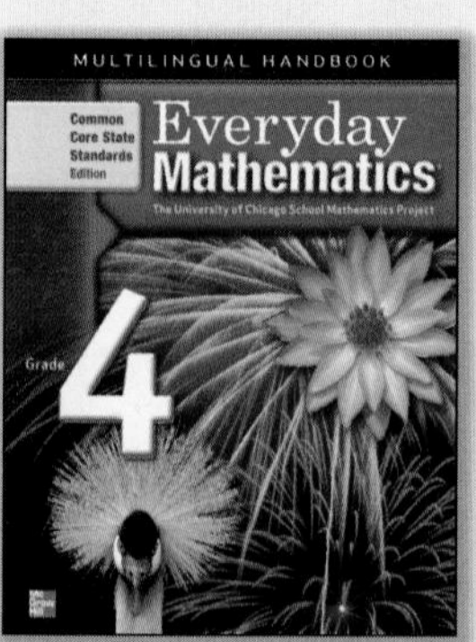

Multilingual Handbook
Previews concepts and vocabulary. It is written in six languages.
Pages 77–98

Planning Tips

Multiage Classroom

Companion Lessons from Grades 3 and 5 can help you meet instructional needs of a multiage classroom. The full Scope and Sequence can be found in the Appendix.

Grade 3	4•1, 4•2, 4•4		1•11	1•11, 7•7	9•4, 9•5	9•11, 9•12	9•9	2•2, 5•5	2•2, 7•6, 7•8	2•2	
Grade 4	**5•1**	**5•2**	**5•3**	**5•4**	**5•5**	**5•6**	**5•7**	**5•8**	**5•9**	**5•10**	**5•11**
Grade 5	2•8			2•7			2•9	2•10	7•2	2•7	

Pacing for Success

Pacing depends on a number of factors, such as students' individual needs and how long your school has been using *Everyday Mathematics*. At the beginning of Unit 5, you may want to use tools available at www.everydaymathonline.com to help you set your pace.

Home Support

Unit 5 Family Letter (English/Spanish) provides families with an overview, Do-Anytime Activities, Building Skills through Games, a list of vocabulary, and answers to the daily homework (Study Links). Family Letters in English, Spanish, and seven other languages are also available online.

Study Links are the daily homework assignments. They consist of active projects and ongoing review problems.

Home Support Resources

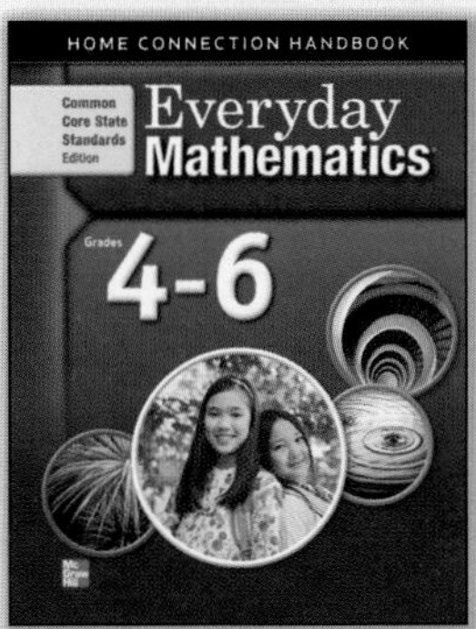

Home Connection Handbook
Offers ideas and reproducible masters for communicating with families. See Table of Contents for unit information.

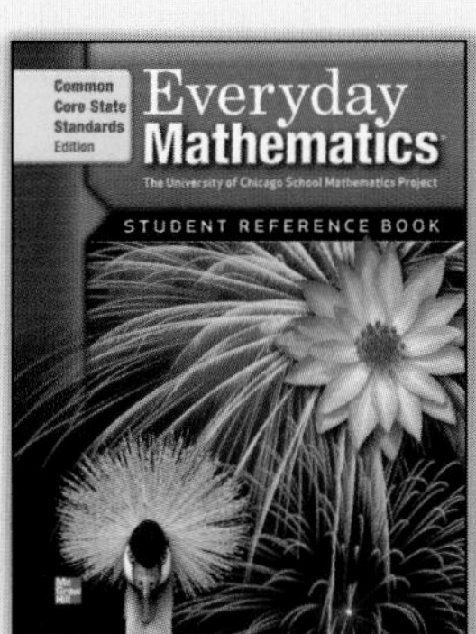

Student Reference Book
Provides a resource for students and parents.

Pages 4, 233, 252–255, 258, 259, 264, 271, 276, 277, 279–281, 297, 301–305

Technology Resources

Materials

Technology Resources www.everydaymathonline.com

ePresentations | eToolkit | Algorithms Practice | EM Facts Workshop Game™ | Family Letters | Assessment Management | Common Core State Standards | Curriculum Focal Points | Interactive Teacher's Lesson Guide

Lesson	Masters	Manipulative Kit	Other Items
5•1	Game Masters, pp. 461 and 506 Study Link Master, p. 139 Teaching Aid Master, p. 430 *Differentiation Handbook,* p. 140	per group: 4 each of number cards 1–10; slate; tape measure or ruler; base-10 blocks	Multiplication/Division Facts Table*; calculator
5•2	Game Master, p. 488 Transparency of *Math Masters,* p. 488* Study Link Master, p. 140 Teaching Masters, pp. 141 and 142	per partnership: 4 each of number cards 0–9 or a ten-sided die; slate	index cards*; demonstration clock*; calculator*
5•3	Teaching Masters, pp. 143, 145, and 146 Study Link Master, p. 144 *Differentiation Handbook,* p. 140	per partnership: 8 each of number cards 1–10; base-10 blocks	demonstration clock*; calculator
5•4	Teaching Masters, pp. 147, 149, and 150 Game Master, p. 488 Study Link Master, p. 148	per partnership: 4 each of number cards 0–9 or a ten-sided die	calculator
5•5	Teaching Aid Master, p. 403 or 431 Study Link Master, p. 151 Teaching Masters, pp. 152 and 153 Transparencies of *Math Masters,* pp. 432 and 433	slate; tape measure or ruler; base-10 blocks	erasable marker; transparent tape
5•6	Game Master, p. 489* Teaching Aid Masters, p. 388* or 389*, and p. 403 or 431 Teaching Masters, pp. 155 and 156 Study Link Master, p. 154 Transparencies of *Math Masters,* pp. 432 and 433	per partnership: deck of number cards; base-10 blocks; slate	erasable marker; transparent tape
5•7	Teaching Aid Masters, pp. 434 and 435 Transparency of *Math Masters,* p. 434* Teaching Masters, pp. 158–161 Study Link Master, p. 157 Game Master, p. 506	slate; per partnership: 4 each of number cards 1–10	index cards*; dictionary*; Multiplication/Division Facts Table; scissors; chart paper; colored pencils and markers
5•8	Teaching Masters, pp. 162, 164, and 165 Teaching Aid Master, p. 388* or 389* Study Link Master, p. 163 Game Master, p. 487*	1 six-sided die	1 ream of copy paper; 1 empty carton used to pack 10 reams of paper; *How Much Is a Million?*; calculator
5•9	Teaching Aid Master, p. 388* or 389* Transparency of *Math Masters,* p. 166* Study Link Master, p. 167 Game Masters, pp. 496 and 497 Teaching Master, p. 168		calculator
5•10	Study Link Master, p. 169 Teaching Aid Masters, pp. 410, 414, and 416* Teaching Masters, pp. 170 and 171	slate	pen or colored pencil
5•11	Teaching Aid Masters, pp. 419–421* and 426*; Study Link Master, p. 172 Game Masters, pp. 487, 492, 493, and 506	per partnership: 4 each of number cards 0–9, 1 six-sided die; slate	tape
5•12	Assessment Masters, pp. 174–178 Study Link Masters, pp. 173–176	slate	

*Denotes optional materials

Mathematical Background

The discussion below highlights the major content ideas presented in Unit 5 and helps establish instructional priorities.

Extending Multiplication Skills

(Lessons 5◆1 and 5◆2)

Lesson 5-1 extends the basic multiplication facts (3 * 4) to products of ones and tens (3 * 40 or 30 * 4) and products of tens and tens (30 * 40). These skills, useful in their own right, are important prerequisites for the intelligent use of estimation and calculators and in the development of multiplication and division algorithms.

You may expect that most students will have had experience with products of ones and tens. The activities in this lesson are designed to review and solidify this knowledge and extend it to products of tens and tens.

Lesson 5-2 introduces the basic principles of multiplication with multidigit numbers. The key idea is that a product, such as 53 * 68, may be broken down into sums of "partial products" (50 * 60, 50 * 8, 3 * 60, and 3 * 8). Every part of one factor is multiplied by every part of the other factor. The partial products are then added together to find the answer. To do this efficiently, of course, one needs to have a quick and sure sense for extended facts, such as 50 * 60 = 3,000 and 50 * 8 = 400. Learning extended multiplication facts is the focus of Lesson 5-1.

To learn more about extending multiplication skills, see Section 16.3.3 of the *Teacher's Reference Manual.*

Multiplication Algorithms

(Lessons 5•5–5•7)

Project Note

To teach U.S. traditional multiplication, see Algorithm Project 5.

For each of the four basic operations, *Everyday Mathematics* has selected a "focus algorithm"—an algorithm that all students are expected to learn. One purpose of focus algorithms is to provide students with a common language with which to share solution strategies. The focus algorithm for multiplication is the **partial-products algorithm.** Although students are encouraged to use whatever algorithm they like to solve problems, they will be asked on occasion to use the partial-products algorithm.

As explained in the lessons, when using the partial-products algorithm, one starts from the left (so that the most important products—the largest—are attended to first and the smallest ones last). Each part of the calculation, or each **partial product,** is written on a separate line. Adding partial products is fairly simple and has the additional benefit of providing practice with column addition.

Partial Products Algorithm

63	
* 24	
1,200	← 20 [60s] or 20 * 60
60	← 20 [3s] or 20 * 3
240	← 4 [60s] or 4 * 60
+ 12	← 4 [3s] or 4 * 3
1,512	

The partial-products algorithm exploits the ideas of the *Multiplication Wrestling* game (see Lesson 5-2): Every part of one factor is multiplied by every part of the other factor. It is important to "talk to oneself" or to say aloud what is going on. For example, in the problem in the margin, it is not 2 times 6, but 20 times 60, or 20 [60s].

The **lattice algorithm,** which is introduced in Lesson 5-7, is a useful alternative to the partial-products algorithm. This ancient method, invented in India, is popular among students because it relies only on simple computations.

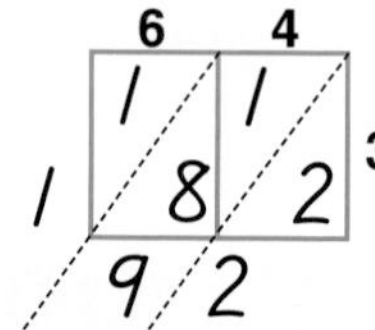

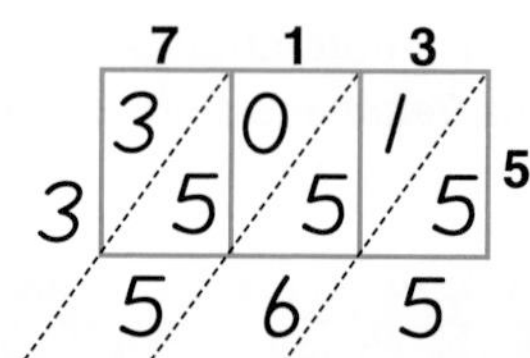

Section 11.2.3 of the *Teacher's Reference Manual* contains more information about multiplication algorithms.

Magnitude Estimates

(Lessons 5•4 and 5•6)

It is often useful simply to know a very rough "ballpark" into which an answer might fall: less than one, in the ones, or tens, or hundreds, or thousands, and so on. In science and other applications, "orders of magnitude" are powers of ten, and **magnitude estimates** give a power-of-10 "ballpark."

Lesson 5-4 introduces a routine that will be practiced many times from now until the end of the year. It invites students to estimate in advance where the answers to problems will fall and to mark their estimates on a magnitude bar. Eventually, that explicit check-off routine will become

another matter of "inner speech": "Is the answer I'm looking for in the tens? Hundreds? Thousands?" With such intuition, students can make many decisions and almost automatically know when they have mis-keyed the calculator and gotten a silly result or when information they have read or heard doesn't make sense. (For example, promoters of parades and other events often claim attendance figures so huge that each spectator would be confined to an impossibly small space.)

Magnitude Bar

0.1s	1s	10s	100s	1,000s	10,000s	100,000s	1,000,000s

Consult Section 16.1 of the *Teacher's Reference Manual* for additional information on magnitude estimates.

Rounding and Making Smart Estimates (Lessons 5•3–5•6 and 5•10)

More often than most people suppose, an estimate is as useful as an exact answer. In certain situations, "exact" answers are even impossible to find. Finally, counts and measures given exactly to the very last digit may be misleading—they may imply a degree of accuracy which they do not possess.

In school mathematics, a lot of attention has been given to rounding numbers to specified places. While this is an important subskill (just as memorizing basic addition facts is important), it is far more important to develop good judgment about when to round, how accurate an estimate is needed, and how accurate an estimate is possible, independent of how "good" one might wish an estimate to be.

To further investigate rounding and making smart estimates, refer to Section 16.2 in the *Teacher's Reference Manual.*

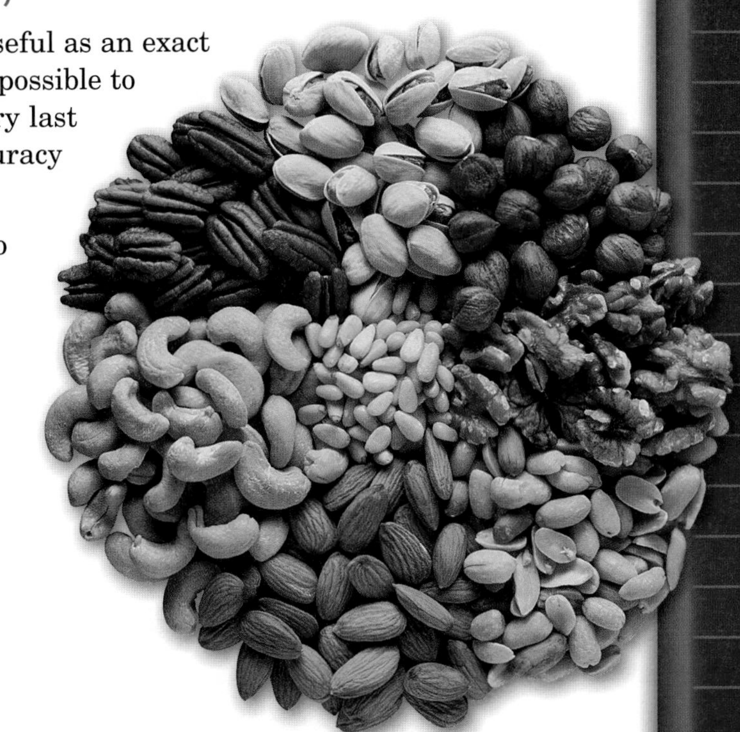

Project Note

Use Project 7, Numbers, Mayan Style, to provide practice converting between Mayan numerals and base-ten numerals. See the *Differentiation Handbook* for modifications to Project 7.

Place-Value Structure of Big Numbers (Lesson 5•8)

Much of the power of the familiar base-ten place-value system of numeration comes from the regularity of progression from place to place. Moving to the left, place values increase by multiples of ten, allowing for the representation of whole numbers as large as necessary. Moving to the right, place values decrease by multiples of one-tenth, allowing for the representation of decimals as small as necessary.

In estimating with large numbers, it is important to understand the progression by multiples of one thousand, as well as by multiples of ten. A million is a thousand thousands, a billion is a thousand millions, a trillion is a thousand billions, and so on. Many adults don't understand the consequences of those relationships—that a billion is not just a little bigger than a million but a thousand times bigger—so they can make little sense of public finance, which these days runs heavily into millions, billions, and trillions of dollars. The authors hope to enlighten students in these matters, not all at once, but through many experiences.

In Lesson 5-8, numbers up to a million (and beyond) are represented progressively as dots on paper, reams of dot paper, cartons of reams of dot paper, and (as a project) the enormous number of dots in a roomful of dot paper. For example, 1 is to 1,000 as a dot is to a half-page of dots. One thousand is to 1,000,000 as the number of dots on a half-sheet of paper is to the number of dots on a ream of dot paper. During the rest of the school year, help students get a sense of numerical differences in magnitude and the roles of multiples of 10 and 1,000.

Further information on place-value structure in large numbers can be found in the *Teacher's Reference Manual* in Section 16.1.2.

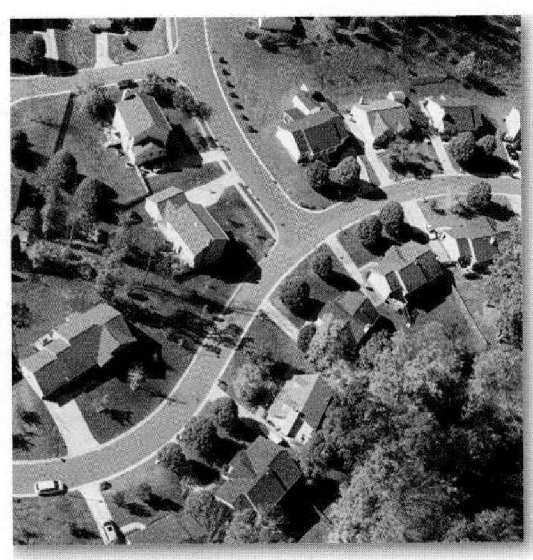

Powers of 10 and Scientific Notation (Lessons 5◆8 and 5◆9)

It is difficult to work very large or very small numbers in their full written form, and it is seldom necessary or sensible to do so. On many calculators, if the numbers in an operation exceed eight digits, they can't be entered; if an answer exceeds eight digits, an error message is given.

In the world outside of school, large numbers are nearly always written with such words as *million, billion,* and so on, substituted for digits. Huge numbers, such as those astronomers use to describe the universe, are usually shown with the help of powers of 10. Very small numbers, which are common in science, are often given in terms of such units as the *nanometer* (one billionth of a meter) or with negative powers of 10.

Common Methods for Writing Extremely Large or Small Numbers		
Town budget	\$8 million	$\$8 * 10^6$
World population for the year 2000	6 billion people	$6 * 10^9$ people
Light-year (distance light travels in a year)	6 trillion miles	$6 * 10^{12}$ mi
Wavelength of ultraviolet radiation (shortest)	4 nanometers	$4 * 10^{-9}$ m

These lessons begin to deal with essential skills for learning science and for functioning in a world of calculators and computers—skills that are more important than paper-and-pencil methods of multiplying or dividing with large numbers or small decimals.

See Section 10.1.2 of the *Teacher's Reference Manual* for more information concerning powers of 10 and scientific notation.

5•1 Extended Multiplication Facts

Objective To extend basic multiplication facts to products of ones and tens and products of tens and tens.

www.everydaymathonline.com

ePresentations

eToolkit

Algorithms Practice

EM Facts Workshop Game™

Family Letters

Assessment Management

Common Core State Standards

Curriculum Focal Points

Interactive Teacher's Lesson Guide

1 Teaching the Lesson

Key Concepts and Skills

- Solve basic multiplication facts. [Operations and Computation Goal 3]
- Use basic multiplication facts to compute fact extensions. [Operations and Computation Goal 3]
- Use repeated addition and arrays to model multiplication. [Operations and Computation Goal 7]
- Describe rules to solve problems involving products of ones and tens and products of tens and tens. [Patterns, Functions, and Algebra Goal 1]

Key Activities

Students use multiple methods to solve extended multiplication facts. They play *Beat the Calculator* to practice solving extended facts.

Ongoing Assessment: Informing Instruction See page 316.

Ongoing Assessment: Recognizing Student Achievement Use journal page 107. [Operations and Computation Goal 3]

Key Vocabulary

extended multiplication facts

Materials

Math Journal 1, pp. 106 and 107
Student Reference Book, p. 233
Math Masters, p. 461
per group: 4 each of number cards 1–10 ◆ slate ◆ base-10 blocks ◆ Multiplication/Division Facts Table (optional) ◆ calculator

2 Ongoing Learning & Practice

Finding Personal References for Customary Units of Length
Math Journal 1, p. 98
tape measure or ruler
Students use tape measures or rulers to find personal references for customary units of length.

Math Boxes 5•1
Math Journal 1, p. 108
Students practice and maintain skills through Math Box problems.

Study Link 5•1
Math Masters, p. 139
Students practice and maintain skills through Study Link activities.

3 Differentiation Options

READINESS

Playing *Multiplication Top-It*
Student Reference Book, p. 264
Math Masters, p. 506
per partnership: 4 each of number cards 1–10 (from the Everything Math Deck, if available), calculator (optional)
Students practice multiplication facts.

EXTRA PRACTICE

Solving Multiplication/Division Puzzles
Math Masters, p. 430
Students practice extended multiplication and division facts.

ELL SUPPORT

Building a Math Word Bank
Differentiation Handbook, p. 140
Students add the term *extended fact* to their Math Word Banks.

Advance Preparation

***Teacher's Reference Manual,* Grades 4–6** pp. 16, 107–111

Getting Started

Mental Math and Reflexes

Pose multiplication facts and extended facts.
Suggestions:

●○○ $3 * 3 = 9$
$9 * 2 = 18$
$8 * 5 = 40$
$6 * 4 = 24$

●●○ $9 * 4 = 36$
$6 * 8 = 48$
$7 * 7 = 49$
$8 * 9 = 72$

●●● $70 * 5 = 350$
$8 * 40 = 320$
$90 * 50 = 4,500$
$70 * 30 = 2,100$

Math Message

Solve the problems.

- *6 apples cost 40¢ each. What is the total cost?*
- *There are 40 cans of tennis balls, with 3 balls per can. How many balls are there in all?*

1 Teaching the Lesson

Math Message Follow-Up

Discuss students' solutions. Try to include a variety of explanations, such as:

▷ Repeated addition: Each apple costs 40 cents, so 6 apples cost 40¢ + 40¢ + 40¢ + 40¢ + 40¢ + 40¢; that is 240¢, or $2.40.

▷ Array pictures: Using base-10 blocks, show 6 rows with 4 longs (tens) in each row. Or, draw an array with 6 rows and 40 dots in each row.

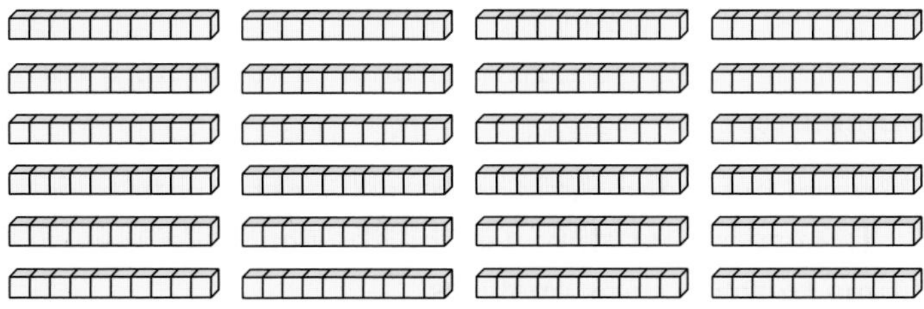

$6 * 40 = 240$

▷ "10-times-as-many" language: If the apples cost 4¢ each, then 6 apples would cost $6 * 4$¢, or 24¢. Because the apples cost 40¢ each, 6 apples must cost 10 times as much; that is $10 * 24$¢ = 240¢, or $2.40.

▷ Multiplication comparison: What amount is 6 times as much as 40¢? 240¢, or $2.40.

Tell students that in this lesson they will extend their work with basic multiplication facts to develop a shortcut for working with multiples of 10.

Interactive whiteboard-ready ePresentations are available at www.everydaymathonline.com to help you teach the lesson.

As students share their strategies, record them on the board and leave them up for reference throughout the lesson.

AUDITORY ◆ KINESTHETIC ◆ TACTILE ◆ VISUAL

Links to the Future

In Lesson 5-5 students review the partial-products algorithm for multiplication of multidigit numbers. In Unit 6 students are introduced to the partial-quotients algorithm. For both algorithms, automaticity with extended multiplication facts is essential.

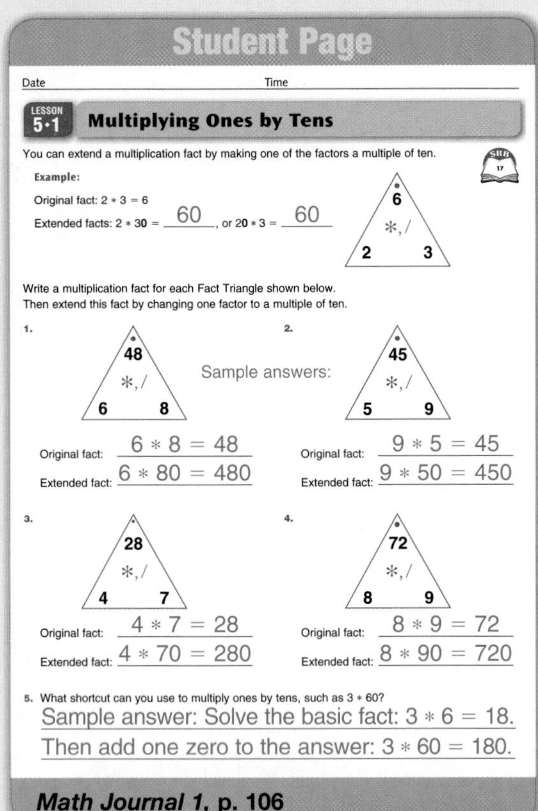

Student Page

Date Time

LESSON 5·1 **Multiplying Ones by Tens**

You can extend a multiplication fact by making one of the factors a multiple of ten.

Example:

Original fact: 2 * 3 = 6

Extended facts: 2 * 30 = 60, or 20 * 3 = 60

Write a multiplication fact for each Fact Triangle shown below.
Then extend this fact by changing one factor to a multiple of ten.

Sample answers:

1. Original fact: 6 * 8 = 48
Extended fact: 6 * 80 = 480

2. Original fact: 9 * 5 = 45
Extended fact: 9 * 50 = 450

3. Original fact: 4 * 7 = 28
Extended fact: 4 * 70 = 280

4. Original fact: 8 * 9 = 72
Extended fact: 8 * 90 = 720

5. What shortcut can you use to multiply ones by tens, such as 3 * 60?
Sample answer: Solve the basic fact: 3 * 6 = 18. Then add one zero to the answer: 3 * 60 = 180.

Math Journal 1, p. 106

Ongoing Assessment: Informing Instruction

Watch for students who simply attach zeros to the product without understanding why. Point out that 3 * 20, for example, is equivalent to 3 * 2 * 10 and to 6 * 10.

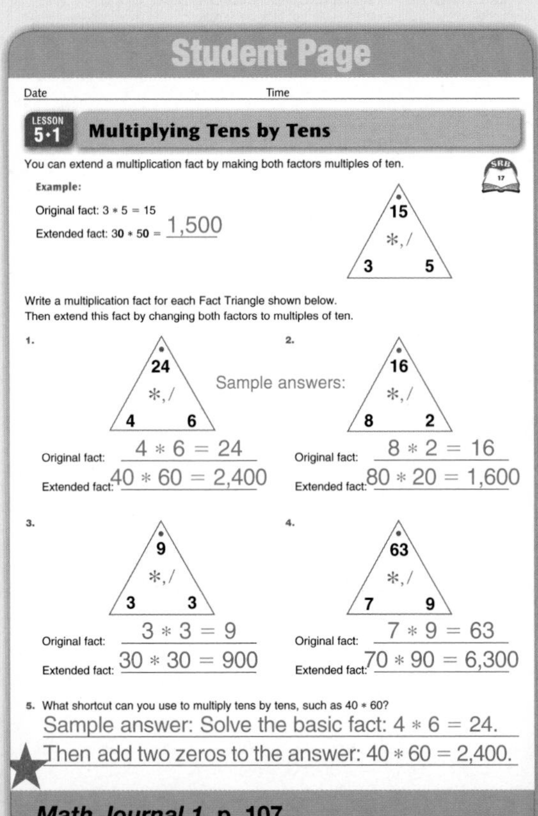

Student Page

Date Time

LESSON 5·1 **Multiplying Tens by Tens**

You can extend a multiplication fact by making both factors multiples of ten.

Example:

Original fact: 3 * 5 = 15

Extended fact: 30 * 50 = 1,500

Write a multiplication fact for each Fact Triangle shown below.
Then extend this fact by changing both factors to multiples of ten.

Sample answers:

1. Original fact: 4 * 6 = 24
Extended fact: 40 * 60 = 2,400

2. Original fact: 8 * 2 = 16
Extended fact: 80 * 20 = 1,600

3. Original fact: 3 * 3 = 9
Extended fact: 30 * 30 = 900

4. Original fact: 7 * 9 = 63
Extended fact: 70 * 90 = 6,300

5. What shortcut can you use to multiply tens by tens, such as 40 * 60?
Sample answer: Solve the basic fact: 4 * 6 = 24. Then add two zeros to the answer: 40 * 60 = 2,400.

Math Journal 1, p. 107

▶ Developing a Rule for Multiplying Ones by Tens

PARTNER ACTIVITY

ELL

(*Math Journal 1*, p. 106)

Ask students to turn to the example at the top of journal page 106. To support English language learners, discuss the meanings of the terms *original fact* and *extended fact*. Then have students solve the two extended facts.

Students may use explanations like those suggested in the Math Message Follow-Up or as shown below.

▷ Think money: 30¢ = 3 dimes. 2 * 3 dimes = 6 dimes, or 60¢.

▷ Rewrite multiples of 10 as "tens": Write 2 * 30 as 2 * 3 tens, which equals 6 tens, or 60.

▷ Ask themselves: *What number is 2 times as many as 30?*

Adjusting the Activity

ELL

Have students use base-10 blocks to model the multiplication with arrays. For example, for the extended fact 2 * 30, first have students make an array consisting of 2 rows with 3 cubes in each row to show 2 * 3. Then ask students to make an array consisting of 2 rows with 3 longs in each row to show 2 * 30.

AUDITORY ◆ KINESTHETIC ◆ TACTILE ◆ VISUAL

Have students complete the journal page. They should write an **extended multiplication fact** (either ones * tens or tens * ones) for each basic fact shown by a Fact Triangle. Partners then work together to write a shortcut rule for multiplying ones by tens.

Bring the class together to share students' shortcuts. Sample answer: Solve the basic fact and attach one zero to the answer. For example, to solve 3 * 20, solve the basic fact 3 * 2 = 6, and then attach one zero to get 60. Have students stand up if they wrote a similar shortcut.

Pose several extended-facts problems for students to solve on their slates. To ensure that they use the shortcut rule, give them very little time to write their answers.

▶ Developing a Rule for Multiplying Tens by Tens

PARTNER ACTIVITY

(*Math Journal 1*, p. 107)

Ask students to turn to the example at the top of journal page 107 and solve the extended fact.

Some of the ways used earlier to model the multiplication of ones and tens are too cumbersome to model the multiplication of tens and tens. For example, an array of base-10 blocks for 30 * 50 would be huge. To find this product using repeated addition would require using 50 as an addend 30 times.

Encourage explanations like the following:

▷ Think money: 50¢ = 5 dimes. 30 * 5 dimes = 150 dimes. 150 dimes equals 1,500 cents, so 30 * 50 = 1,500.

▷ Use "10-times-as-much" language: Three 5s equals 15, so three 50s is 10 times as much, or 150. Thirty 50s is 10 times as much as 150, or 1,500.

▷ Ask themselves: *What number is 30 times as many as 50?*

Have students complete the journal page. They should write an extended multiplication fact (tens * tens) for each basic fact shown by a Fact Triangle. Students then work independently to write a shortcut rule for multiplying tens by tens.

Pose several extended-facts problems for students to solve on their slates. To ensure that they use the shortcut rule, give them very little time to write their answers.

Ongoing Assessment: Recognizing Student Achievement

Journal page 107 Problem 5

Use **journal page 107, Problem 5** to assess students' ability to explain how to use basic facts to compute fact extensions. Students are making adequate progress if their shortcut mentions solving the basic fact and then attaching as many zeros to the product as there are in the factors. Some students may mention that this shortcut can also be used when multiplying tens by hundreds, hundreds by hundreds, and so on.

[Operations and Computation Goal 3]

▸ Playing *Beat the Calculator*

(*Student Reference Book,* p. 233; *Math Masters,* p. 461)

Have students play *Beat the Calculator* to practice solving extended multiplication facts.

Adjusting the Activity

Cut apart the gameboard on *Math Masters,* page 461 so some students can first focus on multiplying ones by tens and later tens by tens. Additionally, encourage students to use the Multiplication/Division Facts Table as necessary.

*

*

AUDITORY ◆ KINESTHETIC ◆ TACTILE ◆ VISUAL

Student Page

Games

Beat the Calculator

Multiplication Facts

Materials
☐ number cards 1–10 (4 of each)
☐ 1 calculator
☐ *Beat the Calculator* Gameboard (optional) (*Math Masters,* p. 461)

Players 3

Skill Mental multiplication skills

Object of the game To multiply numbers without a calculator faster than a player using one.

Directions

1. One player is the "Caller," one is the "Calculator," and one is the "Brain."
2. Shuffle the deck and place it number-side down on the table.
3. The Caller draws 2 cards from the number deck and asks for their product.
4. The Calculator solves the problem using a calculator. The Brain solves it without a calculator. The Caller decides who got the answer first.
5. The Caller continues to draw 2 cards at a time from the number deck and ask for their product.
6. Players trade roles every 10 turns or so.

Example The Caller draws a 10 and a 5 and calls out "10 times 5." The Brain and the Calculator each solve the problem. The Caller decides who got the answer first.

Extended Multiplication Facts

In this version of the game, the Caller:

- Draws 2 cards from the number deck.
- Attaches a 0 to either one of the factors, or to both factors, before asking for the product.

Example If the Caller turns over a 4 and an 8, he or she may make up any one of the following problems:

4 * 80 40 * 8 40 * 80

Student Reference Book, p. 233

2 Ongoing Learning & Practice

▶ Finding Personal References for Customary Units of Length

PARTNER ACTIVITY

(*Math Journal 1,* p. 98)

Have students use their rulers or tape measures to find common objects that are approximately 1 inch, 1 foot, and 1 yard in length. Remind them to look for objects that are easy to find or readily available. For example, body parts are especially useful as personal references for certain units of length.

Then ask students to draw a diagram to show how the measurement units—inches, feet, and yards—are related. Diagrams may look similar to the following:

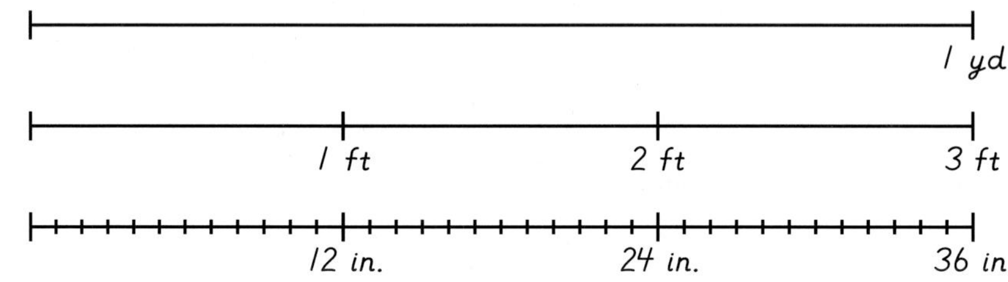

Other students may find it helpful to record measurement quantities in a table. *For example:*

Yards	Feet	Inches
	1	12
	2	24
1	3	36

▶ Math Boxes 5•1

INDEPENDENT ACTIVITY

(*Math Journal 1,* p. 108)

Mixed Practice Math Boxes in this lesson are paired with Math Boxes in Lesson 5-3. The skill in Problem 6 previews Unit 6 content.

Writing/Reasoning Have students write a response to the following: *One comparison statement for Problem 2a is 2,000 is 40 times as many as 50. Write another comparison statement to match the multiplication equation you wrote in Problem 2a.* 2,000 is 50 times as many as 40. *Now write two comparison statements to match the multiplication equation in Problem 2b.* 21,000 is 300 times as many as 70. 21,000 is 70 times as many as 300.

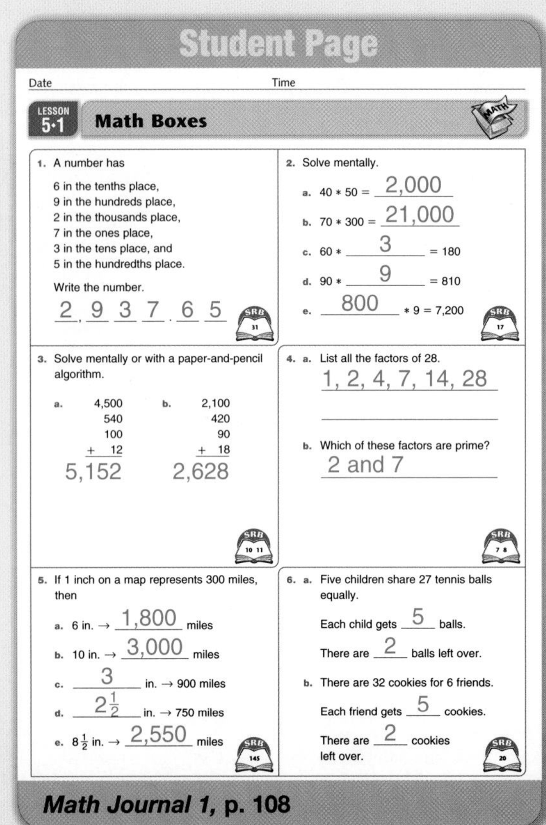

Student Page

Date Time

LESSON 5•1 **Math Boxes**

1. A number has
6 in the tenths place,
9 in the hundreds place,
2 in the thousands place,
7 in the ones place,
3 in the tens place, and
5 in the hundredths place.
Write the number.
2 9 3 7 . 6 5

2. Solve mentally.
a. 40 ∗ 50 = 2,000
b. 70 ∗ 300 = 21,000
c. 60 ∗ 3 = 180
d. 90 ∗ 9 = 810
e. 800 ∗ 9 = 7,200

3. Solve mentally or with a paper-and-pencil algorithm.
a. 4,500 + 540 + 100 + 12 = 5,152
b. 2,100 + 420 + 90 + 18 = 2,628

4. a. List all the factors of 28.
1, 2, 4, 7, 14, 28
b. Which of these factors are prime?
2 and 7

5. If 1 inch on a map represents 300 miles, then
a. 6 in. → 1,800 miles
b. 10 in. → 3,000 miles
c. 3 in. → 900 miles
d. $2\frac{1}{2}$ in. → 750 miles
e. $8\frac{1}{2}$ in. → 2,550 miles

6. a. Five children share 27 tennis balls equally.
Each child gets 5 balls.
There are 2 balls left over.
b. There are 32 cookies for 6 friends.
Each friend gets 5 cookies.
There are 2 cookies left over.

Math Journal 1, p. 108

Study Link 5•1

INDEPENDENT ACTIVITY

(*Math Masters,* p. 139)

Home Connection Students find products and quotients involving multiples of 10, 100, and 1,000.

3 Differentiation Options

READINESS

PARTNER ACTIVITY

Playing *Multiplication Top-It*

5–15 Min

(*Student Reference Book,* p. 264; *Math Masters,* p. 506)

To provide practice with basic multiplication facts, have students play *Multiplication Top-It.*

NOTE For facts practice through 12 $*$ 12, have students include number cards 11 and 12.

EXTRA PRACTICE

INDEPENDENT ACTIVITY

Solving Multiplication/Division Puzzles

5–15 Min

FACTS PRACTICE

(*Math Masters,* p. 430)

To provide practice with extended facts, have students solve multiplication/division puzzles. Use *Math Masters,* page 430 to create multiplication/division puzzles that meet individual needs, or have students create and solve their own problems.

ELL SUPPORT

SMALL-GROUP ACTIVITY

Building a Math Word Bank

5–15 Min

(*Differentiation Handbook,* p. 140)

To provide language support for multiplication facts, have students use the Word Bank Template found on *Differentiation Handbook,* page 140. Ask students to write the term *extended fact,* draw pictures or give examples that represent the term, and write other words that describe it. See the *Differentiation Handbook* for more information.

Study Link Master

Name Date Time

STUDY LINK 5•1 **Multiplication/Division Puzzles**

Solve the multiplication/division puzzles mentally. Fill in the blank boxes.

Examples:

*, /	300	2,000
2	600	4,000
3	900	6,000

*, /	80	50
4	320	200
8	640	400

1.

*, /	70	400
8	560	3,200
9	630	3,600

2.

*, /	5	7
80	400	560
600	3,000	4,200

3.

*, /	9	4
50	450	200
7,000	63,000	28,000

4.

*, /	500	600
7	3,500	4,200
4	2,000	2,400

5.

*, /	90	80
30	2,700	2,400
700	63,000	56,000

6.

*, /	4,000	500
9	36,000	4,500
20	80,000	10,000

Make up and solve some puzzles of your own. Answers vary.

7.

*, /		

8.

*, /		

Practice

9. 1.48 = 0.56 + 0.92
10. 1.13 = 2.86 − 1.73
11. 19.11 − 10.94 = 8.17
12. 0.77 = 0.52 + 0.25

Math Masters, p. 139

Teaching Aid Master

Name Date Time

Multiplication/Division Puzzles

Solve the multiplication/division puzzles mentally. Fill in the blank boxes.

Examples:

*, /	400	6,000
5	2,000	30,000
8	3,200	48,000

*, /	90	20
3	270	60
7	630	140

Answers vary.

1.

*, /		

2.

*, /		

3.

*, /		

4.

*, /		

5.

*, /		

6.

*, /		

Make up and solve some puzzles of your own.

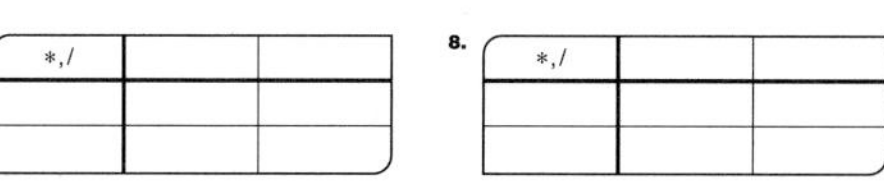

7.

*, /		

8.

*, /		

Math Masters, p. 430

5•2 Multiplication Wrestling

Objectives To provide practice with extended multiplication facts; and to introduce the basic principles of multiplication with multidigit numbers.

www.everydaymathonline.com

ePresentations

eToolkit

Algorithms Practice

EM Facts Workshop Game™

Family Letters

Assessment Management

Common Core State Standards

Curriculum Focal Points

Interactive Teacher's Lesson Guide

1 Teaching the Lesson

Key Concepts and Skills

- Write numbers in expanded notation.
  [Number and Numeration Goal 4]
- Add multidigit numbers.
  [Operations and Computation Goal 2]
- Use basic facts to compute extended facts.
  [Operations and Computation Goal 3]
- Solve multidigit multiplication problems.
  [Operations and Computation Goal 4]
- Evaluate numeric expressions containing parentheses.
  [Patterns, Functions, and Algebra Goal 3]
- Use the Distributive Property of Multiplication over Addition.
  [Patterns, Functions, and Algebra Goal 4]

Key Activities

Students use their knowledge of extended multiplication facts to play *Multiplication Wrestling.* This game prepares students for the partial-products algorithm, which will be introduced in Lesson 5•5.

Ongoing Assessment: Informing Instruction See page 322.

Materials

Student Reference Book, p. 253
Study Link 5•1
Math Masters, p. 488
transparency of *Math Masters,* p. 488 (optional) ◆ per partnership: 4 each of number cards 0–9 (from the Everything Math Deck, if available) or a ten-sided die ◆ slate ◆ index cards (optional)

2 Ongoing Learning & Practice

Interpreting a Data Table

Math Journal 1, p. 109
demonstration clock (optional) ◆ calculator (optional)
Students solve problems based on data about recent U.S. presidents.

Ongoing Assessment: Informing Instruction See page 323.

Math Boxes 5•2

Math Journal 1, p. 110
Students practice and maintain skills through Math Box problems.

Ongoing Assessment: Recognizing Student Achievement
Use Math Boxes, Problem 3.
[Patterns, Functions, and Algebra Goal 2]

Study Link 5•2

Math Masters, p. 140
Students practice and maintain skills through Study Link activities.

3 Differentiation Options

READINESS

Reviewing Partial-Sums Addition

Math Masters, p. 141
Students practice the partial-sums addition method.

ENRICHMENT

Judging a *Multiplication Wrestling* Competition

Math Masters, p. 142
Students use estimation to determine the winner of a *Multiplication Wrestling* competition.

Advance Preparation

For Part 1, make copies of *Math Masters,* page 488 (at least 1 per student). Make enough copies so that some are always on hand for playing *Multiplication Wrestling.*

***Teacher's Reference Manual,* Grades 4–6** pp. 9, 10, 126–132

Getting Started

Mental Math and Reflexes

FACTS PRACTICE

Pose extended multiplication facts problems. *Suggestions:*

●○○	●●○	●●●
4 ∗ 50 = 200	20 ∗ 40 = 800	70 ∗ 800 = 56,000
30 ∗ 7 = 210	50 ∗ 40 = 2,000	600 ∗ 40 = 24,000
70 ∗ 8 = 560	90 ∗ 30 = 2,700	900 ∗ 900 = 810,000

Math Message

Use each of the numbers 2, 4, 6, and 8 to fill in the blanks on the left side of the = sign so you get the largest possible answer.

(____ + ____) ∗ (____ + ____) = ?

Study Link 5·1 Follow-Up

Students compare answers and review shortcuts for solving multiplication problems in which one or more of the factors is a multiple of 10.

1 Teaching the Lesson

Math Message Follow-Up

SMALL-GROUP DISCUSSION

Algebraic Thinking Have students share their solutions in small groups. There are three possible combinations of the numbers:

$$(2 + 4) * (6 + 8) = 84$$

$$(2 + 6) * (4 + 8) = 96$$

$$(2 + 8) * (4 + 6) = 100$$

Each of these combinations of numbers can be arranged in many different ways because the order in which two numbers are added or multiplied does not affect the answer (the turn-around rule). The largest possible answer is 100.

Playing *Multiplication Wrestling*

PARTNER ACTIVITY

(*Student Reference Book,* p. 253; *Math Masters,* p. 488)

Tell students that in this lesson they will learn to play a game that provides computation practice. Players must calculate four partial products and then find the sum of the partial products.

Review the rules of *Multiplication Wrestling* on *Student Reference Book,* page 253 with the class.

Links to the Future

Playing *Multiplication Wrestling* prepares students for the partial-products algorithm, introduced in Lesson 5-5.

Student Page

Games

Multiplication Wrestling

Materials □ 1 *Multiplication Wrestling* Worksheet for each player (*Math Masters,* p. 488)

□ number cards 0–9 (4 of each) or 1 ten-sided die

Players 2

Skill Partial-products algorithm

Object of the game To get the larger product of two 2-digit numbers.

Directions

1. Shuffle the deck of cards and place it number-side down on the table.
2. Each player draws 4 cards and forms two 2-digit numbers. Players should form their 2 numbers so that their product is as large as possible.
3. Players create 2 "wrestling teams" by writing each of their numbers as a sum of 10s and 1s.
4. Each player's 2 teams wrestle. Each member of the first team (for example, 70 and 5) is multiplied by each member of the second team (for example, 80 and 4). Then the 4 products are added.
5. **Scoring:** The player with the larger product wins the round and receives 1 point.
6. To begin a new round, each player draws 4 new cards to form 2 new numbers. A game consists of 3 rounds.

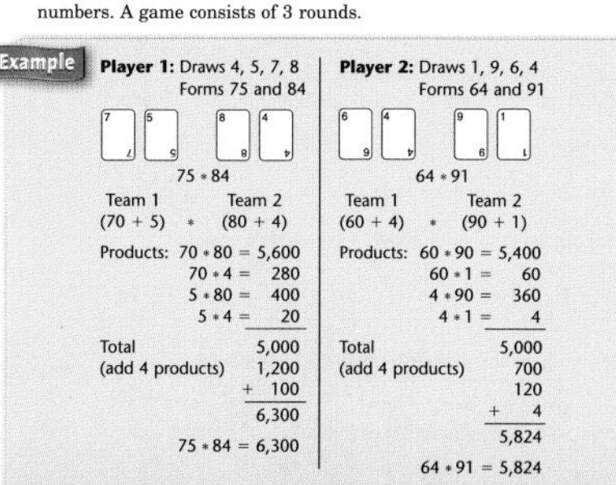

Example

Player 1: Draws 4, 5, 7, 8
Forms 75 and 84

75 ∗ 84

Team 1 (70 + 5) ∗ Team 2 (80 + 4)

Products: 70 ∗ 80 = 5,600
70 ∗ 4 = 280
5 ∗ 80 = 400
5 ∗ 4 = 20

Total (add 4 products): 5,000 + 1,200 + 100 = 6,300

75 ∗ 84 = 6,300

Player 2: Draws 1, 9, 6, 4
Forms 64 and 91

64 ∗ 91

Team 1 (60 + 4) ∗ Team 2 (90 + 1)

Products: 60 ∗ 90 = 5,400
60 ∗ 1 = 60
4 ∗ 90 = 360
4 ∗ 1 = 4

Total (add 4 products): 5,000 + 700 + 120 + 4 = 5,824

64 ∗ 91 = 5,824

***Student Reference Book,* p. 253**

Game Master

Name ____________ Date ____________ Time ____________

Multiplication Wrestling Record Sheet

Round 1 Cards: ______ ______ ______ ______

Numbers formed: ______ * ______

Teams: (______ + ______) * (______ + ______)

Products: ______ * ______ = ______

______ * ______ = ______

______ * ______ = ______

______ * ______ = ______

Total (add 4 products): ______

Round 2 Cards: ______ ______ ______ ______

Numbers formed: ______ * ______

Teams: (______ + ______) * (______ + ______)

Products: ______ * ______ = ______

______ * ______ = ______

______ * ______ = ______

______ * ______ = ______

Total (add 4 products): ______

Round 3 Cards: ______ ______ ______ ______

Numbers formed: ______ * ______

Teams: (______ + ______) * (______ + ______)

Products: ______ * ______ = ______

______ * ______ = ______

______ * ______ = ______

______ * ______ = ______

Total (add 4 products): ______

***Math Masters,* p. 488**

Student Page

Date ____________ Time ____________

LESSON 5•2 **Presidential Information**

The following table shows the dates on which the most recent presidents of the United States were sworn in and their ages at the time they were sworn in.

President	Date Sworn In	Age
F. D. Roosevelt	March 4, 1933	51
Truman	April 12, 1945	60
Eisenhower	January 20, 1953	62
Kennedy	January 20, 1961	43
Johnson	November 22, 1963	55
Nixon	January 20, 1969	56
Ford	August 9, 1974	61
Carter	January 20, 1977	52
Reagan	January 20, 1981	69
G. H. Bush	January 20, 1989	64
Clinton	January 20, 1993	46
G. W. Bush	January 20, 2001	54

1. What is the median age (the middle age) of the presidents at the time they were sworn in? $55\frac{1}{2}$ years
2. What is the range of their ages (the difference between the ages of the oldest and the youngest)? 26 years
3. Who was president for the longest time? F. D. Roosevelt
4. Who was president for the shortest time? Ford
5. Presidents are elected to serve for 1 term. A term lasts 4 years. Which presidents served only 1 term or less than 1 term? Kennedy, Ford, Carter, G. H. Bush
6. Which president was sworn in about 28 years after Roosevelt? Kennedy
7. Roosevelt was born on January 30, 1882. If he were alive today, about how old would he be? As of January 30, 2007: 125 years old

***Math Journal 1,* p. 109**

Adjusting the Activity

ELL

Acting out "tag team" wrestling may help students better understand the rules of *Multiplication Wrestling.*

Using the example 75 ∗ 84, have students write each number as the sum of the values of the digits: 70 + 5 and 80 + 4. Record 70 and 5 on separate index cards of one color and 80 and 4 on separate index cards of another color. Explain that 70 and 5 are one team, and 80 and 4 are a different team.

Select four students to hold the cards. Remind students that in a tag-team wrestling match, a person never wrestles someone from the same team. So, 70 and 5 cannot wrestle each other, nor can 80 and 4. Therefore, 70 wrestles 80 and then 4. Next, 5 wrestles 80 and then 4. Have students stand next to each other as they "wrestle," and record the product after each "wrestling match."

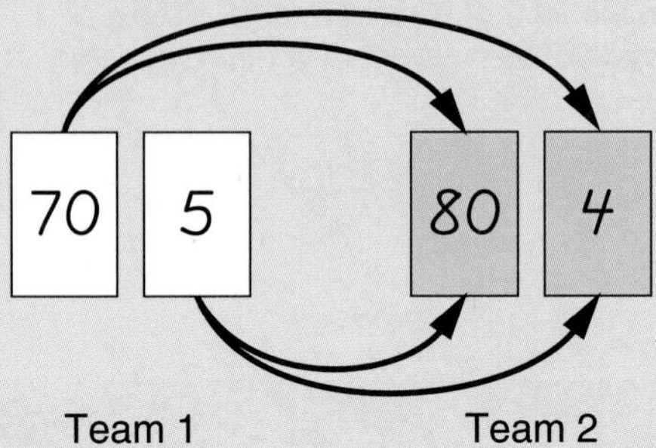

Team 1 Team 2

AUDITORY ◆ KINESTHETIC ◆ TACTILE ◆ VISUAL

The record sheet on *Math Masters,* page 488 is designed to help students organize and keep track of their computations. All students should use this page to record their work for the first 3-round game they play.

Use a transparency of *Math Masters,* page 488 to demonstrate how to fill in the record sheet. When they have learned the game, many students will not need worksheets to record their results. They may simply write their calculations on a blank sheet of paper.

Ask students about the patterns they noticed and the strategies they used while playing and completing the record sheet. For example, some students may note that for each set of four cards drawn, there are many ways of forming 2-digit numbers. The goal is to form two pairs that will yield the largest product.

Ongoing Assessment: Informing Instruction

Watch for students who correctly determine the partial products but then add incorrectly. Encourage students to write their partial products so that the digits in each number are aligned according to their value.

2 Ongoing Learning & Practice

Interpreting a Data Table

INDEPENDENT ACTIVITY

(*Math Journal 1,* p. 109)

Social Studies Link Students solve problems based on data about the 12 most recent presidents of the United States.

Ongoing Assessment: Informing Instruction

In Problem 4, watch for students who look only at the years of Ford's and Kennedy's terms and therefore conclude that Kennedy was president for the shortest time. Actually, Kennedy was president for a little more than 2 years and 10 months, while Ford was president for less than 2 years and 6 months.

You may wish to use the context of journal page 109 to pose word problems involving intervals of time. Students may use the demonstration clock, calculators, or anything else that may help. Some students may find it helpful to use an open number line to illustrate the strategy of counting up in years, and possibly even days. For the first suggestion given below, students might draw an open number line like the one shown here. Students mark off the starting year and count up in years, while recording the elapsed time.

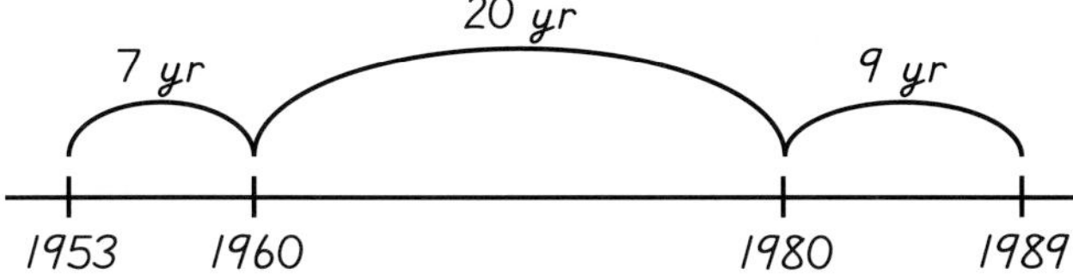

Have students record their answers on slates. Encourage students to share their strategies. *Suggestions:*

- How many years passed between the swearing in of Eisenhower and the swearing in of G. H. Bush? 36 years Between Carter and Reagan? 4 years
- Approximately how much time passed between the swearing in of Johnson and the swearing in of Nixon? 5 years, 59 days Between Nixon and Ford? 5 years, 201 days

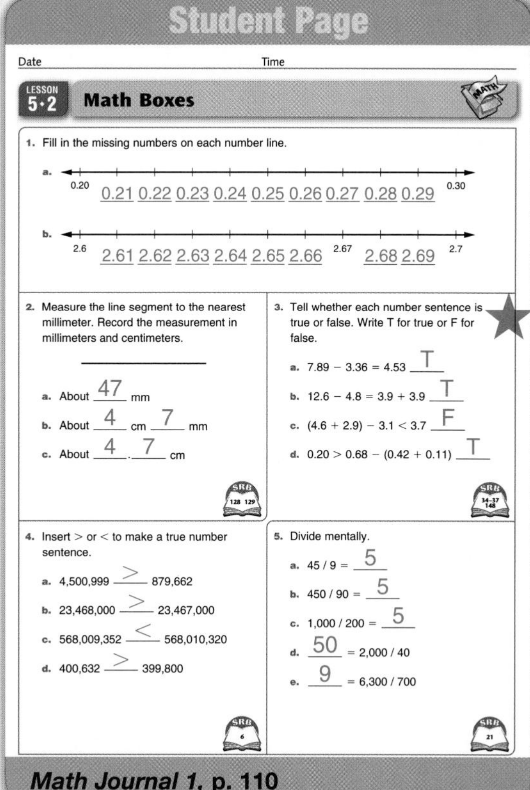

Student Page

Date Time

LESSON 5·2 **Math Boxes**

1. Fill in the missing numbers on each number line.

a. 0.20, 0.21, 0.22, 0.23, 0.24, 0.25, 0.26, 0.27, 0.28, 0.29, 0.30

b. 2.6, 2.61, 2.62, 2.63, 2.64, 2.65, 2.66, 2.67, 2.68, 2.69, 2.7

2. Measure the line segment to the nearest millimeter. Record the measurement in millimeters and centimeters.

a. About 47 mm

b. About 4 cm 7 mm

c. About 4.7 cm

SRB 128 129

3. Tell whether each number sentence is true or false. Write T for true or F for false.

a. 7.89 − 3.36 = 4.53 T

b. 12.6 − 4.8 = 3.9 + 3.9 T

c. (4.6 + 2.9) − 3.1 < 3.7 F

d. 0.20 > 0.68 − (0.42 + 0.11) T

SRB 34-37 148

4. Insert > or < to make a true number sentence.

a. 4,500,999 > 879,662

b. 23,468,000 > 23,467,000

c. 568,009,352 < 568,010,320

d. 400,632 > 399,800

SRB 6

5. Divide mentally.

a. 45 / 9 = 5

b. 450 / 90 = 5

c. 1,000 / 200 = 5

d. 50 = 2,000 / 40

e. 9 = 6,300 / 700

SRB 21

Math Journal 1, p. 110

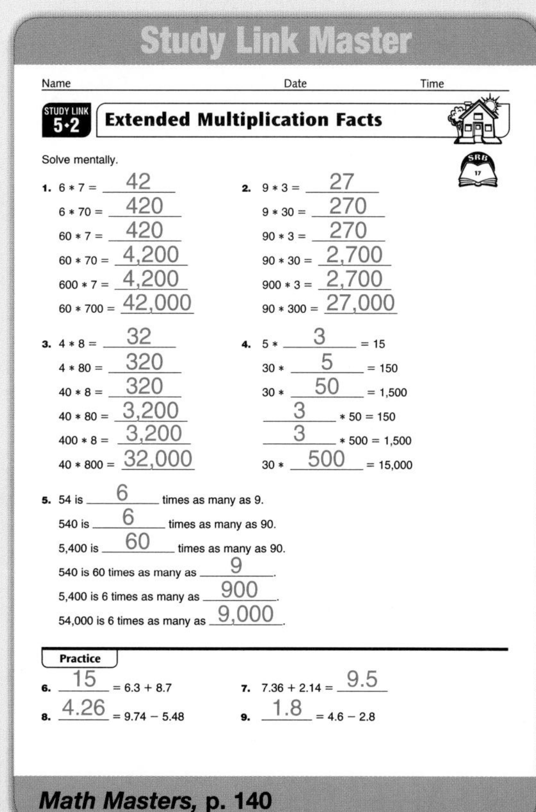

Study Link Master

Name Date Time

STUDY LINK 5·2 **Extended Multiplication Facts**

SRB 17

Solve mentally.

1. 6 * 7 = 42
6 * 70 = 420
60 * 7 = 420
60 * 70 = 4,200
600 * 7 = 4,200
60 * 700 = 42,000

2. 9 * 3 = 27
9 * 30 = 270
90 * 3 = 270
90 * 30 = 2,700
900 * 3 = 2,700
90 * 300 = 27,000

3. 4 * 8 = 32
4 * 80 = 320
40 * 8 = 320
40 * 80 = 3,200
400 * 8 = 3,200
40 * 800 = 32,000

4. 5 * 3 = 15
30 * 5 = 150
30 * 50 = 1,500
3 * 50 = 150
3 * 500 = 1,500
30 * 500 = 15,000

5. 54 is 6 times as many as 9.
540 is 6 times as many as 90.
5,400 is 60 times as many as 90.
540 is 60 times as many as 9.
5,400 is 6 times as many as 900.
54,000 is 6 times as many as 9,000.

Practice

6. 15 = 6.3 + 8.7

7. 7.36 + 2.14 = 9.5

8. 4.26 = 9.74 − 5.48

9. 1.8 = 4.6 − 2.8

Math Masters, p. 140

Teaching Master

Name Date Time

LESSON 5•2

Partial-Sums Addition

Example: 2,000 + 280 + 300 + 42 = ?

	2,000	
	280	
	300	
	+ 42	
Add the thousands:	2,000	
Add the hundreds:	500	(200 + 300)
Add the tens:	120	(80 + 40)
Add the ones:	+ 2	
Find the total:	2,622	

Solve each problem.

1. 800 + 120 + 160 + 24 = 1,104
2. 700 + 420 + 50 + 30 = 1,200
3. 832 = 600 + 180 + 40 + 12
4. 3,008 = 2,400 + 160 + 420 + 28
5. 1,854 = 1,500 + 90 + 240 + 24
6. 5,600 + 420 + 400 + 30 = 6,450

Math Masters, **p. 141**

Teaching Master

Name Date Time

LESSON 5•2

A *Multiplication Wrestling* Competition

1. Twelve players entered a *Multiplication Wrestling* competition. The numbers they chose are shown in the following table. The score of each player is the product of the two numbers. For example, Aidan's score is 741, because 13 * 57 = 741. Which of the 12 players do you think has the highest score? Answers vary.

Group A	Group B	Group C
Aidan: 13 * 57	Indira: 15 * 73	Miguel: 17 * 35
Colette: 13 * 75	Jelani: 15 * 37	Rex: 17 * 53
Emily: 31 * 75	Kuniko: 51 * 37	Sarah: 71 * 53
Gunnar: 31 * 57	Liza: 51 * 73	Tanisha: 71 * 35

Check your guess with the following procedure. *Do not do any arithmetic for Steps 2 and 3.*

2. In each pair below, cross out the player with the lower score. Find that player's name in the table above and cross it out as well.

Aidan; Colette	Indira; Jelani	Miguel; Rex
Emily; Gunnar	Kuniko; Liza	Sarah; Tanisha

3. Two players are left in Group A. Cross out the one with the lower score. Two players are left in Group B. Cross out the one with the lower score. Two players are left in Group C. Cross out the one with the lower score.

   Which 3 players are still left? Emily, Liza, and Sarah

4. Of the 3 players who are left, which player has the lowest score? Emily
   Cross out that player's name.

5. There are 2 players left. What are their scores? Liza's is 3,723; Sarah's is 3,763.

6. Who won the competition? Sarah

Math Masters, **p. 142**

▶ Math Boxes 5•2

(*Math Journal 1,* p. 110)

Mixed Practice Math Boxes in this lesson are paired with Math Boxes in Lesson 5-4. The skill in Problem 5 previews Unit 6 content.

Ongoing Assessment: Recognizing Student Achievement

Math Boxes Problem 3

Use **Math Boxes, Problem 3** to assess students' ability to determine whether a number sentence is true or false. Students are making adequate progress if they can use mental arithmetic, a paper-and-pencil algorithm, or a calculator to determine whether the number sentences are true or false. Some students may be able to suggest how to change a false number sentence to make it true.

[Patterns, Functions, and Algebra Goal 2]

▶ Study Link 5•2

(*Math Masters,* p. 140)

Home Connection Students practice extended multiplication facts.

3 Differentiation Options

READINESS

▶ Reviewing Partial-Sums Addition

(*Math Masters,* p. 141)

To explore partial-sums addition in preparation for adding partial products in *Multiplication Wrestling*, have students find the sum of four multidigit numbers. The problems are presented horizontally to provide practice in correctly aligning the digits in a vertical format.

ENRICHMENT

▶ Judging a *Multiplication Wrestling* Competition

(*Math Masters,* p. 142)

To apply students' understanding of the Distributive Property of Multiplication over Addition, have them use estimation strategies to determine which player in a *Multiplication Wrestling* competition has the highest score. On the back of *Math Masters,* page 142, ask students to explain how they solved Problem 4 and to show their work for Problem 5.

5·3 Estimating Sums

Objectives To provide practice deciding whether estimation is appropriate in a given situation; and to provide practice estimating sums.

Technology Resources www.everydaymathonline.com

ePresentations

eToolkit

Algorithms Practice

EM Facts Workshop Game™

Family Letters

Assessment Management

Common Core State Standards

Curriculum Focal Points

Interactive Teacher's Lesson Guide

1 Teaching the Lesson

Key Concepts and Skills

- Estimate sums.
  [Operations and Computation Goal 6]
- Compare appropriate situations for the use of exact answers and estimates.
  [Operations and Computation Goal 6]
- Use a travel map to find driving distance and driving time.
  [Data and Chance Goal 2]

Key Activities

Students discuss an example of a problem that can be solved by estimation. They use a travel map to determine approximate distances and times between cities. Then they estimate the total distance and the total driving time for a trip.

Ongoing Assessment: Informing Instruction See page 328.

Ongoing Assessment: Recognizing Student Achievement
Use journal page 113.
[Operations and Computation Goal 6]

Key Vocabulary

estimation ◆ round

Materials

Math Journal 1, pp. 112 and 113
Study Link 5•2
Math Masters, p. 143
calculator ◆ demonstration clock (optional)

2 Ongoing Learning & Practice

Playing *Product Pile-Up*
Student Reference Book, p. 259
per partnership: 8 each of number cards 1–10 (from the Everything Math Deck, if available)
Students maintain automaticity with multiplication facts.

Math Boxes 5•3
Math Journal 1, p. 111
Students practice and maintain skills through Math Box problems.

Study Link 5•3
Math Masters, p. 144
Students practice and maintain skills through Study Link activities.

3 Differentiation Options

READINESS

Finding "Closer-To" Numbers with Base-10 Blocks
Math Masters, p. 145
base-10 blocks
Students explore rounding numbers.

ENRICHMENT

Solving a Traveling Salesperson Problem
Math Journal 1, p. 112
Math Masters, p. 146
Students use estimation skills to find the shortest route between four cities.

EXTRA PRACTICE

Solving Elapsed-Time Problems
Math Journal 1, p. 112
demonstration clock (optional) ◆ calculator (optional)
Students solve elapsed-time problems.

ELL SUPPORT

Building a Math Word Bank
Differentiation Handbook, p. 140
Students add the terms *estimation* and *round* to their Math Word Banks.

Advance Preparation

Make one copy of *Math Masters,* page 143 for every two students. Cut them in half and place them near the Math Message.

***Teacher's Reference Manual,* Grades 4–6** pp. 260–264

Getting Started

Mental Math and Reflexes

Write multidigit addition problems on the board. Students estimate the sums. They indicate "thumbs-up" if the answer is greater than 100 for the ●○○ problems and greater than 1,000 for the ●●○ and ●●● problems. Have students explain their strategies. *Suggestions:* Sample answers are given.

●○○ 52 + 49 50 + 50 = 100
22 + 49 20 + 50 = 70
37 + 54 35 + 55 = 90
21 + 47 + 68 20 + 50 + 70 = 140

●●○ 786 + 293 800 + 300 = 1,100
496 + 257 500 + 250 = 750
865 + 439 900 + 400 = 1,300
572 + 314 600 + 300 = 900

●●● 316 + 145 + 459 300 + 150 + 450 = 900
125 + 239 + 353 100 + 250 + 350 = 700
673 + 314 + 249 700 + 300 + 250 = 1,250
588 + 467 + 218 600 + 500 + 200 = 1,300

Math Message

Take an answer sheet (Math Masters, *page 143*) *and complete it.*

Study Link 5·2 Follow-Up

Have students discuss Problem 5. Point out that these are comparison problems involving multiplication. Have students discuss the patterns they found in their answers.

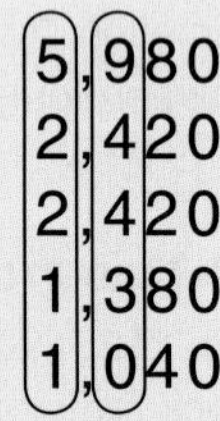

One method is to add the thousands and then the hundreds.

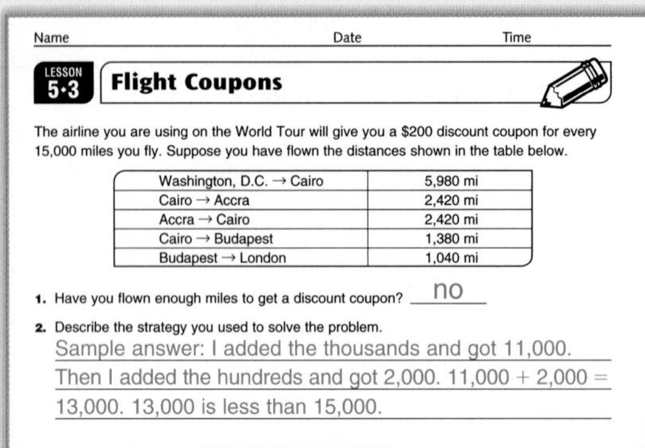

Name Date Time

LESSON 5·3 **Flight Coupons**

The airline you are using on the World Tour will give you a $200 discount coupon for every 15,000 miles you fly. Suppose you have flown the distances shown in the table below.

Washington, D.C. → Cairo	5,980 mi
Cairo → Accra	2,420 mi
Accra → Cairo	2,420 mi
Cairo → Budapest	1,380 mi
Budapest → London	1,040 mi

1. Have you flown enough miles to get a discount coupon? no
2. Describe the strategy you used to solve the problem.
Sample answer: I added the thousands and got 11,000. Then I added the hundreds and got 2,000. 11,000 + 2,000 = 13,000. 13,000 is less than 15,000.

Math Masters, page 143

1 Teaching the Lesson

▶ Math Message Follow-Up

(*Math Masters,* p. 143)

Ask students what methods they used to solve the problem. Ask questions like the following:

- Did anyone figure out the exact number of miles traveled using paper and pencil?
- Using a calculator?
- Did anyone use **estimation?**

On the board, list the distances traveled and ask someone who estimated the total distance to describe his or her estimation method.

If no one mentions it, demonstrate the following method on the board: Add the thousands first (11,000 miles). Next add the hundreds (2,000 miles). (*See margin.*) The *estimated total distance,* using thousands and hundreds, is 11,000 + 2,000, or 13,000 miles—far short of the 15,000 miles required to get a discount coupon.

One idea that should emerge from this discussion is that it is not necessary to find the *exact total* number of miles to answer the question. This point needs to be emphasized. Students will be reluctant to use estimation unless they are convinced of its usefulness in certain situations.

Ask those students who used estimation to check their estimates by using a calculator to find the exact number of miles they have traveled so far.

Note that the method of estimation described previously is consistent with the left-to-right partial-sums algorithm, in which the sums of the thousands, the hundreds, the tens, and the ones are recorded separately and then added. (*See margin.*)

In this lesson students use their estimation skills to figure out how many days are needed to reach a destination during a driving trip that includes four U.S. cities. Students will estimate mileage and time to find the solution.

Examining a Travel Map

WHOLE-CLASS DISCUSSION

(*Math Journal 1,* p. 112)

Social Studies Link Ask students to turn to the Estimated U.S. Distances and Driving Times map on journal page 112. Briefly discuss the information the map provides.

The map displays distances and driving times between major U.S. cities. These are based on travel from the center or downtown of one city to the center or downtown of another city.

- ▷ The number *above* the line between two cities is the distance in miles between the cities based on the fastest or most commonly traveled roads.
- ▷ The notation *below* the line is an estimate of the time it would take to drive the distance under normal conditions at the posted speed limits.

Example: The map indicates that the distance between Chicago and St. Louis is 302 miles. The notation "5:40" means that the trip would take about 5 hours and 40 minutes.

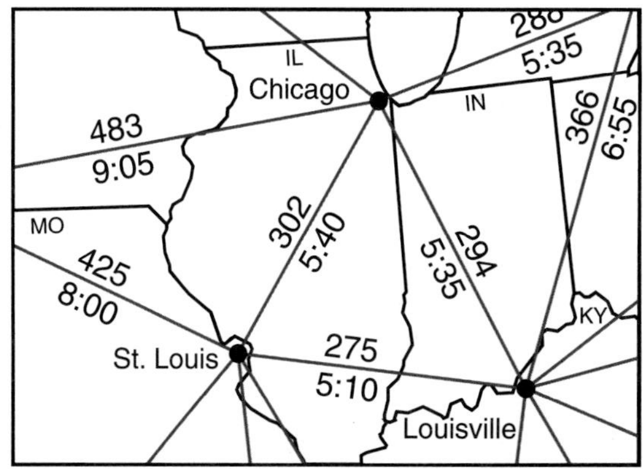

NOTE Point out that although the cities on the map are connected by straight lines, the roads themselves do not necessarily run in a straight line.

Adjusting the Activity

ELL

This lesson provides multiple opportunities to introduce words that may be new to English language learners, such as *route, driving distance, driving time, sensible,* and *destination.* As you encounter each word during the lesson, be sure to write it on the board and discuss its meaning.

AUDITORY • KINESTHETIC • TACTILE • VISUAL

Partial-Sums Algorithm

	5,980
	2,420
	2,420
	1,380
	+ 1,040
Add thousands:	11,000
Add hundreds:	2,000
Add tens:	240
Add ones:	+ 0
Add partial sums:	13,240

Student Page

Date Time

LESSON 5•3 **Planning a Driving Trip**

Use the map on journal page 112. Start at your hometown. Plan a driving trip that takes you to 4 other cities on the map. If your hometown is not on the map, find the nearest city on the map to your hometown. Start your driving trip from this city.

Example: Start in Chicago. Drive to St. Louis, Louisville, Birmingham, and then New Orleans.

1. Record your routes, driving distances, and driving times in the table. Sample answers:

From...To	Driving Distance (miles)	Driving Time (hours:minutes)	Rounded Time (hours)
Chicago to St. Louis	3 0 2	5 : 40	6
St. Louis to Louisville	2 7 5	5 : 10	5
Louisville to Birmingham	3 6 7	6 : 55	7
Birmingham to New Orleans	3 4 2	6 : 25	6

2. Estimate how many *miles* you will drive in all. About 1,300 miles
3. Estimate how many *hours* you will drive in all. About 24 hours
4. Tell how many *days* it will take to complete the trip if you plan to drive about 8 hours each day and then stop somewhere for the night. 3 days
5. Explain how you solved Problems 2–4.

Sample answer: I rounded each distance to the nearest hundred, and then added them. I added the rounded times to get the estimated hours. I divided the estimated 24 hours by 8 to get 3 days.

Math Journal 1, p. 113

Discuss distance and time measurements.

- How do you think the distances and travel times between cities were obtained? Up-to-date maps were used to find routes and distances between cities. A typical speed, such as 55 miles per hour, was assumed for all drivers and all routes.

- If the distances and times were measured again, would it be reasonable to expect the same results? Expect the same, or very close, results. There may be two or more equally good routes, with slightly different distances and times.

- What is a sensible way of reporting distances and travel times? Would you see exact numbers? Would you use estimates within a certain range or numbers rounded to a certain place? If so, what is a sensible range or place to **round** to? Although the reported distances are fairly accurate, it is probably not sensible to report long distances between cities to the nearest mile. It might be better to round distances to the nearest 10 miles. Since driving times are even less reliable due to weather, traffic, road construction, and so on, it is probably sensible to think that driving times may be off by up to $\frac{1}{2}$ hour for each 5 hours reported on the travel map. Therefore, round times to the nearest hour.

Adjusting the Activity

When rounding times to the nearest hour, remind students that 30 minutes is one-half of an hour; it is halfway between two consecutive hours. For example, 2:30 is halfway between 2:00 and 3:00. A time that is less than 30 minutes after the hour is rounded down. A time that is 30 or more minutes after the hour is rounded up. Have students use clocks to work through several problems. *For example:*

	lower time	higher time	rounded time
Round 5:20 to nearest hour.	5:00	6:00	5:00
Round 3:45 to nearest hour.	3:00	4:00	4:00
Round 6:30 to nearest hour.	6:00	7:00	7:00

AUDITORY ◆ KINESTHETIC ◆ TACTILE ◆ VISUAL

Ongoing Assessment: Informing Instruction

As students complete Problem 4, watch for those who think they must reach one of the cities named by driving exactly 8 hours each day. It is assumed that overnight stops are made anywhere along the route when about 8 hours have been driven. Remind students that the 8-hour average is used to calculate the days it takes to reach the destination, not the absolute driving time each day.

▶ Planning a Trip

(*Math Journal 1,* pp. 112 and 113)

Ask students to read the instructions for "Planning a Driving Trip" on journal page 113. Make sure they understand the purpose of the activity—to determine how many *days* it will take them to reach their destination. Do they need to find the *exact total* driving time, or will an *estimate* do?

You will probably want to model a sample trip with the class. For each city-to-city part of the trip, record the distance and driving time given on the travel map on journal page 112.

▷ To estimate the total distance, find the sum of the distances by adding only the hundreds and tens. Ignore digits in the ones place.

▷ To estimate the total driving time, first round each time to the nearest hour. Then add the rounded times.

Have students complete Problem 5 independently.

Ongoing Assessment: Recognizing Student Achievement

Journal page 113 Problem 5

Use **journal page 113, Problem 5** to assess students' ability to explain how they used estimation to solve addition problems. Students are making adequate progress if their explanation involves "close-but-easier" numbers. Some students may be able to describe more than one way to solve the problems.

[Operations and Computation Goal 6]

2 Ongoing Learning & Practice

Playing *Product Pile-Up*

PARTNER ACTIVITY

FACTS PRACTICE

(*Student Reference Book,* p. 259)

Students play *Product Pile-Up* to maintain automaticity with multiplication facts. See Lesson 4-3 for additional information.

Math Boxes 5•3

INDEPENDENT ACTIVITY

(*Math Journal 1,* p. 111)

Mixed Practice Math Boxes in this lesson are paired with Math Boxes in Lesson 5-1. The skill in Problem 6 previews Unit 6 content.

Writing/Reasoning Have students write a response to the following: *Explain how you solved Problem 5.* Sample answer: I multiplied 4 ∗ 200 to get 800 miles. I knew that 1 centimeter represents 200 miles, so 0.5 centimeters represents 100 miles. 800 + 100 = 900

Study Link 5•3

INDEPENDENT ACTIVITY

ELL

(*Math Masters,* p. 144)

Home Connection Students estimate sums. If the estimate is greater than or equal to 1,500, students find the exact sum. If the estimate is less than 1,500, students do not need to solve the problem. Emphasize to English language learners that they do not have to solve all the problems.

3 Differentiation Options

READINESS

SMALL-GROUP ACTIVITY

5–15 Min

Finding "Closer-To" Numbers with Base-10 Blocks

(*Math Masters,* p. 145)

To provide experience with estimation skills by finding the "closer-to" number when rounding, have students use base-10 blocks to build

▷ the number to be rounded,

▷ the nearest multiple of 10 or 100 less than the number, and

▷ the nearest multiple of 10 or 100 greater than the number.

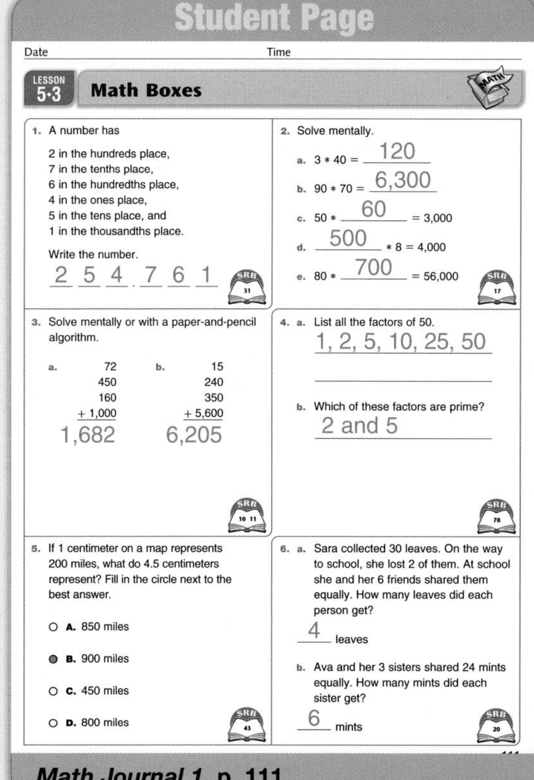

Student Page

Date Time

LESSON 5•3 **Math Boxes**

1. A number has 2 in the hundreds place, 7 in the tenths place, 6 in the hundredths place, 4 in the ones place, 5 in the tens place, and 1 in the thousandths place. Write the number. 2 5 4 . 7 6 1

2. Solve mentally.
a. 3 ∗ 40 = 120
b. 90 ∗ 70 = 6,300
c. 50 ∗ 60 = 3,000
d. 500 ∗ 8 = 4,000
e. 80 ∗ 700 = 56,000

3. Solve mentally or with a paper-and-pencil algorithm.
a. 72 + 450 + 160 + 1,000 = 1,682
b. 15 + 240 + 350 + 5,600 = 6,205

4. a. List all the factors of 50. 1, 2, 5, 10, 25, 50
b. Which of these factors are prime? 2 and 5

5. If 1 centimeter on a map represents 200 miles, what do 4.5 centimeters represent? Fill in the circle next to the best answer.
○ A. 850 miles
● B. 900 miles
○ C. 450 miles
○ D. 800 miles

6. a. Sara collected 30 leaves. On the way to school, she lost 2 of them. At school she and her 6 friends shared them equally. How many leaves did each person get? 4 leaves
b. Ava and her 3 sisters shared 24 mints equally. How many mints did each sister get? 6 mints

Math Journal 1, p. 111

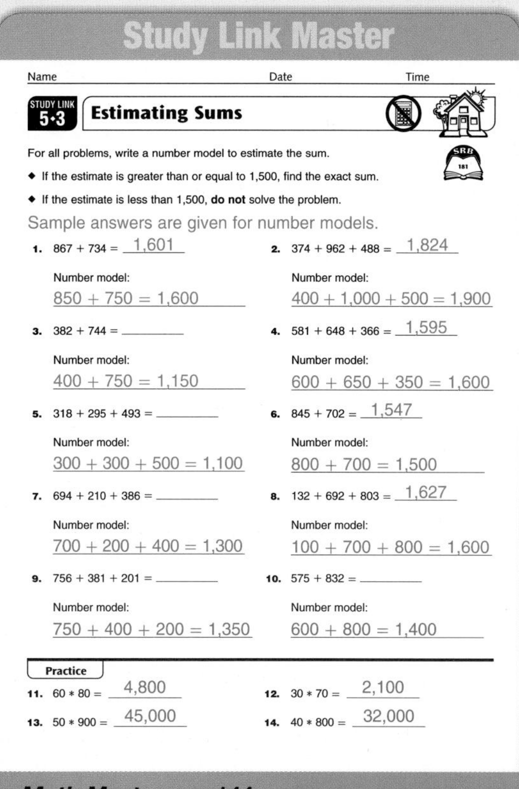

Study Link Master

Name Date Time

STUDY LINK 5•3 **Estimating Sums**

For all problems, write a number model to estimate the sum.
- If the estimate is greater than or equal to 1,500, find the exact sum.
- If the estimate is less than 1,500, **do not** solve the problem.

Sample answers are given for number models.

1. 867 + 734 = 1,601 Number model: 850 + 750 = 1,600
2. 374 + 962 + 488 = 1,824 Number model: 400 + 1,000 + 500 = 1,900
3. 382 + 744 = ____ Number model: 400 + 750 = 1,150
4. 581 + 648 + 366 = 1,595 Number model: 600 + 650 + 350 = 1,600
5. 318 + 295 + 493 = ____ Number model: 300 + 300 + 500 = 1,100
6. 845 + 702 = 1,547 Number model: 800 + 700 = 1,500
7. 694 + 210 + 386 = ____ Number model: 700 + 200 + 400 = 1,300
8. 132 + 692 + 803 = 1,627 Number model: 100 + 700 + 800 = 1,600
9. 756 + 381 + 201 = ____ Number model: 750 + 400 + 200 = 1,350
10. 575 + 832 = ____ Number model: 600 + 800 = 1,400

Practice

11. 60 ∗ 80 = 4,800
12. 30 ∗ 70 = 2,100
13. 50 ∗ 900 = 45,000
14. 40 ∗ 800 = 32,000

Math Masters, p. 144

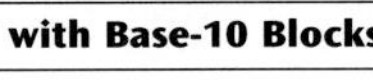

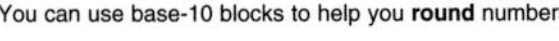

Name Date Time

LESSON 5·3 **"Closer To" with Base-10 Blocks**

You can use base-10 blocks to help you **round** numbers.

Example: Round 64 to the nearest ten.

- Build a model for 64 with base-10 blocks.
- *Think:* What **multiples of 10** are nearest to 64?
  If I take the ones (cubes) away, I would have **60**.
  If I add more ones to make the next ten, I would have **70**.
- Build models for 60 and 70.

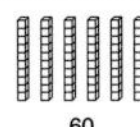

60

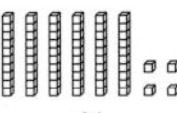

64

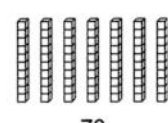

70

Think: Is 64 closer to 60 or 70? 64 is closer to 60. So, 64 rounded to the nearest ten is 60.

Build models to help you choose the closer number.

1. Round 87 to the nearest ten.
   List the three numbers you will build models for: 80, 87, 90
   87 is closer to 90. So, 87 rounded to the nearest ten is 90.
2. Round 43 to the nearest ten.
   List the three numbers you will build models for: 40, 43, 50
   43 is closer to 40. So, 43 rounded to the nearest ten is 40.
3. Round 138 to the nearest ten.
   List the three numbers you will build models for: 130, 138, 140
   138 is closer to 140. So, 138 rounded to the nearest ten is 140.
4. Round 138 to the nearest *hundred*.
   List the three numbers you will build models for: 100, 138, 200
   138 is closer to 100. So, 138 rounded to the nearest hundred is 100.

***Math Masters,* p. 145**

NOTE To teach a standard procedure for rounding whole numbers to the nearest ten and hundred, see www.everydaymathonline.com.

Teaching Master

Name Date Time

LESSON 5·3 **A Traveling Salesperson Problem**

A salesperson plans to visit several cities. To save time and money, the trip should be as short as possible. If the salesperson were visiting only a few cities, it would be possible to figure the shortest route in a reasonable time. But what if the trip includes 10 cities? There would be 3,628,800 possible routes! Computer scientists are trying to find ways to solve this problem on the computer without having to do an impossible number of calculations.

Think like a computer. Imagine that you begin a trip in Seattle and have to visit Denver, Birmingham, and Bangor for business.

1. Estimate to find the shortest *route* that would include each city. Use the map on journal page 112.
2. Describe your route between each of the four cities.
   Sample answer: Seattle to Boise to Salt Lake City to Denver (totals 1,361 miles); then Denver to Dallas to Birmingham (totals 1,431 miles); then Birmingham to Washington, D.C., to New York City to Boston to Bangor (totals 1,408 miles). The total mileage is 4,200 miles.

Try This

3. Describe a route that includes each city that would take the shortest amount of *time*.
   Sample answer: Looking at the map, the route described above should be the shortest because the shortest distances are also shown as the shortest times.

***Math Masters,* p. 146**

ENRICHMENT

INDEPENDENT ACTIVITY

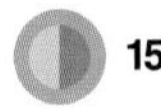

15–30 Min

▶ Solving a Traveling Salesperson Problem

(*Math Journal 1,* p. 112; *Math Masters,* p. 146)

Portfolio Ideas

To apply students' understanding of estimating sums, have them use journal page 112 to plan a route connecting four cities, beginning in Washington State and ending in Maine. The route should have the shortest total *driving distance*. To extend this problem, students may also find the route with the shortest total *driving time*.

EXTRA PRACTICE

SMALL-GROUP ACTIVITY

15–30 Min

▶ Solving Elapsed-Time Problems

(*Math Journal 1,* p. 112)

To provide extra practice with elapsed-time problems, you may wish to use the context of journal page 112 to pose word problems. Students may use a demonstration clock, calculators, or anything else that may help. Some students may find it helpful to use an open number line to illustrate the strategy of counting up in hours and minutes. In the first suggestion given below, students might draw a diagram like the one shown here. Students mark off the starting time and count up in hours and then in minutes, while recording the actual and elapsed time.

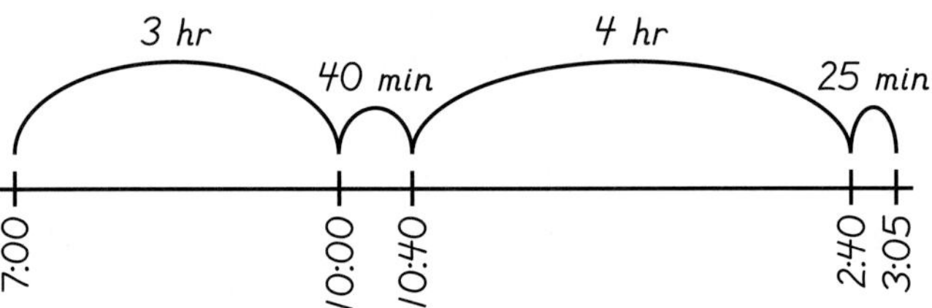

Encourage students to share their strategies. *Suggestions:*

▷ Brynn is taking a trip from New York City, NY to Bangor, ME. If she leaves at 7:00 A.M. and travels through Boston, MA, what time will she arrive in Bangor? 3:05 P.M.

▷ Esteban is delivering produce from Seattle, WA to San Francisco, CA by way of Salt Lake City, UT. How long will the trip take him? 29 hr, 20 min

ELL SUPPORT

SMALL-GROUP ACTIVITY

5–15 Min

▶ Building a Math Word Bank

(*Differentiation Handbook,* p. 140)

To provide language support for estimation, have students use the Word Bank Template found on *Differentiation Handbook,* page 140. Ask students to write the terms *estimation* and *round,* draw pictures representing the terms, and write other words that describe them. See the *Differentiation Handbook* for more information.

5•4 Estimating Products

Objective To provide practice estimating whether a product is in the tens, hundreds, thousands, or more.

www.everydaymathonline.com

ePresentations

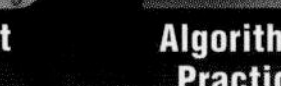
eToolkit

Algorithms Practice

EM Facts Workshop Game™

Family Letters

Assessment Management

Common Core State Standards

Curriculum Focal Points

Interactive Teacher's Lesson Guide

1 Teaching the Lesson

Key Concepts and Skills

- Solve problems involving products where factors are multiples of 10, 100, 1,000, and so on.
  [Operations and Computation Goal 3]
- Estimate whether a product is in the tens, hundreds, thousands, or more.
  [Operations and Computation Goal 6]
- Explore meanings of *average*.
  [Data and Chance Goal 2]

Key Activities

Students make magnitude estimates for products and mark their estimates on a magnitude bar that shows tens, hundreds, thousands, and so on.

Key Vocabulary

rough estimate ◆ magnitude estimate

Materials

Math Journal 1, pp. 114 and 115
Study Link 5•3
Math Masters, p. 147
calculator

2 Ongoing Learning & Practice

Playing *Multiplication Wrestling*
Student Reference Book, p. 253
Math Masters, p. 488
per partnership: 4 each of number cards 0–9 (from the Everything Math Deck, if available) or a ten-sided die
Students practice calculating partial products and finding the sum of the partial products.

Ongoing Assessment: Recognizing Student Achievement
Use *Math Masters,* page 488.
[Patterns, Functions, and Algebra Goal 4]

Math Boxes 5•4
Math Journal 1, p. 116
Students practice and maintain skills through Math Box problems.

Study Link 5•4
Math Masters, p. 148
Students practice and maintain skills through Study Link activities.

3 Differentiation Options

READINESS

Rounding Whole Numbers Using a Number Line
Math Masters, p. 149
Students use curved number lines to practice rounding.

ENRICHMENT

Finding Missing Numbers and Digits
Math Masters, p. 150
Students use estimation to find missing numbers and digits in multiplication number sentences.

EXTRA PRACTICE

5-Minute Math
5-Minute Math™, pp. 19, 95, and 182
Students estimate products.

Advance Preparation

For the Math Message, make one copy of *Math Masters,* page 147 for every three students. Cut the masters apart and place them near the Math Message. For Part 1, find out the total number of fourth graders and the total enrollment in your school.

***Teacher's Reference Manual,* Grades 4–6** pp. 260–264

Getting Started

Mental Math and Reflexes

Continue to focus on multiplying by tens. This work will prepare students for the partial-products algorithm that is introduced in Lesson 5-5. *Suggestions:*

●○○ 5 * 40 = 200
2 * 60 = 120
40 * 20 = 800

●●○ 40 * 60 = 2,400
70 * 30 = 2,100
50 * 90 = 4,500

●●● 60 * 700 = 42,000
70 * 800 = 56,000
90 * 400 = 36,000

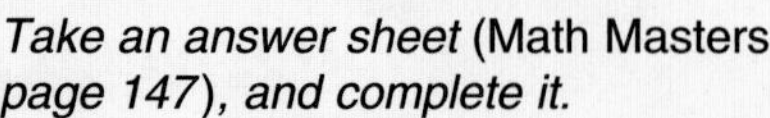

Math Message

Take an answer sheet (Math Masters, *page 147*), *and complete it.*

Study Link 5·3 Follow-Up

Partners compare answers. Have students share their strategies for estimating sums.

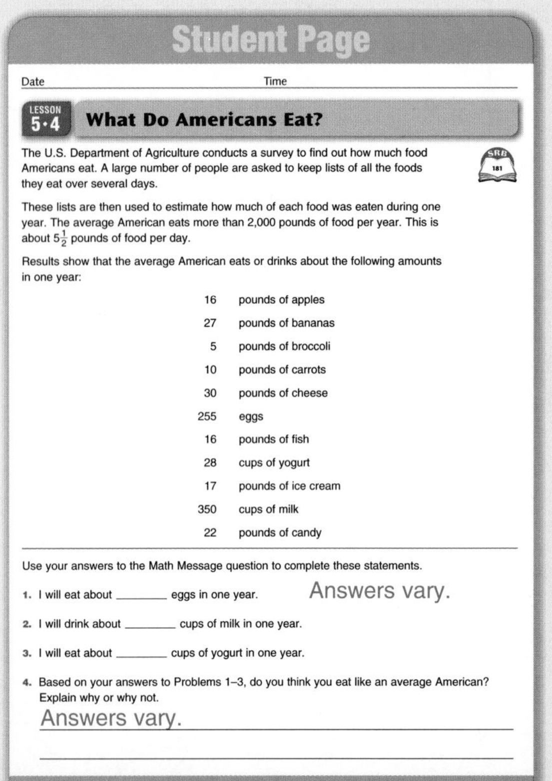

Student Page

Date ______ Time ______

LESSON 5·4 **What Do Americans Eat?**

The U.S. Department of Agriculture conducts a survey to find out how much food Americans eat. A large number of people are asked to keep lists of all the foods they eat over several days.

SRB 181

These lists are then used to estimate how much of each food was eaten during one year. The average American eats more than 2,000 pounds of food per year. This is about $5\frac{1}{2}$ pounds of food per day.

Results show that the average American eats or drinks about the following amounts in one year:

16	pounds of apples
27	pounds of bananas
5	pounds of broccoli
10	pounds of carrots
30	pounds of cheese
255	eggs
16	pounds of fish
28	cups of yogurt
17	pounds of ice cream
350	cups of milk
22	pounds of candy

Use your answers to the Math Message question to complete these statements.

1. I will eat about ______ eggs in one year. Answers vary.
2. I will drink about ______ cups of milk in one year.
3. I will eat about ______ cups of yogurt in one year.
4. Based on your answers to Problems 1–3, do you think you eat like an average American? Explain why or why not.
Answers vary.

Math Journal 1, p. 114

1 Teaching the Lesson

▶ Math Message Follow-Up

WHOLE-CLASS DISCUSSION

(*Math Journal 1,* p. 114)

Ask someone to read aloud the first two paragraphs of "What Do Americans Eat?" on journal page 114. Give students a minute or two to read the survey results and then discuss them. *Suggestions*

- Does any of this information surprise you?
- Do you think any of this information has changed since it was collected? Probably yes. The eating habits of Americans change over time. This survey was taken in 2002.
- What is meant by the "average" American? Does everyone eat more than 2,000 pounds of food per year, or about $5\frac{1}{2}$ pounds per day? Some people eat $5\frac{1}{2}$ pounds of food per day; some eat more than $5\frac{1}{2}$ pounds, and some eat less than $5\frac{1}{2}$ pounds per day. If all the food eaten by all Americans were divided into equal shares, each person's share would then be more than 2,000 pounds of food per year, or about $5\frac{1}{2}$ pounds per day. The average American is one who eats an equal share each day.

▶ Using the Food-Survey Data to Make Magnitude Estimates

WHOLE-CLASS ACTIVITY

(*Math Journal 1,* p. 114; *Math Masters,* p. 147)

Pose problems like the following. Ask students to make **rough estimates** for the answers and describe how they made their estimates. After each estimate is made, ask someone to find the exact answer using a calculator.

- About how many pounds of bananas might the students in our class eat in one year? Will the answer be in the tens, hundreds, thousands, ten-thousands, or more? Sample answer: The average American eats 27 pounds of bananas per year. That is about 30 pounds per year. There are 25 students in our class, so that is about 750 pounds per year. The answer is in the hundreds.
- About how many glasses of milk might *all the fourth-grade students in our school* drink in one year? Will the answer be in the tens, hundreds, thousands, ten-thousands, or more? (You will need to give the fourth-grade school population.)
- About how many cups of yogurt might *all the students in our school* eat in 1 year? Will the answer be in the tens, hundreds, thousands, ten thousands, or more? (You will need to give the school population.) Answers vary.
- About how many eggs might an average family of four eat in 1 year? Will the answer be in the tens, hundreds, thousands, ten thousands, or more? Sample answer: The average person eats 255 eggs per year. A number model for the exact answer is $255 * 4 = \_\_\_$. Round 255 to the nearest hundred to get 300; $300 * 4 = 1{,}200$. Or, round 255 down to 250, because it is a close number and easy to use; $250 * 4 = 1{,}000$. Both rough estimates are in the thousands, but very close to 1,000.
- The average person's life expectancy in the United States is about 77 years. About how many pounds of cheese might an average person eat in a lifetime? Will the answer be in the tens, hundreds, thousands, ten thousands, or more? Thousands, $30 * 80 = 2{,}400$

Finally, have students use their answers in the Math Message to compare their consumption of certain foods to that of an average American. Students must convert their weekly results to 1-year totals. Ask volunteers to describe how they might do this. If no one mentions it, suggest the following procedure:

1. Multiply the total amount eaten in one week by 100. This gives the total amount eaten in 100 weeks, which is about 2 years.
2. Divide the result by 2. This gives the total amount eaten in about 1 year.

Have students record their 1 year totals at the bottom of journal page 114.

NOTE A rough estimate is an estimate of the magnitude of an answer. Will the answer be in the tens? In the hundreds? In the thousands? A rough estimate is also called a **magnitude estimate.**

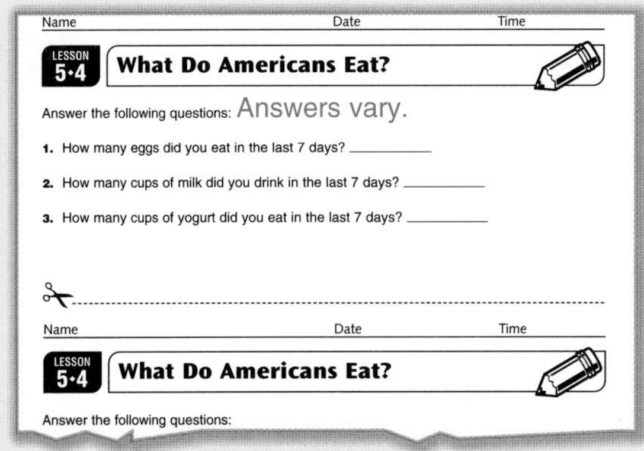
Name Date Time

LESSON 5•4 **What Do Americans Eat?**

Answer the following questions: Answers vary.

1. How many eggs did you eat in the last 7 days? ______
2. How many cups of milk did you drink in the last 7 days? ______
3. How many cups of yogurt did you eat in the last 7 days? ______

Name Date Time

LESSON 5•4 **What Do Americans Eat?**

Answer the following questions:

Math Masters, page 147

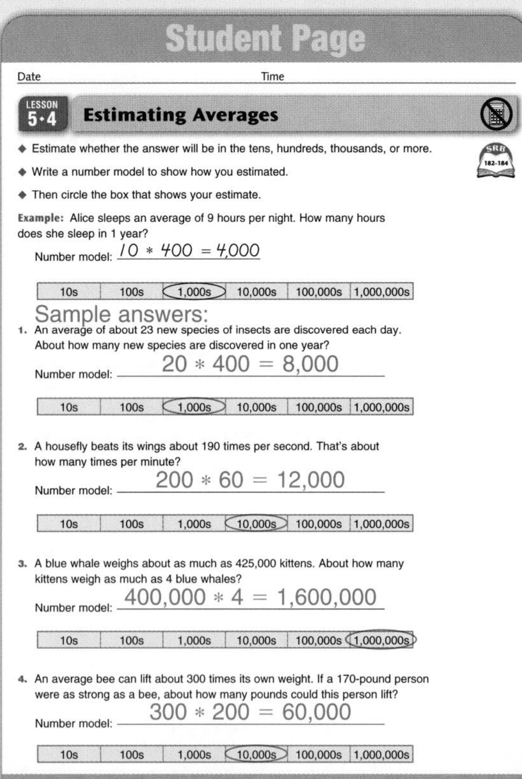
Student Page

Date Time

LESSON 5·4 **Estimating Averages**

- Estimate whether the answer will be in the tens, hundreds, thousands, or more.
- Write a number model to show how you estimated.
- Then circle the box that shows your estimate.

Example: Alice sleeps an average of 9 hours per night. How many hours does she sleep in 1 year?

Number model: $10 * 400 = 4{,}000$

10s	100s	(1,000s)	10,000s	100,000s	1,000,000s

Sample answers:

1. An average of about 23 new species of insects are discovered each day. About how many new species are discovered in one year?

Number model: $20 * 400 = 8{,}000$

10s	100s	(1,000s)	10,000s	100,000s	1,000,000s

2. A housefly beats its wings about 190 times per second. That's about how many times per minute?

Number model: $200 * 60 = 12{,}000$

10s	100s	1,000s	(10,000s)	100,000s	1,000,000s

3. A blue whale weighs about as much as 425,000 kittens. About how many kittens weigh as much as 4 blue whales?

Number model: $400{,}000 * 4 = 1{,}600{,}000$

10s	100s	1,000s	10,000s	100,000s	(1,000,000s)

4. An average bee can lift about 300 times its own weight. If a 170-pound person were as strong as a bee, about how many pounds could this person lift?

Number model: $300 * 200 = 60{,}000$

10s	100s	1,000s	(10,000s)	100,000s	1,000,000s

Math Journal 1, **p. 115**

Estimating Averages

PARTNER ACTIVITY

(*Math Journal 1,* p. 115)

These problems focus on estimating the magnitude of an answer. Students need to make only rough estimates that tell whether the answer will be in the tens, hundreds, thousands, or more.

NOTE This skill is isolated so students will realize the importance of making rough estimates when they solve computation problems with or without a calculator. There will be many opportunities for making more precise estimates in the lessons that follow.

Discuss the example with the class. Students can complete the rest of the page with their partners using any estimation method that works for them. Bring the class together to discuss estimation strategies. Then have students check their estimates by finding the exact answers using a calculator.

Adjusting the Activity

Use the example at the top of journal page 115 to illustrate two meanings for "average sleep time." Ask students how they would determine the average nightly sleep time for the entire class. Then ask students how Alice's average sleep time of 9 hours may have been calculated. Sample answer: Alice's nightly sleep times were recorded for at least one week; for example, M: 9 hr, T: 8 hr, W: 9 hr, Th: 8 hr, F: 7 hr, S: 11 hr, S: 11 hr. The "equal share" mean of 9 hours is a good representation of the data. The longer sleep times on the weekend offset some shorter weekday times like Friday.

AUDITORY ◆ KINESTHETIC ◆ TACTILE ◆ VISUAL

Game Master

Name Date Time

***Multiplication Wrestling* Record Sheet**

Round 1 Cards: ___ ___ ___ ___
Numbers formed: ___ * ___
Teams: (___ + ___) * (___ + ___)
Products: ___ * ___ = ___
___ * ___ = ___
___ * ___ = ___
___ * ___ = ___
Total (add 4 products): ___

Round 2 Cards: ___ ___ ___ ___
Numbers formed: ___ * ___
Teams: (___ + ___) * (___ + ___)
Products: ___ * ___ = ___
___ * ___ = ___
___ * ___ = ___
___ * ___ = ___
Total (add 4 products): ___

Round 3 Cards: ___ ___ ___ ___
Numbers formed: ___ * ___
Teams: (___ + ___) * (___ + ___)
Products: ___ * ___ = ___
___ * ___ = ___
___ * ___ = ___
___ * ___ = ___
Total (add 4 products): ___

Math Masters, **p. 488**

2 Ongoing Learning & Practice

Playing *Multiplication Wrestling*

PARTNER ACTIVITY

(*Student Reference Book,* p. 253; *Math Masters,* p. 488)

Students play *Multiplication Wrestling* to practice calculating partial products and finding the sum of the partial products. See Lesson 5-2 for additional information.

Ongoing Assessment: Recognizing Student Achievement

Math Masters Page 488

Use ***Math Masters,* page 488** to assess students' ability to use the distributive property of multiplication over addition in the context of the partial-products algorithm. Students are making adequate progress if they can write each factor as the sum of tens and ones and find the four partial products.

Some students may be able to demonstrate the use of this property with decimals or mixed numbers. For example, $4.2 * 3.5 = (4 * 3) + (4 * 0.5) + (0.2 * 3) + (0.2 * 0.5)$ or $5\frac{1}{2} * 6\frac{1}{3} = (5 * 6) + (5 * \frac{1}{3}) + (\frac{1}{2} * 6) + (\frac{1}{2} * \frac{1}{3})$.

[Patterns, Functions, and Algebra Goal 4]

Math Boxes 5•4

INDEPENDENT ACTIVITY

(*Math Journal 1,* p. 116)

Mixed Practice Math Boxes in this lesson are paired with Math Boxes in Lesson 5-2. The skill in Problem 5 previews Unit 6 content.

Writing/Reasoning Have students write a response to the following: *For Problem 5, explain a shortcut you might use to solve the division problems.* Sample answer: I used basic division facts to solve the problems. For 350 / 7, I thought 35 / 7 = 5. I know 350 / 7 is 10 times as much, so 350 / 7 = 5 ∗ 10 = 50. For 5,600 / 800, I thought 56 / 8 = 7. 800 ∗ 7 = 5,600, so 7 is the answer.

Study Link 5•4

(*Math Masters,* p. 148)

Home Connection Students make magnitude estimates for multiplication problems. Remind students to write a number model for each estimate.

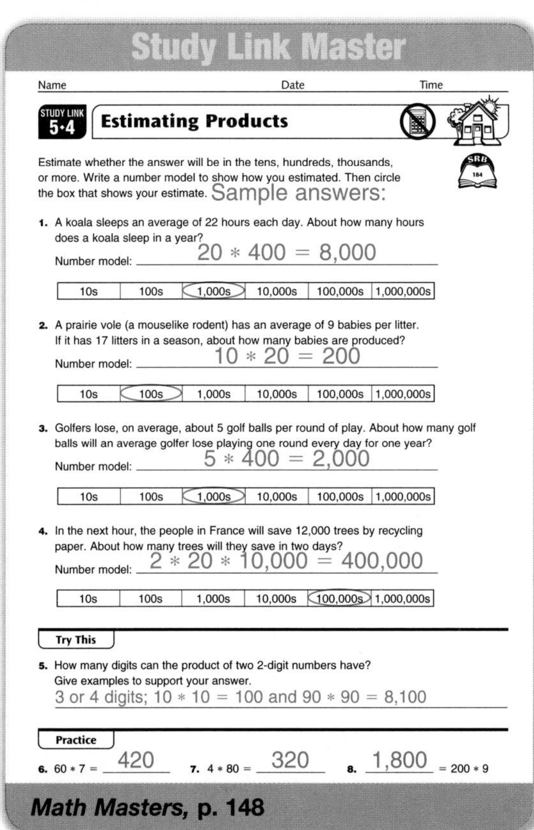

Study Link Master

Name Date Time

STUDY LINK 5•4 **Estimating Products**

Estimate whether the answer will be in the tens, hundreds, thousands, or more. Write a number model to show how you estimated. Then circle the box that shows your estimate. Sample answers:

1. A koala sleeps an average of 22 hours each day. About how many hours does a koala sleep in a year?
Number model: 20 ∗ 400 = 8,000

10s	100s	(1,000s)	10,000s	100,000s	1,000,000s

2. A prairie vole (a mouselike rodent) has an average of 9 babies per litter. If it has 17 litters in a season, about how many babies are produced?
Number model: 10 ∗ 20 = 200

10s	(100s)	1,000s	10,000s	100,000s	1,000,000s

3. Golfers lose, on average, about 5 golf balls per round of play. About how many golf balls will an average golfer lose playing one round every day for one year?
Number model: 5 ∗ 400 = 2,000

10s	100s	(1,000s)	10,000s	100,000s	1,000,000s

4. In the next hour, the people in France will save 12,000 trees by recycling paper. About how many trees will they save in two days?
Number model: 2 ∗ 20 ∗ 10,000 = 400,000

10s	100s	1,000s	10,000s	(100,000s)	1,000,000s

Try This

5. How many digits can the product of two 2-digit numbers have? Give examples to support your answer.
3 or 4 digits; 10 ∗ 10 = 100 and 90 ∗ 90 = 8,100

Practice

6. 60 ∗ 7 = 420
7. 4 ∗ 80 = 320
8. 1,800 = 200 ∗ 9

Math Masters, **p. 148**

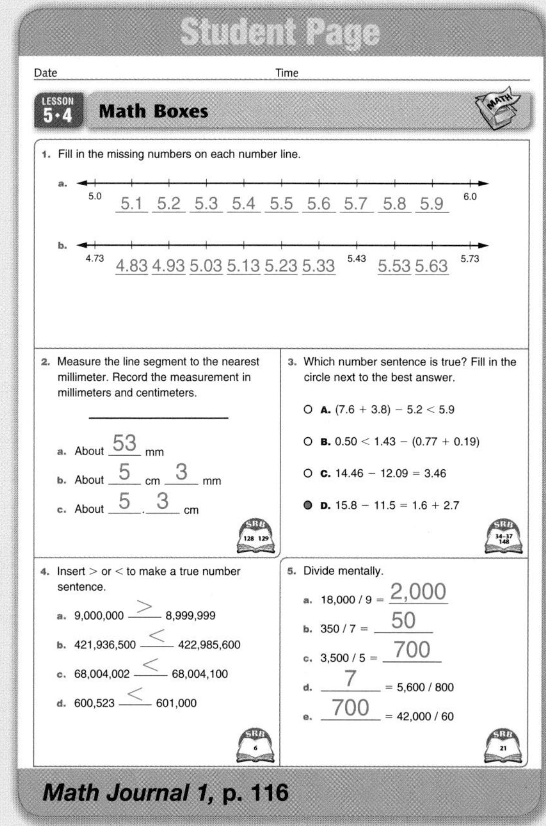

Student Page

Date Time

LESSON 5•4 **Math Boxes**

1. Fill in the missing numbers on each number line.
a. 5.0, 5.1, 5.2, 5.3, 5.4, 5.5, 5.6, 5.7, 5.8, 5.9, 6.0
b. 4.73, 4.83, 4.93, 5.03, 5.13, 5.23, 5.33, 5.43, 5.53, 5.63, 5.73

2. Measure the line segment to the nearest millimeter. Record the measurement in millimeters and centimeters.
a. About 53 mm
b. About 5 cm 3 mm
c. About 5.3 cm

3. Which number sentence is true? Fill in the circle next to the best answer.
○ A. (7.6 + 3.8) − 5.2 < 5.9
○ B. 0.50 < 1.43 − (0.77 + 0.19)
○ C. 14.46 − 12.09 = 3.46
● D. 15.8 − 11.5 = 1.6 + 2.7

4. Insert > or < to make a true number sentence.
a. 9,000,000 > 8,999,999
b. 421,936,500 < 422,985,600
c. 68,004,002 < 68,004,100
d. 600,523 < 601,000

5. Divide mentally.
a. 18,000 / 9 = 2,000
b. 350 / 7 = 50
c. 3,500 / 5 = 700
d. 7 = 5,600 / 800
e. 700 = 42,000 / 60

Math Journal 1, **p. 116**

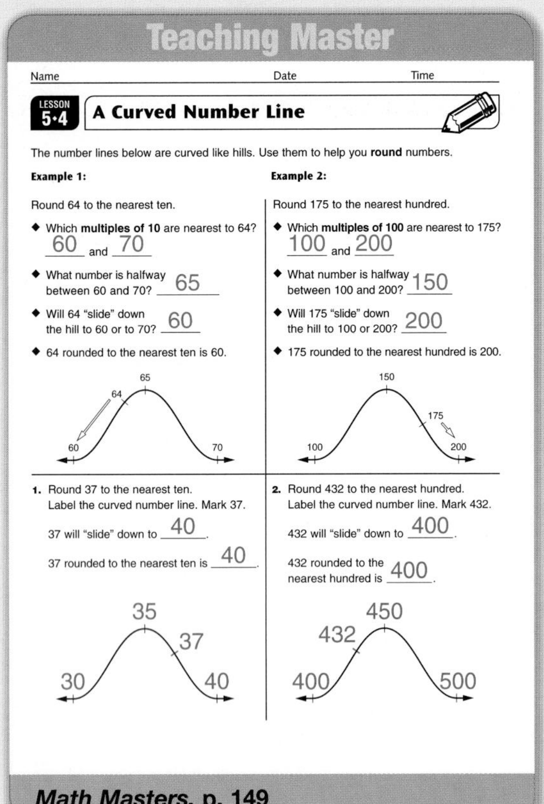

Teaching Master

Name ____________ Date ____________ Time ____________

LESSON 5·4 **A Curved Number Line**

The number lines below are curved like hills. Use them to help you **round** numbers.

Example 1:	**Example 2:**
Round 64 to the nearest ten.	Round 175 to the nearest hundred.
◆ Which **multiples of 10** are nearest to 64? 60 and 70	◆ Which **multiples of 100** are nearest to 175? 100 and 200
◆ What number is halfway between 60 and 70? 65	◆ What number is halfway between 100 and 200? 150
◆ Will 64 "slide" down the hill to 60 or to 70? 60	◆ Will 175 "slide" down the hill to 100 or 200? 200
◆ 64 rounded to the nearest ten is 60.	◆ 175 rounded to the nearest hundred is 200.

1. Round 37 to the nearest ten. Label the curved number line. Mark 37.
   37 will "slide" down to 40.
   37 rounded to the nearest ten is 40.

2. Round 432 to the nearest hundred. Label the curved number line. Mark 432.
   432 will "slide" down to 400.
   432 rounded to the nearest hundred is 400.

Math Masters, **p. 149**

Teaching Master

Name ____________ Date ____________ Time ____________

LESSON 5·4 **Missing Numbers and Digits**

1. Complete the number sentences.
   - Fill in the circles using the numbers 3, 4, 6, or 7.
   - Fill in the rectangles using the numbers 47, 62, 74, or 86.
   - Some numbers will be used more than once.

   a. (7) × [47] = 329
   b. (3) × [86] = 258
   c. (6) × [62] = 372
   d. (4) × [62] = 248
   e. (6) × [74] = 444
   f. (4) × [74] = 296

2. For each problem, fill in the squares using the digits 4, 6, and 7.

   a. 64 × 7 = 448
   b. 46 × 7 = 322
   c. 67 × 4 = 268

3. Use the digits 6, 7, 8, and 9 to make the largest product possible.
   876 × 9 = 7,884

4. Use the digits 6, 7, 8, and 9 to make the smallest product possible.
   789 × 6 = 4,734

Math Masters, **p. 150**

3 Differentiation Options

READINESS

INDEPENDENT ACTIVITY

5–15 Min

▶ Rounding Whole Numbers Using a Number Line

(*Math Masters,* p. 149)

To explore rounding whole numbers, have students plot numbers on a curved number line to see which way the numbers will "slide." Have students describe how they rounded their numbers. Encourage vocabulary such as *top, bottom, endpoint, middle, closer,* and *farther*.

ENRICHMENT

INDEPENDENT ACTIVITY

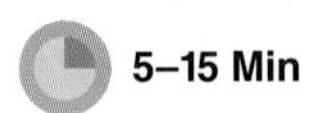

5–15 Min

▶ Finding Missing Numbers and Digits

(*Math Masters,* p. 150)

To apply students' understanding of estimates, have them use estimation to find the missing numbers and digits in multiplication number sentences. Ask students to describe the strategies they used to solve the problems.

EXTRA PRACTICE

SMALL-GROUP ACTIVITY

5–15 Min

▶ *5-Minute Math*

To offer students more experience with estimating products, see *5-Minute Math,* pages 19, 95, and 182.

5•5 Partial-Products Multiplication (Part 1)

Objectives To review and provide practice with the partial-products algorithm for 1-digit multipliers.

Technology Resources www.everydaymathonline.com

ePresentations

eToolkit

Algorithms Practice

EM Facts Workshop Game™

Family Letters

Assessment Management

Common Core State Standards

Curriculum Focal Points

Interactive Teacher's Lesson Guide

1 Teaching the Lesson

Key Concepts and Skills

- Write numbers in expanded notation. [Number and Numeration Goal 4]
- Add multidigit numbers. [Operations and Computation Goal 2]
- Use basic facts to compute extended facts. [Operations and Computation Goal 3]
- Use the partial-products algorithm to solve multiplication problems with 1-digit multipliers. [Operations and Computation Goal 4]
- Estimate whether a product is in the tens, hundreds, thousands, or more. [Operations and Computation Goal 6]
- Apply the Distributive Property of Multiplication over Addition. [Patterns, Functions, and Algebra Goal 4]

Key Activities

Students practice the partial-products algorithm for 1-digit multipliers.

Ongoing Assessment: Informing Instruction See page 339.

Ongoing Assessment: Recognizing Student Achievement Use journal page 118. [Operations and Computation Goal 4]

Key Vocabulary

partial-products method ◆ partial product

Materials

Math Journal 1, pp. 118 and 119
Study Link 5•4
Math Masters, p. 403 or 431
slate

2 Ongoing Learning & Practice

Estimating Lengths Using Personal References
Math Journal 1, pp. 98 and 120
tape measure or ruler
Students use personal references for customary units of length to estimate lengths of objects.

Math Boxes 5•5
Math Journal 1, p. 117
Students practice and maintain skills through Math Box problems.

Study Link 5•5
Math Masters, p. 151
Students practice and maintain skills through Study Link activities.

3 Differentiation Options

READINESS

Modeling Multiplication with Base-10 Blocks
transparencies of *Math Masters,* pp. 432 and 433 ◆ base-10 blocks ◆ erasable marker ◆ transparent tape
Students explore the partial-products algorithm using a concrete model.

READINESS

Exploring Patterns in Extended Facts
Math Masters, p. 152
base-10 blocks
Students explore patterns in extended facts.

ENRICHMENT

Solving an Old Puzzle
Math Masters, p. 153
Students use multiplication to solve an old puzzle about houses, cats, whiskers, and fleas.

Advance Preparation

For the optional Readiness activity in Part 3, make transparencies of *Math Masters,* pages 432 and 433 and tape them together.

***Teacher's Reference Manual,* Grades 4–6** pp. 39, 40, 126–132

Getting Started

Mental Math and Reflexes

Pose extended multiplication facts problems. *Suggestions:*

●○○ 4 * 50 = 200
30 * 7 = 210
6 * 40 = 240

●●○ 20 * 40 = 800
50 * 80 = 4,000
70 * 60 = 4,200

●●● 30 * 500 = 15,000
800 * 700 = 560,000
900 * 600 = 540,000

Math Message

Paul's new baby sister sleeps about 16 hours per day. About how many hours does she sleep in one week?

Study Link 5·4 Follow-Up

Partners compare answers. Students should focus on the number models they wrote for their estimates.

1 Teaching the Lesson

▶ Math Message Follow-Up

Have students share solution strategies.

Students may have tried either of these written strategies:

▷ Use an algorithm to find the product of 7 and 16.

▷ Use repeated addition: Add 16 seven times.

Or, they may have used one of these mental strategies:

▷ Multiply 8 * 7. 56
Double the result. 56 + 56 = 112

▷ Multiply 20 * 7. 140
Subtract 4 * 7 from the result. 140 – 28 = 112

If no one shares it, suggest the following strategy:

▷ Multiply 10 * 7. 70
Multiply 6 * 7. 42
Add the results. 70 + 42 = 112

Tell the class that this last strategy makes use of the place value of each digit. It is the strategy on which the partial-products method, the multiplication method students will review in this lesson, is based.

▶ Finding Products Mentally

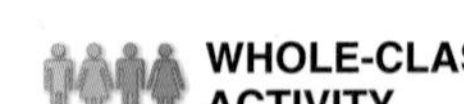

Pose "easy" multiplication problems involving 1-digit times 2-digit numbers. Have students solve them mentally, write the answers on their slates, and at a signal, display the answers. Emphasize to students that they may write partial answers on their slates, but not the original problem. Ask them to circle the final answer.

Discuss solution strategies after each problem. Do not insist that students use the last strategy mentioned in the Math Message Follow-Up, but encourage its use. Keep this activity brief, especially if students can solve the problems with ease. *Suggestions:*

- 3 * 54 = 162
- 8 * 37 = 296
- 24 * 4 = 96
- 6 * 83 = 498
- 7 * 62 = 434
- 15 * 9 = 135

Demonstrating the Partial-Products Algorithm for 1-Digit Multipliers

(*Math Masters,* p. 403 or 431)

Give each student a sheet of computation grid paper (*Math Masters,* page 403 or 431). Write the following problem on the board. If you think your class is not ready to start with a 3-digit factor, start with a 1-digit times 2-digit problem instead.

$$\begin{array}{r} 869 \\ \underline{*\quad 6} \end{array}$$

Ask the class to estimate whether the answer will be in the tens, hundreds, thousands, or more. thousands *About how many thousands?* About 5 thousands, but less than 6 thousands. 869 is close to, but less than, 1,000.

Next, have students find the exact product on their grid paper. Ask a volunteer to demonstrate a solution method on the board. If others used different methods, ask them to demonstrate them.

If no one used the **partial-products method** for multiplying, demonstrate it on the board. (*See margin.*)

▷ In this method, multiplication is usually done from left to right. This ensures that the most important products—the largest ones—are calculated first. But it is not incorrect for a student to multiply from right to left.

▷ Each part of the calculation, that is, each **partial product,** is written on a separate line. Then the partial products are added. This is usually very simple and has the benefit of providing practice with column addition.

Pose a few more multiplication problems until most students seem to understand the partial-products method.

Ongoing Assessment: Informing Instruction

When students are explaining the steps in the partial-products algorithm, watch for those who say "6 * 8": the 8 in the problem to the right, for example, is in the hundreds place and has a value of 800, not 8. Encourage students to think and say "6 [800s]" or "6 * 800." The notation 6 [800s], introduced in *Third Grade Everyday Mathematics*, is read as "6 eight-hundreds."

NOTE Like the addition and subtraction algorithms in Unit 2, the partial-products algorithm is a "low-stress" algorithm. Even if students have used a standard multiplication algorithm or some other multiplication method in the past, ask them to use the partial-products algorithm to solve the problems in this lesson.

	1,000s	100s	10s	1s	
		8	6	9	
*				6	
	4	8	0	0	← 6 [800s] or 6 * 800
		3	6	0	← 6 [60s] or 6 * 60
+			5	4	← 6 [9s] or 6 * 9
	5,	2	1	4	

Student Page

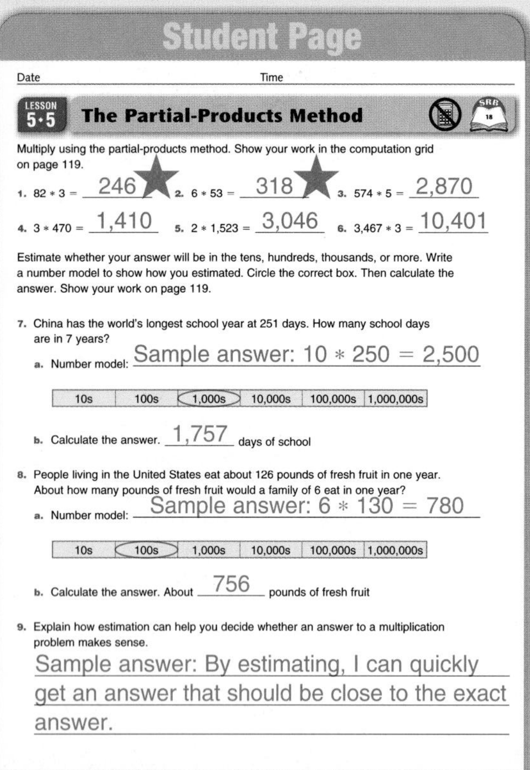

Date Time

LESSON 5·5 **The Partial-Products Method**

Multiply using the partial-products method. Show your work in the computation grid on page 119.

1. 82 * 3 = 246 ★
2. 6 * 53 = 318 ★
3. 574 * 5 = 2,870
4. 3 * 470 = 1,410
5. 2 * 1,523 = 3,046
6. 3,467 * 3 = 10,401

Estimate whether your answer will be in the tens, hundreds, thousands, or more. Write a number model to show how you estimated. Circle the correct box. Then calculate the answer. Show your work on page 119.

7. China has the world's longest school year at 251 days. How many school days are in 7 years?
   a. Number model: Sample answer: $10 * 250 = 2,500$

10s	100s	(1,000s)	10,000s	100,000s	1,000,000s

   b. Calculate the answer. 1,757 days of school

8. People living in the United States eat about 126 pounds of fresh fruit in one year. About how many pounds of fresh fruit would a family of 6 eat in one year?
   a. Number model: Sample answer: $6 * 130 = 780$

10s	(100s)	1,000s	10,000s	100,000s	1,000,000s

   b. Calculate the answer. About 756 pounds of fresh fruit

9. Explain how estimation can help you decide whether an answer to a multiplication problem makes sense.
   Sample answer: By estimating, I can quickly get an answer that should be close to the exact answer.

Math Journal 1, p. 118

Using the Partial-Products Algorithm with 1-Digit Multipliers

INDEPENDENT ACTIVITY

COMPUTATION PRACTICE

(*Math Journal 1,* pp. 118 and 119)

Students complete journal page 118 independently. Partners compare their answers.

Adjusting the Activity

Encourage students to write the number model for the partial products if they are not using mental math to solve the extended facts. *For example:*

$$4 \text{ [300s] or } 4 * 300 = 1,200$$

AUDITORY ◆ KINESTHETIC ◆ TACTILE ◆ VISUAL

Ongoing Assessment: Recognizing Student Achievement

Journal page 118 Problems 1 and 2 ★

Use **journal page 118, Problems 1 and 2** to assess students' ability to use the partial-products algorithm to multiply a 1-digit number by a 2-digit number. Students are making adequate progress if they can correctly calculate and then add the partial products. Some students may be able to solve Problems 3–6, which involve the multiplication of a 1-digit number by a 3- or 4-digit number.

[Operations and Computation Goal 4]

2 Ongoing Learning & Practice

Estimating Lengths Using Personal References

INDEPENDENT ACTIVITY

(*Math Journal 1,* pp. 98 and 120)

Students use their personal references for customary units of length to help them estimate the lengths of various classroom objects in inches, feet, and yards. Then they measure these objects with rulers or tape measures to check the accuracy of their estimates.

Student Page

Date Time

LESSON 5·5 **My Measurement Collection for Units of Length**

Use your personal references on journal page 98 to estimate the length or height of an object or distance in inches, feet, or yards. Describe the object or distance, and record your estimate in the table below. Then measure the object or distance, and record the actual measurement in the table.

SRB 128 130

Object or Distance	Estimated Length	Actual Length
Answers vary.		

Math Journal 1, p. 120

Math Boxes 5·5

INDEPENDENT ACTIVITY

(*Math Journal 1,* p. 117)

Mixed Practice Math Boxes in this lesson are paired with Math Boxes in Lesson 5-7. The skill in Problem 5 previews Unit 6 content.

Writing/Reasoning Have students write a response to the following: *Donato said that there is more than one correct answer for each of the estimates in Problem 2. Do you agree or disagree? Explain.* Sample answer: Yes. There can be more than one correct answer because it depends on the place value to which students round. For example, the following are both reasonable estimates for Problem 2b: 600 + 1,800 + 2,400 = 4,800 and 600 + 2,000 + 2,000 = 4,600.

Study Link 5•5

INDEPENDENT ACTIVITY

(*Math Masters,* p. 151)

Home Connection Students practice using the partial-products algorithm to find products with 1-digit multipliers.

3 Differentiation Options

READINESS

SMALL-GROUP ACTIVITY

Modeling Multiplication with Base-10 Blocks

(*Math Masters,* pp. 432 and 433)

To explore the partial-products algorithm using a concrete model, have students model 1-digit times 2-digit multiplication problems with base-10 blocks. Place taped transparencies of *Math Masters,* pages 432 and 433 on a table. To model 4 ∗ 28, use an erasable marker to mark off a portion of the grid that is 4 squares high and 28 squares wide (4 by 28).

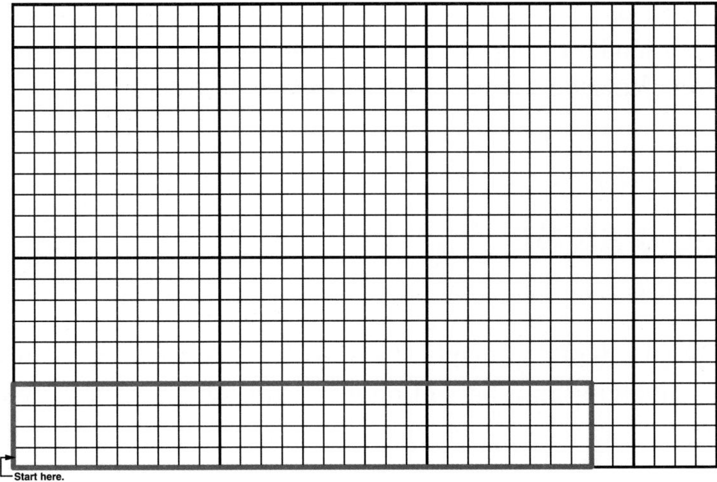

Array model of 4 ∗ 28

Student Page

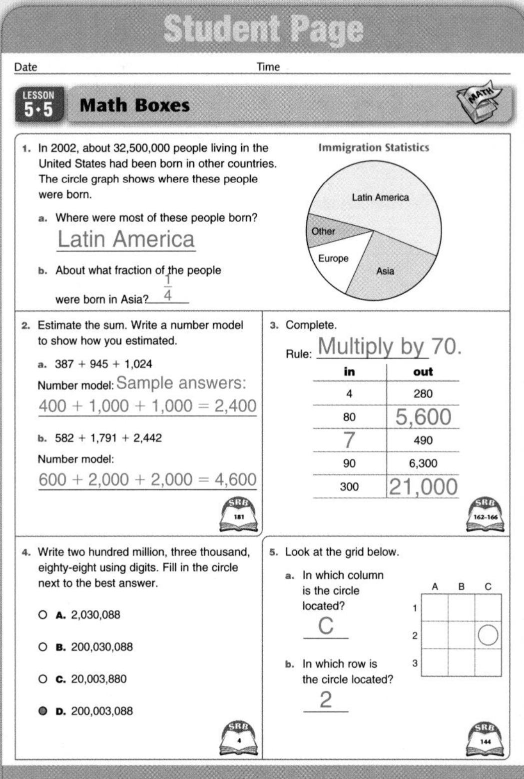

Date Time

LESSON 5•5 **Math Boxes**

1. In 2002, about 32,500,000 people living in the United States had been born in other countries. The circle graph shows where these people were born.
   a. Where were most of these people born? Latin America
   b. About what fraction of the people were born in Asia? $\frac{1}{4}$

2. Estimate the sum. Write a number model to show how you estimated.
   a. 387 + 945 + 1,024
   Number model: Sample answers: 400 + 1,000 + 1,000 = 2,400
   b. 582 + 1,791 + 2,442
   Number model: 600 + 2,000 + 2,000 = 4,600

3. Complete.
   Rule: Multiply by 70.

in	out
4	280
80	5,600
7	490
90	6,300
300	21,000

4. Write two hundred million, three thousand, eighty-eight using digits. Fill in the circle next to the best answer.
   - ○ A. 2,030,088
   - ○ B. 200,030,088
   - ○ C. 20,003,880
   - ● D. 200,003,088

5. Look at the grid below.
   a. In which column is the circle located? C
   b. In which row is the circle located? 2

Math Journal 1, p. 117

Study Link Master

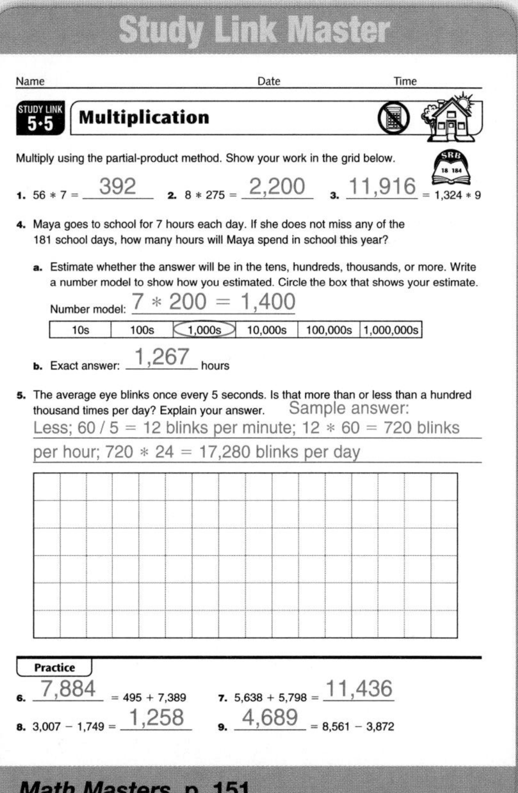

Name Date Time

STUDY LINK 5•5 **Multiplication**

Multiply using the partial-product method. Show your work in the grid below.

1. 56 ∗ 7 = 392
2. 8 ∗ 275 = 2,200
3. 11,916 = 1,324 ∗ 9
4. Maya goes to school for 7 hours each day. If she does not miss any of the 181 school days, how many hours will Maya spend in school this year?
   a. Estimate whether the answer will be in the tens, hundreds, thousands, or more. Write a number model to show how you estimated. Circle the box that shows your estimate.
   Number model: 7 ∗ 200 = 1,400

10s	100s	(1,000s)	10,000s	100,000s	1,000,000s

   b. Exact answer: 1,267 hours
5. The average eye blinks once every 5 seconds. Is that more than or less than a hundred thousand times per day? Explain your answer. Sample answer: Less; 60 / 5 = 12 blinks per minute; 12 ∗ 60 = 720 blinks per hour; 720 ∗ 24 = 17,280 blinks per day

Practice

6. 7,884 = 495 + 7,389
7. 5,638 + 5,798 = 11,436
8. 3,007 − 1,749 = 1,258
9. 4,689 = 8,561 − 3,872

Math Masters, p. 151

Teaching Master

Name Date Time

LESSON 5·5 **Patterns in Extended Facts**

1. Use base-10 blocks to help you solve the problems in the first 2 columns. Use the patterns to help you solve the problems in the third column. Use a calculator to check your work.

2 * 1 = 2	20 * 1 = 20	200 * 1 = 200
2 * 10 = 20	20 * 10 = 200	200 * 10 = 2,000
2 * 100 = 200	20 * 100 = 2,000	200 * 100 = 20,000

2. Use what you learned in Problem 1 to help you solve the problems in the table below. Use a calculator to check your work.

2 * 4 = 8	20 * 4 = 80	200 * 4 = 800
2 * 40 = 80	20 * 40 = 800	200 * 40 = 8,000
2 * 400 = 800	20 * 400 = 8,000	200 * 400 = 80,000

3. Explain how knowing 2 * 4 can help you find the answer to 20 * 40.
Sample answer: I know 2 * 4 = 8, so 20 * 40 is just 8 with two zeros added on, or 800. I added on two zeros because there is a total of two zeros in the numerals 20 and 40.

4. Make up and solve some problems of your own that use this pattern.
Answers vary.

Math Masters, p. 152

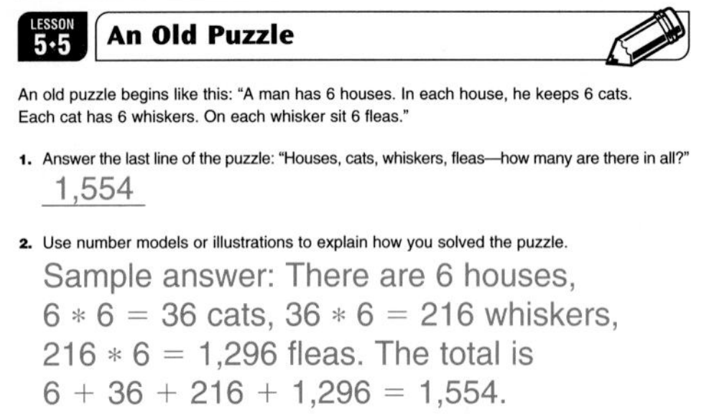

Name Date Time

LESSON 5·5 **An Old Puzzle**

An old puzzle begins like this: "A man has 6 houses. In each house, he keeps 6 cats. Each cat has 6 whiskers. On each whisker sit 6 fleas."

1. Answer the last line of the puzzle: "Houses, cats, whiskers, fleas—how many are there in all?"
1,554

2. Use number models or illustrations to explain how you solved the puzzle.
Sample answer: There are 6 houses, 6 * 6 = 36 cats, 36 * 6 = 216 whiskers, 216 * 6 = 1,296 fleas. The total is 6 + 36 + 216 + 1,296 = 1,554.

Math Masters, page 153

Ask students to cover the array using as few base-10 blocks as possible.

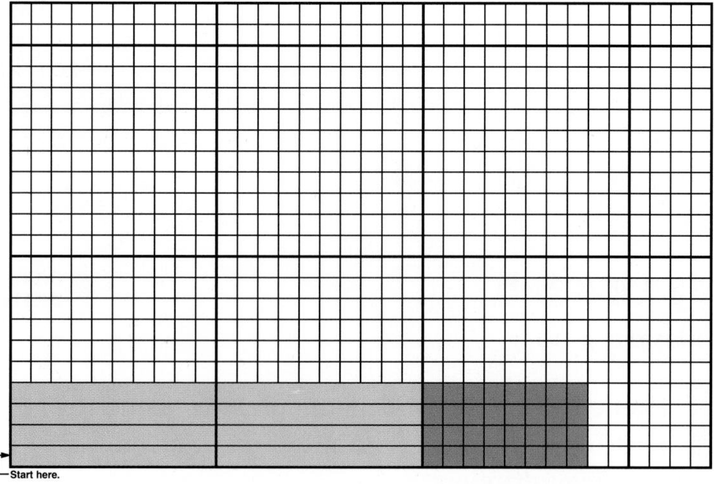

Base-10 block model of 4 * 28

Now match each part of the 4-by-28 array with a partial product.

- ▷ There are 2 longs in each of 4 rows. These cover $4 * 20 = 80$ squares.
- ▷ There are 8 cubes in each of 4 rows. These cover $4 * 8 = 32$ squares.
- ▷ The longs and cubes cover $80 + 32 = 112$ squares in all.

Erase the transparencies. Use the transparencies and base-10 blocks to solve additional 1-digit times 2-digit problems.

READINESS

PARTNER ACTIVITY

▶ Exploring Patterns in Extended Facts

5–15 Min

(*Math Masters,* p. 152)

To explore patterns in extended facts, have students use base-10 blocks to model the problems on *Math Masters,* page 152. Have students describe the patterns they see in Problem 1.

ENRICHMENT

PARTNER ACTIVITY

▶ Solving an Old Puzzle

5–15 Min

(*Math Masters,* p. 153)

To apply students' multiplication skills, have them solve an old puzzle involving numbers of houses, cats, whiskers, and fleas.

5•6 Partial-Products Multiplication (Part 2)

Objectives To introduce and provide practice with the partial-products algorithm for 2-digit multipliers.

Technology Resources www.everydaymathonline.com

ePresentations

eToolkit

Algorithms Practice

EM Facts Workshop Game™

Family Letters

Assessment Management

Common Core State Standards

Curriculum Focal Points

Interactive Teacher's Lesson Guide

1 Teaching the Lesson

Key Concepts and Skills

- Write numbers in expanded notation. [Number and Numeration Goal 4]
- Use the partial-products algorithm to solve multiplication problems with 2-digit multipliers. [Operations and Computation Goal 4]
- Estimate whether a product is in the tens, hundreds, thousands, or more. [Operations and Computation Goal 6]
- Apply the Distributive Property of Multiplication over Addition. [Patterns, Functions, and Algebra Goal 4]

Key Activities

Students learn how to extend the partial-products algorithm to 2-digit multipliers. They make rough estimates and then use the partial-products method.

Ongoing Assessment: Recognizing Student Achievement Use Mental Math and Reflexes. [Operations and Computation Goal 6]

Ongoing Assessment: Informing Instruction See page 345.

Materials

Math Journal 1, pp. 122 and 123
Study Link 5•5
Math Masters, p. 403 or 431; p. 388 or 389 (optional)
slate

2 Ongoing Learning & Practice

Playing *Name That Number*
Student Reference Book, p. 254
Math Masters, p. 489 (optional)
per partnership: deck of number cards (the Everything Math Deck, if available)
Students practice representing numbers in different ways.

Math Boxes 5•6
Math Journal 1, p. 121
Students practice and maintain skills through Math Box problems.

Study Link 5•6
Math Masters, p. 154
Students practice and maintain skills through Study Link activities.

3 Differentiation Options

READINESS
Modeling Multiplication with Base-10 Blocks
transparencies of *Math Masters,* pp. 432 and 433 ◆ base-10 blocks ◆ erasable marker ◆ transparent tape
Students explore the partial-products algorithm using a concrete model.

ENRICHMENT
Scoring a Dart Game
Math Masters, p. 155
Students solve a multistep number story involving a dart game.

ENRICHMENT
Solving Venn Diagram Puzzles
Math Masters, p. 156
Students apply their understanding of extended multiplication and division facts.

ENRICHMENT
Writing Multiplication Number Stories
Students write and solve multiplication number stories.

Advance Preparation

For Part 1, place copies of *Math Masters,* page 403 or 431 near the Math Message. For the optional Readiness activity in Part 3, make transparencies of *Math Masters,* pages 432 and 433, and tape them together.

***Teacher's Reference Manual,* Grades 4–6** pp. 39, 40, 126–132, 260, 261

Getting Started

Mental Math and Reflexes ★

Write multiplication problems on the board. Have students write number models to show their estimates. *Suggestions:* Sample answers are given.

●○○ 3 * 52 3 * 50 = 150
4 * 26 4 * 30 = 120
9 * 74 10 * 74 = 740

●●○ 8 * 632 8 * 600 = 4,800
6 * 569 6 * 600 = 3,600
3 * 248 3 * 250 = 750

●●● 2 * 7,414 2 * 7,500 = 15,000
5 * 8,299 5 * 8,000 = 40,000
7 * 6,172 7 * 6,000 = 42,000

Math Message

Solve the following problems on a computation grid:

*4 * 29 =* 116 *803 * 6 =* 4,818

*3 * 260 =* 780 *418 * 7 =* 2,926

Study Link 5·5 Follow-Up

Have students compare answers and share how they decided whether an average person blinks more than or fewer than 100,000 times per day.

NOTE For additional practice using a standard procedure for rounding whole numbers to the nearest ten and hundred, see www.everydaymathonline.com.

Ongoing Assessment: Recognizing Student Achievement

Mental Math and Reflexes ★

Use **Mental Math and Reflexes** to assess students' ability to estimate reasonable solutions to whole-number multiplication problems. Students are making adequate progress if they can write appropriate number models for the ●○○ and ●●○ problems. Some students may be able to estimate products for the ●●● problems.

[Operations and Computation Goal 6]

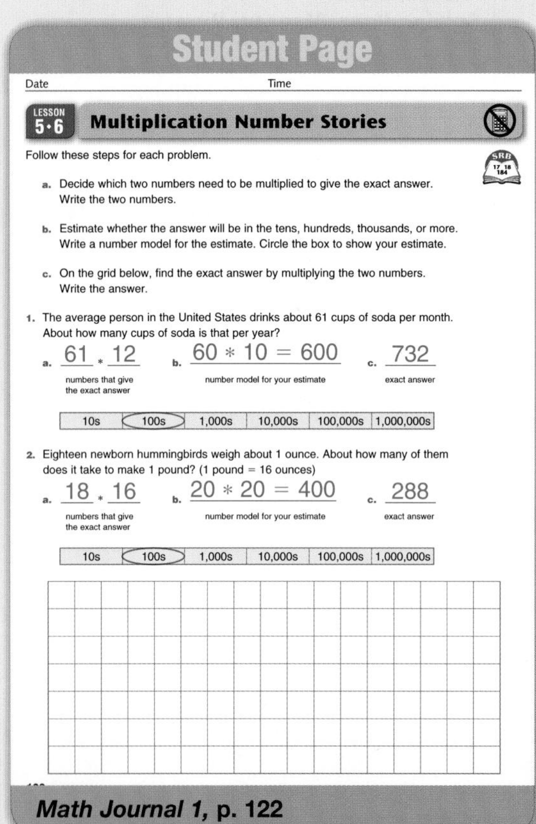

Student Page

Date Time

LESSON 5·6 **Multiplication Number Stories**

SRB 17 18 184

Follow these steps for each problem.

a. Decide which two numbers need to be multiplied to give the exact answer. Write the two numbers.

b. Estimate whether the answer will be in the tens, hundreds, thousands, or more. Write a number model for the estimate. Circle the box to show your estimate.

c. On the grid below, find the exact answer by multiplying the two numbers. Write the answer.

1. The average person in the United States drinks about 61 cups of soda per month. About how many cups of soda is that per year?

a. 61 * 12 (numbers that give the exact answer) b. 60 * 10 = 600 (number model for your estimate) c. 732 (exact answer)

10s	(100s)	1,000s	10,000s	100,000s	1,000,000s

2. Eighteen newborn hummingbirds weigh about 1 ounce. About how many of them does it take to make 1 pound? (1 pound = 16 ounces)

a. 18 * 16 (numbers that give the exact answer) b. 20 * 20 = 400 (number model for your estimate) c. 288 (exact answer)

10s	(100s)	1,000s	10,000s	100,000s	1,000,000s

Math Journal 1, p. 122

1 Teaching the Lesson

▶ Math Message Follow-Up

WHOLE-CLASS DISCUSSION

Go over the answers. Ask:

- How would you solve 4 * 29 in your head? Sample answer: Multiply 4 * 30 and then subtract 4 from the product.
- How would you solve 803 * 6 in your head? Sample answer: Multiply 800 * 6 and 3 * 6 and then add the two products.

▶ Estimating Products

PARTNER ACTIVITY

(*Math Journal 1,* pp. 122 and 123)

Tell students that in this lesson they will apply the partial-products algorithm to multiply a 2-digit number by a 2-digit number.

For each problem on pages 122 and 123, students first decide which two numbers need to be multiplied to give the exact answer (Step a). In Step b, they make a rough estimate of that product and write a number model that shows how they made that estimate. They should not do Step c at this time. Do Problem 1 as a class:

Step a An average person drinks about 61 cups of soda in 1 month. In 1 year, a person will drink 12 times that amount. To find the amount of soda a person drinks in one year, you would multiply 12 ∗ 61. Write 12 ∗ 61, but do not calculate the exact answer at this time.

Step b To estimate the answer, round 12 to 10 and write a number model for the rough estimate: 10 ∗ 61 = 610. Or round 61 to 60 and write a number model for the rough estimate: 12 ∗ 60 = 720. Looking at the number models, you can tell that the answer will be in the hundreds, so circle "100s."

Have students work with a partner to complete Steps a and b for the rest of the problems.

Student Page

Date Time

LESSON 5·6 **Multiplication Number Stories** *continued*

3. A test found that a lightbulb lasts an average of 63 days after being turned on. About how many hours is that?

a. 63 , 24 (numbers that give the exact answer) b. 60 ∗ 20 = 1,200 (number model for your estimate) c. 1,512 (exact answer)

10s | 100s | (1,000s) | 10,000s | 100,000s | 1,000,000s

4. A full-grown oak tree loses about 78 gallons of water through its leaves per day. About how many gallons of water is that per year?

a. 78 , 365 (numbers that give the exact answer) b. 80 ∗ 400 = 32,000 (number model for your estimate) c. 28,470 (exact answer)

10s | 100s | 1,000s | (10,000s) | 100,000s | 1,000,000s

Math Journal 1, p. 123

Extending the Partial-Products Algorithm to 2-Digit Multipliers

(*Math Journal 1,* pp. 122 and 123)

Demonstrate how to use the partial-products algorithm to find the exact answer and check the estimate for Problem 1 on journal page 122. (*See margin.*) Work from left to right. Point out that each part of one factor is multiplied by each part of the other factor.

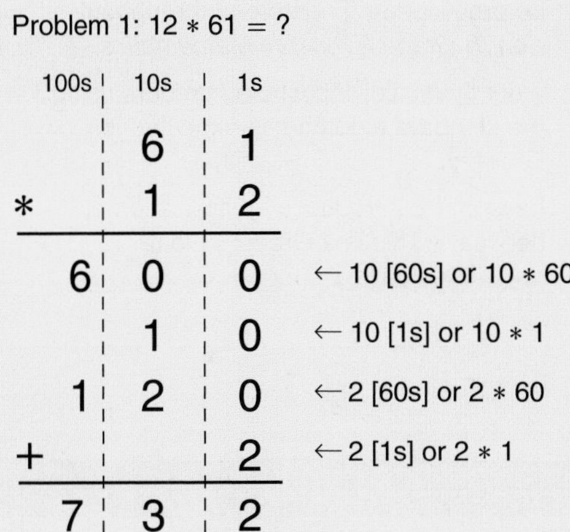

Problem 1: 12 ∗ 61 = ?
100s 10s 1s
6 1
∗ 1 2
6 0 0 ← 10 [60s] or 10 ∗ 60
1 0 ← 10 [1s] or 10 ∗ 1
1 2 0 ← 2 [60s] or 2 ∗ 60
+ 2 ← 2 [1s] or 2 ∗ 1
7 3 2

Ongoing Assessment: Informing Instruction

As students say each step, watch for those who say, for example "1 times 6" instead of "10 sixties" or "10 times 60." Remind students to consider the value of each digit.

Do several more problems with the class. *Suggestions:*

- 18 ∗ 52 = 936
- 29 ∗ 73 = 2,117
- 26 ∗ 34 = 884
- 28 ∗ 434 = 12,152

Adjusting the Activity

Organize the multiplication problems as follows:
12 ∗ 61 = (10 + 2) ∗ (60 + 1)

	60	1
10	600	10
2	120	2

Students then add the partial products in the table to find the total: 600 + 10 + 120 + 2 = 732.

AUDITORY ◆ KINESTHETIC ◆ TACTILE ◆ VISUAL

Algorithm Project The focus of this lesson is partial products. To teach U.S. traditional multiplication, see Algorithm Project 5 on page A21.

▶ Using the Partial-Products Algorithm

PARTNER ACTIVITY
COMPUTATION PRACTICE

(*Math Journal 1,* pp. 122 and 123)

Students complete the remaining problems on journal pages 122 and 123 in the same way. They check their estimates and complete Step c by finding the exact answer using the partial-products algorithm.

Adjusting the Activity

Ask students to respond to the following question in a Math Log or on an Exit Slip (*Math Masters,* page 388 or 389): *Explain how the partial-products algorithm is similar to finding a team's score in a game of* Multiplication Wrestling.

Look for students to note that every part of one factor is multiplied by every part of the other factor.

AUDITORY ◆ KINESTHETIC ◆ TACTILE ◆ VISUAL

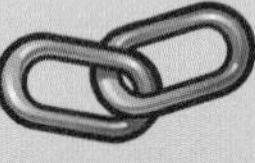

Links to the Future

Do not expect all students to master the partial-products algorithm for two 2-digit multipliers at this time. This algorithm will be practiced and reinforced throughout *Fourth Grade Everyday Mathematics.*

Fluently multiplying whole numbers using the standard algorithm is expected in Grade 5.

Lesson 9-8 introduces multiplication of decimals. This is a Grade 5 Goal.

2 Ongoing Learning & Practice

▶ Playing *Name That Number*

PARTNER ACTIVITY

(*Student Reference Book,* p. 254; *Math Masters,* p. 489)

Students play *Name That Number* to practice representing numbers in different ways. See Lesson 2-2 for additional information.

▶ Math Boxes 5•6

INDEPENDENT ACTIVITY

(*Math Journal 1,* p. 121)

Mixed Practice Math Boxes in this lesson are linked with Math Boxes in Lessons 5-8 and 5-10. The skill in Problem 5 previews Unit 6 content.

Writing/Reasoning Have students write a response to the following: *Devon wrote 342,000 for Problem 4a. Explain the error he might have made.* Sample answer: He wrote 342 thousands, not 342 thousandths.

Student Page

Date Time

LESSON 5•6 **Math Boxes**

1. a. Measure the line segment to the nearest $\frac{1}{4}$ inch.
About 5 inches
b. Draw a line segment that is half as long as the one above.
c. How long is the line segment you drew? About $2\frac{1}{2}$ inches

2. Estimate the product. Write a number model to show how you estimated.
a. 48 * 21
Number model: Sample answers: 50 * 20 = 1,000
b. 98 * 72
Number model: 100 * 70 = 7,000

3. Multiply. Use the partial-products method.
2,236 = 52 * 43

			4	3
	*		5	2
	2	0	0	0
		1	5	0
			8	0
+				6
	2	2	3	6

4. Write each number using digits.
a. three hundred forty-two thousandths
0.342
b. six and twenty-five hundredths
6.25

5. If you remove 7 gallons per day from a 65-gallon water tank, how many days will it take to empty the tank?
About 10 days

Math Journal 1, p. 121

▶ Study Link 5•6

INDEPENDENT ACTIVITY
COMPUTATION PRACTICE

(*Math Masters,* p. 154)

Home Connection Students practice using the partial-products algorithm with 2-digit multipliers.

3 Differentiation Options

READINESS

SMALL-GROUP ACTIVITY

15–30 Min

Modeling Multiplication with Base-10 Blocks

(*Math Masters,* pp. 432 and 433)

To explore the partial-products algorithm using a concrete model, have students use base-10 blocks to model multiplication problems involving two 2-digit numbers.

Place taped transparencies of *Math Masters,* pages 432 and 433 on a table. To model 17 ∗ 32, use an erasable marker to mark off a portion of the grid that is 17 squares high and 32 squares wide (17 by 32).

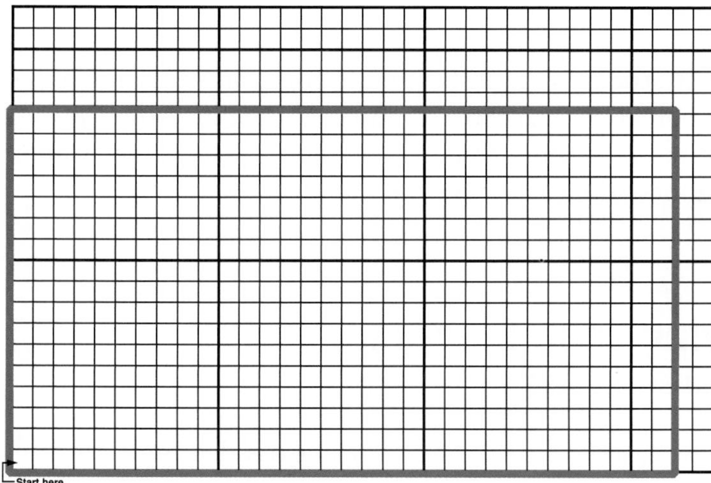

Array model of 17 ∗ 32

Ask students to cover the array using as few base-10 blocks (flats, longs, and cubes) as possible.

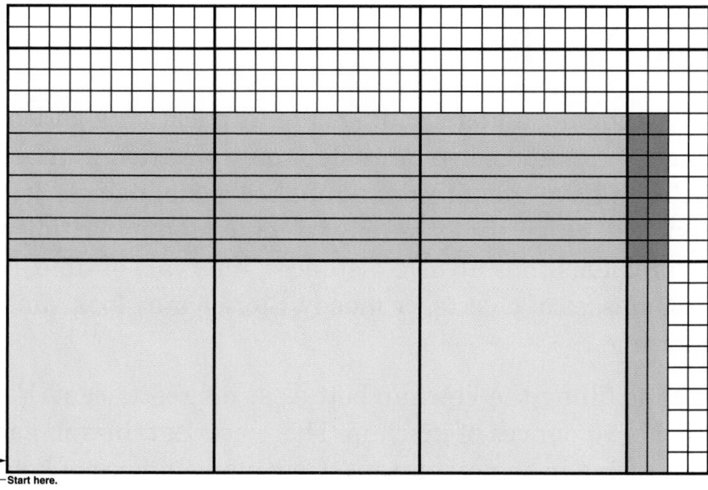

Base-10 block model of 17 ∗ 32

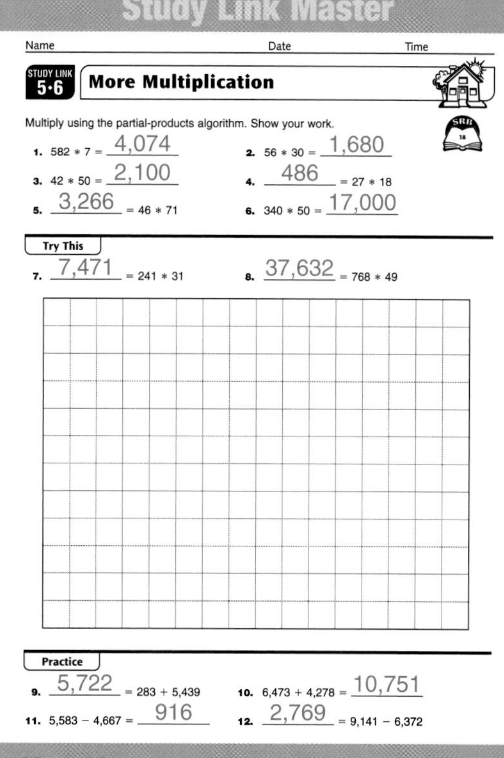

Study Link Master

Name Date Time

STUDY LINK 5·6 **More Multiplication**

Multiply using the partial-products algorithm. Show your work.

1. 582 ∗ 7 = 4,074
2. 56 ∗ 30 = 1,680
3. 42 ∗ 50 = 2,100
4. 486 = 27 ∗ 18
5. 3,266 = 46 ∗ 71
6. 340 ∗ 50 = 17,000

Try This

7. 7,471 = 241 ∗ 31
8. 37,632 = 768 ∗ 49

Practice

9. 5,722 = 283 + 5,439
10. 6,473 + 4,278 = 10,751
11. 5,583 − 4,667 = 916
12. 2,769 = 9,141 − 6,372

Math Masters, p. 154

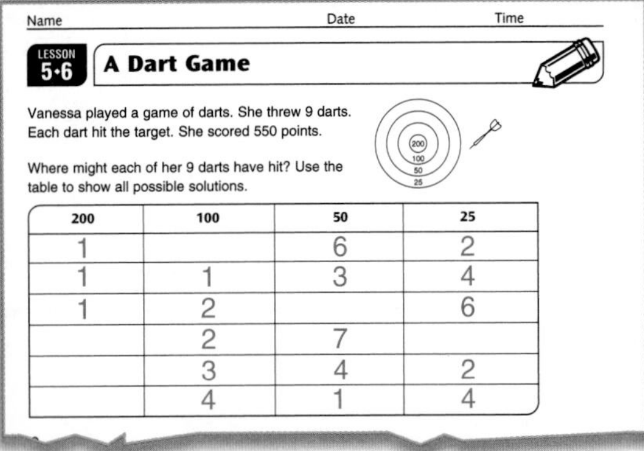

Name Date Time

LESSON 5·6 **A Dart Game**

Vanessa played a game of darts. She threw 9 darts. Each dart hit the target. She scored 550 points.

Where might each of her 9 darts have hit? Use the table to show all possible solutions.

200	100	50	25
1		6	2
1	1	3	4
1	2		6
	2	7	
	3	4	2
	4	1	4

Math Masters, page 155

Now match each part of the 17-by-32 array with a partial product.

▷ Match the 3 flats with $10 * 30 = 300$. These cover 300 squares.

▷ Match the 2 vertical longs with $10 * 2 = 20$. These cover 20 squares.

▷ There are 7 rows with 3 longs in each row. These cover $7 * 30 = 210$ squares.

▷ There are 7 rows with 2 cubes in each row. These cover $7 * 2 = 14$ squares.

▷ There are 544 $(300 + 20 + 210 + 14)$ cubes in all.

Erase the transparencies. Use the transparencies and base-10 blocks to model and solve other 2-digit-times-2-digit problems.

ENRICHMENT

INDEPENDENT ACTIVITY

▶ Scoring a Dart Game

5–15 Min

(*Math Masters,* p. 155)

To apply students' multidigit multiplication skills, have them use various strategies to solve a multistep number story involving a dart game with more than one possible answer. Ask students to explain how they know they found all the solutions.

ENRICHMENT

PARTNER ACTIVITY

▶ Solving Venn Diagram Puzzles

5–15 Min

(*Math Masters,* p. 156)

To apply students' understanding of extended multiplication and division facts, have them solve Venn diagram puzzles based on factors.

ENRICHMENT

PARTNER ACTIVITY

▶ Writing Multiplication Number Stories

5–15 Min

To apply students' understanding of multiplication algorithms, have them write and solve multistep multiplication number stories. Then have them record a number model using a letter for the unknown. Some students may be interested in writing and solving problems that involve distances, intervals of time, liquid volumes, masses of objects, or money. Stories may look similar to the following:

▷ Simon is filling the ketchup bottles at his restaurant. Each bottle holds 16 ounces of ketchup. There are 12 tables in each room and 3 rooms in the restaurant. How many ounces of ketchup will he need to fill one bottle for each table? Answer: 576 oz; Number model with unknown: $(12 * 3) * 16 = n$; Number model with answer: $(12 * 3) * 16 = 576$

Provide opportunities for students to revise and share their writing. Then have partners solve each other's problems.

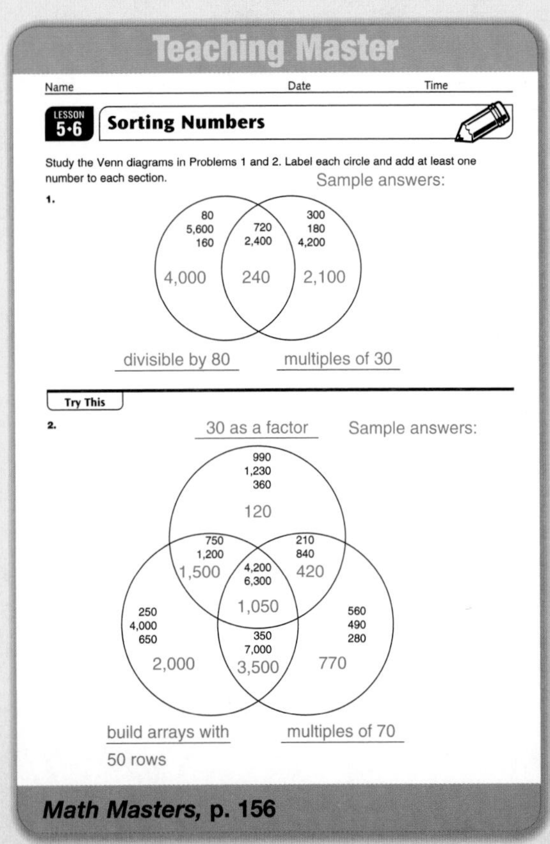

Teaching Master

Name Date Time

LESSON 5·6 **Sorting Numbers**

Study the Venn diagrams in Problems 1 and 2. Label each circle and add at least one number to each section.

Sample answers:

1\. divisible by 80: 80, 5,600, 160, 4,000
Both: 720, 2,400, 240
multiples of 30: 300, 180, 4,200, 2,100

Try This

2\. Sample answers:
30 as a factor: 990, 1,230, 360, 120
30 as a factor and build arrays with 50 rows: 750, 1,200, 1,500
30 as a factor and multiples of 70: 210, 840, 420
All three: 4,200, 6,300, 1,050
build arrays with 50 rows: 250, 4,000, 650, 2,000
build arrays with 50 rows and multiples of 70: 350, 7,000, 3,500
multiples of 70: 560, 490, 280, 770

Math Masters, p. 156

5•7 Lattice Multiplication

Objectives To review and provide practice with the lattice method for multiplication.

www.everydaymathonline.com

ePresentations

eToolkit

Algorithms Practice

EM Facts Workshop Game™

Family Letters

Assessment Management

Common Core State Standards

Curriculum Focal Points

Interactive Teacher's Lesson Guide

1 Teaching the Lesson

Key Concepts and Skills

- Add single-digit numbers. [Operations and Computation Goal 2]
- Solve basic multiplication facts. [Operations and Computation Goal 3]
- Use the lattice method to solve multiplication problems with 1- and 2-digit multipliers. [Operations and Computation Goal 4]

Key Activities

Students review the lattice method for multiplication with 1- and 2-digit multipliers. They practice using this multiplication algorithm.

Key Vocabulary

lattice ◆ lattice method (for multiplication)

Materials

Math Journal 1, p. 124
Study Link 5•6
Math Masters, p. 434
transparency of *Math Masters,* p. 434 (optional) ◆ slate ◆ index cards (optional) ◆ dictionary (optional)

2 Ongoing Learning & Practice

Playing *Multiplication Top-It*
Student Reference Book, p. 264
Math Masters, p. 506
per partnership: 4 each of number cards 1–10 (from the Everything Math Deck, if available)
Students practice multiplication facts.

Ongoing Assessment: Recognizing Student Achievement
Use *Math Masters*, page 506.
[Operations and Computation Goal 3]

Math Boxes 5•7
Math Journal 1, p. 125
Students practice and maintain skills through Math Box problems.

Study Link 5•7
Math Masters, p. 157
Students practice and maintain skills through Study Link activities.

3 Differentiation Options

READINESS

Exploring Fact Lattice Patterns
Math Masters, pp. 161 and 435
Multiplication/Division Facts Table ◆ colored pencils
Students explore the use of the lattice grid for multiplication.

ENRICHMENT

Investigating Napier's Rods
Math Masters, pp. 158–160
scissors
Students investigate Napier's Rods, a seventeenth-century multiplication method.

ELL SUPPORT

Creating Visuals for Multiplication Algorithms
chart paper ◆ markers ◆ colored pencils
Students make posters to display multiplication algorithms.

Advance Preparation

***Teacher's Reference Manual,* Grades 4–6** pp. 126–132

Getting Started

Mental Math and Reflexes

Pose multiplication facts and extended facts. *Suggestions:*

●○○ 5 ∗ 6 = 30
6 ∗ 3 = 18
6 ∗ 4 = 24
7 ∗ 3 = 21

●●○ 7 ∗ 4 = 28
9 ∗ 8 = 72
8 ∗ 7 = 56
7 ∗ 7 = 49

●●● 6 ∗ 60 = 360
8 ∗ 50 = 400
70 ∗ 90 = 6,300
80 ∗ 30 = 2,400

Math Message

What do you think the missing digits are?

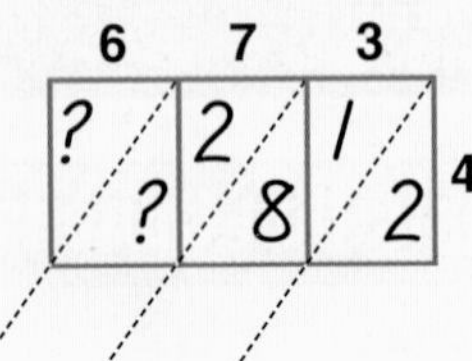

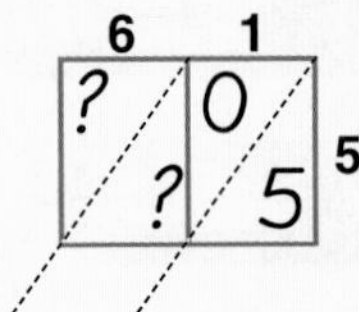

Study Link 5·6 Follow-Up

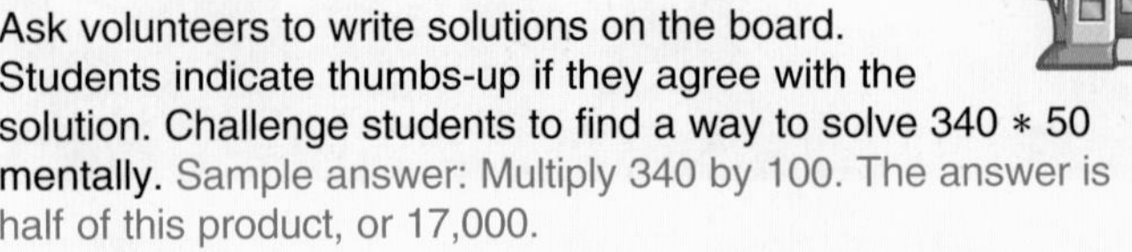

Ask volunteers to write solutions on the board. Students indicate thumbs-up if they agree with the solution. Challenge students to find a way to solve 340 ∗ 50 mentally. Sample answer: Multiply 340 by 100. The answer is half of this product, or 17,000.

Algorithm Project The focus of this lesson is lattice multiplication. To teach U.S. traditional multiplication, see Algorithm Project 5 on page A21.

Links to the Future

Fluently multiplying whole numbers using the standard algorithm is expected in Grade 5.

1 Teaching the Lesson

▶ Math Message Follow-Up

Students share answers. The pair of digits in each cell names the product of two digits outside the **lattice**—one above the cell of the lattice and the other to the right of the cell of the lattice. Thus, the missing digits in the first lattice form the product of 6 and 4 (24). The missing digits in the second lattice form the product of 6 and 5 (30).

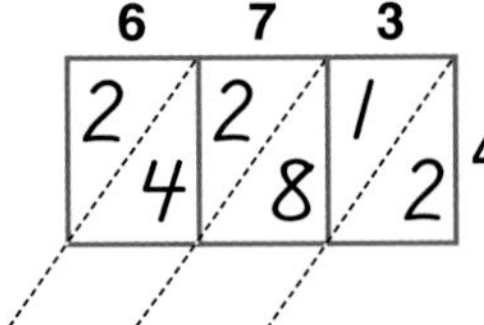

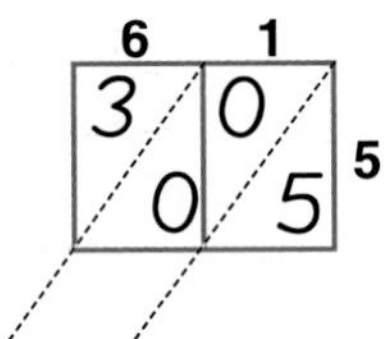

Tell students that in this lesson they will review the **lattice method** for multiplication. Introduced in *Third Grade Everyday Mathematics,* this algorithm relies almost entirely on the recall of basic multiplication facts. If students do not yet have a favorite multiplication algorithm, the lattice method is a good one to suggest.

Demonstrating the Lattice Method for 1-Digit Multipliers

WHOLE-CLASS ACTIVITY

(*Math Masters,* p. 434)

Demonstrate the lattice method using the following examples. Students should show their work using the computation grids on *Math Masters,* page 434.

Example: Use the lattice method to multiply 3 * 45.

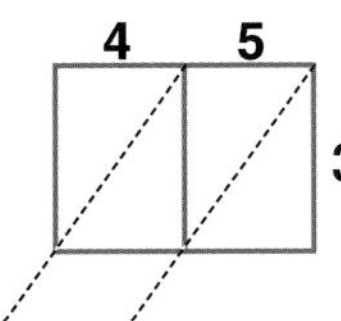

A lattice usually consists of two or more cells with diagonals. Write 4 and 5 above the cells of the lattice. Write 3 on the right side.

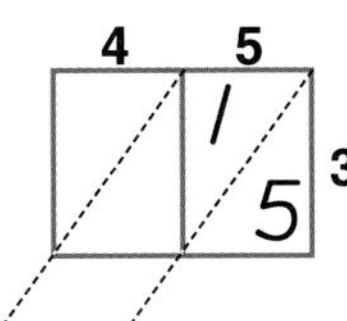

Multiply 3 * 5. Write the answer as shown.

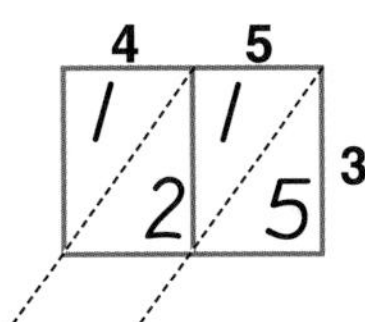

Multiply 3 * 4. Write the answer as shown.

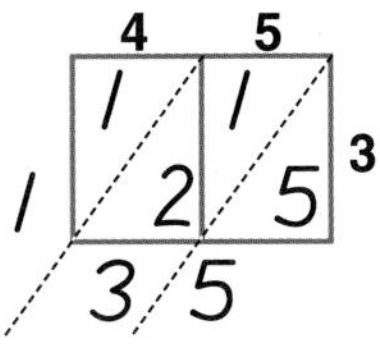

Starting at the right, add the numbers inside the lattice along each diagonal. Read the answer starting on the left side of the lattice and continuing across the bottom. 3 * 45 = 135.

The sum of the numbers along a diagonal may be a 2-digit number. When this happens, write the ones digit in the answer space and the tens digit at the top of the next diagonal.

Example: Use the lattice method to multiply 7 * 89.

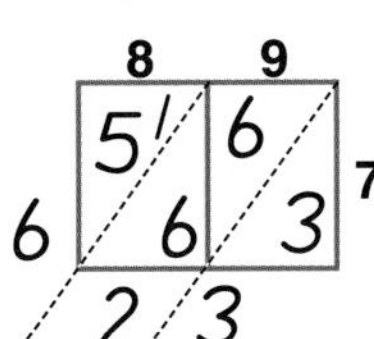

The sum of the numbers in the middle diagonal is 12. Write 2 in the answer space and 1 at the top of the next diagonal. Then add the numbers in that diagonal.

Read the answer: 7 * 89 = 623.

Practicing the Lattice Method for 1-Digit Multipliers

PARTNER ACTIVITY

(*Math Journal 1,* p. 124)

Students complete Problems 1–5 independently. Partners check each other's work.

NOTE The lattice method is a very efficient algorithm, no matter how many digits are in the factors. For problems with 1- and 2-digit multipliers, the lattice method takes about the same amount of time as the partial-products algorithm or the traditional multiplication algorithm. For problems with three or more digits in the factors, the lattice method is much faster and much more likely to yield a correct answer.

Adjusting the Activity

ELL

Have students look up the term *lattice* in the dictionary and think of places where they might see lattices, such as a gate, a window, or a patio. Have students discuss why this word is used to describe the multiplication algorithm.

AUDITORY ◆ KINESTHETIC ◆ TACTILE ◆ VISUAL

Student Page

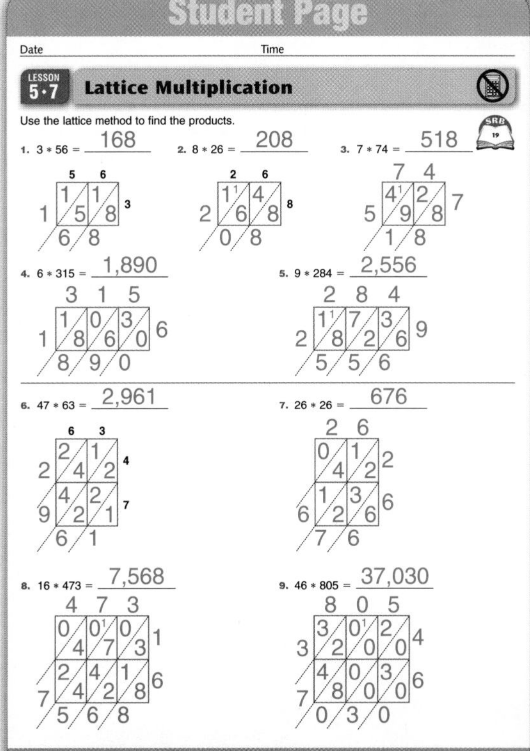

Date Time

LESSON 5·7 **Lattice Multiplication**

Use the lattice method to find the products.

1. 3 * 56 = 168
2. 8 * 26 = 208
3. 7 * 74 = 518
4. 6 * 315 = 1,890
5. 9 * 284 = 2,556
6. 47 * 63 = 2,961
7. 26 * 26 = 676
8. 16 * 473 = 7,568
9. 46 * 805 = 37,030

Math Journal 1, p. 124

Adjusting the Activity

Consider these suggestions for students who need help with the lattice method.

▷ Use an index card to mark the place when adding along each diagonal.

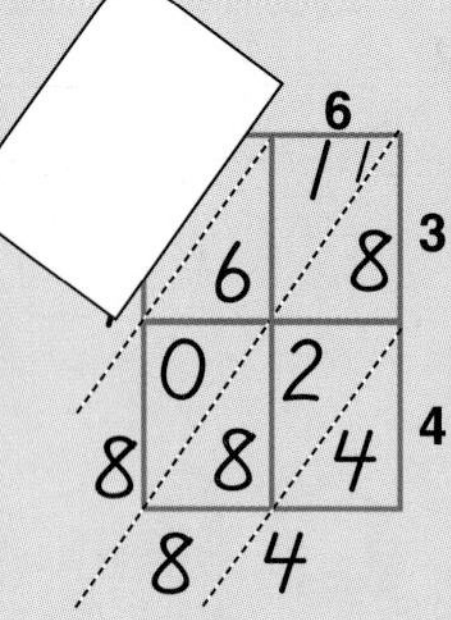

▷ Cross out the factors of the problem before adding so those numbers are not accidentally added with the numbers within the grid.

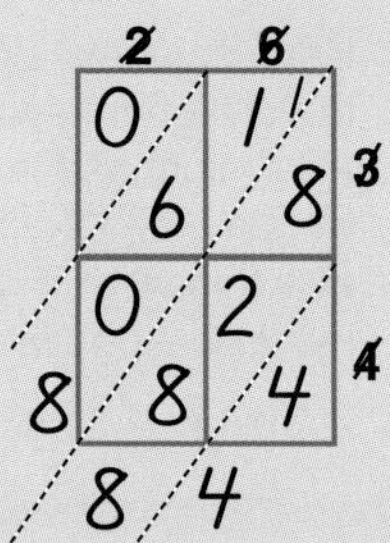

▷ Extend the diagonal lines through the lattice as shown.

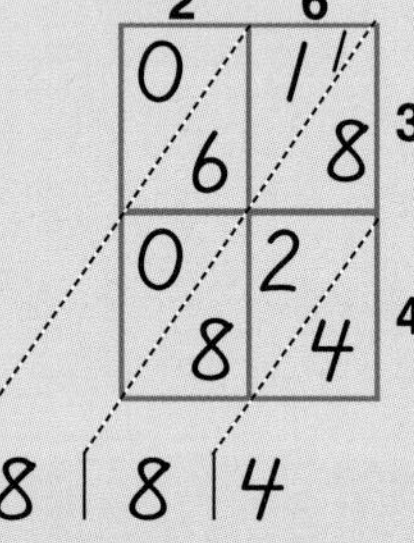

AUDITORY ◆ KINESTHETIC ◆ TACTILE ◆ VISUAL

▶ Demonstrating the Lattice Method for 2-Digit Multipliers

WHOLE-CLASS ACTIVITY

(*Math Masters,* p. 434)

Demonstrate the lattice method for 2-digit multipliers using the example below. Use a transparency of *Math Masters,* page 434 or copy the lattices onto the board. Students should show their work on the lattice grids.

Example: Use the lattice method to multiply 34 ∗ 26.

Write 26 above the lattice. Write 34 on the right side.

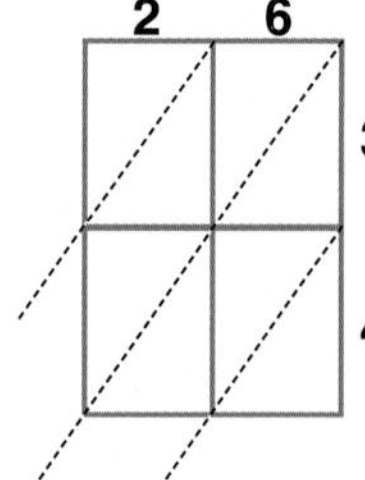

Multiply 3 ∗ 6. Then multiply 3 ∗ 2.

Multiply 4 ∗ 6. Then multiply 4 ∗ 2.

Write the answers as shown.

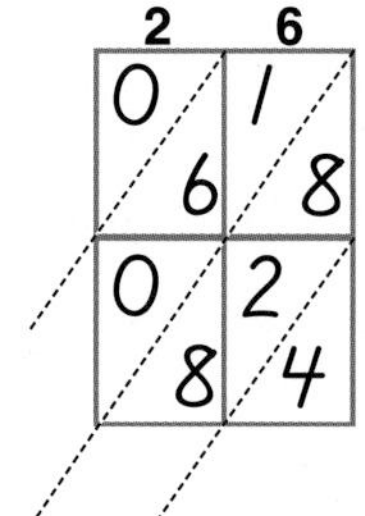

Starting at the right, add the numbers inside the lattice along each diagonal. The sum of the numbers along the second diagonal is 8 + 2 + 8 = 18. Write 8 in the answer space and 1 at the top of the next diagonal.

Read the answer: 34 ∗ 26 = 884.

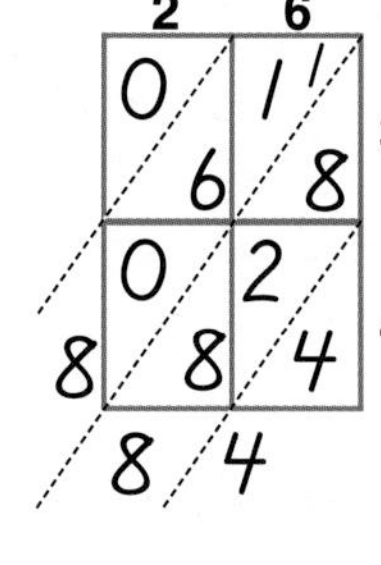

The lattice method for multiplication may seem like a trick. It is not, of course, and place value is evident within the lattice.

thousands hundreds tens ones

▶ Practicing the Lattice Method with 2-Digit Multipliers

PARTNER ACTIVITY

(*Math Journal 1,* p. 124)

Students complete Problems 6–9 independently. Partners check each other's work.

2 Ongoing Learning & Practice

Playing *Multiplication Top-It*

FACTS PRACTICE

(*Student Reference Book,* p. 264; *Math Masters,* p. 506)

Students play *Multiplication Top-It* to maintain automaticity with multiplication facts. See Lesson 3-3 for additional information.

NOTE For facts practice through 12 ∗ 12, have students include number cards 11 and 12.

Ongoing Assessment: Recognizing Student Achievement

***Math Masters* Page 506**

Use ***Math Masters,* page 506** to assess students' automaticity with basic multiplication facts. Students are making adequate progress if they can name the product of the factors generated by the two cards. Some students may play a variation of the game and demonstrate the ability to mentally solve 2-digit by 1-digit multiplication problems.

[Operations and Computation Goal 3]

Math Boxes 5•7

(*Math Journal 1,* p. 125)

Mixed Practice Math Boxes in this lesson are paired with Math Boxes in Lesson 5-5. The skill in Problem 5 previews Unit 6 content.

Writing/Reasoning Have students write a response to the following: *In Problem 1, about how many minutes does Seema spend doing chores, eating, and relaxing each day?* About 288 minutes ***Explain how you got your answer.*** Sample answer: I multiplied 24 by 60 to find out how many minutes are in a day: 24 ∗ 60 = 1,440 minutes. Seema spends about $\frac{1}{5}$ of a day on those activities, so 1,440 / 5 = 288 minutes.

Study Link 5•7

(*Math Masters,* p. 157)

Home Connection Students use the lattice method to solve multiplication problems. Students are asked to solve Problem 7 by using both the lattice method and the partial-products method.

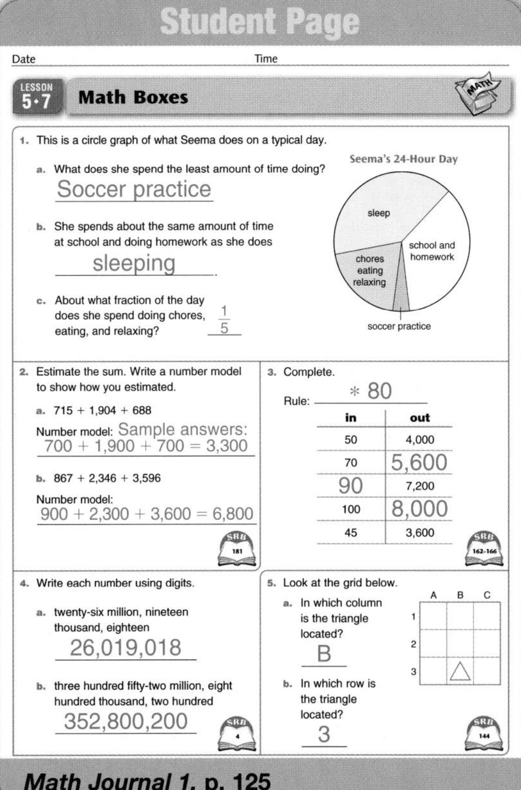

Student Page

Date Time

LESSON 5•7 **Math Boxes**

1. This is a circle graph of what Seema does on a typical day.

a. What does she spend the least amount of time doing? Soccer practice

b. She spends about the same amount of time at school and doing homework as she does sleeping.

c. About what fraction of the day does she spend doing chores, eating, and relaxing? 1/5

2. Estimate the sum. Write a number model to show how you estimated.

a. 715 + 1,904 + 688
Number model: Sample answers: 700 + 1,900 + 700 = 3,300

b. 867 + 2,346 + 3,596
Number model: 900 + 2,300 + 3,600 = 6,800

3. Complete.

Rule: ∗ 80

in	out
50	4,000
70	5,600
90	7,200
100	8,000
45	3,600

4. Write each number using digits.

a. twenty-six million, nineteen thousand, eighteen 26,019,018

b. three hundred fifty-two million, eight hundred thousand, two hundred 352,800,200

5. Look at the grid below.

a. In which column is the triangle located? B

b. In which row is the triangle located? 3

Math Journal 1, p. 125

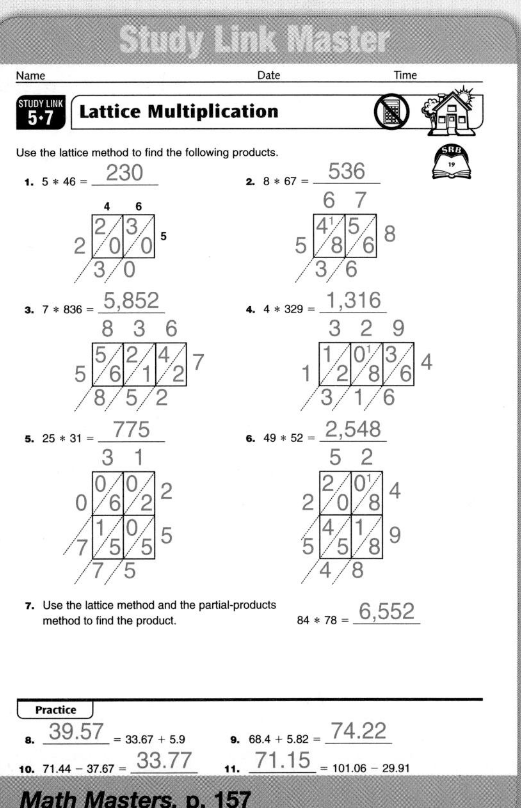

Study Link Master

Name Date Time

STUDY LINK 5•7 **Lattice Multiplication**

Use the lattice method to find the following products.

1. 5 ∗ 46 = 230

2. 8 ∗ 67 = 536

3. 7 ∗ 836 = 5,852

4. 4 ∗ 329 = 1,316

5. 25 ∗ 31 = 775

6. 49 ∗ 52 = 2,548

7. Use the lattice method and the partial-products method to find the product. 84 ∗ 78 = 6,552

Practice

8. 39.57 = 33.67 + 5.9

9. 68.4 + 5.82 = 74.22

10. 71.44 − 37.67 = 33.77

11. 71.15 = 101.06 − 29.91

Math Masters, p. 157

Teaching Master

Name Date Time

LESSON 5·7 **Fact Lattice Patterns**

1. Look at a Multiplication/Division Facts Table. Find the shaded diagonal showing the doubles facts.
2. Find the doubles facts on the Fact Lattice on *Math Masters,* page 435. Shade the doubles facts lightly with a colored pencil.
3. Compare the two fact tables. Sample answers:
   a. List 3 things the tables have in common.
   Both show multiplication and division facts for the factors 1–9; both are a square shape; both show the square products along a diagonal; both show the factors along the top and one side.
   b. List 3 things that are different on the Fact Lattice.
   Lists factors in reverse; shows factors from 0–9, not 1–10; shows zeros in 10s place for numbers < 10; has diagonal lines between the 10s and 1s place for products; shows factors on the right; and does not shade square products.
4. Describe 2 patterns that you see on the Fact Lattice. Sample answers:
   a. Not counting zero as a factor, in the 9s columns and rows, the digit of the 10s place goes up by 1 while the digit for the 1s place goes down by 1.
   b. The bottom (1s) digits in the 2s column and rows repeat a pattern on 0, 2, 4, 6, 8.
5. Which of your Fact Lattice patterns is also in the Multiplication/Division Facts Table in your journal?
   Sample answer: The 9s pattern is in the fact table.

Math Masters, **p. 161**

Teaching Master

Name Date Time

LESSON 5·7 **Napier's Rods**

Scottish mathematician John Napier (1550–1617) devised a multiplication method using rods made of bone, wood, or heavy paper. These rods were used to solve multiplication and division problems.

Example 1: 4 * 67 = 268

Example 2: 8 * 5,239 = 41,912

Cut out the rods on *Math Masters,* page 159. Use the rods and the board on *Math Masters,* page 160 to solve the following problems and some of your own. Use another method to check your answers.

1. 5 * 79 = 395
2. 7 * 92 = 644
3. 1,416 = 6 * 236
4. 52,569 = 9 * 5,841

Try This

5. Show a friend how you would use Napier's Rods to solve 3 * 407 or 9 * 5,038.

Math Masters, **p. 158**

3 Differentiation Options

READINESS

PARTNER ACTIVITY

5–15 Min

▶ Exploring Fact Lattice Patterns

(*Math Masters,* pp. 161 and 435)

To explore the use of the lattice grid for multiplication, have students find patterns in the Fact Lattice (*Math Masters,* page 435).

ENRICHMENT

INDEPENDENT ACTIVITY

15–30 Min

▶ Investigating Napier's Rods

(*Math Masters,* pp. 158–160)

To apply students' understanding of lattice multiplication, have them use Napier's Rods to solve problems.

Discuss students' responses to Problem 5. Students may note that when solving a problem with 0 as a digit in one of the factors, a space is left between the rods where the 0 rod would be.

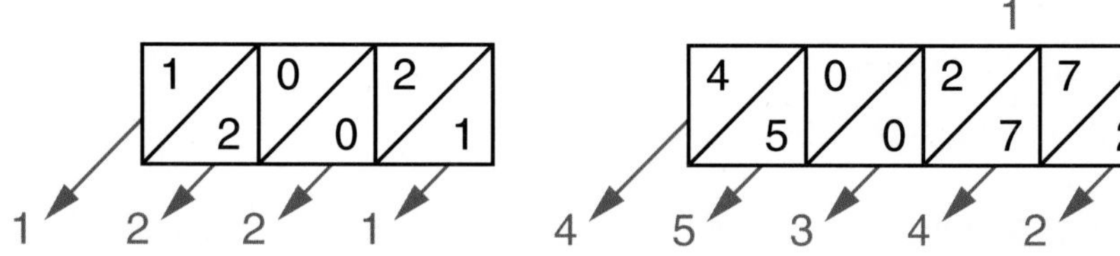

ELL SUPPORT

SMALL-GROUP ACTIVITY

15–30 Min

▶ Creating Visuals for Multiplication Algorithms

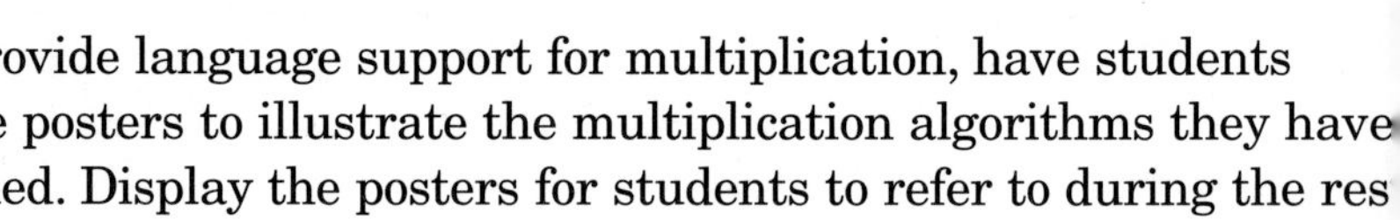

To provide language support for multiplication, have students make posters to illustrate the multiplication algorithms they have learned. Display the posters for students to refer to during the rest of the unit.

Planning Ahead

For use in Part 1 and the optional Enrichment activity in Part 3 of Lesson 5-8, borrow a ream of copy paper and an empty carton used to pack 10 reams of paper.

5•8 Big Numbers

Objective To provide practice reading, writing, and comparing large numbers using patterns in the base-ten place-value system.

Technology Resources www.everydaymathonline.com

ePresentations

eToolkit

Algorithms Practice

EM Facts Workshop Game™

Family Letters

Assessment Management

Common Core State Standards

Curriculum Focal Points

Interactive Teacher's Lesson Guide

1 Teaching the Lesson

Key Concepts and Skills

- Read and write whole numbers to hundred billions. [Number and Numeration Goal 1]
- Identify digits and their values in whole numbers to hundred billions. [Number and Numeration Goal 1]
- Use multiplication to solve a multistep problem. [Operations and Computation Goals 3 and 4]
- Make reasonable estimates. [Operations and Computation Goal 6]

Key Activities

Students use a place-value chart to help them read and write numbers up to the billions place. Students use dot paper to explore the relationships among a thousand, a million, and a billion.

Ongoing Assessment: Recognizing Student Achievement Use a Math Log or Exit Slip (*Math Masters,* page 388 or 389). [Operations and Computation Goal 3]

Key Vocabulary

million ◆ billion

Materials

Math Journal 1, pp. 126 and 127
Student Reference Book, p. 4
Study Link 5•7
Math Masters, p. 162; p. 388 or 389 (optional)
1 ream of copy paper ◆ 1 empty carton used to pack 10 reams of paper ◆ calculator

2 Ongoing Learning & Practice

Analyzing a Data Table
Math Journal 1, p. 128
Students analyze data on Internet users.

Ongoing Assessment: Informing Instruction See page 359.

Math Boxes 5•8
Math Journal 1, p. 129
Students practice and maintain skills through Math Box problems.

Study Link 5•8
Math Masters, p. 163
Students practice and maintain skills through Study Link activities.

3 Differentiation Options

READINESS

Playing *High-Number Toss*
Student Reference Book, p. 252
Math Masters, p. 487 (optional)
calculator ◆ 1 six-sided die
Students practice place-value skills.

ENRICHMENT

Estimating the Number of Dots and the Weight of Paper Needed to Fill the Classroom
Math Masters, p. 164
calculator
Students apply their understanding of the relationships among thousands, millions, and billions.

ENRICHMENT

Exploring Big Numbers in *How Much Is a Million?*
Math Masters, p. 165
Students explore big numbers.

Advance Preparation

For Part 1, draw a place-value chart on the board like the one at the bottom of journal page 126. Make the columns as long as possible. You will use this chart in several lessons. If possible, use semipermanent chalk. For the second optional Enrichment activity in Part 3, obtain a copy of ***How Much Is a Million?*** by David M. Schwartz (Mulberry Books, 1993).

***Teacher's Reference Manual,* Grades 4–6** pp. 59, 60, 259, 260

Getting Started

Mental Math and Reflexes

Have students display a number on their calculators for their partners to read. Have them also take turns dictating numbers for their partners to display on their calculators.

Math Message

Read page 4 in your Student Reference Book. *Be prepared to discuss how commas in large numbers are helpful.*

Study Link 5·7 Follow-Up

For Problem 7, have students discuss which multiplication method they prefer and explain why they chose it.

1 Teaching the Lesson

▶ Math Message Follow-Up

(*Student Reference Book,* p. 4)

On the board, draw four sets of three dashed lines, separated by commas. Write labels next to the commas as shown below. Remind students that in large numbers, groups of three digits are separated by commas.

Use this as a template to practice reading and writing numbers. Write 14,413,236,610 from the *Student Reference Book* example on the template. The strategy for reading this or any other large number is simple.

▷ Read each group of digits separated by commas as a 3-digit number.

▷ Read the appropriate label associated with the comma to the right for each group of three digits.

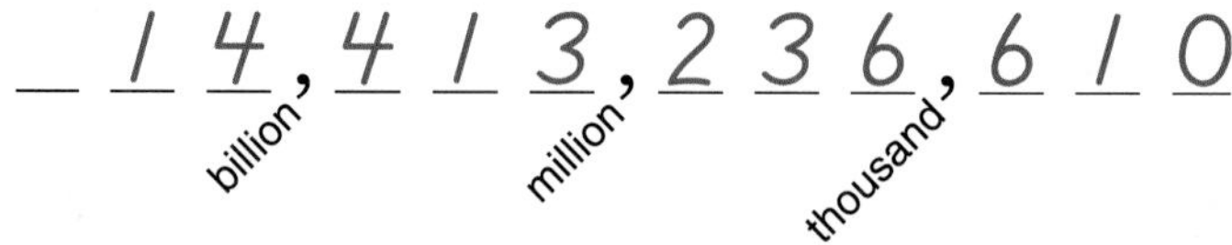

Erase the number and write other examples. Have volunteers read the numbers aloud. Students indicate thumbs-up if they agree with the answer. *Suggestions:*

- 5,000 5 thousand
- 900,000 900 thousand
- 123,450 123 thousand, 450
- 9,000,000 9 million
- 9,500,000 9 million, 500 thousand
- 23,000,000,000 23 billion
- 52,405,072 52 million, 405 thousand, 72
- 183,007,694,718 183 billion, 7 million, 694 thousand, 718

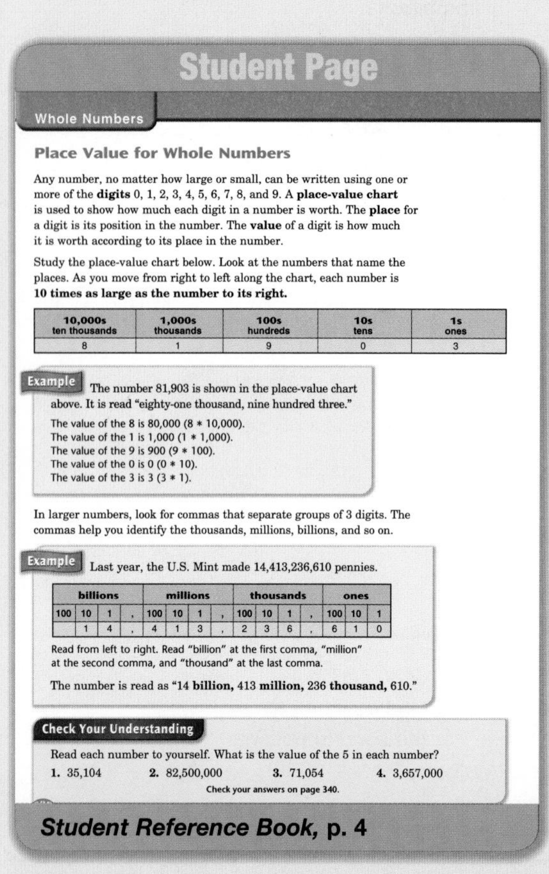

Student Page

Whole Numbers

Place Value for Whole Numbers

Any number, no matter how large or small, can be written using one or more of the **digits** 0, 1, 2, 3, 4, 5, 6, 7, 8, and 9. A **place-value chart** is used to show how much each digit in a number is worth. The **place** for a digit is its position in the number. The **value** of a digit is how much it is worth according to its place in the number.

Study the place-value chart below. Look at the numbers that name the places. As you move from right to left along the chart, each number is **10 times as large as the number to its right.**

10,000s ten thousands	1,000s thousands	100s hundreds	10s tens	1s ones
8	1	9	0	3

Example The number 81,903 is shown in the place-value chart above. It is read "eighty-one thousand, nine hundred three."

The value of the 8 is 80,000 (8 * 10,000).
The value of the 1 is 1,000 (1 * 1,000).
The value of the 9 is 900 (9 * 100).
The value of the 0 is 0 (0 * 10).
The value of the 3 is 3 (3 * 1).

In larger numbers, look for commas that separate groups of 3 digits. The commas help you identify the thousands, millions, billions, and so on.

Example Last year, the U.S. Mint made 14,413,236,610 pennies.

billions				millions				thousands				ones		
100	10	1	,	100	10	1	,	100	10	1	,	100	10	1
	1	4	,	4	1	3	,	2	3	6	,	6	1	0

Read from left to right. Read "billion" at the first comma, "million" at the second comma, and "thousand" at the last comma.

The number is read as "14 **billion,** 413 **million,** 236 **thousand,** 610."

Check Your Understanding

Read each number to yourself. What is the value of the 5 in each number?

1. 35,104 **2.** 82,500,000 **3.** 71,054 **4.** 3,657,000

Check your answers on page 340.

***Student Reference Book,* p. 4**

Reverse the procedure; that is, name numbers and ask volunteers to write the numerals on the template.

Tell students that in this lesson they will explore the relationships among a thousand, a million, and a billion.

Reading and Writing Big Numbers

WHOLE-CLASS ACTIVITY

(*Math Journal 1,* p. 126)

It is more convenient to use a place-value chart than to label commas as thousand, million, and so on.

The place-value chart on journal page 126 separates places into groups of three and labels these groups as ones, thousands, **millions,** and **billions.** The chart also includes commas to separate the groups of three digits.

The chart includes a label for each individual place at the top of its column. For example, the labels for the thousands columns are 100Th (100 thousands), 10Th (10 thousands), and 1Th (1 thousands). Use the following example to show students that the place-value name for each column indicates how much a digit in that column is worth.

Thousands				Ones		
100Th	10Th	1Th	,	100	10	1
4	0	0	,	0	0	0
	4	0	,	0	0	0
		4	,	0	0	0

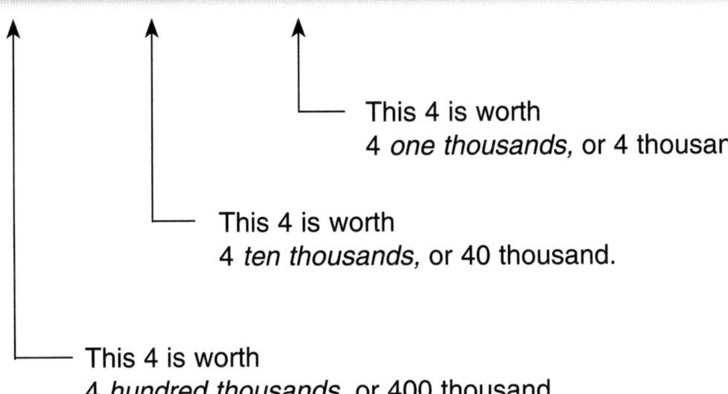
This 4 is worth
4 *one thousands,* or 4 thousand.
This 4 is worth
4 *ten thousands,* or 40 thousand.
This 4 is worth
4 *hundred thousands,* or 400 thousand.

Enter numbers in the place-value chart on the board and have students read them. Then name several numbers, and ask volunteers to write them in the chart.

Assign journal page 126 to the class.

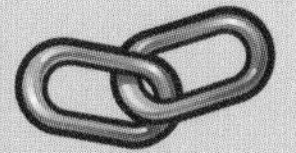

Links to the Future

In Lessons 2-3 and 2-4, students worked with numbers through the hundred-millions place. This is the first exposure to numbers in the billions. Reading, writing, and identifying digits and their values in numbers beyond 1,000,000,000 is a Grade 5 Goal.

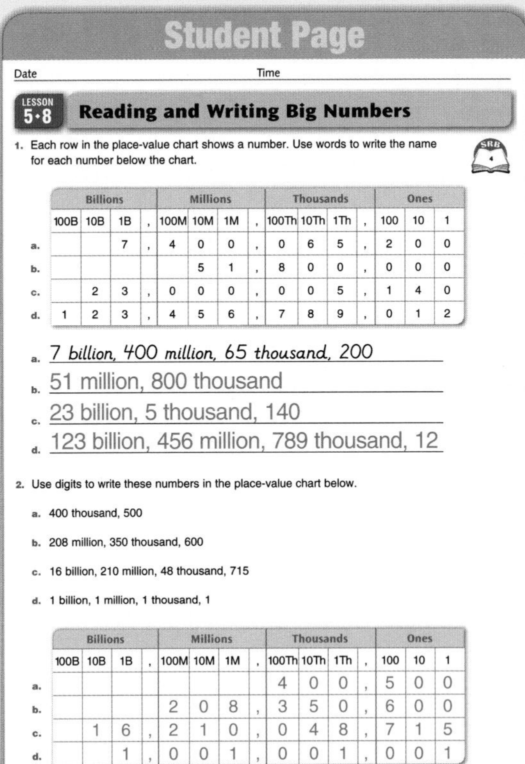

Student Page

Date Time

LESSON 5•8 **Reading and Writing Big Numbers**

1. Each row in the place-value chart shows a number. Use words to write the name for each number below the chart.

	Billions				Millions				Thousands				Ones		
	100B	10B	1B	,	100M	10M	1M	,	100Th	10Th	1Th	,	100	10	1
a.			7	,	4	0	0	,	0	6	5	,	2	0	0
b.						5	1	,	8	0	0	,	0	0	0
c.		2	3	,	0	0	0	,	0	0	5	,	1	4	0
d.	1	2	3	,	4	5	6	,	7	8	9	,	0	1	2

a. 7 billion, 400 million, 65 thousand, 200

b. 51 million, 800 thousand

c. 23 billion, 5 thousand, 140

d. 123 billion, 456 million, 789 thousand, 12

2. Use digits to write these numbers in the place-value chart below.

a. 400 thousand, 500

b. 208 million, 350 thousand, 600

c. 16 billion, 210 million, 48 thousand, 715

d. 1 billion, 1 million, 1 thousand, 1

	Billions				Millions				Thousands				Ones		
	100B	10B	1B	,	100M	10M	1M	,	100Th	10Th	1Th	,	100	10	1
a.									4	0	0	,	5	0	0
b.					2	0	8	,	3	5	0	,	6	0	0
c.		1	6	,	2	1	0	,	0	4	8	,	7	1	5
d.			1	,	0	0	1	,	0	0	1	,	0	0	1

Math Journal 1, p. 126

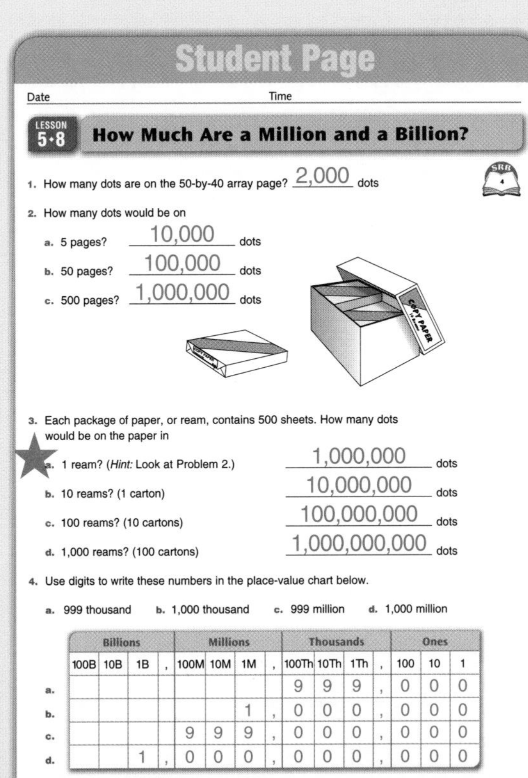

Student Page

Date Time

LESSON 5•8 **How Much Are a Million and a Billion?**

1. How many dots are on the 50-by-40 array page? 2,000 dots

2. How many dots would be on

a. 5 pages? 10,000 dots

b. 50 pages? 100,000 dots

c. 500 pages? 1,000,000 dots

3. Each package of paper, or ream, contains 500 sheets. How many dots would be on the paper in

a. 1 ream? (*Hint:* Look at Problem 2.) 1,000,000 dots

b. 10 reams? (1 carton) 10,000,000 dots

c. 100 reams? (10 cartons) 100,000,000 dots

d. 1,000 reams? (100 cartons) 1,000,000,000 dots

4. Use digits to write these numbers in the place-value chart below.

a. 999 thousand b. 1,000 thousand c. 999 million d. 1,000 million

	Billions				Millions				Thousands				Ones		
	100B	10B	1B	,	100M	10M	1M	,	100Th	10Th	1Th	,	100	10	1
a.									9	9	9	,	0	0	0
b.							1	,	0	0	0	,	0	0	0
c.					9	9	9	,	0	0	0	,	0	0	0
d.			1	,	0	0	0	,	0	0	0	,	0	0	0

Math Journal 1, p. 127

Teaching Master

Name Date Time

LESSON 5·8 A 50-by-40 Array

Math Masters, p. 162

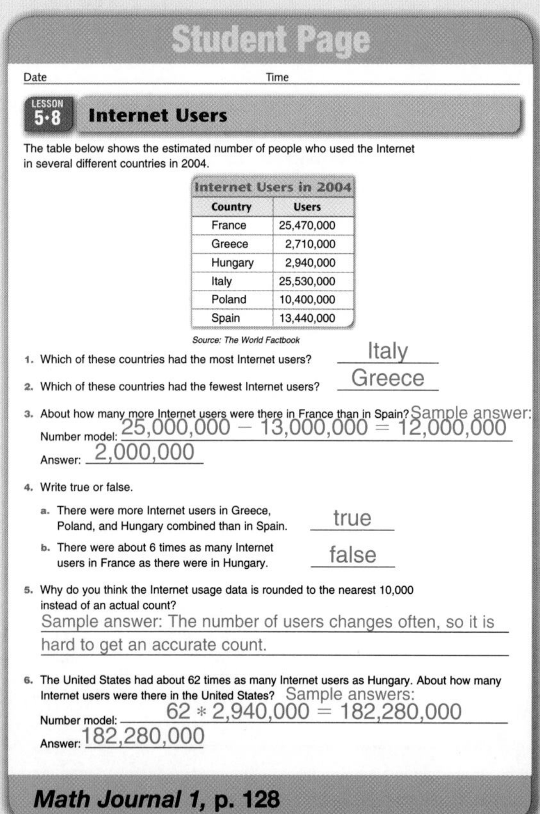
Student Page

Date Time

LESSON 5·8 Internet Users

The table below shows the estimated number of people who used the Internet in several different countries in 2004.

Internet Users in 2004	
Country	Users
France	25,470,000
Greece	2,710,000
Hungary	2,940,000
Italy	25,530,000
Poland	10,400,000
Spain	13,440,000

Source: The World Factbook

1. Which of these countries had the most Internet users? Italy
2. Which of these countries had the fewest Internet users? Greece
3. About how many more Internet users were there in France than in Spain? Sample answer:
Number model: 25,000,000 − 13,000,000 = 12,000,000
Answer: 2,000,000
4. Write true or false.
   a. There were more Internet users in Greece, Poland, and Hungary combined than in Spain. true
   b. There were about 6 times as many Internet users in France as there were in Hungary. false
5. Why do you think the Internet usage data is rounded to the nearest 10,000 instead of an actual count?
Sample answer: The number of users changes often, so it is hard to get an accurate count.
6. The United States had about 62 times as many Internet users as Hungary. About how many Internet users were there in the United States? Sample answers:
Number model: 62 ∗ 2,940,000 = 182,280,000
Answer: 182,280,000

Math Journal 1, p. 128

▶ Exploring the Relationships among a Thousand, a Million, and a Billion

(*Math Journal 1,* p. 127; *Math Masters,* p. 162)

If you have a ream of copy paper and a packing carton, display them. Tell the class that a ream contains 500 sheets and that a full carton contains 10 reams. Working with a partner, students complete journal page 127.

Compare strategies and answers. Use the ream and empty carton to support the discussion. Have students share how they found the number of dots on *Math Masters,* page 162. Sample answers:

▷ There are 20 squares with 100 dots each; that is 20 [100s], or 2,000.

▷ The dots form a 50-by-40 array; that is 50 [40s], or 50 ∗ 40, or 2,000.

▷ There are 1,000 dots on a half-sheet; that is 2,000 dots on a full sheet.

Review strategies for determining that there are 1 million dots in a ream:

▷ There are 1,000 dots per half-sheet and 1,000 half-sheets per ream of 500; that is 1,000 [1,000s], or 1 million.

▷ There are 2,000 dots per sheet and 500 sheets; that is 500 [2,000s], or 1 million.

Use the answers to Problems 3a and 3d to illustrate that 1 billion is equivalent to 1,000 million:

▷ 1 ream contains paper with a total of 1 million dots (Problem 3a), so 1,000 reams must contain paper with 1,000 million dots. But 1,000 reams contain paper with 1 billion dots (Problem 3d), so 1,000 million and 1 billion are the same number.

Ongoing Assessment: Recognizing Student Achievement

Math Log or Exit Slip

Use a **Math Log** or an **Exit Slip** (*Math Masters,* page 388 or 389) to assess students' ability to use extended multplication facts in a problem-solving situation. Have students describe how they determined on journal page 127, Problem 3a that a ream of paper would have 1 million dots. Students are making adequate progress if they can explain in words, with pictures, or with number models how 2,000 dots on one page can be used to determine the number of dots on 500 pages. Some students may be able to explain how they used this information to solve problems 3b–3d.

[Operations and Computation Goal 3]

Analyzing a Data Table

(*Math Journal 1,* p. 128)

Social Studies Link Students answer questions about the number of Internet users in several countries in Region 2.

Ongoing Assessment: Informing Instruction

Watch for students who use estimation strategies rather than calculate exact answers to solve the problems. Have them explain why estimation is appropriate.

When students have completed the journal page, ask them to look at Problems 3 and 6. Ask: *How is the way you compared the number of Internet users in France and in Spain different from how you compared the number of Internet users in the United States and in Hungary?* Sample answer: For France and Spain, I used subtraction to compare. But for the United States and Hungary, I used multiplication. Point out that the difference between the numbers of Internet users in the United States and in Hungary is so large that it is almost equal to the number for the United States. When differences are this big, it is usually more useful to use multiplication to compare the numbers, because multiplication gives a better sense of how much bigger one quantity is than another.

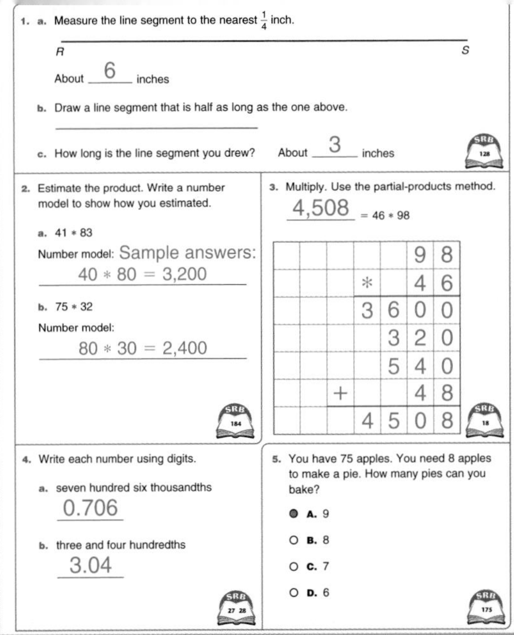

1. a. Measure the line segment to the nearest $\frac{1}{4}$ inch.
R ——— S
About 6 inches
b. Draw a line segment that is half as long as the one above.
c. How long is the line segment you drew? About 3 inches

2. Estimate the product. Write a number model to show how you estimated.
a. 41 * 83
Number model: Sample answers: 40 * 80 = 3,200
b. 75 * 32
Number model: 80 * 30 = 2,400

3. Multiply. Use the partial-products method.
4,508 = 46 * 98

			9	8
		*	4	6
	3	6	0	0
		3	2	0
		5	4	0
	+		4	8
	4	5	0	8

4. Write each number using digits.
a. seven hundred six thousandths 0.706
b. three and four hundredths 3.04

5. You have 75 apples. You need 8 apples to make a pie. How many pies can you bake?
● A. 9
○ B. 8
○ C. 7
○ D. 6

Math Journal 1, p. 129

Math Boxes 5•8

(*Math Journal 1,* p. 129)

Mixed Practice Math Boxes in this lesson are linked with Math Boxes in Lessons 5-6 and 5-10. The skill in Problem 5 previews Unit 6 content.

Writing/Reasoning Have students write a response to the following: *Explain how you determined the number of pies for Problem 5.* Sample answer: Because 75 / 8 = 9 R3 or $9\frac{3}{8}$, there are enough apples for only 9 pies.

Study Link 5•8

(*Math Masters,* p. 163)

Home Connection Students solve a place-value puzzle involving the four basic operations.

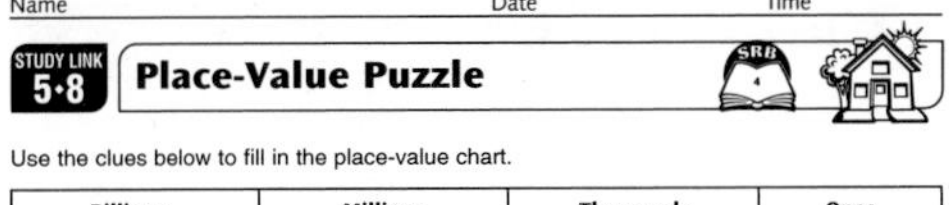

Name Date Time

STUDY LINK 5•8 **Place-Value Puzzle**

Use the clues below to fill in the place-value chart.

Billions				Millions				Thousands				Ones		
100B	10B	1B	,	100M	10M	1M	,	100Th	10Th	1Th	,	100	10	1
	9	2		1	0	6		9	5	4		8	7	3

1. Find $\frac{1}{2}$ of 24. Subtract 4. Write the result in the hundreds place.
2. Find $\frac{1}{2}$ of 30. Divide the result by 3. Write the answer in the ten-thousands place.
3. Find 30 ÷ 10. Double the result. Write it in the one-millions place.
4. Divide 12 by 4. Write the answer in the ones place.
5. Find 9 * 8. Reverse the digits in the result. Divide by 3. Write the answer in the hundred-thousands place.
6. Double 8. Divide the result by 4. Write the answer in the one-thousands place.
7. In the one-billions place, write the even number greater than 0 that has not been used yet.
8. Write the answer to 5 ÷ 5 in the hundred-millions place.
9. In the tens place, write the odd number that has not been used yet.
10. Find the sum of all the digits in the chart so far. Divide the result by 5, and write it in the ten-billions place.
11. Write 0 in the empty column whose place value is less than billions.
12. Write the number in words. For example, 17,450,206 could be written as "17 million, 450 thousand, 206."
92 billion, 106 million, 954 thousand, 873

Practice

13. 74 * 5 = 370
14. 3,168 = 396 * 8
15. 1,656 = 92 * 18
16. 56 * 47 = 2,632

Math Masters, p. 163

Suppose you filled your classroom from floor to ceiling with dot paper (2,000 dots per sheet).

1. About how many dots do you think there would be on all the paper needed to fill your classroom? Make a check mark next to your guess. Answers vary.

_____ less than a million
_____ between a million and a half billion
_____ between half a billion and a billion
_____ more than a billion

2. One ream of paper weighs about 5 pounds and has 500 sheets of paper. About how many pounds would the paper needed to fill your classroom weigh? Make a check mark next to your guess. Answers vary.

_____ less than 100,000 pounds
_____ between 100,000 pounds and 500,000 pounds
_____ between 500,000 pounds and a million pounds
_____ more than a million pounds

3. Now, work with your group to make more accurate estimates for Problems 1 and 2. Explain what you did.

My group's estimates: Sample answers:

Number of dots: 56,700,000,000 dots

Weight of the paper: 283,500 lb

Sample answer:

A ream of paper is about 2 in. high, so 6 reams will be about 1 ft tall. It will take about 60 reams to reach the ceiling. The floor is about 27 reams by 35 reams, so 945 reams will cover it. To fill the room, it will take about 56,700 reams.

Math Masters, p. 164

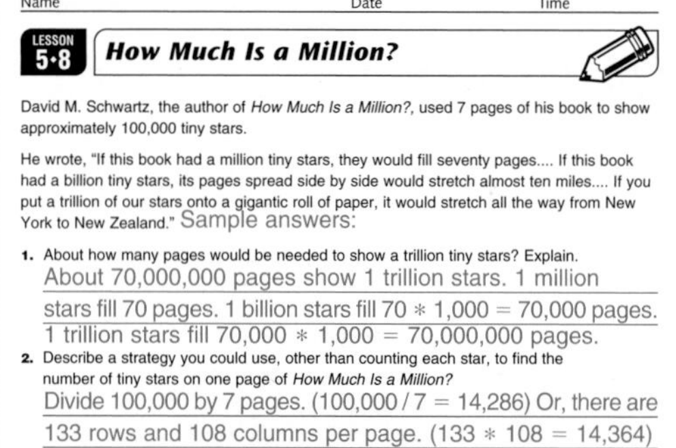
Name Date Time

LESSON 5·8 **How Much Is a Million?**

David M. Schwartz, the author of *How Much Is a Million?*, used 7 pages of his book to show approximately 100,000 tiny stars.

He wrote, "If this book had a million tiny stars, they would fill seventy pages.... If this book had a billion tiny stars, its pages spread side by side would stretch almost ten miles.... If you put a trillion of our stars onto a gigantic roll of paper, it would stretch all the way from New York to New Zealand." Sample answers:

1. About how many pages would be needed to show a trillion tiny stars? Explain.
About 70,000,000 pages show 1 trillion stars. 1 million stars fill 70 pages. 1 billion stars fill 70 * 1,000 = 70,000 pages. 1 trillion stars fill 70,000 * 1,000 = 70,000,000 pages.

2. Describe a strategy you could use, other than counting each star, to find the number of tiny stars on one page of *How Much Is a Million?*
Divide 100,000 by 7 pages. (100,000 / 7 = 14,286) Or, there are 133 rows and 108 columns per page. (133 * 108 = 14,364)

Math Masters, page 165

READINESS

▶ Playing *High-Number Toss*

PARTNER ACTIVITY · 15–30 Min

(*Student Reference Book,* p. 252; *Math Masters,* p. 487)

To provide experience with place-value skills, have students play *High-Number Toss*. See Lesson 2-7 for additional information.

ENRICHMENT

▶ Estimating the Number of Dots and the Weight of Paper Needed to Fill the Classroom

SMALL-GROUP ACTIVITY · 15–30 Min

(*Math Masters,* p. 164)

To apply students' understanding of the relationships among thousands, millions, and billions, have them devise and carry out a strategy to see how many dots (on dot paper) would fill a classroom.

Points of reference:

▷ Approximately 56,700 reams of paper would be needed to fill a 25-by-25-by-10 ft classroom (a 625 sq ft classroom with a 10 ft ceiling).

▷ About 283,500 pounds, or 140 tons, of paper would fill the same classroom. 56,700 reams * 5 pounds = 283,500 pounds.

ENRICHMENT

▶ Exploring Big Numbers in *How Much Is a Million?*

PARTNER ACTIVITY · 5–15 Min

(*Math Masters,* p. 165)

Literature Link To further explore students' understanding of the relationships among thousands, millions, and billions to millions, billions, and trillions, have students read and answer questions about ***How Much Is a Million?*** by David M. Schwartz (Mulberry Books, 1993).

5•9 Powers of 10

Objective To introduce exponential notation for powers of 10 as a way of naming the values of places in our base-ten system.

Technology Resources www.everydaymathonline.com

Presentations

eToolkit

Algorithms Practice

EM Facts Workshop Game™

Family Letters

Assessment Management

Common Core State Standards

Curriculum Focal Points

Interactive Teacher's Lesson Guide

1 Teaching the Lesson

Key Concepts and Skills

- Read and write large numbers; identify the digits and their values. [Number and Numeration Goal 1]
- Use exponential notation to represent powers of 10. [Number and Numeration Goal 4]
- Use expanded notation to represent powers of 10. [Number and Numeration Goal 4]
- Identify and describe patterns in a place-value table. [Patterns, Functions, and Algebra Goal 1]

Key Activities

Students fill in a place-value chart that shows place-value headings expressed as powers of 10. They use exponential notation to represent powers of 10.

Ongoing Assessment: Recognizing Student Achievement
Use a Math Log or Exit Slip (*Math Masters,* page 388 or 389).
[Patterns, Functions, and Algebra Goal 1]

Key Vocabulary

scientific notation ◆ trillion ◆ quadrillion ◆ quintillion ◆ sextillion ◆ powers of 10 ◆ exponent

Materials

Math Journal 1, p. 130
Student Reference Book, p. 271
Study Link 5•8
Math Masters, p. 388 or 389 (optional)
transparency of *Math Masters,* p. 166 (optional) ◆ calculator

2 Ongoing Learning & Practice

Playing *Polygon Pair-Up*
Student Reference Book, p. 258
Polygon Pair-Up Property Cards and Polygon Cards (*Math Masters,* pp. 496 and 497)
Students practice naming properties of polygons.

Math Boxes 5•9
Math Journal 1, p. 131
Students practice and maintain skills through Math Box problems.

Study Link 5•9
Math Masters, p. 167
Students practice and maintain skills through Study Link activities.

3 Differentiation Options

ENRICHMENT

Investigating Powers of 10 on a Calculator
Math Masters, p. 168
calculator
Students explore exponential notation on a calculator.

EXTRA PRACTICE

5-Minute Math
5-Minute Math™, pp. 2, 3, and 7
Students use exponential notation.

ELL SUPPORT

Building Background for Mathematics Words
Students find various ways of using the word *power.*

Advance Preparation

For Part 1, draw a place-value chart on the board like the one on journal page 130, or use a transparency of *Math Masters,* page 166.

***Teacher's Reference Manual,* Grades 4–6** pp. 94–98, 259, 260

Getting Started

Mental Math and Reflexes

Write large numbers through the billions on the board, and have volunteers read them aloud. *Suggestions:*

●○○	●●○	●●●
396,467	3,654,987	5,123,467,890
283,950	17,834,567	8,312,945,607
712,945	527,000,348	3,980,246,571

Ask questions such as:

- What digit is in the millions place?
- What is the value of the digit *x*?
- How many billions are there?

Math Message

Find the largest number you can in the World Tour section of your Student Reference Book.

Study Link 5·8 Follow-Up

The number in the place-value chart should be 92,106,954,873. Accept either of the following ways to write the number:

▷ 92 billion, 106 million, 954 thousand, 873

▷ ninety-two billion, one hundred six million, nine hundred fifty-four thousand, eight hundred seventy-three

1 Teaching the Lesson

▶ Math Message Follow-Up

(*Student Reference Book,* p. 271)

Divide students into small groups so they can compare answers. You might give them a few additional minutes to look for an even larger number. Then have the groups report their answers and write them in the place-value chart on the board.

Discuss the answers. The largest numbers in the World Tour section of the *Student Reference Book* are found on page 271.

The total population of the world is given in the table near the bottom of the page. Although this is not the largest number in the World Tour section, it is probably the largest number that most students will recognize at this time.

The largest number in the World Tour section is found in the other table on page 271. The approximate weight (mass) of Earth is listed as $6.6 * 10^{21}$ tons. This number is read as "6 point 6 times 10 to the 21st power."

Numbers written in this form are said to be in **scientific notation.** This is how the number looks, written out:

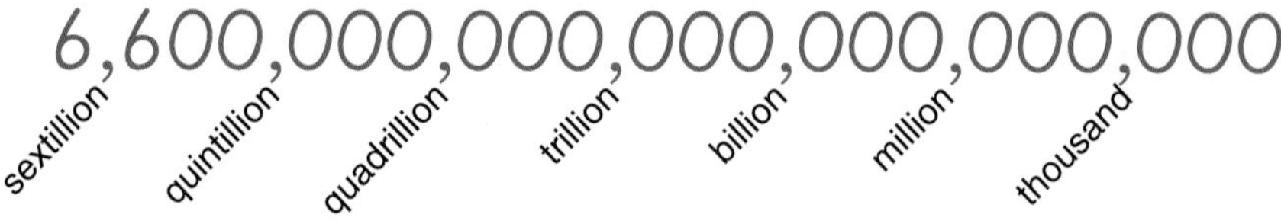

Write this 22-digit number on the board, including the labels for thousands, millions, billions, and so on. Point out the place-value group names that are used for numbers larger than billions, namely **trillions, quadrillions, quintillions,** and **sextillions.**

Ask students to read the number by using the name labels written beside the commas. 6 sextillion, 600 quintillion

Student Page

World Tour

Facts About the World

Continents are large land masses. There are seven continents on the Earth, although Europe and Asia are sometimes thought of as one continent. Most continents contain many countries, but there are no countries at all in Antarctica.

A **country** is a territory and the people who live there under one government. The number of countries in the world often changes as countries split apart or join with other countries. At this time, there are about 200 countries in the world.

Population is the number of people who live in a certain region. Population growth is the change in the population every year after all births and deaths are accounted for. The **population growth rate** is the increase (or decrease) in population per year, written as a percent.

Dimensions of the Earth

Equatorial circumference*: about 24,900 miles (40,000 kilometers)

Equatorial diameter:** about 7,930 miles (12,760 kilometers)

Volume: 2.6×10^{11} cubic miles (1.1×10^{12} cubic kilometers)

Weight (mass): 6.6×10^{21} tons (6.0×10^{21} metric tons)

Total world water area: about 139,433,000 square miles (361,129,000 square kilometers)

*Circumference is the distance around a circle or sphere.

**Diameter is the distance measured by a straight line passing from one side of a circle or sphere, through the center, to the other side.

The world's population is now increasing by about 200,000 people per day, or about 75 million people per year. Over the last 40 years, the world's population has about doubled. It reached the 6 billion mark in 1999. World population is expected to reach about 9 billion people by the year 2050.

The Continents

Continent	Population*	Percent of World Population	Area (sq miles)	Percent of Land Area
North America	509,000,000	8.0%	8,300,000	14.8%
South America	367,000,000	5.8	6,800,000	12.1
Europe	799,000,000	12.5	4,100,000	7.3
Asia	3,797,000,000	59.5	16,700,000	29.8
Africa	874,000,000	13.7	11,500,000	20.5
Australia	32,000,000	0.5	3,300,000	5.9
Antarctica	0	0.0	5,400,000	9.6
World Totals	**6,378,000,000 (about 6.4 billion)**	**100.0%**	**56,100,000**	**100.0%**

*Data are for the year 2004. World population growth rate for the year 2004: about 1.2% per year

***Student Reference Book,* p. 271**

Introducing Exponential Notation for Powers of 10

(*Math Journal 1,* p. 130)

In preparation for later work with scientific notation, it is useful to show how place-value headings can be expressed as powers of 10 using exponential notation.

1. Review the place-value headings that students are familiar with on journal page 130—ones, tens, hundreds, and so on. Ask them to write the standard numerals in Row 1 of the place-value chart.
2. Review the relationship between the value of each place and the place to its right. The value of each place is 10 times the value of the place to its right. Students complete the 10-times-as-much pattern in Row 2.
3. Tell students that numbers like 100, 1,000, and 10,000 are called **powers of 10.** They are numbers that can be expressed as products whose factors are 10. Have students fill in Row 3 of the chart on their journal page.
4. Instead of repeating the factor 10, we can use the shorthand introduced in the Math Message Follow-Up. For example, $10 * 10$ can be written as 10^2 (read "10 to the second power" or "10 squared"). $10 * 10 * 10$ can be written as 10^3 (read "10 to the third power" or "10 cubed"). The raised digit, called the **exponent,** tells how many times 10 is used as a factor. Ask students to fill in Row 4 of the chart on their journal page.

Student Page

Date | Time

LESSON 5•9 **Place Value and Powers of 10**

Millions	Hundred Thousands	Ten Thousands	Thousands	Hundreds	Tens	Ones
1,000,000	100,000	10,000	1,000	100	10	1
10 [100,000s]	10 [10,000s]	10 [1,000s]	10 [100s]	10 [10s]	10 [1s]	10 [tenths]
$10 * 10 * 10 * 10 * 10 * 10$	$10 * 10 * 10 * 10 * 10$	$10 * 10 * 10 * 10$	$10 * 10 * 10$	$10 * 10$	10	
10^6	10^5	10^4	10^3	10^2	10^1	10^0

Fill in this place-value chart as follows:

1. Write standard numbers in Row 1.
2. In Row 2, write the value of each place to show that it is 10 times the value of the place to its right.
3. In Row 3, write the place values as products of 10s.
4. In Row 4, show the values as powers of 10. Use exponents. The exponent shows how many times 10 is used as a factor. It also shows how many zeros are in the standard number.

Math Journal 1, p. 130

Math Masters, page 166 is identical to *Math Journal 1,* page 130.

Links to the Future

The discussions of exponential notation and scientific notation are exposures to the topics. They will be revisited more formally in later grades. The use of exponential notation is a Grade 5 Goal, and the use of scientific notation is a Grade 6 Goal.

5. Have students explore the calculator key sequences used to raise 10 to a certain power.

TI-15:

Key Sequence: 10 [^] 3 [Enter]

Display: 1000

Casio *fx*-55:

Key Sequence: 3 [10^x]

Display: 1000

or

Key Sequence: 10 [x^y] 3 [=]

Display: 1000

6. Ask students to look for patterns in their completed charts. The patterns should include the following:

▷ The exponent tells how many zeros are in the number in Row 1. For example, look at the thousands place: the exponent is 3, and the number 1,000 has 3 zeros.

▷ The exponent tells how many columns are to the right. For example, look at the hundreds place: the exponent is 2. There are 2 columns to the right of the hundreds place—the tens place and the ones place.

▷ In moving left one place, the exponent increases by 1. For example, start in the thousands place. The exponent is 3. Move left one place to the ten-thousands place. The exponen here is 4.

▷ In moving right one place, the exponent decreases by 1. For example, start in the hundreds place. The exponent is 2. Move right one place to the tens place. The exponent here is 1.

NOTE The pattern in the table shows 10^0 is another name for 1. This illustrates a more general mathematical definition: Any non-zero number to the zero power is defined as 1. For example, $347^0 = 1$.

Adjusting the Activity

Ask students to find another name for 10^{-1}. Suggest that they extend the patterns in Rows 1 and 4. Each number in Row 1 is $\frac{1}{10}$ of the number to its left. So if a column is added to the right of the ones column, it would have $\frac{1}{10}$ in Row 1 and would be labeled Tenths. Because the exponents decrease by 1 in moving one place to the right, the tenths place would have 10^{-1} in Row 4. 10^{-1} is another name for $\frac{1}{10}$.

AUDITORY ♦ KINESTHETIC ♦ TACTILE ♦ VISUAL

Ongoing Assessment: Recognizing Student Achievement

Math Log or Exit Slip

Use a **Math Log** or an **Exit Slip** (*Math Masters,* page 388 or 389) to assess students' ability to describe numeric patterns. Have students describe the pattern in one of the rows in the table on journal page 130. Students are making adequate progress if they note that the value of each place is 10 times the value of the place to its right and $\frac{1}{10}$ the value of the place to its left. Some students may be able to extend this pattern past millions and ones.

[Patterns, Functions, and Algebra Goal 1]

2 Ongoing Learning & Practice

Playing *Polygon Pair-Up*

PARTNER ACTIVITY

(*Student Reference Book,* p. 258; *Math Masters,* pp. 496 and 497)

Students play *Polygon Pair-Up* to practice identifying properties of polygons. See Lesson 1-6 for additional information.

Math Boxes 5•9

INDEPENDENT ACTIVITY

(*Math Journal 1,* p. 131)

Mixed Practice Math Boxes in this lesson are paired with Math Boxes in Lesson 5-11. The skill in Problem 6 previews Unit 6 content.

Writing/Reasoning Have students write a response to the following: *For Problem 3, can intersecting lines be perpendicular lines? Explain.* Sample answer: Yes. Perpendicular lines intersect at right angles and intersecting lines intersect at any angle.

Study Link 5•9

INDEPENDENT ACTIVITY

(*Math Masters,* p. 167)

Home Connection Students identify and sort names for powers of 10.

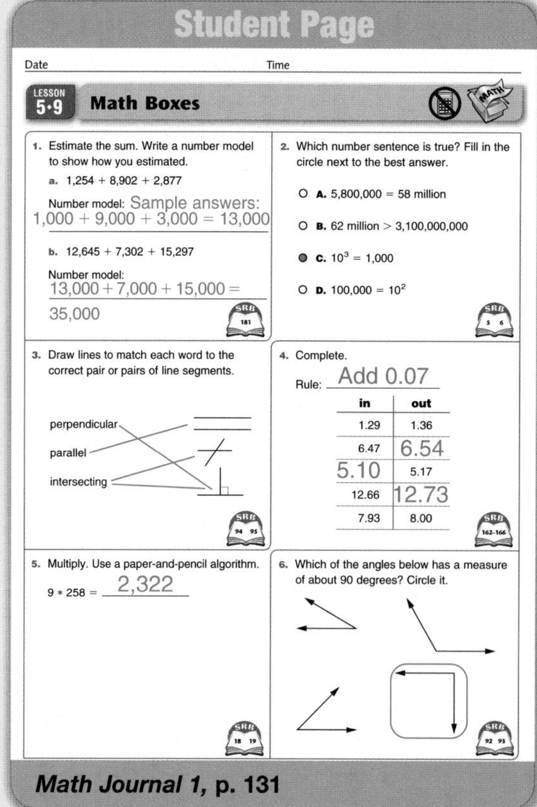

Student Page

Date Time

LESSON 5•9 **Math Boxes**

1. Estimate the sum. Write a number model to show how you estimated.
   a. 1,254 + 8,902 + 2,877
   Number model: Sample answers: 1,000 + 9,000 + 3,000 = 13,000
   b. 12,645 + 7,302 + 15,297
   Number model: 13,000 + 7,000 + 15,000 = 35,000

2. Which number sentence is true? Fill in the circle next to the best answer.
   - A. 5,800,000 = 58 million
   - B. 62 million > 3,100,000,000
   - ● C. 10^3 = 1,000
   - D. 100,000 = 10^2

3. Draw lines to match each word to the correct pair or pairs of line segments.
   perpendicular
   parallel
   intersecting

4. Complete.
   Rule: Add 0.07

in	out
1.29	1.36
6.47	6.54
5.10	5.17
12.66	12.73
7.93	8.00

5. Multiply. Use a paper-and-pencil algorithm.
   9 * 258 = 2,322

6. Which of the angles below has a measure of about 90 degrees? Circle it.

Math Journal 1, p. 131

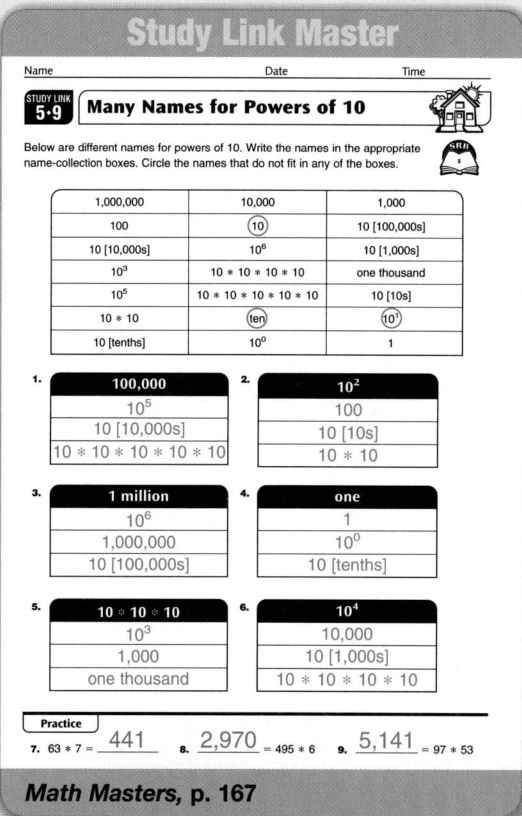

Study Link Master

Name Date Time

STUDY LINK 5•9 **Many Names for Powers of 10**

Below are different names for powers of 10. Write the names in the appropriate name-collection boxes. Circle the names that do not fit in any of the boxes.

1,000,000	10,000	1,000
100	(10)	10 [100,000s]
10 [10,000s]	10^6	10 [1,000s]
10^3	10 * 10 * 10 * 10	one thousand
10^5	10 * 10 * 10 * 10 * 10	10 [10s]
10 * 10	(ten)	(10^1)
10 [tenths]	10^0	1

1. **100,000**: 10^5; 10 [10,000s]; 10 * 10 * 10 * 10 * 10
2. **10^2**: 100; 10 [10s]; 10 * 10
3. **1 million**: 10^6; 1,000,000; 10 [100,000s]
4. **one**: 1; 10^0; 10 [tenths]
5. **10 * 10 * 10**: 10^3; 1,000; one thousand
6. **10^4**: 10,000; 10 [1,000s]; 10 * 10 * 10 * 10

Practice

7. 63 * 7 = 441
8. 2,970 = 495 * 6
9. 5,141 = 97 * 53

Math Masters, p. 167

Teaching Master

Name Date Time

LESSON 5•9 **Powers of 10 on a Calculator**

Experiment to see what happens when your calculator can no longer display all of the digits in a power of 10.

Clear your calculator's memory, then program it to multiply over and over by 10 as follows:

Calculator	Key Sequence
Calculator A	On/Off and Clear together
	Op1 × 10 Op1 10 Op1 Op1 Op1 ...
Calculator B	AC
	10 × × = = = ...

1. What is the largest power of 10 that your calculator can display before it switches from decimal notation to exponential notation?
   1 billion (Calculator A); 10 million (Calculator B)

2. Write what the calculator displays after it switches from decimal notation to exponential notation.
   9 1 × 10^10 (Calculator A); 1. 08× (Calculator B)

3. If there are different kinds of calculators in your classroom, is the largest power of 10 that they can display the same or different from your calculator? If it is different, tell how. Write your answer on the back of this page. Answers vary.

Try This

4. What is the smallest power of 10 that your calculator can display before it switches from decimal notation to exponential notation?
   0.0000000001 (Calculator A); 0.0000001 (Calculator B)

   Explain what you did to find out.
   Sample answer: I followed the steps above but pressed the division key instead of the multiplication key.

***Math Masters,* p. 168**

3 Differentiation Options

ENRICHMENT

INDEPENDENT ACTIVITY

5–15 Min

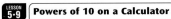

▶ Investigating Powers of 10 on a Calculator

(*Math Masters,* p. 168)

To further explore exponential notation, have students investigate how calculators display powers of 10 and the patterns they show. If more than one kind of calculator is available, have students compare the ways the different calculators perform these functions.

EXTRA PRACTICE

SMALL-GROUP ACTIVITY

5–15 Min

▶ *5-Minute Math*

To offer students more experience with exponential notation, see *5-Minute Math,* pages 2, 3, and 7.

ELL SUPPORT

SMALL-GROUP ACTIVITY

5–15 Min

▶ Building Background for Mathematics Words

To provide language support for exponential notation, have students think of as many ways to use the word *power* as they can. *For example:*

- ▷ The President of the United States has the *power* to veto bills sent from Congress.
- ▷ The United States armed forces are a mighty *power* in the world.
- ▷ A battery *powers* this CD player.
- ▷ He *powered* up (or *powered* down) the computer.
- ▷ Her new car has *power* windows.
- ▷ 100 and 0.1 are *powers* of 10.

5•10 Rounding and Reporting Large Numbers

Objectives To discuss sensible ways of reporting a count when a large number of items has been counted; and to practice rounding numbers.

Technology Resources www.everydaymathonline.com

ePresentations

eToolkit

Algorithms Practice

EM Facts Workshop Game™

Family Letters

Assessment Management

Common Core State Standards

Curriculum Focal Points

Interactive Teacher's Lesson Guide

1 Teaching the Lesson

Key Concepts and Skills

- Read and write whole numbers; identify digits and their values. [Number and Numeration Goal 1]
- Describe differences between estimates and exact counts. [Operations and Computation Goal 6]
- Round numbers to a given place. [Operations and Computation Goal 6]
- Use data presented in a table. [Data and Chance Goal 2]

Key Activities

Students discuss the reliability of large population counts, such as numbers of marathon runners and attendance figures for sports events. They review and practice rounding to a given place.

Ongoing Assessment: Recognizing Student Achievement
Use Mental Math and Reflexes.
[Operations and Computation Goal 3]

Key Vocabulary

rounding (to a certain place)

Materials

Math Journal 1, p. 132
Study Link 5•9
slate

2 Ongoing Learning & Practice

Math Boxes 5•10
Math Journal 1, p. 133
Students practice and maintain skills through Math Box problems.

Study Link 5•10
Math Masters, p. 169
Students practice and maintain skills through Study Link activities.

3 Differentiation Options

READINESS

Using Number Lines to Find the Halfway Point
Math Masters, p. 170
Students explore locating large numbers on a number line.

ENRICHMENT

Rounding Bar Graph Data
Math Masters, p. 171
Students visually round numbers represented on a bar graph.

EXTRA PRACTICE

Taking a 50-Facts Test
Math Masters, pp. 410 and 414; p. 416 (optional)
pen or colored pencil
Students take a 50-facts test. They use a line graph to record individual and optional class scores.

EXTRA PRACTICE

5-Minute Math
5-Minute Math™, pp. 15, 91, and 92
Students practice rounding whole numbers.

Advance Preparation

***Teacher's Reference Manual,* Grades 4–6** pp. 261–264

Getting Started

Mental Math and Reflexes ★ 

Pose multiplication facts and extended facts. *Suggestions:*

●○○	●●○	●●●
9 * 2 = 18	9 * 9 = 81	40 * 9 = 360
4 * 4 = 16	6 * 8 = 48	50 * 7 = 350
3 * 8 = 24	6 * 7 = 42	70 * 80 = 5,600
5 * 4 = 20	9 * 6 = 54	30 * 90 = 2,700

Math Message

A newspaper reported that 20,344 participants ran in the 2004 Boston Marathon. Do you think that number is exactly correct? Be ready to explain your answer.

Study Link 5·9 Follow-Up

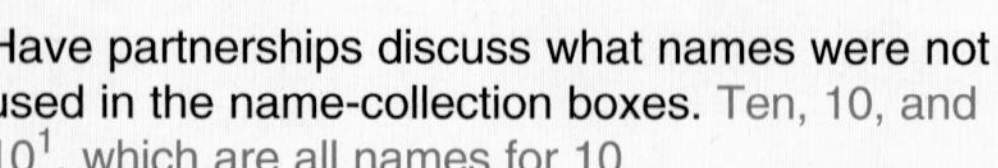

Have partnerships discuss what names were not used in the name-collection boxes. Ten, 10, and 10^1, which are all names for 10

Ongoing Assessment: Recognizing Student Achievement

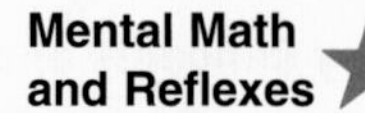

Mental Math and Reflexes ★

Use **Mental Math and Reflexes** to assess students' automaticity with multiplication facts. Students are making adequate progress if they demonstrate automaticity with the ●○○ and ●●○ problems. Some students may demonstrate automaticity with the extended facts in the ●●● problems.

[Operations and Computation Goal 3]

1 Teaching the Lesson

▶ Math Message Follow-Up

WHOLE-CLASS DISCUSSION

On the board, write the reported numbers of runners for the 1994 and 2004 Boston Marathons:

1994: 9,059

2004: 20,344

Have students discuss the reliability of these numbers.

- Do you think *exactly* that many people ran in each race? Why or why not? Probably not. It is difficult to keep track of every person who competes. A person may register to run but then not run for many possible reasons.
- How do you think the counts of runners were obtained? When runners register for a race, each person is given a number to wear, and that person's name and number are recorded on a list.

NOTE These are the official counts of the number of *entrants* in each race, not the number of actual *starters* or *finishers.* A count of finishers is likely to be more accurate than a count of entrants or starters, because officials check off the runners' numbers as they cross the finish line.

In counting large numbers of items (especially things that change constantly), it is probably impossible to come up with a number that is exactly right, down to the last single item. Large counts that are reported without rounding appear to be more accurate than they really are. In these cases, a rounded count is a more honest report about the number of things counted.

Tell students that in this lesson they will practice rounding whole numbers to a certain place.

Reviewing Rounding

WHOLE-CLASS DISCUSSION

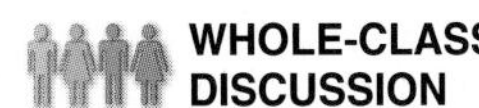

Use the marathon counts to review **rounding** a number to a certain place. Remind students about the steps in rounding a number. For example, to round 20,344 to the nearest hundred follow these steps:

1. Mark the digit in the place you are rounding to. — 20,344
2. Replace all digits to the right of this digit with zeros. This is the *lower number*. — 20,300
3. Add 1 to the digit in the place you are rounding to. This is the higher number. — 20,400
4. Ask yourself: "Is the number I am rounding closer to the lower number or the higher number?" — lower
5. Round to the number that is closer. If the number you are rounding is halfway between the lower and higher numbers, round to the higher number. — 20,300

Work together as a class to round both marathon counts to the nearest thousand, to the nearest hundred, and to the nearest ten.

	Lower number	Higher number	Rounded number
Round 9,059 to the nearest thousand.	9,000	10,000	9,000
Round 9,059 to the nearest hundred.	9,000	9,100	9,100
Round 9,059 to the nearest ten.	9,050	9,060	9,060
Round 20,344 to the nearest thousand.	20,000	21,000	20,000
Round 20,344 to the nearest hundred.	20,300	20,400	20,300
Round 20,344 to the nearest ten.	20,340	20,350	20,340

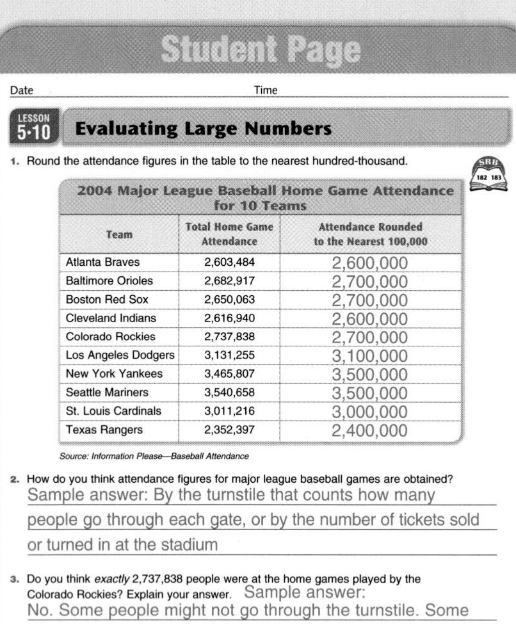

Student Page

Date Time

LESSON 5•10 **Evaluating Large Numbers**

1. Round the attendance figures in the table to the nearest hundred-thousand.

2004 Major League Baseball Home Game Attendance for 10 Teams

Team	Total Home Game Attendance	Attendance Rounded to the Nearest 100,000
Atlanta Braves	2,603,484	2,600,000
Baltimore Orioles	2,682,917	2,700,000
Boston Red Sox	2,650,063	2,700,000
Cleveland Indians	2,616,940	2,600,000
Colorado Rockies	2,737,838	2,700,000
Los Angeles Dodgers	3,131,255	3,100,000
New York Yankees	3,465,807	3,500,000
Seattle Mariners	3,540,658	3,500,000
St. Louis Cardinals	3,011,216	3,000,000
Texas Rangers	2,352,397	2,400,000

Source: Information Please—Baseball Attendance

2. How do you think attendance figures for major league baseball games are obtained?
Sample answer: By the turnstile that counts how many people go through each gate, or by the number of tickets sold or turned in at the stadium

3. Do you think *exactly* 2,737,838 people were at the home games played by the Colorado Rockies? Explain your answer. Sample answer:
No. Some people might not go through the turnstile. Some people who bought tickets might not go. With so many people, mistakes are easily made.

4. You rounded the figures in the table above to the nearest hundred-thousand. Which teams have the same attendance figures based on these rounded numbers?
The Braves and Indians; the Orioles, Red Sox, and Rockies; and the Yankees and Mariners

Math Journal 1, p. 132

Adjusting the Activity

ELL

Use number lines to help students visualize this rounding method. *For example:*

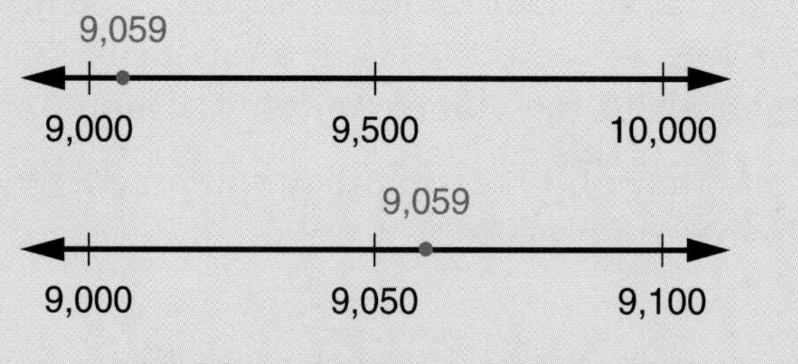

AUDITORY ◆ KINESTHETIC ◆ TACTILE ◆ VISUAL

Summarize by asking students to pretend they are writing a newspaper report of the 1994 (or 2004) marathon. Ask: *Which version of the marathon count would you report—9,059, 9,060, 9,100, or 9,000? Explain your answer.* Sample answer: The number of runners who actually started the race might have differed from the official registrant list by at least 10 to 20, and maybe even by 100. This suggests rounding to the nearest hundred, or 9,100, because it is a more realistic count.

▶ Rounding Baseball Team Attendance Figures

(*Math Journal 1,* p. 132)

Students complete journal page 132. To support English language learners, discuss the meaning of *attendance figures.* Clarify the difference between the meaning of *figure* in this context compared to a geometric *figure.*

Adjusting the Activity

Pose the following question: The teams shown in the table on journal page 132 have between 25,000 and 50,000 attendees per game. Inaccurate counting could well lead to a 2 percent error in the number of attendees or an error of about 1,000 per game. Each team plays about 81 home games. Ask: *What might be the total error in attendees for an entire season?* As large as 50,000 to 100,000 per season This explains why rounding to the nearest 100,000 is a very realistic thing to do.

AUDITORY ◆ KINESTHETIC ◆ TACTILE ◆ VISUAL

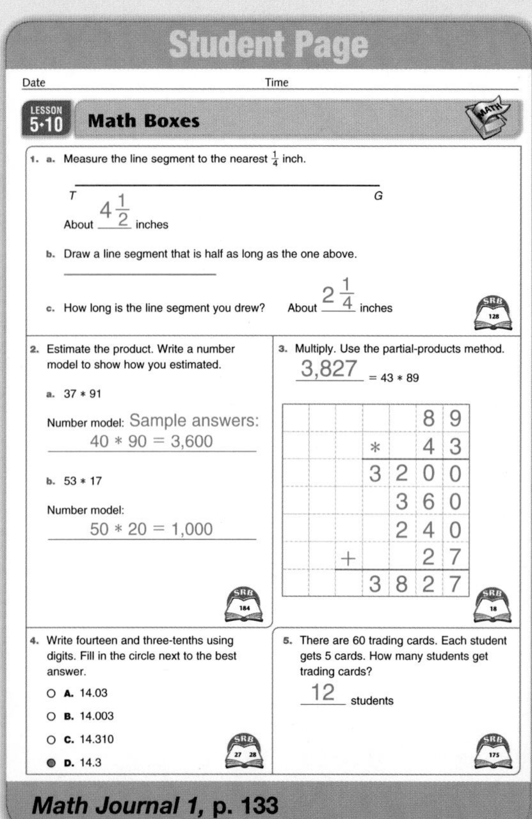

Student Page

Date Time

LESSON 5•10 **Math Boxes**

1. a. Measure the line segment to the nearest $\frac{1}{4}$ inch.
T G
About $4\frac{1}{2}$ inches
b. Draw a line segment that is half as long as the one above.
c. How long is the line segment you drew? About $2\frac{1}{4}$ inches

2. Estimate the product. Write a number model to show how you estimated.
a. 37 ∗ 91
Number model: Sample answers: 40 ∗ 90 = 3,600
b. 53 ∗ 17
Number model: 50 ∗ 20 = 1,000

3. Multiply. Use the partial-products method.
3,827 = 43 ∗ 89

		8	9
	∗	4	3
3	2	0	0
	3	6	0
	2	4	0
+		2	7
3	8	2	7

4. Write fourteen and three-tenths using digits. Fill in the circle next to the best answer.
○ A. 14.03
○ B. 14.003
○ C. 14.310
● D. 14.3

5. There are 60 trading cards. Each student gets 5 cards. How many students get trading cards?
12 students

Math Journal 1, p. 133

2 Ongoing Learning & Practice

▶ Math Boxes 5•10

(*Math Journal 1,* p. 133)

Mixed Practice Math Boxes in this lesson are paired with Math Boxes in Lessons 5-6 and 5-8. The skill in Problem 5 previews Unit 6 content.

Study Link 5•10

INDEPENDENT ACTIVITY

(*Math Masters,* p. 169)

Home Connection Students round basketball stadium seating capacities to the nearest thousand. They round population census data to the nearest million.

3 Differentiation Options

READINESS

INDEPENDENT ACTIVITY

5–15 Min

Using Number Lines to Find the Halfway Point

(*Math Masters,* p. 170)

To explore locating large numbers on a number line, have students find halfway points on segments of number lines. Then have them plot a number less than or greater than the halfway number.

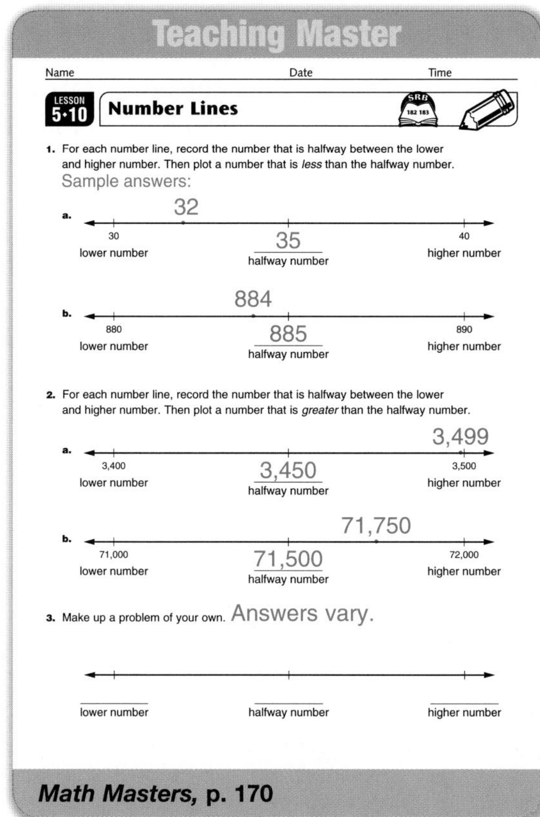

Teaching Master

Name Date Time

LESSON 5•10 **Number Lines**

1. For each number line, record the number that is halfway between the lower and higher number. Then plot a number that is *less* than the halfway number.
Sample answers:

a. 32
30 lower number; 35 halfway number; 40 higher number

b. 884
880 lower number; 885 halfway number; 890 higher number

2. For each number line, record the number that is halfway between the lower and higher number. Then plot a number that is *greater* than the halfway number.

a. 3,499
3,400 lower number; 3,450 halfway number; 3,500 higher number

b. 71,750
71,000 lower number; 71,500 halfway number; 72,000 higher number

3. Make up a problem of your own. Answers vary.

lower number; halfway number; higher number

Math Masters, p. 170

Study Link Master

Name Date Time

STUDY LINK 5•10 **Rounding**

1. Round the seating capacities in the table below to the nearest thousand.

Women's National Basketball Association Seating Capacity of Home Courts

Team	Seating Capacity	Rounded to the Nearest 1,000
Charlotte Sting	24,042	24,000
Cleveland Rockers	20,562	21,000
Detroit Shock	22,076	22,000
New York Liberty	19,763	20,000
Phoenix Mercury	19,023	19,000
Sacramento Monarchs	17,317	17,000
San Antonio Stars	18,500	19,000
Seattle Storm	17,072	17,000

2. Look at your rounded numbers. Which stadiums have about the same capacity?
Mercury and Stars; Monarchs and Storm

3. Round the population figures in the table below to the nearest million.

U.S. Population by Official Census from 1940 to 2000

Year	Population	Rounded to the Nearest Million
1940	132,164,569	132,000,000
1960	179,323,175	179,000,000
1980	226,542,203	227,000,000
2000	281,421,906	281,000,000

Source for both tables: The World Almanac and Book of Facts 2004

Practice

4. 4,152 = 692 ∗ 6
5. 798 = 38 ∗ 21
6. 44 ∗ 73 = 3,212

Math Masters, p. 169

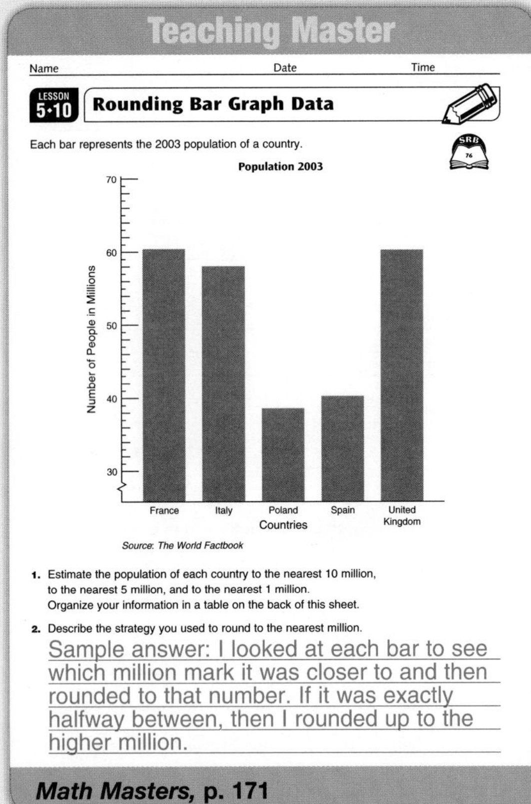

Teaching Master
Name
Date
Time
LESSON 5•10
Rounding Bar Graph Data
Each bar represents the 2003 population of a country.
Population 2003
Number of People in Millions
70
60
50
40
30
France
Italy
Poland
Spain
United Kingdom
Countries
Source: The World Factbook
1. Estimate the population of each country to the nearest 10 million, to the nearest 5 million, and to the nearest 1 million. Organize your information in a table on the back of this sheet.
2. Describe the strategy you used to round to the nearest million.
Sample answer: I looked at each bar to see which million mark it was closer to and then rounded to that number. If it was exactly halfway between, then I rounded up to the higher million.

Math Masters, **p. 171**

NOTE To provide practice with pictographs, have students create a pictograph to represent the data in the bar graph on *Math Masters,* page 171. Remind students that they need to use a key. Suggest that each picture or symbol represent 10 million people.

ENRICHMENT

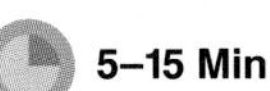

▶ Rounding Bar Graph Data

(*Math Masters,* p. 171)

To apply students' understanding of rounding, have them use population data represented on a bar graph to practice visually rounding numbers. Direct students' attention to the break near the bottom of the vertical axis of the graph. Students should note that the vertical axis begins at 30 million, not at 0.

In Problem 1, students organize the information in a table. Sample answer:

Population in 2003

Country	Nearest 10 million	Nearest 5 million	Nearest 1 million
France	60 million	60 million	61 million
Italy	60 million	60 million	58 million
Poland	40 million	40 million	39 million
Spain	40 million	40 million	41 million
U.K.	60 million	60 million	60 million

Have students discuss the advantages and disadvantages of rounding to each place specified in the problem. Sample answer: It is easier to round to the nearest 10 million because the 10 millions are marked on the graph. If the bars are almost the same height, it is easier to compare them if you round to the nearest million.

EXTRA PRACTICE

▶ Taking a 50-Facts Test

(*Math Masters,* pp. 410, 414, and 416)

See Lesson 3-4 for details regarding the administration of the 50-facts test and the recording and graphing of individual and optional class results.

EXTRA PRACTICE

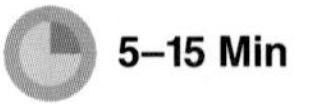

▶ *5-Minute Math*

To offer students more experience with rounding numbers, see *5-Minute Math,* pages 15, 91, and 92.

5•11 Comparing Data

Objective To guide students as they look up and compare numerical data, including geographical measurements.

www.everydaymathonline.com

ePresentations

eToolkit

Algorithms Practice

EM Facts Workshop Game™

Family Letters

Assessment Management

Common Core State Standards

Curriculum Focal Points

Interactive Teacher's Lesson Guide

1 Teaching the Lesson

Key Concepts and Skills

- Read and write large numbers. [Number and Numeration Goal 1]
- Develop the meaning of percent as per 100. [Number and Numeration Goal 5]
- Compare large numbers. [Number and Numeration Goal 6]
- Use a table of information. [Data and Chance Goal 2]

Key Activities

Students use the World Tour section of the *Student Reference Book* to look up population, area, and climate data for countries and capitals of Europe. They identify the maximum and minimum values for each count or measure. They compare counts and measures by comparing the initial digits of the numbers.

Materials

Math Journal 1, p. 134
Student Reference Book, pp. 279–281, 294 (optional), 297, 301, and 304
Study Link 5•10
Math Masters, p. 426 (optional)
slate

2 Ongoing Learning & Practice

Updating the World Tour

Math Journal 1, pp. 171–173, 178, and 179
Student Reference Book, pp. 276, 277, 279–281, 297, 302–305
Math Masters, pp. 419–421 (optional)
Students continue their World Tour by traveling from Cairo, Egypt, to Budapest, Hungary. They update their Route Map and complete the Country Notes for Hungary. Students who are keeping a Route Log update it.

Solving Addition and Subtraction Number Stories

Math Journal 1, pp. 134A and 134B
Students solve addition and subtraction number stories.

Math Boxes 5•11

Math Journal 1, p. 135
Students practice and maintain skills through Math Box problems.

Ongoing Assessment: Recognizing Student Achievement

Use Math Boxes, Problems 2a–2d. [Number and Numeration Goal 6]

Study Link 5•11

Math Masters, p. 172
Students practice and maintain skills through Study Link activities.

3 Differentiation Options

READINESS

Playing *Number Top-It*

Student Reference Book, p. 255
Math Masters, pp. 492, 493, and 506
per partnership: 4 each of number cards 0–9 (from the Everything Math Deck, if available) ◆ tape
Students practice comparing numbers.

EXTRA PRACTICE

Playing *High-Number Toss*

Student Reference Book, p. 252
Math Masters, p. 487
per partnership: 1 six-sided die
Students practice comparing numbers.

Advance Preparation

For the optional Readiness activity in Part 3, make a place-value mat by taping together *Math Masters*, pages 492 and 493.

 ***Teacher's Reference Manual,* Grades 4–6** pp. 230, 261–264

Getting Started

Mental Math and Reflexes

Write pairs of numbers on the board. Students record the larger number on their slates. *Suggestions:*

●○○ 3,482 and 3,982 3,982
6,005 and 6,500 6,500
8,600 and 8,599 8,600

●●○ 35,281 and 34,975 35,281
78,004 and 78,400 78,400
238,756 and 209,899 238,756

●●● 984,063 and 984,065 984,065
1,239,462 and 1,239,362 1,239,462
5,400,780 and 5,410,780 5,410,780

Math Message

Find the table listing the tallest mountains on page 304 in your Student Reference Book. *Which digits tell you that Everest is taller than K-2?*

ten thousands *thousands* *hundreds* *tens* *ones*

Study Link 5·10 Follow-Up

Have students compare their rounded numbers for the census data. Ask which 20-year span showed the greatest growth. 1980 to 2000

Unit
feet

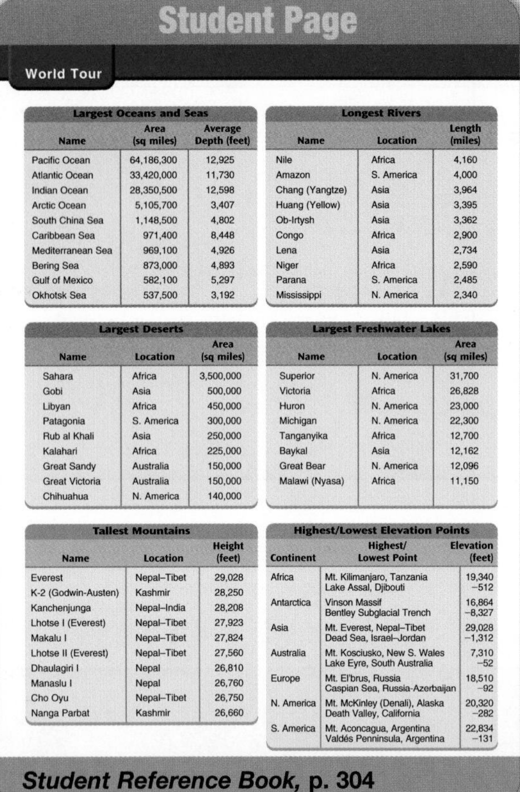

Student Page

World Tour

Largest Oceans and Seas		
Name	Area (sq miles)	Average Depth (feet)
Pacific Ocean	64,186,300	12,925
Atlantic Ocean	33,420,000	11,730
Indian Ocean	28,350,500	12,598
Arctic Ocean	5,105,700	3,407
South China Sea	1,148,500	4,802
Caribbean Sea	971,400	8,448
Mediterranean Sea	969,100	4,926
Bering Sea	873,000	4,893
Gulf of Mexico	582,100	5,297
Okhotsk Sea	537,500	3,192

Longest Rivers		
Name	Location	Length (miles)
Nile	Africa	4,160
Amazon	S. America	4,000
Chang (Yangtze)	Asia	3,964
Huang (Yellow)	Asia	3,395
Ob-Irtysh	Asia	3,362
Congo	Africa	2,900
Lena	Asia	2,734
Niger	Africa	2,590
Parana	S. America	2,485
Mississippi	N. America	2,340

Largest Deserts		
Name	Location	Area (sq miles)
Sahara	Africa	3,500,000
Gobi	Asia	500,000
Libyan	Africa	450,000
Patagonia	S. America	300,000
Rub al Khali	Asia	250,000
Kalahari	Africa	225,000
Great Sandy	Australia	150,000
Great Victoria	Australia	150,000
Chihuahua	N. America	140,000

Largest Freshwater Lakes		
Name	Location	Area (sq miles)
Superior	N. America	31,700
Victoria	Africa	26,828
Huron	N. America	23,000
Michigan	N. America	22,300
Tanganyika	Africa	12,700
Baykal	Asia	12,162
Great Bear	N. America	12,096
Malawi (Nyasa)	Africa	11,150

Tallest Mountains		
Name	Location	Height (feet)
Everest	Nepal–Tibet	29,028
K-2 (Godwin-Austen)	Kashmir	28,250
Kanchenjunga	Nepal–India	28,208
Lhotse I (Everest)	Nepal–Tibet	27,923
Makalu I	Nepal–Tibet	27,824
Lhotse II (Everest)	Nepal–Tibet	27,560
Dhaulagiri I	Nepal	26,810
Manaslu I	Nepal	26,760
Cho Oyu	Nepal–Tibet	26,750
Nanga Parbat	Kashmir	26,660

Highest/Lowest Elevation Points		
Continent	Highest/ Lowest Point	Elevation (feet)
Africa	Mt. Kilimanjaro, Tanzania Lake Assal, Djibouti	19,340 −512
Antarctica	Vinson Massif Bentley Subglacial Trench	16,864 −8,327
Asia	Mt. Everest, Nepal–Tibet Dead Sea, Israel–Jordan	29,028 −1,312
Australia	Mt. Kosciusko, New S. Wales Lake Eyre, South Australia	7,310 −52
Europe	Mt. El'brus, Russia Caspian Sea, Russia-Azerbaijan	18,510 −92
N. America	Mt. McKinley (Denali), Alaska Death Valley, California	20,320 −282
S. America	Mt. Aconcagua, Argentina Valdés Penninsula, Argentina	22,834 −131

Student Reference Book, p. 304

1 Teaching the Lesson

▶ Math Message Follow-Up

WHOLE-CLASS ACTIVITY

(*Student Reference Book,* p. 294 (optional); p. 304)

Social Studies Link On the board, draw a unit box like the one in the margin. Write the names and heights of Everest and K-2, and underline the digit in the ten-thousands place in each numeral.

Everest 29,028
K-2 28,250

Point out that this digit (2) is the same for both numbers, so it cannot be used to decide which mountain is higher.

Now underline the second digit (thousands) in each numeral. Use a double underline, because these digits are different. Everest has one more thousand than K-2. So Everest is higher.

Everest 29,028
K-2 28,250

The remaining 3 digits in each number can be ignored, because they are in the hundreds or smaller. Only the first 2 digits (the ten-thousands and thousands digits) are needed to determine that Everest is higher than K-2.

Repeat this routine by comparing the heights of K-2 and Kanchenjunga and then the heights of Lhotse I and Makalu I.

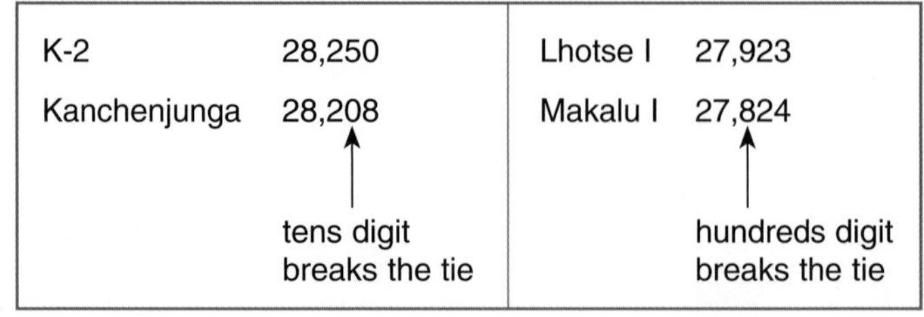

K-2 28,250
Kanchenjunga 28,208
tens digit breaks the tie
Lhotse I 27,923
Makalu I 27,824
hundreds digit breaks the tie

Finally, use the Oceans and Seas table shown on the same page of the *Student Reference Book*. Compare the depths of the Indian and Arctic Oceans. (You need to look only at the ten-thousands place.) Compare the depths of the Arctic Ocean and the South China Sea. (You need to look only at the thousands place.)

Adjusting the Activity

Refer students to *Student Reference Book,* page 294 for more information about how geographical measurements such as heights of mountains, depths of oceans, and lengths of rivers are obtained.

AUDITORY ◆ KINESTHETIC ◆ TACTILE ◆ VISUAL

Looking Up and Comparing Data about the Countries in Europe

INDEPENDENT ACTIVITY

(*Math Journal 1,* p. 134; *Student Reference Book,* pp. 279–281, 297, and 301; *Math Masters,* p. 426)

Social Studies Link Students complete journal page 134 by looking up the information in the World Tour section of the *Student Reference Book.*

▷ Country population and area data are listed in the Country Profiles on pages 279–281.

▷ Temperature data are listed in the Climate and Elevation of Capital Cities table on page 297.

▷ Percent of a country's population that is 0–14 years old is listed in the Population Data table on page 301.

Adjusting the Activity

ELL

Have students shade 10-by-10 grids to interpret the Percent of Population Ages 0–14 data in the table on *Student Reference Book,* page 301. *For example:*

▷ The percent of population ages 0–14 for Ethiopia is 47. This means that 47 out of every 100 Ethiopians are 14 years old or younger. Have students shade 47 squares on a 10-by-10 grid (*Math Masters,* page 426). The shaded squares, $\frac{47}{100}$, represent the percent of the Ethiopian population that is 14 years old or younger.

▷ The percent of population ages 0–14 for the United States is 21. Have students shade 21 squares on a 10-by-10 grid (*Math Masters,* page 426). The shaded squares, $\frac{21}{100}$, represent the percent of the U.S. population that is 14 years old or younger.

AUDITORY ◆ KINESTHETIC ◆ TACTILE ◆ VISUAL

Links to the Future

In Unit 9 of *Fourth Grade Everyday Mathematics,* students will rename fourths, fifths, tenths, and hundredths as decimals and percents.

Student Page

Date ____ Time ____

Traveling to Europe

It is time to leave Africa. Your destination is Region 2—the continent of Europe. You and your classmates will fly from Cairo, Egypt to Budapest, Hungary. Before exploring Hungary, you will collect information about the countries in Region 2. You may even decide to visit another country in Europe after your stay in Budapest.

SRB 280 297 301

Use the World Tour section of your *Student Reference Book* to answer the questions.

1. Which country in Region 2 has

a. the largest population? France (country) 60,424,000 (population)

b. the smallest population? Iceland (country) 294,000 (population)

c. the largest area? France (country) 211,200 sq mi. (area)

d. the smallest area? Netherlands (country) 16,000 sq mi. (area)

Use the Climate and Elevation of Capital Cities table on page 297.

2. From December to February, which capital in Region 2 has

a. the warmest weather? Athens (capital) Greece (country) 56/45°F (temperatures)

b. the coolest weather? Oslo (capital) Norway (country) 32/20°F (temperatures)

c. the greatest amount of rain? Rome (capital) Italy (country) 3.3 (inches rainfall)

d. the least amount of rain? Warsaw (capital) Poland (country) 1.2 (inches rainfall)

Use the Population Data table on page 301.

3. Which country in Region 2 has

a. the greatest percent of population ages 0–14? Iceland (country) 23 (percent)

b. the smallest percent of population ages 0–14? Italy (country) 14 (percent)

Math Journal 1, p. 134

Student Page

Date Time

LESSON 5•11 **Water, Water Everywhere**

Solve each problem below. Record a number model for the problem using a letter for the unknown. You may want to use two number models for some of the problems. Then write a summary number model with your answer in place of the letter.

Sample number models are given.

1. The world's largest lake is the Caspian Sea, with an area of about 143,200 square miles. The second largest lake, Lake Superior, has an area of about 31,320 square miles. What is the approximate total area of both lakes?

   Answer: About 174,520 square miles

   143,200 + 31,320 = *t* (number model with unknown)

   143,200 + 31,320 = 174,520 (number model with answer)

2. The Nile River in Egypt is about 4,132 miles long. The longest river in the United States, the Missouri River, stretches about 2,540 miles. How much longer is the Nile River than the Missouri River?

   Answer: About 1,592 miles

   4,132 – 2,540 = *m* (number model with unknown)

   4,132 – 2,540 = 1,592 (number model with answer)

3. To grow a single orange, it takes about 13.8 gallons of water. A tomato is made of 95% water, but takes only 3 gallons of water to grow it. How much more water is needed to grow an orange than a tomato?

   Answer: About 10.8 gallons

   13.8 – 3 = *m* (number model with unknown)

   13.8 – 3 = 10.8 (number model with answer)

Math Journal 1, p. 134A

Student Page

Date Time

LESSON 5•11 **Water, Water Everywhere** *continued*

Sample number models are given.

4. The average depth of the ocean is 4,267 meters. The deepest spot, Challenger Deep in the Mariana Trench near Guam, is about 11,030 meters below the surface. How much deeper is Challenger Deep than the average depth of the ocean?

   Answer: About 6,763 meters

   11,030 – 4,267 = *d* (number model with unknown)

   11,030 – 4,267 = 6,763 (number model with answer)

5. The total annual rainfall for the three wettest inhabited places in the world is 1,416 inches. In the wettest place, Cherrapunji, India, it rains about 498 inches per year. In the second wettest place, Mawsynram, India, it rains about 467 inches per year. About how many inches per year does it rain in the third wettest place, Waialeale, Hawaii?

   Answer: About 451 in.

   1416 – 498 – 467 = *r* (number model(s) with unknown)

   1416 – 498 – 467 = 451 (number model(s) with answer)

6. Alaska, the biggest state in the United States, has more miles of rivers and streams than any other state. The next four highest ranked states are California with 211,513 miles; Texas with 191,228 miles; Montana with 176,750 miles; and Nevada with 143,750 miles. The top five states have 1,088,241 miles of rivers and streams. How many miles of rivers and streams does Alaska have?

   Answer: About 365,000 miles

   211,513 + 191,228 + 176,750 + 143,750 = 723,241; 1,088,241 – 723,241 = *m* (number model(s) with unknown)

   211,513 + 191,228 + 176,750 + 143,750 = 723,241; 1,088,241 – 723,241 = 365,000 (number model(s) with answer)

Math Journal, p. 134B

2 Ongoing Learning & Practice

Updating the World Tour

INDEPENDENT ACTIVITY

(*Math Journal 1,* pp. 171–173, 178, and 179; *Student Reference Book,* pp. 276, 277, 279–281, 297, and 302–305; *Math Masters,* pp. 419–421)

Social Studies Link Students follow the established World Tour routine.

- They update the Route Map by drawing a line segment to connect Cairo, Egypt, and Budapest, Hungary.
- They use the World Tour section of the *Student Reference Book* to locate facts about Hungary and Budapest and fill in the Country Notes pages for this country and capital.
- If students are using a Route Log, they update it.

Solving Addition and Subtraction Number Stories

PARTNER ACTIVITY

(*Math Journal 1,* pp. 134A and 134B)

Students solve addition and subtraction number stories about water. They find the answer, record a number model with an unknown, and then record a summary number model.

Math Boxes 5•11

INDEPENDENT ACTIVITY

(*Math Journal 1,* p. 135)

Mixed Practice Math Boxes in this lesson are paired with Math Boxes in Lesson 5-9. The skill in Problem 6 previews Unit 6 content.

Ongoing Assessment: Recognizing Student Achievement

Math Boxes Problems 2a–2d

Use **Math Boxes, Problems 2a–2d** to assess students' ability to compare numbers up to 1 billion. Students are making adequate progress if they can insert > and < symbols to make true number sentences. Some students may be able to solve Problem 2e, which involves exponential notation for powers of 10.

[Number and Numeration Goal 6]

Study Link 5•11

INDEPENDENT ACTIVITY

(*Math Masters,* p. 172)

Home Connection Students compare numerical data. They practice reading numbers in the billions.

3 Differentiation Options

READINESS

PARTNER ACTIVITY

Playing *Number Top-It*

5–15 Min

(*Student Reference Book,* p. 255; *Math Masters,* pp. 492, 493, and 506)

To explore comparing large numbers, have students play *Number Top-It.* Players make a place-value mat by taping together *Math Masters,* pages 492 and 493. Students compare two numbers by seeing them, one under the other, with the same-place digits aligned. Students compare the values of the aligned pairs of digits, starting on the left. *For example:*

5,274,906 5,293,881	
	The millions digits are the same; their value is 5,000,000 each.
	The hundred-thousands digits are the same; their value is 200,000 each.
	The ten-thousands digits are not the same; 90,000 is greater than 70,000, so 5,293,881 is greater than 5,274,906.

Have students record a few rounds of play on *Math Masters,* page 506 and then choose one of the rounds to explain how they knew which number was greater.

EXTRA PRACTICE

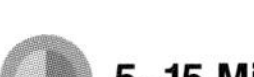

PARTNER ACTIVITY

Playing *High-Number Toss*

5–15 Min

(*Student Reference Book,* p. 252; *Math Masters,* p. 487)

To practice comparing numbers, have students play *High-Number Toss*. See Lesson 2-7 for additional information.

Student Page

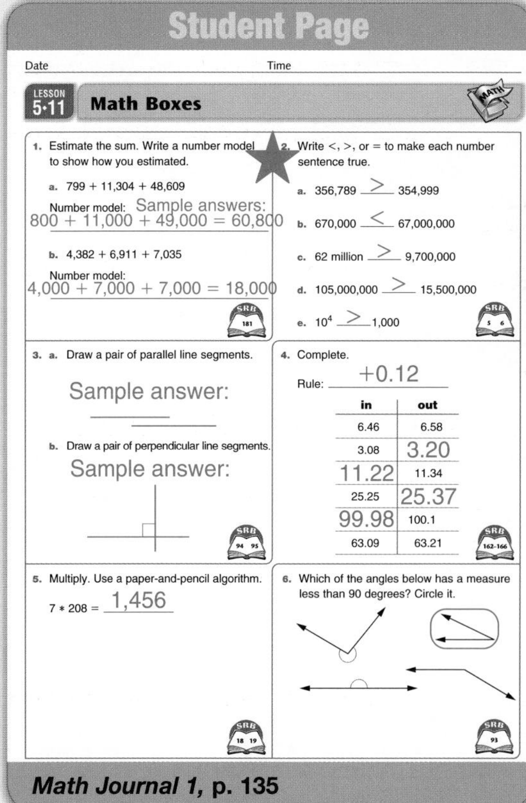

Date Time

LESSON 5·11 **Math Boxes**

1. Estimate the sum. Write a number model to show how you estimated.
   a. 799 + 11,304 + 48,609
   Number model: Sample answers: 800 + 11,000 + 49,000 = 60,800
   b. 4,382 + 6,911 + 7,035
   Number model: 4,000 + 7,000 + 7,000 = 18,000

2. Write <, >, or = to make each number sentence true.
   a. 356,789 > 354,999
   b. 670,000 < 67,000,000
   c. 62 million > 9,700,000
   d. 105,000,000 > 15,500,000
   e. 10^4 > 1,000

3. a. Draw a pair of parallel line segments.
   Sample answer:
   b. Draw a pair of perpendicular line segments.
   Sample answer:

4. Complete.
   Rule: +0.12

in	out
6.46	6.58
3.08	3.20
11.22	11.34
25.25	25.37
99.98	100.1
63.09	63.21

5. Multiply. Use a paper-and-pencil algorithm.
   7 * 208 = 1,456

6. Which of the angles below has a measure less than 90 degrees? Circle it.

Math Journal 1, p. 135

Study Link Master

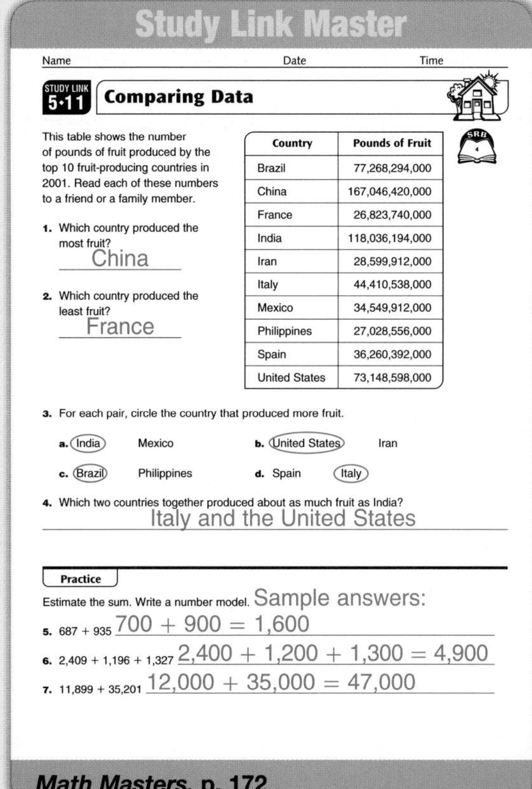

Name Date Time

STUDY LINK 5·11 **Comparing Data**

This table shows the number of pounds of fruit produced by the top 10 fruit-producing countries in 2001. Read each of these numbers to a friend or a family member.

Country	Pounds of Fruit
Brazil	77,268,294,000
China	167,046,420,000
France	26,823,740,000
India	118,036,194,000
Iran	28,599,912,000
Italy	44,410,538,000
Mexico	34,549,912,000
Philippines	27,028,556,000
Spain	36,260,392,000
United States	73,148,598,000

1. Which country produced the most fruit? China
2. Which country produced the least fruit? France
3. For each pair, circle the country that produced more fruit.
   a. (India) Mexico
   b. (United States) Iran
   c. (Brazil) Philippines
   d. Spain (Italy)
4. Which two countries together produced about as much fruit as India? Italy and the United States

Practice

Estimate the sum. Write a number model. Sample answers:

5. 687 + 935 700 + 900 = 1,600
6. 2,409 + 1,196 + 1,327 2,400 + 1,200 + 1,300 = 4,900
7. 11,899 + 35,201 12,000 + 35,000 = 47,000

Math Masters, p. 172

5•12 Progress Check 5

Objective To assess students' progress on mathematical content through the end of Unit 5.

1 Looking Back: Cumulative Assessment

Input student data from Progress Check 5 into the **Assessment Management Spreadsheets.**

Materials

- Study Link 5•11
- *Assessment Handbook,* pp. 84–91, 174–178, 220, and 262–265
- slate

CONTENT ASSESSED	LESSON(S)	ASSESSMENT ITEMS: SELF	ORAL/SLATE	WRITTEN PART A	WRITTEN PART B	OPEN RESPONSE
Read and write whole numbers through millions; identify digits and their values. [Number and Numeration Goal 1]	5•1–5•3, 5•5, 5•7, 5•11		1, 4			✓
Write powers of 10 in exponential notation. [Number and Numeration Goal 4]	5•6, 5•9		3			
Order whole numbers through millions. [Number and Numeration Goal 6]	5•2, 5•4, 5•8, 5•9, 5•11				20	
Solve extended multiplication facts. [Operations and Computation Goal 3]	5•1–5•7			13–15	18, 19	
Multiply multidigit whole numbers. [Operations and Computation Goal 4]	5•4–5•11	1, 2		3–6	16b, 17b	✓
Make estimates for addition and multiplication problems. [Operations and Computation Goal 6]	5•3–5•11	3	2	1, 2	16a, 17a	✓
Add and subtract decimals. [Operations and Computation Goal 2]	5•2, 5•4, 5•9, 5•11	4		7–11		
Measure line segments to the nearest $\frac{1}{4}$ in. and 0.5 cm. [Measurement and Reference Frames Goal 1]	5•2, 5•4, 5•6, 5•8, 5•10, 5•11	5		12	21	
Find and use rules for simple functions. [Patterns, Functions, and Algebra Goal 1]	5•5, 5•7, 5•9, 5•11	6		13–15		
Apply the Distributive Property of Multiplication over Addition. [Patterns, Functions, and Algebra Goal 4]	5•4–5•11			3–6	16b, 17b	

2 Looking Ahead: Preparing for Unit 6

Math Boxes 5•12

Study Link 5•12: Unit 6 Family Letter

Materials

- *Math Journal 1,* p. 136
- *Math Masters,* pp. 173–176

Getting Started

Math Message • Self Assessment

Complete the Self Assessment (Assessment Handbook, *page 174*).

Study Link 5+11 Follow-Up

Have students compare answers. Ask volunteers to explain how they solved Problem 4.

1 Looking Back: Cumulative Assessment

Math Message Follow-Up

(Self Assessment, *Assessment Handbook,* p. 174)

The Self Assessment offers students the opportunity to reflect upon their progress.

Oral and Slate Assessments

Problem 2 provides summative information and can be used for grading purposes. Problems 1, 3, and 4 provide formative information that can be useful in planning future instruction.

Oral Assessment

1. Write numbers through billions on the board. Have students read them aloud.
2. Pose addition problems. Ask students to describe the strategy they use to estimate the sum. *Suggestions:*

   Sample answers:

   - 639 + 752 600 + 800 = 1,400
   - 456 + 892 450 + 900 = 1,350
   - 1,395 + 2,142 1,500 + 2,000 = 3,500
   - 3,849 + 7,026 4,000 + 7,000 = 11,000

Slate Assessment

3. Write powers of 10 in standard notation, as products whose factors are 10, and in words. Students use exponential notation to name the powers of 10. *Suggestions:*

   - 100 10^2
   - 10,000 10^4
   - 10 ∗ 10 ∗ 10 10^3
   - 10 ∗ 10 ∗ 10 ∗ 10 ∗ 10 10^5
   - one million 10^6

Assessment Master

Name Date Time

LESSON 5+12 **Self Assessment** Progress Check 5

Think about each skill listed below. Assess your own progress by checking the most appropriate box.

Skills	I can do this on my own and explain how to do it.	I can do this on my own.	I can do this if I get help or look at an example.
1. Multiply numbers like these: 23 ∗ 5 214 ∗ 3			
2. Multiply numbers like these: 26 ∗ 31 78 ∗ 64			
3. Estimate sums like this: 493 + 262 is about 800			
4. Add and subtract decimals like these: 8.4 + 6.3 14.75 − 8.32			
5. Measure line segments in inches and centimeters.			
6. Complete a "What's My Rule?" table.			

Assessment Handbook, **p. 174**

Assessment Master

Name Date Time

LESSON 5+12 **Written Assessment** Progress Check 5

Part A

Circle the number closest to the sum. Write a number model for the estimate.

1. 486 + 732 900 (1,200) 1,500 1,800

   Number model: Sample answer: 500 + 700 = 1,200

2. 515 + 987 + 264 1,000 1,400 (1,800) 2,200

   Number model: Sample answer: 500 + 1,000 + 300 = 1,800

Use the partial-products algorithm to multiply.

3. 5 ∗ 57 = 285
4. 42 ∗ 6 = 252
5. 241 ∗ 3 = 723
6. 32 ∗ 50 = 1,600

Add or subtract.

7. 9.6 + 7.3 = 16.9
8. 2.63 + 4.15 = 6.78
9. 8.9 − 5.3 = 3.6
10. 12.86 − 9.34 = 3.52

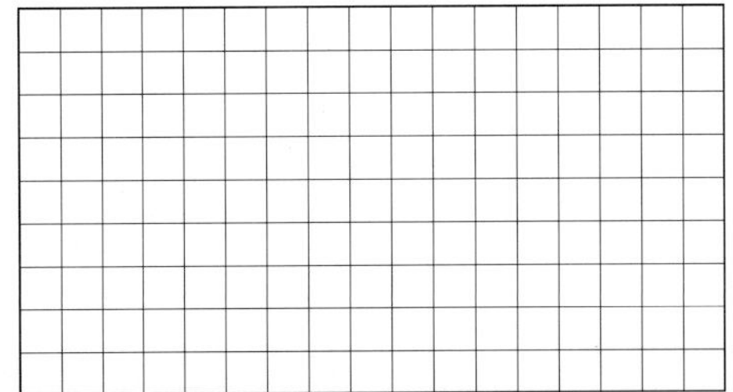

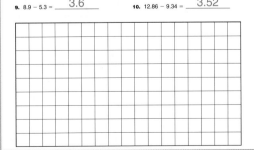

Assessment Handbook, **p. 175**

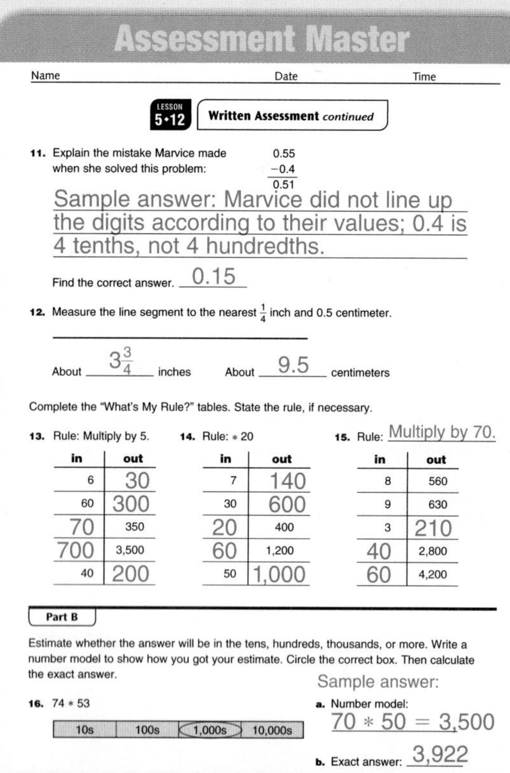
Assessment Handbook, p. 176

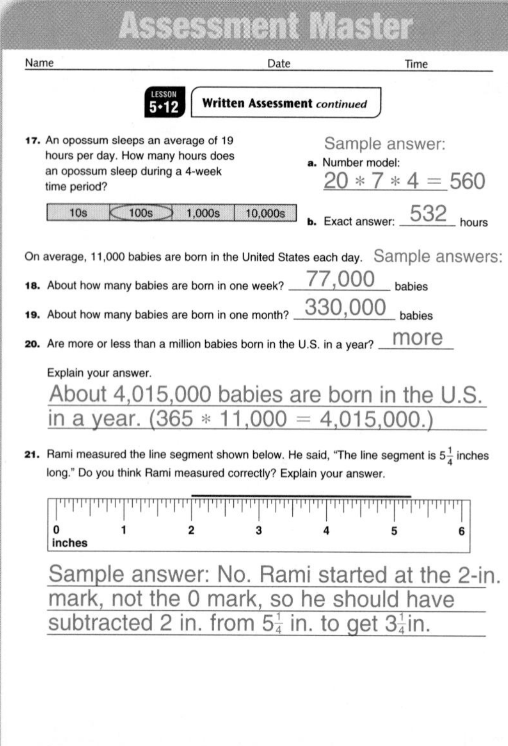
Assessment Handbook, p. 177

4. Write numbers through the billions on the board. Pose questions such as the following:
   - Which digit is in the millions place?
   - What is the value of the digit *x*?
   - How many billions are there?

▶ Written Assessment

INDEPENDENT ACTIVITY

(*Assessment Handbook,* pp. 175–177)

Part A Recognizing Student Achievement

Problems 1–15 provide summative information and may be used for grading purposes.

Problem(s)	Description
1, 2	Estimate sums.
3–6	Multiply multidigit whole numbers.
7–11	Add and subtract decimals.
12	Measure to the nearest $\frac{1}{4}$ in. and 0.5 cm.
13–15	Multiply using "What's My Rule?" tables.

Part B Informing Instruction

Problems 16–21 provide formative information that can be useful in planning future instruction.

Problem(s)	Description
16a, 17a	Estimate products.
16b, 17b	Multiply multidigit whole numbers.
18–20	Multiply using extended facts.
21	Measure to the nearest $\frac{1}{4}$ in. and 0.5 cm when the 0-mark of the ruler is not positioned at the end of an object.

Use the checklists on pages 263 and 265 of the *Assessment Handbook* to record results. Then input the data into the **Assessment Management Spreadsheets** to keep an ongoing record of students' progress toward Grade-Level Goal

▶ Open Response

INDEPENDENT ACTIVITY

(*Assessment Handbook,* p. 178)

Walking Away with a Million Dollars

The open-response item requires students to apply concepts and skills from Unit 5 to solve a multistep problem. See *Assessment Handbook,* pages 87–91 for rubrics and students' work samples for this problem.

2 Looking Ahead: Preparing for Unit 6

Math Boxes 5·12

INDEPENDENT ACTIVITY

(*Math Journal 1,* p. 136)

Mixed Practice This Math Boxes page previews Unit 6 content.

Study Link 5·12: Unit 6 Family Letter

INDEPENDENT ACTIVITY

(*Math Masters,* pp. 173–176)

Home Connection The Unit 6 Family Letter provides parents and guardians with information and activities related to Unit 6 topics.

Study Link Masters

Name Date Time

STUDY LINK 5·12 **Unit 6: Family Letter**

Division; Map Reference Frames; Measures of Angles

The first four lessons and the last lesson of Unit 6 focus on understanding the division operation, developing a method for dividing whole numbers, and solving division number stories.

Though most adults reach for a calculator to do a long-division problem, it is useful to know a paper-and-pencil procedure for computations such as 567 ÷ 6 and 15)235. Fortunately, there is a method that is similar to the one most of us learned in school but is much easier to understand and use. This method is called the **partial-quotients method.**

Students have had considerable practice with extended division facts, such as 420 ÷ 7 = 60, and questions, such as "About how many 12s are in 150?" Using the partial-quotients method, your child will apply these skills to build partial quotients until the exact quotient and remainder are determined.

Full-circle (360°) protractor

This unit also focuses on numbers in map coordinate systems. For maps of relatively small areas, rectangular coordinate grids are used. For world maps and the world globe, the system of latitude and longitude is used to locate places.

Because this global system is based on angle measures, the class will practice measuring and drawing angles with full-circle (360°) and half-circle (180°) protractors. If you have a protractor, ask your child to show you how to use this tool.

Half-circle (180°) protractor

The class is well into the World Tour. Students have visited Africa and are now traveling in Europe. They are beginning to see how numerical information about a country helps them get a better understanding of the country—its size, climate, location, and population distribution—and how these characteristics affect the way people live. Your child may want to share with you information about some of the countries the class has visited. Encourage your child to take materials about Europe to school, such as magazine articles, travel brochures, and articles in the travel section of your newspaper.

Please keep this Family Letter for reference as your child works through Unit 6.

Math Masters, pp. 173–176

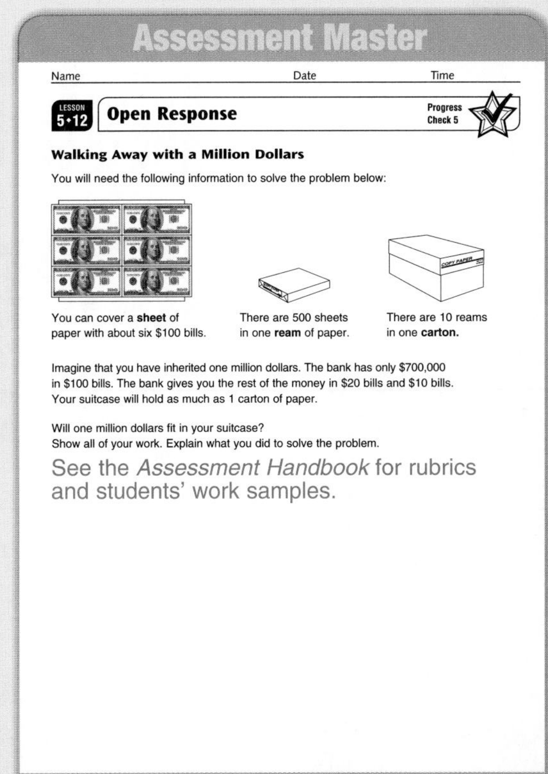

Assessment Master

Name Date Time

LESSON 5·12 **Open Response** Progress Check 5

Walking Away with a Million Dollars

You will need the following information to solve the problem below:

You can cover a **sheet** of paper with about six $100 bills.

There are 500 sheets in one **ream** of paper.

There are 10 reams in one **carton.**

Imagine that you have inherited one million dollars. The bank has only $700,000 in $100 bills. The bank gives you the rest of the money in $20 bills and $10 bills. Your suitcase will hold as much as 1 carton of paper.

Will one million dollars fit in your suitcase?
Show all of your work. Explain what you did to solve the problem.

See the *Assessment Handbook* for rubrics and students' work samples.

Assessment Handbook, p. 178

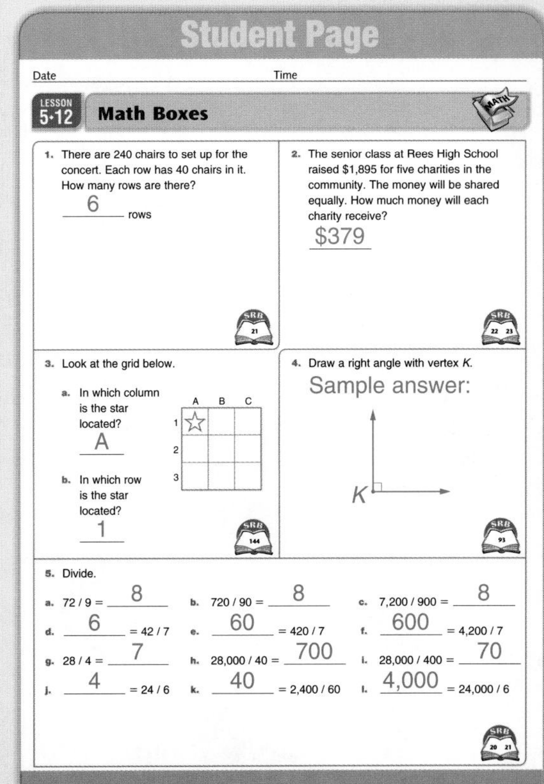

Student Page

Date Time

LESSON 5·12 **Math Boxes**

1. There are 240 chairs to set up for the concert. Each row has 40 chairs in it. How many rows are there? 6 rows

2. The senior class at Rees High School raised $1,895 for five charities in the community. The money will be shared equally. How much money will each charity receive? $379

3. Look at the grid below.
a. In which column is the star located? A
b. In which row is the star located? 1

4. Draw a right angle with vertex *K*. Sample answer:

5. Divide.
a. 72 / 9 = 8
b. 720 / 90 = 8
c. 7,200 / 900 = 8
d. 6 = 42 / 7
e. 60 = 420 / 7
f. 600 = 4,200 / 7
g. 28 / 4 = 7
h. 28,000 / 40 = 700
i. 28,000 / 400 = 70
j. 4 = 24 / 6
k. 40 = 2,400 / 60
l. 4,000 = 24,000 / 6

Math Journal 1, p. 136

Division; Map Reference Frames; Measures of Angles

Overview

Unit 6 begins with four lessons and ends with one lesson that focus on understanding the division operation, developing a method for dividing whole numbers, and solving division number stories. Unit 6 also emphasizes numbers in map coordinate systems and extends informal work with rotations and angles. Unit 6 has four main areas of focus:

- **To provide practice solving multiplication and division number stories,**
- **To introduce the division algorithm and the concept of remainders as fractions or decimals,**
- **To provide practice drawing, measuring, and naming angles using half-circle and full-circle protractors, and**
- **To introduce latitude and longitude and to utilize letter-number pairs and ordered pairs on a grid system.**

CCSS Linking to the Common Core State Standards

The content of Unit 6 addresses the Common Core State Standards for Mathematics in *Number and Operations in Base Ten* and *Measurement and Data.* The correlation of the Common Core State Standards to the *Everyday Mathematics* Grade 4 lessons begins on page CS1.

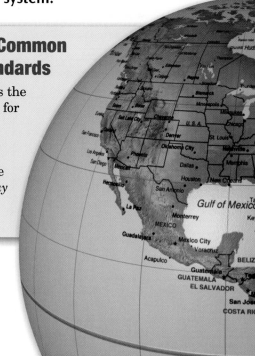

Contents

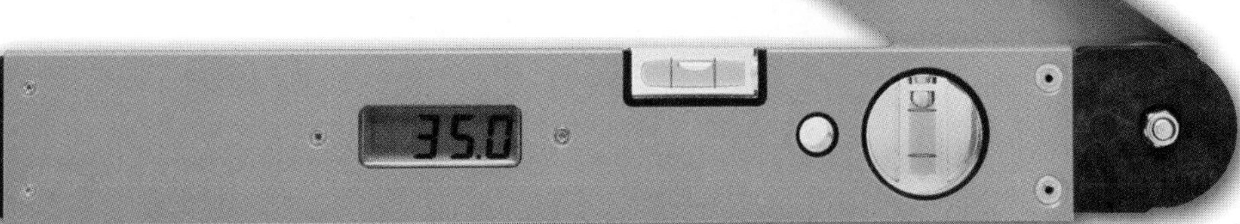

Learning In Perspective

	Lesson Objectives	Links to the Past	Links to the Future
6•1	To provide practice solving multiplication and division number stories by using diagrams to organize information.	Grade 4: Practice basic multiplication and division facts; practice extended multiplication facts (Units 3 and 5). Grades 1–3: Explore division as equal sharing. Solve division problems by direct modeling, arrays, and other methods.	Grades 4–6: Applications and maintenance to develop proficiency with the focus division algorithm, the partial-quotients method. Grade 4: Extend the partial quotients method to decimals divided by a whole number. (Unit 9)
6•2	To guide the exploration of a variety of strategies to solve equal-grouping division number stories.	Grades 1–3: Solve equal-sharing and equal-grouping division problems by using counters, pictures, and diagrams.	Grade 5: Use tiles to model and solve number stories involving ratios of part of a set to the whole set. Grade 6: Model rate and ratio problems with proportions; solve proportions by cross multiplication and other methods.
6•3	To introduce and provide practice with a "low-stress" division algorithm for 1-digit divisors.	Grade 4: Practice basic multiplication and division facts; practice extended multiplication facts (Units 3 and 5). Grades 1–3: Explore division as equal sharing. Solve division problems by direct modeling, arrays, and other methods.	Grades 5 and 6: Applications and maintenance.
6•4	To introduce the expression of remainders as fractions or decimals; and to provide practice interpreting remainders in division problems.	Grade 4: Introduce division vocabulary: *dividend, divisor,* and *quotient.* Explore the relationship between fractions and division. (Unit 3) Grade 3: Introduce the term *remainder.*	Grades 5 and 6: Solve division number stories and interpret remainders.
6•5	To review rotations; and to guide students as they make and use a full-circle protractor.	Grades 1–3: Use straws, geoboards, and body turns to demonstrate rotations and angles. Grade 3: Use the terms *right angle, clockwise,* and *counterclockwise.*	Grade 4: Describe and create designs, such as frieze patterns, that include rotated figures. (Unit 10) Grade 6: Study rotations of a figure and rotation symmetry.
6•6	To provide practice using a full-circle protractor to measure and draw angles less than 360°.	Grade 4: Use straws to model angles and name the parts of an angle. (Unit 1) Grade 3: Construct an angle measurer from a folded and labeled circle; find the approximate size of various angles, in degrees.	Grades 4–6: Applications and maintenance, including playing *Angle Tangle* to practice estimating the measure of, and then measuring, angles.
6•7	To guide students as they classify angles as acute, right, obtuse, straight, and reflex; and to provide practice using a half-circle protractor to measure and draw angles.	Grade 3: Use a string to act out "square corners" (right angles) and other angles. Determine that there are 360° in a circle and 180° in a half circle.	Grade 5: Define vertical and adjacent angles; study relationships between angles formed by intersecting lines. Grade 6: Define supplementary angles; study relationships between angles formed by parallel lines and a transversal.
6•8	To guide students in the use of letter-number pairs and ordered pairs of numbers to locate points on a grid; and to provide practice using a map scale.	Grade 3: Introduce using ordered pairs to locate points on a coordinate grid.	Grade 5: Transform ordered number pairs and explore the resulting transformations of geometric figures. Grade 6: Explore the relations between endpoints and midpoints of line segments drawn on coordinate grids.
6•9	To introduce latitude and longitude; to provide practice finding the latitude and longitude of places on a globe and a map; and to identify places given the latitude and longitude.	Grade 4: Define parallel lines. (Unit 1) Grade 3: Use ordered number pairs to locate and plot points on a coordinate grid.	Grade 4: Use grid coordinates to identify regions, give directions, and describe routes on a map (Units 7–12); construct a model globe that shows latitude and longitude in terms of angles (Project 1). Grades 5 and 6: Applications and maintenance.
6•10	To provide practice with a "low-stress" division algorithm for 2-digit divisors.	Grade 4: Practice basic multiplication and division facts; practice extended multiplication facts (Units 3 and 5). Grades 1–3: Explore division as equal sharing. Solve division problems by direct modeling, arrays, and other methods.	Grades 5 and 6: Applications and maintenance.

	Key Concepts and Skills	Grade 4 Goals*
6•1	Describe the inverse relationship between multiplication and division.	Operations and Computation Goal 3
	Solve multiplication and division number stories.	Operations and Computation Goals 3 and 4
	Use repeated addition, skip counting, and arrays to model multiplication.	Operations and Computation Goal 7
	Write number models to represent multiplication and division number stories.	Patterns, Functions, and Algebra Goal 2
	Write number models containing grouping symbols.	Patterns, Functions, and Algebra Goal 3
6•2	Identify and use multiples of 10.	Number and Numeration Goal 3
	Add multiples of 10.	Operations and Computation Goal 1
	Apply extended multiplication facts to long-division situations.	Operations and Computation Goal 3
	Solve equal-grouping division number stories.	Operations and Computation Goal 4
	Write number models to represent multiplication and division number stories.	Patterns, Functions, and Algebra Goal 2
6•3	Identify and use multiples of 10.	Number and Numeration Goal 3
	Add multiples of 10.	Operations and Computation Goal 1
	Subtract multidigit numbers.	Operations and Computation Goal 2
	Apply extended multiplication facts to long-division situations.	Operations and Computation Goal 3
	Solve equal-grouping division number stories.	Operations and Computation Goal 4
6•4	Use multiples to solve division problems.	Number and Numeration Goal 3
	Solve division number stories and interpret remainders.	Operations and Computation Goal 4
	Use arrays to model division.	Operations and Computation Goal 7
	Write number models to represent division number stories.	Patterns, Functions, and Algebra Goal 2
	Write number models containing grouping symbols.	Patterns, Functions, and Algebra Goal 3
6•5	Use multiples of 30.	Number and Numeration Goal 3
	Form angles of a given measure.	Measurement and Reference Frames Goal 1
	Describe right angles.	Geometry Goal 1
	Rotate objects a given number of degrees.	Geometry Goal 3
	Investigate the relationship between rotations and degrees.	Geometry Goal 3
6•6	Draw and measure angles with a full-circle protractor.	Measurement and Reference Frames Goal 1
	Use ray and line segment vocabulary.	Geometry Goal 1
	Describe a circle as having 360°.	Geometry Goal 2
	Rotate objects a given number of degrees.	Geometry Goal 3
6•7	Add and subtract to find unknown angle measures.	Operations and Computation Goal 2
	Use reference points to estimate the measures of angle; use a half-circle protractor to measure and draw angles.	Measurement and Reference Frames Goal 1
	Classify angles according to their measure.	Geometry Goal 1
6•8	Use a map scale.	Operations and Computation Goal 7
	Estimate distances on a map.	Measurement and Reference Frames Goal 1
	Use ordered number pairs to locate points on a map.	Measurement and Reference Frames Goal 4
	Use letter-number pairs to locate points and regions on a map.	Measurement and Reference Frames Goal 4
6•9	Multiply multidigit numbers to determine miles from the equator.	Operations and Computation Goal 4
	Locate positions on the global coordinate grid system.	Measurement and Reference Frames Goal 4
	Describe parallel and intersecting lines in terms of latitude and longitude.	Geometry Goal 1
	Identify Earth as a sphere divided into hemispheres.	Geometry Goal 2
6•10	Identify and use multiples of 10.	Number and Numeration Goal 3
	Add multiples of 10.	Operations and Computation Goal 1
	Subtract multidigit numbers.	Operations and Computation Goal 2
	Apply extended multiplication facts to long-division situations.	Operations and Computation Goal 3
	Solve equal-grouping division number stories and problems.	Operations and Computation Goal 4

*See the Appendix for a complete list of Grade 4 Goals.

A Balanced Curriculum

Ongoing Practice

Mental Math and Reflexes activities promote speed and accuracy in mental computation.

Math Boxes offer mixed practice and are paired across lessons as shown in the brackets below. This makes them useful as assessment tools. The last one or two boxes on each page preview the next unit's content.

Mixed practice	[6•1, 6•3], [6•2, 6•4], [6•5, 6•7], [6•6, 6•9], [6•8, 6•10]
Mixed practice with multiple choice	6•2, 6•4, 6•7, 6•9, 6•10
Mixed practice with writing/reasoning opportunity	6•1, 6•3, 6•6, 6•7, 6•8, 6•10

Study Links are daily homework assignments that review the content of the lesson and often contain ongoing facts practice or computation practice.

5-Minute Math problems are offered for additional practice in Lesson 6•4.

EM Facts Workshop Game provides online practice of basic facts and computation.

EXTRA PRACTICE **Extra Practice** activities are included in Lessons 6•2, 6•3, 6•4, 6•5, 6•6, 6•8, 6•9, and 6•10.

Practice through Games

Games are an essential component of practice in the *Everyday Mathematics* program. Games offer skills practice and promote strategic thinking. See the *Differentiation Handbook* for ways to adapt games to meet students' needs.

Lesson	Game	Skill Practiced
6•1	*Division Arrays*	Modeling the relationship between multiplication and division [OC Goal 3]
6•2	*High-Number Toss*	Identifying values of digits in places and comparing numbers [NN Goals 1 and 6]
6•2	*Buzz* and *Bizz-Buzz*	Naming multiples and common multiples [NN Goal 3]
6•3	*Beat the Calculator*	Practicing extended multiplication facts [OC Goal 3]
6•3, 6•4, 6•6, 6•10	*Division Dash*	Dividing 2- or 3-digit dividends by 1-digit divisors [OC Goal 4]
6•5	*Robot*	Modeling rotations expressed as both fractions of turns and degree measures [GEO Goal 3]
6•6	*Angle Add-Up*	Solving addition and subtraction problems to find the measures of unknown angles [OC Goal 2]
6•6, 6•8	*Angle Tangle*	Estimating and measuring angles [MRF Goal 1]
6•8	*Grid Search*	Using letter-number pairs to locate regions on a coordinate grid [MRF Goal 4]
6•9	*Over and Up Squares*	Locating and plotting points on a coordinate grid [MRF Goal 4]

[NN] Number and Numeration | [OC] Operations and Computation | [DC] Data and Chance
[MRF] Measurement and Reference Frames | [GEO] Geometry | [PFA] Patterns, Functions, and Algebra

Problem Solving 

Experts at problem solving and mathematical modeling generally do these things:

- Identify the problem.
- Decide what information is needed to solve the problem.
- Play with and study the data to find patterns and meaning.
- Identify and use mathematical procedures to solve the problem.
- Decide whether the solution makes sense and whether it can be applied to other problems.

The table below lists some of the opportunities in this unit for students to practice these strategies.

Lessons that teach *through* problem solving, not just *about* problem solving

Lesson	Activity
6•1–6•4	Use division or multiplication to solve number stories.
6•4	Interpret remainders in problem contexts.
6•5	Measure elapsed time in degrees.
6•7	Draw angles.
6•8	Locate points and estimate distances on a map.
6•9	Locate places on a globe and on world and regional maps.

See Chapter 18: Problem Solving in the *Teacher's Reference Manual* for more information.

The Language of Mathematics

Everyday Mathematics provides lesson-specific suggestions to help all students acquire, process, and express mathematical ideas. Throughout Unit 6, there are lesson-specific language development notes that address the needs of English language learners, indicated by ELL.

ELL SUPPORT Activities to support English language learners are in Part 3 of Lessons 6•3, 6•5, 6•6, and 6•7.

The *English Learners Handbook* and the *Differentiation Handbook* have suggestions for promoting language development and acquisition of mathematics vocabulary. See Unit 6 in each handbook.

Literacy Connection

Lesson 6•4 *A Remainder of One,* by Elinor J. Pinczes, Houghton Mifflin Harcourt, 2002

Lesson 6•7 *Sir Cumference and the Great Knight of Angleland,* by Cindy Neuschwander, Charlesbridge Publishing, 2001

Lesson 6•9 *Sea Clocks: The Story of Longitude,* by Louise Borden, Margaret K. McElderry Books, 2004

For more literacy connections, see the *Home Connection Handbook,* Grades 4–6.

Unit 6 Vocabulary

acute angle
angle (∠)
axis
base line
clockwise
clockwise rotation
counterclockwise rotation
degree
dividend
divisor
equal-groups notation
equator
full-circle protractor
half-circle protractor
hemisphere
index of locations
latitude (lines)
letter-number pair
longitude (lines)
map scale
meridian bar
mixed number
Multiplication/Division Diagram
North Pole
obtuse angle
ordered number pair
parallels
partial quotient
prime meridian
quotient
reflex angle
remainder
right angle
rotation
sides (of an angle)
South Pole
sphere
straight angle
turn
vertex (of an angle)

Cross-Curricular Links 

Literature – Lessons 6•4, 6•7, 6•9

Social Studies – Lessons 6•5, 6•7, 6•8, 6•9

Balanced Assessment

Daily Assessments

- **Recognizing Student Achievement** – A daily assessment that is included in every lesson to evaluate students' progress toward the Grade 4 Grade-Level Goals.
- **Informing Instruction** – Notes that appear throughout the unit to help anticipate students' common errors and suggest appropriate problem-solving strategies.

Lesson	Recognizing Student Achievement	Informing Instruction
6•1	Write number models to represent number stories. [PFA Goal 2]	Recognize the inverse relationship between multiplication and division.
6•2	Solve open sentences using multiplication and division facts. [PFA Goal 2]	
6•3	Solve division problems and number stories with 1-digit divisors and 2-digit dividends. [OC Goal 4]	Use another name for an equal quantity. Use multiples that are not too large.
6•4	Solve decimal addition and subtraction problems. [OC Goal 2]	
6•5	Create a bar graph. [DC Goal 1]	Use different strategies to determine the results of the turn of a straw.
6•6	Draw angles with measures less than or greater than 90°. [MRF Goal 1]	Use a full-circle protractor appropriately.
6•7	Identify places in decimals and the values of the digits in those places. [NN Goal 1]	Measure carefully with a protractor.
6•8	Compare coordinate grid systems. [MRF Goal 4]	
6•9	Solve multidigit multiplication number stories. [OC Goal 4]	Understand latitude and longitude in degrees and directions.
6•10	Solve problems involving the division of multidigit whole numbers by 1-digit divisors. [OC Goal 4]	

[NN] Number and Numeration
[MRF] Measurement and Reference Frames
[OC] Operations and Computation
[GEO] Geometry
[DC] Data and Chance
[PFA] Patterns, Functions, and Algebra

Portfolio Opportunities

The following lessons provide opportunities to gather samples of students' mathematical writings, drawings, and creations to add balance to the assessment process: Lessons 6•1, 6•4, 6•7, 6•8, 6•10, and 6•11.

See pages 16 and 17 in the *Assessment Handbook* for more information about portfolios and how to use them.

Unit Assessment

Progress Check 6 – A cumulative assessment of concepts and skills taught in Unit 6 and in previous units, providing information for evaluating students' progress and planning for future instruction. These assessments include oral/slate, written, and open-response activities, as shown below in the sample Progress Check lesson opener.

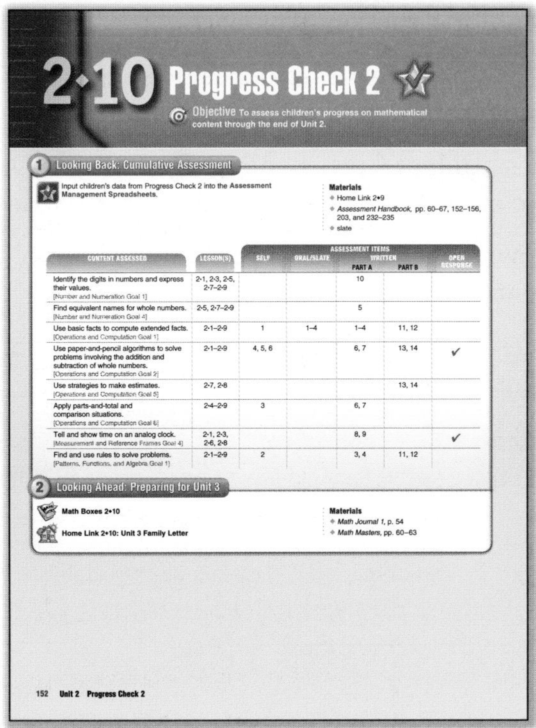

2·10 Progress Check 2

Objective To assess children's progress on mathematical content through the end of Unit 2.

1 Looking Back: Cumulative Assessment

Input children's data from Progress Check 2 into the Assessment Management Spreadsheets.

Materials
- Home Link 2•9
- *Assessment Handbook,* pp. 60–67, 152–156, 203, and 232–235
- slate

CONTENT ASSESSED	LESSON(S)	ASSESSMENT ITEMS				
		SELF	ORAL/SLATE	WRITTEN PART A	WRITTEN PART B	OPEN RESPONSE
Identify the digits in numbers and express their values. [Number and Numeration Goal 1]	2·1, 2·3, 2·5, 2·7–2·9			10		
Find equivalent names for whole numbers. [Number and Numeration Goal 4]	2·5, 2·7–2·9			5		
Use basic facts to compute extended facts. [Operations and Computation Goal 1]	2·1–2·9	1	1–4	1–4	11, 12	
Use paper-and-pencil algorithms to solve problems involving the addition and subtraction of whole numbers. [Operations and Computation Goal 2]	2·1–2·9	4, 5, 6		6, 7	13, 14	✓
Use strategies to make estimates. [Operations and Computation Goal 5]	2·7, 2·8				13, 14	
Apply parts-and-total and comparison situations. [Operations and Computation Goal 6]	2·4–2·9	3		6, 7		
Tell and show time on an analog clock. [Measurement and Reference Frames Goal 4]	2·1, 2·3, 2·6, 2·8			8, 9		✓
Find and use rules to solve problems. [Patterns, Functions, and Algebra Goal 1]	2·1–2·9	2		3, 4	11, 12	

2 Looking Ahead: Preparing for Unit 3

Math Boxes 2•10

Home Link 2•10: Unit 3 Family Letter

Materials
- *Math Journal 1,* p. 54
- *Math Masters,* pp. 60–63

152 Unit 2 Progress Check 2

Core Assessment Resources

Assessment Handbook

- **Unit 6 Assessment Overview,** pages 92–99
- **Unit 6 Assessment Masters,** pages 179–183
- **Unit 6 Individual Profiles of Progress,** pages 266, 267, and 302
- **Unit 6 Class Checklists,** pages 268, 269, and 303
- **Mid-Year Assessment,** pages 100, 101, and 228–233
- **Quarterly Checklist: Quarter 2,** pages 296 and 297
- **Math Logs,** pages 306–308
- **Exit Slip,** page 311
- **Other Student Assessment Forms,** pages 304, 305, 309, and 310

Assessment Management Spreadsheets

The Assessment Management Spreadsheets consist of the Digital Class Checklists and Individual Profile of Progress Checklists. Use them to monitor, record, and report student progress.

Addressing All Needs

Differentiated Instruction

Adjusting the Activity – suggests adaptations that target advanced learners, English language learners, or learners who need additional instructional support.

ELL SUPPORT / ELL – provides lesson-specific suggestions to help English language learners understand and process the mathematical content.

READINESS – accesses students' prior knowledge or previews content that prepares students to engage in the lesson's Part 1 activities.

EXTRA PRACTICE – provides additional opportunities to apply the mathematical content of the lesson.

ENRICHMENT – enables students to apply or further explore the mathematical content of the lesson.

Lesson	Adjusting the Activity	ELL Support/ ELL	Readiness	Extra Practice	Enrichment
6•1	•	•	•		•
6•2	•	•	•	•	
6•3	•	•	•	•	•
6•4	•	•	•	•	•
6•5	•	•	•	•	•
6•6		•	•	•	•
6•7		•	•		•
6•8	•	•	•	•	•
6•9	•			•	•
6•10			•	•	•

Additional Resources

Differentiation Handbook
Provides ideas and strategies for differentiating instruction.
Pages 83–89

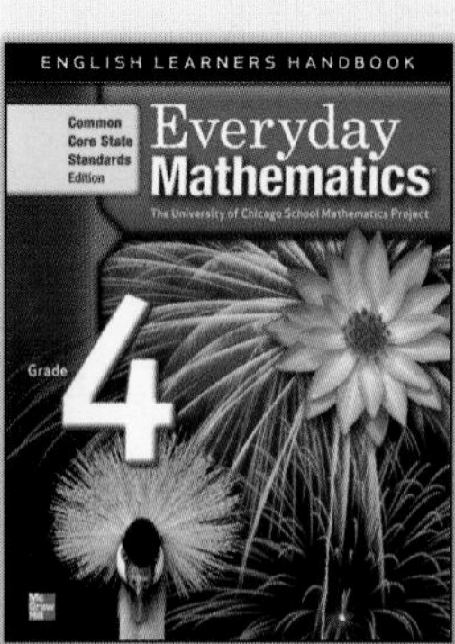

English Learners Handbook
Contains lesson-specific comprehension strategies.
Pages 50–59

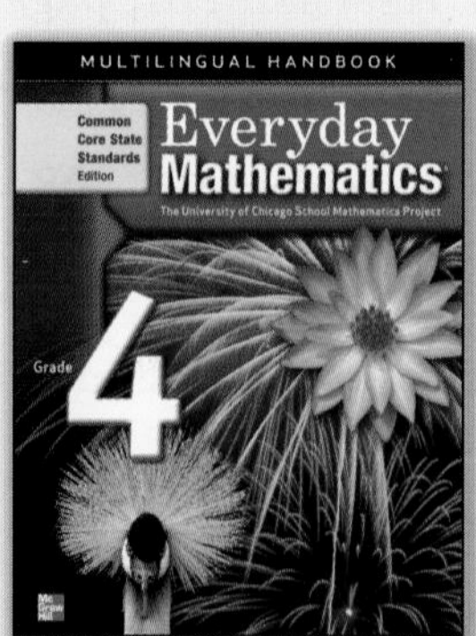

Multilingual Handbook
Previews concepts and vocabulary. It is written in six languages.
Pages 99–118

Planning Tips

Multiage Classroom

Companion Lessons from Grades 3 and 5 can help you meet instructional needs of a multiage classroom. The full Scope and Sequence can be found in the Appendix.

Grade 3	4•6	9•1			6•3	6•3, 6•7, 6•8	6•7, 6•8	10•10		
Grade 4	**6•1**	**6•2**	**6•3**	**6•4**	**6•5**	**6•6**	**6•7**	**6•8**	**6•9**	**6•10**
Grade 5	2•4, 12•5		4•2	4•6	3•4, 3•5	3•4	3•4	9•2, 9•3	3•5	4•2

Pacing for Success

Pacing depends on a number of factors, such as students' individual needs and how long your school has been using *Everyday Mathematics*. At the beginning of Unit 6, you may want to use tools available at www.everydaymathonline.com to help you set your pace.

Home Support

Unit 6 Family Letter (English/Spanish) provides families with an overview, Do-Anytime Activities, Building Skills through Games, a list of vocabulary, and answers to the daily homework (Study Links). Family Letters in English, Spanish, and seven other languages are also available online.

Study Links are the daily homework assignments. They consist of active projects and ongoing review problems.

Home Support Resources

Home Connection Handbook
Offers ideas and reproducible masters for communicating with families. See Table of Contents for unit information.

Student Reference Book
Provides a resource for students and parents.

Pages 92, 93, 142, 230, 233, 234, 240, 241, 250–252, 257, 272, 273, 276, 277, 280, 282–293, 297, 301–305

Technology Resources

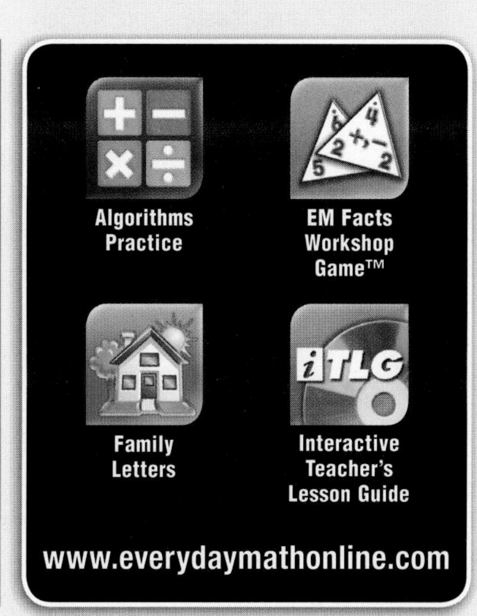

Materials

Technology Resources www.everydaymathonline.com

ePresentations

eToolkit

Algorithms Practice

EM Facts Workshop Game™

Family Letters

Assessment Management

Common Core State Standards

Curriculum Focal Points

Interactive Teacher's Lesson Guide

Lesson	Masters	Manipulative Kit	Other Items
6•1	Teaching Aid Master, p. 437* Transparency of *Math Masters,* p. 436* Study Link Master, p. 177 Game Master, p. 470	per partnership: 1 each of number cards 6–18, 1 six-sided die; slate	Multiplication/Division Facts Table*; counters
6•2	Teaching Aid Master, p. 436 Study Link Master, p. 178 Game Master, p. 487 Teaching Master, p. 179	per partnership: 1 six-sided die; base-10 blocks*; slate	Multiplication/Division Facts Table*
6•3	Teaching Aid Masters, pp. 403, 436*, and 438* Study Link Master, p. 180 Teaching Master, p. 181 Game Masters, pp. 461 and 471	per group: 4 each of number cards 1–10; slate	chart paper; markers; 10 nickels*; calculator
6•4	Study Link Master, p. 182 Game Master, p. 471 Teaching Masters, pp. 183 and 184	per partnership: 4 each of number cards 1–9; slate; centimeter cubes	13 sticks of gum*; *A Remainder of One;* counters*
6•5	Study Link Master, p. 185 Teaching Masters, pp. 186–189 *Differentiation Handbook,* p. 140	drinking straws	demonstration clock; scissors; calculator*
6•6	Teaching Aid Master, p. 389* Transparency of *Math Masters,* p. 439 Study Link Master, p. 190 Game Masters, pp. 457, 471, and 507–509 Teaching Master, p. 191	per partnership: 4 each of number cards 1–9; drinking straw for demonstration purposes	straightedge; scissors; full-circle protractor; waxed paper; colored pencils; dictionary; dry-erase markers
6•7	Study Link Master, p. 192 Teaching Aid Masters, pp. 388 or 389 and 419–421* Teaching Master, p. 193		half-circle protractor; protractor for demonstration purposes; chart paper; straightedge; rope or string; glue or tape; *Sir Cumference and the Great Knight of Angleland*
6•8	Teaching Aid Masters, pp. 388* or 389* and 440 Study Link Master, p. 194 Game Masters, pp. 457 and 486	compass*; slate	protractor; road atlas*; masking tape and index cards, or rope and colored tape; straightedge
6•9	Study Link Master, p. 195 Game Master, p. 494 Teaching Master, p. 196 Teaching Aid Master, p. 388 or 389	per partnership: 2 six-sided dice	globe; world map; colored pencils; *Sea Clocks: The Story of Longitude*; per group: flat world political map, 1 penny, scissors
6•10	Teaching Aid Masters, pp. 413, 414, 416*, 436*, and 438 Study Link Master, p. 197 Teaching Master, p. 198 Game Master, p. 471	per partnership: 4 each of number cards 1–9; base-10 blocks*; slate	pen or colored pencil
6•11	Assessment Masters, pp. 179–183 and 228–233* Study Link Masters, pp. 199–202	slate	straightedge; full-circle protractor; half-circle protractor

*Denotes optional materials

Mathematical Background

The discussion below highlights the major content ideas presented in Unit 6 and helps establish instructional priorities.

Multiplication and Division Number Stories (Lesson 6◆1)

Students have solved multiplication and division number stories in previous lessons. Lesson 6-1 extends that work and utilizes Multiplication/Division Diagrams. Such diagrams are a means of organizing information in number stories. These diagrams contain a row of boxes for representing the units in the problem, as shown below.

tables	students per table	total students
t	6	33

There are 33 students. Each table can seat 6 students. How many tables are needed?

If a Multiplication/Division Diagram is correctly constructed, it reveals what to do to solve the problem. The number in the right column is the product of the other two. The number in the left column (or middle column) can be found by dividing the number in the right column by the number in the middle column (or left column). For example, in the situation shown above, the answer is found by dividing 33 by 6 and rounding the quotient up to 6. After students have decided what to do to solve the problem, they can write a number model to represent the problem using a variable for the unknown.

Multiplication/Division Diagrams are useful tools in problem solving but are not intended as content to be mastered.

To learn more about multiplication and division number stories, see Section 18.4.1 of the *Teacher's Reference Manual.*

Six packs of drinks are familiar examples of "equal groups."

Project Note

To teach U.S. traditional long division, see Algorithm Project 7.

The Partial-Quotients Division Algorithm (Lessons 6◆2, 6◆3, and 6◆10)

Division is a way of answering the question "How many of these are in that?" or "How many [*n*s] are in *m*?" Lesson 6-2 develops the concept of division through solving equal-grouping division number stories by using multiples of 10.

Lesson 6-3 introduces a paper-and-pencil division algorithm. It is offered as an alternative to the traditional U.S. long-division algorithm, which is hard for most students to learn and apply. Picking the right digits for the quotient and then multiplying and subtracting can be both difficult and confusing.

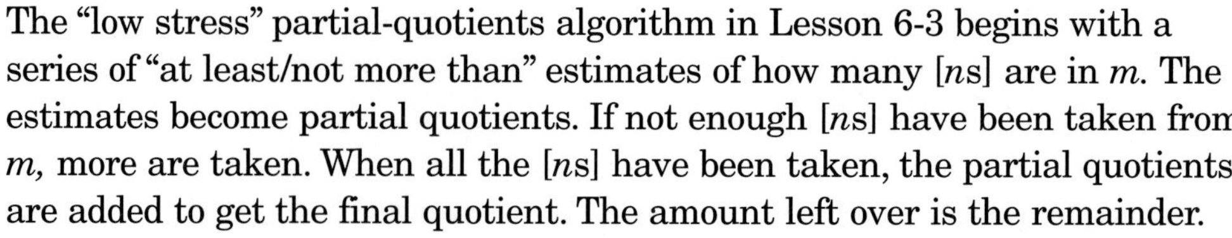

Unit 6 Organizer

The "low stress" partial-quotients algorithm in Lesson 6-3 begins with a series of "at least/not more than" estimates of how many [*n*s] are in *m*. The estimates become partial quotients. If not enough [*n*s] have been taken from *m*, more are taken. When all the [*n*s] have been taken, the partial quotients are added to get the final quotient. The amount left over is the remainder.

For example, $158 \div 12$ can be thought of as the question "How many [12s] are in 158?" Students should begin with multiples of 10, because they are simple to work with. A quick mental calculation shows that there are at least 10 [12s] in 158 ($10 * 12 = 120$) but fewer than 20 [12s] (since $20 * 12 = 240$). Students record 10 as the first partial quotient and remove (subtract) 10 [12s] from 158, leaving 38.

The next question is, "How many [12s] are in the remaining 38?" Some students might know the answer right away (since 3 [12s] are 36), or they might sneak up on it: "More than 1, more than 2, a little more than 3, but not as many as 4. . . ." Taking out 3 [12s] leaves 2, which is less than 12. There are no more [12s], so students can stop looking for partial quotients.

To obtain the final answer, students add the partial quotients: $10 + 3 = 13$. They note what, if anything, is left over—in this problem, 2. The quotient is 13, and the remainder is 2.

Example 1:

12)158		How many [12s] are in 158? At least 10.
– 120	10	Use 10 as the first partial quotient. $10 * 12 = 120$
38		Subtract. At least 3 [12s] are left.
– 36	3	Use 3 as the second partial quotient. $3 * 12 = 36$
2	13	Subtract. Add the partial quotients. $10 + 3 = 13$
↑	↑	
Remainder	**Quotient**	**Answer: 13 R2**

Note

Division with remainder is also known as integer division. Some calculators have a special key, often Int÷, for this operation.

It is important to note that, in following this algorithm, students may not all use the same series of partial quotients. In Example 2 below, a student has used 2 as the second partial quotient. Subtracting 2 [12s] leaves 14 still unaccounted for. 14 consists of another [12], with 2 left over. The student would reach the final answer in three steps rather than two. One way is not better than another.

Example 2:

12)158		How many [12s] are in 158? At least 10.
– 120	10	Use 10 as the first partial quotient. $10 * 12 = 120$
38		Subtract. At least 2 [12s] are left.
– 24	2	Use 2 as the second partial quotient. $2 * 12 = 24$
14		Subtract. At least 1 [12] is left.
– 12	1	Use 1 as the third partial quotient. $1 * 12 = 12$
2	13	Subtract. Add the partial quotients. $10 + 2 + 1 = 13$
↑	↑	
Remainder	**Quotient**	**Answer: 13 R2**

One advantage of this algorithm is that students can use numbers that are easy for them to work with. Students who are good estimators and confident of their extended multiplication facts will need to list only a few partial quotients to arrive at a final quotient. Other students will be more comfortable taking smaller steps. More important than the specific steps a student follows is that the student understands how and why this algorithm works and can use it to get an accurate answer.

The partial-quotients algorithm is the focus division algorithm for *Everyday Mathematics,* to be learned by all students. However, if some students learn another algorithm and prefer it, they should feel free to use it.

Students are reminded that there are several equivalent notations for division. The first one in the margin, $12\overline{)246}$, is convenient when carrying out the partial-quotients algorithm or the conventional long-division algorithm.

The second notation, $246 \div 12$, is familiar. The answer is 20 R6. Because a form like $246 \div 12 = 20$ R6 is not a proper mathematical sentence, the authors prefer to use an arrow when there is a nonzero remainder: $246 \div 12 \rightarrow 20$ R6. This is a subtlety that need not be enforced with students.

The notation 246/12 is less common in elementary mathematics but is the usual form in secondary and higher mathematics. It has the advantage of reinforcing the connection between division and fractions—also shown by the fraction notation $\frac{246}{12}$, which can be thought of as "246 divided by 12."

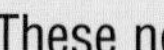

Note

These notations for division are equivalent:

$12\overline{)246}$

$246 \div 12$

246/12

$\frac{246}{12}$

To further investigate the partial-quotients division algorithm, refer to Section 11.2.4 of the *Teacher's Reference Manual.*

Expressing and Interpreting Remainders (Lesson 6♦4)

In some whole-number division problems, it may be desirable to express the remainder as a fraction or decimal; for example, if a cost of \$14 is to be shared by 4 people, each person's share is better represented as $\$3\frac{1}{2}$ or \$3.50, rather than 3 R2 dollars.

Students will discover the shortcut for writing a remainder as a fraction:

- Use the remainder as the numerator of the fraction.
- Use the divisor as the denominator of the fraction.

Then the answer to the division can be written as a mixed number by attaching the fraction to the quotient. If appropriate, the fraction can be converted to a decimal, and the answer given as a decimal.

Students consider the role of the remainder in a variety of division number stories and decide how to report the answer.

Remainder that becomes part of the answer

- A rope 14 feet long is cut into 4 pieces of equal length. How long is each piece? $3\frac{2}{4}$ feet, $3\frac{1}{2}$ feet, or 3 feet 6 inches

Remainder that cannot be further split up

- Four children agree to divide a set of 14 toy cars equally. What is each child's share? 3 cars, with 2 left over that can't be split up

Remainder that is ignored

- Ann has $14 to buy notebooks that cost $4 each. How many notebooks can she buy? 3 notebooks, with $2 left over

Remainder that indicates the answer should be rounded up

- Joe has 14 photographs. He can fit 4 photos on a page in his photo album. How many pages must he use to include all 14 photos? 4 pages; 3 pages will hold only 12 photos, so he needs to use a fourth page.

Consult Section 11.2.4 of the *Teacher's Reference Manual* for additional information on expressing and interpreting remainders.

Measures of Rotations and Angles

(Lessons 6◆5–6◆7)

In *Third Grade Everyday Mathematics,* students worked extensively with straws to explore rotations and angles formed by rotations. Students then extended these concepts to measure angles in a very informal way.

In Lesson 6-5, straws are used to review rotations and familiarize students with the circular protractor. Lessons 6-6 and 6-7 explore the use of the circular protractor and half-circle protractor as precision tools. Both types of protractors are used to measure given angles and to construct angles of given measures.

Sometimes angle diagrams may be confusing. Figure 1 in the margin shows a 90° angle that has been marked with arcs in three different ways. The arcs in the first two angles have arrowheads and indicate a $\frac{1}{4}$-clockwise turn and a $\frac{1}{4}$-counterclockwise turn, respectively. The arc in the third angle has no arrowhead, so no particular direction of rotation is indicated. Each of these three angles has the same measure—90°. The direction information in two of the diagrams may be useful in a particular situation, but it does not affect the angle measure of 90°.

In many angle diagrams, no arc is drawn to indicate the direction of rotation, as in the first angle in Figure 2. Without the arc, this angle could represent either the second angle in Figure 2 or the third angle—a reflex angle. The convention is that if no arc or other indication is given, the smaller of the two angles should be used.

When an angle is decomposed into non-overlapping parts, the angle measure of the whole is the sum of the angle measures of the parts. In Lessons 6-6 and 6-7, students use this idea to solve addition and subtraction problems to find unknown angle measures.

For additional information about measures of rotations and angles, see Section 13.4.1 of the *Teacher's Reference Manual.*

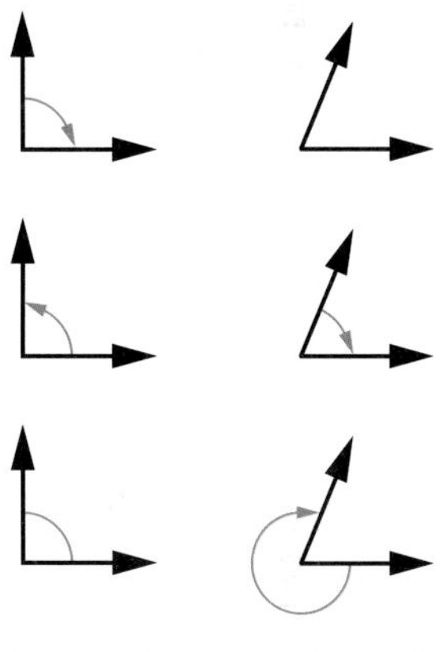

Figure 1 Figure 2

Note

Students may find construction of angles more difficult than measurement of angles. Have students practice drawing and measuring angles throughout the school year. To practice, have someone give a measure between 0° and 180° and ask students to construct an angle with that measure.

Map Coordinate Systems

(Lessons 6◆8 and 6◆9)

Map models of the world generally locate points on 2-dimensional surfaces (including surfaces of spheres). Hence, two pieces of information (or "coordinates") are needed to specify each location. If you were in an airplane and concerned about collisions with the ground or other aircraft, a third piece of information—altitude—would also be important.

The reference frames for flat maps of local areas are much like standard 2-dimensional coordinate systems, except that the intervals on one edge of the maps are often specified by letters of the alphabet instead of numbers. On such maps, the two pieces of distance information—the letter and number coordinates—are used to find specific locations and to move between locations.

Lesson 6-8 considers rectangular coordinate grids for maps. Map coordinates are used in two ways: to identify regions on a map and to identify a point where two grid lines intersect. You may want to use a U.S. road atlas to illustrate the use of an index of locations and letter-number grid coordinates.

Project Notes

Use Project 1, Making a Cutaway Globe, to reinforce work with latitude and longitude.

Use Project 2, Using a Magnetic Compass, to introduce reading a compass and finding directions using degree measurements. See the *Differentiation Handbook* for modifications to Projects 1 and 2.

Lesson 6-9 introduces the coordinate system used to locate points on the world globe. Again, two pieces of numerical information—latitude and longitude—suffice to locate any particular place on Earth's surface. (Earth is assumed to be a smooth surface, ignoring the fact that a location might be on top of a mountain or under the surface of an ocean.)

But latitude and longitude are not distances. They are given in degrees that can be considered either as angle measures (of angles with vertices at the center of Earth) or as numbers that tell how far and in what direction to go along arcs of circles.

Section 15.4.1 of the *Teacher's Reference Manual* contains more information about map coordinate systems.

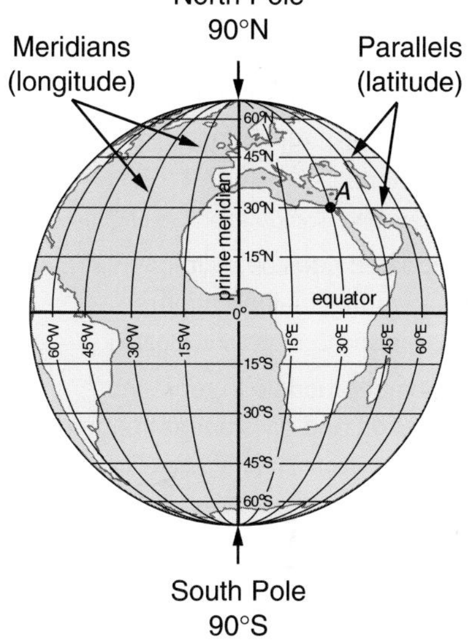

Point *A* is located at 30°N, 30°E.

Goode's homotosine projection of the world divides the world into six lobes.

6•1 Multiplication and Division Number Stories

 **Objective** To provide practice solving multiplication and division number stories by using diagrams to organize information.

Technology Resources www.everydaymathonline.com

ePresentations

eToolkit

Algorithms Practice

EM Facts Workshop Game™

Family Letters

Assessment Management

Common Core State Standards

Curriculum Focal Points

Interactive Teacher's Lesson Guide

1 Teaching the Lesson

Key Concepts and Skills

- Describe the inverse relationship between multiplication and division.
  [Operations and Computation Goal 3]
- Solve multiplication and division number stories.
  [Operations and Computation Goals 3 and 4]
- Use repeated addition, skip counting, and arrays to model multiplication.
  [Operations and Computation Goal 7]
- Write number models to represent multiplication and division number stories.
  [Patterns, Functions, and Algebra Goal 2]
- Write number models containing grouping symbols.
  [Patterns, Functions, and Algebra Goal 3]

Key Activities

Students use Multiplication/Division Diagrams to organize information in number stories and write number models for the problems.

 **Ongoing Assessment: Informing Instruction** See page 403.

 **Ongoing Assessment: Recognizing Student Achievement**
Use journal pages 138 and 139.
[Patterns, Functions, and Algebra Goal 2]

Key Vocabulary

Multiplication/Division Diagram

Materials

Math Journal 1, pp. 138 and 139
Math Masters, p. 437 (optional)
transparency of *Math Masters,* p. 436 (optional) ◆ slate ◆ counters (optional) ◆ Multiplication/Division Facts Table (optional)

2 Ongoing Learning & Practice

Solving Extended Facts
Math Journal 1, p. 140
Students solve extended multiplication facts.

 **Math Boxes 6•1**
Math Journal 1, p. 137
Students practice and maintain skills through Math Box problems.

 **Study Link 6•1**
Math Masters, p. 177
Students practice and maintain skills through Study Link activities.

3 Differentiation Options

READINESS

Playing *Division Arrays*
Student Reference Book, p. 240
Math Masters, p. 470
per partnership: 1 each of number cards 6–18 (from the Everything Math Deck, if available), 1 six-sided die ◆ counters
Students review the relationship between multiplication and division using a concrete model.

ENRICHMENT

Writing Multiplication/Division Number Stories
Students apply their understanding of the inverse relationship between multiplication and division.

Advance Preparation

 ***Teacher's Reference Manual,* Grades 4–6** pp. 19, 107–111, 304–306

Getting Started

Mental Math and Reflexes

Pose fact pairs to highlight the inverse relationship between multiplication and division. *Suggestions:*

●○○	2 ∗ 5 = 10	10 / 5 = 2	●●○	7 ∗ 4 = 28	28 / 4 = 7	●●●	7 ∗ 8 = 56	56 / 7 = 8
	3 ∗ 6 = 18	18 / 6 = 3		8 ∗ 3 = 24	24 / 8 = 3		6 ∗ 7 = 42	42 / 6 = 7
	5 ∗ 4 = 20	20 / 4 = 5		5 ∗ 9 = 45	45 / 9 = 5		8 ∗ 9 = 72	72 / 8 = 9

Math Message

There are 6 rows of chairs. There are 4 chairs in each row. How many chairs are there in all?

1 Teaching the Lesson

Math Message Follow-Up

(*Math Masters,* pp. 436 and 437)

Algebraic Thinking Have students share their answers and strategies. Such strategies may include using counters; drawing pictures; making arrays; counting by 1s, 4s, or 6s; repeatedly adding 4s or 6s; doubling; or knowing that 4 ∗ 6 = 24 or 6 ∗ 4 = 24. (*See margin.*)

Review the **Multiplication/Division Diagram** as a way of keeping track of the information in the number story. Draw the following diagram on the board (or use a transparency of *Math Masters,* page 436), and record the given information. Use a variable to represent the unknown.

rows	chairs per row	total chairs
6	4	*t*

In this problem, the number of groups and the number of objects in each group are known. The total number of objects is sought.

Point out that multiplication can be used to find the total number of objects. Write "Number model with unknown:" below the diagram. Ask students to give a number model that represents the number story using a letter for the unknown, and record it on the board. Number model with unknown: $6 * 4 = t$ Now erase the variable in the diagram and replace it with the answer. Write "Summary number model:" and ask students to give a number model with the answer in place of the unknown. Record the summary number model on the board. Summary number model: $6 * 4 = 24$

Have students use the relationship between multiplication and division to check if their answers make sense. There are 6 rows of chairs with 4 chairs in each row. There are 24 total chairs. $24 \div 6 = 4$

Tell students that in this lesson they will use Multiplication/Division Diagrams to help them solve division number stories.

Interactive whiteboard-ready ePresentations are available at www.everydaymathonline.com to help you teach the lesson.

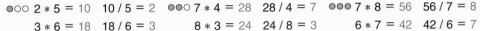

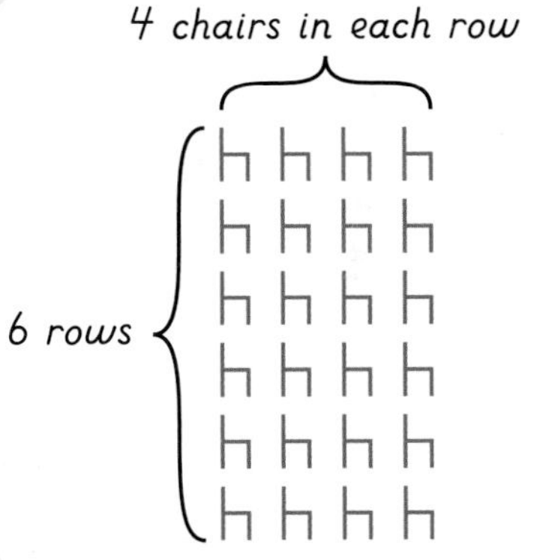

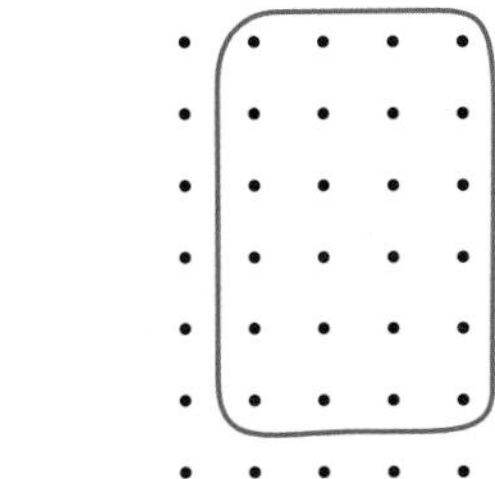

Array sketched using *Math Masters,* page 437

Links to the Future

In Unit 12 of *Fourth Grade Everyday Mathematics* students solve rate problems. Rate problems, like the problems students will encounter in this lesson, often contain the word *per,* which means *in each* or *for each.*

rows	chairs per row	total chairs

*,/	1	2	3	4	5	6	7	8	9	10
1	1									10
2		4								20
3			9							30
4				~~16~~				(32)		40

Solving Division Number Stories

WHOLE-CLAS ACTIVITY

(*Math Masters,* p. 436)

Algebraic Thinking Because the format of the Multiplication/Division Diagram is identical for multiplication and division, the diagram also helps reinforce the inverse relationship between the two operations.

Pose the following problem: Jenna and Salim are setting up chair for the class play. There are 32 chairs. Their teacher asked them to arrange the chairs so that there are 4 rows with the same number of chairs in each row. How many chairs should Jenna and Salim put in each row?

Explain that this is an *equal-sharing* problem. In equal-sharing problems, the number of groups (rows) and the total number of objects (chairs) are known. The number of objects in each group (chairs per row) is sought.

Draw a Multiplication/Division Diagram on the board, or use a transparency of *Math Masters,* page 436. (*See margin.*)

Guide students through the following steps:

Step 1: Decide what you need to find out. How many chairs will be in each row? Write a variable for the unknown in the "chairs per row" column.

Step 2: Identify the data (information) you need to solve the problem. The total number of chairs to be shared and the number of rows that will share them Write the data in the appropriate columns.

Step 3: Decide what to do to find the answer. Divide. 32 chairs must be shared (divided) equally by 4 rows. Write a number model to represent the problem using a variable for the unknown. Number model with unknown: $32 / 4 = c$

Step 4: Do the computation. Encourage students to use counters, use a Multiplication/Division Facts Table, or draw an array. Replace the variable in the diagram with the answer to the computation. 8

rows	chairs per row	total chairs
4	~~c~~ 8	32

Adjusting the Activity

Have students use a Multiplication/Division Facts Table for division. For example, to find the answer to 32 / 4, move across the 4s row to the cell containing 32. Then move up the column containing 32 to find the answer, 8, at the top. Tell students they can think of the arrow (*see margin*) from the 4 to the 32 as a representation of the question: "How many 4s are in 32?"

AUDITORY ◆ KINESTHETIC ◆ TACTILE ◆ VISUAL

Step 5: Below the diagram, write the answer with the unit and write a number model to summarize the number story.

Answer: 8 chairs per row

Summary number model: 32 / 4 = 8

Ask students to use the relationship between multiplication and division to check if their answers make sense. 32 chairs are arranged in 4 rows. There are 8 chairs in each row. $4 * 8 = 32$

Ongoing Assessment: Informing Instruction

Watch for students who recognize the inverse relationship between multiplication and division and solve the problem by thinking “4 times what number equals 32?” Help them write a number model that represents their thinking: $4 * c = 32$.

Now pose an *equal-grouping* problem in which the number of objects per group (chairs per row) and the total number of objects (chairs) are known and the number of groups (rows) is sought.

The school custodian is setting up chairs for a parent meeting. There are 43 chairs. The principal asked the custodian to place 7 chairs in each row. How many rows of chairs will there be? Guide students through Steps 1–5.

rows	chairs per row	total chairs
6	7	43

Number model with unknown: $43 / 7 = r$

Answer: 6 rows (1 chair left over)

Summary number model: $43 / 7 \rightarrow 6$ R1

Have students use the relationship between multiplication and division to check if their answers make sense. 43 chairs are arranged with 7 chairs in each row. There are 6 rows of 7 chairs with 1 chair left over. $(6 * 7) + 1 = 43$

NOTE When the result of division is expressed as a quotient and non-zero remainder, the authors prefer to use an arrow rather than an equal sign, as in $43 \div 7 \rightarrow 6$ R1. The arrow is read as “is,” “yields,” or “results in.” This is because $43 \div 7 = 6$ R1 is not a proper number sentence. However, this is a subtle usage that need not be required of students.

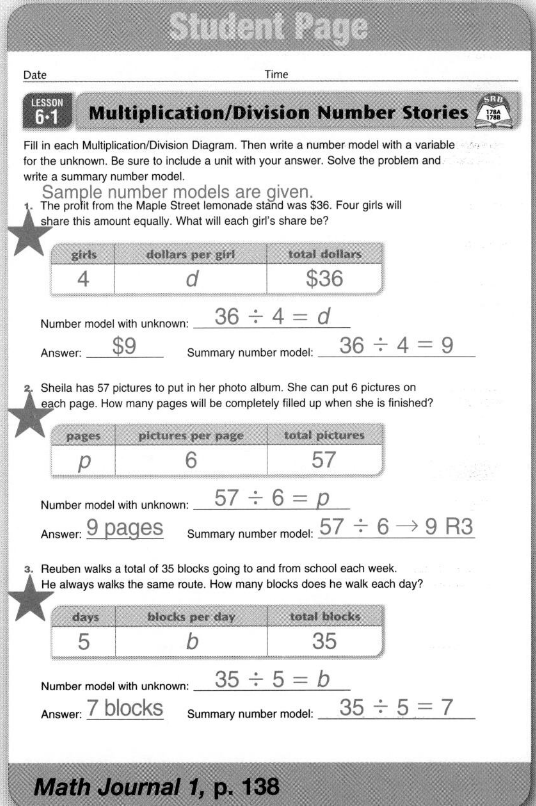

Student Page

Date Time

LESSON 6·1 **Multiplication/Division Number Stories**

Fill in each Multiplication/Division Diagram. Then write a number model with a variable for the unknown. Be sure to include a unit with your answer. Solve the problem and write a summary number model.

Sample number models are given.

1. The profit from the Maple Street lemonade stand was $36. Four girls will share this amount equally. What will each girl's share be?

girls	dollars per girl	total dollars
4	*d*	$36

Number model with unknown: $36 \div 4 = d$

Answer: $9 Summary number model: $36 \div 4 = 9$

2. Sheila has 57 pictures to put in her photo album. She can put 6 pictures on each page. How many pages will be completely filled up when she is finished?

pages	pictures per page	total pictures
p	6	57

Number model with unknown: $57 \div 6 = p$

Answer: 9 pages Summary number model: $57 \div 6 \rightarrow 9$ R3

3. Reuben walks a total of 35 blocks going to and from school each week. He always walks the same route. How many blocks does he walk each day?

days	blocks per day	total blocks
5	*b*	35

Number model with unknown: $35 \div 5 = b$

Answer: 7 blocks Summary number model: $35 \div 5 = 7$

Math Journal 1, p. 138

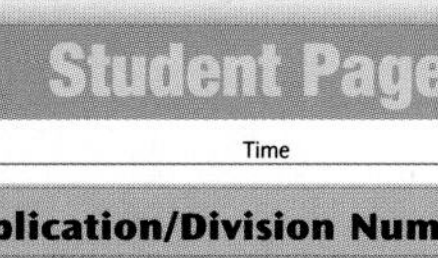

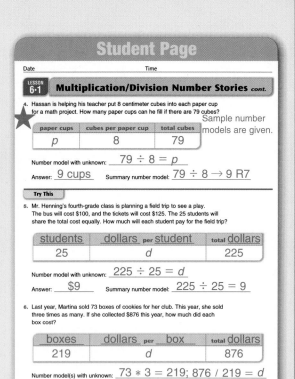

Student Page

Date Time

LESSON 6·1 Multiplication/Division Number Stories *cont.*

4. Hassan is helping his teacher put 8 centimeter cubes into each paper cup for a math project. How many paper cups can he fill if there are 79 cubes?

Sample number models are given.

paper cups	cubes per paper cup	total cubes
p	8	79

Number model with unknown: $79 \div 8 = p$

Answer: 9 cups Summary number model: $79 \div 8 \rightarrow 9$ R7

Try This

5. Mr. Henning's fourth-grade class is planning a field trip to see a play. The bus will cost $100, and the tickets will cost $125. The 25 students will share the total cost equally. How much will each student pay for the field trip?

students	dollars per student	total dollars
25	d	225

Number model with unknown: $225 \div 25 = d$

Answer: $9 Summary number model: $225 \div 25 = 9$

6. Last year, Martina sold 73 boxes of cookies for her club. This year, she sold three times as many. If she collected $876 this year, how much did each box cost?

boxes	dollars per box	total dollars
219	d	876

Number model(s) with unknown: $73 * 3 = 219$; $876 / 219 = d$

Answer: $4

Summary number model(s): $73 * 3 = 219$; $876 / 219 = 4$

Math Journal 1, **p. 139**

Student Page

Date Time

LESSON 6·1 Extended Multiplication Facts

1. $9 * 5 = 45$
$9 * 50 = 450$
$90 * 5 = 450$
$90 * 50 = 4{,}500$
$900 * 5 = 4{,}500$
$90 * 500 = 45{,}000$

2. $8 * 7 = 56$
$8 * 70 = 560$
$80 * 7 = 560$
$80 * 70 = 5{,}600$
$800 * 7 = 5{,}600$
$80 * 700 = 56{,}000$

3. $4 * 9 = 36$
$4 * 90 = 360$
$40 * 9 = 360$
$40 * 90 = 3{,}600$
$400 * 9 = 3{,}600$
$40 * 900 = 36{,}000$

4. $6 * 3 = 18$
$60 * 3 = 180$
$60 * 30 = 1{,}800$
$3 * 60 = 180$
$3 * 600 = 1{,}800$
$30 * 600 = 18{,}000$

5. $6 * 8 = 48$
$6 * 80 = 480$
$60 * 80 = 4{,}800$
$60 * 8 = 480$
$6 * 800 = 4{,}800$
$6 * 8{,}000 = 48{,}000$

6. $8 * 3 = 24$
$8 * 300 = 2{,}400$
$80 * 30 = 2{,}400$
$8 * 30 = 240$
$80 * 3 = 240$
$800 * 300 = 240{,}000$

Math Journal 1, **p. 140**

▶ Solving Number Stories

(*Math Journal 1,* pp. 138 and 139)

Students solve Problems 1–4 on their own. Encourage them to work with a partner, as necessary, to solve Problems 5 and 6.

Ongoing Assessment: Recognizing Student Achievement

Journal pages 138 and 139 Problems 1–4

Use **journal pages 138 and 139, Problems 1–4** to assess students' ability to write number models to represent number stories. Students are making adequate progress if the number models accurately reflect the content of the multiplication and division number stories and include the correct use of symbols. Some students may be able to explain the connection between the Multiplication/Division Diagrams and the number models.

[Patterns, Functions, and Algebra Goal 2]

2 Ongoing Learning & Practice

▶ Solving Extended Facts

(*Math Journal 1,* p. 140)

Students solve extended multiplication facts. Some problems require students to find the product; others ask for one of the factors.

▶ Math Boxes 6·1

(*Math Journal 1,* p. 137)

Mixed Practice Math Boxes in this lesson are paired with Math Boxes in Lesson 6-3. The skill in Problem 5 previews Unit 7 content.

Writing/Reasoning Have students write a response to the following: *Explain how you rounded the number in Problem 2 to the nearest ten million.* Sample answer: 409,381,886 is between 400,000,000 and 410,000,000. The number halfway between the lower number and the higher number is 405,000,000. 409,381,886 is closer to the higher number, so I rounded to 410,000,000.

▶ Study Link 6·1

(*Math Masters,* p. 177)

Home Connection Students use Multiplication/Division Diagrams to help them solve problems.

3 Differentiation Options

READINESS

PARTNER ACTIVITY

▸ Playing *Division Arrays*

5–15 Min

(*Student Reference Book,* p. 240; *Math Masters,* p. 470)

To explore the relationship between multiplication and division using a concrete model, have students play *Division Arrays.* Consider having students record rounds of play on *Math Masters,* page 470.

ENRICHMENT

PARTNER ACTIVITY

▸ Writing Multiplication/Division Number Stories

5–15 Min

ELL

Algebraic Thinking To apply students' understanding of the inverse relationship between multiplication and division, have them write and solve multiplication and division number stories. Have them record a number model using a letter for the unknown and a summary number model. Some students may be interested in writing and solving multistep problems and problems that involve distances, intervals of time, liquid volumes, masses of objects, or money. Stories may look similar to the following:

▷ Yataiva divided 450 pennies equally among the tellers at a bank. One roll has 50 pennies, and each teller got 3 rolls. How many tellers are there? Number model with unknown: $(450 \div 50) \div 3 = t$; Answer: 3 tellers; Summary number model: $(450 \div 50) \div 3 = 3$

To support English language learners, provide an opportunity for students to share and revise their writing. *For example:*

▷ Read problems aloud or have students read their own problems aloud.

▷ Have partners read and comment on each other's drafts.

▷ Have students edit problems as a whole-class activity.

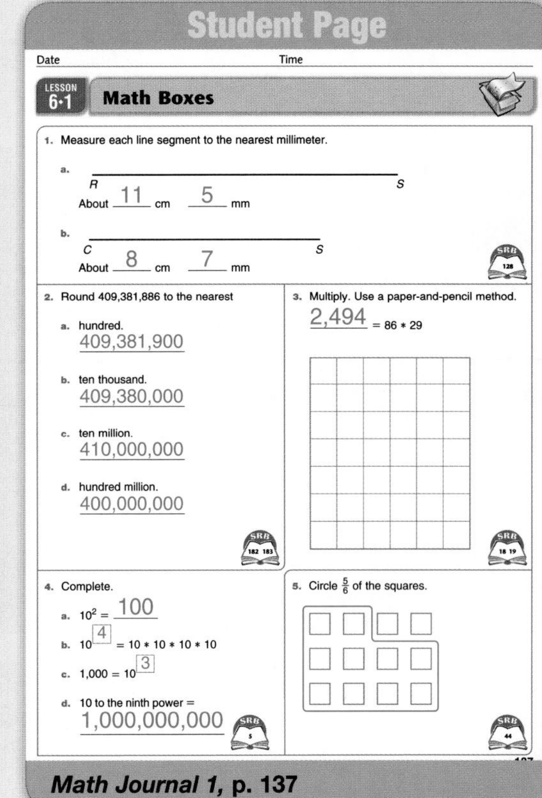

Student Page

Date Time

LESSON 6•1 **Math Boxes**

1. Measure each line segment to the nearest millimeter.

a. R S
About 11 cm 5 mm

b. C S
About 8 cm 7 mm

2. Round 409,381,886 to the nearest

a. hundred. 409,381,900

b. ten thousand. 409,380,000

c. ten million. 410,000,000

d. hundred million. 400,000,000

3. Multiply. Use a paper-and-pencil method.
2,494 = 86 ∗ 29

4. Complete.

a. $10^2 =$ 100

b. $10^{4} = 10 * 10 * 10 * 10$

c. $1{,}000 = 10^{3}$

d. 10 to the ninth power = 1,000,000,000

5. Circle $\frac{5}{6}$ of the squares.

Math Journal 1, p. 137

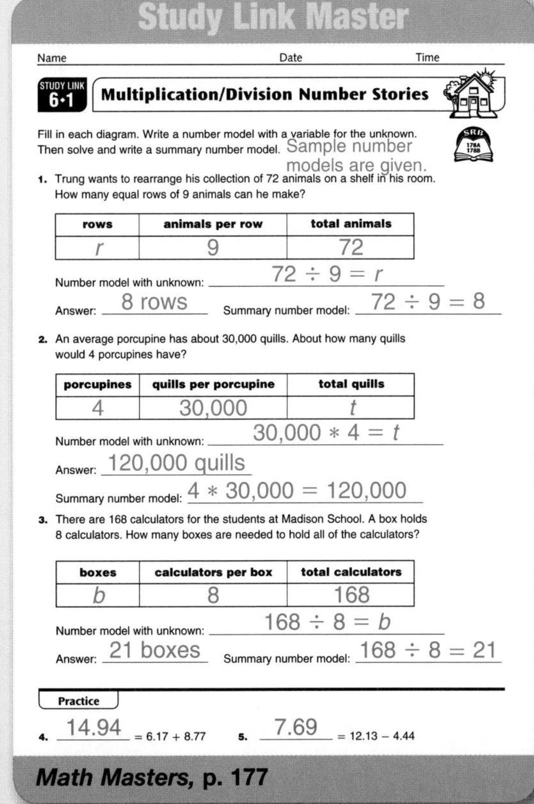

Study Link Master

Name Date Time

STUDY LINK 6•1 **Multiplication/Division Number Stories**

Fill in each diagram. Write a number model with a variable for the unknown. Then solve and write a summary number model. Sample number models are given.

1. Trung wants to rearrange his collection of 72 animals on a shelf in his room. How many equal rows of 9 animals can he make?

rows	animals per row	total animals
r	9	72

Number model with unknown: $72 \div 9 = r$

Answer: 8 rows Summary number model: $72 \div 9 = 8$

2. An average porcupine has about 30,000 quills. About how many quills would 4 porcupines have?

porcupines	quills per porcupine	total quills
4	30,000	t

Number model with unknown: $30{,}000 * 4 = t$

Answer: 120,000 quills

Summary number model: $4 * 30{,}000 = 120{,}000$

3. There are 168 calculators for the students at Madison School. A box holds 8 calculators. How many boxes are needed to hold all of the calculators?

boxes	calculators per box	total calculators
b	8	168

Number model with unknown: $168 \div 8 = b$

Answer: 21 boxes Summary number model: $168 \div 8 = 21$

Practice

4. 14.94 = 6.17 + 8.77 5. 7.69 = 12.13 – 4.44

Math Masters, p. 177

6•2 Strategies for Division

Objective To guide the exploration of a variety of strategies to solve equal-grouping division number stories.

Technology Resources www.everydaymathonline.com

ePresentations

eToolkit

Algorithms Practice

EM Facts Workshop Game™

Family Letters

Assessment Management

Common Core State Standards

Curriculum Focal Points

Interactive Teacher's Lesson Guide

1 Teaching the Lesson

Key Concepts and Skills

- Identify and use multiples of 10.
  [Number and Numeration Goal 3]
- Add multiples of 10.
  [Operations and Computation Goal 1]
- Apply extended multiplication facts to long-division situations.
  [Operations and Computation Goal 3]
- Solve equal-grouping division number stories.
  [Operations and Computation Goal 4]
- Write number models to represent multiplication and division number stories.
  [Patterns, Functions, and Algebra Goal 2]

Key Activities

Students explore a multiples-of-10 strategy as one of many ways to solve equal-grouping division number stories.

Key Vocabulary

equal-groups notation ◆ quotient ◆ remainder

Materials

Math Journal 1, pp. 142 and 143
Study Link 6•1
Math Masters, p. 436
base-10 blocks (optional) ◆ slate ◆
Multiplication/Division Facts Table (optional)

2 Ongoing Learning & Practice

Playing *High-Number Toss*
Student Reference Book, p. 252
Math Masters, p. 487
per partnership: 1 six-sided die
Students practice place-value skills and comparing numbers.

Math Boxes 6•2
Math Journal 1, p. 141
Students practice and maintain skills through Math Box problems.

Ongoing Assessment: Recognizing Student Achievement
Use Math Boxes, Problems 2a–2c.
[Patterns, Functions, and Algebra Goal 2]

Study Link 6•2
Math Masters, p. 178
Students practice and maintain skills through Study Link activities.

3 Differentiation Options

READINESS

Finding Multiples of 10 and 100
Math Masters, p. 179
Students practice extended multiplication/division facts.

EXTRA PRACTICE

Playing *Buzz* and *Bizz-Buzz*
Student Reference Book, p. 234
Students practice naming multiples and common multiples.

Advance Preparation

***Teacher's Reference Manual,* Grades 4–6** pp. 19, 107–111, 304–306

Getting Started

Mental Math and Reflexes

Display a Multiplication/Division Diagram. Explain that you are thinking of things that are packaged in equal groups.

packages	___ per package	total ___

Ask: *How many are*

●○○ 2 [6s]? 12	●●○ 4 [7s]? 28	●●● 8 [90s]? 720
20 [6s]? 120	4 [70s]? 280	80 [90s]? 7,200
5 [6s]? 30	9 [3s]? 27	7 [60s]? 420
50 [6s]? 300	9 [30s]? 270	70 [60s]? 4,200

Math Message

A box holds 6 chocolate candies. How many boxes are needed to hold 134 chocolate candies?

Study Link 6·1 Follow-Up

Have students use the inverse operations to check their answers to Problems 1–5.

1 Teaching the Lesson

Math Message Follow-Up

Algebraic Thinking Remind students that by packing 134 chocolate candies into the boxes, they are dividing 134 chocolates into groups of 6. The problem is a division problem: How many [6s] are in 134?

Discuss with students that the 134 chocolates could be divided into groups of other sizes besides 6. For example, they could be divided into 13 groups of 10, with 4 chocolates left over: 134 / 10 → 13 R4. But the 134 chocolates cannot be divided into boxes with 0 chocolates in each box. That is, division by 0 is not possible.

On the board, write the problem in four of the ways that division problems can be written:

$$134 \div 6$$

$$6\overline{)134}$$

$$134 / 6$$

$$\frac{134}{6}$$

Ask several students to give their solutions to the Math Message problem and to describe their strategies. *Four possible strategies:*

▷ Use a Multiplication/Division Diagram to organize the information in the problem. Some students may think "What number times 6 equals 134?" while others may reason "134 divided by 6 equals what number?"

boxes	candies per box	total candies
b	6	134

▷ Take 134 cubes. Divide the cubes into as many groups of 6 cubes as possible. 22 groups, 2 cubes left over

▷ Draw a picture.

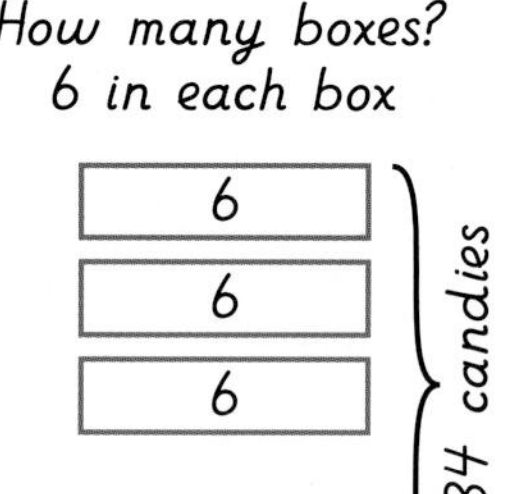

How many [6s] in 134?

▷ Break 134 into smaller "friendly numbers." *For example:*

- 120 + 14 = 134. There are 20 [6s] in 120 and 2 [6s] in 14 with 2 left over. 20 + 2 = 22, so there are 22 [6s] in 134 with 2 left over.

- 60 + 60 + 14 = 134. There are 10 [6s] in 60, 10 [6s] in 60, and 2 [6s] in 14 with 2 left over. 10 + 10 + 2 = 22, so there are 22 [6s] in 134 with 2 left over.

Tell students that there are many ways to solve equal-grouping division problems. One strategy, multiples-of-10, is introduced in this lesson.

Links to the Future

This method for solving equal-grouping division number stories is formalized in the following lesson. In Lesson 6-10, after students have had opportunities to practice division with 1-digit divisors, students work with 2-digit divisors.

▶ Using Multiples to Solve Division Problems

Explain the following multiples strategy as one way to solve the Math Message problem:

Ask if there are at least 10 [6s] in 134. Yes, because 10 ∗ 6 = 60. Write this on the board as shown: 10 [6s] = 60.

Then ask if there are at least 20 [6s] in 134. Yes, because 20 ∗ 6 = 120. Ask if there are at least 30 [6s] in 134. No, because 30 ∗ 6 = 180. Record these multiples on the board.

20 [6s] = 120

30 [6s] = 180

10 [6s] is far less than the required total of 134. 30 [6s] is far greater than 134. 20 [6s] is just 14 short of 134. You need 20 boxes to hold 120 candies. Ask: *How many boxes do you need t hold the remaining 14 candies?* 2 boxes will hold 12 candies. The are 2 candies left over. Therefore, there is not an exact number o [6s] in 134; 22 is the **quotient,** and the 2 left over is the **remainder.** Write the answer on the board in two ways. To support English language learners, label the *quotient* and *remainder* in each of the example problems.

$6\overline{)134} \rightarrow$ 22 R2 and $134 \div 6 \rightarrow$ 22 R2

NOTE When students confront a division problem such as 134 ÷ 6, they should ask themselves, "How many 6s are there in 134?" A good way to keep track of the number of 6s is to use **equal-groups notation:** 10 [6s] are 60, 20 [6s] are 120, 21 [6s] are 126, and so forth.

If you choose not to use the equal-groups notation, you can write 10 ∗ 6 in place of 10 [6s], and 20 ∗ 6 in place of 20 [6s]. But continue to read 10 ∗ 6 as "10 sixes," and 20 ∗ 6 as "20 sixes."

Pose and solve equal-grouping division problems that are similar to the Math Message problem. Show how multiples can be used for each problem. Encourage students to use the relationship between multiplication and division to check their answers.

Example 1: The school used 336 bottles of water at Parents' Night. How many 8-packs is that?

This is a division problem. The 336 bottles are divided into groups of 8. The problem is to find how many [8s] there are in 336.

packs	bottles per pack	total bottles
p	8	336

1. Make a list of the number of bottles in 1, 2, 3, 4, and 5 groups of 8. Also make a list of the number of bottles in 10, 20, 30, 40, and 50 groups of 8.

   1 [8] = 8   10 [8s] = 80

   2 [8s] = 16   20 [8s] = 160

   3 [8s] = 24   30 [8s] = 240

   4 [8s] = 32   40 [8s] = 320

   5 [8s] = 40   50 [8s] = 400

2. Use the list to make a sequence of estimates for the number of [8s] in 336. *For example:*

   10 [8s] = 80 (far too small)

   20 [8s] = 160 (too small)

   30 [8s] = 240 (too small, but close)

   40 [8s] = 320 (too small, but closer)

   50 [8s] = 400 (too much)

40 [8s] is 16 short of 336; 40 [8s] + 2 [8s] = 336 (exact agreement)

So there are 40 + 2, or 42 [8s] in 336, with no remainder. We now know that 42 packs of water, with 8 in each pack, were used for Parents' Night. Write this as

$8\overline{)336} = 42$ or $336 \div 8 = 42$.

Example 2: Each table seats 4 people. How many tables are needed to seat 195 people?

This is a division problem. The 195 people are divided into groups of 4. The problem is to find how many [4s] there are in 195.

tables	people per table	total people
t	4	195

1. Begin by making a list of the number of people in 10, 20, 30, 40, and 50 groups of 4. Show students that it is not necessary to also make a list of the number in 1, 2, 3, 4, and 5 groups of 4. For example, since 30 [4s] = 120, it is clear that 3 [4s] = 12.

Student Page

Date   Time

LESSON 6·2 **Solving Division Problems**

For Problems 1–6, fill in the multiples-of-10 list if it is helpful. If you prefer to solve the division problems in another way, show your work.

Sample number models are given.

1. José's class baked 64 cookies for the school bake sale. Students put 4 cookies in each bag. How many bags of 4 cookies did they make?

   10 [4s] = 40   Number model with unknown: $64 \div 4 = b$

   20 [4s] = 80   Answer: 16 bags

   30 [4s] = 120   Summary number model: $64 \div 4 = 16$

   40 [4s] = 160

   50 [4s] = 200

2. The community center bought 276 cans of soda for a picnic. How many 6-packs is that?

   10 [6s] = 60   Number model with unknown: $276 \div 6 = p$

   20 [6s] = 120   Answer: 46 6-packs

   30 [6s] = 180   Summary number model: $276 \div 6 = 46$

   40 [6s] = 240

   50 [6s] = 300

3. Each lunch table at Johnson Elementary School seats 5 people. How many tables are needed to seat 191 people?

   10 [5s] = 50   Number model with unknown: $191 \div 5 = t$

   20 [5s] = 100   Answer: 39 tables

   30 [5s] = 150   Summary number model: $191 \div 5 \rightarrow 38$ R1

   40 [5s] = 200

   50 [5s] = 250

Math Journal 1, **p. 142**

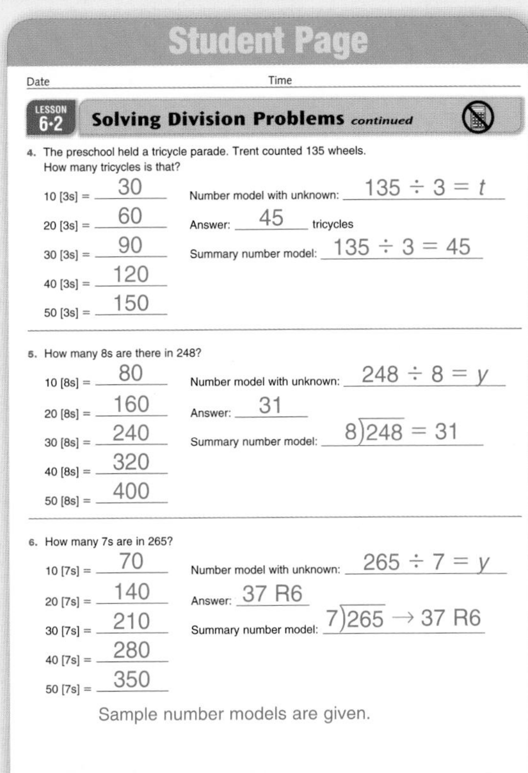

Student Page

Date   Time

LESSON 6·2 **Solving Division Problems** *continued*

4. The preschool held a tricycle parade. Trent counted 135 wheels. How many tricycles is that?

   10 [3s] = 30   Number model with unknown: $135 \div 3 = t$

   20 [3s] = 60   Answer: 45 tricycles

   30 [3s] = 90   Summary number model: $135 \div 3 = 45$

   40 [3s] = 120

   50 [3s] = 150

5. How many 8s are there in 248?

   10 [8s] = 80   Number model with unknown: $248 \div 8 = y$

   20 [8s] = 160   Answer: 31

   30 [8s] = 240   Summary number model: $8\overline{)248} = 31$

   40 [8s] = 320

   50 [8s] = 400

6. How many 7s are in 265?

   10 [7s] = 70   Number model with unknown: $265 \div 7 = y$

   20 [7s] = 140   Answer: 37 R6

   30 [7s] = 210   Summary number model: $7\overline{)265} \rightarrow 37$ R6

   40 [7s] = 280

   50 [7s] = 350

Sample number models are given.

Math Journal 1, **p. 143**

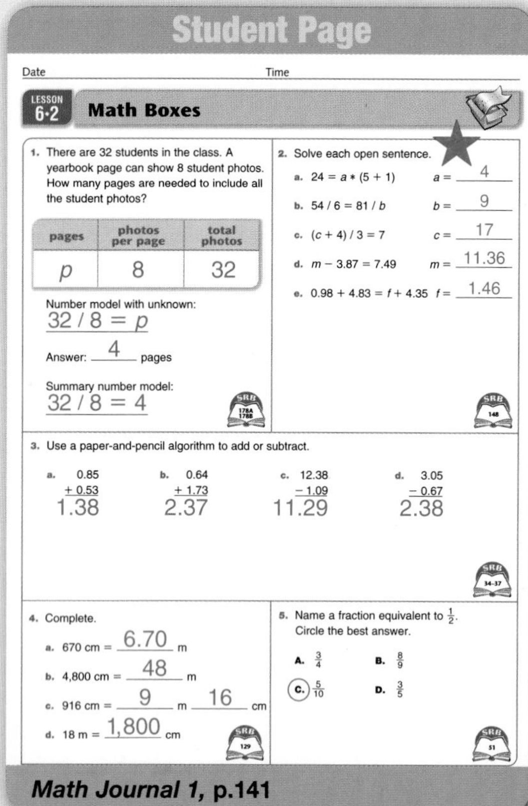
Student Page

Date Time

LESSON 6·2 **Math Boxes**

1. There are 32 students in the class. A yearbook page can show 8 student photos. How many pages are needed to include all the student photos?

pages	photos per page	total photos
p	8	32

Number model with unknown: 32 / 8 = p

Answer: 4 pages

Summary number model: 32 / 8 = 4

2. Solve each open sentence.

a. 24 = a * (5 + 1) a = 4

b. 54 / 6 = 81 / b b = 9

c. (c + 4) / 3 = 7 c = 17

d. m − 3.87 = 7.49 m = 11.36

e. 0.98 + 4.83 = f + 4.35 f = 1.46

3. Use a paper-and-pencil algorithm to add or subtract.

a. 0.85 + 0.53 = 1.38 b. 0.64 + 1.73 = 2.37 c. 12.38 − 1.09 = 11.29 d. 3.05 − 0.67 = 2.38

4. Complete.

a. 670 cm = 6.70 m

b. 4,800 cm = 48 m

c. 916 cm = 9 m 16 cm

d. 18 m = 1,800 cm

5. Name a fraction equivalent to $\frac{1}{2}$. Circle the best answer.

A. $\frac{3}{4}$ B. $\frac{8}{9}$ (C.) $\frac{5}{10}$ D. $\frac{3}{5}$

Math Journal 1, p.141

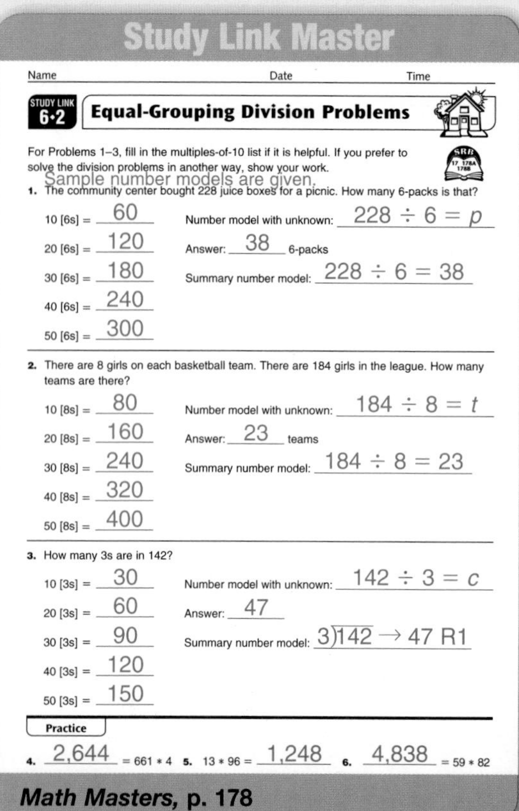
Study Link Master

Name Date Time

STUDY LINK 6·2 **Equal-Grouping Division Problems**

For Problems 1–3, fill in the multiples-of-10 list if it is helpful. If you prefer to solve the division problems in another way, show your work.

Sample number models are given.

1. The community center bought 228 juice boxes for a picnic. How many 6-packs is that?

10 [6s] = 60
20 [6s] = 120
30 [6s] = 180
40 [6s] = 240
50 [6s] = 300

Number model with unknown: 228 ÷ 6 = p

Answer: 38 6-packs

Summary number model: 228 ÷ 6 = 38

2. There are 8 girls on each basketball team. There are 184 girls in the league. How many teams are there?

10 [8s] = 80
20 [8s] = 160
30 [8s] = 240
40 [8s] = 320
50 [8s] = 400

Number model with unknown: 184 ÷ 8 = t

Answer: 23 teams

Summary number model: 184 ÷ 8 = 23

3. How many 3s are in 142?

10 [3s] = 30
20 [3s] = 60
30 [3s] = 90
40 [3s] = 120
50 [3s] = 150

Number model with unknown: 142 ÷ 3 = c

Answer: 47

Summary number model: 3)142 → 47 R1

Practice

4. 2,644 = 661 * 4 5. 13 * 96 = 1,248 6. 4,838 = 59 * 82

Math Masters, p. 178

10 [4s] = 40

20 [4s] = 80

30 [4s] = 120

40 [4s] = 160

50 [4s] = 200

2. Use the list to make a sequence of estimates for the number of [4s] in 195. *For example:*

30 [4s] = 120 (too small)

40 [4s] = 160 (too small, but closer)

50 [4s] = 200 (just a bit too much)

40 [4s] is 35 short of 195; 40 [4s] + 8 [4s] = 192 (only 3 short)

So there are 40 + 8, or 48 [4s] in 195, with a remainder of 3. Write this as 4)195 → 48 R3 or 195 ÷ 4 → 48 R3.

3. Point out the answer and ask students whether 48 R3 tables is the solution to the problem. No. The remainder indicates that 3 people would be left over. Therefore, 49 tables are actually needed to seat 195 people with 4 per table.

Lead students through several more problems on the board, asking, *How many* [ns] *are there in* m? Each *n* should be a 1-digit number; each *m* should be a 2- or 3-digit number.

▶ Practicing Division Strategies

(*Math Journal 1,* pp. 142 and 143; *Math Masters,* p. 436)

Encourage students to use a variety of strategies to solve the problems on journal pages 142 and 143. Have copies of *Math Masters,* page 436 available so students can use Multiplication/Division Diagrams to organize the information in the problems.

Adjusting the Activity

ELL

Have students use a Multiplication/Division Facts table, and begin by listing the numbers in 1, 2, 3, 4, and 5 groups of *n* before listing the numbers in 10, 20, 30, 40, and 50 groups of *n.*

AUDITORY ◆ KINESTHETIC ◆ TACTILE ◆ VISUAL

2 Ongoing Learning & Practice

▶ Playing *High-Number Toss*

(*Student Reference Book,* p. 252; *Math Masters,* p. 487)

Students play *High-Number Toss* to practice place-value skills and comparing numbers. See Lesson 2-7 for additional information.

Math Boxes 6•2

INDEPENDENT ACTIVITY

(*Math Journal 1,* p. 141)

Mixed Practice Math Boxes in this lesson are paired with Math Boxes in Lesson 6-4. The skill in Problem 5 previews Unit 7 content.

Ongoing Assessment: Recognizing Student Achievement

Math Boxes Problems 2a–2c

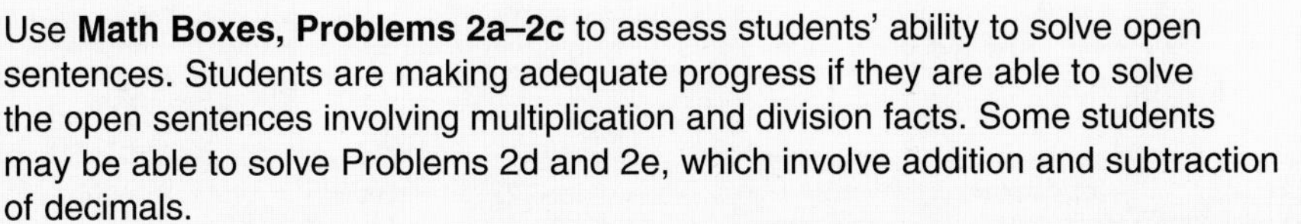

Use **Math Boxes, Problems 2a–2c** to assess students' ability to solve open sentences. Students are making adequate progress if they are able to solve the open sentences involving multiplication and division facts. Some students may be able to solve Problems 2d and 2e, which involve addition and subtraction of decimals.

[Patterns, Functions, and Algebra Goal 2]

Study Link 6•2

INDEPENDENT ACTIVITY

(*Math Masters,* p. 178)

Home Connection Students solve equal-grouping division stories.

3 Differentiation Options

READINESS

INDEPENDENT ACTIVITY

5–15 Min

Finding Multiples of 10 and 100

(*Math Masters,* p. 179)

To explore the relationship between extended multiplication and division facts, have students complete Fact Triangles on *Math Masters,* page 179.

EXTRA PRACTICE

SMALL-GROUP ACTIVITY

5–15 Min

Playing *Buzz* and *Bizz-Buzz*

(*Student Reference Book,* p. 234)

To practice naming multiples and common multiples, have students play the games *Buzz* and *Bizz-Buzz.* Before playing the game, remind students that a whole number is a multiple of each of its factors.

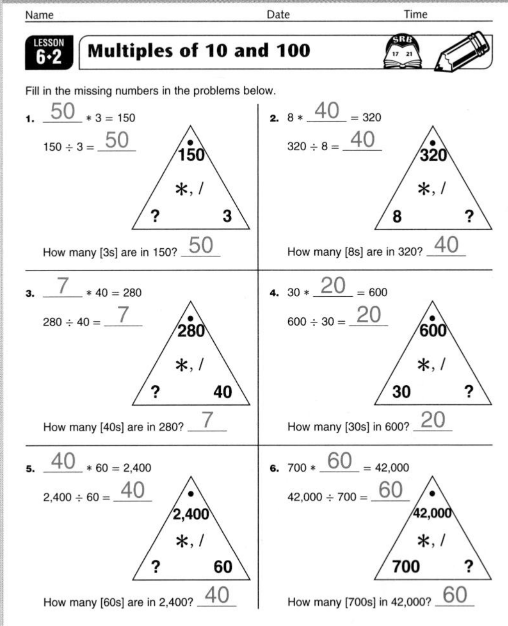

Teaching Master

Name Date Time

LESSON 6•2 **Multiples of 10 and 100**

Fill in the missing numbers in the problems below.

1. 50 ∗ 3 = 150
150 ÷ 3 = 50
How many [3s] are in 150? 50

2. 8 ∗ 40 = 320
320 ÷ 8 = 40
How many [8s] are in 320? 40

3. 7 ∗ 40 = 280
280 ÷ 40 = 7
How many [40s] are in 280? 7

4. 30 ∗ 20 = 600
600 ÷ 30 = 20
How many [30s] in 600? 20

5. 40 ∗ 60 = 2,400
2,400 ÷ 60 = 40
How many [60s] are in 2,400? 40

6. 700 ∗ 60 = 42,000
42,000 ÷ 700 = 60
How many [700s] in 42,000? 60

7. Explain how solving one problem in each set helps you solve the other two problems.
Sample answer: I solved the multiplication problem and then used the relationship between ∗ and / to solve the division problems.

Math Masters, p. 179

Student Page

Games

Buzz Games

Buzz

Materials none

Players 5–10

Skill Finding multiples of a number and common multiples of two numbers

Object of the game To correctly say either "BUZZ" or the next number when it is your turn.

Directions

1. Players sit in a circle and choose a leader. The leader names any whole number from 3 to 9. This number is the BUZZ number. The leader also chooses the STOP number. The STOP number should be at least 30.
2. The player to the left of the leader begins the game by saying "one." Play continues clockwise with each player saying either the next whole number or "BUZZ."
3. A player must say "BUZZ" instead of the next number if:
   - The number is the BUZZ number or a multiple of the BUZZ number; or
   - The number contains the BUZZ number as one of its digits.
4. If a player makes an error, the next player starts with 1.
5. Play continues until the STOP number is reached.
6. For the next round, the player to the right of the leader becomes the new leader.

Example The BUZZ number is 4. Play should proceed as follows: 1, 2, 3, BUZZ, 5, 6, 7, BUZZ, 9, 10, 11, BUZZ, 13, BUZZ, 15, and so on.

Bizz-Buzz

Bizz-Buzz is played like *Buzz,* except the leader names 2 numbers: a BUZZ number and a BIZZ number.

Players say:

1. "BUZZ" if the number is a multiple of the BUZZ number.
2. "BIZZ" if the number is a multiple of the BIZZ number.
3. "BIZZ-BUZZ" if the number is a multiple of both the BUZZ number and the BIZZ number.

Example The BUZZ number is 6, and the BIZZ number is 3. Play should proceed as follows: 1, 2, BIZZ, 4, 5, BIZZ-BUZZ, 7, 8, BIZZ, 10, 11, BIZZ-BUZZ, 13, 14, BIZZ, 16, and so on. The numbers 6 and 12 are replaced by "BIZZ-BUZZ" since 6 and 12 are multiples of both 6 and 3.

Student Reference Book, p. 234

6•3 The Partial-Quotients Division Algorithm, Part 1

Objectives To introduce and provide practice with a "low-stress" division algorithm for 1-digit divisors.

www.everydaymathonline.com

ePresentations

eToolkit

Algorithms Practice

EM Facts Workshop Game™

Family Letters

Assessment Management

Common Core State Standards

Curriculum Focal Points

Interactive Teacher's Lesson Guide

1 Teaching the Lesson

Key Concepts and Skills

- Identify and use multiples of 10.
  [Number and Numeration Goal 3]
- Add multiples of 10.
  [Operations and Computation Goal 1]
- Subtract multidigit numbers.
  [Operations and Computation Goal 2]
- Apply extended multiplication facts to long-division situations.
  [Operations and Computation Goal 3]
- Solve equal-grouping division number stories.
  [Operations and Computation Goal 4]

Key Activities

Students learn and practice a paper-and-pencil algorithm for division that permits them to build up the quotient by working with "easy" numbers.

Ongoing Assessment: Informing Instruction
See pages 413 and 416.

Ongoing Assessment: Recognizing Student Achievement
Use journal pages 144 and 145.
[Operations and Computation Goal 4]

Key Vocabulary

dividend ◆ divisor ◆ partial quotient

Materials

Math Journal 1, pp. 144 and 145
Study Link 6•2
Math Masters, p. 403; pp. 436 and 438 (optional)
slate

2 Ongoing Learning & Practice

Reviewing Place Value in Decimals
Math Journal 1, p. 146
Students solve problems involving various basic skills with decimals.

Math Boxes 6•3
Math Journal 1, p. 147
Students practice and maintain skills through Math Box problems.

Study Link 6•3
Math Masters, p. 180
Students practice and maintain skills through Study Link activities.

3 Differentiation Options

READINESS

Playing *Beat the Calculator*
Student Reference Book, p. 233
Math Masters, p. 461
per group: 4 each of number cards 1–10 (from the Everything Math Deck, if available), calculator
Students practice extended multiplication facts.

ENRICHMENT

Determining the Cost of Pens
Math Masters, p. 181
10 nickels (optional)
Students use clues to solve a division number story.

EXTRA PRACTICE

Playing *Division Dash*
Student Reference Book, p. 241
Math Masters, p. 471
per partnership: 4 each of number cards 1–9 (from the Everything Math Deck, if available)
Students practice dividing 2- or 3-digit dividends by 1-digit divisors.

ELL SUPPORT

Building Vocabulary
chart paper ◆ markers
Students display and label parts of division number models.

Advance Preparation

Make 1 or 2 copies of *Math Masters,* page 403 for each student. Have extra copies available throughout this unit.

***Teacher's Reference Manual,* Grades 4–6** pp. 132–140

Mental Math and Reflexes

FACTS PRACTICE

Pose true or false problems involving equal groups. *Suggestions:*

●○○ There are at least 2 [5s] in 11. true
There are at least 3 [2s] in 5. false
There are at least 4 [3s] in 14. true

●●○ There are at least 7 [6s] in 45. true
There are at least 9 [8s] in 67. false
There are at least 8 [9s] in 75. true

●●● There are at least 10 [8s] in 92. true
There are at least 30 [6s] in 157. false
There are at least 40 [9s] in 391. true

Math Message

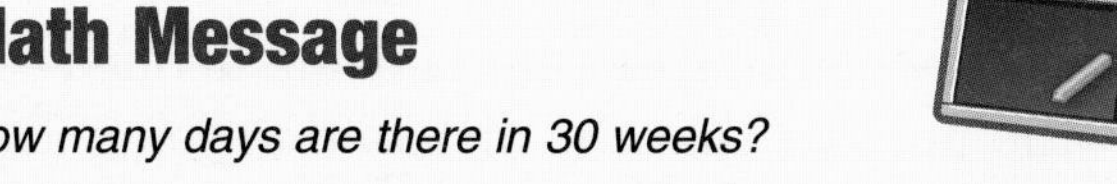

How many days are there in 30 weeks?

How many weeks are there in 98 days?

Study Link 6·2 Follow-Up

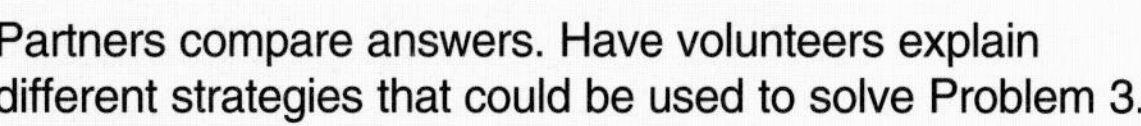

Partners compare answers. Have volunteers explain different strategies that could be used to solve Problem 3.

1 Teaching the Lesson

Math Message Follow-Up

WHOLE-CLASS ACTIVITY

PROBLEM SOLVING

Algebraic Thinking In the first problem, the number of weeks is known; students find the number of days by multiplying by 7. In the second problem, the total number of days is given; students divide by 7 to find the number of weeks.

weeks	days per week	total days
30	7	~~t~~ 210

weeks	days per week	total days
~~w~~ 14	7	98

Introducing the Partial-Quotients Algorithm

WHOLE-CLASS ACTIVITY

ELL

(*Math Masters,* pp. 403 and 438)

This lesson formally introduces the partial-quotients algorithm.

Begin with an equal-grouping division problem like the following:

- Amy is 127 days older than Bob. How many weeks older is Amy?

Briefly work through the steps mentioned in the previous lessons:

Step 1: Decide what you need to find out. How many weeks older is Amy? Write a variable in the "weeks" column.

Ongoing Assessment: Informing Instruction

Watch for students who do not understand where the numeral 7 came from because they did not see a 7 in the problem and did not equate a week with 7 days. Remind students that using another name for an equal quantity is often necessary to solve problems.

Teaching Aid Master

Name Date Time

Easy Multiples SRB 17

100 ∗ ______ = ______ 50 ∗ ______ = ______ 20 ∗ ______ = ______ 10 ∗ ______ = ______ 5 ∗ ______ = ______ 2 ∗ ______ = ______ 1 ∗ ______ = ______	100 ∗ ______ = ______ 50 ∗ ______ = ______ 20 ∗ ______ = ______ 10 ∗ ______ = ______ 5 ∗ ______ = ______ 2 ∗ ______ = ______ 1 ∗ ______ = ______
100 ∗ ______ = ______ 50 ∗ ______ = ______ 20 ∗ ______ = ______ 10 ∗ ______ = ______ 5 ∗ ______ = ______ 2 ∗ ______ = ______ 1 ∗ ______ = ______	100 ∗ ______ = ______ 50 ∗ ______ = ______ 20 ∗ ______ = ______ 10 ∗ ______ = ______ 5 ∗ ______ = ______ 2 ∗ ______ = ______ 1 ∗ ______ = ______

Math Masters, p. 438

w	7	127

number of days in all and the number of days per week. Write the data in the appropriate spaces in the diagram. (*See margin.*)

Step 3: Decide what to do to find the answer. 127 days must be equally grouped (divided) so that there are 7 days in each week. Write a number model to represent the problem using a variable for the unknown. Number model with unknown: $127 / 7 = w$

Step 4: Do the computation. Model the following algorithm while students follow along with paper and pencil.

1. Write the problem in the traditional form: $7\overline{)127}$. Point out that the **dividend**—the number that is being divided—is 127. The **divisor**—the number that the dividend is being divided by—is 7. To support English language learners, label the dividend and the divisor on the board.

2. Draw a vertical line so that the problem looks like the problem below. The vertical line will separate subtractions from partial quotients.

$$7\overline{)127}\;\Big|$$

3. Suggest that one way to proceed is to use a series of "at least/not more than" multiples of the divisor. A good strategy is to start with easy numbers, such as 100 times the divisor or 10 times the divisor.

   - Are there at least 100 [7s] in 127? No, because $100 * 7 = 700$, which is more than 127.
   - Are there at least 10 [7s] in 127? Yes, because $10 * 7 = 70$, which is less than 127.
   - Are there at least 20 [7s]? No, because $20 * 7 = 140$, which is more than 127.
   - So there are at least 10 [7s], but not more than 20 [7s]. Try 10.

   Write $10 * 7$, or 70, under 127. Write 10 at the right. 10 is the first **partial quotient.** Partial quotients will be used to build up the final quotient.

   ```
   7)127 |
      70 | 10   (The first partial quotient) 10 * 7 = 70
   ```

4. The next step is to find out how much is left to divide. Subtract 70 from 127.

   ```
   7)127 |
    - 70 | 10   (The first partial quotient) 10 * 7 = 70
      57 |      Subtract. 57 is left to divide.
   ```

Adjusting the Activity

Suggest that students first make a list of "easy" multiples of the divisor. For example, if the divisor is 7, students might make the following list:

$100 * 7 = 700$
$50 * 7 = 350$
$20 * 7 = 140$
$10 * 7 = 70$
$5 * 7 = 35$
$2 * 7 = 14$
$1 * 7 = 7$

Depending on the students and the divisor, the list can be extended or reduced.

Students can use their list of easy multiples to take the guesswork out of successive multiples and focus on solving the division problem.

Students will realize that they can work more quickly if they begin with a more extensive list of multiples. *Math Masters,* page 438 provides an optional form for writing multiples.

AUDITORY ◆ KINESTHETIC ◆ TACTILE ◆ VISUAL

5. Now find the number of 7s in 57. Following are two ways to do this:

▷ Use a fact family: $8 * 7 = 56$, so there are at least 8 [7s] in 57. Record as follows:

```
7)127 |
 - 70 | 10  (The first partial quotient) 10 * 7 = 70
   57 |     Subtract. 57 is left to divide.
   56 |  8  (The second partial quotient) 8 * 7 = 56
```

▷ Use "at least / not more than" multiples with easy numbers. For example, ask:

- Are there at least 10 [7s] in 57? No, because $10 * 7 = 70$.
- Are there at least 5 [7s]? Yes, because $5 * 7 = 35$.

Next, subtract 35 from 57 and continue by asking:

- How many 7s are in 22? 3

```
7)127 |
 - 70 | 10  (The first partial quotient) 10 * 7 = 70
   57 |     Subtract. 57 is left to divide.
 - 35 |  5  (The second partial quotient) 5 * 7 = 35
   22 |     Subtract. 22 is left to divide.
   21 |  3  (The third partial quotient) 3 * 7 = 21
```

6. For both ways, the division is complete when the subtraction leaves a number less than the divisor (7 in this example). The final step is to add the partial quotients—the numbers of 7s that were subtracted. 18 is the quotient. There is 1 left over. So, 1 is the remainder.

```
7)127 |        7)127 |
 - 70 | 10      - 70 | 10
   57 |           57 |
 - 56 |  8      - 35 |  5
    1   18        22 |
                - 21 |  3
                   1   18
```

7. Have students record the final answer in the traditional position above the dividend. To support English language learners, label the quotient and the remainder.

```
   18 R1
7)127
```

8. Conclude by interpreting the answer: Amy is 18 weeks and 1 day older than Bob.

tep 5: Record the answer and write a number model to summarize ie number story.

nswer: 18 weeks and 1 day older than Bob

ummary number model: $127 / 7 \rightarrow 18$ R1

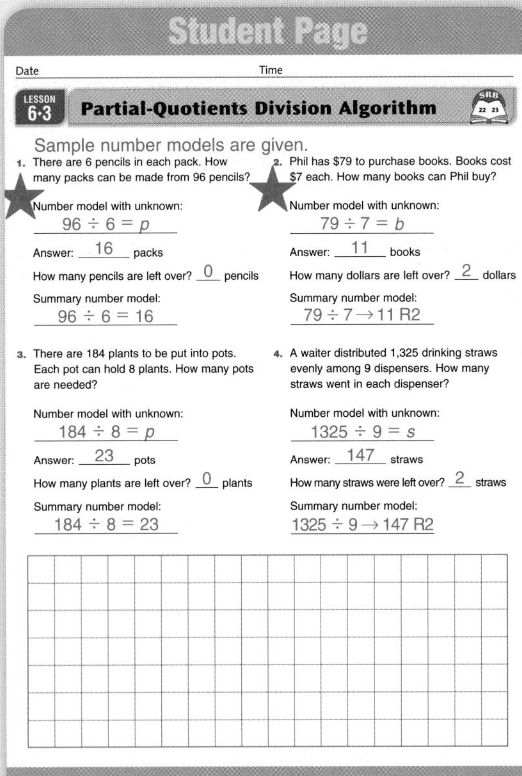

Student Page

Date Time

LESSON 6·3 **Partial-Quotients Division Algorithm** SRB 22 23

Sample number models are given.

1. There are 6 pencils in each pack. How many packs can be made from 96 pencils?

Number model with unknown: 96 ÷ 6 = *p*

Answer: 16 packs

How many pencils are left over? 0 pencils

Summary number model: 96 ÷ 6 = 16

2. Phil has $79 to purchase books. Books cost $7 each. How many books can Phil buy?

Number model with unknown: 79 ÷ 7 = *b*

Answer: 11 books

How many dollars are left over? 2 dollars

Summary number model: 79 ÷ 7 → 11 R2

3. There are 184 plants to be put into pots. Each pot can hold 8 plants. How many pots are needed?

Number model with unknown: 184 ÷ 8 = *p*

Answer: 23 pots

How many plants are left over? 0 plants

Summary number model: 184 ÷ 8 = 23

4. A waiter distributed 1,325 drinking straws evenly among 9 dispensers. How many straws went in each dispenser?

Number model with unknown: 1325 ÷ 9 = *s*

Answer: 147 straws

How many straws were left over? 2 straws

Summary number model: 1325 ÷ 9 → 147 R2

Math Journal 1, p. 144

Lead students through several more problems on the board. Ask: *How many* [ns] *are there in* m*?* Each *n* should be a 1-digit number; each *m* should be a 2- or 3-digit number. Some students may be ready for a 2-digit divisor. *Suggestions:*

- How many [4s] are there in 92? 23
- How many [3s] are there in 87? 29
- How many [7s] are there in 301? 43
- How many [8s] are there in 925? 115 R5
- How many [12s] are there in 588? 49
- How many [15s] are there in 556? 37 R1

Have the class pose a division problem, and ask partnerships to try to find the answer. Have volunteers share their work with the class. Look for students who got the same results in different ways.

Ongoing Assessment: Informing Instruction

Watch for students using multiples that are not too large and that are easy to work with. Using such multiples may require more steps, but it will make the work go faster. Also, students should not be concerned if they pick a multiple that is too large. If that happens, they will quickly realize that they have a subtraction problem involving a larger number below.

▶ Using the Partial-Quotients Algorithm

INDEPENDENT ACTIVITY

(*Math Journal 1,* pp. 144 and 145)

Students use the partial-quotients algorithm to solve number stories and computation problems. Have copies of *Math Masters,* pages 436 and 438 readily available for students who choose to use them. Encourage students to use the relationship between multiplication and division to check their answers.

Ongoing Assessment: Recognizing Student Achievement

Journal pages 144 and 145 Problems 1, 2, 5

Use **journal pages 144** and **145, Problems 1, 2,** and **5** to assess students' ability to solve division problems and number stories with 1-digit divisors and 2-digit dividends. Students are making adequate progress if they are able to compute the answers using the partial-quotients division algorithm. Some students may be able to solve Problems 3, 4, and 6–8, which involve 2-digit divisors or 3- or 4-digit dividends.

[Operations and Computation Goal 4]

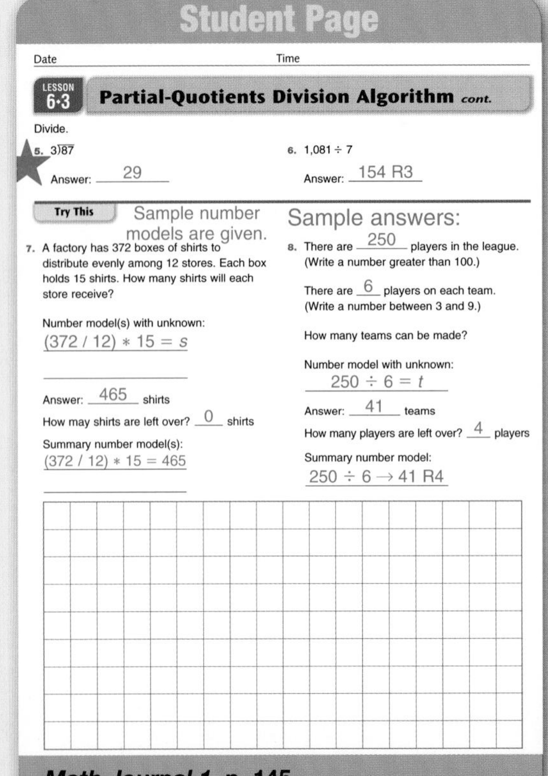

Student Page

Date Time

LESSON 6·3 **Partial-Quotients Division Algorithm** *cont.*

Divide.

5. 3)87

Answer: 29

6. 1,081 ÷ 7

Answer: 154 R3

Try This

Sample number models are given.

Sample answers:

7. A factory has 372 boxes of shirts to distribute evenly among 12 stores. Each box holds 15 shirts. How many shirts will each store receive?

Number model(s) with unknown: (372 / 12) ∗ 15 = *s*

Answer: 465 shirts

How may shirts are left over? 0 shirts

Summary number model(s): (372 / 12) ∗ 15 = 465

8. There are 250 players in the league. (Write a number greater than 100.)

There are 6 players on each team. (Write a number between 3 and 9.)

How many teams can be made?

Number model with unknown: 250 ÷ 6 = *t*

Answer: 41 teams

How many players are left over? 4 players

Summary number model: 250 ÷ 6 → 41 R4

Math Journal 1, p. 145

2 Ongoing Learning & Practice

▶ Reviewing Place Value in Decimals

(*Math Journal 1,* p. 146)

Students solve problems involving ordering of decimals, naming place value in decimals, and reading and writing decimals.

▶ Math Boxes 6•3

(*Math Journal 1,* p. 147)

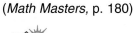

Mixed Practice Math Boxes in this lesson are paired with Math Boxes in Lesson 6-1. The skill in Problem 5 previews Unit 7 content.

Writing/Reasoning Have students write a response to the following: *Explain how the exponent in Problem 4a changes the value of 10.* Sample answer: The exponent tells how many times the base 10 is used as a factor. For example, $10^4 = 10 * 10 * 10 * 10$, or 10,000.

▶ Study Link 6•3

(*Math Masters,* p. 180)

Home Connection Students practice using the partial-quotients division algorithm.

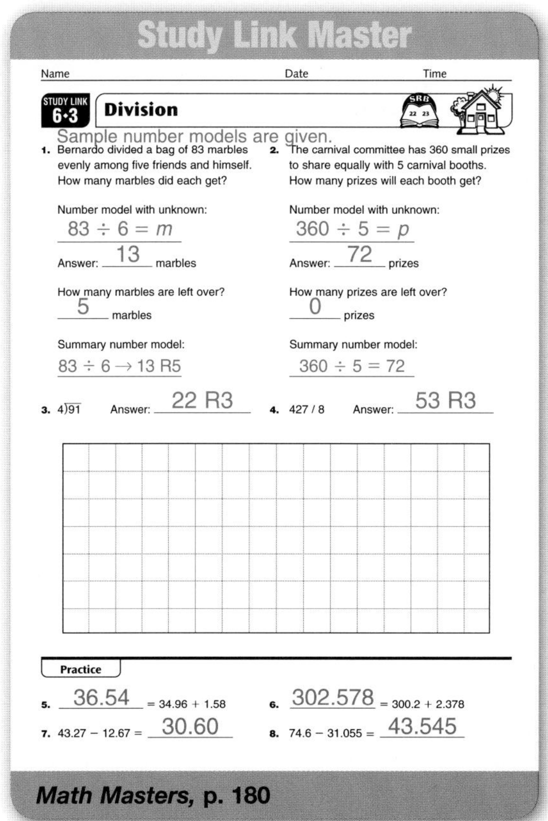

Study Link Master

Name ____ Date ____ Time ____

STUDY LINK 6•3 **Division**

Sample number models are given.

1. Bernardo divided a bag of 83 marbles evenly among five friends and himself. How many marbles did each get?
   Number model with unknown: 83 ÷ 6 = *m*
   Answer: 13 marbles
   How many marbles are left over? 5 marbles
   Summary number model: 83 ÷ 6 → 13 R5

2. The carnival committee has 360 small prizes to share equally with 5 carnival booths. How many prizes will each booth get?
   Number model with unknown: 360 ÷ 5 = *p*
   Answer: 72 prizes
   How many prizes are left over? 0 prizes
   Summary number model: 360 ÷ 5 = 72

3. 4)91 Answer: 22 R3
4. 427 / 8 Answer: 53 R3

Practice

5. 36.54 = 34.96 + 1.58
6. 302.578 = 300.2 + 2.378
7. 43.27 − 12.67 = 30.60
8. 74.6 − 31.055 = 43.545

Math Masters, p. 180

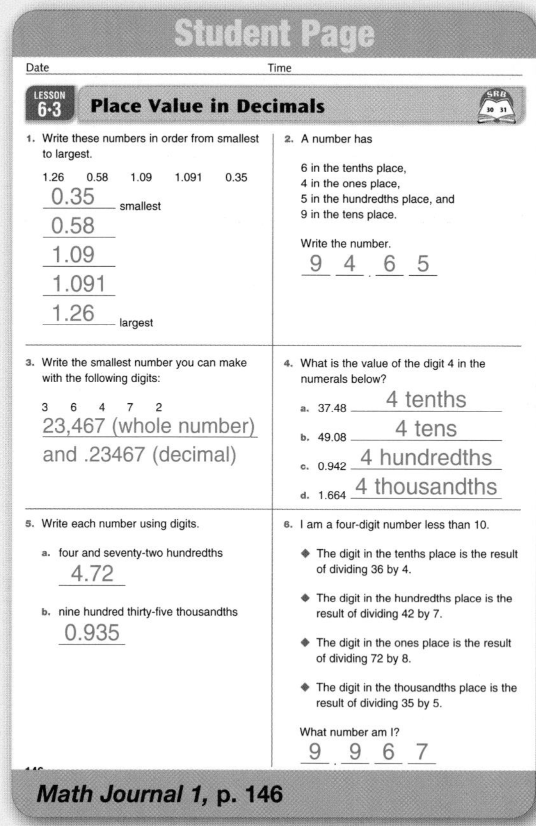

Student Page

Date ____ Time ____

LESSON 6•3 **Place Value in Decimals**

1. Write these numbers in order from smallest to largest.
   1.26 0.58 1.09 1.091 0.35
   0.35 smallest
   0.58
   1.09
   1.091
   1.26 largest

2. A number has
   6 in the tenths place,
   4 in the ones place,
   5 in the hundredths place, and
   9 in the tens place.
   Write the number. 9 4 . 6 5

3. Write the smallest number you can make with the following digits:
   3 6 4 7 2
   23,467 (whole number) and .23467 (decimal)

4. What is the value of the digit 4 in the numerals below?
   a. 37.48 4 tenths
   b. 49.08 4 tens
   c. 0.942 4 hundredths
   d. 1.664 4 thousandths

5. Write each number using digits.
   a. four and seventy-two hundredths 4.72
   b. nine hundred thirty-five thousandths 0.935

6. I am a four-digit number less than 10.
   - The digit in the tenths place is the result of dividing 36 by 4.
   - The digit in the hundredths place is the result of dividing 42 by 7.
   - The digit in the ones place is the result of dividing 72 by 8.
   - The digit in the thousandths place is the result of dividing 35 by 5.

   What number am I? 9 . 9 6 7

Math Journal 1, p. 146

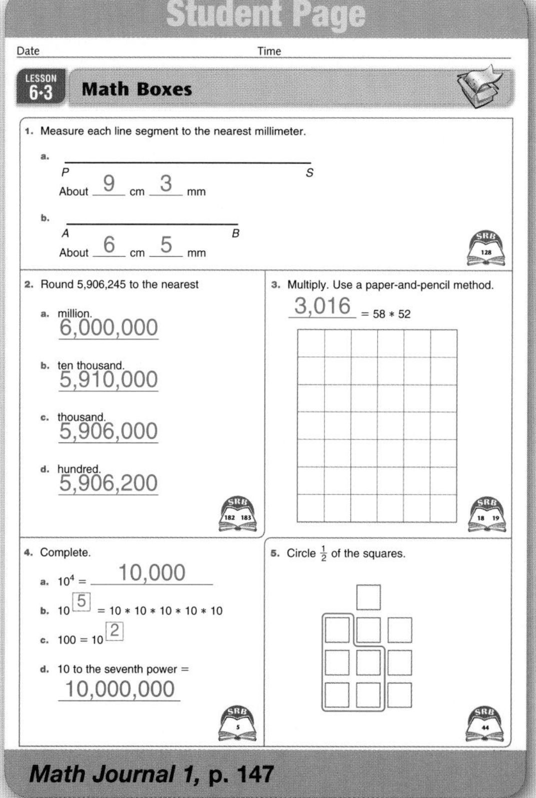

Student Page

Date ____ Time ____

LESSON 6•3 **Math Boxes**

1. Measure each line segment to the nearest millimeter.
   a. P———S About 9 cm 3 mm
   b. A———B About 6 cm 5 mm

2. Round 5,906,245 to the nearest
   a. million. 6,000,000
   b. ten thousand. 5,910,000
   c. thousand. 5,906,000
   d. hundred. 5,906,200

3. Multiply. Use a paper-and-pencil method.
   3,016 = 58 ∗ 52

4. Complete.
   a. 10^4 = 10,000
   b. 10^{5} = 10 ∗ 10 ∗ 10 ∗ 10 ∗ 10
   c. 100 = 10^{2}
   d. 10 to the seventh power = 10,000,000

5. Circle $\frac{1}{2}$ of the squares.

Math Journal 1, p. 147

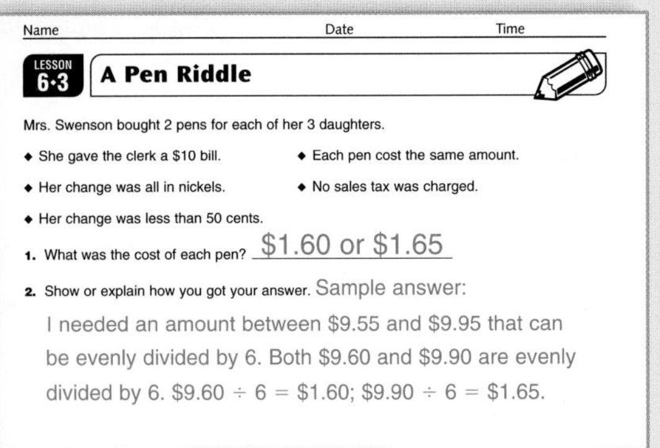
Name Date Time

LESSON 6·3 **A Pen Riddle**

Mrs. Swenson bought 2 pens for each of her 3 daughters.

- She gave the clerk a $10 bill.
- Each pen cost the same amount.
- Her change was all in nickels.
- No sales tax was charged.
- Her change was less than 50 cents.

1. What was the cost of each pen? $1.60 or $1.65
2. Show or explain how you got your answer. Sample answer: I needed an amount between $9.55 and $9.95 that can be evenly divided by 6. Both $9.60 and $9.90 are evenly divided by 6. $9.60 ÷ 6 = $1.60; $9.90 ÷ 6 = $1.65.

Math Masters, page 181

3 Differentiation Options

READINESS

SMALL-GROUP ACTIVITY

5–15 Min

▶ Playing *Beat the Calculator*

(*Student Reference Book,* p. 233; *Math Masters,* p. 461)

To provide experience with extended multiplication facts, students play a version of *Beat the Calculator* in which the caller attaches a 0 to one or both of the factors shown on the cards.

ENRICHMENT

INDEPENDENT ACTIVITY

5–15 Min

▶ Determining the Cost of Pens

(*Math Masters,* p. 181)

To apply students' understanding of division, have them use clues to find the cost of several pens. Encourage students to use money to model the problem if necessary.

EXTRA PRACTICE

PARTNER ACTIVITY

5–15 Min

▶ Playing *Division Dash*

(*Student Reference Book,* p. 241; *Math Masters,* p. 471)

To practice dividing 2- or 3-digit dividends by 1-digit divisors, have students play *Division Dash.* See Lesson 6-4 for additional information.

ELL SUPPORT

SMALL-GROUP ACTIVITY

5–15 Min

▶ Building Vocabulary

To provide language support for division, have students write division number models on chart paper in the following ways:

$42 / 5 \rightarrow 8\text{ R2}$ $\quad \frac{42}{5} \rightarrow 8\text{ R2}$ $\quad 42 \div 5 \rightarrow 8\text{ R2}$ $\quad 5\overline{)42}$ with 8 R2 above

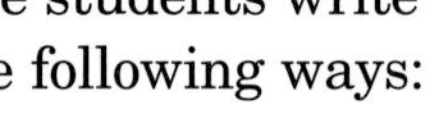

Have students do the following for each number model:

- ▷ Label and underline the *dividend* (number being divided) in red.
- ▷ Label and underline the *divisor* (the number the dividend is being divided by) in blue.
- ▷ Label and circle the *quotient* in a third color.
- ▷ Label and circle the *remainder* in a fourth color.

Point out that both the quotient and the remainder are part of the answer. Display this chart throughout the division lessons.

Student Page

Games

Division Dash

Materials □ number cards 1–9 (4 of each)
□ 1 score sheet

Players 1 or 2

Skill Division of 2-digit by 1-digit numbers

Object of the game To reach 100 in the fewest divisions possible.

Player 1		Player 2	
Quotient	Score	Quotient	Score

Directions

1. Prepare a score sheet like the one shown at the right.
2. Shuffle the cards and place the deck number-side down on the table.
3. Each player follows the instructions below:
   - Turn over 3 cards and lay them down in a row, from left to right. Use the 3 cards to generate a division problem. The 2 cards on the left form a 2-digit number. This is the *dividend.* The number on the card at the right is the *divisor.*
   - Divide the 2-digit number by the 1-digit number and record the result. This result is your quotient. Remainders are ignored. Calculate mentally or on paper.
   - Add your quotient to your previous score and record your new score. (If this is your first turn, your previous score was 0.)
4. Players repeat Step 3 until one player's score is 100 or more. The first player to reach at least 100 wins. If there is only one player, the object of the game is to reach 100 in as few turns as possible.

Example

Turn 1: Bob draws 6, 4, and 5. He divides 64 by 5. Quotient = 12. Remainder is ignored. The score is 12 + 0 = 12.

Turn 2: Bob then draws 8, 2, and 1. He divides 82 by 1. Quotient = 82. The score is 82 + 12 = 94.

Turn 3: Bob then draws 5, 7, and 8. He divides 57 by 8. Quotient = 7. Remainder is ignored. The score is 7 + 94 = 101. Bob has reached 100 in 3 turns and the game ends.

64 is the dividend. 5 is the divisor.

Quotient	Score
12	12
82	94
7	101

***Student Reference Book,* p. 241**

6•4 Expressing and Interpreting Remainders

Objectives To introduce the expression of remainders as fractions or decimals; and to provide practice interpreting remainders in division problems.

Technology Resources www.everydaymathonline.com

ePresentations

eToolkit

Algorithms Practice

EM Facts Workshop Game™

Family Letters

Assessment Management

Common Core State Standards

Curriculum Focal Points

Interactive Teacher's Lesson Guide

1 Teaching the Lesson

Key Concepts and Skills

- Use multiples to solve division problems. [Number and Numeration Goal 3]
- Solve division number stories and interpret remainders. [Operations and Computation Goal 4]
- Use arrays to model division. [Operations and Computation Goal 7]
- Write number models to represent division number stories. [Patterns, Functions, and Algebra Goal 2]
- Write number models containing grouping symbols. [Patterns, Functions, and Algebra Goal 3]

Key Activities

Students express remainders in division problems as fractions that become part of mixed-number answers or as decimals. They solve other division problems in which the remainder is either rounded up or ignored.

Key Vocabulary

mixed number

Materials

Math Journal 1, pp. 148 and 149
Study Link 6•3
slate ◆ 13 sticks of gum (optional)

2 Ongoing Learning & Practice

Playing *Division Dash*
Student Reference Book, p. 241
Math Masters, p. 471
per partnership: 4 each of number cards 1–9 (from the Everything Math Deck, if available)
Students practice dividing 2- and 3-digit dividends by 1-digit divisors.

Math Boxes 6•4
Math Journal 1, p. 150
Students practice and maintain skills through Math Box problems.

Ongoing Assessment: Recognizing Student Achievement
Use Math Boxes, Problem 3.
[Operations and Computation Goal 2]

Study Link 6•4
Math Masters, p. 182
Students practice and maintain skills through Study Link activities.

3 Differentiation Options

READINESS

Exploring Remainders in Literature
Math Masters, p. 183
centimeter cubes
Students read *A Remainder of One,* create arrays, and record number models based on the story.

ENRICHMENT

Solving a Multiples Number Story
Math Masters, p. 184
counters (optional)
Students solve a division number story by finding multiples.

EXTRA PRACTICE

5-Minute Math
5-Minute Math™, pp. 20 and 25
Students practice solving division problems.

Advance Preparation

For the optional Readiness activity in Part 3, obtain the book ***A Remainder of One*** by Elinor J. Pinczes (Houghton Mifflin Harcourt, 2002).

***Teacher's Reference Manual,* Grades 4–6** pp. 68, 69, 132–140

Getting Started

Mental Math and Reflexes

Pose division facts. *Suggestions:*

●○○ $12 \div 6 = 2$
$16 \div 4 = 4$
$30 \div 6 = 5$
$70 \div 7 = 10$

●●○ $21 \div 3 = 7$
$32 \div 4 = 8$
$27 \div 3 = 9$
$24 \div 6 = 4$

●●● $72 \div 9 = 8$
$42 \div 7 = 6$
$36 \div 4 = 9$
$63 \div 9 = 7$

Math Message

Three students share 13 sticks of gum. How many sticks of gum does each student get if they receive equal shares?

students	sticks of gum per student	total sticks of gum
3	g	13

Study Link 6·3 Follow-Up

Have students compare answers. Ask volunteers to share different ways to solve the problems.

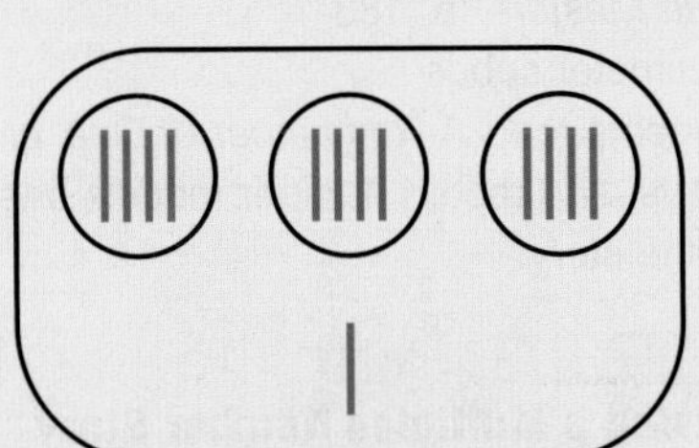

13 sticks of gum shared equally by 3 students

$13 / 3 = x$

13 sticks of gum.
3 students.
$3 * x = 13$

1 Teaching the Lesson

▶ Math Message Follow-Up

Algebraic Thinking Point out that 4 R1 is a correct answer to the Math Message problem, but that this answer will not satisfy the three students who want to know who gets the last piece of gum.

Ask students to draw a simple picture to organize the information in the problem. Have several volunteers draw their pictures on the board.

Ask: *What do the quotient 4 and remainder 1 represent?* Each student can have 4 sticks of gum, and 1 stick will be left.
Ask: *Should the 1 stick be ignored?* No. That would be a waste. The context of the problem indicates that the remainder should be made part of the answer.

One way to do this is to divide the remainder among the 3 students. Draw a rectangle to represent one stick of gum and divide it into thirds. Label each section $\frac{1}{3}$.

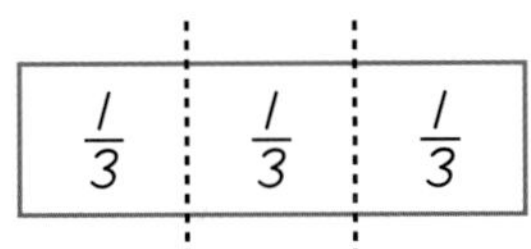

Adjusting the Activity

Act out the problem using actual sticks of gum. Open the thirteenth stick and break it into 3 equal pieces.

AUDITORY ♦ KINESTHETIC ♦ TACTILE ♦ VISUAL

Therefore, each student will receive $4\frac{1}{3}$ sticks of gum. Another way to say this is $4\frac{1}{3}$ sticks of gum *per* student. Explain that $4\frac{1}{3}$ is called a **mixed number.**

Students can check their answers by multiplying $3 * 4$ and adding the remainder of 1. $(3 * 4) + 1 = 13$

Links to the Future

In Unit 7 of *Fourth Grade Everyday Mathematics,* students will continue their exploration of mixed numbers in their work with number lines, regions, and collections.

▶ Expressing Remainders as Fractions or Decimals

WHOLE-CLASS ACTIVITY

Tell students that in this lesson they will solve division number stories in which something must be done with the remainder in order to provide a useful answer. In the following examples, the remainder is expressed as a fraction or decimal.

Ask students to draw a simple picture to organize the information for each problem below.

Example 1: Four brothers are given 35 fruit bars. They agree to share the bars equally. How many fruit bars will each boy get?

This is a division problem: $35 / 4 \rightarrow 8$ R3. If they each get 8 fruit bars, 3 fruit bars would still need to be divided.

Sketch the 3 fruit bars on the board. Divide each into fourths to represent the 4 boys sharing each bar.

If each boy takes one piece of each bar, he will have $8\frac{3}{4}$ fruit bars.

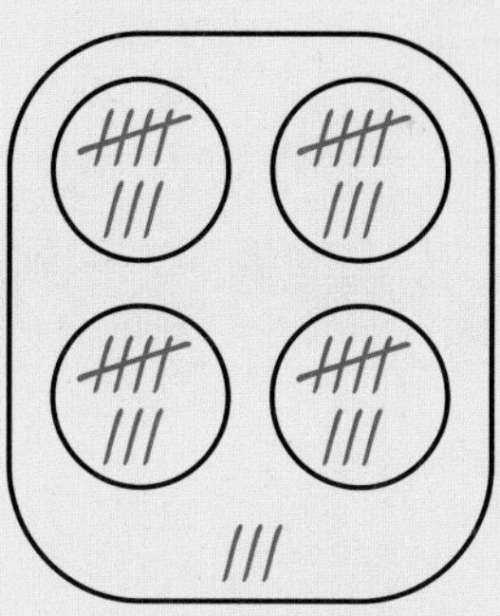

35 fruit bars shared equally by 4 brothers $35 / 4 = x$

Some students will discover the shortcut for writing a remainder as a fraction:

1. Make the remainder the *numerator* of the fraction.
2. Make the divisor the *denominator* of the fraction.

Then write the answer as a mixed number in which the remainder is now expressed as a fraction.

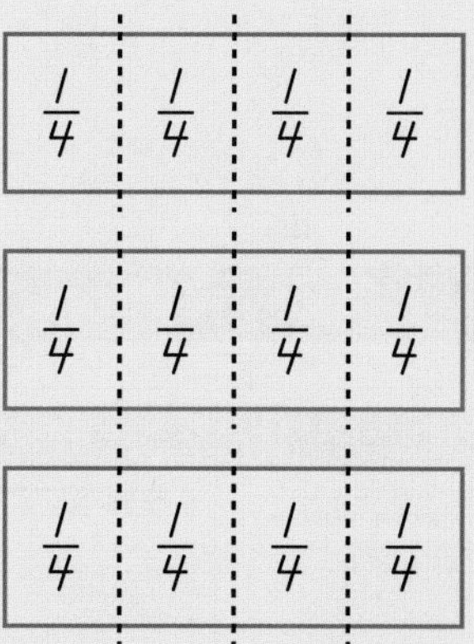

The 3 remaining bars shared equally by 4 brothers $\frac{1}{4} + \frac{1}{4} + \frac{1}{4} = \frac{3}{4}$

In some problems, especially those involving money, it may be preferable to change the fraction to an equivalent decimal.

Example 2: Four people split the cost of a \$15 present equally. What is each person's share? $15 \div 4 \rightarrow 3$ R3.

Using the remainder as the numerator of the fraction and the divisor as the denominator leads to the answer $\$3\frac{3}{4}$, or \$3.75. Sketch a dollar bill on the board. Divide it into fourths to show that $\frac{3}{4}$ of \$1.00 = \$0.75.

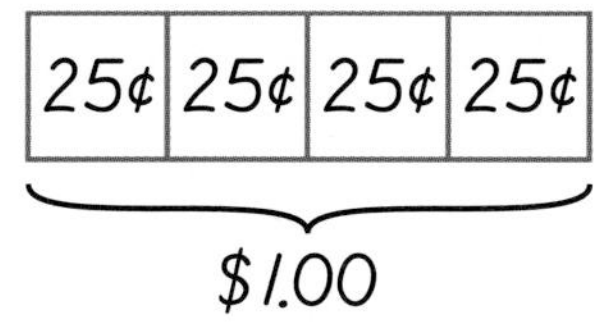

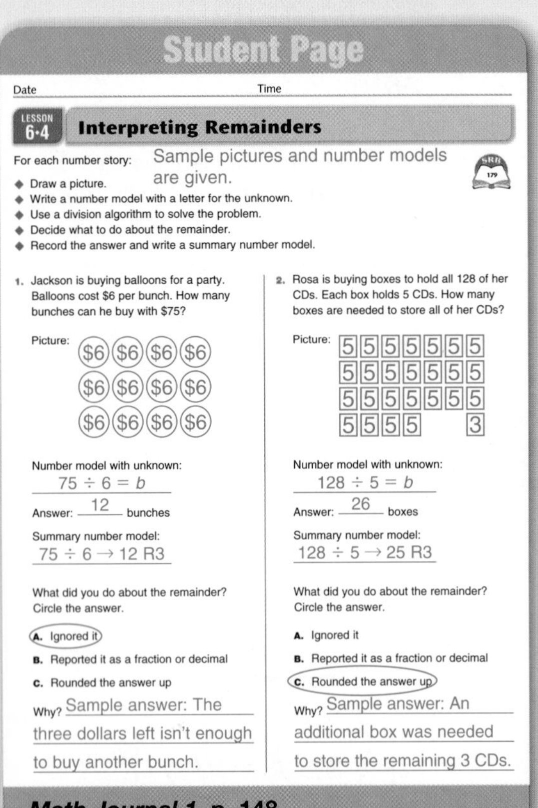

Student Page

Date Time

LESSON 6·4 **Interpreting Remainders**

For each number story: Sample pictures and number models are given.

- Draw a picture.
- Write a number model with a letter for the unknown.
- Use a division algorithm to solve the problem.
- Decide what to do about the remainder.
- Record the answer and write a summary number model.

1. Jackson is buying balloons for a party. Balloons cost $6 per bunch. How many bunches can he buy with $75?

Picture: $6 $6 $6 $6 / $6 $6 $6 $6 / $6 $6 $6 $6

Number model with unknown: $75 \div 6 = b$

Answer: 12 bunches

Summary number model: $75 \div 6 \rightarrow 12$ R3

What did you do about the remainder? Circle the answer.

A. Ignored it (circled)
B. Reported it as a fraction or decimal
C. Rounded the answer up

Why? Sample answer: The three dollars left isn't enough to buy another bunch.

2. Rosa is buying boxes to hold all 128 of her CDs. Each box holds 5 CDs. How many boxes are needed to store all of her CDs?

Picture: 5 5 5 5 5 5 5 / 5 5 5 5 5 5 5 / 5 5 5 5 5 5 5 / 5 5 5 5 3

Number model with unknown: $128 \div 5 = b$

Answer: 26 boxes

Summary number model: $128 \div 5 \rightarrow 25$ R3

What did you do about the remainder? Circle the answer.

A. Ignored it
B. Reported it as a fraction or decimal
C. Rounded the answer up (circled)

Why? Sample answer: An additional box was needed to store the remaining 3 CDs.

Math Journal 1, p. 148

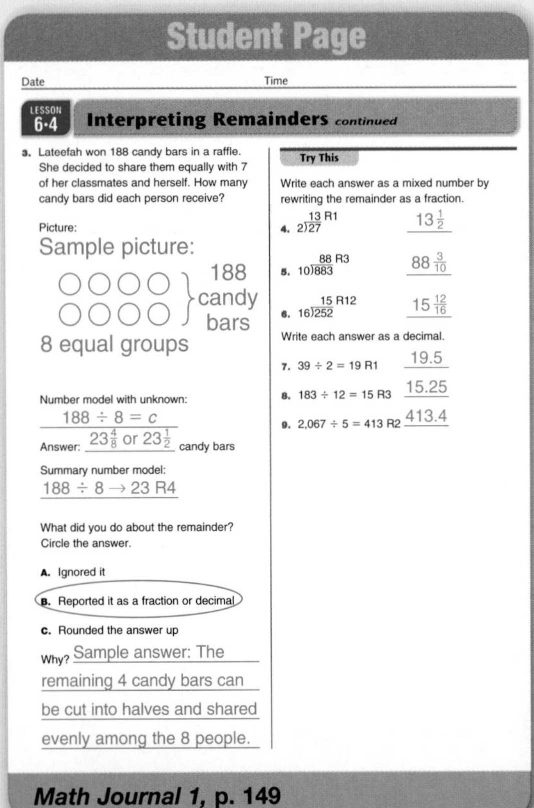

Student Page

Date Time

LESSON 6·4 **Interpreting Remainders** *continued*

3. Lateefah won 188 candy bars in a raffle. She decided to share them equally with 7 of her classmates and herself. How many candy bars did each person receive?

Picture: Sample picture: 8 equal groups, 188 candy bars

Number model with unknown: $188 \div 8 = c$

Answer: $23\frac{4}{8}$ or $23\frac{1}{2}$ candy bars

Summary number model: $188 \div 8 \rightarrow 23$ R4

What did you do about the remainder? Circle the answer.

A. Ignored it
B. Reported it as a fraction or decimal (circled)
C. Rounded the answer up

Why? Sample answer: The remaining 4 candy bars can be cut into halves and shared evenly among the 8 people.

Try This

Write each answer as a mixed number by rewriting the remainder as a fraction.

4. $2\overline{)27}$ 13 R1 — $13\frac{1}{2}$
5. $10\overline{)883}$ 88 R3 — $88\frac{3}{10}$
6. $16\overline{)252}$ 15 R12 — $15\frac{12}{16}$

Write each answer as a decimal.

7. $39 \div 2 = 19$ R1 — 19.5
8. $183 \div 12 = 15$ R3 — 15.25
9. $2{,}067 \div 5 = 413$ R2 — 413.4

Math Journal 1, p. 149

▶ Interpreting Remainders in Problem Contexts

The remainder in a division number story should not always be converted to a fraction or decimal and retained as part of the answer. Depending on the situation, the remainder might be ignored because it is a leftover amount that cannot be split up further. Or, it might indicate that the answer should be rounded up. Discuss examples that illustrate these other situations. For each problem, ask students to draw a simple picture to organize the information.

Remainder that is ignored

- Three children wish to divide a set of 16 toy cars equally. What is each child's share?

Each child can have 5 cars, and there is 1 car left over. Unlike the 1 stick of gum in the Math Message problem that could be cut into equal parts, the 1 remaining toy car cannot be divided up. Therefore, the remainder is considered a "leftover" amount.

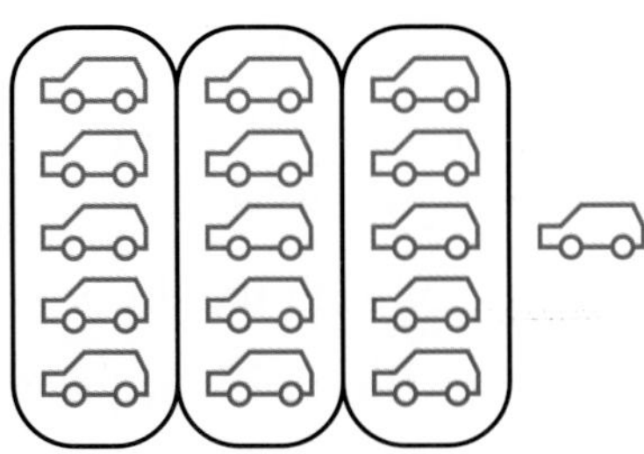

Remainder that is ignored

- Ann has $18 to buy notebooks that cost $4 each. How many notebooks can she buy?

The division is $18 \div 4 \rightarrow 4$ R2. Ann can buy 4 notebooks and will have $2 left. The remainder can be ignored. Note that Ann will have $2 left, but the answer to the question is 4 (notebooks).

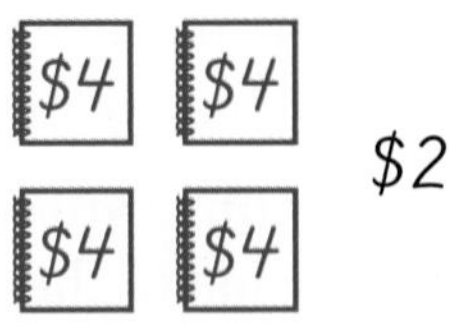

Remainder that indicates the answer should be rounded up

- Esteban has 29 photographs. He can fit 6 photos on each page of his photo album. How many pages must he use to hold all 29 photos?

The division is $29 \div 6 \rightarrow 4$ R5, or $4\frac{5}{6}$. Esteban needs $4\frac{5}{6}$ pages to include all 29 photos. Four pages hold only 24 photos and are not enough. Esteban must use a fifth page to hold the last 5 photos. He must use 5 pages in all, which is $4\frac{5}{6}$ rounded up to the next whole number.

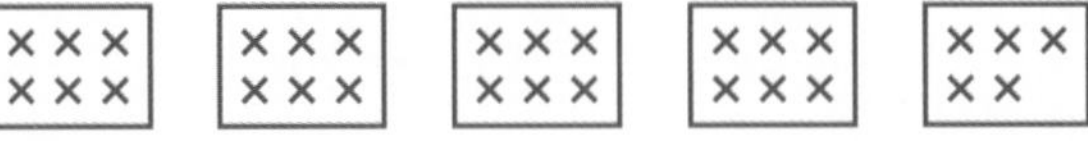

▶ Solving Division Problems and Interpreting Remainders

(*Math Journal 1,* pp. 148 and 149)

Encourage students to think about each remainder and the different ways in which it should be interpreted as they complete journal pages 148 and 149.

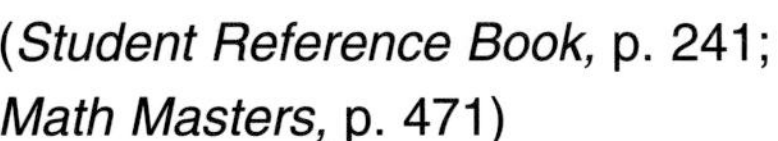

2 Ongoing Learning & Practice

▶ Playing *Division Dash*

(*Student Reference Book,* p. 241; *Math Masters,* p. 471)

Students play *Division Dash* to practice dividing 2- or 3-digit dividends by 1-digit divisors.

Adjusting the Activity

Use this game variation as appropriate:
Have students place only the 2 and 5 cards in the divisor pile.

AUDITORY ◆ KINESTHETIC ◆ TACTILE ◆ VISUAL

▶ Math Boxes 6·4

(*Math Journal 1,* p. 150)

Mixed Practice Math Boxes in this lesson are paired with Math Boxes in Lesson 6-2. The skill in Problem 5 previews Unit 7 content.

Ongoing Assessment: Recognizing Student Achievement

Math Boxes Problem 3 

Use **Math Boxes, Problem 3** to assess students' ability to solve decimal addition and subtraction problems. Students are making adequate progress if they compute the correct sums and differences. Some students may be able to explain how to use ballpark estimates or the relationship between addition and subtraction to check their answers.

[Operations and Computation Goal 2]

▶ Study Link 6·4

(*Math Masters,* p. 182)

Home Connection Students practice using a division algorithm and interpreting the remainder.

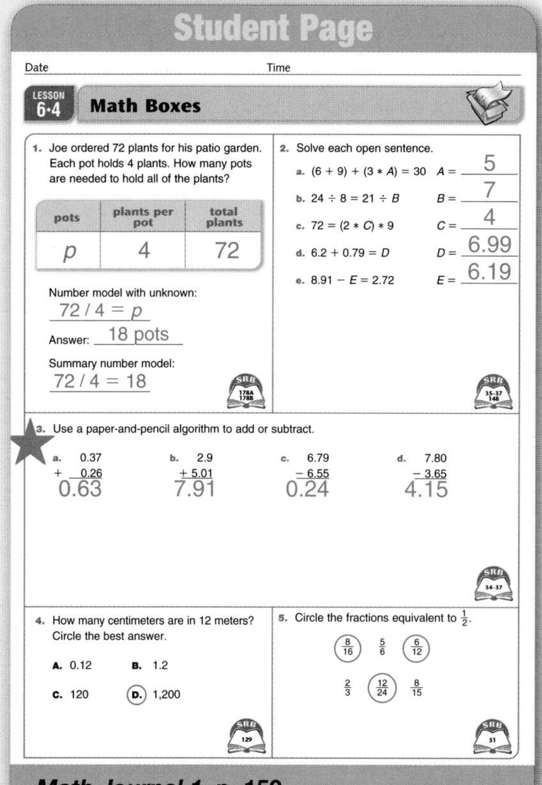

Student Page

Date Time

LESSON 6·4 **Math Boxes**

1. Joe ordered 72 plants for his patio garden. Each pot holds 4 plants. How many pots are needed to hold all of the plants?

pots	plants per pot	total plants
p	4	72

Number model with unknown: 72 / 4 = p

Answer: 18 pots

Summary number model: 72 / 4 = 18

2. Solve each open sentence.

a. (6 + 9) + (3 ∗ A) = 30 A = 5
b. 24 ÷ 8 = 21 ÷ B B = 7
c. 72 = (2 ∗ C) ∗ 9 C = 4
d. 6.2 + 0.79 = D D = 6.99
e. 8.91 − E = 2.72 E = 6.19

3. Use a paper-and-pencil algorithm to add or subtract.

a. 0.37 + 0.26 = 0.63
b. 2.9 + 5.01 = 7.91
c. 6.79 − 6.55 = 0.24
d. 7.80 − 3.65 = 4.15

4. How many centimeters are in 12 meters? Circle the best answer.

A. 0.12 B. 1.2
C. 120 D. 1,200 (circled)

5. Circle the fractions equivalent to $\frac{1}{2}$.

$\frac{8}{16}$ (circled) $\frac{5}{6}$ $\frac{6}{12}$ (circled)
$\frac{2}{3}$ $\frac{12}{24}$ (circled) $\frac{8}{15}$

Math Journal 1, p. 150

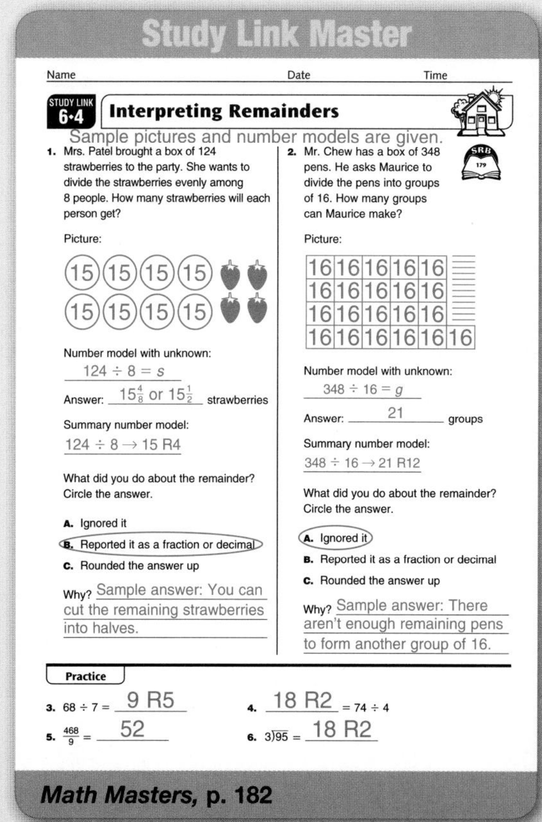

Study Link Master

Name Date Time

STUDY LINK 6·4 **Interpreting Remainders**

Sample pictures and number models are given.

1. Mrs. Patel brought a box of 124 strawberries to the party. She wants to divide the strawberries evenly among 8 people. How many strawberries will each person get?

Picture: 15 15 15 15 / 15 15 15 15

Number model with unknown: 124 ÷ 8 = s

Answer: $15\frac{4}{8}$ or $15\frac{1}{2}$ strawberries

Summary number model: 124 ÷ 8 → 15 R4

What did you do about the remainder? Circle the answer.

A. Ignored it
B. Reported it as a fraction or decimal (circled)
C. Rounded the answer up

Why? Sample answer: You can cut the remaining strawberries into halves.

2. Mr. Chew has a box of 348 pens. He asks Maurice to divide the pens into groups of 16. How many groups can Maurice make?

Picture: 16 16 16 16 16 / 16 16 16 16 16 / 16 16 16 16 16 / 16 16 16 16 16 16

Number model with unknown: 348 ÷ 16 = g

Answer: 21 groups

Summary number model: 348 ÷ 16 → 21 R12

What did you do about the remainder? Circle the answer.

A. Ignored it (circled)
B. Reported it as a fraction or decimal
C. Rounded the answer up

Why? Sample answer: There aren't enough remaining pens to form another group of 16.

Practice

3. 68 ÷ 7 = 9 R5
4. 18 R2 = 74 ÷ 4
5. $\frac{468}{9}$ = 52
6. 3)95 = 18 R2

Math Masters, p. 182

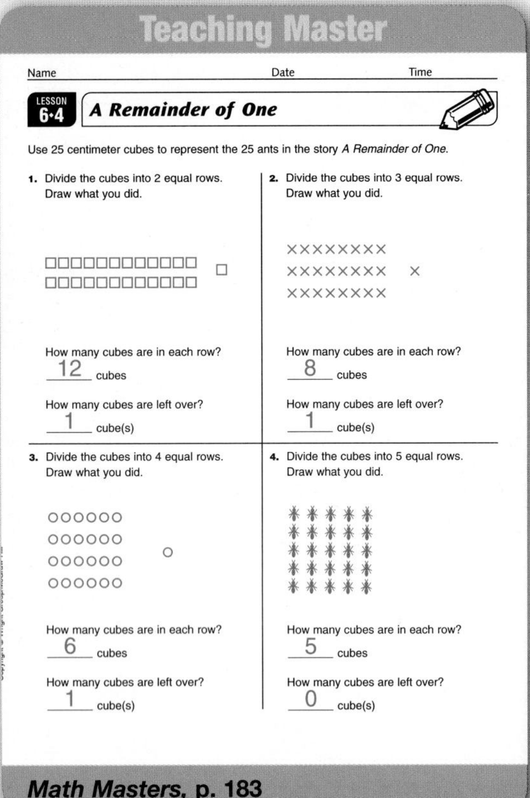
Teaching Master

Name Date Time

LESSON 6•4 **A Remainder of One**

Use 25 centimeter cubes to represent the 25 ants in the story *A Remainder of One.*

1. Divide the cubes into 2 equal rows. Draw what you did.

How many cubes are in each row? 12 cubes

How many cubes are left over? 1 cube(s)

2. Divide the cubes into 3 equal rows. Draw what you did.

How many cubes are in each row? 8 cubes

How many cubes are left over? 1 cube(s)

3. Divide the cubes into 4 equal rows. Draw what you did.

How many cubes are in each row? 6 cubes

How many cubes are left over? 1 cube(s)

4. Divide the cubes into 5 equal rows. Draw what you did.

How many cubes are in each row? 5 cubes

How many cubes are left over? 0 cube(s)

Math Masters, **p. 183**

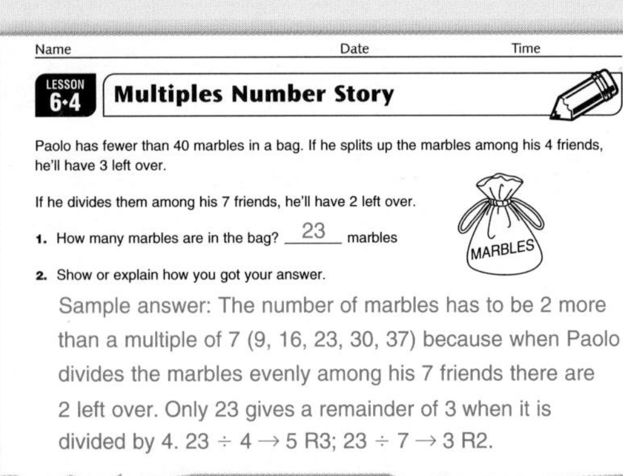
Name Date Time

LESSON 6•4 **Multiples Number Story**

Paolo has fewer than 40 marbles in a bag. If he splits up the marbles among his 4 friends, he'll have 3 left over.

If he divides them among his 7 friends, he'll have 2 left over.

1. How many marbles are in the bag? 23 marbles

2. Show or explain how you got your answer.

Sample answer: The number of marbles has to be 2 more than a multiple of 7 (9, 16, 23, 30, 37) because when Paolo divides the marbles evenly among his 7 friends there are 2 left over. Only 23 gives a remainder of 3 when it is divided by 4. 23 ÷ 4 → 5 R3; 23 ÷ 7 → 3 R2.

Math Masters, page 184

3 Differentiation Options

READINESS

SMALL-GROUP ACTIVITY

15–30 Min

▶ Exploring Remainders in Literature

(*Math Masters,* p. 183)

Literature Link To explore the concept of remainders, have students read and discuss the book ***A Remainder of One*** by Elinor J. Pinczes (Houghton Mifflin Harcourt, 2002). For each situation in the story, ask students to create arrays using centimeter cubes and record their work on *Math Masters,* page 183. Have students describe the arrays and tell how they determined the number of rows. Encourage the use of vocabulary from this unit.

ENRICHMENT

INDEPENDENT ACTIVITY

5–15 Min

▶ Solving a Multiples Number Story

(*Math Masters,* p. 184)

To apply students' understanding of multiples, factors, and division and remainders, have them solve a marble-sharing number story. Encourage students to model the problem with counters if necessary.

EXTRA PRACTICE

SMALL-GROUP ACTIVITY

5–15 Min

▶ *5-Minute Math*

To offer students more experience with division, see *5-Minute Math,* pages 20 and 25.

6•5 Rotations and Angles

Objectives To review rotations; and to guide students as they make and use a full-circle protractor.

Technology Resources www.everydaymathonline.com

ePresentations

eToolkit

Algorithms Practice

EM Facts Workshop Game™

Family Letters

Assessment Management

Common Core State Standards

Curriculum Focal Points

Interactive Teacher's Lesson Guide

1 Teaching the Lesson

Key Concepts and Skills

- Use multiples of 30.
  [Number and Numeration Goal 3]
- Form angles of a given measure.
  [Measurement and Reference Frames Goal 1]
- Describe right angles.
  [Geometry Goal 1]
- Rotate objects a given number of degrees.
  [Geometry Goal 3]
- Investigate the relationship between rotations and degrees.
  [Geometry Goal 3]

Key Activities

Students review clockwise rotations. They make a full-circle protractor by measuring rotations in degrees; then they use the protractor to form angles of given measures.

Students solve problems that involve measuring elapsed time in degrees.

Ongoing Assessment: Informing Instruction See page 427.

Key Vocabulary

rotation • turn • clockwise • degree • right angle

Materials

Math Journal 1, pp. 152 and 153
Study Link 6•4
drinking straws • demonstration clock

2 Ongoing Learning & Practice

Making a Bar Graph

Math Journal 1, p. 154
Student Reference Book, p. 301
Students make a bar graph showing percent of population (ages 0–14) for Region 2 countries.

Ongoing Assessment: Recognizing Student Achievement
Use journal page 154.
[Data and Chance Goal 1]

Solving Elapsed-Time Problems

Math Journal 1, pp. 154A and 154B
demonstration clock (optional) •
calculator (optional)
Students solve elapsed-time problems.

Math Boxes 6•5

Math Journal 1, p. 151
Students practice and maintain skills through Math Box problems.

Study Link 6•5

Math Masters, p. 185
Students practice and maintain skills through Study Link activities.

3 Differentiation Options

READINESS

Matching Alternate Time Displays

Math Masters, pp. 186–188
scissors
Students match alternate ways of naming time.

ENRICHMENT

Measuring Elapsed Time in Degrees

Math Journal 1, pp. 152 and 153
Math Masters, p. 189
Students determine elapsed time for 1° increments on a clock face.

EXTRA PRACTICE

Playing *Robot*

Students practice making rotations of a given size.

ELL SUPPORT

Building a Math Word Bank

Differentiation Handbook, p. 140
Students add the term *degree* to their Math Word Banks.

Advance Preparation

***Teacher's Reference Manual,* Grades 4–6** pp. 178–180

Getting Started

Mental Math and Reflexes

Have students imagine standing in the center of a clock with their right hand extended as the minute hand. Ask them to rotate their bodies to make turns such as the following:

●○○ $\frac{1}{2}$ turn clockwise
$\frac{1}{4}$ turn clockwise
full turn clockwise

●●○ 90° turn clockwise
180° turn clockwise
360° turn clockwise

●●● $\frac{3}{4}$ turn counterclockwise
$\frac{3}{4}$ turn clockwise
$\frac{1}{2}$ turn counterclockwise

Math Message

How many minutes does it take the minute hand to move through a full turn on the face of a clock? 60 min *A $\frac{1}{2}$ turn?* 30 min *A $\frac{1}{4}$ turn?* 15 min

Study Link 6·4 Follow-Up

Have students discuss how they handled the remainders in Problems 1 and 2.

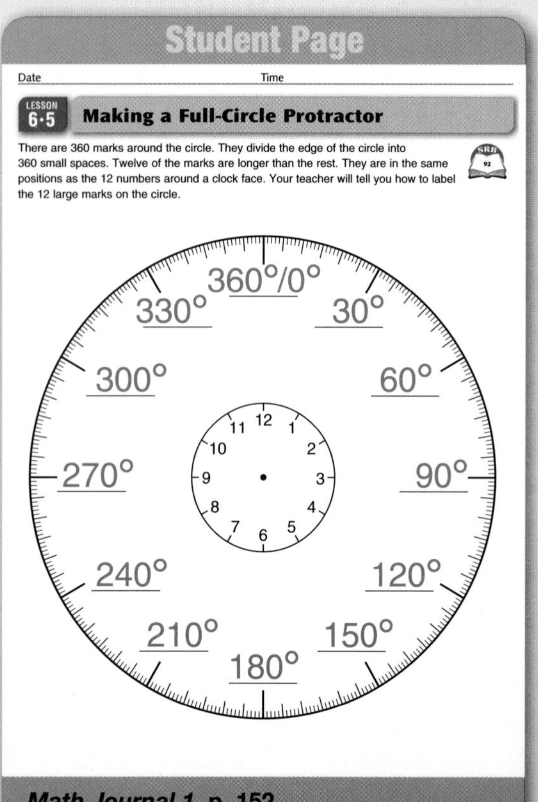

Student Page
Date
Time
LESSON 6·5
Making a Full-Circle Protractor
There are 360 marks around the circle. They divide the edge of the circle into 360 small spaces. Twelve of the marks are longer than the rest. They are in the same positions as the 12 numbers around a clock face. Your teacher will tell you how to label the 12 large marks on the circle.
360°/0°
30°
60°
90°
120°
150°
180°
210°
240°
270°
300°
330°
12
1
2
3
4
5
6
7
8
9
10
11

Math Journal 1, p. 152

1 Teaching the Lesson

▶ Math Message Follow-Up

WHOLE-CLASS ACTIVITY

The Math Message reminds students who used *Third Grade Everyday Mathematics* of previous experiences with **rotations.** Review answers using a clock with an hour and minute hand or a demonstration clock to model movements of the minute hand.

Pose additional problems: A $\frac{3}{4}$ turn? 45 min A $\frac{1}{6}$ turn? 10 min A $\frac{1}{3}$ turn? 20 min A $\frac{2}{3}$ turn? 40 min

▷ For a $\frac{3}{4}$ turn—Since there are 3 five-minute intervals in $\frac{1}{4}$ of a turn ($3 = \frac{1}{4}$ of 12), there are three times as many in $\frac{3}{4}$ of a turn, or 9 five-minute intervals. Therefore, it takes the minute hand 45 minutes to move through $\frac{3}{4}$ of a **turn.**

▷ For a $\frac{1}{6}$ turn—Since there are 12 five-minute intervals in 1 full turn of the minute hand, there are 2 five-minute intervals in $\frac{1}{6}$ of a turn. Therefore, it takes the minute hand 10 minutes to move through a $\frac{1}{6}$ turn.

▷ For a $\frac{2}{3}$ turn—Since there are 4 five-minute intervals in $\frac{1}{3}$ of a turn ($4 = \frac{1}{3}$ of 12), there are twice as many in $\frac{2}{3}$ of a turn, or 8 five-minute intervals. Therefore, it takes the minute hand 40 minutes to move through $\frac{2}{3}$ of a turn.

▶ Investigating Rotations and Degree Measures

WHOLE-CLASS ACTIVITY
ELL

(*Math Journal 1*, p. 152)

Tell the class that in this lesson they will investigate the markings on a full-circle protractor and compare them to familiar markings on an analog clock.

Discuss the marked circle on journal page 152.

- ▷ There are three different lengths of marks.
- ▷ The shortest marks divide the circle into 360 small spaces. $360 * 1° = 360°$
- ▷ The longest marks are in the same positions as the 12 numbers around a clock face. These 12 long marks divide the circle into 12 spaces. $12 * 30° = 360°$
- ▷ The middle-size marks divide the circle into 72 spaces. $72 * 5° = 360°$

Ask students to write 0° beneath the large mark at the 12 o'clock position on the circle.

Ask students to fold a straw in half. Show them how to place it on the circle on journal page 152. The bend of the straw should touch the center of the circle, and both halves of the straw should point to the 0-degree mark.

Keeping one part of the straw pointing to the 0-degree mark, move the other half of the straw **clockwise** to the first large mark, or $\frac{1}{12}$ of a turn.

Links to the Future

Students will discuss *counterclockwise* rotations in Lesson 6-6.

The straw-halves form an angle. Remind students that angles are measured in **degrees** and that the degree symbol (°) is often used in place of the word *degree*. To support English language learners, write *degree* on the board and explain that this word has different meanings when it is used to measure angles and temperature.

Now show students how to measure the straw angle they just made: To measure the angle, count the number of small spaces created by the shortest marks. (*See note in margin.*) 30 spaces, so the angle measures 30 degrees, or 30° Ask students to write 30° at the first large mark on the circle.

Tell students to move the straw-half back to its original position and then repeat the routine for a $\frac{1}{4}$ turn. (*See margin.*)

- What is the measure of the angle? 90° Ask students to write 90° at the $\frac{1}{4}$-turn mark on the circle. (*See margin.*)

Ongoing Assessment: Informing Instruction

Watch for the different strategies that students use to determine that the result of a $\frac{1}{4}$ turn of the straw is an angle that measures 90°.

- ▷ Count the 90 spaces along the circle between the sides of the straw.
- ▷ Recognize that the angle is 3 times as large as the first angle, and multiply by 3 to get 90°.
- ▷ Recognize that the angle is a **right angle,** and right angles measure 90°.

NOTE Think of an angle as "in motion" opening from 0° to the desired angle. For example, to measure a 15° angle, start with a 0° angle and open the angle to 1°, 2°, and so on until 15° is reached. Thinking this way can help students realize that counting the spaces in between the marks of the protractor is more accurate than counting the marks.

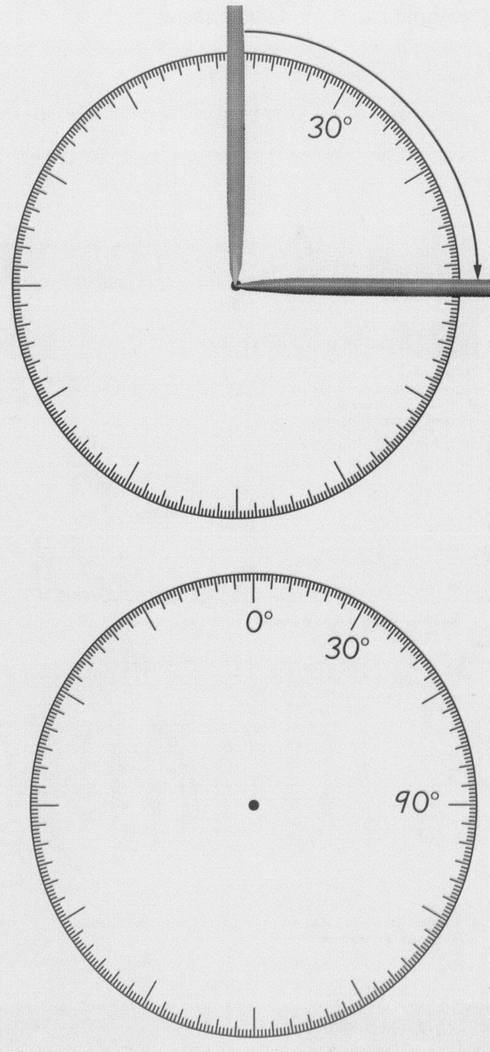

Student Page

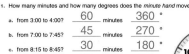

Date Time

LESSON 6·5 **Clock Angles**

Use the clock below and the full-circle protractor on journal page 152 to help you answer the questions.

SRB 92 141

1. How many minutes and how many degrees does the *minute hand* move

a. from 3:00 to 4:00? 60 minutes 360 °
b. from 7:00 to 7:45? 45 minutes 270 °
c. from 8:15 to 8:45? 30 minutes 180 °
d. from 6:30 to 6:50? 20 minutes 120 °
e. from 5:15 to 5:30? 15 minutes 90 °
f. from 1:00 to 1:10? 10 minutes 60 °
g. from 12:00 to 12:05? 5 minutes 30 °
h. from 5:00 to 5:01? 1 minutes 6 °

Try This

2. How many degrees does the *hour hand* move

a. in 1 hour? 30 °
b. in $\frac{1}{2}$ hour? 15 °
c. in 10 minutes? 5 °

3. Explain how you solved Problem 2c.

Sample answer: I know that the hour hand moves 30° in 1 hour. There are 6 groups of 10 minutes in 1 hour (60 minutes). So there are 6 groups of 5° in 30°, or 30°/ 6 = 5°.

***Math Journal 1,* p. 153**

Adjusting the Activity

Have students describe a strategy for labeling the remaining large tick marks without using the folded straw. Sample answer: Count by 30s; each large tick mark corresponds to a multiple of 30.

AUDITORY ◆ KINESTHETIC ◆ TACTILE ◆ VISUAL

Student Page

Date Time

LESSON 6·5 **Population Bar Graph**

The table below shows the percent of the population (number of people out of 100) who are 14 years old or younger in the Region 2 countries.

SRB 76 301

Country	Percent of Population Ages 0–14
France	19
Greece	15
Hungary	16
Iceland	23
Italy	14
Netherlands	18
Norway	20
Poland	18
Spain	15
United Kingdom	19

1. Make a bar graph to display the information given in the table above.

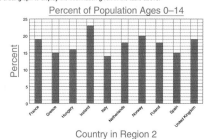

Percent of Population Ages 0–14

Percent: 0, 5, 10, 15, 20, 25

France, Greece, Hungary, Iceland, Italy, Netherlands, Norway, Poland, Spain, United Kingdom

Country in Region 2

2. Why might it be important to know what percent of the population of a country is 0 through 14 years of age?

Sample answer: A government will know how much money to give schools for grades 8 and below.

***Math Journal 1,* p. 154**

- What is another name for a 90-degree angle? A right angle
  To support English language learners, review the different meanings of *right* discussed in Unit 1—*right* answer, *right* hand, *right* angle.

Now tell students to move the straw-half back to its original position, and then repeat the procedure for a full turn.

- What is the measure of the angle? 360°

Ask students to write 360° at the full-turn mark on the circle, right next to the 0° mark. Have students label the rest of the large tick marks on the circle until all 12 marks have been labeled.

▶ Forming Angles of Given Measures

WHOLE-CLASS ACTIVITY

(*Math Journal 1,* p. 152)

Direct students to use their bent straws to form angles of various degree measures. For example, *Show me a 120° angle; a 45° angle; a 77° angle.*

▶ Measuring Elapsed Time in Degrees

PARTNER ACTIVITY

PROBLEM SOLVING

(*Math Journal 1,* pp. 152 and 153)

Students solve problems and share solution strategies about the number of degrees the minute and hour hands of a clock move in a given amount of time.

2 Ongoing Learning & Practice

▶ Making a Bar Graph

INDEPENDENT ACTIVITY

(*Math Journal 1,* p. 154; *Student Reference Book,* p. 301)

Social Studies Link Students make a bar graph to show percent of population (ages 0–14 years) for Region 2 countries. Direct students to page 301 of the *Student Reference Book* for additional data.

Ongoing Assessment: Recognizing Student Achievement

Journal page 154

Use **journal page 154** to assess students' ability to create a bar graph. Students are making adequate progress if they can draw the bars at the appropriate height on the graph. Some students may be able to provide a title and label each axis.

[Data and Chance Goal 1]

Problems

(*Math Journal 1,* pp. 154A and 154B)

Students solve elapsed-time problems. Students may use the demonstration clock, calculators, or anything else that may help. Some students may find it helpful to use an open number line to illustrate the strategy of counting up in hours and minutes. See Lesson 3-6 for more information.

Math Boxes 6•5

INDEPENDENT ACTIVITY

(*Math Journal 1,* p. 151)

Mixed Practice Math Boxes in this lesson are paired with Math Boxes in Lesson 6-7. The skill in Problem 6 previews Unit 7 content.

Study Link 6•5

INDEPENDENT ACTIVITY

(*Math Masters,* p. 185)

Home Connection Students follow directions, given as fractions of turns and distances, to trace a path on a coordinate grid. When reviewing answers, point out that the length of each horizontal line segment equals the difference of the *x*-coordinates and that the length of each vertical line segment equals the difference of the *y*-coordinates.

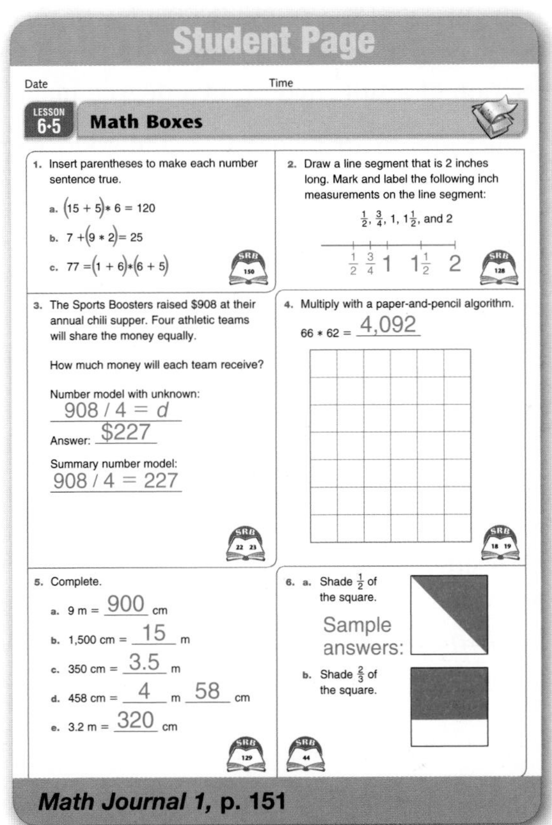

Student Page

Date Time

LESSON 6•5 **Math Boxes**

1. Insert parentheses to make each number sentence true.
   a. (15 + 5) ∗ 6 = 120
   b. 7 + (9 ∗ 2) = 25
   c. 77 = (1 + 6) ∗ (6 + 5)

2. Draw a line segment that is 2 inches long. Mark and label the following inch measurements on the line segment: $\frac{1}{2}$, $\frac{3}{4}$, 1, $1\frac{1}{2}$, and 2

   $\frac{1}{2}$ $\frac{3}{4}$ 1 $1\frac{1}{2}$ 2

3. The Sports Boosters raised $908 at their annual chili supper. Four athletic teams will share the money equally.
   How much money will each team receive?
   Number model with unknown: 908 / 4 = *d*
   Answer: $227
   Summary number model: 908 / 4 = 227

4. Multiply with a paper-and-pencil algorithm.
   66 ∗ 62 = 4,092

5. Complete.
   a. 9 m = 900 cm
   b. 1,500 cm = 15 m
   c. 350 cm = 3.5 m
   d. 458 cm = 4 m 58 cm
   e. 3.2 m = 320 cm

6. a. Shade $\frac{1}{2}$ of the square.
   b. Shade $\frac{2}{3}$ of the square.
   Sample answers:

Math Journal 1, p. 151

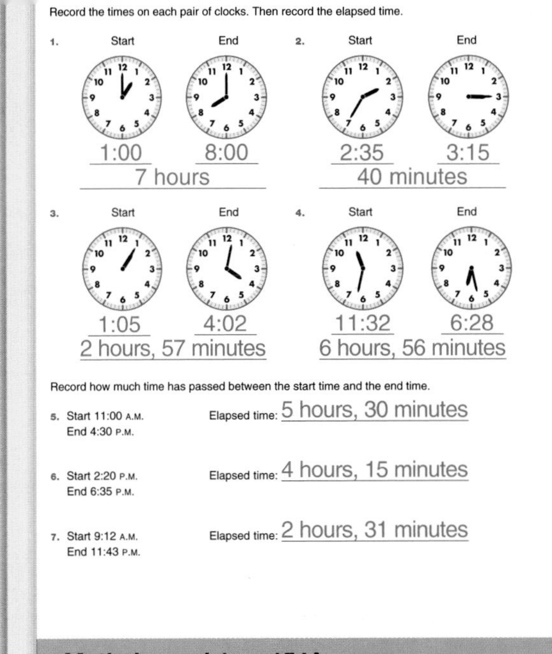

Record the times on each pair of clocks. Then record the elapsed time.

1. Start 1:00 End 8:00 — 7 hours
2. Start 2:35 End 3:15 — 40 minutes
3. Start 1:05 End 4:02 — 2 hours, 57 minutes
4. Start 11:32 End 6:28 — 6 hours, 56 minutes

Record how much time has passed between the start time and the end time.

5. Start 11:00 A.M. End 4:30 P.M. Elapsed time: 5 hours, 30 minutes
6. Start 2:20 P.M. End 6:35 P.M. Elapsed time: 4 hours, 15 minutes
7. Start 9:12 A.M. End 11:43 P.M. Elapsed time: 2 hours, 31 minutes

Math Journal 1, p. 154A

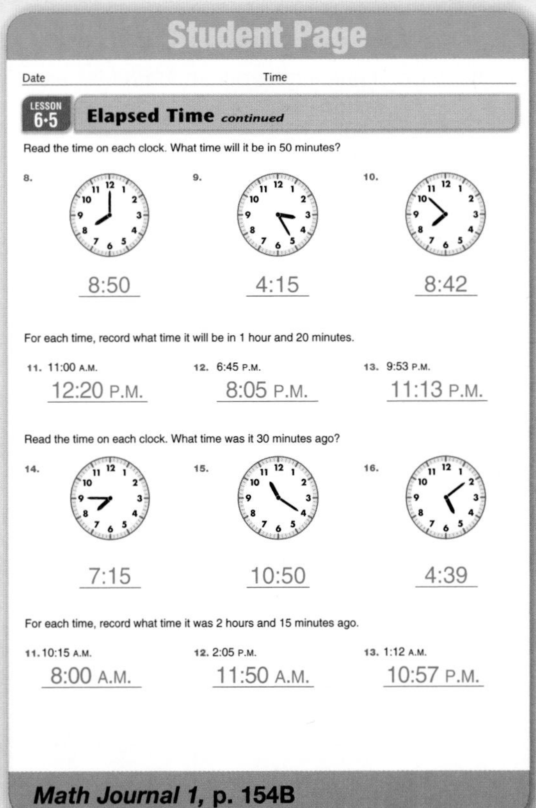

Student Page

Date Time

LESSON 6•5 **Elapsed Time** *continued*

Read the time on each clock. What time will it be in 50 minutes?

8. 8:50
9. 4:15
10. 8:42

For each time, record what time it will be in 1 hour and 20 minutes.

11. 11:00 A.M. 12:20 P.M.
12. 6:45 P.M. 8:05 P.M.
13. 9:53 P.M. 11:13 P.M.

Read the time on each clock. What time was it 30 minutes ago?

14. 7:15
15. 10:50
16. 4:39

For each time, record what time it was 2 hours and 15 minutes ago.

11. 10:15 A.M. 8:00 A.M.
12. 2:05 P.M. 11:50 A.M.
13. 1:12 A.M. 10:57 P.M.

Math Journal 1, p. 154B

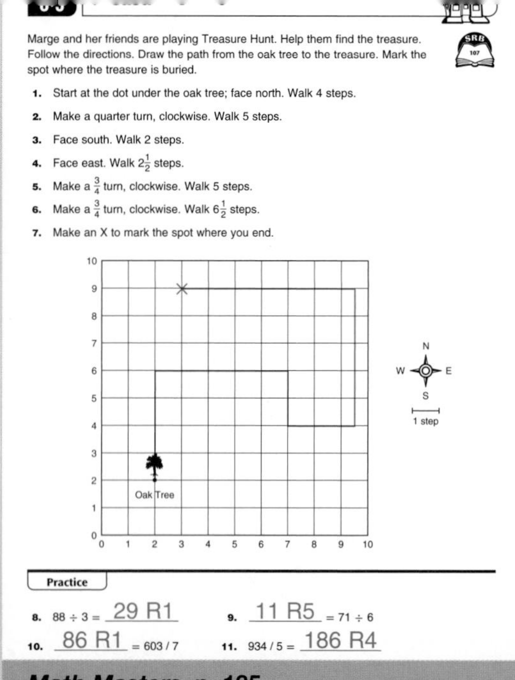

Marge and her friends are playing Treasure Hunt. Help them find the treasure. Follow the directions. Draw the path from the oak tree to the treasure. Mark the spot where the treasure is buried.

1. Start at the dot under the oak tree; face north. Walk 4 steps.
2. Make a quarter turn, clockwise. Walk 5 steps.
3. Face south. Walk 2 steps.
4. Face east. Walk $2\frac{1}{2}$ steps.
5. Make a $\frac{3}{4}$ turn, clockwise. Walk 5 steps.
6. Make a $\frac{3}{4}$ turn, clockwise. Walk $6\frac{1}{2}$ steps.
7. Make an X to mark the spot where you end.

Practice

8. 88 ÷ 3 = 29 R1
9. 11 R5 = 71 ÷ 6
10. 86 R1 = 603 / 7
11. 934 / 5 = 186 R4

Math Masters, p. 185

Alternate ways of naming time from *Math Masters,* pages 186–188

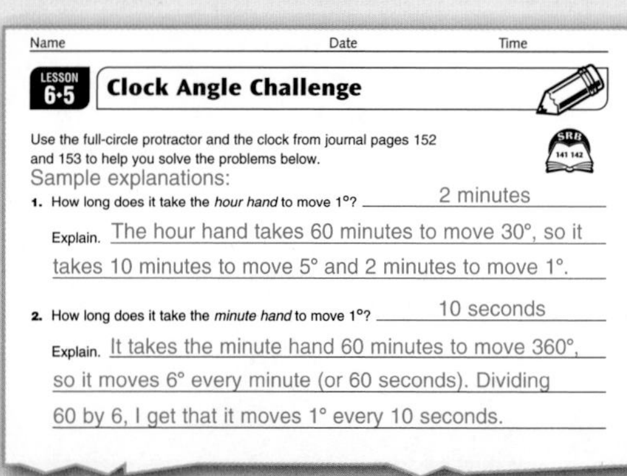

Name Date Time

LESSON 6·5 **Clock Angle Challenge**

Use the full-circle protractor and the clock from journal pages 152 and 153 to help you solve the problems below.

Sample explanations:

1. How long does it take the *hour hand* to move 1°? 2 minutes

Explain. The hour hand takes 60 minutes to move 30°, so it takes 10 minutes to move 5° and 2 minutes to move 1°.

2. How long does it take the *minute hand* to move 1°? 10 seconds

Explain. It takes the minute hand 60 minutes to move 360°, so it moves 6° every minute (or 60 seconds). Dividing 60 by 6, I get that it moves 1° every 10 seconds.

Math Masters, page 189

READINESS

PARTNER ACTIVITY

5–15 Min

▶ Matching Alternate Time Displays

(*Math Masters,* pp. 186–188)

To explore alternate ways of naming time, have students match cards that indicate the same time in analog, digital, and word forms.

ENRICHMENT

INDEPENDENT ACTIVITY

5–15 Min

▶ Measuring Elapsed Time in Degrees

(*Math Journal 1,* pp. 152 and 153; *Math Masters,* p. 189)

To further investigate the relationship between elapsed time and angle measures, have students use the full-circle protractor on journal page 152 to determine how long it takes the minute and the hour hands to move 1 degree.

EXTRA PRACTICE

PARTNER ACTIVITY

5–15 Min

▶ Playing *Robot*

To practice rotations expressed as both fractions of turns and degree measures, have students play *Robot.* One partner is the "Controller" and the other is the "Robot." The Controller picks a destination. The Controller gives the Robot directions for the amount of each turn and the number of steps to take until the Robot reaches the destination. The amount of each turn may be given as a fraction of a full turn or as a degree measure.

Example: "Make a half-turn clockwise and go forward 5 steps. Now turn clockwise a quarter-turn (90 degrees), and go back 3 steps."

ELL SUPPORT

PARTNER ACTIVITY

5–15 Min

▶ Building a Math Word Bank

(*Differentiation Handbook,* p. 140)

To provide language support for angle rotations, have students use the Word Bank template found on *Differentiation Handbook,* page 140. Ask students to write the term *degree,* draw a picture or give an example to represent the term, and write other related words. See the *Differentiation Handbook* for more information.

6•6 Using a Full-Circle Protractor

Objective To provide practice using a full-circle protractor to measure and draw angles less than 360°.

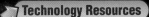

www.everydaymathonline.com

Presentations

eToolkit

Algorithms Practice

EM Facts Workshop Game™

Family Letters

Assessment Management

Common Core State Standards

Curriculum Focal Points

Interactive Teacher's Lesson Guide

1 Teaching the Lesson

Key Concepts and Skills

- Draw and measure angles with a full-circle protractor. [Measurement and Reference Frames Goal 1]
- Use ray and line segment vocabulary. [Geometry Goal 1]
- Describe a circle as having 360°. [Geometry Goal 2]
- Rotate objects a given number of degrees. [Geometry Goal 3]

Key Activities

Students use transparent protractors to measure and draw angles.

Ongoing Assessment: Informing Instruction See page 434.

Ongoing Assessment: Recognizing Student Achievement Use an Exit Slip (*Math Masters,* page 389). [Measurement and Reference Frames Goal 1]

Key Vocabulary

angle (∠) ◆ sides (of an angle) ◆ vertex (of an angle) ◆ clockwise rotation ◆ counterclockwise rotation ◆ full-circle protractor

Materials

Math Journal 1, p. 155
Student Reference Book, pp. 92 and 142
Study Link 6•5
Math Masters, p. 389 (optional)
transparency of *Math Masters,* p. 439 ◆ drinking straw for demonstration purposes ◆ straightedge

2 Ongoing Learning & Practice

Playing *Division Dash*

Student Reference Book, p. 241
Math Masters, p. 471
per partnership: 4 each of number cards 1–9 (from the Everything Math Deck, if available)
Students practice dividing 2- or 3-digit dividends by 1-digit divisors.

Math Boxes 6•6

Math Journal 1, p. 156
Students practice and maintain skills through Math Box problems.

Study Link 6•6

Math Masters, p. 190
full-circle protractor
Students practice and maintain skills through Study Link activities.

3 Differentiation Options

READINESS

Making and Using a Waxed-Paper Protractor

Math Masters, p. 191
waxed paper ◆ scissors
Students make and use a waxed-paper protractor.

ENRICHMENT

Playing *Angle Add-Up*

Math Masters, pp. 507–509
per partnership: 4 of each of number cards 1–8 and 1 of each of number cards 0 and 9 (from the Everything Math Deck, if available) ◆ full-circle protractor (transparency of *Math Masters,* p. 439) ◆ dry-erase markers ◆ straightedge
Students draw angles and then use addition and subtraction to find the measures of unknown angles.

EXTRA PRACTICE

Playing *Angle Tangle*

Student Reference Book, p. 230
Math Masters, p. 457
full-circle protractor ◆ straightedge
Students practice estimating and measuring angles.

ELL SUPPORT

Building Background for Mathematics Words

colored pencils ◆ dictionary
Students discuss the meanings of the terms *clockwise* and *counterclockwise.*

Advance Preparation

For Part 1 and the optional Enrichment activity in Part 3, make enough transparencies of *Math Masters,* page 439 so each student will have a full-circle protractor and there will be a reserve supply for future activities.

***Teacher's Reference Manual,* Grades 4–6** pp. 178–180, 225

Getting Started

Mental Math and Reflexes

Students make different angle openings with their arms. Have students begin each angle with arms in the 12 o'clock position and use clockwise movement. *Suggestions:*

●○○	●●○	●●●
90°	less than 90°	270°
45°	more than 90°	120°
180°	more than 180°	355°

Math Message

Read the top half of page 92 in your Student Reference Book. *Be prepared to tell some things that all angles have in common.*

Study Link 6·5 Follow-Up

Consider having a student go through the motions as you go over the answer. Find an empty space on the classroom floor. Mark a starting point. The student should step heel-to-toe while following the directions.

1 Teaching the Lesson

▶ Math Message Follow-Up

WHOLE-CLASS ACTIVITY

ELL

(*Student Reference Book,* p. 92)

Draw an angle on the board. As you review the parts of an angle, label them. To support English language learners, leave this drawing on the board throughout the lesson as a visual reference.

- ▷ An **angle** is formed by 2 rays or 2 line segments that have the same endpoint.
- ▷ The rays or line segments are called the **sides** of the angle.
- ▷ The endpoint is called the **vertex** of the angle.
- ▷ ∠ is the symbol for *angle*.
- ▷ If the vertex of an angle is point *T*, the angle can be named ∠*T*, or angle *T*.

Tell students that in this lesson they will learn how to measure angles of varying degrees.

▶ Demonstrating Angles and Rotations

WHOLE-CLASS ACTIVITY

In Lesson 6-5, angles were used to represent **clockwise rotations.** Angles can also be used to represent **counterclockwise rotations.** To demonstrate, ask a student to fold a straw in half and hold it against the board. Rotate one half of the straw counterclockwise about $\frac{1}{3}$ of a turn. Ask another student to draw a line along each side of the straw to form an angle.

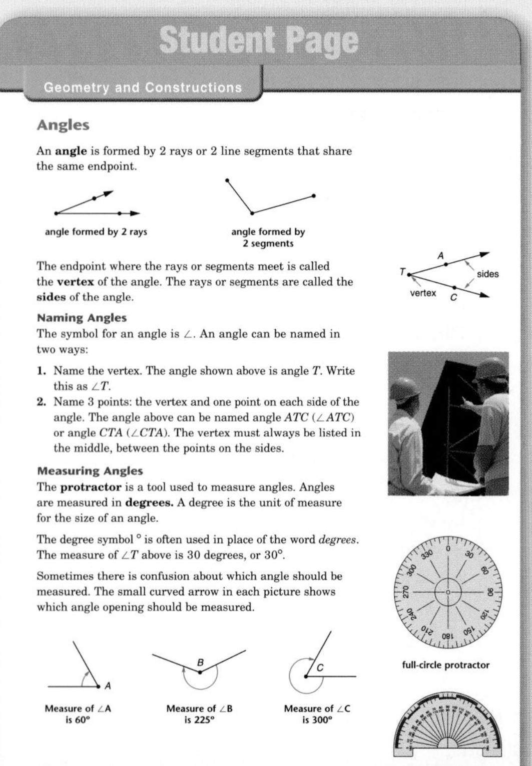

Student Page

Geometry and Constructions

Angles

An **angle** is formed by 2 rays or 2 line segments that share the same endpoint.

angle formed by 2 rays
angle formed by 2 segments

The endpoint where the rays or segments meet is called the **vertex** of the angle. The rays or segments are called the **sides** of the angle.

Naming Angles

The symbol for an angle is ∠. An angle can be named in two ways:

1. Name the vertex. The angle shown above is angle *T*. Write this as ∠*T*.
2. Name 3 points: the vertex and one point on each side of the angle. The angle above can be named angle *ATC* (∠*ATC*) or angle *CTA* (∠*CTA*). The vertex must always be listed in the middle, between the points on the sides.

Measuring Angles

The **protractor** is a tool used to measure angles. Angles are measured in **degrees.** A degree is the unit of measure for the size of an angle.

The degree symbol ° is often used in place of the word *degrees*. The measure of ∠*T* above is 30 degrees, or 30°.

Sometimes there is confusion about which angle should be measured. The small curved arrow in each picture shows which angle opening should be measured.

Measure of ∠A is 60°

Measure of ∠B is 225°

Measure of ∠C is 300°

full-circle protractor

half-circle protractor

Student Reference Book, p. 92

Draw a directional arc to show that this angle represents a counterclockwise rotation. Name the vertex. Then use the angle symbol to name the angle. (*See below.*) Write *counterclockwise rotation* next to the angle.

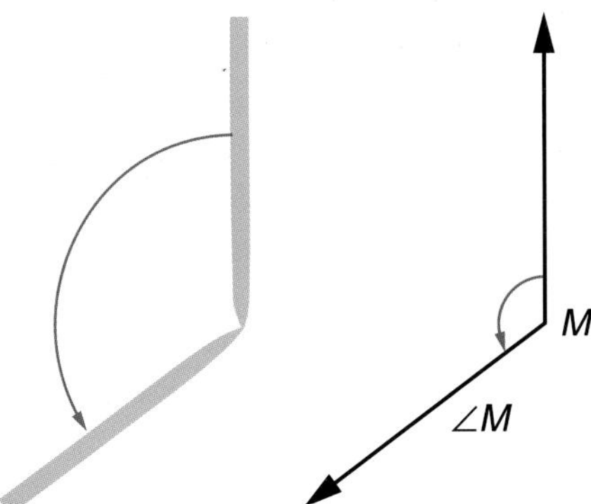

Using a straw to demonstrate a counterclockwise rotation

Using a Full-Circle Protractor

WHOLE-CLASS ACTIVITY

(*Math Journal 1,* p. 155; *Student Reference Book,* p. 142; *Math Masters,* p. 439)

Distribute the squares from the transparencies of *Math Masters,* page 439. Explain that **full-circle protractors** are tools used to measure angles. Write *full-circle protractor* on the board.

Show students how to use the full-circle protractor to measure angle B on page 142 of the *Student Reference Book*. Point out that the marks on the edge are labeled from 0° to 360° in a clockwise direction. Therefore, students must be careful to measure the angle in a clockwise direction.

Ask them to measure reflex angle C. To support English language learners, write *reflex angle* on the board and discuss its meaning.

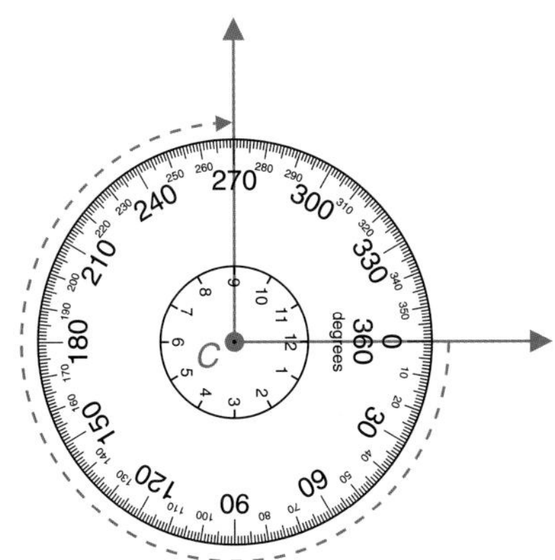

Angle C measures 270°.

Students work in partnerships to measure the angles on journal page 155.

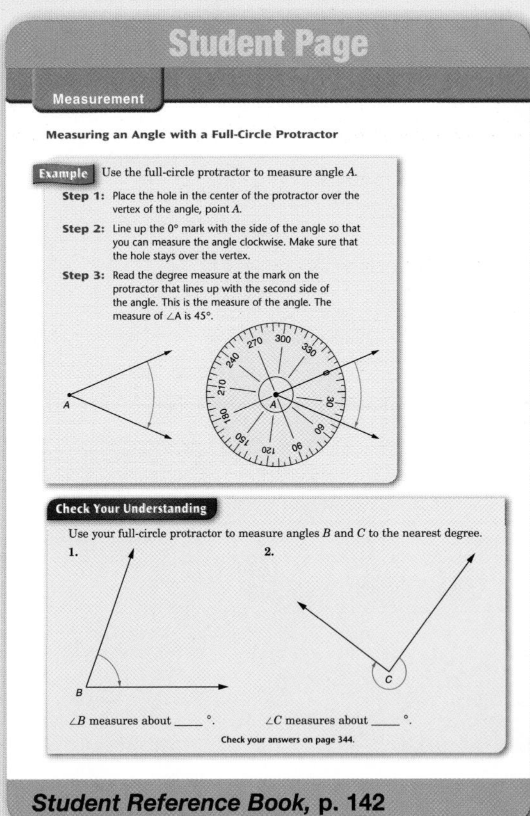

Student Page
Measurement
Measuring an Angle with a Full-Circle Protractor
Example Use the full-circle protractor to measure angle A.
Step 1: Place the hole in the center of the protractor over the vertex of the angle, point A.
Step 2: Line up the 0° mark with the side of the angle so that you can measure the angle clockwise. Make sure that the hole stays over the vertex.
Step 3: Read the degree measure at the mark on the protractor that lines up with the second side of the angle. This is the measure of the angle. The measure of ∠A is 45°.
Check Your Understanding
Use your full-circle protractor to measure angles B and C to the nearest degree.
1.
2.
∠B measures about ____°.
∠C measures about ____°.
Check your answers on page 344.

Student Reference Book, p. 142

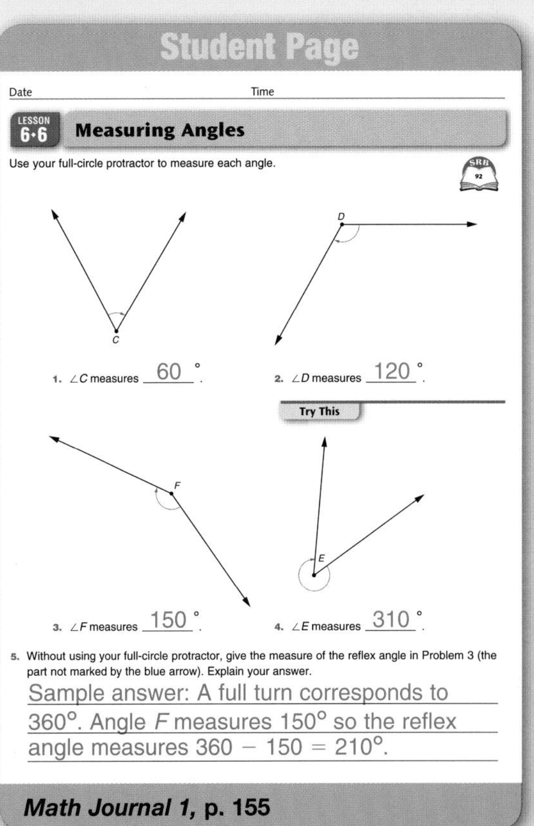

Student Page
Date
Time
LESSON 6•6
Measuring Angles
Use your full-circle protractor to measure each angle.
SRB 92
1. ∠C measures 60 °.
2. ∠D measures 120 °.
Try This
3. ∠F measures 150 °.
4. ∠E measures 310 °.
5. Without using your full-circle protractor, give the measure of the reflex angle in Problem 3 (the part not marked by the blue arrow). Explain your answer.
Sample answer: A full turn corresponds to 360°. Angle F measures 150° so the reflex angle measures 360 − 150 = 210°.

Math Journal 1, p. 155

Ongoing Assessment: Informing Instruction

Watch for students who

- ▷ line up the 0° mark on the full-circle protractor with the right-hand side of the angle and incorrectly read the protractor in a counterclockwise direction.

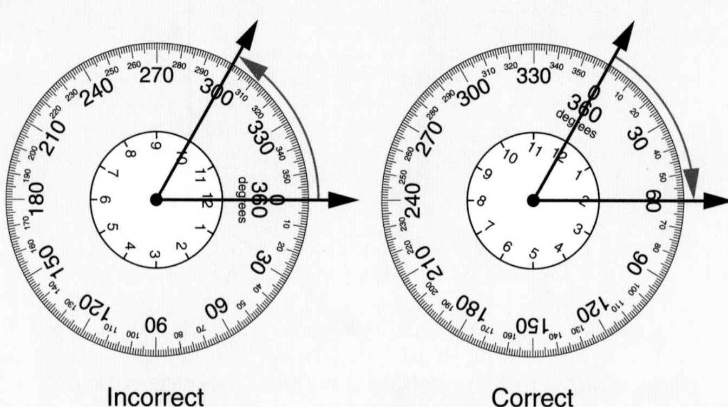

- ▷ do not place the center of the full-circle protractor at the vertex of the angle.
- ▷ have difficulty measuring angles like angle *A* below that do not have one side of the angle parallel to the bottom of the page.

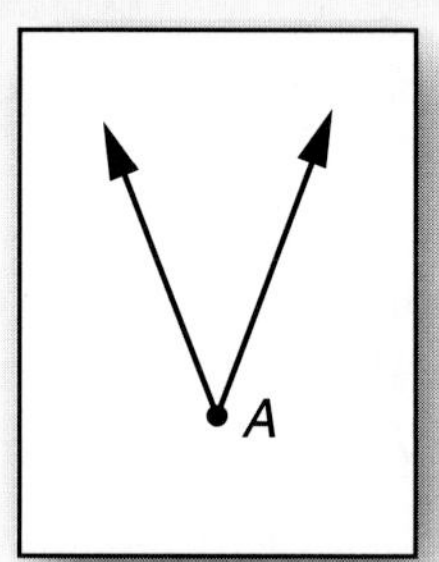

Discuss Problem 5 with students. Explain that angle measures can be added and subtracted to find unknown angle measures. For example, suppose you want to know the measure of the reflex angle in Problem 1. Angle *C* measures 60° and a full turn measures 360°. If a stands for the measure of the reflex angle, then $60° + a = 360°$, or $360° - 60° = a$. So, $a = 300°$.

Drawing an Angle

Have students use a straightedge and their full-circle protractors to draw a 60° angle. (*See margin.*) Ask someone to describe how he or she drew the angle.

Step 1: Draw a ray.

Step 2: Place the center of the full-circle protractor on the endpoint of the ray, and align the 0° mark with the ray. Make a dot on the paper at the 60° mark.

Step 3: Draw a second ray from the endpoint of the first ray through the dot.

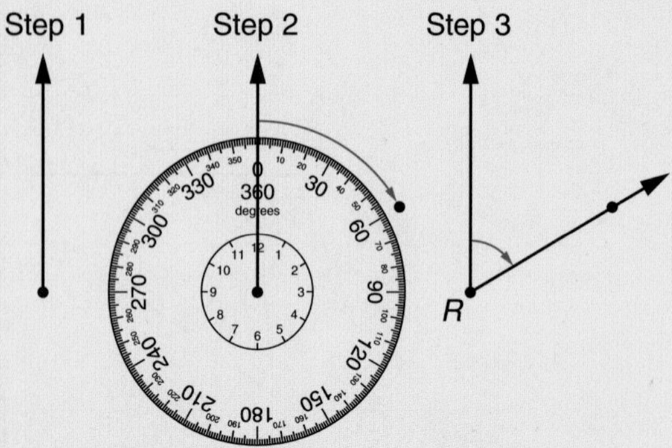

Using a full-circle protractor and a straightedge to draw an angle

Remind students to draw an arc with an arrowhead to identify the direction of the rotation and use a letter to name the vertex point.

Have partners take turns: One partner names a degree measure; the other draws an angle with that degree measure.

Ongoing Assessment: Recognizing Student Achievement

Exit Slip

Use an **Exit Slip** (*Math Masters,* page 389) to assess students' ability to draw angles with measures less than or greater than 90°. Ask students to draw one angle that measures less than 90° and one angle that measures more than 90°. Students should then use the full-circle protractor to measure the angles and record their measures. Students are making adequate progress if they are able to draw angles measuring less and more than 90°. Some students may be able to correctly measure the angles to within a few degrees.

[Measurement and Reference Frames Goal 1]

2 Ongoing Learning & Practice

Playing *Division Dash*

PARTNER ACTIVITY

(*Student Reference Book,* p. 241; *Math Masters,* p. 471)

Students play *Division Dash* to practice dividing 2- or 3-digit dividends by 1-digit divisors. See Lesson 6-4 for additional information.

Math Boxes 6•6

INDEPENDENT ACTIVITY

(*Math Journal 1,* p. 156)

Mixed Practice Math Boxes in this lesson are paired with Math Boxes in Lesson 6-9. The skill in Problem 5 previews Unit 7 content.

Writing/Reasoning Have students write a response to the following: *Winnona said there isn't enough information provided in Problem 2 to answer the question. Do you agree or disagree? Explain your answer.* Sample answer: I disagree. There are 52 weeks in 1 year, so I multiplied 34 by 52 to get the number of minutes Juan spends on the phone in 1 year.

Study Link 6•6

INDEPENDENT ACTIVITY

(*Math Masters,* p. 190)

Home Connection Students use a full-circle protractor to measure angles.

Student Page

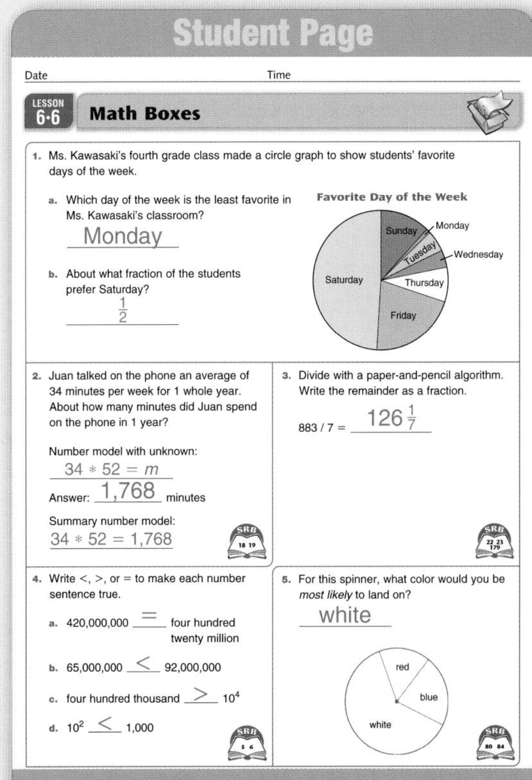

Date Time

LESSON 6•6 **Math Boxes**

1. Ms. Kawasaki's fourth grade class made a circle graph to show students' favorite days of the week.
   a. Which day of the week is the least favorite in Ms. Kawasaki's classroom? Monday
   b. About what fraction of the students prefer Saturday? $\frac{1}{2}$

2. Juan talked on the phone an average of 34 minutes per week for 1 whole year. About how many minutes did Juan spend on the phone in 1 year?
   Number model with unknown: 34 ∗ 52 = m
   Answer: 1,768 minutes
   Summary number model: 34 ∗ 52 = 1,768

3. Divide with a paper-and-pencil algorithm. Write the remainder as a fraction.
   883 / 7 = $126\frac{1}{7}$

4. Write <, >, or = to make each number sentence true.
   a. 420,000,000 = four hundred twenty million
   b. 65,000,000 < 92,000,000
   c. four hundred thousand > 10^4
   d. 10^2 < 1,000

5. For this spinner, what color would you be *most likely* to land on? white

Math Journal 1, p. 156

Study Link Master

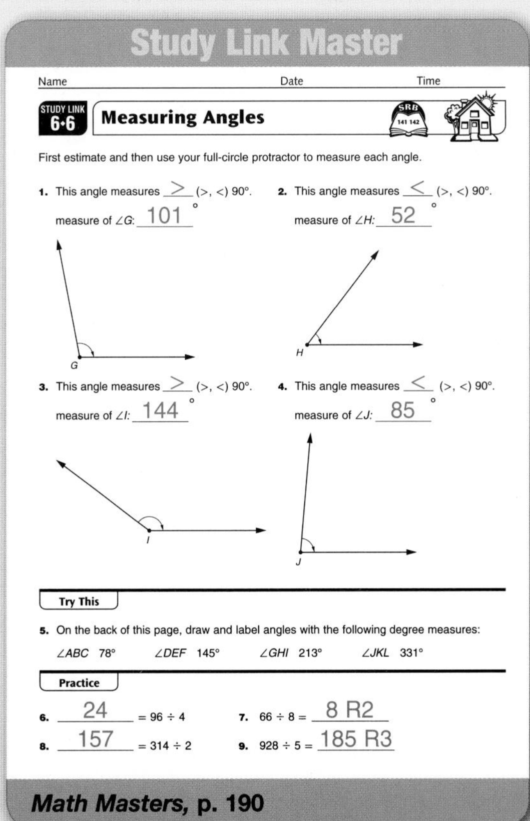

Name Date Time

STUDY LINK 6•6 **Measuring Angles**

First estimate and then use your full-circle protractor to measure each angle.

1. This angle measures > (>, <) 90°. measure of ∠G: 101°
2. This angle measures < (>, <) 90°. measure of ∠H: 52°
3. This angle measures > (>, <) 90°. measure of ∠I: 144°
4. This angle measures < (>, <) 90°. measure of ∠J: 85°

Try This

5. On the back of this page, draw and label angles with the following degree measures:
   ∠ABC 78° ∠DEF 145° ∠GHI 213° ∠JKL 331°

Practice

6. 24 = 96 ÷ 4
7. 66 ÷ 8 = 8 R2
8. 157 = 314 ÷ 2
9. 928 ÷ 5 = 185 R3

Math Masters, p. 190

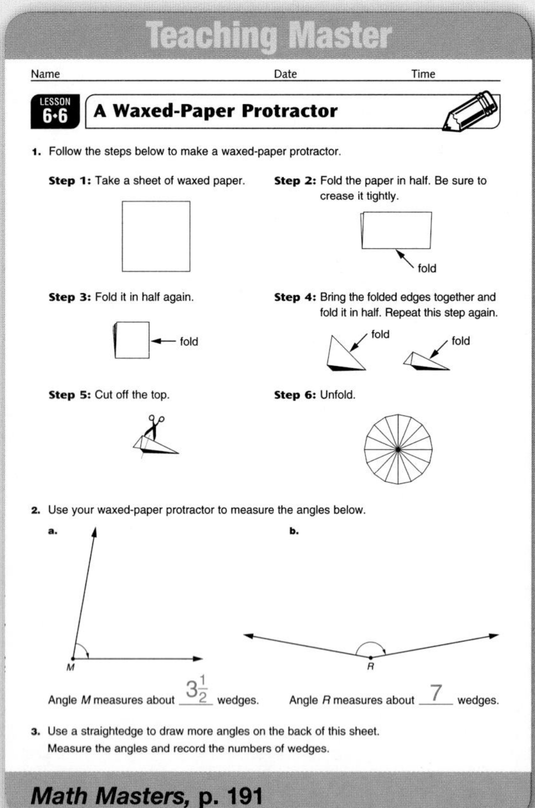
Teaching Master

Name Date Time

LESSON 6•6 **A Waxed-Paper Protractor**

1. Follow the steps below to make a waxed-paper protractor.

Step 1: Take a sheet of waxed paper.

Step 2: Fold the paper in half. Be sure to crease it tightly.

Step 3: Fold it in half again.

Step 4: Bring the folded edges together and fold it in half. Repeat this step again.

Step 5: Cut off the top.

Step 6: Unfold.

2. Use your waxed-paper protractor to measure the angles below.

a. Angle *M* measures about $3\frac{1}{2}$ wedges.

b. Angle *R* measures about 7 wedges.

3. Use a straightedge to draw more angles on the back of this sheet. Measure the angles and record the numbers of wedges.

Math Masters, p. 191

Game Master

Name Date Time

Angle Add-Up

Materials
- ☐ number cards 1–8 (4 of each)
- ☐ number cards 0 and 9 (1 of each)
- ☐ dry-erase marker
- ☐ straightedge
- ☐ full-circle protractor (transparency of *Math Masters,* p. 439)
- ☐ *Angle Add-Up* Record Sheet (*Math Masters,* p. 509)

Players 2

Skills
- ◆ Drawing angles of a given measure
- ◆ Recognizing angle measures as additive
- ◆ Solving addition and subtraction problems to find the measures of unknown angles

Objective To score the most points in 3 rounds.

Directions

1. Shuffle the cards and place the deck number-side down on the table.
2. In each round, each player draws the number of cards indicated on the Record Sheet.
3. Each player uses the number cards to fill in the blanks and form angle measures so the unknown angle measure is as large as possible.
4. Players add or subtract to find the measure of the unknown angle and record it in the circle on the Record Sheet. The measure of the unknown angle is the player's score for the round.
5. Each player uses a full-circle protractor, straightedge, and marker to show that the angle measure of the whole is the sum of the angle measures of the parts.
6. Players play 3 rounds for a game. The player with the largest total number of points at the end of the 3 rounds wins the game.

Math Masters, p. 507

3 Differentiation Options

READINESS

SMALL-GROUP ACTIVITY

15–30 Min

Making and Using a Waxed-Paper Protractor

(*Math Masters,* p. 191)

To explore the use of a protractor to measure angles, have students make and then use a waxed-paper protractor to approximate the measure of angles using standard angles as reference. Have students record the measurements as "wedges" and fractions of "wedges."

ENRICHMENT

PARTNER ACTIVITY

5–15 Min

Playing *Angle Add-Up*

(*Math Masters,* pp. 439 and 507–509)

To further explore the idea that angle measures are additive, have students draw angles and then use addition and subtraction to find the measures of unknown angles. Note that Round 1 requires students to use addition to find the unknown angle measure. Rounds 2 and 3 require subtraction. The given measures of 90° and 180° degrees provide practice with complementary and supplementary angles.

Before they play the game, tell students that the notation m∠*ABC* shown on the record sheet means "the measure of angle *ABC*."

EXTRA PRACTICE

PARTNER ACTIVITY

5–15 Min

Playing *Angle Tangle*

(*Student Reference Book,* p. 230; *Math Masters,* p. 457)

To practice estimating and measuring angles, have students play *Angle Tangle*. See Lesson 6-8 for additional information.

ELL SUPPORT

SMALL-GROUP ACTIVITY

5–15 Min

Building Background for Mathematics Words

To provide language support for angle rotations, discuss the meanings of the words *clockwise* and *counterclockwise.* Explain that *counter* can be a noun with many meanings. Ask students to provide some examples. Kitchen counter, using counters to make an array Explain that *counter-* can also be used as a prefix. Have students look up words in the dictionary that have the prefix *counter-*. Countermove, counterattack, counterbalance Clarify the meaning of *counter* in this context. Consider labeling a clock with an arrow arcing to the right labeled "clockwise" and an arrow arcing to the left labeled "counterclockwise."

6•7 The Half-Circle Protractor

Objectives To guide students as they classify angles as acute, right, obtuse, straight, and reflex; and to provide practice using a half-circle protractor to measure and draw angles.

Technology Resources www.everydaymathonline.com

Presentations

eToolkit

Algorithms Practice

EM Facts Workshop Game™

Family Letters

Assessment Management

Common Core State Standards

Curriculum Focal Points

Interactive Teacher's Lesson Guide

1 Teaching the Lesson

Key Concepts and Skills

- Add and subtract to find unknown angle measures. [Operations and Computation Goal 2]
- Use reference points to estimate the measures of angles; use a half-circle protractor to measure and draw angles. [Measurement and Reference Frames Goal 1]
- Classify angles according to their measure. [Geometry Goal 1]

Key Activities

Students identify types of angles. They measure and draw angles with a half-circle protractor. They identify an angle as obtuse or acute to help them determine which protractor scale to use. They add and subtract to find unknown angle measures.

Ongoing Assessment: Recognizing Student Achievement Use Mental Math and Reflexes. [Number and Numeration Goal 1]

Ongoing Assessment: Informing Instruction See page 440.

Key Vocabulary

acute angle ◆ obtuse angle ◆ reflex angle ◆ straight angle ◆ half-circle protractor ◆ base line

Materials

Math Journal 1, pp. 157 and 158
Study Link 6•6 ◆ half-circle protractor ◆ protractor for demonstration purposes ◆ straightedge ◆ chart paper

2 Ongoing Learning & Practice

World Tour Option: Visiting Europe

Math Journal 1, p. 171 (optional); pp. 172, 173, 180, and 181
Student Reference Book, pp. 276, 277, 280, 284, 285, 297, and 302–305
Math Masters, pp. 419–421 (optional)
Students resume the World Tour in Europe.

Math Boxes 6•7

Math Journal 1, p. 159
Students practice and maintain skills through Math Box problems.

Study Link 6•7

Math Masters, p. 192
protractor
Students practice and maintain skills through Study Link activities.

3 Differentiation Options

READINESS

Modeling Angles

Student Reference Book, p. 93
rope or string
Students model angles with a rope.

ENRICHMENT

Measuring Angles in Triangles

Math Masters, p. 193
straightedge ◆ protractor ◆ glue or tape
Students determine that the sum of the measures of the angles of any triangle is 180°.

ENRICHMENT

Exploring Angles in Literature

Math Masters, p. 388 or 389
Students read *Sir Cumference and the Great Knight of Angleland.*

ELL SUPPORT

Building Background for Mathematics Words

Students create a graphic organizer for the word *angle.*

Advance Preparation

For the optional Enrichment activity in Part 3, obtain the book ***Sir Cumference and the Great Knight of Angleland*** by Cindy Neuschwander (Charlesbridge Publishing, 2001).

***Teacher's Reference Manual,* Grades 4–6** pp. 44–46, 178–180, 234–236

Getting Started

Mental Math and Reflexes 

Write decimals on the board and have volunteers read them aloud. *Suggestions:*

●○○	●●○	●●●
3.45	12.358	10.005
0.27	60.893	2.6074
6.89	83.591	26.0801

Ask questions such as:

- What digit is in the hundredths place?
- What is the value of the digit *x*?

Math Message

Complete the Math Message problems on journal page 157.

Study Link 6·6 Follow-Up

Students compare answers. Make sure they understand that the directional arc shows the path and direction of the rotation.

Ongoing Assessment: Recognizing Student Achievement

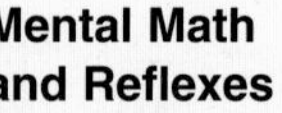

Mental Math and Reflexes

Use **Mental Math and Reflexes** to assess students' ability to identify places in decimals and the values of the digits in those places. Students are making adequate progress if they can correctly identify and express the values of digits through thousandths. Some students may correctly identify and express the values of digits through ten thousandths.

[Number and Numeration Goal 1]

1 Teaching the Lesson

▶ Math Message Follow-Up

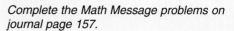

WHOLE-CLASS ACTIVITY

ELL

(*Math Journal 1,* p. 157)

In discussing the answers, talk about the angles in terms of rotations: $\angle A$ is less than a $\frac{1}{4}$ turn, $\angle B$ is more than a $\frac{1}{4}$ turn but less than a $\frac{1}{2}$ turn, and $\angle C$ is between a $\frac{1}{2}$ turn and 1 full turn. Call attention to the names for the various types of angles. To support English language learners, write the names on chart paper next to an example of each. Display the chart paper throughout the unit.

▷ An **acute angle** measures between 0° and 90°.

▷ An **obtuse angle** measures between 90° and 180°.

▷ A **reflex angle** measures between 180° and 360°.

Remind students that a 90° angle is called a *right angle.*

Complete the list of angle names by mentioning that a 180° angle is called a **straight angle.** Ask: *Why is this a good name for this angle?* In a 180° angle, the two sides meet to form a straight line.

Links to the Future

Identifying and describing acute, obtuse, straight, and reflex angles is a Grade 5 Goal.

Introducing the Half-Circle Protractor

Have students examine their half-circle protractors. Students can use either the protractor on the Geometry Template or any other protractor. If some students' protractors do not have labels for the 0° and 180° marks, have them write the labels. The marks may smear and disappear later, but they are helpful for this introduction to the half-circle protractor.

Ask partnerships to decide how the **half-circle protractor** is different from the full-circle protractor they used in the previous lesson. Review observations. Have students indicate "thumbs-up" if they had a similar answer.

▷ The curved edge of the protractor is a half circle. The edge of the full-circle protractor is a full circle.

▷ There are two scales on the half-circle protractor: one scale goes from 0° to 180° in a clockwise direction and the other from 0° to 180° in a counterclockwise direction. To support English language learners, discuss the meaning of *scale* in this context.

▷ The 0° mark on one side of the half-circle protractor is connected with the 180° mark on the other side by a line segment. This segment is the **base line** of the protractor.

▷ The midpoint of the base line is the center of the half-circle protractor. There is often a hole at the center.

Measuring Angles with a Half-Circle Protractor

(*Math Journal 1,* p. 157)

Draw an angle on the board or overhead projector, but omit the arc that indicates the direction of the rotation. Mention that without the directional arc, this angle could represent a rotation less than 180° or a rotation greater than 180°. Draw directional arcs with arrowheads to show the two possible angles. Explain that if no arc is shown, the smaller of the two angles is intended. (*See margin.*)

Draw another angle on the board or overhead. Use your demonstration protractor to show how to measure the angle.

1. Students should first estimate whether the angle measures more or less than 90°. Ask: *Is the angle acute or obtuse?* They can also use 45° and 180° as reference angles to refine their estimate. If students develop this good habit, they will seldom read the wrong scale.
2. Put the center of the protractor over the vertex of the angle.
3. Move the protractor so that one side of the angle is on the base line, as shown in the margin. Make sure the center of the protractor remains over the vertex.

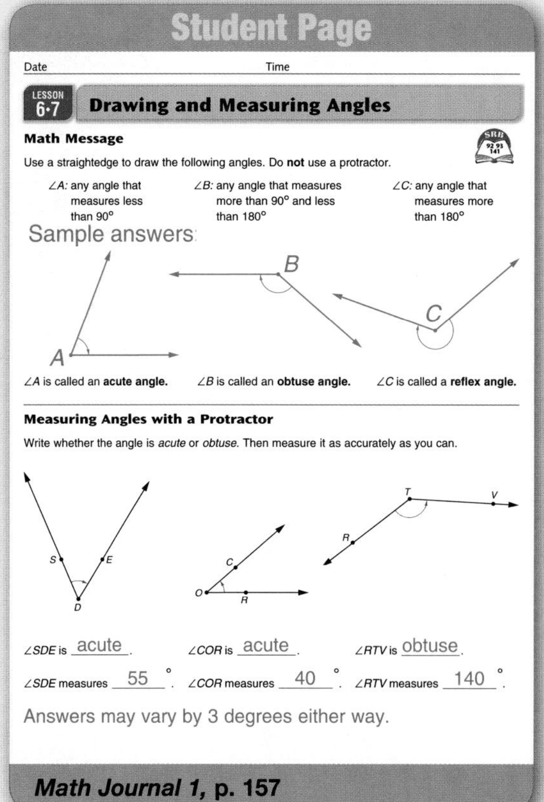

Student Page

Date Time

LESSON 6·7 **Drawing and Measuring Angles**

Math Message

Use a straightedge to draw the following angles. Do **not** use a protractor.

∠*A*: any angle that measures less than 90°
∠*B*: any angle that measures more than 90° and less than 180°
∠*C*: any angle that measures more than 180°

Sample answers:

∠*A* is called an **acute angle.** ∠*B* is called an **obtuse angle.** ∠*C* is called a **reflex angle.**

Measuring Angles with a Protractor

Write whether the angle is *acute* or *obtuse*. Then measure it as accurately as you can.

∠*SDE* is acute. ∠*COR* is acute. ∠*RTV* is obtuse.

∠*SDE* measures 55°. ∠*COR* measures 40°. ∠*RTV* measures 140°.

Answers may vary by 3 degrees either way.

Math Journal 1, p. 157

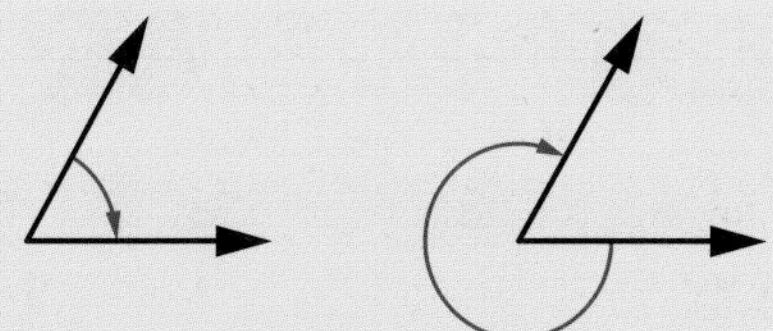

The arc indicates which angle to consider.

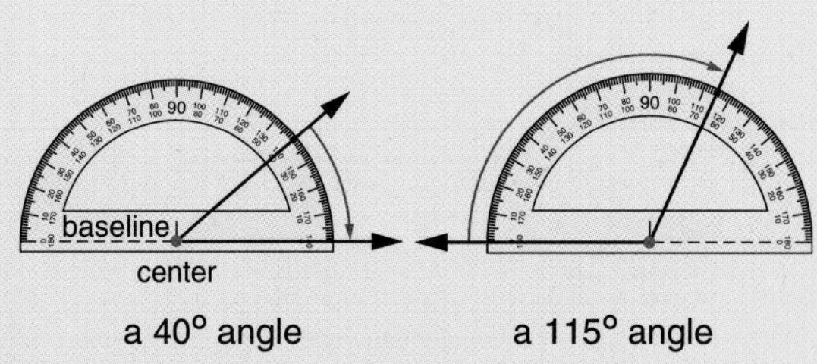

a 40° angle a 115° angle

Ongoing Assessment: Informing Instruction

Watch that students are measuring carefully. A difference of 3 degrees either way should be enough leeway.

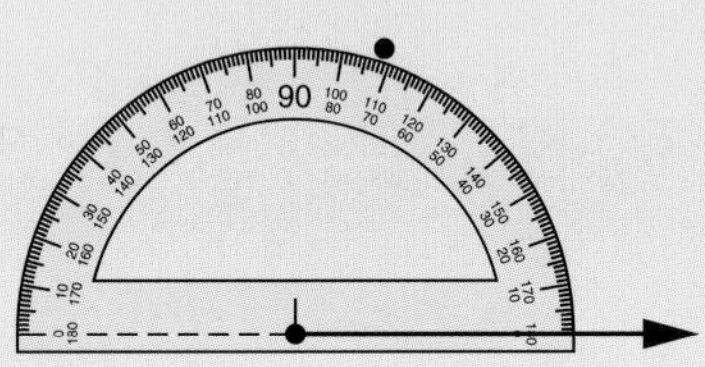

Student Page

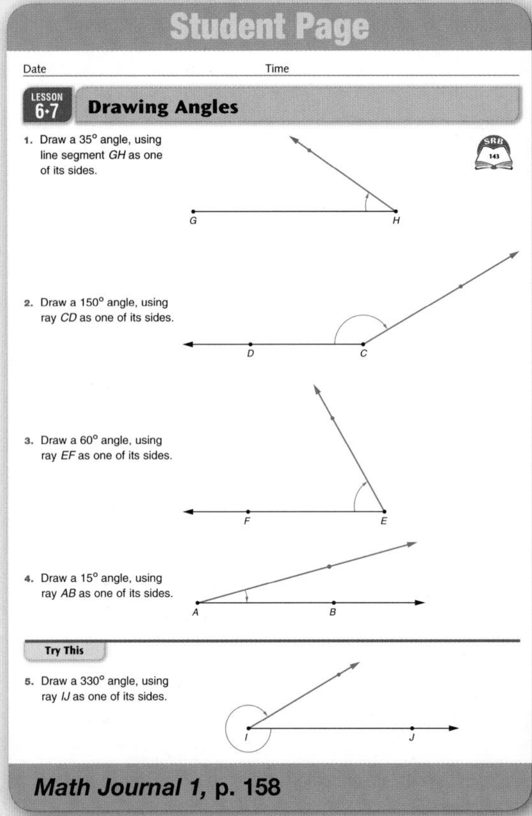

Date Time

LESSON 6·7 **Drawing Angles**

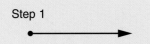

1. Draw a 35° angle, using line segment *GH* as one of its sides.
2. Draw a 150° angle, using ray *CD* as one of its sides.
3. Draw a 60° angle, using ray *EF* as one of its sides.
4. Draw a 15° angle, using ray *AB* as one of its sides.

Try This

5. Draw a 330° angle, using ray *IJ* as one of its sides.

Math Journal 1, p. 158

4. Find the place where the other side of the angle crosses a mark on the edge of the protractor.
5. Decide which of the two 0°-to-180° scales to use to determine the degree measure of the angle. If it is acute, use the smaller number; if it is obtuse, use the larger number.

Ask students to measure angles *SDE, COR,* and *RTV* at the bottom of journal page 157 and compare their measurements.

▶ Drawing Angles with a Half-Circle Protractor

INDEPENDENT ACTIVITY

(*Math Journal 1,* p. 158)

Have students complete Problem 1 on journal page 158 with a partner or on their own. Ask students to describe a procedure for using a half-circle protractor to draw angles while you or a student demonstrates at the board or overhead. One method:

1. Draw a ray.
2. Place the center of the protractor at the endpoint of the ray so that the base line is along the ray.
3. Use the scale that shows 0° where the ray crosses the edge of the protractor. Make a dot where the other ray should cross the edge of the protractor.
4. Draw a ray from the vertex through the dot.

Have students complete journal page 158 on their own. Remind students that they can check whether they have chosen the appropriate scale by noting if the angle is acute or obtuse.

Share strategies for Problem 5, which requires students to draw a reflex angle. Sample strategy: Subtract 330° from 360° (= 30°). Draw a 30° angle; then draw an arc on the "outside" of the angle.

▶ Adding and Subtracting to Find Missing Angle Measures

WHOLE-CLASS ACTIVITY

Show students that you can add and subtract angle measures to find unknown angle measures. Draw the diagram below on the board or overhead.

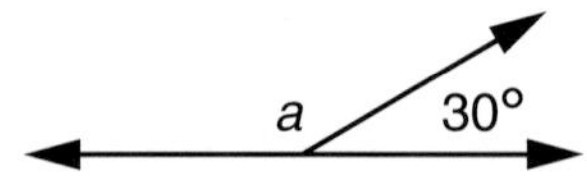

Point out that a straight angle measures 180° and the smaller angle measures 30°. Let a stand for the measure of the missing angle. Explain to students that the angle measure of the whole is the sum of the angle measures of the parts. Therefore, $30° + a = 180°$, so $a = 150°$.

Pose additional problems on the board using either a straight angle or a 90° angle as the main angle. Have students use addition or subtraction to find the missing angle measures.

2 Ongoing Learning & Practice

World Tour Option: Visiting Europe

SMALL-GROUP ACTIVITY

(*Math Journal 1,* pp. 171–173, 180, and 181; *Student Reference Book,* pp. 276, 277, 280, 284, 285, 297, and 302–305; *Math Masters,* pp. 419–421)

Social Studies Link If you have chosen to extend the scope of the World Tour for your class, divide students into groups of 4 or 5. Each group visits one of the remaining countries in Europe and records their country data on journal pages 180 and 181, or on *Math Masters,* pages 419 and 420.

Math Boxes 6•7

INDEPENDENT ACTIVITY

(*Math Journal 1,* p. 159)

Mixed Practice Math Boxes in this lesson are paired with Math Boxes in Lesson 6-5. The skill in Problem 6 previews Unit 7 content.

Writing/Reasoning Have students write a response to the following: *Wei said that both squares in Problem 6 have $\frac{1}{3}$ shaded. Do you agree or disagree? Explain your answer.* Sample answer: I disagree. Both of the squares are divided into three parts and both of the squares have one part shaded. However, only A shows $\frac{1}{3}$ because A is divided into equal parts. The three parts in B are not equal.

Study Link 6•7

INDEPENDENT ACTIVITY

(*Math Masters,* p. 192)

Home Connection Students measure angles using a half-circle protractor. Some students may prefer to use a full-circle protractor from Lesson 6-6.

3 Differentiation Options

READINESS

Modeling Angles

SMALL-GROUP ACTIVITY

5–15 Min

(*Student Reference Book,* p. 93)

To explore estimating angle measures using a concrete model, have students use rope to model angles. (*See margin.*) Ask the "vertex" to tell the two "points" the type of angle or the measure of the angle that they should form. Have students use *Student Reference Book,* page 93 as a guide.

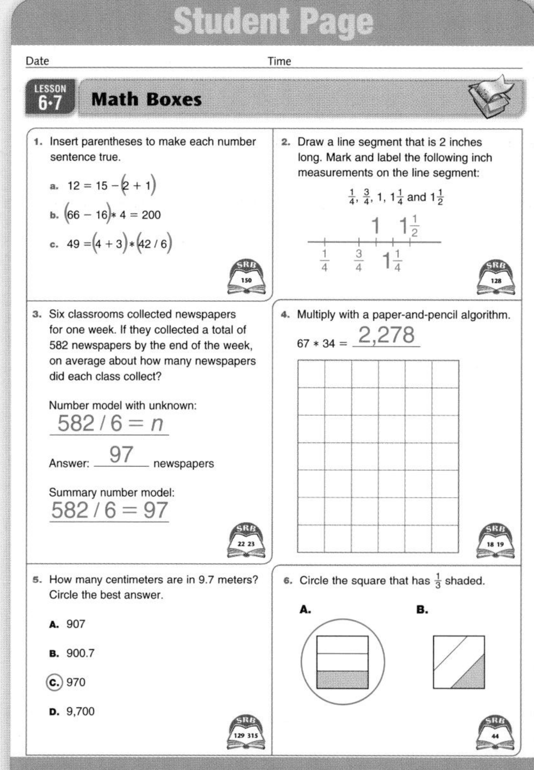

Student Page

Date Time

LESSON 6•7 **Math Boxes**

1. Insert parentheses to make each number sentence true.
   a. 12 = 15 − (2 + 1)
   b. (66 − 16) ∗ 4 = 200
   c. 49 = (4 + 3) ∗ (42 / 6)

SRB 150

2. Draw a line segment that is 2 inches long. Mark and label the following inch measurements on the line segment:
   $\frac{1}{4}$, $\frac{3}{4}$, 1, $1\frac{1}{4}$ and $1\frac{1}{2}$

SRB 128

3. Six classrooms collected newspapers for one week. If they collected a total of 582 newspapers by the end of the week, on average about how many newspapers did each class collect?
   Number model with unknown: 582 / 6 = *n*
   Answer: 97 newspapers
   Summary number model: 582 / 6 = 97

SRB 22 23

4. Multiply with a paper-and-pencil algorithm.
   67 ∗ 34 = 2,278

SRB 18 19

5. How many centimeters are in 9.7 meters? Circle the best answer.
   A. 907
   B. 900.7
   (C.) 970
   D. 9,700

SRB 129 315

6. Circle the square that has $\frac{1}{3}$ shaded.
   A. B.

SRB 44

Math Journal 1, p. 159

Three students, acting as points, use rope to represent line segments and form an acute angle.

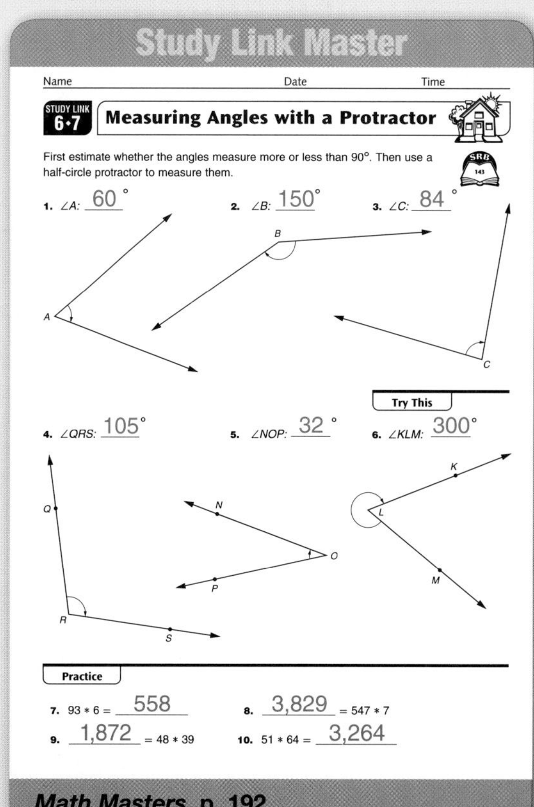

Study Link Master

Name Date Time

STUDY LINK 6•7 **Measuring Angles with a Protractor**

First estimate whether the angles measure more or less than 90°. Then use a half-circle protractor to measure them.

SRB 143

1. ∠A: 60°
2. ∠B: 150°
3. ∠C: 84°

Try This

4. ∠QRS: 105°
5. ∠NOP: 32°
6. ∠KLM: 300°

Practice

7. 93 ∗ 6 = 558
8. 3,829 = 547 ∗ 7
9. 1,872 = 48 ∗ 39
10. 51 ∗ 64 = 3,264

Math Masters, p. 192

Teaching Master

Name Date Time

LESSON 6•7 **Exploring Triangle Measures**

You need 2 sheets of paper, a straightedge, and a protractor.

1. Draw a large triangle on each sheet of paper. The 2 triangles should not look the same.
2. Label the vertices of one triangle *A, B,* and *C.* Label the vertices of the other triangle *D, E,* and *F.* Be sure to write the labels inside the triangles.
3. Using your protractor, measure each angle as accurately as you can. Record the degree measures in the tables below.
4. Find the sum of the degree measures in triangle *ABC* and in triangle *DEF.*

Sample answers:

Angle	Degree Measure
∠A	About 45°
∠B	About 45°
∠C	About 90°
Sum	About 180°

Angle	Degree Measure
∠D	About 60°
∠E	About 60°
∠F	About 60°
Sum	About 180°

5. Write a true statement about the sum of the measures of the 3 angles of a triangle.
The sum of the angle measures of a triangle is 180°.

Math Masters, p. 193

ENRICHMENT

▶ Measuring Angles in Triangles

15–30 Min

(*Math Masters,* p. 193)

To apply students' understanding of measuring angles, have them draw two triangles, measure the angles, and find the sum of the angle measures for each triangle. The sum of the students' measures of the angles of a triangle should range from 170° to 190°, with most sums close to 180°.

Guide students as they "prove" that the sum of the measures of the angles of any triangle is 180°. Have them cut off the three corners of one of their triangles and arrange them so that the three angles touch each other but do not overlap. From this, it should be clear that the angles form a straight angle, and so the sum of their measures is 180°.

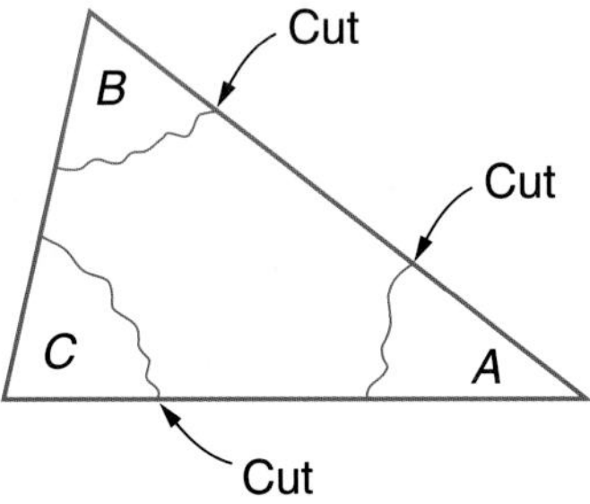

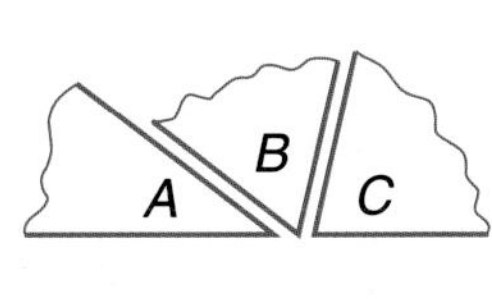

Encourage students to extend this exploration to "prove" that the sum of the measures of the angles of any quadrilateral is 360°. Students may reason that since any quadrilateral can be divided into two triangles, the sum of the angles is twice 180°, or 360°.

ENRICHMENT

▶ Exploring Angles in Literature

(*Math Masters,* p. 388 or 389)

Literature Link To further explore the half-circle protractor and angles, have students read and discuss ***Sir Cumference and the Great Knight of Angleland*** by Cindy Neuschwander (Charlesbridge Publishing, 2001). In a Math Log or on an Exit Slip, ask students to summarize what Radius learned on his quest.

ELL SUPPORT

▶ Building Background for Mathematics Words

To provide language support for angles, have students create a graphic organizer for the word *angle.* They may list words and draw pictures that are connected to the word *angle.* See *Differentiation Handbook,* page 34 for more information.

6•8 Rectangular Coordinate Grids for Maps

Objectives To guide students in the use of letter-number pairs and ordered pairs of numbers to locate points on a grid; and to provide practice using a map scale.

Technology Resources www.everydaymathonline.com

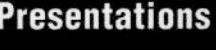
Presentations

eToolkit

Algorithms Practice

EM Facts Workshop Game™

Family Letters

Assessment Management

Common Core State Standards

Curriculum Focal Points

Interactive Teacher's Lesson Guide

1 Teaching the Lesson

Key Concepts and Skills

- Use a map scale. [Operations and Computation Goal 7]
- Estimate distances on a map. [Measurement and Reference Frames Goal 1]
- Use ordered number pairs to locate points on a map. [Measurement and Reference Frames Goal 4]
- Use letter-number pairs to locate points and regions on a map. [Measurement and Reference Frames Goal 4]

Key Activities

Students use letter-number pairs to find locations on a map of Ireland. They use ordered pairs of numbers to identify points, give directions, and describe routes on a campground map. Students use a map scale to estimate distances.

Ongoing Assessment: Recognizing Student Achievement Use a Math Log or Exit Slip (*Math Masters,* page 388 or 389). [Measurement and Reference Frames Goal 4]

Key Vocabulary

index of locations ◆ letter-number pair ◆ ordered number pair ◆ map scale

Materials

Math Journal 1, pp. 161–163
Study Link 6•7
Math Masters, p. 388 or 389 (optional)
compass (optional) ◆ slate ◆ road atlas (optional)

2 Ongoing Learning & Practice

Playing *Angle Tangle*
Student Reference Book, p. 230
Math Masters, p. 457
protractor ◆ straightedge
Students practice estimating the measures of angles and measuring angles.

Finding Real-Life Angle Measures
Math Journal 1, pp. 163A and 163B
Students practice finding unknown angle measures.

Math Boxes 6•8
Math Journal 1, p. 160
Students practice and maintain skills through Math Box problems.

Study Link 6•8
Math Masters, p. 194
Students practice and maintain skills through Study Link activities.

3 Differentiation Options

READINESS

Moving on a Coordinate Grid
masking tape and index cards, or rope and colored tape
Students describe the locations of points and plot points on a life-size coordinate grid.

ENRICHMENT

Playing *Grid Search*
Student Reference Book, pp. 250 and 251
Math Masters, p. 486
Students practice naming and locating grid squares and develop search strategies.

EXTRA PRACTICE

Plotting and Naming Points on a Coordinate Grid
Math Masters, p. 440
Students plot and name points on a coordinate grid.

Advance Preparation

For Part 1, you may want to use a road atlas of the United States to illustrate the use of indexes and letter-number grid coordinates.

***Teacher's Reference Manual,* Grades 4–6** pp. 249–252

Getting Started

Mental Math and Reflexes

Pose multiplication and division number stories.
Suggestions:

●○○ 3 boxes of beads; 4 beads per box: How many beads in all? 12

12 cups divided equally between 2 trays: How many cups per tray? 6

●●○ 8 boxes of cupcakes; 6 cupcakes per box: How many cupcakes in all? 48

5 shirts per rack; 45 shirts in all: How many racks? 9

●●● 4 crates of tennis balls; 8 cans per crate; 3 balls per can: How many tennis balls in all? 96

180 seats in all; 10 seats per row; 6 rows per section: How many sections? 3

Math Message

Turn to journal page 161. Find the city of Tralee on the map. Be prepared to explain how you found it.

Study Link 6•7 Follow-Up

Students compare answers. The final problem is more difficult because the angle is a reflex angle and the half-circle protractor cannot directly measure angles greater than 180°. Have students share their strategies. One possible strategy: The smaller angle has a measure of 60°. Subtract 60° from 360° to get 300°, which is the measure of the reflex angle.

1 Teaching the Lesson

▶ Math Message Follow-Up

WHOLE-CLASS ACTIVITY

(*Math Journal 1,* p. 161)

Social Studies Link The map on journal page 161 shows the island of Ireland. Ask students how they found Tralee. Make sure they know how to use the **index of locations.** Look up Tralee in the list above the map. It is located in square B-2. Find column B and row 2. The column and row overlap at a square region. Tralee is located in this region.

- Why is this **letter-number pair** method useful for finding places on a map? It limits the search to a small part of the map.

Have students find other locations on the map.

Point out that in the Math Message students used letter-number pairs to locate *regions* on a map. In the remainder of the lesson, students will use ordered number pairs to locate specific *points* on a campground map.

NOTE The larger part of the island is the Republic of Ireland. The smaller northern part is Northern Ireland, a part of the United Kingdom.

Student Page

Date Time

LESSON 6•8 **A Map of the Island of Ireland**

Bantry	B-1	Dublin	F-4	Lahinch	B-4	Omagh	E-7
Belfast	F-7	Dundalk	F-6	Larne	F-7	Tralee	B-2
Carlow	E-3	Galway	C-4	Limerick	C-3	Tuam	C-5
Castlebar	B-6	Gort	C-4	Mullingar	E-5	Westport	B-5
Derry	E-8	Kilkee	B-3	Navan	E-5	Wicklow	F-4

Math Journal 1, p. 161

▶ Using Ordered Pairs to Locate Points on a Map

WHOLE-CLASS ACTIVITY

PROBLEM SOLVING

(*Math Journal 1,* p. 162)

Ask students to look at the campground map and symbols on journal page 162. Tell them that these are standard symbols for United States topographic maps and most conventional road maps. Students should notice that the map has been drawn on a rectangular coordinate grid. Remind them that they can locate points by naming **ordered number pairs,** such as (0,3) and (7,6).

To review the concept that the order of the numbers in an ordered pair is important, ask students which ordered pair—(3,7) or (7,3)—names a point in Blue Lake. To find point (3,7), start at 0, go 3 to the right, and then go up 7. To find point (7,3), start at 0, go 7 to the right, and then go up 3. The ordered pair (3,7) names a point in Blue Lake; (7,3) does not.

Then ask students to name an ordered pair that describes the location of the ranger station. Some students may name (6,1), but point out that $(5\frac{1}{2}, 1\frac{1}{2})$ is a better answer because the station is located in the middle of a grid square.

Practice naming ordered pairs with other examples, including points that are between grid lines.

Adjusting the Activity

A "ladder" metaphor may help some students plot ordered number pairs. The first number tells where to put the ladder. The second tells how high to climb. Or have students locate points by making heel-to-toe steps from the origin (0,0) to named points (*x*,*y*). Students chant "over" as they move to the *x*-coordinate and then "up" as they move to the *y*-coordinate.

AUDITORY ◆ KINESTHETIC ◆ TACTILE ◆ VISUAL

Math Log or Exit Slip

Use a **Math Log** or an **Exit Slip** (*Math Masters,* page 388 or 389) to assess students' understanding of coordinate grid systems. Ask students to compare the grid system on the map of Ireland to the one on the campground map. Students are making adequate progress if they mention the following:

▷ The grid of the map of Ireland identifies square regions using letter-number pairs.

▷ The grid of the campground map identifies points using ordered pairs of numbers.

▷ The order in a letter-number pair is not important, but the order of the numbers in an ordered number pair is important.

[Measurement and Reference Frames Goal 4]

Estimating Distances on a Map

(*Math Journal 1,* pp. 162 and 163)

Point out the **map scale** on journal page 162. To support English language learners, write *map scale* on the board and explain that the scale tells the relationship between the measured distance on the map and the actual distance. Students should notice that each side of a grid square represents 0.2 kilometers.

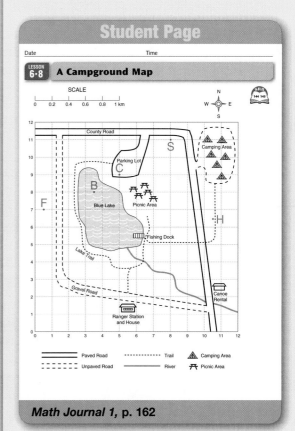

Student Page

Date Time

LESSON 6•8 **A Campground Map**

SCALE: 0 0.2 0.4 0.6 0.8 1 km

County Road; Parking Lot; Camping Area; Blue Lake; Picnic Area; Fishing Dock; Lake Trail; Gravel Road; Canoe Rental; Ranger Station and House

Paved Road; Unpaved Road; Trail; River; Camping Area; Picnic Area

Math Journal 1, p. 162

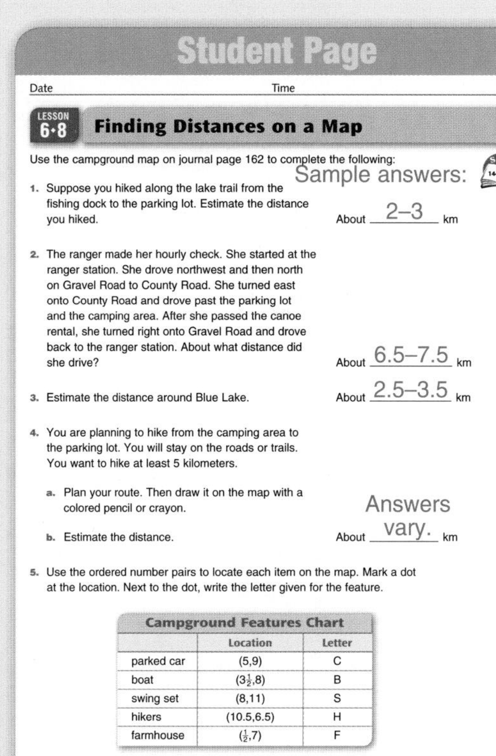
Student Page

Date Time

LESSON 6•8 **Finding Distances on a Map**

Use the campground map on journal page 162 to complete the following:

Sample answers:

1. Suppose you hiked along the lake trail from the fishing dock to the parking lot. Estimate the distance you hiked. About 2–3 km
2. The ranger made her hourly check. She started at the ranger station. She drove northwest and then north on Gravel Road to County Road. She turned east onto County Road and drove past the parking lot and the camping area. After she passed the canoe rental, she turned right onto Gravel Road and drove back to the ranger station. About what distance did she drive? About 6.5–7.5 km
3. Estimate the distance around Blue Lake. About 2.5–3.5 km
4. You are planning to hike from the camping area to the parking lot. You will stay on the roads or trails. You want to hike at least 5 kilometers.
   a. Plan your route. Then draw it on the map with a colored pencil or crayon.
   b. Estimate the distance. About Answers vary. km
5. Use the ordered number pairs to locate each item on the map. Mark a dot at the location. Next to the dot, write the letter given for the feature.

Campground Features Chart

	Location	Letter
parked car	(5,9)	C
boat	$(3\frac{1}{2},8)$	B
swing set	(8,11)	S
hikers	(10.5,6.5)	H
farmhouse	$(\frac{1}{2},7)$	F

Math Journal 1, p. 163

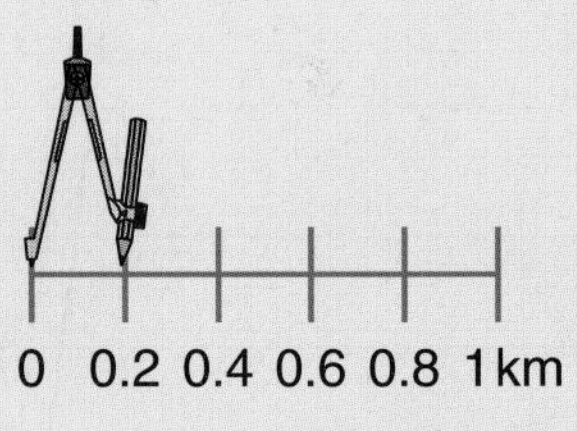

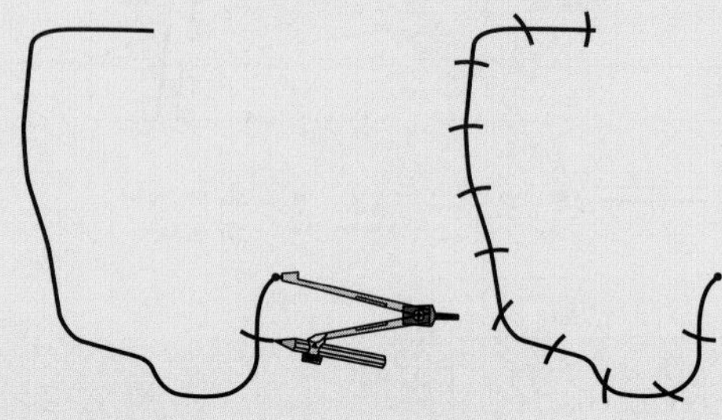

Using a compass to estimate the distance around an irregular shape

Ask students to estimate the distance along Lake Trail from the fishing dock to the parking lot and to record it on journal page 163. Have students compare estimates and strategies:

▷ Count the number of squares the trail passes through. 15 Each side of a grid square represents a distance of 0.2 kilometers, so the length of the trail is about 3 kilometers.

▷ Make a mark on the edge of a sheet of paper. Place that mark at the beginning point of the trail with the edge of the paper along the trail. When the trail turns, make a mark on the edge and turn the paper so the edge follows the trail. When you reach the end of the trail, make a final mark. Measure the distance between the first and last marks on the paper. Then use the map scale to estimate the actual distance.

▷ Use a traditional compass. On the map scale, set the opening of the compass to represent 0.2 kilometers. Place the anchor point at the fishing dock and swing the pencil point, marking off about 0.2 km along the trail. Place the anchor point on this mark and swing the pencil point, marking off the next 0.2 km along the trail. Continue to the end of the trail. Count the number of compass swings and estimate the distance. 11 or 12 compass swings, or about 2.2 to 2.4 km

Ask: *Why are the estimates obtained by the last two methods above probably less than the actual length?* Each segment on the paper's edge or each compass swing measures the path as though it were made up of straight pieces. Such a path would be a little shorter than the actual curved path.

Have partnerships complete the journal page and share results.

Student Page

Date Time

LESSON 6·8 **Dartboard Angles**

A regulation dartboard is made up of 20 equal sectors. The measure of each sector's angle is 18 degrees.

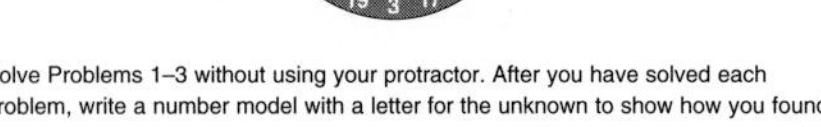

Solve Problems 1–3 without using your protractor. After you have solved each problem, write a number model with a letter for the unknown to show how you found your answer.

1. Draw ∠*ABC* around sectors 14, 9, 12, 5, 20, and 1. What is the measure of ∠*ABC*?

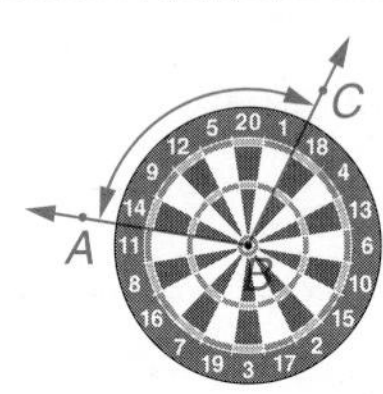

Measure of ∠*ABC* = 108 ° Sample answer:

Number model with unknown: 18 + 18 + 18 + 18 + 18 + 18 = *m*

***Math Journal 1*, p. 163A**

2 Ongoing Learning & Practice

▶ Playing *Angle Tangle*

(*Student Reference Book,* p. 230; *Math Masters,* p. 457)

Students play *Angle Tangle* to practice estimating and measuring angles.

Adjusting the Activity

Use this game variation as appropriate: Have students draw and measure reflex angles. Their drawings should include the directional arc in the appropriate place.

AUDITORY ◆ KINESTHETIC ◆ TACTILE ◆ VISUAL

▶ Finding Real-Life Angle Measures

INDEPENDENT ACTIVITY

(*Math Journal 1,* pp. 163A and 163B)

Students practice finding unknown angle measures using real-life examples. Using addition and subtraction, students find missing measures on a dartboard.

▶ Math Boxes 6•8

INDEPENDENT ACTIVITY

(*Math Journal 1,* p. 160)

Mixed Practice Math Boxes in this lesson are paired with Math Boxes in Lesson 6-10. The skill in Problem 6 previews Unit 7 content.

Writing/Reasoning Have students write a response to the following: *Explain how to use the* in *and* out *numbers in Problem 2 to determine the rule.* Sample answer: The first two rows have both the *in* and *out* numbers. The *out* numbers are smaller than the *in* numbers, so I thought the rule might involve subtraction. I subtracted the *out* number from the *in* number in both rows and got 1.5 for an answer, so I knew the rule was –1.5.

▶ Study Link 6•8

INDEPENDENT ACTIVITY

(*Math Masters,* p. 194)

Home Connection Students plot and label points on a coordinate grid. They write the ordered number pair for each point.

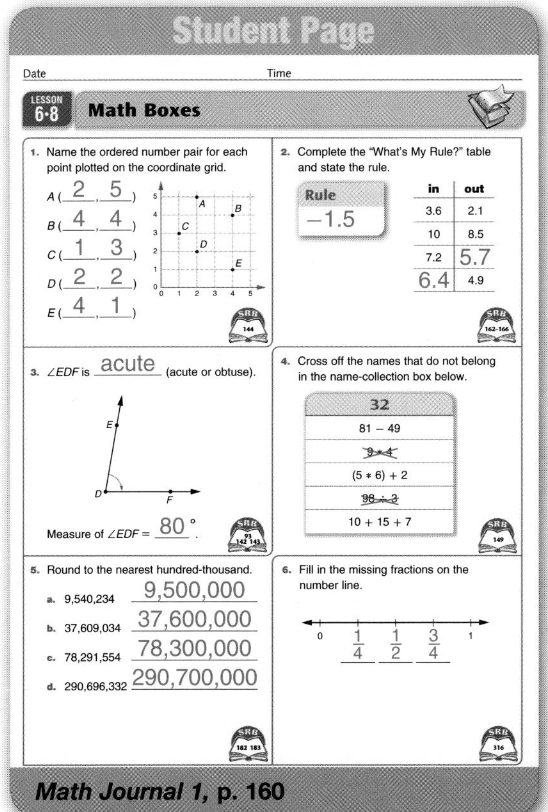

Student Page

Date Time

LESSON 6•8 **Math Boxes**

1. Name the ordered number pair for each point plotted on the coordinate grid.
A (2, 5)
B (4, 4)
C (1, 3)
D (2, 2)
E (4, 1)

2. Complete the "What's My Rule?" table and state the rule.

Rule: −1.5

in	out
3.6	2.1
10	8.5
7.2	5.7
6.4	4.9

3. ∠EDF is acute (acute or obtuse).
Measure of ∠EDF = 80°.

4. Cross off the names that do not belong in the name-collection box below.

32
81 − 49
~~9 * 4~~
(5 * 6) + 2
~~98 ÷ 3~~
10 + 15 + 7

5. Round to the nearest hundred-thousand.
a. 9,540,234 9,500,000
b. 37,609,034 37,600,000
c. 78,291,554 78,300,000
d. 290,696,332 290,700,000

6. Fill in the missing fractions on the number line.
0 $\frac{1}{4}$ $\frac{1}{2}$ $\frac{3}{4}$ 1

Math Journal 1, p. 160

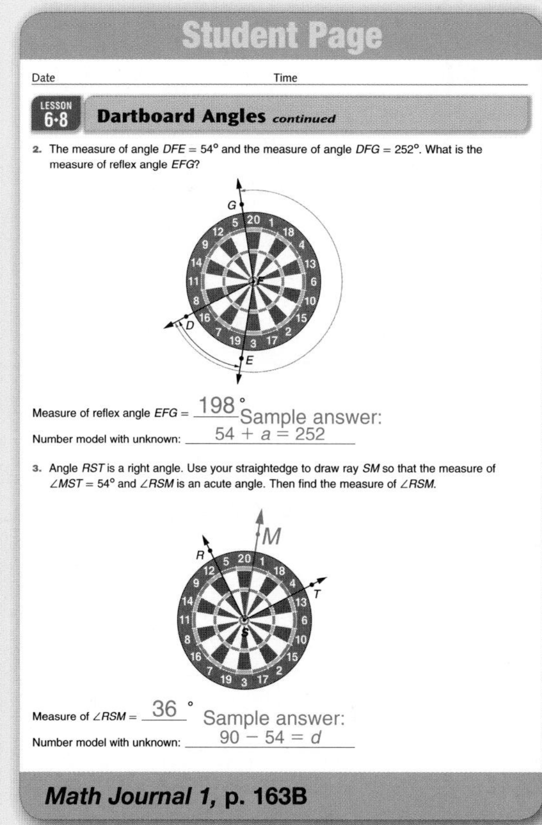

Student Page

Date Time

LESSON 6•8 **Dartboard Angles** *continued*

2. The measure of angle *DFE* = 54° and the measure of angle *DFG* = 252°. What is the measure of reflex angle *EFG*?

Measure of reflex angle *EFG* = 198°
Number model with unknown: Sample answer: 54 + a = 252

3. Angle *RST* is a right angle. Use your straightedge to draw ray *SM* so that the measure of ∠*MST* = 54° and ∠*RSM* is an acute angle. Then find the measure of ∠*RSM*.

Measure of ∠*RSM* = 36°
Number model with unknown: Sample answer: 90 − 54 = d

Math Journal 1, p. 163B

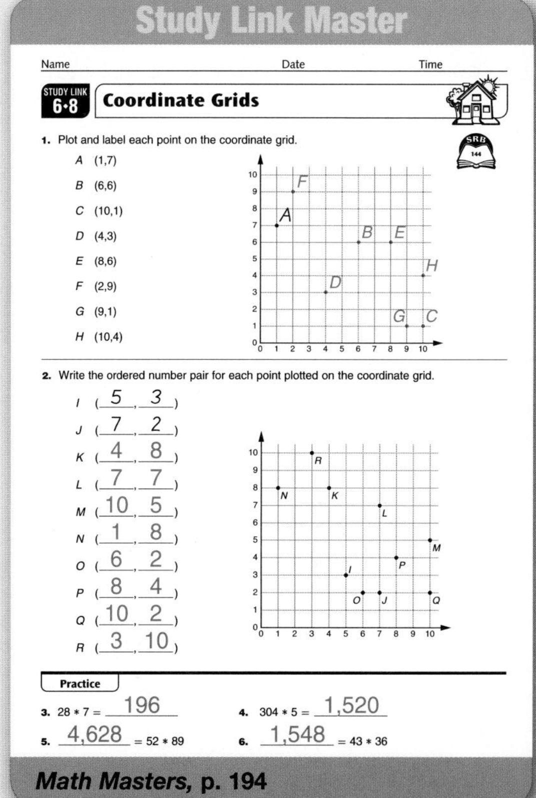

Study Link Master

Name Date Time

STUDY LINK 6•8 **Coordinate Grids**

1. Plot and label each point on the coordinate grid.
A (1,7)
B (6,6)
C (10,1)
D (4,3)
E (8,6)
F (2,9)
G (9,1)
H (10,4)

2. Write the ordered number pair for each point plotted on the coordinate grid.
I (5, 3)
J (7, 2)
K (4, 8)
L (7, 7)
M (10, 5)
N (1, 8)
O (6, 2)
P (8, 4)
Q (10, 2)
R (3, 10)

Practice

3. 28 * 7 = 196
4. 304 * 5 = 1,520
5. 4,628 = 52 * 89
6. 1,548 = 43 * 36

Math Masters, p. 194

3 Differentiation Options

READINESS

▶ Moving on a Coordinate Grid

To provide experience locating ordered pairs, create or have students help you create a life-size 6-by-6 coordinate grid on the floor. *Suggestions:*

- ▷ Use masking tape to mark off the x-axis and y-axis on carpet or a tile floor. Use index card "tents" (two colors) to mark the points on each axis.
- ▷ Tie two ropes together to create the x-axis and y-axis. Use two colors of electrical tape at regular intervals to mark the points on each axis. (*See margin.*)

Place objects on the coordinate grid. Have students describe their location.

Give directions for students to follow to "plot" themselves on the grid. For example, *Walk over 3 blue steps. Now walk up 5 red steps.*

The book is located at blue 3, red 5.

ENRICHMENT

PARTNER ACTIVITY

▶ Playing *Grid Search*

(*Student Reference Book,* pp. 250 and 251; *Math Masters,* p. 486)

To apply students' understanding of coordinate grids, have them play *Grid Search.* Expect students to develop strategies for zeroing in on the area where the queen has been hidden. They may also invent variations—add more knights, add a king worth 7 points, and so on.

Student Page

Games

Grid Search

Materials ☐ 1 sheet of *Grid Search* Grids for each player (*Math Masters,* p. 486)

Players 2

Skill Deduction; developing a search strategy

Object of the game To locate the opponent's queen on a coordinate grid in the fewest turns possible.

Directions

Players sit so that they cannot see what the other player is doing. Each player uses 2 grids like those shown at the right.

Advance Preparation Before the start of the game, each player secretly decides where to place a queen and 6 knights on their Grid 1. They write the letter Q to record the location of the queen and the letter K to record the location of each knight.

- ♦ The queen may be placed on any square.
- ♦ The knights may also be placed on any squares, as long as the queen and the knights can all be connected without skipping squares.

My Pieces (Grid 1)

Opponent's Pieces (Grid 2)

These are acceptable arrangements of the pieces:

These are *not* acceptable arrangements because the pieces cannot be connected without skipping squares.

Student Reference Book, p. 250

EXTRA PRACTICE

▶ Plotting and Naming Points on a Coordinate Grid

(*Math Masters,* p. 440)

To practice plotting and labeling points (including those between grid lines) on a coordinate grid, have students complete *Math Masters,* page 440. Fill in the page to create a new set of problems for students each time they use the master or have students create and solve their own problems.

Planning Ahead

In Part 1 of Lesson 6-9, you will need a world globe and a wall map.

6•9 Global Coordinate Grid System

Objectives To introduce latitude and longitude; to provide practice finding the latitude and longitude of places on a globe and a map; and to identify places given the latitude and longitude.

Technology Resources www.everydaymathonline.com

Presentations

eToolkit

Algorithms Practice

EM Facts Workshop Game™

Family Letters

Assessment Management

Common Core State Standards

Curriculum Focal Points

Interactive Teacher's Lesson Guide

1 Teaching the Lesson

Key Concepts and Skills

- Multiply multidigit numbers to determine miles from the equator.
  [Operations and Computation Goal 4]
- Locate positions on the global coordinate grid system.
  [Measurement and Reference Frames Goal 4]
- Describe parallel and intersecting lines in terms of latitude and longitude.
  [Geometry Goal 1]
- Identify Earth as a sphere divided into hemispheres.
  [Geometry Goal 2]

Key Activities

Students locate and discuss important features of the world globe. They use latitude and longitude to locate places on a globe, a world map, and regional maps.

Ongoing Assessment: Informing Instruction See page 453.

Key Vocabulary

sphere ◆ North Pole ◆ South Pole ◆ axis ◆ equator ◆ prime meridian ◆ hemisphere ◆ latitude (lines) ◆ longitude (lines) ◆ parallels ◆ meridian bar

Materials

Math Journal 1, p. 164
Student Reference Book, pp. 272, 273, and 282–293
Study Link 6•8
globe ◆ world map

2 Ongoing Learning & Practice

Playing *Over and Up Squares*
Student Reference Book, p. 257
Math Masters, p. 494
per partnership: colored pencils, 2 six-sided dice
Students practice coordinate grid skills.

Math Boxes 6•9
Math Journal 1, p. 165
Students practice and maintain skills through Math Box problems.

Ongoing Assessment: Recognizing Student Achievement
Use Math Boxes, Problem 2.
[Operations and Computation Goal 4]

Study Link 6•9
Math Masters, p. 195
Students practice and maintain skills through Study Link activities.

3 Differentiation Options

ENRICHMENT

Using Time to Determine Longitude
Math Masters, p. 388 or 389
Students read *Sea Clocks: The Story of Longitude.*

EXTRA PRACTICE

Locating Places with Latitude and Longitude
Math Masters, p. 196
per group: flat world political map, 1 penny, scissors
Students use latitude and longitude to locate places on a map.

Advance Preparation

For the optional Enrichment activity in Part 3, obtain a copy of ***Sea Clocks: The Story of Longitude*** by Louise Bordon (Margaret K. McElderry Books, 2004).

***Teacher's Reference Manual,* Grades 4–6** pp. 251, 252, 254

Getting Started

Mental Math and Reflexes

Write decimals on the board and have volunteers read them aloud. *Suggestions:*

●○○	●●○	●●●
0.1	0.379	1.0498
2.56	50.123	2.0501
14.78	96.478	11.0063

Ask questions such as:

- What digit is in the tenths place?
- What is the value of the digit *x*?

Math Message

Make a list of the things that you know about the world globe. Write down one question that you have about the world globe.

Study Link 6·8 Follow-Up

Have students compare answers.

1 Teaching the Lesson

▶ Math Message Follow-Up

Make one list of things students already know (or think they kno about the world globe and a second list of questions students wou like answered. During the discussion that follows, refer to the list when facts are reviewed or questions are answered.

Tell students that in this lesson they will explore the coordinate grid system used to locate points on the world globe.

▶ Studying a World Globe

(*Student Reference Book,* pp. 272 and 273)

Mention that Earth is close to being a perfect **sphere;** that is, all points on Earth's surface are about the same distance from the center of Earth. With the help of the class, locate and discuss som of the important features of the globe.

1. The **North Pole** and **South Pole:** Demonstrate how Earth rotates as students share observations:
   - ▷ Earth rotates about an **axis** (an imaginary line through its center) connecting the two poles. Viewed from above the North Pole, Earth rotates counterclockwise.
   - ▷ All points on the surface of Earth, except the two poles, mov east as Earth rotates.
2. The **equator:** Point out that the equator is a circle and that every point on it is the same distance from each pole.
3. The **prime meridian:** Unlike the equator, the prime meridia is a semicircle (half circle). It connects the poles and passes through the Royal Observatory at Greenwich, England—near London. It was established when England was the foremost seafaring nation.

Student Page

World Tour

Latitude and Longitude

You sometimes use a world globe or a flat map to locate countries, cities, rivers, and so forth. Reference lines are drawn on globes and maps to make places easier to find.

Latitude

Lines that go east and west around the Earth are called **lines of latitude.** The **equator** is a special line of latitude. Every point on the equator is the same distance from the North Pole and the South Pole. Lines of latitude are called **parallels** because each one is a circle that is parallel to the equator.

Latitude is measured in **degrees.** The symbol for degrees is (°). Lines north of the equator are labeled °N. Lines south of the equator are labeled °S. The number of degrees tells how far north or south of the equator a place is. The area north of the equator is called the **Northern Hemisphere.** The area south of the equator is called the **Southern Hemisphere.**

Examples The latitude of Cairo, Egypt, is 30°N. We say that Cairo is 30 degrees north of the equator.

The latitude of Durban, South Africa, is 30°S. Durban is in the Southern Hemisphere.

The latitude of the North Pole is 90°N. The latitude of the South Pole is 90°S. The poles are the points farthest north and farthest south on Earth.

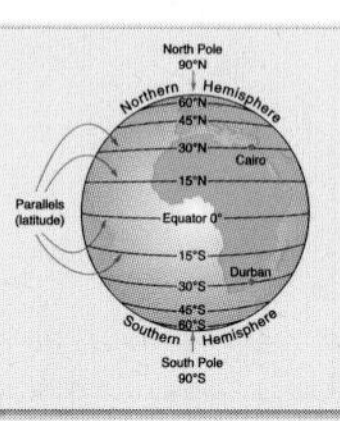

Longitude

A second set of lines runs from north to south. These are semicircles (half-circles) that connect the poles. They are called **lines of longitude** or **meridians.** The meridians are not parallel since they meet at the poles.

The **prime meridian** is the special meridian labeled 0°. The prime meridian passes through Greenwich, near London, England. Another special meridian falls on, or close to, the **International Date Line.** This meridian is labeled 180° and is exactly opposite the prime meridian, on the other side of the world.

Student Reference Book, **p. 272**

4. The **hemispheres:** Demonstrate how the equator and the prime meridian each partition Earth into half-spheres, or hemispheres.

   ▷ The Northern Hemisphere is the half-sphere north of the equator. The Southern Hemisphere is the half-sphere south of the equator.

   ▷ The Western Hemisphere is the half-sphere west of the prime meridian. The Eastern Hemisphere is the half-sphere east of the prime meridian.

5. The **latitude** and **longitude lines:** Point out the grid that circles the globe.

   ▷ The latitude lines are circles above and below the equator. Because these circles are parallel to the equator, they are often called **parallels.**

   ▷ The longitude lines are semicircles that connect the poles. The semicircles of longitude are not parallel, since they meet at the poles.

Be sure to emphasize that longitude is represented by semicircles and latitude by full circles.

Introducing the System for Locating Places on the Globe

Social Studies Link Emphasize that all latitude and longitude readings must have two parts: a *number of degrees* and a *direction* with reference to the equator or prime meridian. The only exceptions are 0° latitude and either 0° or 180° longitude; the direction is not included because it is not needed.

Point out that degrees are printed on, or near, the latitude and longitude lines on the globe. But the directions (N, S, E, and W) are not printed on the globe, and students must attach a direction to each latitude and longitude reading they make.

▷ Latitudes north of the equator (Northern Hemisphere) are labeled °N or °North.

▷ Latitudes south of the equator (Southern Hemisphere) are labeled °S or °South.

▷ Longitudes west of the prime meridian (Western Hemisphere) are labeled °W or °West.

▷ Longitudes east of the prime meridian (Eastern Hemisphere) are labeled °E or °East.

Then demonstrate how to locate a point on the globe in relation to the prime meridian and the equator. On the globe, the degrees east and west of the prime meridian are shown along the equator. Most globes have a **meridian bar** that shows degrees north and south of the equator.

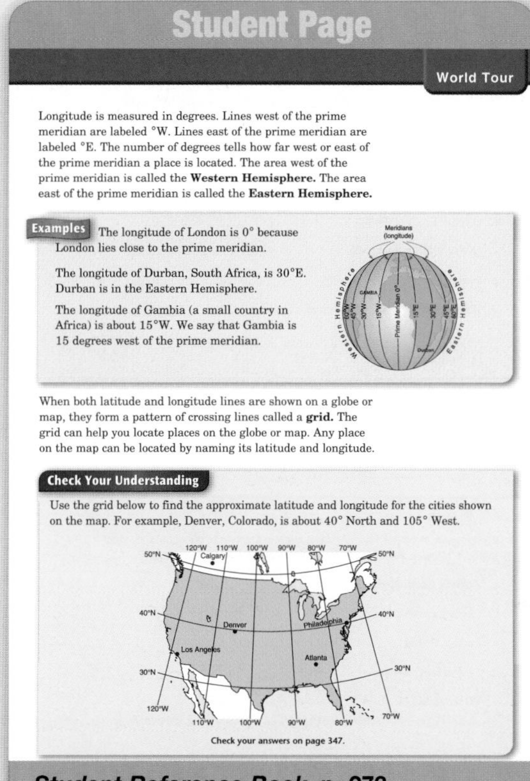

Student Page

World Tour

Longitude is measured in degrees. Lines west of the prime meridian are labeled °W. Lines east of the prime meridian are labeled °E. The number of degrees tells how far west or east of the prime meridian a place is located. The area west of the prime meridian is called the **Western Hemisphere.** The area east of the prime meridian is called the **Eastern Hemisphere.**

Examples The longitude of London is 0° because London lies close to the prime meridian.

The longitude of Durban, South Africa, is 30°E. Durban is in the Eastern Hemisphere.

The longitude of Gambia (a small country in Africa) is about 15°W. We say that Gambia is 15 degrees west of the prime meridian.

When both latitude and longitude lines are shown on a globe or map, they form a pattern of crossing lines called a **grid.** The grid can help you locate places on the globe or map. Any place on the map can be located by naming its latitude and longitude.

Check Your Understanding

Use the grid below to find the approximate latitude and longitude for the cities shown on the map. For example, Denver, Colorado, is about 40° North and 105° West.

Check your answers on page 347.

Student Reference Book, p. 273

Adjusting the Activity

Students and adults often confuse the words latitude (parallels) and longitude (meridians). Suggest and sketch visuals such as “latitudes are like rungs on a ladder to climb north or south of the equator,” and “longitude lines are long half-circle paths to the poles.”

AUDITORY ♦ KINESTHETIC ♦ TACTILE ♦ VISUAL

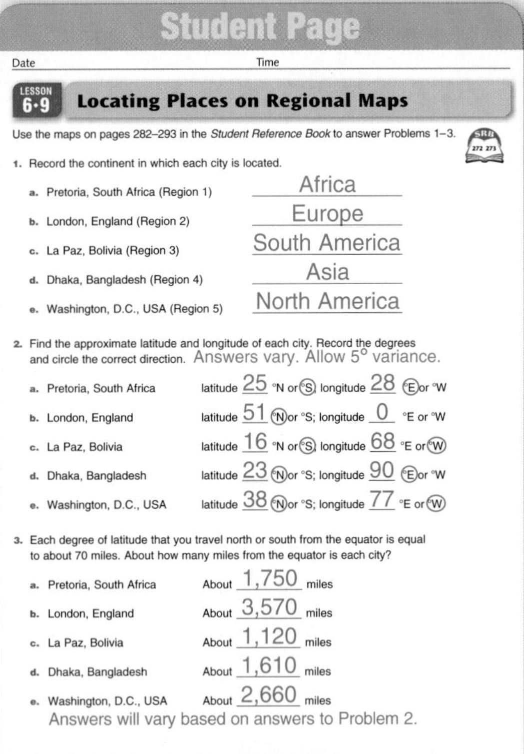

Student Page

Date Time

LESSON 6·9 **Locating Places on Regional Maps**

Use the maps on pages 282–293 in the *Student Reference Book* to answer Problems 1–3. SRB 272 273

1. Record the continent in which each city is located.
   a. Pretoria, South Africa (Region 1) Africa
   b. London, England (Region 2) Europe
   c. La Paz, Bolivia (Region 3) South America
   d. Dhaka, Bangladesh (Region 4) Asia
   e. Washington, D.C., USA (Region 5) North America

2. Find the approximate latitude and longitude of each city. Record the degrees and circle the correct direction. Answers vary. Allow 5° variance.
   a. Pretoria, South Africa latitude 25 °N or (°S); longitude 28 (°E) or °W
   b. London, England latitude 51 (°N) or °S; longitude 0 °E or °W
   c. La Paz, Bolivia latitude 16 °N or (°S); longitude 68 °E or (°W)
   d. Dhaka, Bangladesh latitude 23 (°N) or °S; longitude 90 (°E) or °W
   e. Washington, D.C., USA latitude 38 (°N) or °S; longitude 77 °E or (°W)

3. Each degree of latitude that you travel north or south from the equator is equal to about 70 miles. About how many miles from the equator is each city?
   a. Pretoria, South Africa About 1,750 miles
   b. London, England About 3,570 miles
   c. La Paz, Bolivia About 1,120 miles
   d. Dhaka, Bangladesh About 1,610 miles
   e. Washington, D.C., USA About 2,660 miles
   Answers will vary based on answers to Problem 2.

Math Journal 1, p. 164

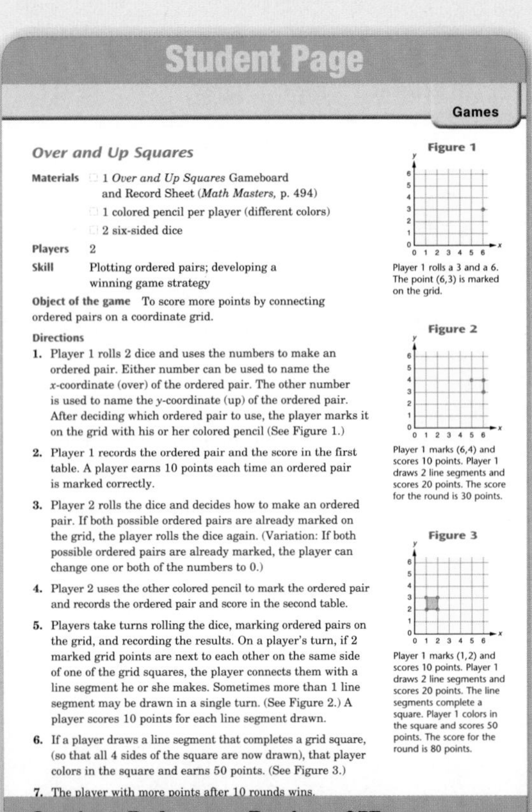

Student Page

Games

Over and Up Squares

Materials 1 *Over and Up Squares* Gameboard and Record Sheet (*Math Masters,* p. 494)
1 colored pencil per player (different colors)
2 six-sided dice

Players 2

Skill Plotting ordered pairs; developing a winning game strategy

Object of the game To score more points by connecting ordered pairs on a coordinate grid.

Directions

1. Player 1 rolls 2 dice and uses the numbers to make an ordered pair. Either number can be used to name the *x*-coordinate (over) of the ordered pair. The other number is used to name the *y*-coordinate (up) of the ordered pair. After deciding which ordered pair to use, the player marks it on the grid with his or her colored pencil (See Figure 1.)
2. Player 1 records the ordered pair and the score in the first table. A player earns 10 points each time an ordered pair is marked correctly.
3. Player 2 rolls the dice and decides how to make an ordered pair. If both possible ordered pairs are already marked on the grid, the player rolls the dice again. (Variation: If both possible ordered pairs are already marked, the player can change one or both of the numbers to 0.)
4. Player 2 uses the other colored pencil to mark the ordered pair and records the ordered pair and score in the second table.
5. Players take turns rolling the dice, marking ordered pairs on the grid, and recording the results. On a player's turn, if 2 marked grid points are next to each other on the same side of one of the grid squares, the player connects them with a line segment he or she makes. Sometimes more than 1 line segment may be drawn in a single turn. (See Figure 2.) A player scores 10 points for each line segment drawn.
6. If a player draws a line segment that completes a grid square, (so that all 4 sides of the square are now drawn), that player colors in the square and earns 50 points. (See Figure 3.)
7. The player with more points after 10 rounds wins.

Figure 1

Player 1 rolls a 3 and a 6. The point (6,3) is marked on the grid.

Figure 2

Player 1 marks (6,4) and scores 10 points. Player 1 draws 2 line segments and scores 20 points. The score for the round is 30 points.

Figure 3

Player 1 marks (1,2) and scores 10 points. Player 1 draws 2 line segments and scores 20 points. The line segments complete a square. Player 1 colors in the square and scores 50 points. The score for the round is 80 points.

Student Reference Book, p. 257

To make it easier to read latitude, you can rotate the globe so that the meridian bar is close to the place you want to locate.

Examples:

▷ Start at the point where the equator and prime meridian meet. Then move along the equator 45° West of the prime meridian. Next move 60° North along the 45° West semicircle. You should end up just off the southern tip of Greenland.

▷ Find the city of Durban in South Africa. It is near the 30° South parallel. Move up the longitude semicircle to the equator. This shows that Durban is about 30° East of the prime meridian. Thus, the location of Durban is about 30° South, 30° East.

▷ Find the place at 36° North and 140° East. Use the degree scale along the equator to find 140° East of the prime meridian Rotate the globe so that the meridian bar is next to 140° East. Use the meridian bar to find 36° North latitude. Tokyo, Japan, is adjacent to the meridian bar at this latitude. The location of Tokyo is about 36° North, 140° East.

NOTE The words *latitude* and *longitude* need not be used when naming locations. Also, the words North, South, East, and West can be abbreviated. Thus, the location of Durban, for example, can be written as about 30°S and 30°E. The north or south location is always named first, followed by the east or west location.

▶ Locating Places on a World Map

Have the class gather around a wall map of the world. Repeat the routine that you followed above using the globe.

Name several well-known places. Ask volunteers to identify these on the map and then find the latitude and longitude for each.

Specify several places by giving the latitude and longitude for each. Ask volunteers to locate and name each place.

▶ Locating Places on Regional Maps

(*Math Journal 1,* p. 164; *Student Reference Book,* pp. 282–293)

Have students use the continent maps on pages 282–293 in the *Student Reference Book* to locate cities and find the approximate latitude and longitude of each city. Find the answers for Pretoria in Problems 1–3 with the class. Then have partnerships complete the rest of the problems.

Most locations do not fall exactly on the lines of latitude and longitude. In such cases, students must estimate the degrees of latitude and longitude. Allow a 5-degree variance in their answers but expect that generally they should not be off by more than a degree or two.

Ongoing Assessment: Informing Instruction

Watch for students who have difficulty using the continent maps, because only a portion of the world is shown on each map. Remind them that the lines of latitude and longitude on the continent maps are labeled to show both a number of degrees and a direction (N, S, E, or W).

2 Ongoing Learning & Practice

Playing *Over and Up Squares*

PARTNER ACTIVITY

(*Student Reference Book,* p. 257; *Math Masters,* p. 494)

Students play *Over and Up Squares* to practice locating points and plotting points on a coordinate grid.

Adjusting the Activity

Use these game variations as appropriate:

▷ Have students play the game in teams to share strategies and skills or eliminate the line segment and square aspects of the game.

▷ Have students choose and name their own points, thus emphasizing the importance of strategy.

AUDITORY ◆ KINESTHETIC ◆ TACTILE ◆ VISUAL

Math Boxes 6◆9

INDEPENDENT ACTIVITY

(*Math Journal 1,* p. 165)

Mixed Practice Math Boxes in this lesson are paired with Math Boxes in Lesson 6-6. The skill in Problem 5 previews Unit 7 content.

Ongoing Assessment: Recognizing Student Achievement

Math Boxes Problem 2

Use **Math Boxes, Problem 2** to assess students' ability to solve multidigit multiplication number stories. Students are making adequate progress if they are able to perform the computation correctly. Some students may make a ballpark estimate or use the relationship between multiplication and division to check their answers. [Operations and Computation Goal 4]

Study Link 6◆9

INDEPENDENT ACTIVITY

(*Math Masters,* p. 195)

Home Connection Using a picture of the globe, students label important parts of the global grid system.

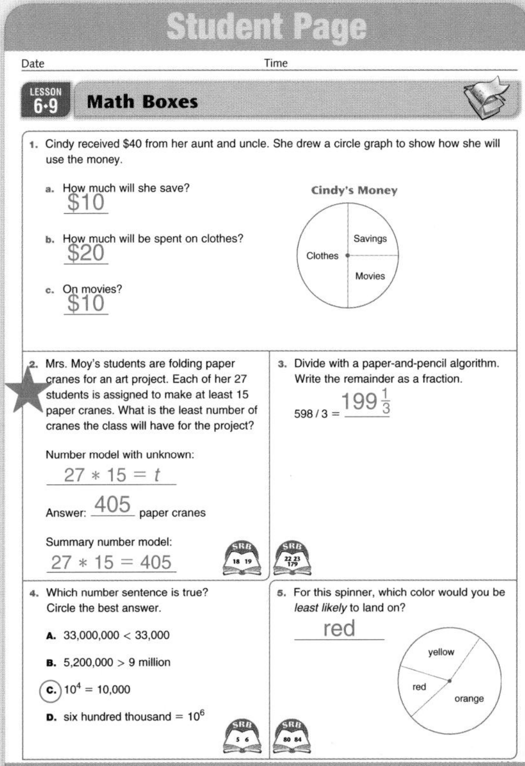

Student Page

Date Time

LESSON 6◆9 **Math Boxes**

1. Cindy received $40 from her aunt and uncle. She drew a circle graph to show how she will use the money.

a. How much will she save? $10

b. How much will be spent on clothes? $20

c. On movies? $10

2. Mrs. Moy's students are folding paper cranes for an art project. Each of her 27 students is assigned to make at least 15 paper cranes. What is the least number of cranes the class will have for the project?

Number model with unknown: $27 * 15 = t$

Answer: 405 paper cranes

Summary number model: $27 * 15 = 405$

3. Divide with a paper-and-pencil algorithm. Write the remainder as a fraction.

$598 / 3 = 199\frac{1}{3}$

4. Which number sentence is true? Circle the best answer.

A. 33,000,000 < 33,000

B. 5,200,000 > 9 million

C. $10^4 = 10{,}000$

D. six hundred thousand = 10^6

5. For this spinner, which color would you be *least likely* to land on? red

Math Journal 1, p. 165

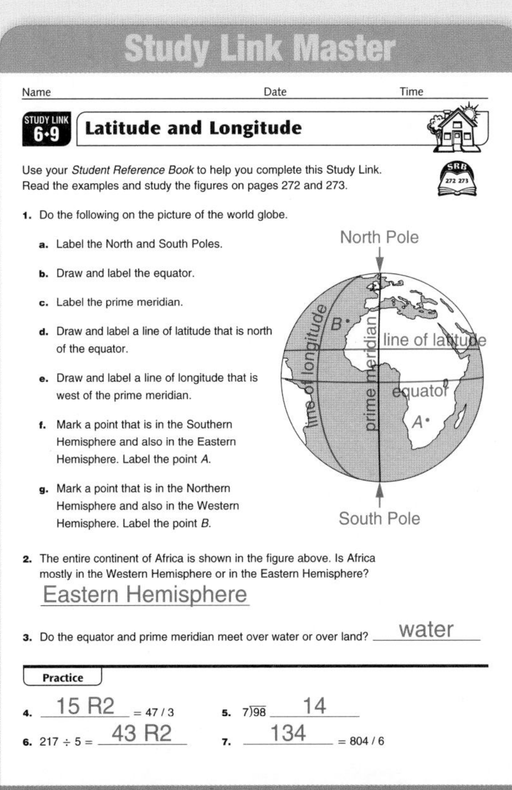

Study Link Master

Name Date Time

STUDY LINK 6◆9 **Latitude and Longitude**

Use your *Student Reference Book* to help you complete this Study Link. Read the examples and study the figures on pages 272 and 273.

1. Do the following on the picture of the world globe.

a. Label the North and South Poles.

b. Draw and label the equator.

c. Label the prime meridian.

d. Draw and label a line of latitude that is north of the equator.

e. Draw and label a line of longitude that is west of the prime meridian.

f. Mark a point that is in the Southern Hemisphere and also in the Eastern Hemisphere. Label the point *A.*

g. Mark a point that is in the Northern Hemisphere and also in the Western Hemisphere. Label the point *B.*

2. The entire continent of Africa is shown in the figure above. Is Africa mostly in the Western Hemisphere or in the Eastern Hemisphere? Eastern Hemisphere

3. Do the equator and prime meridian meet over water or over land? water

Practice

4. 15 R2 = 47 / 3

5. 7)98 14

6. 217 ÷ 5 = 43 R2

7. 134 = 804 / 6

Math Masters, p. 195

3 Differentiation Options

ENRICHMENT

▶ Using Time to Determine Longitude

30+ Min

(*Math Masters,* p. 388 or 389)

Literature Link To apply students' understanding of longitude, have them read ***Sea Clocks: The Story of Longitude*** by Louise Bordon (Margaret K. McElderry Books, 2004). The book tells how John Harrison created the first accurate sea clock, allowing sailors to know more accurately their location at sea by giving them the correct home port time.

Have students explain, in a Math Log or on an Exit Slip, why knowing the correct home port and sea time helped sailors determine longitude at sea. Each hour is marked by exactly 15 degrees of longitude. If it is noon on a ship sailing west and 3 P.M. at the home port, the ship is 45° west of home port. If a clock on a ship sailing east reads 3 P.M. and the home port time is noon, the ship is 45° east of home port.

EXTRA PRACTICE

▶ Locating Places with Latitude and Longitude

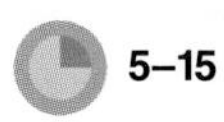
5–15 Min

(*Math Masters,* p. 196)

To practice locating places using latitude and longitude, have small groups use a world political map, a penny, and the Latitude and Longitude Cards cut from *Math Masters,* page 196.

1. Have students shuffle the Latitude and Longitude Cards separately and put them facedown in two piles.
2. Team 1 draws a Latitude Degree Card and then flips a penny to find whether it is north (heads) or south (tails). The latitude and direction are recorded, and the card is returned facedown to the bottom of the pile.
3. Team 1 now draws a Longitude Card and flips the penny to find whether it is east (heads) or west (tails). The longitude and direction are recorded, and the card is returned to the bottom of the pile.
4. The team uses the information to locate and record the country or body of water indicated by the coordinates.
5. Teams take turns until each team has located 10 places. The team with the most land locations is the winner.

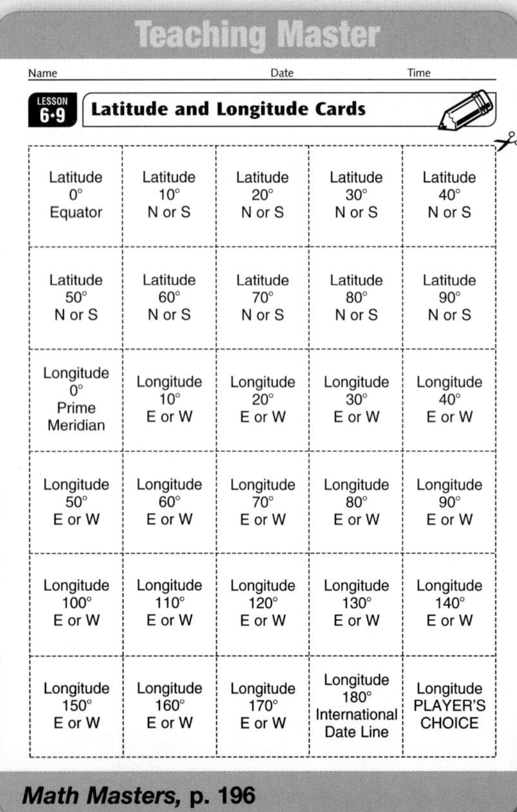

Teaching Master

Name Date Time

LESSON 6·9 Latitude and Longitude Cards

Latitude 0° Equator	Latitude 10° N or S	Latitude 20° N or S	Latitude 30° N or S	Latitude 40° N or S
Latitude 50° N or S	Latitude 60° N or S	Latitude 70° N or S	Latitude 80° N or S	Latitude 90° N or S
Longitude 0° Prime Meridian	Longitude 10° E or W	Longitude 20° E or W	Longitude 30° E or W	Longitude 40° E or W
Longitude 50° E or W	Longitude 60° E or W	Longitude 70° E or W	Longitude 80° E or W	Longitude 90° E or W
Longitude 100° E or W	Longitude 110° E or W	Longitude 120° E or W	Longitude 130° E or W	Longitude 140° E or W
Longitude 150° E or W	Longitude 160° E or W	Longitude 170° E or W	Longitude 180° International Date Line	Longitude PLAYER'S CHOICE

Math Masters, p. 196

6•10 The Partial-Quotients Division Algorithm, Part 2

Objective To provide practice with a "low-stress" division algorithm for 2-digit divisors.

Technology Resources www.everydaymathonline.com

Presentations

eToolkit

Algorithms Practice

EM Facts Workshop Game™

Family Letters

Assessment Management

Common Core State Standards

Curriculum Focal Points

Interactive Teacher's Lesson Guide

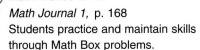

1 Teaching the Lesson

Key Concepts and Skills

- Identify and use multiples of 10.
  [Number and Numeration Goal 3]
- Add multiples of 10.
  [Operations and Computation Goal 1]
- Subtract multidigit numbers.
  [Operations and Computation Goal 2]
- Apply extended multiplication facts to long-division situations.
  [Operations and Computation Goal 3]
- Solve equal-grouping division number stories and problems.
  [Operations and Computation Goal 4]

Key Activities

Students review and practice a paper-and-pencil algorithm for division that permits them to build up the quotient by working with "easy" numbers. Students focus on problems with 2-digit divisors.

Ongoing Assessment: Recognizing Student Achievement
Use journal page 166.
[Operations and Computation Goal 4]

Materials

Math Journal 1, pp. 166 and 167
Study Link 6•9
Math Masters, p. 436 (optional); p. 438
base-10 blocks (optional) ◆ slate

2 Ongoing Learning & Practice

Math Boxes 6•10
Math Journal 1, p. 168
Students practice and maintain skills through Math Box problems.

Study Link 6•10
Math Masters, p. 197
Students practice and maintain skills through Study Link activities.

3 Differentiation Options

READINESS

Playing *Division Dash*
Student Reference Book, p. 241
Math Masters, p. 471
per partnership: 4 each of number cards 1–9 (from the Everything Math Deck, if available)
Students practice dividing 2- or 3-digit dividends by 1-digit divisors.

ENRICHMENT

Performing a "Magic Trick"
Math Masters, p. 198
Students perform and explain a division "magic trick."

EXTRA PRACTICE

Taking a 50-Facts Test
Math Masters, pp. 413 and 414;
p. 416 (optional)
pen or colored pencil
Students take a 50-facts test. They use a line graph to record individual and optional class scores.

Advance Preparation

***Teacher's Reference Manual,* Grades 4–6** pp. 132–140

Getting Started

Mental Math and Reflexes

Pose multiplication facts and extended facts.
Suggestions:

●○○	●●○	●●●
3 ∗ 3 = 9	4 ∗ 9 = 36	90 ∗ 8 = 720
4 ∗ 2 = 8	7 ∗ 7 = 49	8 ∗ 80 = 640
5 ∗ 5 = 25	8 ∗ 3 = 24	60 ∗ 70 = 4,200
10 ∗ 9 = 90	6 ∗ 4 = 24	30 ∗ 90 = 2,700

Math Message

Egg cartons hold 12 eggs. How many cartons do you need to pack 246 eggs?

Study Link 6·9 Follow-Up

Have students check their partner's globe labels and markings.

Algorithm Project The focus of this lesson is partial quotients. To teach U.S. traditional long division, see Algorithm Project 7 on page A31.

Links to the Future

Fluently dividing whole numbers using the standard algorithm is expected in Grade 6.

1 Teaching the Lesson

▶ Math Message Follow-Up

Remind students that by packing 246 eggs into cartons, they are dividing 246 eggs into groups of 12. The problem is a division problem: How many [12s] are in 246?

Write the problem on the board in four of the ways that division problems can be written:

$246 \div 12$ $\quad$ $246 / 12$

$12\overline{)246}$ $\quad$ $\frac{246}{12}$

Ask several students to give their solutions and describe their strategies:

▷ Use a Multiplication/Division Diagram (*Math Masters,* page 436). Some students may think "What number times 12 equals 246?" while others may reason "246 divided by 12 equals what number?"

cartons	eggs per carton	total eggs
c	12	246

▷ Take 2 flats, 4 longs, and 6 cubes. Trade the flats for longs. Divide the longs and cubes into as many groups of 12 cubes as possible. Continue to exchange longs for cubes as necessary. 20 groups, 6 left over

▷ Draw a picture.

12 12 12 12 12 ○ ○
12 12 12 12 12 ○ ○
12 12 12 12 12 ○ ○
12 12 12 12 12

▷ Break 246 into smaller "friendly numbers" such as the following:

- 120 + 120 + 6 = 246. There are 10 [12s] in 120 and 10 [12s] in 120. 10 + 10 = 20, so there are 20 [12s] in 246 with 6 left over.
- 240 + 6 = 246. There are 20 [12s] in 246 with 6 left over.

You need 20 full cartons, plus one other carton to hold the 6 eggs that are left over. So, 21 cartons are needed.

Some students may have used the partial-quotients division algorithm to solve the Math Message problem. Ask a volunteer to explain how the algorithm was used.

Introducing the Partial-Quotients Algorithm with 2-Digit Divisors

WHOLE-CLASS ACTIVITY

(*Math Masters,* p. 438)

Explain that most of the division problems in Unit 6 have involved a 1-digit divisor. In this lesson students will use the partial-quotients division algorithm to solve problems and number stories, like the Math Message, that involve 2-digit divisors.

The algorithm works the same whether you divide by a 2-digit or a 1-digit divisor. As it often helps to write down some easy facts for the divisor first, have copies of *Math Masters,* page 438 readily available. Remind students to use the relationship between multiplication and division to check their answers.

Example 1:

Teddy received a carton of 400 baseball cards from his grandmother. He decided to share them with his classmates. How many cards did Teddy and each of his 21 classmates get?

One way:

22)400	
−220	10
180	
−110	5
70	
−22	1
48	
−22	1
26	
−22	1
4	18

Another way:

22)400	
−220	10
180	
−110	5
70	
−66	3
4	18

Still another way:

22)400	
−220	10
180	
−176	8
4	18

The answer, 18 R4, is the same for each method. Teddy and his classmates each received 18 baseball cards. There were 4 left over.

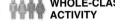

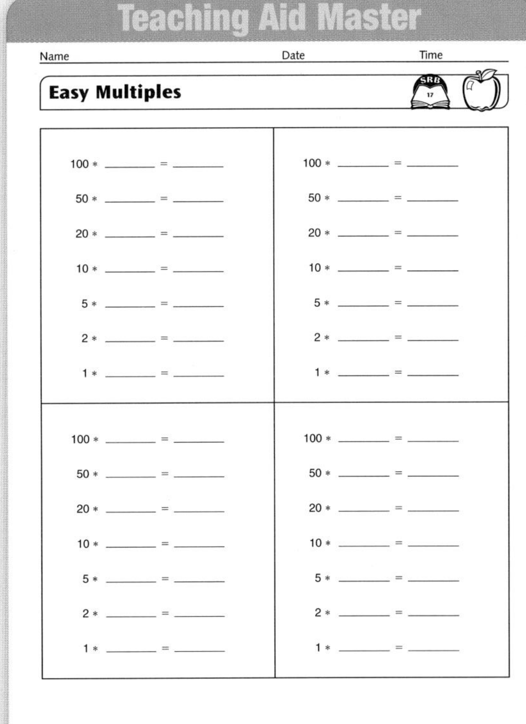

Teaching Aid Master

Name ______ Date ______ Time ______

Easy Multiples

100 * ____ = ____	100 * ____ = ____
50 * ____ = ____	50 * ____ = ____
20 * ____ = ____	20 * ____ = ____
10 * ____ = ____	10 * ____ = ____
5 * ____ = ____	5 * ____ = ____
2 * ____ = ____	2 * ____ = ____
1 * ____ = ____	1 * ____ = ____
100 * ____ = ____	100 * ____ = ____
50 * ____ = ____	50 * ____ = ____
20 * ____ = ____	20 * ____ = ____
10 * ____ = ____	10 * ____ = ____
5 * ____ = ____	5 * ____ = ____
2 * ____ = ____	2 * ____ = ____
1 * ____ = ____	1 * ____ = ____

Math Masters, **p. 438**

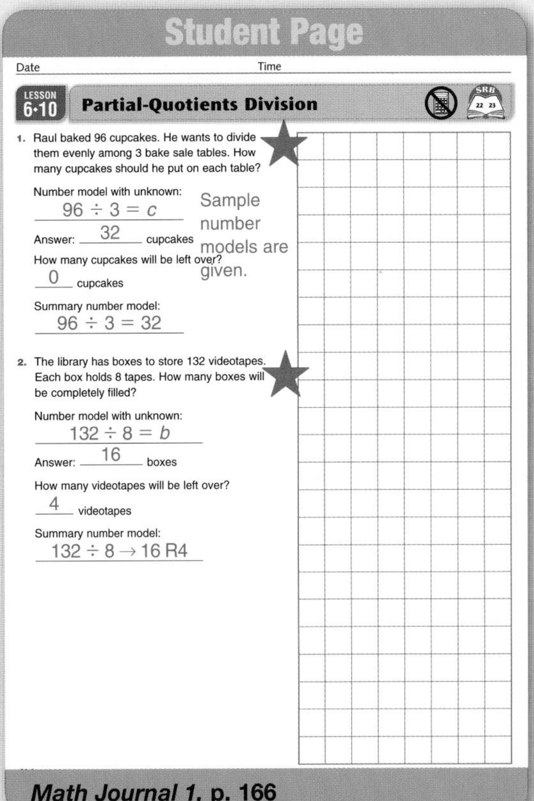

Student Page

Date ______ Time ______

LESSON 6·10 **Partial-Quotients Division**

1. Raul baked 96 cupcakes. He wants to divide them evenly among 3 bake sale tables. How many cupcakes should he put on each table?

Number model with unknown: 96 ÷ 3 = *c*

Answer: 32 cupcakes

How many cupcakes will be left over? 0 cupcakes

Summary number model: 96 ÷ 3 = 32

Sample number models are given.

2. The library has boxes to store 132 videotapes. Each box holds 8 tapes. How many boxes will be completely filled?

Number model with unknown: 132 ÷ 8 = *b*

Answer: 16 boxes

How many videotapes will be left over? 4 videotapes

Summary number model: 132 ÷ 8 → 16 R4

Math Journal 1, **p. 166**

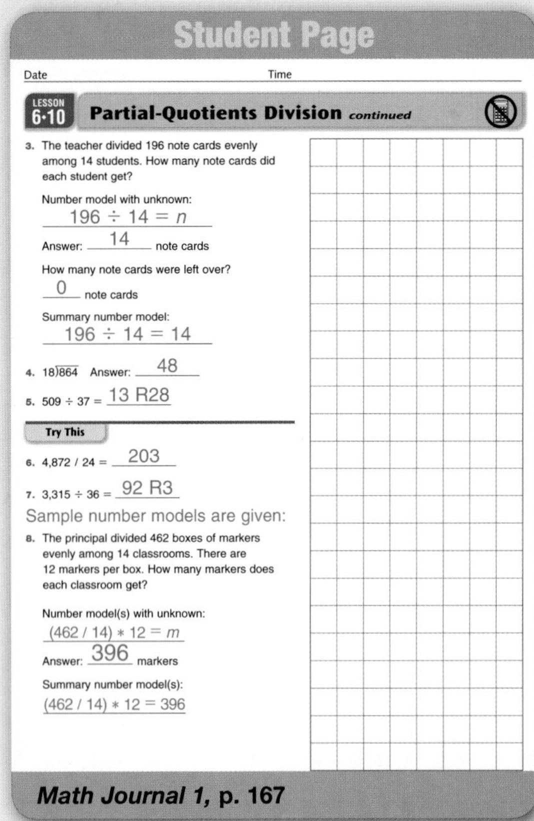

Student Page

Date Time

LESSON 6·10 **Partial-Quotients Division** *continued*

3. The teacher divided 196 note cards evenly among 14 students. How many note cards did each student get?

Number model with unknown: $196 \div 14 = n$

Answer: 14 note cards

How many note cards were left over?

0 note cards

Summary number model: $196 \div 14 = 14$

4. 18)864 Answer: 48

5. 509 ÷ 37 = 13 R28

Try This

6. 4,872 / 24 = 203

7. 3,315 ÷ 36 = 92 R3

Sample number models are given:

8. The principal divided 462 boxes of markers evenly among 14 classrooms. There are 12 markers per box. How many markers does each classroom get?

Number model(s) with unknown: $(462 / 14) * 12 = m$

Answer: 396 markers

Summary number model(s): $(462 / 14) * 12 = 396$

Math Journal 1, p. 167

Student Page

Date Time

LESSON 6·10 **Math Boxes**

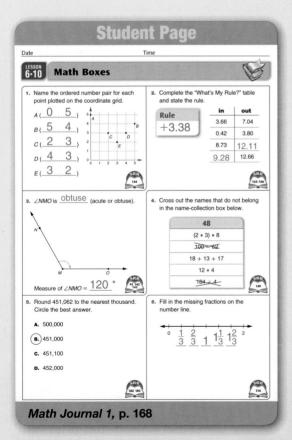

1. Name the ordered number pair for each point plotted on the coordinate grid.

A (0, 5)
B (5, 4)
C (2, 3)
D (4, 3)
E (3, 2)

2. Complete the "What's My Rule?" table and state the rule.

Rule: +3.38

in	out
3.66	7.04
0.42	3.80
8.73	12.11
9.28	12.66

3. ∠NMO is obtuse (acute or obtuse).

Measure of ∠NMO = 120°

4. Cross out the names that do not belong in the name-collection box below.

48
(2 * 3) * 8
~~100 − 62~~
18 + 13 + 17
12 * 4
~~184 ÷ 4~~

5. Round 451,062 to the nearest thousand. Circle the best answer.

A. 500,000
(B.) 451,000
C. 451,100
D. 452,000

6. Fill in the missing fractions on the number line.

0, $\frac{1}{3}$, $\frac{2}{3}$, 1, $1\frac{1}{3}$, $1\frac{2}{3}$, 2

Math Journal 1, p. 168

Example 2:

Sofia was playing with a set of 743 blocks. She decided to arrange them in stacks of 12. How many stacks did Sofia make?

One way:

12)743	
−600	50
143	
−60	5
83	
−60	5
23	
−12	1
11	61

Another way:

12)743	
−600	50
143	
−120	10
23	
−12	1
11	61

Still another way:

12)743	
−600	50
143	
−132	11
11	61

The answer, 61 R11, is the same for each method. Sofia made 61 stacks of 12 blocks. There were 11 blocks left over.

▶ Using the Partial-Quotients Algorithm with 2-Digit Divisors

PARTNER ACTIVITY

COMPUTATION PRACTICE

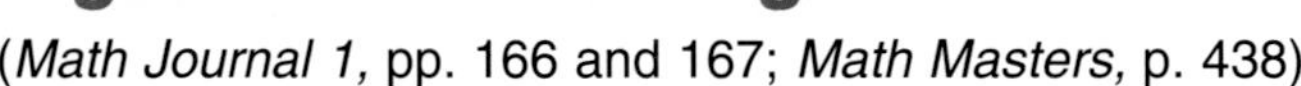

(*Math Journal 1*, pp. 166 and 167; *Math Masters*, p. 438)

Students use the partial-quotients algorithm to solve division problems and number stories on journal pages 166 and 167.

Ongoing Assessment: Recognizing Student Achievement

Journal page 166 Problems 1 and 2

Use **journal page 166, Problems 1 and 2** to assess students' ability to solve problems involving the division of multidigit whole numbers by 1-digit divisors. Students are making adequate progress if they are able to calculate the quotients in Problems 1 and 2 and express the remainder in Problem 2 correctly. Some students may be able to solve Problems 3–8, which involve 2-digit divisors.

[Operations and Computation Goal 4]

2 Ongoing Learning & Practice

▶ Math Boxes 6·10

INDEPENDENT ACTIVITY

(*Math Journal 1*, p. 168)

Mixed Practice Math Boxes in this lesson are paired with Math Boxes in Lesson 6-8. The skill in Problem 6 previews Unit 7 content.

Writing/Reasoning Have students write a response to the following: *True or false? (5,0) and (0,5) are both ordered number pairs that can be used to describe the location of point* A *in Problem 1. Explain your answer.* False. The first number in an ordered number pair tells how far to go to the right, and the second number tells how far to go up. Only (0, 5) tells the location of point *A*.

Study Link 6•10

COMPUTATION PRACTICE — INDEPENDENT ACTIVITY

(*Math Masters,* p. 197)

Home Connection Students practice using the partial-quotients division algorithm for 2-digit divisors. For some problems, they may use a division method of their choice.

3 Differentiation Options

READINESS

COMPUTATION PRACTICE — PARTNER ACTIVITY

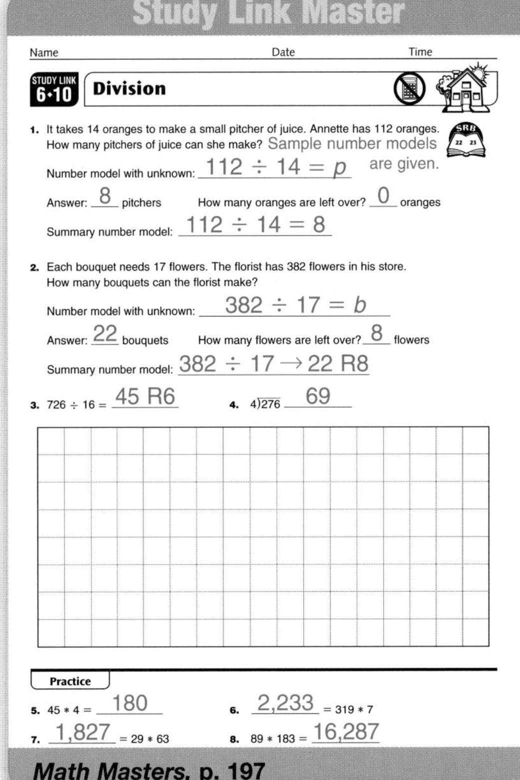

Playing *Division Dash*

15–30 Min

(*Student Reference Book,* p. 241, *Math Masters,* p. 471)

To provide experience with 2- or 3-digit dividends and 1-digit divisors in division problems, have students play *Division Dash.*

ENRICHMENT

INDEPENDENT ACTIVITY

Performing a "Magic Trick"

15–30 Min

(*Math Masters,* p. 198)

To further explore the concept of division, have students use a calculator to perform a division "magic trick."

EXTRA PRACTICE

FACTS PRACTICE — SMALL-GROUP ACTIVITY

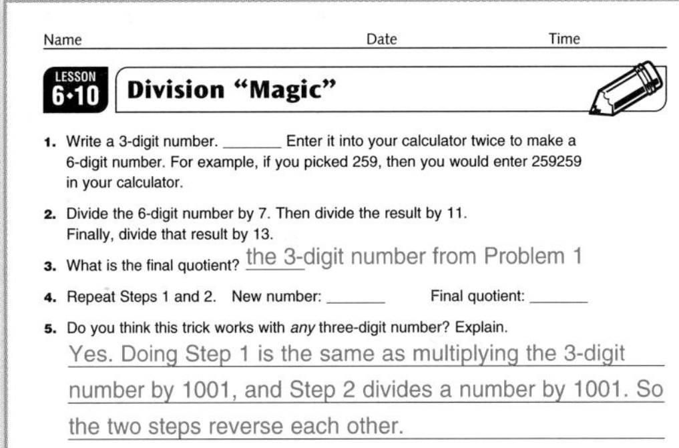

Taking a 50-Facts Test

5–15 Min

(*Math Masters,* pp. 413, 414, and 416)

See Lesson 3-4 for details regarding the administration of the 50-facts test and the recording and graphing of individual and optional class results.

Study Link Master

Name Date Time

STUDY LINK 6•10 **Division**

1. It takes 14 oranges to make a small pitcher of juice. Annette has 112 oranges. How many pitchers of juice can she make? Sample number models are given.

Number model with unknown: $112 \div 14 = p$

Answer: 8 pitchers How many oranges are left over? 0 oranges

Summary number model: $112 \div 14 = 8$

2. Each bouquet needs 17 flowers. The florist has 382 flowers in his store. How many bouquets can the florist make?

Number model with unknown: $382 \div 17 = b$

Answer: 22 bouquets How many flowers are left over? 8 flowers

Summary number model: $382 \div 17 \rightarrow 22$ R8

3. $726 \div 16 =$ 45 R6

4. $4\overline{)276}$ 69

Practice

5. $45 * 4 =$ 180

6. 2,233 $= 319 * 7$

7. 1,827 $= 29 * 63$

8. $89 * 183 =$ 16,287

Math Masters, p. 197

Name Date Time

LESSON 6•10 **Division "Magic"**

1. Write a 3-digit number. ______ Enter it into your calculator twice to make a 6-digit number. For example, if you picked 259, then you would enter 259259 in your calculator.
2. Divide the 6-digit number by 7. Then divide the result by 11. Finally, divide that result by 13.
3. What is the final quotient? the 3-digit number from Problem 1
4. Repeat Steps 1 and 2. New number: ______ Final quotient: ______
5. Do you think this trick works with *any* three-digit number? Explain.
Yes. Doing Step 1 is the same as multiplying the 3-digit number by 1001, and Step 2 divides a number by 1001. So the two steps reverse each other.

Math Masters, page 198

6•11 Progress Check 6

Objective To assess students' progress on mathematical content through the end of Unit 6.

1 Looking Back: Cumulative Assessment

The **Mid-Year Assessment** in the *Assessment Handbook* is a written assessment that you may use to determine how students are progressing toward a range of Grade-Level Goals.

Input student data from Progress Check 6 and the Mid-Year Assessment into the **Assessment Management Spreadsheets**.

Materials

- *Student Reference Book,* pp. 284 and 285
- Study Link 6•10
- *Assessment Handbook,* pp. 92–99, 179–183, 221, and 266–269
- Mid-Year Assessment (*Assessment Handbook,* pp. 100, 101, 228–233, 242, and 243)
- slate; straightedge; half-circle protractor; full-circle protractor

CONTENT ASSESSED	LESSON(S)	ASSESSMENT ITEMS				
		SELF	ORAL/SLATE	WRITTEN		OPEN RESPONSE
				PART A	PART B	
Solve multiplication and division number stories and problems. [Operations and Computation Goal 4]	6•1–6•7, 6•9, 6•10	1, 2		1–5	14, 15	✓
Interpret a remainder in the context of a division problem. [Operations and Computation Goal 4]	6•1–6•4, 6•6, 6•9, 6•10		2	1–3	14	
Make reasonable estimates for whole-number multiplication and division problems and explain how the estimates were obtained. [Operations and Computation Goal 6]	6•2, 6•3, 6•10					✓
Round numbers to a given place. [Operations and Computation Goal 6]	6•1, 6•3, 6•8, 6•10	3		10		
Draw and measure angles with a full-circle or half-circle protractor. [Measurement and Reference Frames Goal 1]	6•5–6•8, 6•10	4, 5		6, 7	11–13	
Use ordered number pairs to locate points on a map. [Measurement and Reference Frames Goal 4]	6•8–6•10	6	4	8		
Classify angles according to their measure. [Geometry Goal 1]	6•5–6•8, 6•10		3	6, 7		
Insert parentheses to make true number sentences. [Patterns, Functions, and Algebra Goal 3]	6•1, 6•2, 6•4, 6•5, 6•7		1	9		

2 Looking Ahead: Preparing for Unit 7

Math Boxes 6•11

Study Link 6•11: Unit 7 Family Letter

Materials

- *Math Journal 1,* p. 169
- *Math Masters,* pp. 199–202

Getting Started

Math Message • Self Assessment

*Complete the Self Assessment (*Assessment Handbook*, page 179).*

Study Link 6·10 Follow-Up

Partners compare answers. Ask volunteers to share different ways to solve the problems.

1 Looking Back: Cumulative Assessment

Math Message Follow-Up

INDEPENDENT ACTIVITY

(Self Assessment, *Assessment Handbook,* p. 179)

The Self Assessment offers students the opportunity to reflect upon their progress.

Oral and Slate Assessments

WHOLE-CLASS ACTIVITY

Problems 1 and 2 provide summative information and can be used for grading purposes. Problems 3 and 4 provide formative information that can be useful in planning future instruction.

Oral Assessment

1. Pose the following problem. Ask students to explain and show how parentheses can be used when writing a number model for this problem.

   When it snows, DeShawn charges \$2 for every sidewalk he shovels and \$3 for every driveway he shovels. If he shovels 6 sidewalks and 3 driveways, how much does he earn? \$21; $(2 * 6) + (3 * 3) = 21$

2. Pose the following problem. Ask students to solve the problem and explain what they did with the remainder.

   Chin and his 3 friends went to the video store. They rented several movies and bought snacks. The total cost was \$21.00. The friends split the bill evenly. How much did each person pay? \$5.25; 21 / 4 → 5 R1 The remainder of 1 represents \$1.00. \$1.00 divided among 4 people is \$0.25.

Slate Assessment

3. Students draw examples of the following types of angles on their slates: acute, obtuse, straight, and reflex.

4. Specify locations in Region 2 by giving the latitude and longitude. Students use *Student Reference Book,* pages 284 and 285 to name the country that is found at each location.

   - 40°N, 5°W Spain
   - 68°N, 15°W Iceland
   - 50°N, 10°E Germany
   - 60°N, 15°E Sweden

Assessment Master

Name Date Time

LESSON 6·11 **Self Assessment** Progress Check 6

Think about each skill listed below. Assess your own progress by checking the most appropriate box.

Skills	I can do this on my own and explain how to do it.	I can do this on my own.	I can do this if I get help or look at an example.
1. Divide numbers like these: 322 ÷ 4, 457 ÷ 3			
2. Divide numbers like these: 181 ÷ 66, 719 ÷ 12			
3. Round numbers to the nearest ten thousand.			
4. Measure angles like these: 25°, 60°, 155°			
5. Draw angles like these: 30°, 95°, 160°			
6. Plot ordered number pairs on a coordinate grid.			

Assessment Handbook, p. 179

Assessment Master

Name Date Time

LESSON 6·11 **Written Assessment** Progress Check 6

Part A Sample number models are given.

1. There are 38 cookies in a box. Tina and her two sisters decide to share them equally. How many whole cookies will each girl get?

   Number model with unknown: $38 \div 3 = c$

   Answer: 12 cookies

   Summary number model: 38 / 3 → 12 R2

2. Grace baked 76 muffins for a class breakfast. She put the muffins on plates. Each plate holds 8 muffins. How many plates were needed to hold all of the muffins?

   Number model with unknown: $76 \div 8 = p$

   Answer: 10 plates

   Summary number model: 76 / 8 → 9 R4

Divide. If there is a remainder, write it as a fraction.

3. 5)84 Answer: $16\frac{4}{5}$
4. 168 ÷ 8 Answer: 21

5. Mrs. Green wants to buy a washing machine and pay for it in 1 year. L-Mart offers two plans, and she wants to choose the cheaper one.

   Plan A: \$7 each week; a total of 52 payments.
   Plan B: \$27 each month; a total of 12 payments.

   Which plan would cost less? Plan B

   Explain your answer.

   Sample answer: Plan A would cost \$7 ∗ 52 = \$364, but Plan B would only cost \$27 ∗ 12 = \$324.

Assessment Handbook, p. 180

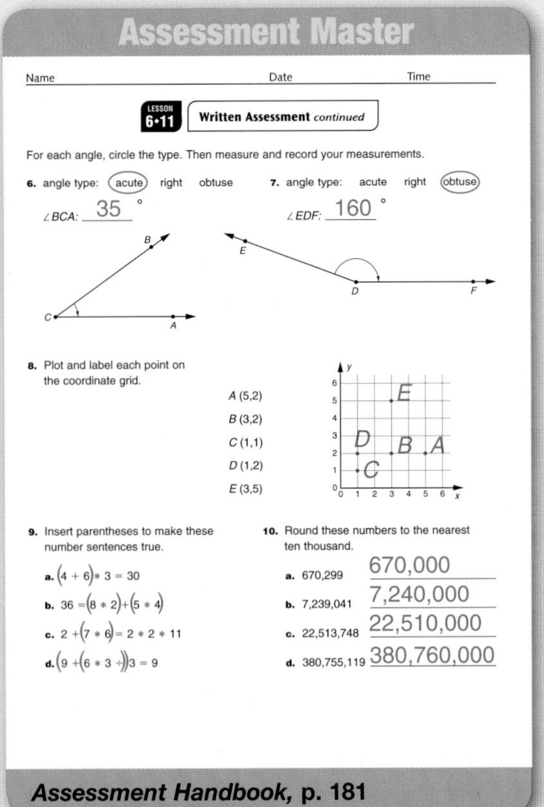

Assessment Master

Name _______ Date _______ Time _______

LESSON 6•11 **Written Assessment** *continued*

For each angle, circle the type. Then measure and record your measurements.

6. angle type: (acute) right obtuse
∠BCA: 35 °

7. angle type: acute right (obtuse)
∠EDF: 160 °

8. Plot and label each point on the coordinate grid.
A (5,2)
B (3,2)
C (1,1)
D (1,2)
E (3,5)

9. Insert parentheses to make these number sentences true.
a. (4 + 6) ∗ 3 = 30
b. 36 = (8 ∗ 2) + (5 ∗ 4)
c. 2 + (7 ∗ 6) = 2 ∗ 2 ∗ 11
d. (9 + (6 ∗ 3 ÷)) 3 = 9

10. Round these numbers to the nearest ten thousand.
a. 670,299 670,000
b. 7,239,041 7,240,000
c. 22,513,748 22,510,000
d. 380,755,119 380,760,000

Assessment Handbook, p. 181

Use the checklists on pages 267 and 269 of the *Assessment Handbook* to record results. Then input the data into the **Assessment Management Spreadsheets** to keep an ongoing record of students' progress toward Grade-Level Goals.

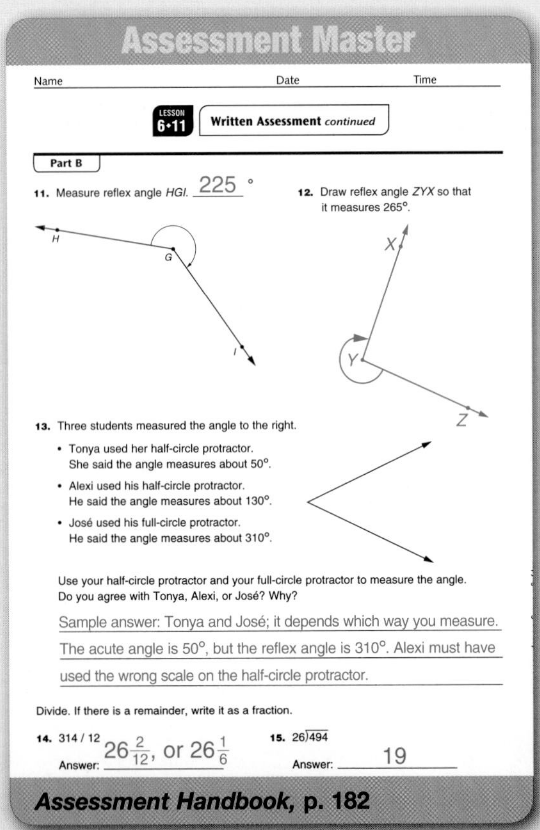

Assessment Master

Name _______ Date _______ Time _______

LESSON 6•11 **Written Assessment** *continued*

Part B

11. Measure reflex angle *HGI*. 225 °

12. Draw reflex angle *ZYX* so that it measures 265°.

13. Three students measured the angle to the right.
- Tonya used her half-circle protractor. She said the angle measures about 50°.
- Alexi used his half-circle protractor. He said the angle measures about 130°.
- José used his full-circle protractor. He said the angle measures about 310°.

Use your half-circle protractor and your full-circle protractor to measure the angle. Do you agree with Tonya, Alexi, or José? Why?

Sample answer: Tonya and José; it depends which way you measure. The acute angle is 50°, but the reflex angle is 310°. Alexi must have used the wrong scale on the half-circle protractor.

Divide. If there is a remainder, write it as a fraction.

14. 314 / 12
Answer: $26\frac{2}{12}$, or $26\frac{1}{6}$

15. 26)494
Answer: 19

Assessment Handbook, p. 182

Written Assessment

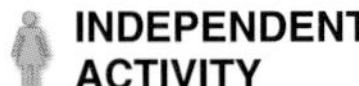

(*Assessment Handbook,* pp. 180–182)

Part A Recognizing Student Achievement

Problems 1–10 provide summative information and may be used for grading purposes.

Problem(s)	Description
1, 2	Solve division number stories; interpret remainders.
3, 4	Divide multidigit numbers by 1-digit divisors; express remainders as fractions.
5	Multiply multidigit numbers and compare them.
6, 7	Classify and measure angles.
8	Plot points on a coordinate grid.
9	Insert parentheses.
10	Round numbers.

Part B Informing Instruction

Problems 11–15 provide formative information that can be useful in planning future instruction.

Problem(s)	Description
11–13	Draw and measure angles.
14, 15	Divide multidigit numbers by 2-digit divisors; express remainders as fractions.

Open Response

(*Assessment Handbook,* p. 183)

A Trip to Adventure Land

The open-response item requires students to apply concepts and skills from Unit 6 to solve a multistep problem. See *Assessment Handbook,* pages 95–99 for rubrics and students' work samples for this problem.

Mid-Year Assessment

(*Assessment Handbook,* pp. 228–233)

The Mid-Year Assessment (*Assessment Handbook,* pages 228–233) provides an additional assessment opportunity that you may use as part of your balanced assessment plan. This assessment covers some of the important concepts and skills presented in *Fourth Grade Everyday Mathematics.* It should be used to complement the ongoing and periodic assessments that appear within lessons and at the end of the units. Please see pages 100 and 101 in the *Assessment Handbook* for further information.

2 Looking Ahead: Preparing for Unit 7

Math Boxes 6•11

INDEPENDENT ACTIVITY

(*Math Journal 1,* p. 169)

Mixed Practice This Math Boxes previews Unit 7 content.

Study Link 6•11: Unit 7 Family Letter

(*Math Masters,* pp. 199–202)

Home Connection The Unit 7 Family Letter provides parents and guardians with information and activities related to Unit 7 topics.

Assessment Master

Name Date Time

LESSON 6•11 **Open Response** Progress Check 6

A Trip to Adventure Land

The students in Ms. Brown's and Mr. Ron's classes at Ridge Elementary School are going on a field trip to Adventure Land. There are 28 students in each class.

Mr. Ron's class secretary has the following information about admission prices:

Adventure Land
Special Group Rates:
One Class—$60.00
Adults (1 for every 10 students)—Free

It costs $80.00 to rent a bus for a day. One bus can hold 66 people.

Calculate the amount of money each student needs to pay for the trip. Explain your strategy below.

See the *Assessment Handbook* for rubrics and students' work samples.

***Assessment Handbook,* p. 183**

Planning Ahead Before students move from *Math Journal 1* to *Math Journal 2,* have them copy the line segments they drew on the Route Map in *Math Journal 1,* pages 172 and 173 onto the Route Map in *Math Journal 2,* pages 330 and 331. This will show their trip route to date. Then they complete the World Tour using the Route Map in *Math Journal 2.*

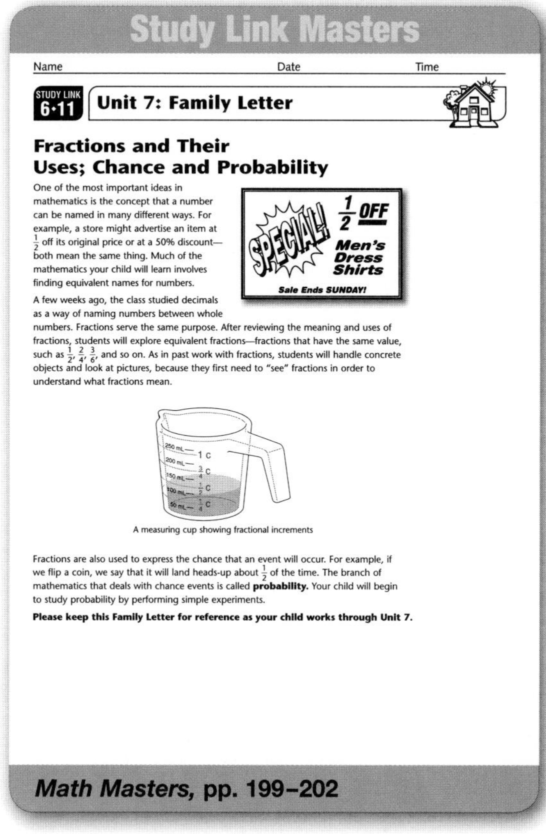

Study Link Masters

Name Date Time

STUDY LINK 6•11 **Unit 7: Family Letter**

Fractions and Their Uses; Chance and Probability

One of the most important ideas in mathematics is the concept that a number can be named in many different ways. For example, a store might advertise an item at $\frac{1}{2}$ off its original price or at a 50% discount—both mean the same thing. Much of the mathematics your child will learn involves finding equivalent names for numbers.

A few weeks ago, the class studied decimals as a way of naming numbers between whole numbers. Fractions serve the same purpose. After reviewing the meaning and uses of fractions, students will explore equivalent fractions—fractions that have the same value, such as $\frac{1}{2}$, $\frac{2}{4}$, $\frac{3}{6}$, and so on. As in past work with fractions, students will handle concrete objects and look at pictures, because they first need to "see" fractions in order to understand what fractions mean.

A measuring cup showing fractional increments

Fractions are also used to express the chance that an event will occur. For example, if we flip a coin, we say that it will land heads-up about $\frac{1}{2}$ of the time. The branch of mathematics that deals with chance events is called **probability.** Your child will begin to study probability by performing simple experiments.

Please keep this Family Letter for reference as your child works through Unit 7.

***Math Masters,* pp. 199–202**

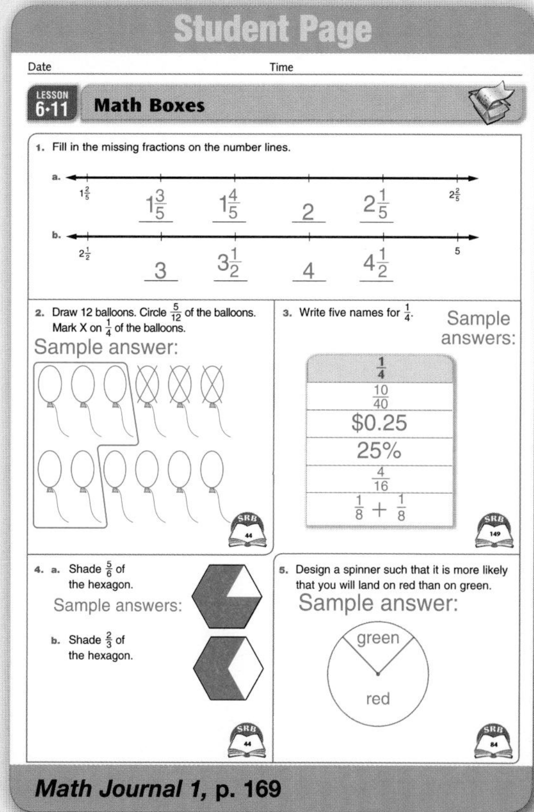

Student Page

Date Time

LESSON 6•11 **Math Boxes**

1. Fill in the missing fractions on the number lines.

a. $1\frac{2}{5}$, $1\frac{3}{5}$, $1\frac{4}{5}$, 2, $2\frac{1}{5}$, $2\frac{2}{5}$

b. $2\frac{1}{2}$, 3, $3\frac{1}{2}$, 4, $4\frac{1}{2}$, 5

2. Draw 12 balloons. Circle $\frac{5}{12}$ of the balloons. Mark X on $\frac{1}{4}$ of the balloons.

Sample answer:

3. Write five names for $\frac{1}{4}$.

Sample answers:

$\frac{1}{4}$
$\frac{10}{40}$
$0.25
25%
$\frac{4}{16}$
$\frac{1}{8} + \frac{1}{8}$

4. a. Shade $\frac{5}{6}$ of the hexagon.

Sample answers:

b. Shade $\frac{2}{3}$ of the hexagon.

5. Design a spinner such that it is more likely that you will land on red than on green.

Sample answer:

***Math Journal 1,* p. 169**

Appendices

Contents

Project

1 Making a Cutaway Globe

Objective To reinforce work with latitude and longitude.

Technology Resources www.everydaymathonline.com

eToolkit

Algorithms Practice

EM Facts Workshop Game™

Family Letters

Assessment Management

Common Core State Standards

Curriculum Focal Points

Interactive Teacher's Lesson Guide

1 Doing the Project

Recommended Use After Unit 6

Key Concepts and Skills

- Identify 90° and 180° angles.
  [Measurement and Reference Frames Goal 1]
- Use degree measurements to mark lines of latitude and longitude.
  [Measurement and Reference Frames Goal 1]
- Use latitude and longitude to locate points on the global grid system.
  [Measurement and Reference Frames Goal 4]
- Identify semicircles.
  [Geometry Goal 2]

Key Activities

Students work with partners to construct a cutaway version of a globe. Then they use latitude and longitude to locate various places on their globe.

Materials

- *Math Masters,* pp. 360 and 361
- transparent tape
- scissors
- straightedge
- 2 or 3 standard-size paper clips
- globe

2 Extending the Project

Students find the point on the globe that is polar opposite to their hometown and name the latitude and longitude for that point.

Students examine latitude and longitude on the Web.

Materials

- computer with Internet access

Advance Preparation

In order for the cutaway globe to work properly, *Math Masters,* page 360 must be copied on cardstock or similar paper. Before beginning the project, you may want to cut apart *Math Masters,* page 360 and follow the instructions that follow to construct a cutaway globe.

You need a globe. You also need to know the approximate latitude and longitude of your school, or use the area where it is located, or a nearby city's latitude and longitude. These can be estimated from the globe or a map in the *Student Reference Book.* They can also be found at several Internet sites; see the end of this project.

It will be helpful if you recruit one or two parents or students to help as students construct their models.

1 Doing the Project

Constructing a Cutaway Globe

(*Math Masters,* pp. 360 and 361)

Divide the class into partnerships and distribute *Math Masters,* page 360. There are two sets of circles and semicircles on the sheet. Students will use them to construct models of two hemispheres and then assemble them to form a full globe. The directions for making the cutaway globe are on *Math Masters,* page 361. You may want to have students read and follow the directions on their own while you and your helpers circulate. Or you may prefer to demonstrate the construction while students follow along and construct their models.

Directions:

1. Carefully cut out one of the circles A along the dashed lines.
2. Cut out one of the semicircles B. Cut the slit marked at 90° on the semicircle.
3. Lay semicircle B on circle A so that the base of the semicircle aligns with the 0° to 180° diameter shown on circle A. Tape the pieces together on both sides of the semicircle. Move semicircle B so that it is perpendicular to circle A.

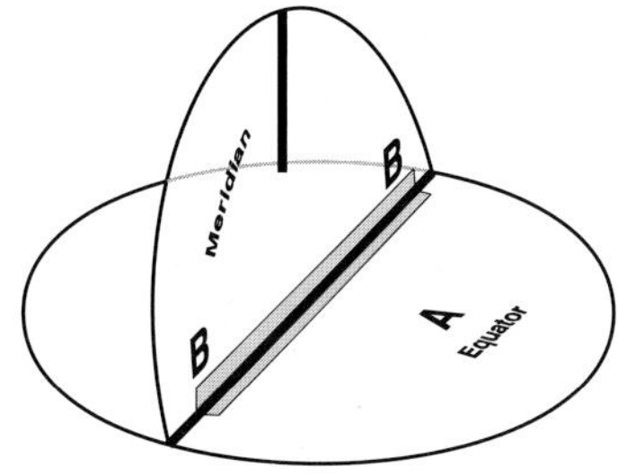

4. Cut out one of the semicircles C. Cut the slit marked at the bottom of the 90° line. Fold the semicircle in half along the 90° line. Fold it back and forth several times to make a good crease. Set semicircle C aside for later use.

Tell students that they have made a cutaway model of the Northern Hemisphere. The circumference of circle A corresponds to the equator. Ask them to point out the North Pole and the prime meridian. (Note that semicircle B shows only the northern half of the prime meridian. The rest of the semicircle is the northern half of the 180° longitude semicircle.)

Ask: *What part of the globe is at the center of circle A?* The center of the globe

Call attention to the degree labels on circle A. The labels from 0° to 180° on each side of the prime meridian correspond to the degree labels along the equator.

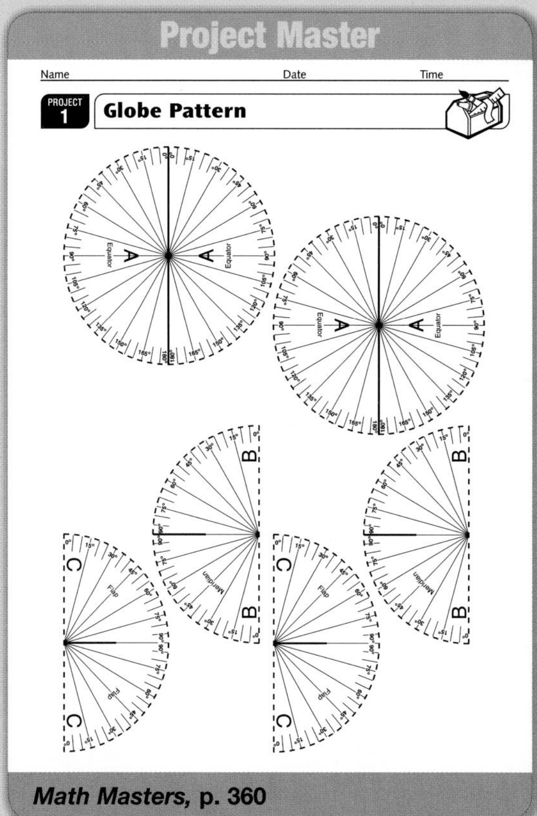

Math Masters, p. 360

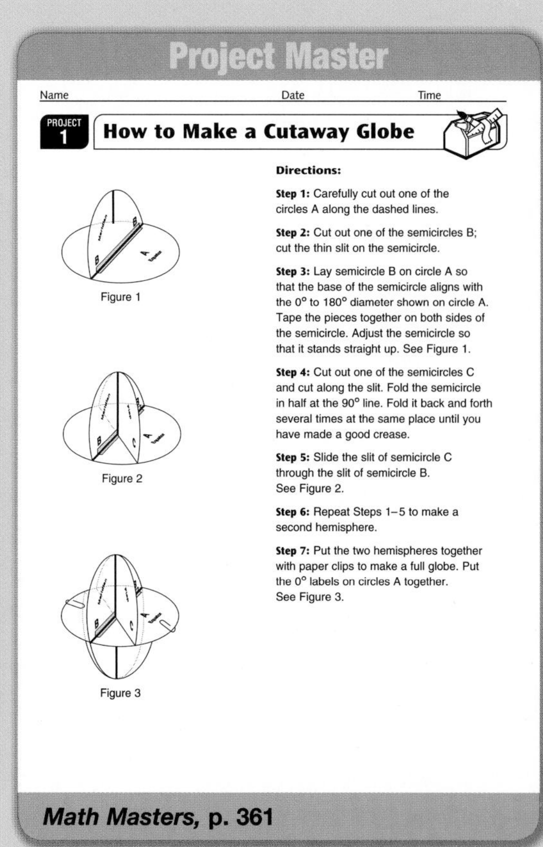

Project Master
Name
Date
Time
PROJECT 1
How to Make a Cutaway Globe
Figure 1
Figure 2
Figure 3

Directions:

Step 1: Carefully cut out one of the circles A along the dashed lines.

Step 2: Cut out one of the semicircles B; cut the thin slit on the semicircle.

Step 3: Lay semicircle B on circle A so that the base of the semicircle aligns with the 0° to 180° diameter shown on circle A. Tape the pieces together on both sides of the semicircle. Adjust the semicircle so that it stands straight up. See Figure 1.

Step 4: Cut out one of the semicircles C and cut along the slit. Fold the semicircle in half at the 90° line. Fold it back and forth several times at the same place until you have made a good crease.

Step 5: Slide the slit of semicircle C through the slit of semicircle B. See Figure 2.

Step 6: Repeat Steps 1–5 to make a second hemisphere.

Step 7: Put the two hemispheres together with paper clips to make a full globe. Put the 0° labels on circles A together. See Figure 3.

Math Masters, p. 361

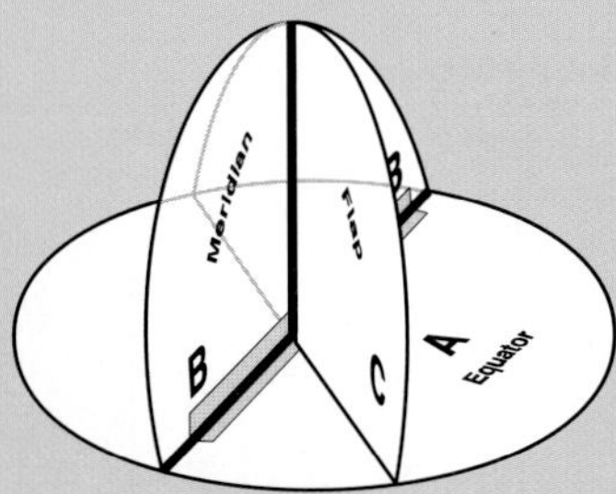

Figure 1

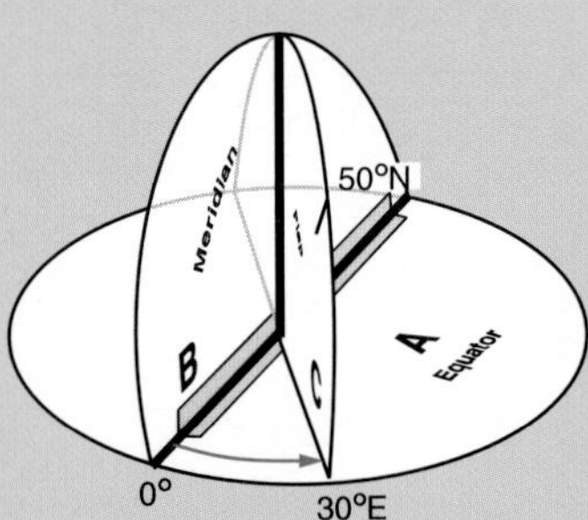

Figure 2

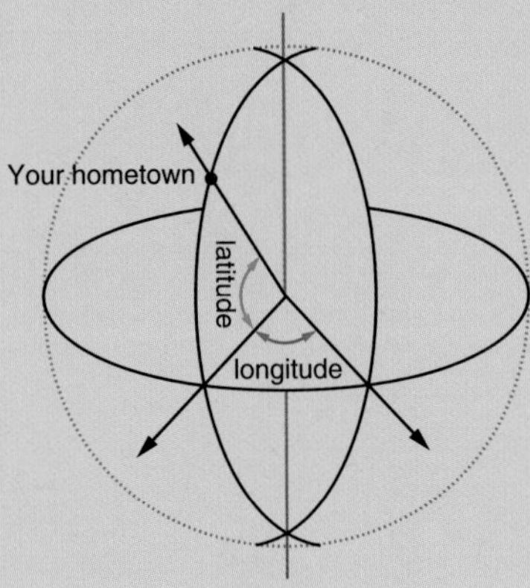

Figure 3

On semicircle B, degree labels from 0° to 90° start at each end of the base. They represent degrees of latitude north of the equator.

Now ask students to take semicircle C, which they had set aside, and slide the slit of this semicircle through the slit of semicircle B. (*See Figure 1.*) If necessary, lengthen the slits for a good fit.

Demonstrate how this movable semicircle can be used to show any combination of latitude and longitude.

Example: Find 50° North, 30° East.

1. With the prime meridian facing the class, find the 30° East mark on circle A. Rotate the right flap of the movable semicircle C to that position.
2. Then, without moving flap C, point to the 50° North mark on it.

The model now shows the location of 50° North, 30° East. Find this location on the globe and compare it with the location on the model. (*See Figure 2.*)

Ask a volunteer to give the approximate latitude and longitude of an important place—preferably the school, hometown, or nearby city. If not already known, these can be estimated from the globe or maps in the *Student Reference Book.* Write them on the board.

Direct students to mark this location on their models by doing the following. (*See Figure 3.*)

1. Move Flap C to show the longitude (east or west on the equator). Then draw a line along the base of the flap.

   This hand-drawn line, along with the base of the prime meridian flap (Flap B), forms an angle on circle A.

   Ask: *What does the degree measure of the angle represent?* The number of degrees of longitude
2. Make a dot on the edge of the flap to show the latitude of the location identified on the board. Draw a line from the center of the model to the dot. This line, along with the base of the flap, forms a second angle.

   Ask: *What does the degree measure of the angle represent?* The number of degrees of latitude north from the equator

NOTE At this point, it is not necessary for students to be able to state that degrees of latitude and longitude are measures of angles whose vertices are at the center of Earth. It is enough that by drawing the angles, students become aware of this fact.

Making a Full Cutaway Globe

Next, ask students to make a second hemisphere out of the remaining circle and semicircles on *Math Masters,* page 360.

Then show how to make a complete cutaway globe—that is, one that shows both the Northern and Southern Hemispheres. (*See Figure 4.*) Partners use paper clips to fasten the bases of their models together, making sure to align the 0° longitude marks on both hemispheres. With this full globe, they can practice finding locations in both hemispheres.

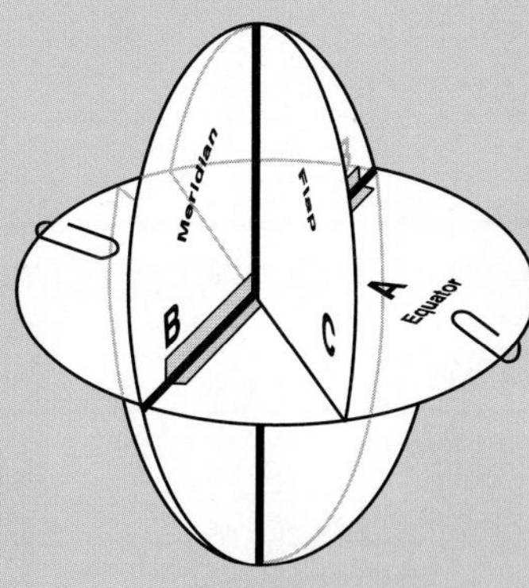

Figure 4

On the board, write other latitude/longitude pairs in the Northern Hemisphere. Ask students to move the flaps on their models to find these locations. Then have them guess on which continent these are located. Check on the globe. *For example:*

20°N,	20°E	Africa
15°N,	105°E	Southeast Asia
45°N,	100°W	North America
50°N,	5°E	Northern Europe
0°S,	60°W	South America

2 Extending the Project

Digging a Tunnel

Ask students to imagine digging a straight tunnel from their hometown through the center of Earth to the surface on the opposite side. Ask them to show the opposite point on their models and to name its latitude and longitude. Have them share strategies. Suggest other starting points for the tunnel.

Looking Up Latitudes and Longitudes

Invite students to look up latitudes and longitudes on the Internet.

For locations in the United States:

- ▷ kids.earth.nasa.gov/trmm/locator.html
- ▷ www.census.gov/geo/www/gazetteer/gazette.html

For locations in the United States and elsewhere:

- ▷ www.infoplease.com/ipa/A0001769.html
- ▷ www.indo.com/cgi-bin/dist

The last site also allows you to calculate the distance between locations.

Project 2

Using a Magnetic Compass

Objective To introduce reading a magnetic compass and finding directions.

Technology Resources www.everydaymathonline.com

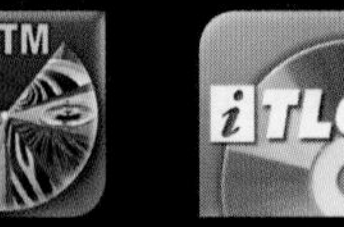

eToolkit | Algorithms Practice | EM Facts Workshop Game™ | Family Letters | Assessment Management | Common Core State Standards | Curriculum Focal Points | Interactive Teacher's Lesson Guide

1 Doing the Project

Recommended Use After Unit 6

Key Concepts and Skills

- Identify degree measurements to find the direction from north on a compass.
  [Measurement and Reference Frames Goal 1]
- Draw a line segment.
  [Geometry Goal 1]
- Identify clockwise rotations.
  [Geometry Goal 3]

Key Activities

Students learn how to orient and read a magnetic compass. Then, working in small groups, they use a magnetic compass to practice finding the direction of objects in relation to north.

Key Vocabulary

compass bearing ◆ magnetic north

Materials

- *Math Masters,* p. 362; p. 363 (optional)

Per group:

- magnetic compass
- 10-foot string
- tape

2 Extending the Project

Students make a floating compass with a steel sewing needle, a bar magnet, a piece of cork, and a dish of water.

Students further investigate orienteering through reading books and Web sites.

Materials

- steel sewing needle
- bar magnet
- piece of cork
- dish of water
- liquid detergent
- *Basic Essentials: Map and Compass*
- computer with Internet access

Advance Preparation

For Part 1, you need a magnetic compass and a copy of *Math Masters,* page 362 for a classroom demonstration. Try to obtain additional compasses for the group activity. Each group of four will need a 10-foot length of string.

For the optional activity in Part 2, you can use ***Basic Essentials: Map and Compass*** by Cliff Jacobson (Falcon, 2007).

1 Doing the Project

Introducing the Magnetic Compass

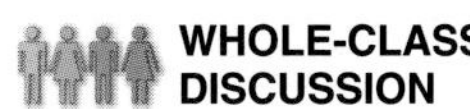

WHOLE-CLASS DISCUSSION

Gather the class around an open space in the classroom. If you have more than one magnetic compass, distribute them for students to examine.

Prompt discussion along the following lines:

- Does anyone know how a magnetic compass works? Earth behaves like a huge magnet. The compass needle is a tiny magnet. Earth's magnetic field exerts a force or pull on the compass needle so that the needle points north.
- How do you use a magnetic compass? Lay the compass flat on a surface or hold it level to the ground. Make sure that there are no metal objects or magnets near the compass. The compass needle will settle down and point north.

Using a Magnetic Compass

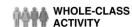

WHOLE-CLASS ACTIVITY

(*Math Masters,* p. 362)

Show students a method for describing the direction of an object from a given point.

1. A paper compass (*Math Masters,* page 362) is laid on a flat surface so that the 0° mark points north.
2. A string is stretched from the center of the paper compass toward the object, making it possible to describe the direction of the object in relation to north.

You will need a magnetic compass to orient the paper compass so that it points north. Here is one way to do it:

1. Lay the paper compass flat on the floor.
2. Place the magnetic compass on the paper compass so that the center of the magnetic compass is over the center of the paper compass. Make sure the letter *N* on both compasses points in the same direction.
3. Gently rotate the paper with the magnetic compass on it until the needle on the magnetic compass points to the letter *N.* Tape the paper compass in place.

Now select a location in the classroom—for example, the class globe. Demonstrate how to find the direction of the globe from the compass, using north as a reference.

1. Have a student hold down one end of a piece of string on the center of the paper compass.
2. Ask another student to pull the string as far as possible in the direction of the object you selected, keeping the string at floor level.

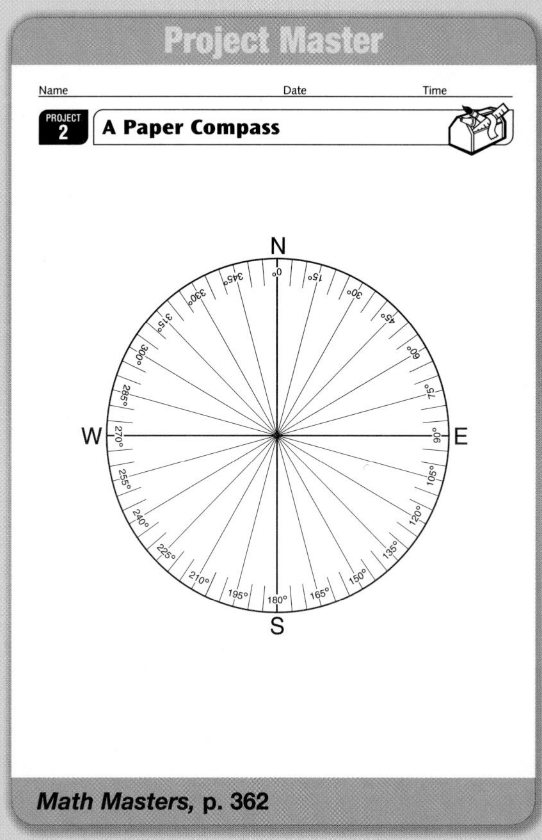

Math Masters, p. 362

NOTE Depending on one's location, a compass may not show "true" north. The U.S. Geological Survey (USGS) maintains a Web site on the National Geomagnetism Program: http://geomag.usgs.gov. Its FAQ page gives basic information and can guide you to the models and calculations that show the variation between "true" and magnetic north for a given location. The National Geophysical Data Center (NGDC) maintains archives of geomagnetic data, models, software, and other information. Their general Web page and FAQ might be helpful: www.ngdc.noaa.gov/geomag

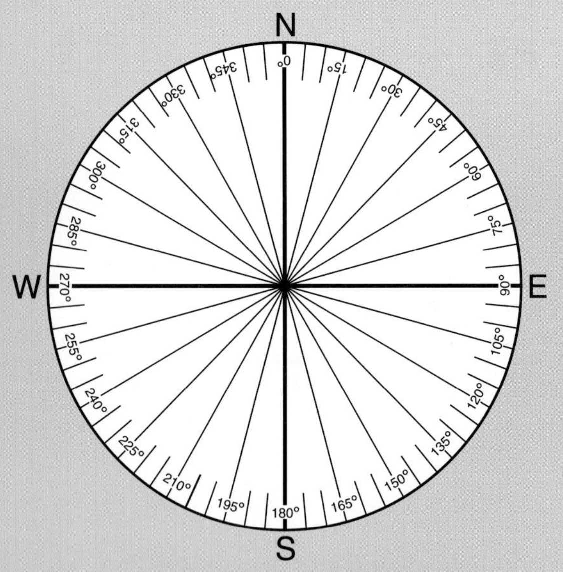

Use a paper compass to determine compass bearings of objects in the classroom.

3. Read the number of degrees at the mark where the string crosses the edge of the paper compass. This gives the direction of the object, using north as a reference. For example, "The globe is 120° clockwise from north," or "The globe has a **compass bearing** of 120°."

Emphasize that this method measures the amount of clockwise rotation from **magnetic north.**

Choose other objects or locations in the classroom. Ask pairs of students to find the objects' direction from north, using the method just described.

▶ Measuring Direction

SMALL-GROUP ACTIVITY

(*Math Masters,* p. 362)

Divide the class into groups of four. Pass out a length of string to each group and a magnetic compass to as many groups as possible. If there are not enough compasses to go around, groups can share.

Ask each group to lay its copy of *Math Masters,* page 362 flat on the desktop and orient it toward north, as described earlier. Then tape the paper compass to the desktop.

Each group now uses its string to find the direction of each corner of the room on its taped paper compass. Students indicate the direction of each corner by drawing a line segment along the string from the center of the paper compass to the edge. Have students record next to each line segment the number of degrees from north.

Bring the class together to share results. Ask: *Why do the results differ from group to group?* The direction of any particular location depends on the point from which the direction is measured. For example, the direction of the classroom globe will vary, depending on where one is standing in the classroom.

2 Extending the Project

Making a Compass

INDEPENDENT ACTIVITY

(*Math Masters,* p. 363)

Math Masters, page 363 provides a brief history of compasses and the directions for making a floating compass with a steel sewing needle, bar magnet, piece of cork, and dish of water.

Finding Out about Compasses and Orienteering

Invite students to learn more about the history and uses of compasses by looking in encyclopedias and books such as ***Basic Essentials: Map and Compass*** by Cliff Jacobson (Falcon, 2007).

Through scouting or camping, some students may be familiar with using a compass to follow a course and might be interested in describing their experiences to the class.

The competitive sport of orienteering involves using a detailed map and a compass to navigate around a course with designated control points. The winner of the competition is the participant who visits the control points in order and in the shortest amount of time. The International Orienteering Federation has a Web site at www.orienteering.org.

Project Master

Name Date Time

PROJECT 2 **Making a Compass**

In ancient times, sailors had only the sun, moon, and stars to aid them in navigation. The most important navigational instrument was the **compass.** The compass was invented more than 1,000 years ago. The first compass was a small bar of magnetized iron that floated on a reed in a bowl of water. The magnet in the iron would make the reed point to the magnetically charged North Pole. Using a compass, sailors could tell in which direction they were traveling.

You, too, can make a floating compass.

1. Magnetize a steel sewing needle by stroking it with one pole of a strong bar magnet. Slowly stroke the needle from end to end **in one direction only.** Be sure to lift your hand up in the air before coming down for another stroke.

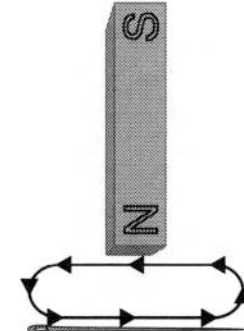

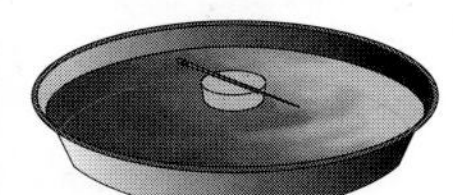

2. Slice a round ($\frac{1}{2}$-inch-thick) piece from a cork stopper. Cut a groove across the center of the top of the cork. Put the needle in the groove.
3. Place the cork into a glass, china, or aluminum dish filled with water. Add a teaspoon of detergent to the water. The detergent will lower the surface tension of the water and prevent the cork from moving to one side of the dish and staying there.

The needle will behave like a compass needle. It will assume a North-South position because of Earth's magnetic field.

Source: Science for the Elementary School. New York: Macmillan, 1993.

***Math Masters,* p. 363**

Project

3 A Carnival Game

Objectives To provide opportunities to analyze a cube-tossing game; and to invent a profitable variation.

Technology Resources www.everydaymathonline.com

eToolkit

Algorithms Practice

EM Facts Workshop Game™

Family Letters

Assessment Management

Common Core State Standards

Curriculum Focal Points

Interactive Teacher's Lesson Guide

1 Doing the Project

Recommended Use After Unit 7

Key Concepts and Skills

- Solve problems involving extended multiplication facts. [Operations and Computation Goal 3]
- Collect and organize data. [Data and Chance Goal 1]
- Conduct a cube-drop experiment. [Data and Chance Goal 4]
- Compare predicted results and experimental results; use results to predict future events. [Data and Chance Goal 4]

Key Activities

Students make a "quilt" out of the 10-by-10 grids they colored in Lesson 7•12. They use their quilt as a target mat for a cube-tossing game.

Then students work in small groups to invent a variation of the game that will show a profit.

Materials

- *Math Journal 2,* p. 215 (optional)
- *Math Masters,* pp. 238 and 242 (as completed by the student, if available); pp. 364 and 365
- calculator
- centimeter cube
- scissors
- transparent tape

2 Extending the Project

Students make up their own games.

Materials

- none

Advance Preparation

You need the data for 1,000 cube drops collected in Lesson 7•12 on *Math Masters,* page 242. If this was not done, combine 20 students' results on 50 drops as described in Part 3 of Lesson 7•12, or generate the data with the students from their results on *Math Journal 2,* page 215. Write this information, including percents for each color, on the board.

Students need their completed copies of *Math Masters,* page 238. If these are not available, copy the master and have students color it as described in the project.

1 Doing the Project

Introducing a Carnival Game

SMALL-GROUP ACTIVITY

(*Math Journal 2,* p. 215; *Math Masters,* pp. 238 and 364)

Constructing a Class "Quilt" Mat

Have students take out the grid they colored on *Math Masters,* page 238. If this is not available, have students color the grid on a blank copy of the master according to the specifications shown on the table. (*See margin.*) They may color the squares in any way they want. The colors may form a pattern or a picture, or they may be arranged randomly.

If there are fewer than 20 students in your class, divide the class into groups of four. If there are 20 or more, divide the class into groups of five. (Any "leftover" students form their own group.) Ask students in each group to cut out their hundreds grids and tape them together to form one row of hundreds grids. (For example, a group of four will make a row of four grids.)

Bring the groups together. Have them tape their rows together to form a rectangular (or nearly rectangular) quilt. For example, a class of 20 would form a quilt with four rows, each row with five grids.

Becoming Familiar with the Game

Introduce the carnival game on *Math Masters,* page 364. A player pays 10¢ for each cube the player tosses onto the class "quilt" mat. The player may win a prize, depending on the color on which the cube lands.

Ask students to complete Problem 1. Bring the class together to compare results.

Tell the class that the table on the board contains the combined results of 50 cube drops by 20 students in Lesson 7-12. Since $20 * 50 = 1,000$, the table shows the number of times, and percent of total times, that a cube landed on each color out of 1,000 drops.

Suggest that the carnival game could be run at a school fair or similar event to raise money for the class—for a party, equipment, or other purposes. Have students complete Problem 2 to find out how much money the class could earn if students sold 1,000 tickets and the results were the same as those on the board.

If you wish, have students actually play the game.

Project Master

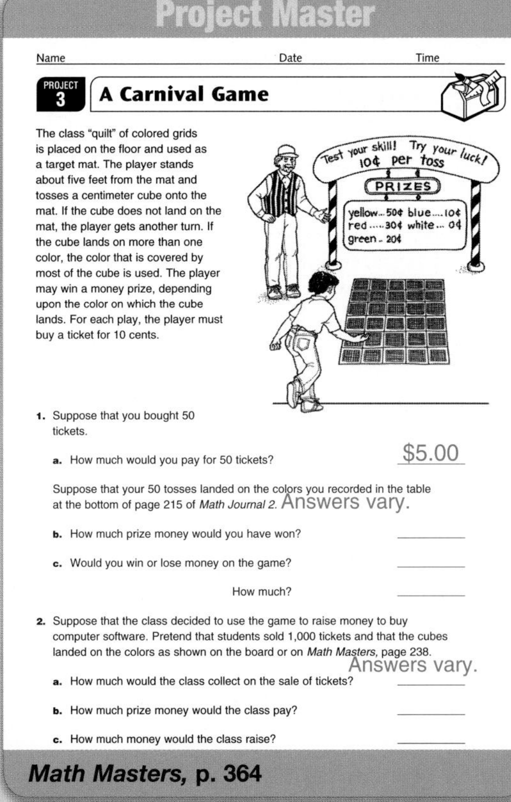

Name Date Time

PROJECT 3 **A Carnival Game**

The class "quilt" of colored grids is placed on the floor and used as a target mat. The player stands about five feet from the mat and tosses a centimeter cube onto the mat. If the cube does not land on the mat, the player gets another turn. If the cube lands on more than one color, the color that is covered by most of the cube is used. The player may win a money prize, depending upon the color on which the cube lands. For each play, the player must buy a ticket for 10 cents.

Test your skill! Try your luck!
10¢ per toss
PRIZES
yellow...50¢ blue....10¢
red.....30¢ white... 0¢
green...20¢

1. Suppose that you bought 50 tickets.
   a. How much would you pay for 50 tickets? $5.00

   Suppose that your 50 tosses landed on the colors you recorded in the table at the bottom of page 215 of *Math Journal 2.* Answers vary.

   b. How much prize money would you have won? ______
   c. Would you win or lose money on the game? ______
   How much? ______

2. Suppose that the class decided to use the game to raise money to buy computer software. Pretend that students sold 1,000 tickets and that the cubes landed on the colors as shown on the board or on *Math Masters,* page 238. Answers vary.
   a. How much would the class collect on the sale of tickets? ______
   b. How much prize money would the class pay? ______
   c. How much money would the class raise? ______

Math Masters, **p. 364**

How to Color the Grid

Color	Number of Squares
yellow	1
red	4
green	10
blue	35
white	50
Total	100

NOTE If you want the taped rows to form a rectangle or square, you may have to ask students to color additional grids.

Project Master

Name Date Time

PROJECT 3 **A Carnival Game** *continued*

3. Work with your group to make up your own version of the carnival game.

a. Record how much you would charge for a ticket and what the prizes would be for each color.

Ticket Price
________ per toss

Prizes	
yellow	________
red	________
green	________
blue	________
white	________

b. Use the results for 1,000 cube drops shown on the board or on *Math Masters,* page 242 to answer the following questions: Answers vary.

Would the class have won or lost money? ________

How much? ________

4. Suppose that the class ran your game on Parents' Night. Answers vary.

a. How many tickets do you estimate the class would sell? ________

b. How much money would the class get from ticket sales? ________

c. About how much money should you expect to pay in prizes? ________

d. About how much money should the class expect to earn? ________

***Math Masters,* p. 365**

▶ Inventing a Variation on the Carnival Game

(*Math Masters,* p. 365)

By now, students should have a fairly good understanding of the rules of the carnival game and the factors that affect the game's profitability. Tell them that each group is to invent its own version of the game. Spend a few minutes discussing things students need to take into consideration, such as the following:

- How much should you charge for a ticket?
- Which colors should win prizes?
- What should the prizes be?
- How will your decisions affect the number of tickets sold?
- Will you make more money if you charge a lot for a ticket and offer large prizes? Or will a high ticket price discourage people from buying tickets?

Students can complete this project over the next few days. Groups can post their ticket prices and prizes near the mat and play each other's games in their free time. To find the total amount of money the class would earn, follow this procedure: Multiply the number of times a cube lands on each color by the amount of the prize for that color. Then add the amounts won for each color.

Example:

Cube lands on		**Prizes**
yellow	1 time	$1 * 50¢ = \$0.50$
red	2 times	$2 * 30¢ = \$0.60$
green	6 times	$6 * 20¢ = \$1.20$
blue	11 times	$11 * 10¢ = \$1.10$
white	30 times	$30 * 0¢ = \$0.00$
	Total:	\$3.40

The 50 tickets cost \$5.00 (50 * 10¢). The players win only \$3.40. The class earns \$1.60; (\$5.00 − \$3.40 = \$1.60).

Have students complete *Math Masters,* page 365.

2 Extending the Project

▶ Creating Other Games

Invite students to make up their own games, establish prices and prizes, and use expected results to calculate prizes paid and profits earned.

Project

Making a Quilt

Objective To guide students as they explore and apply ideas of pattern, symmetry, rotation, and reflection in the context of quilts.

Technology Resources www.everydaymathonline.com

eToolkit

Algorithms Practice

EM Facts Workshop Game™

Family Letters

Assessment Management

Common Core State Standards

Curriculum Focal Points

Interactive Teacher's Lesson Guide

1 Doing the Project

Recommended Use After Unit 10

Key Concepts and Skills

- Identify squares, triangles, and rectangles.
  [Geometry Goal 2]
- Identify lines of symmetry; create patterns with a specified number of lines of symmetry.
  [Geometry Goal 3]
- Identify and use rotations and translations.
  [Geometry Goal 3]
- Identify and extend visual patterns.
  [Patterns, Functions, and Algebra Goal 1]

Key Activities

Students apply their knowledge of symmetry and rotations to make a paper quilt.

Key Vocabulary

patchwork quilt ◆ 9-Patch Pattern ◆ quilting bee

Materials

- *Math Masters,* pp. 366–374 (one per student); p. 375 (at least three copies per student)
- markers, crayons, or colored pencils; or paper of various colors
- one-hole punch
- paste or glue
- scissors
- straightedge
- yarn
- crepe paper (optional)

2 Extending the Project

Students learn more about quilts through literature.

Materials

- *Eight Hands Round: A Patchwork Alphabet*

Advance Preparation

Students need yarn to assemble their quilts. If you wish, collect colored paper or wrapping paper to be cut up for "patches." You may want to make overhead transparencies of *Math Masters,* pages 367 and 371. If you can laminate the patches, the quilt will last longer and look more finished.

For the optional activity in Part 2, obtain copies of ***Eight Hands Round: A Patchwork Alphabet*** by Ann Whitford Paul (HarperCollins, 1996).

Project Master

Name Date Time

Patchwork Quilts

Throughout American history, women have worked together to make **patchwork quilts.** Because cloth was expensive and scarce, quilts were often made out of pieces of worn-out clothing or leftovers from another project. The quilters began by sewing together pieces of different colors, shapes, and textures to create a square pattern. Then they made more "patchwork" squares with the same pattern. When they had enough squares, they sewed them together to form the top of the quilt. Next they added a layer of wool fleece or cotton, called *batting,* and a cloth backing. They made a "sandwich" of the three layers—the backing on the bottom, the batting in the middle, and the patchwork on the top. They stretched the "sandwich" on a wooden frame and sewed the three layers together with tiny stitches.

The quilt was put together at a party, called a **quilting bee.** While cutting and sewing, the women would tell stories and share what went on in their lives. When the quilt was finished, the men joined the women for supper and dancing.

Buggy Wheel

Many patchwork patterns have become traditions. Their names and designs have come from the everyday lives of the people who created them. For example, the "Buggy Wheel" pattern was probably inspired by a trip in a buggy. Along with walking and riding horses, buggies were a popular form of transportation in early America.

Does and Darts

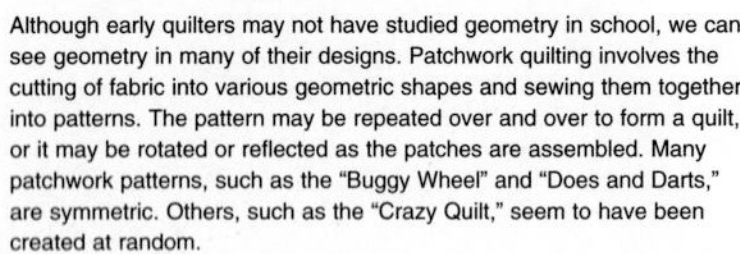

Although early quilters may not have studied geometry in school, we can see geometry in many of their designs. Patchwork quilting involves the cutting of fabric into various geometric shapes and sewing them together into patterns. The pattern may be repeated over and over to form a quilt, or it may be rotated or reflected as the patches are assembled. Many patchwork patterns, such as the "Buggy Wheel" and "Does and Darts," are symmetric. Others, such as the "Crazy Quilt," seem to have been created at random.

Crazy Quilt

The beauty of a quilt lies in its uniqueness. No two patches need ever be the same because there are many possible arrangements of fabrics and colors.

Math Masters, **p. 366**

Project Master

Name Date Time

PROJECT 4

Symmetric Patterns

Each pattern to the right of the "Pinwheel" pattern below has been colored in a different way. Notice how each color arrangement changes the number of lines of symmetry.

Pinwheel Pattern

lines of symmetry: 4 2 1 0

For each pattern below, draw all the lines of symmetry and record the number of lines of symmetry.

1. Bow-Tie Pattern

lines of symmetry: 4 1 2 2

2. Ohio Star Pattern

lines of symmetry: 4 4 0 0

3. Pineapple Log Cabin Pattern

lines of symmetry: 4 4 4 0

Math Masters, **p. 367**

1 Doing the Project

▶ Learning about Quilts

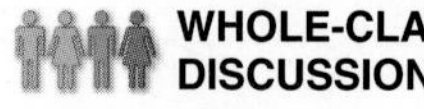

WHOLE-CLASS DISCUSSION

(*Math Masters,* p. 366)

Have students read the article about quilts on *Math Masters,* page 366. Then ask them to discuss it. The discussion should include the following points:

- ▷ Quilting patterns often reflect the lives of the people who create them.
- ▷ Quilting patterns display some of the geometric transformations that students have been studying, such as reflections and rotations, and the symmetries based on these transformations.
- ▷ **Patchwork quilts** were made from available scraps sewn into a square pattern.

Tell students that during this project they will learn more about quilting patterns, and they will use this knowledge to make their own paper quilts.

▶ Examining Lines of Symmetry in Quilting Patterns

PARTNER ACTIVITY

(*Math Masters,* p. 367)

Introduce the activity with a discussion of the Pinwheel Pattern at the top of *Math Masters,* page 367. Students should notice the following details:

- ▷ The original, uncolored pattern has four lines of symmetry.
- ▷ This pattern may be colored in many different ways.
- ▷ The number of lines of symmetry varies, depending on the coloring scheme.

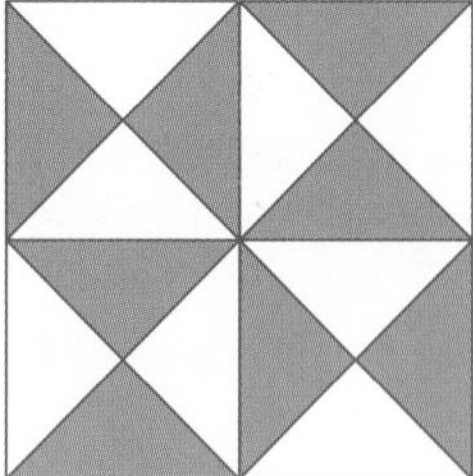

Working with a partner, students examine three other basic patterns and various coloring schemes based on these patterns. Then students draw all the lines of symmetry for each.

After a few minutes, bring the class together and go over the answers. It may be helpful to refer to an overhead transparency of *Math Masters,* page 367.

Designing 9-Patch Patterns

(*Math Masters,* pp. 368–370)

Tell the class that there is a special kind of quilting pattern called the **9-Patch Pattern.** Students will design such patterns of colored squares, triangles, and rectangles.

To make the various pieces, students follow the directions on *Math Masters,* page 368 for coloring the squares on *Math Masters,* page 369. Then they cut the squares into triangles and rectangles as directed on *Math Masters,* page 368.

To assemble a 9-Patch Pattern, students use the 3-by-3 grid on *Math Masters,* page 370. They experiment with different ways to arrange the triangles and rectangles they cut out.

When students have completed a pattern, have them copy it onto a grid on *Math Masters,* page 368. Students should make at least one pattern with four lines of symmetry, one with two lines of symmetry, and one with no lines of symmetry.

Project Master

Name Date Time

PROJECT 4 Traditional 9-Patch Patterns

Some patterns, called **9-Patch Patterns,** look like they are made up of 9 squares. You can make your own 9-Patch Pattern on a 3-by-3 grid.

Take out *Math Masters,* pages 369 and 370. Color 6 squares on *Math Masters,* page 369 in one color and the other 6 in a different color. Cut out the 12 squares. Then make triangles by cutting 6 of the squares in half along a diagonal. Make rectangles by cutting the other 6 squares in half along a line through the middle.

Now arrange some of the pieces on the grid on *Math Masters,* page 370 to make a pattern. Follow the directions below. When you have completed a pattern, draw and color it on one of the 3-by-3 grids below.

1. Make one or two patterns having 4 lines of symmetry.
   Answers vary.

2. Make one or two patterns having 2 lines of symmetry.
   Answers vary.

3. Make one or two patterns having no lines of symmetry.
   Answers vary.

Math Masters, p. 368

Project Master

Name Date Time

PROJECT 4 9-Patch Pattern Pieces

Math Masters, p. 369

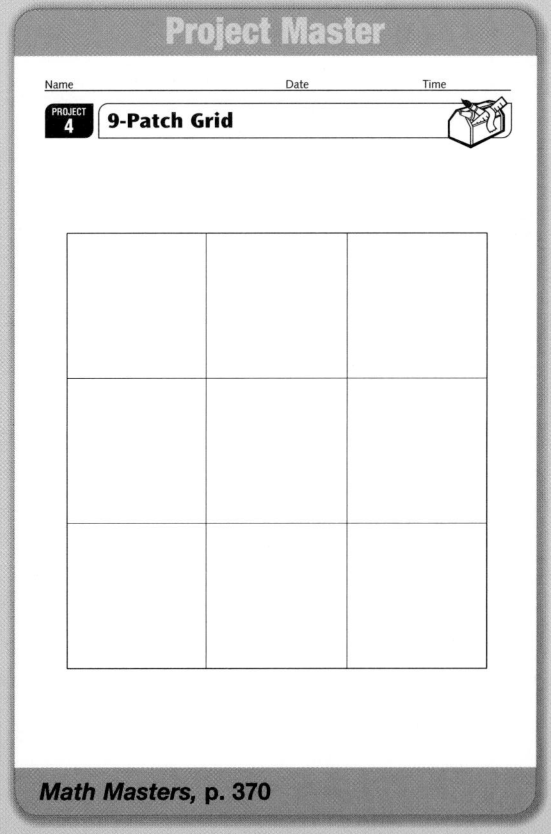
Project Master

Name Date Time

PROJECT 4 9-Patch Grid

Math Masters, p. 370

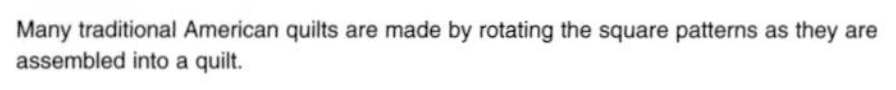
Many traditional American quilts are made by rotating the square patterns as they are assembled into a quilt.

The first patchwork pattern below is a variation of the traditional "Grandmother's Fan" pattern. The patterns to the right of it show the pattern after it has been rotated clockwise a $\frac{1}{4}$, $\frac{1}{2}$, and $\frac{3}{4}$ turn.

starting position

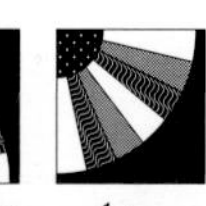
$\frac{1}{4}$ turn

$\frac{1}{2}$ turn

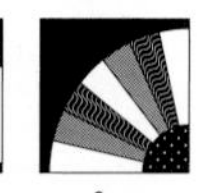
$\frac{3}{4}$ turn

This is what part of the quilt might look like if some of the patterns are rotated:

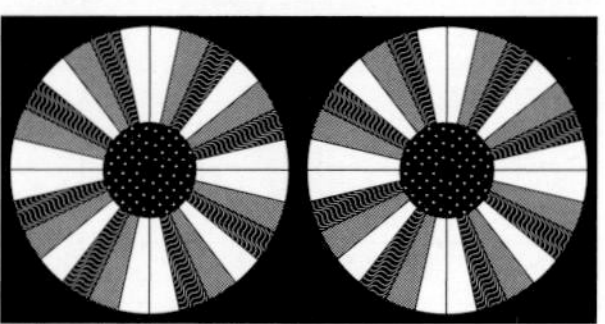

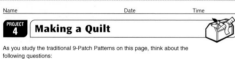

The "Wrench" pattern at the right, also known as the "Monkey Wrench," is a classic pattern that can be found in Amish and Mennonite quilts. Describe what it would look like if it were rotated a $\frac{1}{4}$, $\frac{1}{2}$, and $\frac{3}{4}$ turn.

It would look the same each time.

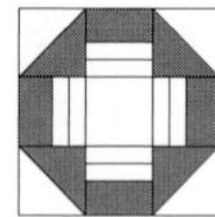

How many lines of symmetry does it have? 4

***Math Masters*, p. 371**

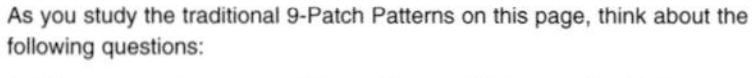

Name Date Time

PROJECT 4 **Making a Quilt**

As you study the traditional 9-Patch Patterns on this page, think about the following questions:

- Do you see where some of the patterns might have gotten their names?
- What are some similarities and differences among the patterns?
- How many lines of symmetry does each pattern have?

Churn Dash

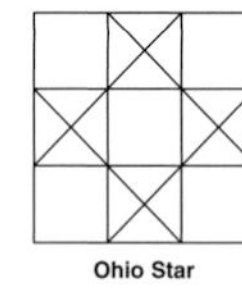
Ohio Star

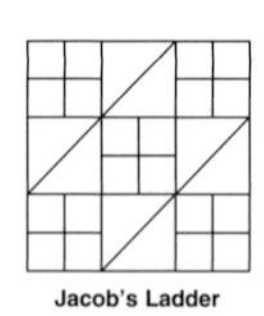
Jacob's Ladder

Storm at Sea

Weather Vane

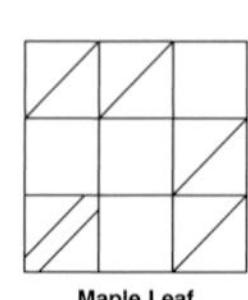
Maple Leaf

***Math Masters*, p. 372**

of Patterns

(*Math Masters,* p. 371)

Briefly review rotations. Ask students to place a closed journal or other book on their desks. Then have them rotate it through various turns. *For example:*

- ▷ Clockwise $\frac{1}{2}$ turn
- ▷ Clockwise $\frac{1}{4}$ turn
- ▷ Counterclockwise $\frac{1}{2}$ turn
- ▷ Counterclockwise $\frac{3}{4}$ turn

Finally, go over *Math Masters,* page 371 with the class. You may want to use an overhead transparency of the master.

▶ Making a Paper Patchwork Quilt

(*Math Masters,* pp. 372–375)

Ask students to examine the traditional 9-Patch Patterns on *Math Masters,* page 372. Like the patterns students created previously, each of these patterns is based on a grid of nine squares. Ask students to speculate about the origin of some of the names, to comment on similarities and differences between the patterns, and to identify the lines of symmetry in each pattern.

Divide the class into groups of three and tell students that they are going to make a patchwork quilt out of paper. Go over the directions for making the quilt on *Math Masters,* page 373. Emphasize these requirements:

- ▷ The pattern that a group chooses may not have more than two lines of symmetry.
- ▷ When the group assembles the quilt, at least one of the patches should be rotated through a $\frac{1}{4}$, $\frac{1}{2}$, or $\frac{3}{4}$ turn.

Then students proceed as follows:

1. Each student cuts out the 3-by-3 grid of squares, including the border with the dots, from three copies of *Math Masters,* page 375.

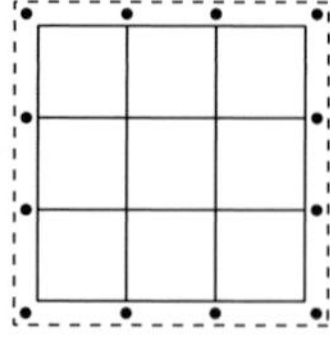

2. Each student cuts out the pieces on *Math Masters,* page 374.
3. Each group chooses one of the patterns on *Math Masters,* page 372 and decides on a coloring scheme.
4. Each student then copies the agreed-upon pattern onto each of the 3-by-3 grids he or she cut out. The pieces cut out from *Math Masters,* page 374 can be used as templates to help in drawing the pattern.

5. Students color each pattern according to the agreed-upon coloring scheme. Alternatively, the pieces cut out from *Math Masters,* page 374 can be traced onto colored paper or wrapping paper. The tracings can be cut out and glued onto the 3-by-3 grid.
6. The students punch holes through each dot on the borders of the 3-by-3 grids. If you have access to a laminating machine, laminate the squares before students punch the holes. The quilts will look more finished and will last longer.

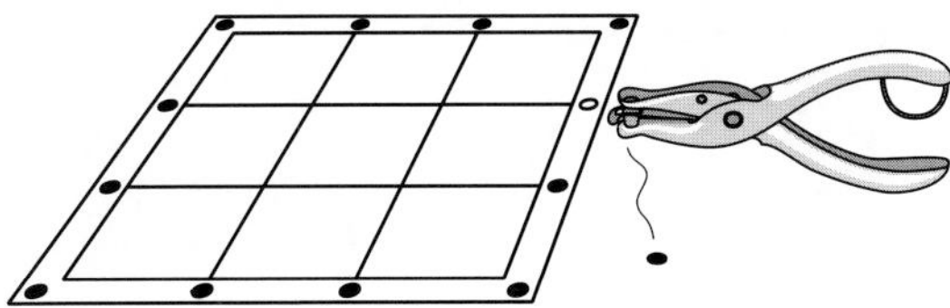

7. When all 3-by-3 "patches" have been completed, students in each group assemble them into a patchwork quilt. They lay the patterns on the floor and arrange them so that the borders of the squares overlap and the holes line up. Students use yarn to fasten the square patterns together by weaving the yarn in and out of the holes.
8. The quilt may be decorated with a ruffle made out of crepe paper. The crepe paper should be pleated and glued around the edges of the quilt.

Summarizing the Project

WHOLE-CLASS ACTIVITY

Ask each group to present its finished quilt to the class and describe how it was designed and put together. Students should point out lines of symmetry, reflections, and rotations in the pattern.

2 Extending the Project

Finding Out about Quilts

INDEPENDENT ACTIVITY

Invite students to learn more about quilts by looking in encyclopedias and books such as ***Eight Hands Round: A Patchwork Alphabet*** by Ann Whitford Paul (HarperCollins, 1996). This informative book speculates on the origins of the names of early American patchwork patterns for each letter in the alphabet.

Project Master

Name Date Time

PROJECT 4 **Making a Quilt** *continued*

Work with two partners to make a quilt.

1. Each of you needs three copies of *Math Masters,* page 375. Cut out the 3-by-3 grid on each sheet. **Make sure you include the border with the dots.**
2. Cut out the quilting pattern shapes on *Math Masters,* page 374.
3. With your partners, choose one of the patterns on *Math Masters,* page 372. Decide on a way to color it. The colored pattern your group chooses **should not have more than two lines of symmetry.** Each group member should then copy this design onto three 3-by-3 grids. Use the pieces you cut out of *Math Masters,* page 374 to trace the pattern onto the 3-by-3 grids. Then color the pattern. Or you can trace the pieces onto colored paper, cut out the tracings, and paste them onto the 3-by-3 grids. Your group should end up with nine square "patches" that **look exactly alike.**
4. Punch holes through the dots along the border of the patches.
5. Lay all 9 square patches on the floor and arrange them so that some of the square patterns are rotated. When your group has agreed on an arrangement, line up the holes on the edges of the squares. Then fasten the pieces together by weaving yarn in and out of the holes. If you wish, make a ruffle for your quilt out of a strip of crepe paper. Pleat and glue the ruffle around the outer edges of the quilt.

Here is an example of a quilt with the "Maple Leaf" pattern:

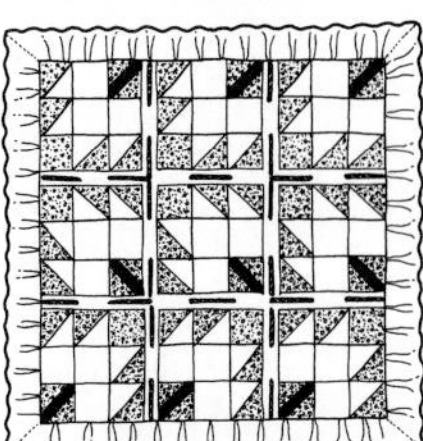

***Math Masters,* p. 373**

NOTE Students are making a 9-Patch Pattern quilt, but this is by no means the only method of quilting. In the spirit of the traditional **quilting bee,** you may wish to serve refreshments after students have completed their quilts.

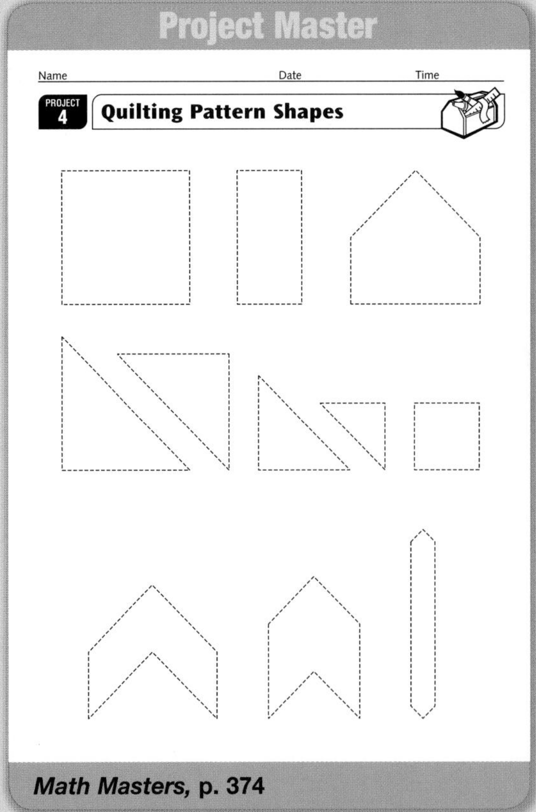

Project Master

Name Date Time

PROJECT 4 **Quilting Pattern Shapes**

***Math Masters,* p. 374**

Project 5

Which Soft Drink Is the Best Buy?

Objective To guide students as they calculate the unit price of various soft drinks and decide which is the best buy.

Technology Resources www.everydaymathonline.com

eToolkit

Algorithms Practice

EM Facts Workshop Game™

Family Letters

Assessment Management

Common Core State Standards

Curriculum Focal Points

Interactive Teacher's Lesson Guide

1 Doing the Project

Recommended Use During or after Unit 12

Key Concepts and Skills

- Round to the nearest fluid ounce.
  [Operations and Computation Goal 6]
- Calculate unit price.
  [Operations and Computation Goal 7]
- Collect and organize data.
  [Data and Chance Goal 1]
- Draw conclusions from data.
  [Data and Chance Goal 2]
- Convert among units of capacity.
  [Measurement and Reference Frames Goal 3]

Key Activities

Students collect soft-drink cups from local businesses and record the prices charged for various sizes of soft drinks. They work in groups to determine which place offers the best soft-drink value.

Key Vocabulary

capacity

Materials

- *Math Masters,* pp. 376 and 377
- soft-drink cups
- measuring cup (fluid ounces)
- about 2 quarts or 2 liters of water or other pourable substance
- stick-on labels
- calculator

2 Extending the Project

Students read magazines and Web sites about consumer issues.

Materials

- computer with Internet access

Advance Preparation

A week or so before beginning the project, divide the class into groups of four or five. Each group is responsible for collecting soft-drink cups of various sizes (small, medium, large) from local businesses (restaurants, fast-food franchises, movie theaters, sports events, concerts, carnivals, and so on)—preferably three different sizes from each of three different places per group. Students should rinse out each cup and label it with its source and price. Collect additional cups for students who may need more. Since it is difficult to write on the surface of some cups, give each group a set of stick-on labels on which to write the information.

Gather enough measuring cups so that each group has one. Each group will also need about 2 liters or 2 quarts of water or other pourable substance, such as sand, navy or lima beans, or unpopped popcorn.

1 Doing the Project

Introducing the Soft-Drink Project

WHOLE-CLASS DISCUSSION

Ask students to share the experiences they had buying soft drinks in various sizes at fast-food restaurants, movie theaters, sports events, concerts, carnivals, and so on.

Then ask students for suggestions for deciding which places and which sizes of soft-drink cups offer the best value.

- How can you use the information you have recorded to make this determination?
- What other information do you need?
- How would you gather this information?

Carrying Out the Project

SMALL-GROUP ACTIVITY

(*Math Masters,* pp. 376 and 377)

These groups can be the same as those that collected the cups. Give each group a measuring cup and enough water or other pourable substance to carry out the investigation. (If possible, each group should work with three sets of three different-sized cups, each set from a different business.)

Students find out how much each container conveniently holds (not filled to the brim). They should round the **capacity** to the nearest fluid ounce. When calculating the price per ounce, ask them to round the answer to the nearest tenth of a cent. Then have students record all information on *Math Masters,* page 376.

After students have finished collecting the data and calculating the unit prices, have each group use *Math Masters,* page 377 to prepare a report describing the data collected and the conclusions drawn from the data. The report might include tables and pictorial representations of the data (for example, bar graphs).

NOTE

1 cup = 8 fluid ounces (fl oz)

1 pint = 2 cups = 16 fl oz

1 quart = 2 pints = 32 fl oz

1 gallon = 4 quarts = 128 fl oz

Project Master

Name Date Time

PROJECT 5 **Which Soft Drink Would You Buy?**

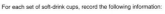

For each set of soft-drink cups, record the following information:

- The name of the place from which the cups come
- The size of the cup (small, medium, or large)
- The price
- The capacity in fluid ounces

Then calculate each unit price in cents per fluid ounce, rounded to the nearest tenth of a cent. Answers vary.

Soft-Drink Cups from			
Size	Price	Capacity (fl oz)	Unit Price (¢/fl oz)

Soft-Drink Cups from			
Size	Price	Capacity (fl oz)	Unit Price (¢/fl oz)

Soft-Drink Cups from			
Size	Price	Capacity (fl oz)	Unit Price (¢/fl oz)

Math Masters, p. 376

Imagine that you have been assigned by *Kids' Consumer Reports* to investigate and report on the prices of soft drinks. Use the information your group recorded on *Math Masters,* page 376 to prepare a group report for the magazine. Your report might contain graphs, tables, and pictures. Try to answer some of the following questions in your report:

- Do small (or medium or large) cups at different places contain the same amount?
- Are prices similar for similar sizes? (For example, are the small-size drinks about the same price at different places?)
- Which places have the least expensive soft drinks? The most expensive soft drinks?
- Is the largest size always the best value?
- Which types of businesses offer better values? (For example, do restaurants generally offer better values than movie theaters?)
- What would you recommend to consumers? Do some places offer free refills? If so, how would this affect your recommendation?

Answers vary.

***Math Masters,* p. 377**

(*Math Masters,* pp. 376 and 377)

Bring the groups together to present their reports. After all the reports have been heard, ask students what conclusions they can draw from their consumer survey. For example, ask: *Is getting the best value the only reason for choosing a particular size?*

2 Extending the Project

▶ Looking at Consumer Magazines

Invite students to look at *Consumer Reports* or other consumer magazines that may be available in the school or local library or on the Internet. Students might report on how measurements of various items are reported—such as dimensions, weight, and capacity—and whether measurements or unit prices are used in determining best buys.

Project

6

Building and Viewing Structures

Objectives To provide practice building structures with cubes, given "blueprints" or side views of the structures; and to provide practice representing structures with diagrams.

Technology Resources www.everydaymathonline.com

eToolkit

Algorithms Practice

EM Facts Workshop Game™

Family Letters

Assessment Management

Common Core State Standards

Curriculum Focal Points

Interactive Teacher's Lesson Guide

1 Doing the Project

Recommended Use During or after Unit 11

Key Concepts and Skills

- Describe and compare plane and solid figures. [Geometry Goal 2]
- Describe 3-D objects from different perspectives. [Geometry Goal 2]
- Use manipulatives to solve problems involving spatial visualization. [Geometry Goal 2]
- Identify and describe reflections of 3-D structures. [Geometry Goal 3]

Key Activities

Students build structures with centimeter cubes on a 4-by-4 grid. They record what they see at eye level for two or more sides of the structure.

Key Vocabulary

blueprint

Materials

- *Math Masters,* pp. 378–380
- at least 25 centimeter cubes (or other size cubes)
- scissors

2 Extending the Project

Students build additional structures.

Materials

- centimeter cubes

Advance Preparation

This project can be done with cubes of any size, as long as students use cubes that are all the same size. If students use cubes other than cm cubes, you will need to make and distribute copies of a Blueprint Mat like the one on *Math Masters,* page 378. It should show squares that are the size of one face of the cubes being used.

Prepare four direction signs for a class demonstration and label them as follows:

↑BACK↑ ↑FRONT↑ ↑LEFT SIDE↑ ↑RIGHT SIDE↑

Arrange a table so that one student can sit at each of the four sides. There should be space on all sides of the table so that the rest of the class can gather around it. Place the direction signs and a copy of *Math Masters,* page 378 on the table.

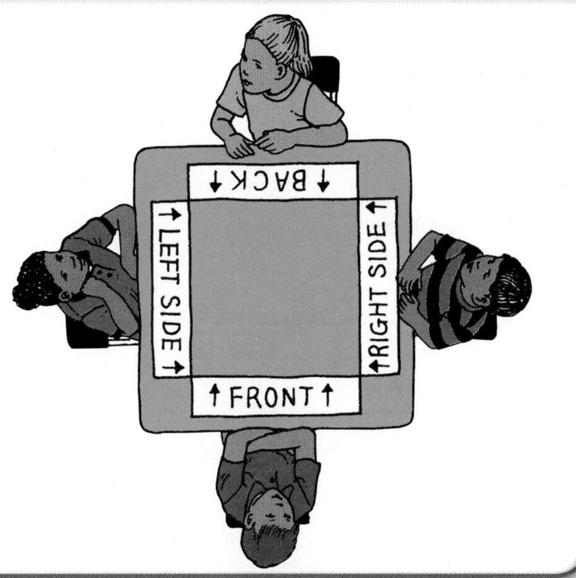

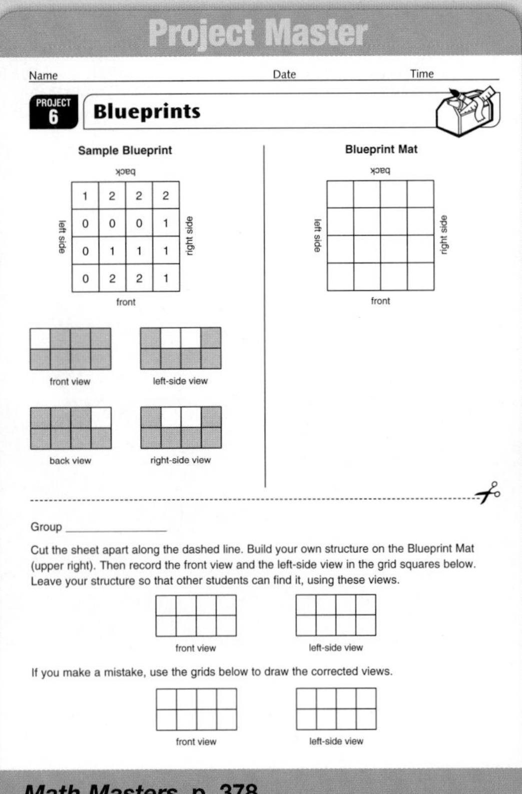

Project Master

Name Date Time

PROJECT 6 **Blueprints**

Sample Blueprint

back

1	2	2	2
0	0	0	1
0	1	1	1
0	2	2	1

left side / right side / front

front view left-side view

back view right-side view

Blueprint Mat

back / left side / right side / front

Group

Cut the sheet apart along the dashed line. Build your own structure on the Blueprint Mat (upper right). Then record the front view and the left-side view in the grid squares below. Leave your structure so that other students can find it, using these views.

front view left-side view

If you make a mistake, use the grids below to draw the corrected views.

front view left-side view

Math Masters, p. 378

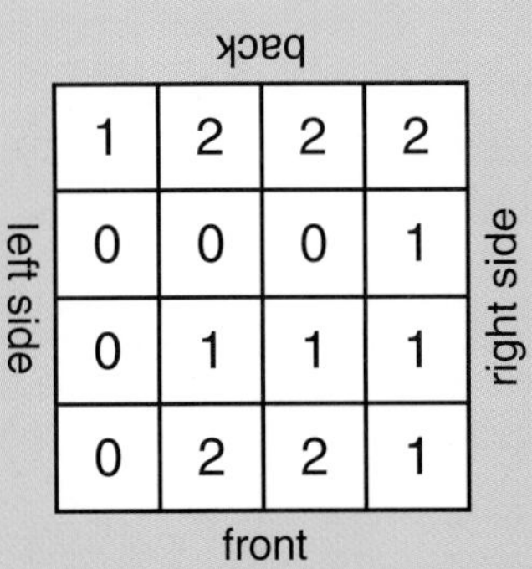

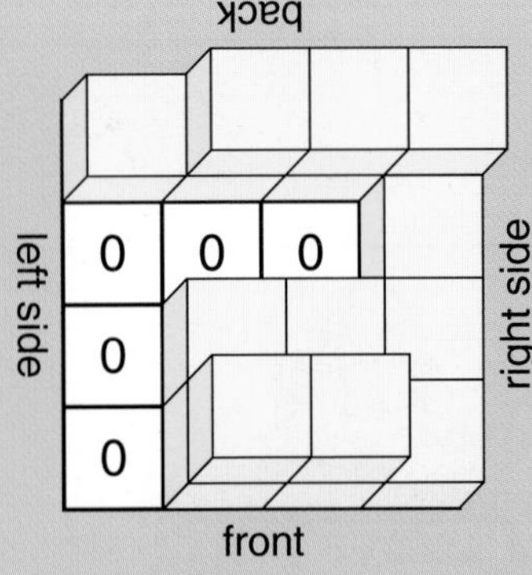

Building a structure on the blueprint

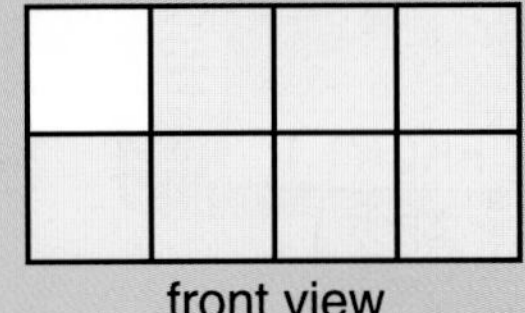

1 Doing the Project

▶ Building a Structure and Recording Four Views of It

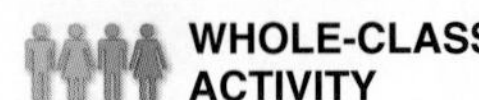

(*Math Masters,* p. 378)

Seat four students at the demonstration table and gather the rest of the class around it. Explain how to use the sample **blueprint** (*Math Masters,* page 378, top left) to build a structure out of cm cubes:

> The number in each square tells how many cubes to stack on the square: Stack 2 cubes on each 2-square, 1 cube on each 1-square, and no cubes on each 0-square.

After students have built the structure, have the student who is seated on the FRONT side of the blueprint stoop down so that the structure is at eye level. The student will then see the front view of the structure.

Ask the student to verify that this view of the structure looks like the shaded grid below the blueprint labeled "front view" (on *Math Masters,* page 378). Be sure to mention that the shaded squares do not show *only* what is in the *front* row of the structure. For example, the *front* row has *no* cubes in the first square on the left. Yet, the last row has *one* cube in that position, so the viewer sees *one* cube, not zero cubes. Similarly, the front row has one cube in the last square on the right. But since the back row has two cubes in that position, the viewer sees two cubes, not one cube.

Ask the other three students at the demonstration table to verify that the appropriate shaded grid below the blueprint (on *Math Masters,* page 378) represents what they actually see. Then ask them to change seats and verify each of the other three views. Let other students do the same, or divide the class into groups of four and ask each group to replicate the structure and verify the views.

Relating the Views of Opposite Sides

(*Math Masters,* pp. 378 and 379)

Have partners share cubes. Students work on the tasks on *Math Masters,* page 379 independently and then compare each other's work. Have students follow the blueprint on *Math Masters,* page 379 but build it on the Blueprint Mat on *Math Masters,* page 378. Bring the class together to discuss the results. Ask questions like the following:

- Is it possible to build two different structures from the same blueprint? no
- How are the views of opposite sides alike? They have the same number of shaded squares.
- How do they differ? The shading pattern is reversed.

Building Structures Based on Two Views

(*Math Masters,* p. 378)

In this activity, each student builds a structure on the Blueprint Mat on *Math Masters,* page 378 (upper right) and then draws the front and left-side views on two grids at the bottom of the page. Then students cut off the lower portion of the master and give it to you. Redistribute these sheets so that no student gets his or her own sheet. Students then walk around and try to find the structures recorded on their sheets.

There are a number of ways to organize this activity. Here is a suggested procedure:

1. Ask students to cut *Math Masters,* page 378 into two parts along the dashed line.
2. Divide the class into two groups—Group A and Group B. Ask students to write their group letter on the lower portion of the master.
3. Each student designs and builds a structure on the Blueprint Mat and draws the front and left-side views on the lower portion of *Math Masters,* page 378.
4. When students have completed Step 3, they raise their hands to signal that they are ready to have you check their work. If students made a mistake, have them correct their work on the second set of grids.
5. After everyone's work has been checked, students hand in the lower portion of the master.
6. Pass out these sheets randomly—Group A's sheets to students in Group B and Group B's sheets to students in Group A. Students then walk about the classroom and try to identify the structures that match their sheets.

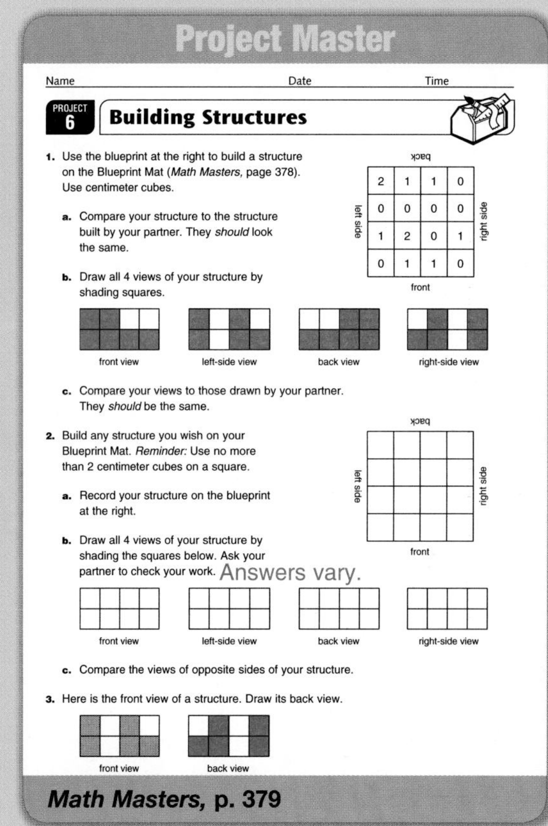

Project Master

Name Date Time

PROJECT 6 **Building Structures**

1. Use the blueprint at the right to build a structure on the Blueprint Mat (*Math Masters,* page 378). Use centimeter cubes.

   back (left side / right side / front)

2	1	1	0
0	0	0	0
1	2	0	1
0	1	1	0

   a. Compare your structure to the structure built by your partner. They *should* look the same.

   b. Draw all 4 views of your structure by shading squares.

   front view left-side view back view right-side view

   c. Compare your views to those drawn by your partner. They *should* be the same.

2. Build any structure you wish on your Blueprint Mat. *Reminder:* Use no more than 2 centimeter cubes on a square.

   back left side right side front

   a. Record your structure on the blueprint at the right.

   b. Draw all 4 views of your structure by shading the squares below. Ask your partner to check your work. Answers vary.

   front view left-side view back view right-side view

   c. Compare the views of opposite sides of your structure.

3. Here is the front view of a structure. Draw its back view.

   front view back view

Math Masters, p. 379

▶ Drawing a Structure

(*Math Masters,* p. 380)

Ask students to solve Problem 1 on *Math Masters,* page 380. Tell them to build the structure with their cubes if it will help.

Go over the answers. Remind students that the shading patterns for views of opposite sides are reversed. The back view should be the reverse of the front view, and the left-side view should be the reverse of the right-side view.

▶ Building Structures Specified by Views of Two Adjacent Sides

(*Math Masters,* pp. 378 and 380)

In Problems 2 and 3 on *Math Masters,* page 380, students are given a front view and a left-side view of a structure. They build structures based on these views and make a blueprint for each structure.

From these activities, students should conclude that it is possible to build different structures from the same two adjacent views (Problem 4a). Furthermore, if students know two adjacent views, they can draw the other two views (see *Math Masters,* page 378). Therefore, it is usually possible to build different structures from the same four views (Problem 4b).

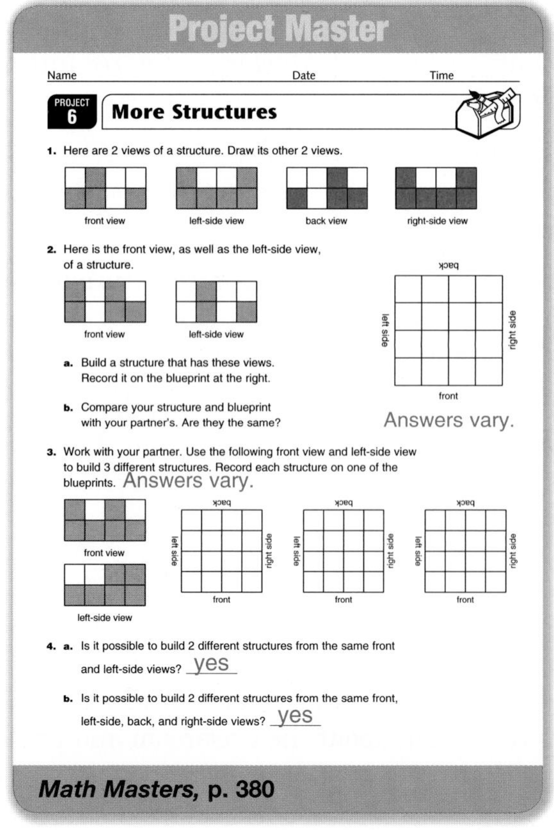

Project Master

Name Date Time

PROJECT 6 **More Structures**

1. Here are 2 views of a structure. Draw its other 2 views.

front view left-side view back view right-side view

2. Here is the front view, as well as the left-side view, of a structure.

front view left-side view

back / left side / right side / front

a. Build a structure that has these views. Record it on the blueprint at the right.

b. Compare your structure and blueprint with your partner's. Are they the same? Answers vary.

3. Work with your partner. Use the following front view and left-side view to build 3 different structures. Record each structure on one of the blueprints. Answers vary.

front view

left-side view

back / left side / right side / front

4. a. Is it possible to build 2 different structures from the same front and left-side views? yes

b. Is it possible to build 2 different structures from the same front, left-side, back, and right-side views? yes

Math Masters, p. 380

2 Extending the Project

Building More Structures

It is not always possible to build two different structures from the same two adjacent views, as shown in the following example:

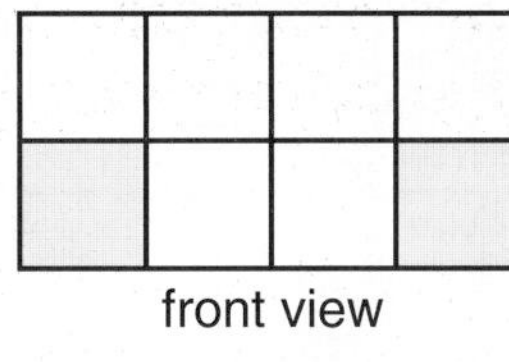

front view

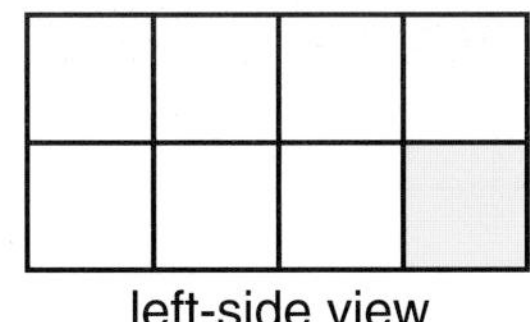

left-side view

Ask students to build the structure above and then try to find another different structure that matches the blueprint. There is only one possible structure, shown in the following blueprint:

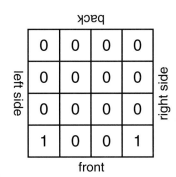

back

left side					right side
	0	0	0	0	
	0	0	0	0	
	0	0	0	0	
	1	0	0	1	

front

Invite students to build and represent structures with blueprint grids other than 4 by 4 (for example, 5 by 5, 4 by 6, and so on) and heights greater than two cubes.

Project
7
Numbers, Mayan Style

Objectives To introduce the Mayan numeration system; and to provide practice converting between Mayan numerals and base-ten numerals.

Technology Resources www.everydaymathonline.com

eToolkit

Algorithms Practice

EM Facts Workshop Game™

Family Letters

Assessment Management

Common Core State Standards

Curriculum Focal Points

Interactive Teacher's Lesson Guide

1 Doing the Project

Recommended Use During or after Unit 5

Key Concepts and Skills

- Identify places in whole numbers and the values of the digits in those places. [Number and Numeration Goal 1]
- Use symbolic notation to represent numbers in base-twenty. [Number and Numeration Goal 1]
- Use extended multiplication facts to convert base-twenty numerals to base-ten numerals. [Operations and Computation Goal 3]
- Use division to convert base-ten numerals to base-twenty numerals. [Operations and Computation Goal 4]

Key Activities

Students work with partners to convert between Mayan numerals and base-ten numerals.

Materials

- *Math Masters,* p. 381
- *Student Reference Book,* p. 293
- map of North America

2 Extending the Project

Students further investigate Mayan numeration through literature.

Materials

- *Secrets of Ancient Cultures: The Maya—Activities and Crafts from a Mysterious Land*
- *The Maya (True Books)*

Advance Preparation

For the optional activity in Part 2, obtain copies of ***Secrets of Ancient Cultures: The Maya—Activities and Crafts from a Mysterious Land*** by Arlette N. Braman and Michelle Nidenoff (Wiley, 2003) and ***The Maya (True Books)*** by Stefanie Takacs (Children's Press, 2004).

1 Doing the Project

Comparing the Mayan Place-Value System to Our Place-Value System

WHOLE-CLASS ACTIVITY

(*Math Masters,* p. 381)

Have students read the article "Numbers, Mayan Style" on *Math Masters,* page 381. Ask a volunteer to locate where the Maya lived on a classroom map or on page 293 of the World Tour section of the *Student Reference Book*.

Review our base-ten place-value numeration system. For example, in the numeral 2,457, the digit 2 stands for 2 [1,000s], the digit 4 for 4 [100s], and so on. (*See margin.*)

If necessary, try a few additional examples to make sure that students understand how our place-value system works before comparing it to the Mayan system.

Next, discuss the Mayan place-value system.

- How many symbols did the Maya use in their numerals? 3
- What are the three symbols? (shell) ● ——
- How many symbols are used in our place-value system? 10

Refer to the example of the Mayan numeral for 837 on *Math Masters,* page 381. Point out each of the "places." Remind students that Mayan numerals read from top to bottom. Students should notice the space that is left between each place. If this space is not shown clearly, it is easy to mistake the place a symbol is in.

- Can there be more than one symbol in a place in the Mayan system? Yes. In the Mayan system, a single dot is one symbol. So two dots are two symbols in one place.
- In our place-value system, can there be more than one symbol in a place? no
- In Mayan numerals, how is the value of the symbols in a place determined? By adding the values of all the symbols in that place

Remind students that in our place-value system, the value of a place is 10 times the value of the preceding place. Thus, the values of the first three places in a numeral for a whole number, from right to left, are 1, 10, and 10 ∗ 10 (or 100). In the Mayan system, the value of a place is 20 times the value of the preceding place. Thus, the values of the first three places, from bottom to top, are 1, 20, and 20 ∗ 20 (or 400).

- What is the value of the next (fourth) place in the Mayan system? 20 ∗ 20 ∗ 20 = 8,000

$$\begin{array}{rr} 2\ [1{,}000\text{s}] = & 2{,}000 \\ 4\ [100\text{s}] = & 400 \\ 5\ [10\text{s}] = & 50 \\ 7\ [1\text{s}] = & +\ \ 7 \\ \hline & 2{,}457 \end{array}$$

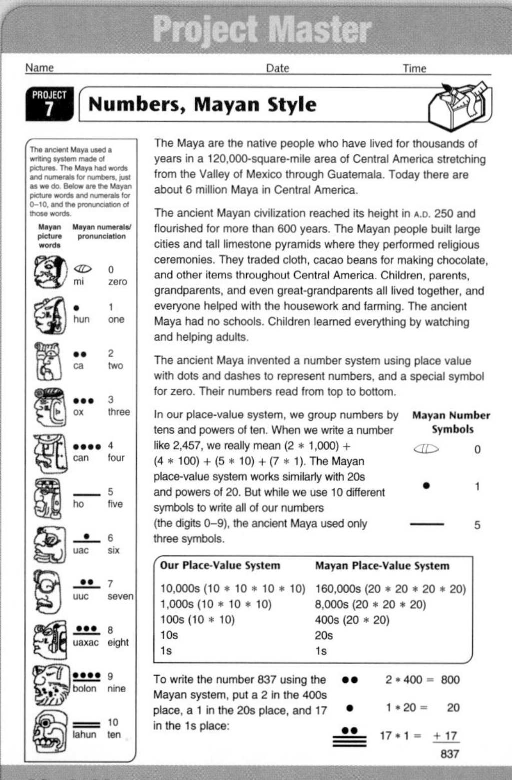
Project Master

Name Date Time

PROJECT 7 **Numbers, Mayan Style**

The ancient Maya used a writing system made of pictures. The Maya had words and numerals for numbers, just as we do. Below are the Mayan picture words and numerals for 0–10, and the pronunciation of those words.

Mayan picture words	Mayan numerals/pronunciation	
	(shell) mi	0 zero
	● hun	1 one
	●● ca	2 two
	●●● ox	3 three
	●●●● can	4 four
	—— ho	5 five
	uac	6 six
	uuc	7 seven
	uaxac	8 eight
	bolon	9 nine
	lahun	10 ten

The Maya are the native people who have lived for thousands of years in a 120,000-square-mile area of Central America stretching from the Valley of Mexico through Guatemala. Today there are about 6 million Maya in Central America.

The ancient Mayan civilization reached its height in A.D. 250 and flourished for more than 600 years. The Mayan people built large cities and tall limestone pyramids where they performed religious ceremonies. They traded cloth, cacao beans for making chocolate, and other items throughout Central America. Children, parents, grandparents, and even great-grandparents all lived together, and everyone helped with the housework and farming. The ancient Maya had no schools. Children learned everything by watching and helping adults.

The ancient Maya invented a number system using place value with dots and dashes to represent numbers, and a special symbol for zero. Their numbers read from top to bottom.

In our place-value system, we group numbers by tens and powers of ten. When we write a number like 2,457, we really mean (2 ∗ 1,000) + (4 ∗ 100) + (5 ∗ 10) + (7 ∗ 1). The Mayan place-value system works similarly with 20s and powers of 20. But while we use 10 different symbols to write all of our numbers (the digits 0–9), the ancient Maya used only three symbols.

Mayan Number Symbols

(shell)	0
●	1
——	5

Our Place-Value System	Mayan Place-Value System
10,000s (10 ∗ 10 ∗ 10 ∗ 10)	160,000s (20 ∗ 20 ∗ 20 ∗ 20)
1,000s (10 ∗ 10 ∗ 10)	8,000s (20 ∗ 20 ∗ 20)
100s (10 ∗ 10)	400s (20 ∗ 20)
10s	20s
1s	1s

To write the number 837 using the Mayan system, put a 2 in the 400s place, a 1 in the 20s place, and 17 in the 1s place:

●●	2 ∗ 400 =	800
●	1 ∗ 20 =	20
	17 ∗ 1 =	+ 17
		837

Math Masters, p. 381

Write each Mayan numeral with digits. Then add.

1. 2,106

— = 5 [400s] = 2,000

— = 5 [20s] = 100

● — = 6 [1s] = 6

2. 2,476

● — = 6 [400s] = 2,400

●●● = 3 [20s] = 60

● ≡ = 16 [1s] = 16

3. 20,023

●● = 2 [8,000s] = 16,000

═ = 10 [400s] = 4,000

● = 1 [20] = 20

●●● = 3 [1s] = 3

Try This

4. Write each base-10 numeral as a Mayan numeral.

a. 153

●●● ≡

b. 1,594

●●●

▶ Converting between Mayan and Base-Ten Numerals

WHOLE-CLASS ACTIVITY

Write the problem below on the board. Discuss how the Mayan numeral in this problem is converted to a base-ten numeral. Then convert several more Mayan numerals as a class. *For example:*

●●●	3 [400s] =	1,200
●●	2 [20s] =	40
●●●● —	9 [1s] =	+ 9
		1,249
●●●● —	9 [20s] =	180
●●●● ≡	19 [1s] =	+ 19
		199

You might also have students make up Mayan numerals for the class to convert.

On the board, write Problems 1–4 shown in the margin. For Problems 1–3, have students write each Mayan numeral with digits and then add. Go over the answers with the class.

For Problem 4, students will write each base-ten numeral as a Mayan numeral. Conversions of base-ten numerals to Mayan numerals involve division. Following are answers for Problem 4.

a. 153

How many [20s] are in 153?

The remainder is 13.

$20\overline{)153}$
−140   7 ●● —
13
7 [20s] in 153
13 [1s] ●●● ═

b. 1,594

How many [400s] are in 1,594?

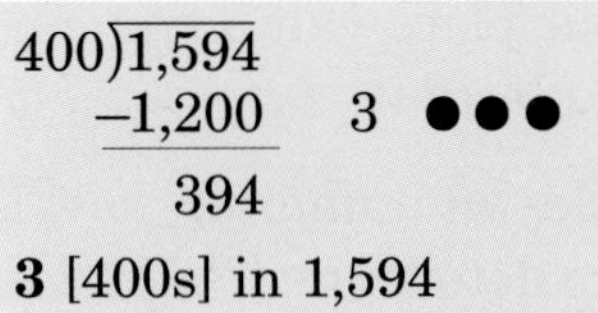
$400\overline{)1,594}$
−1,200   3 ●●●
394
3 [400s] in 1,594

How many [20s] are in 394?

The remainder is 14.

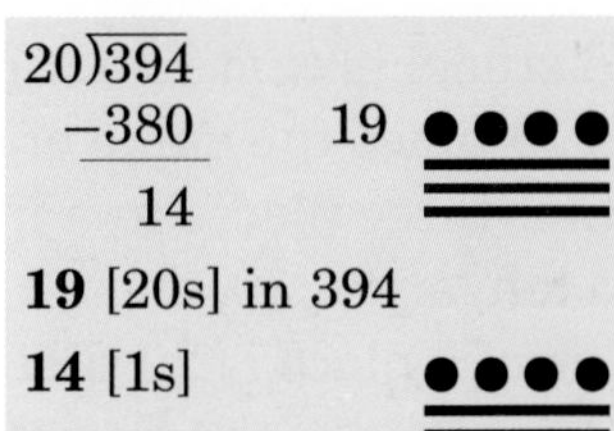
$20\overline{)394}$
−380   19 ●●●● ≡
14
19 [20s] in 394
14 [1s] ●●●● ═

2 Extending the Project

Learning More about the Maya

INDEPENDENT ACTIVITY

Invite students to find out more about the Maya in encyclopedias and in books such as ***Secrets of Ancient Cultures: The Maya—Activities and Crafts from a Mysterious Land*** by Arlette N. Braman and Michelle Nidenoff (Wiley, 2003) and ***The Maya (True Books)*** by Stefanie Takacs (Children's Press, 2004).

This would be a good opportunity to have students use the Internet to research and compare the Mayan numeral system with other numeral systems, for example, the Roman or Babylonian numeral system (which uses a base of 60).

Hindu-Arabic	0	1	2	3	4	5	6	7	8	9	10
Babylonian		▼	▼▼	▼▼▼	▼▼▼▼	▼▼▼ ▼▼	▼▼▼ ▼▼▼	▼▼▼▼ ▼▼▼	▼▼▼▼ ▼▼▼▼	▼▼▼▼▼ ▼▼▼▼	<
Egyptian		ǀ	ǀǀ	ǀǀǀ	ǀǀǀǀ	ǀǀǀ ǀǀ	ǀǀǀ ǀǀǀ	ǀǀǀǀ ǀǀǀ	ǀǀǀǀ ǀǀǀǀ	ǀǀǀ ǀǀǀ ǀǀǀ	∩
Mayan	(shell)	•	••	•••	••••	—	• —	•• —	••• —	•••• —	— —
Greek		α	β	γ	δ	ϵ	ϕ	ζ	η	θ	ι
Roman		I	II	III	IV	V	VI	VII	VIII	IX	X

Students may also want to explore other base systems, such as base five, which is used by people in Kenya. The chart below describes this "one-hand system."

Base-Five Symbol	Base-Five Grouping	Base-Five Symbol
0_{five}		0 fingers
1_{five}	X	1 finger
2_{five}	XX	2 fingers
3_{five}	XXX	3 fingers
4_{five}	XXXX	4 fingers
10_{five}	(XXXXX)	1 hand and 0 fingers
11_{five}	(XXXXX) X	1 hand and 1 finger
12_{five}	(XXXXX) XX	1 hand and 2 fingers
13_{five}	(XXXXX) XXX	1 hand and 3 fingers
14_{five}	(XXXXX) XXXX	1 hand and 4 fingers
20_{five}	(XXXXX) (XXXXX)	2 hands and 0 fingers

Algorithm 1 Project

U.S. Traditional Addition

 **Objective** To introduce U.S. traditional addition.

Technology Resources  www.everydaymathonline.com

 eToolkit

 Algorithms Practice

 EM Facts Workshop Game™

 Family Letters

 Assessment Management

 Common Core State Standards

Curriculum Focal Points

 Interactive Teacher's Lesson Guide

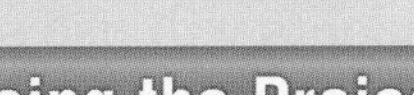

1 Doing the Project

Recommended Use After Lesson 2•7

Key Concepts and Skills

- Identify places in whole numbers and the values of the digits in those places.
  [Number and Numeration Goal 1]
- Use addition facts to find sums of multidigit whole numbers.
  [Operations and Computation Goal 1]
- Add multidigit whole numbers.
  [Operations and Computation Goal 2]
- Write and solve addition number stories.
  [Operations and Computation Goal 2]

Key Activities

Students explore and practice U.S. traditional addition with multidigit whole numbers.

Key Vocabulary

U.S. traditional addition

Materials

- *Math Journal 1* or *2,* pp. 1P–4P
- *Student Reference Book,* p. 24A

2 Extending the Project

Students solve multidigit addition problems, first using the focus algorithm (partial-sums addition) and then using any algorithm they wish.

Materials

- Online Additional Practice, pp. 4A–4D
- *Student Reference Book,* pp. 10, 11, and 24A

Student Page

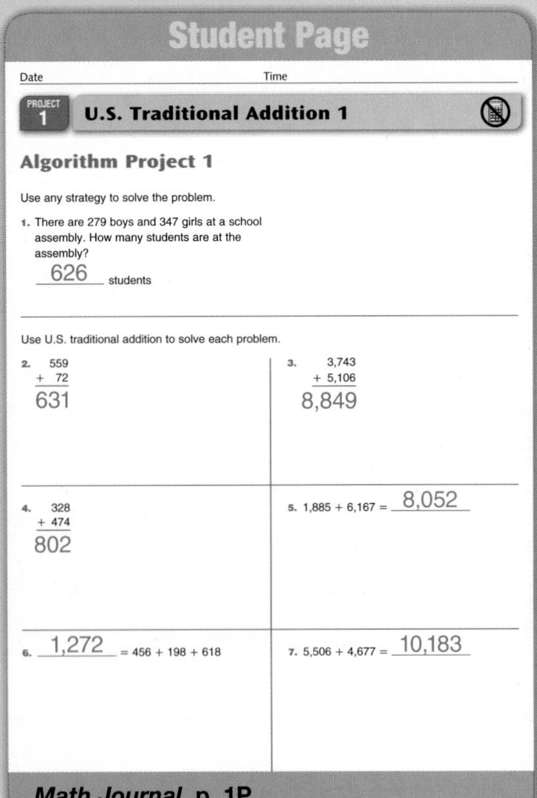

Date Time

PROJECT 1 **U.S. Traditional Addition 1**

Algorithm Project 1

Use any strategy to solve the problem.

1. There are 279 boys and 347 girls at a school assembly. How many students are at the assembly?
626 students

Use U.S. traditional addition to solve each problem.

2. 559 + 72 = 631

3. 3,743 + 5,106 = 8,849

4. 328 + 474 = 802

5. 1,885 + 6,167 = 8,052

6. 1,272 = 456 + 198 + 618

7. 5,506 + 4,677 = 10,183

Math Journal, p. 1P

1 Doing the Project

▶ Solving an Addition Problem

INDEPENDENT ACTIVITY

(*Math Journal 1* or *2,* p. 1P)

Ask students to solve Problem 1 on journal page 1P. Tell them they may use any methods they wish, but they may not use calculators.

▶ Discussing Solutions

WHOLE-CLASS ACTIVITY

(*Math Journal 1* or *2,* p. 1P)

Discuss students' solutions to Problem 1 on journal page 1P. 279 + 347 = 626 students Expect that students will use several different methods, including column addition and partial-sums addition. Some students may also use U.S. traditional addition. *Possible strategies:*

▷ Using column addition

	100s	10s	1s
	2	**7**	**9**
	+ 3	**4**	**7**
Add the numbers in each column.	5	11	16
Trade 10 ones for 1 ten.	5	12	6
Trade 10 tens for 1 hundred.	**6**	**2**	**6**

▷ Using partial-sums addition

		2 7 9
		+ 3 4 7
Add the 100s.	200 + 300 →	5 0 0
Add the 10s.	70 + 40 →	1 1 0
Add the 1s.	9 + 7 →	1 6
Add the partial sums.	500 + 110 + 16 →	**6 2 6**

▷ Using U.S. traditional addition

```
  1 1
  2 7 9
+ 3 4 7
-------
  6 2 6
```

▶ Introducing U.S. Traditional Addition

WHOLE-CLASS ACTIVITY

After you have discussed students' solutions, and even if one or more students used **U.S. traditional addition,** demonstrate it as described below.

Example 1: 279 + 347

Step 1:

Add the 1s: 9 + 7 = 16.
16 = 1 ten + 6 ones
Write 6 in the 1s place below the line.
Write 1 above the numbers in the 10s place.

```
    1
  2 7 9
+ 3 4 7
-------
      6
```

Step 2:

Add the 10s: 1 + 7 + 4 = 12.

12 tens = 1 hundred + 2 tens

Write 2 in the 10s place below the line.

Write 1 above the numbers in the 100s place.

$$\begin{array}{r} \mathbf{1}\,\mathbf{1} \\ 2\,\mathbf{7}\,9 \\ +\;3\,\mathbf{4}\,7 \\ \hline \mathbf{2}\,6 \end{array}$$

Step 3:

Add the 100s: 1 + 2 + 3 = 6.

Write 6 in the 100s place below the line.

$$\begin{array}{r} \mathbf{1}\,1 \\ \mathbf{2}\,7\,9 \\ +\;\mathbf{3}\,4\,7 \\ \hline \mathbf{6}\,2\,6 \end{array}$$

279 + 347 = 626

There are 626 students at the assembly.

NOTE Throughout the discussion of U.S. traditional addition, be sure that students understand the values of the digits. For instance, in Step 2 of Example 1, 1 + 7 + 4 = 12 means 1 ten + 7 tens + 4 tens = 12 tens (1 hundred + 2 tens) or 10 + 70 + 40 = 120.

Example 2: 8,654 + 4,789

Step 1:

Add the 1s: 4 + 9 = 13.

13 = 1 ten + 3 ones

Write 3 in the 1s place below the line.

Write 1 above the numbers in the 10s place.

$$\begin{array}{r} \mathbf{1} \\ 8\,6\,5\,\mathbf{4} \\ +\;4\,7\,8\,\mathbf{9} \\ \hline \mathbf{3} \end{array}$$

Step 2:

Add the 10s: 1 + 5 + 8 = 14.

14 tens = 1 hundred + 4 tens

Write 4 in the 10s place below the line.

Write 1 above the numbers in the 100s place.

$$\begin{array}{r} \mathbf{1}\,\mathbf{1} \\ 8\,6\,\mathbf{5}\,4 \\ +\;4\,7\,\mathbf{8}\,9 \\ \hline \mathbf{4}\,3 \end{array}$$

Step 3:

Add the 100s: 1 + 6 + 7 = 14.

14 hundreds = 1 thousand + 4 hundreds

Write 4 in the 100s place below the line.

Write 1 above the numbers in the 1,000s place.

$$\begin{array}{r} \mathbf{1}\,\mathbf{1}\,1 \\ 8\,\mathbf{6}\,5\,4 \\ +\;4\,\mathbf{7}\,8\,9 \\ \hline \mathbf{4}\,4\,3 \end{array}$$

Step 4:

Add the 1,000s: 1 + 8 + 4 = 13.

13 thousands = 1 ten thousand + 3 thousands

Write 3 in the 1,000s place below the line.

Write 1 in the 10,000s place below the line.

$$\begin{array}{r} \mathbf{1}\,1\,1 \\ \mathbf{8}\,6\,5\,4 \\ +\;\mathbf{4}\,7\,8\,9 \\ \hline \mathbf{1}\,\mathbf{3}\,4\,4\,3 \end{array}$$

8,654 + 4,789 = 13,443

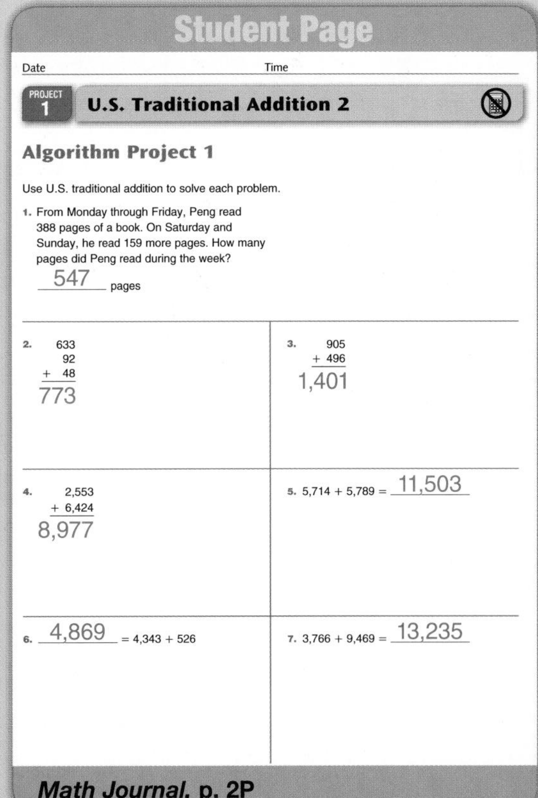

Student Page

Date Time

PROJECT 1 **U.S. Traditional Addition 2**

Algorithm Project 1

Use U.S. traditional addition to solve each problem.

1. From Monday through Friday, Peng read 388 pages of a book. On Saturday and Sunday, he read 159 more pages. How many pages did Peng read during the week?
   547 pages

2. 633 + 92 + 48 = 773

3. 905 + 496 = 1,401

4. 2,553 + 6,424 = 8,977

5. 5,714 + 5,789 = 11,503

6. 4,869 = 4,343 + 526

7. 3,766 + 9,469 = 13,235

Math Journal, p. 2P

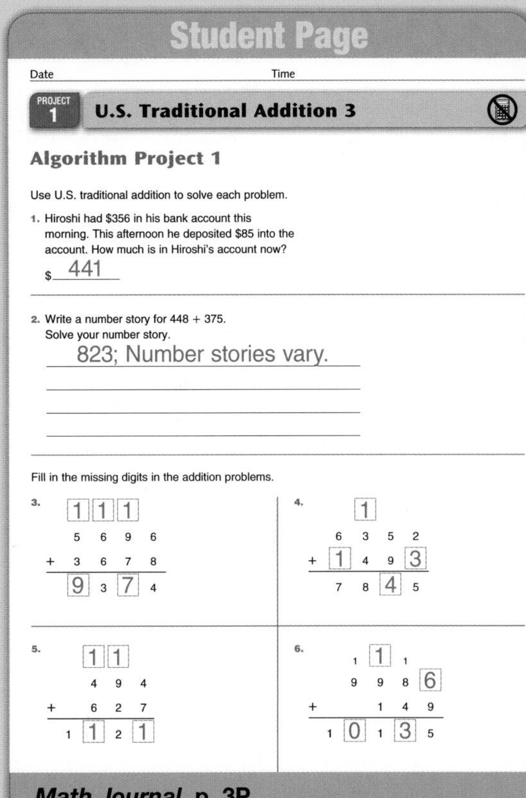

Student Page

Date Time

PROJECT 1 **U.S. Traditional Addition 3**

Algorithm Project 1

Use U.S. traditional addition to solve each problem.

1. Hiroshi had $356 in his bank account this morning. This afternoon he deposited $85 into the account. How much is in Hiroshi's account now?
   $ 441

2. Write a number story for 448 + 375. Solve your number story.
   823; Number stories vary.

Fill in the missing digits in the addition problems.

3. (1 1 1) 5 6 9 6 + 3 6 7 8 = 9 3 7 4

4. (1) 6 3 5 2 + 1 4 9 3 = 7 8 4 5

5. (1 1) 4 9 4 + 6 2 7 = 1 1 2 1

6. (1 1 1) 9 9 8 6 + 1 4 9 = 1 0 1 3 5

Math Journal, p. 3P

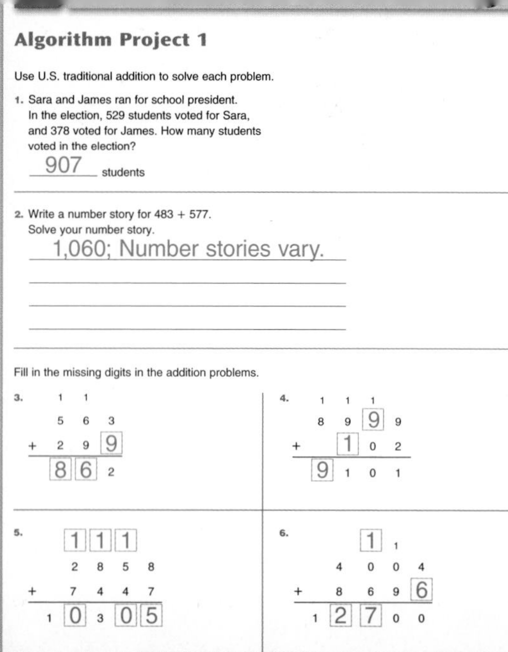
Algorithm Project 1

Use U.S. traditional addition to solve each problem.

1. Sara and James ran for school president. In the election, 529 students voted for Sara, and 378 voted for James. How many students voted in the election?
   907 students

2. Write a number story for 483 + 577. Solve your number story.
   1,060; Number stories vary.

Fill in the missing digits in the addition problems.

3.
```
    1 1
    5 6 3
+   2 9 [9]
  [8][6] 2
```

4.
```
    1 1 1
    8 9 [9] 9
+    [1] 0 2
  [9] 1 0 1
```

5.
```
   [1][1][1]
    2 8 5 8
+   7 4 4 7
 1 [0] 3 [0][5]
```

6.
```
      [1] 1
    4 0 0 4
+   8 6 9 [6]
 1 [2][7] 0 0
```

Math Journal, p. 4P

Go to www.everydaymathonline.com to access the additional practice pages.

Online Master

Name Date Time

PROJECT 1 **Partial-Sums Addition** Online Additional Practice

Algorithm Project 1

Use partial-sums addition to solve each problem.

1. There were 596 people in the audience when the concert began. During the concert, 55 more people came. How many people attended the concert?
   651 people

2. 447 + 955 = 1,402

3. 5,689 + 8,139 = 13,828

4. 306 + 462 = 768

5. 3,746 + 6,255 = 10,001

6. 2,094 = 299 + 1,795

7. 784 + 889 = 1,673

Online Additional Practice, p. 4A

Suggestions:

▷ 56 + 49 = ? 105

▷ 774 + 68 = ? 842

▷ 482 + 315 = ? 797

▷ 6,556 + 3,984 = ? 10,540

▷ 528 + 933 + 295 = ? 1,756

▷ 5,088 + 6,515 = ? 11,603

▶ Practicing U.S. Traditional Addition

(*Math Journal 1* or *2,* pp. 1P–4P; *Student Reference Book,* p. 24A)

When students are ready, have them solve Problems 2–7 on journal page 1P. They may find the example on *Student Reference Book,* page 24A helpful.

Journal pages 2P–4P provide students with additional practice using U.S. traditional addition. Use these journal pages as necessary.

2 Extending the Project

▶ Solving Multidigit Addition Problems

(Online Additional Practice, pp. 4A–4D; *Student Reference Book,* pp. 10, 11, and 24A)

Online practice pages 4A–4D provide students with additional practice solving multidigit addition problems. Use these pages as necessary.

Encourage students to use the focus algorithm (partial-sums addition) to solve the problems on practice page 4A. Invite them to use any algorithm they wish to solve the problems on the remaining pages.

Students may find the examples on *Student Reference Book,* pages 10, 11, and 24A helpful.

Algorithm **2** Project

U.S. Traditional Addition: Decimals

Objective To introduce U.S. traditional addition with decimals.

Technology Resources www.everydaymathonline.com

eToolkit

Algorithms Practice

EM Facts Workshop Game™

Family Letters

Assessment Management

Common Core State Standards

Curriculum Focal Points

Interactive Teacher's Lesson Guide

1 Doing the Project

Recommended Use After Lesson 4•5

Key Concepts and Skills

- Identify places in whole numbers and decimals and the values of the digits in those places.
  [Number and Numeration Goal 1]
- Use addition facts to find sums of decimals.
  [Operations and Computation Goal 1]
- Add decimals.
  [Operations and Computation Goal 2]
- Write and solve addition number stories with decimals.
  [Operations and Computation Goal 2]

Key Activities

Students explore and practice U.S. traditional addition with decimals.

Materials

- ◆ *Math Journal 1* or *2,* pp. 5P–8P
- ◆ *Student Reference Book,* p. 40A
- ◆ $1 and $10 bills (*Math Masters,* p. 428; optional)
- ◆ dimes and pennies (optional)
- ◆ base-10 blocks (optional)

2 Extending the Project

Students solve decimal addition problems, first using the focus algorithm (partial-sums addition) and then using any algorithm they choose.

Materials

- ◆ Online Additional Practice, pp. 8A–8D
- ◆ *Student Reference Book,* pp. 34–36 and 40A

Student Page

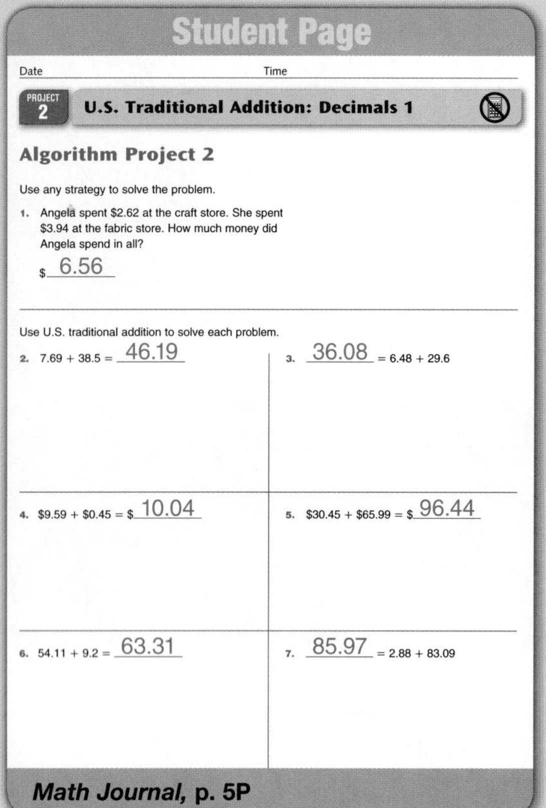
Date Time

PROJECT 2 **U.S. Traditional Addition: Decimals 1**

Algorithm Project 2

Use any strategy to solve the problem.

1. Angela spent $2.62 at the craft store. She spent $3.94 at the fabric store. How much money did Angela spend in all?

$ 6.56

Use U.S. traditional addition to solve each problem.

2. 7.69 + 38.5 = 46.19
3. 36.08 = 6.48 + 29.6
4. $9.59 + $0.45 = $ 10.04
5. $30.45 + $65.99 = $ 96.44
6. 54.11 + 9.2 = 63.31
7. 85.97 = 2.88 + 83.09

Math Journal, p. 5P

1 Doing the Project

▶ Solving a Decimal Addition Problem

INDEPENDENT ACTIVITY

(*Math Journal 1* or *2,* p. 5P)

Ask students to solve Problem 1 on journal page 5P. Tell them they may use base-10 blocks, play money, paper and pencil, or any other tools they wish, except calculators.

▶ Discussing Solutions

WHOLE-CLASS ACTIVITY

(*Math Journal 1* or *2,* p. 5P)

Discuss students' solutions to Problem 1 on journal page 5P. $2.62 + $3.94 = $6.56 Expect that students will use several different methods, including base-10 blocks, play money, and partial-sums addition. Some students may also use U.S. traditional addition. *Possible strategies:*

▷ Modeling with base-10 blocks

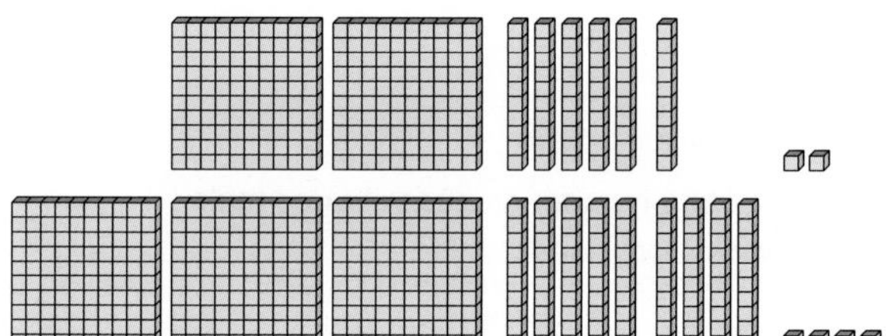

Show 2.62 and 3.94 with blocks.

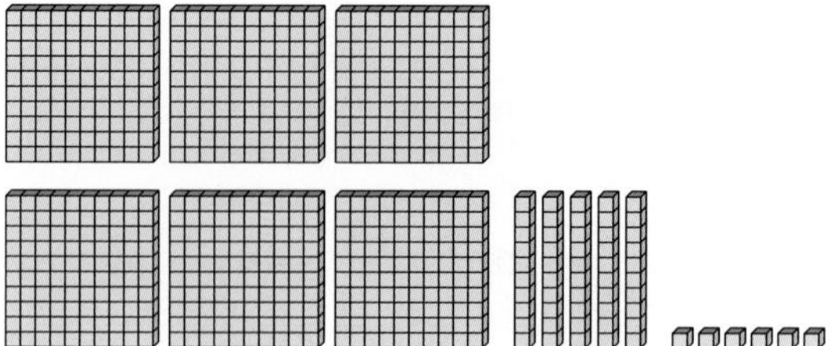

Trade 10 longs for 1 flat.

$2.62 + $3.94 = $6.56

▷ Using shorthand pictures of base-10 blocks

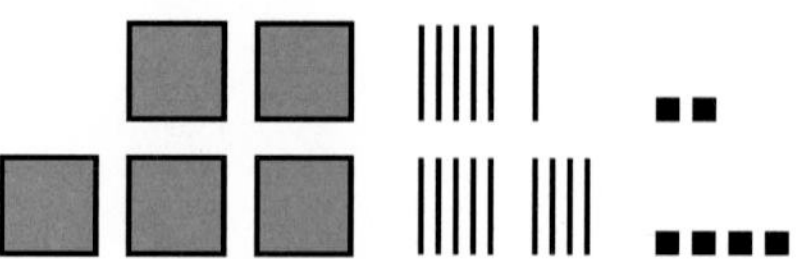

Draw a picture for each number.

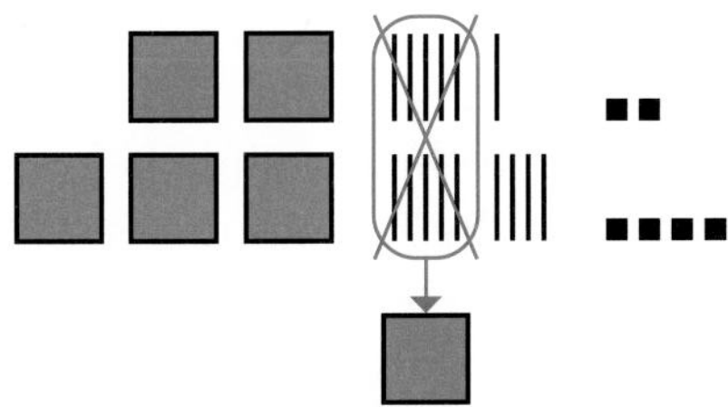

Draw a ring around 10 longs and trade them for 1 flat.

This drawing shows 6.56.

\$2.62 + \$3.94 = \$6.56

▷ Using partial-sums addition

		2.62
		+ 3.94
Add the 1s.	2 + 3 →	5.00
Add the 0.1s.	0.6 + 0.9 →	1.50
Add the 0.01s.	0.02 + 0.04 →	0.06
Add the partial sums.	5.00 + 1.50 + 0.06 →	**6.56**

▷ Using U.S. traditional addition

$$\begin{array}{r} {}^{1} \\ 2.62 \\ +\,3.94 \\ \hline 6.56 \end{array}$$

Introducing U.S. Traditional Addition for Decimals

WHOLE-CLASS ACTIVITY

After you have discussed students' solutions, and even if one or more students used U.S. traditional addition, demonstrate it again as described below.

Example 1: \$2.62 + \$3.94

Step 1:

Start with the 0.01s: 2 + 4 = 6.

$$\begin{array}{r} 2.6\mathbf{2} \\ +\,3.9\mathbf{4} \\ \hline \mathbf{6} \end{array}$$

Step 2:

Add the 0.1s: 6 + 9 = 15.
15 tenths = 1 whole + 5 tenths

$$\begin{array}{r} {}^{1} \\ 2.\mathbf{6}2 \\ +\,3.\mathbf{9}4 \\ \hline \mathbf{5}6 \end{array}$$

Step 3:

Add the 1s: 1 + 2 + 3 = 6.
Remember to include the decimal point in the answer.

$$\begin{array}{r} {}^{\mathbf{1}} \\ \mathbf{2}.62 \\ +\,\mathbf{3}.94 \\ \hline \mathbf{6}.56 \end{array}$$

\$2.62 + \$3.94 = \$6.56

Angela spent \$6.56 in all.

NOTE Throughout the discussion of U.S. traditional addition, be sure that students understand the values of the digits. For instance, in Step 1 of Example 1, 2 + 4 = 6 means 2 hundredths + 4 hundredths = 6 hundredths, or 0.02 + 0.04 = 0.06. The same structure applies to the carry digits.

Algorithm Project 2

Use U.S. traditional addition to solve each problem.

1. José had $5.98 in his wallet. He found 75¢ under his bed. How much money does José have now?
$ 6.73

2. 3.9 + 4.48 = 8.38

3. 0.8 + 9.94 = 10.74

4. 34.94 = 6.76 + 28.18

5. 1.09 + 24.58 = 25.67

6. 53.84 = 1.03 + 52.81

7. 3.8 + 77.92 = 81.72

Math Journal, p. 6P

places when adding decimals so that tenths are added to tenths, ones to ones, and so on. In the example below, write 4.6 as 4.60 so that both numbers have the same number of digits after the decimal point.

Example 2: 9.82 + 4.6

Step 1:

Start with the 0.01s: 2 + 0 = 2.

```
  9.82
+ 4.60
     2
```

Step 2:

Add the 0.1s: 8 + 6 = 14.
14 tenths = 1 whole + 4 tenths

```
  1
  9.82
+ 4.60
    42
```

Step 3:

Add the 1s: 1 + 9 + 4 = 14.
14 ones = 1 ten + 4 ones
Remember to include the decimal point in the answer.

```
  1
  9.82
+ 4.60
 14.42
```

9.82 + 4.6 = 14.42

You may want to work several more examples with the whole cla

Suggestions:

▷ 25.3 + 5.78 = ? 31.08

▷ 10.3 + 7.55 = ? 17.85

▷ 59.4 + 3.65 = ? 63.05

▷ $1.99 + $45.63 = ? $47.62

▷ 36.55 + 9.8 = ? 46.35

▷ $45.09 + $38.71 = ? $83.80

Student Page

Date Time

PROJECT 2 **U.S. Traditional Addition: Decimals 3**

Algorithm Project 2

Use U.S. traditional addition to solve each problem.

1. There is a flower growing in Kayla's garden. It was 22.48 centimeters tall. In three months, it grew 8.6 centimeters. How tall is the flower now?
31.08 centimeters

2. Write a number story for $3.80 + $5.12. Solve your number story.
$8.92; Number stories vary.

Fill in the missing digits in the addition problems.

3.
```
   1 1
   3.8 5
+  6.6 7
  10.5 2
```

4.
```
 1 1 1
   49.09
+   6.91
   56.00
```

5.
```
 1 1
   29.42
+   0.97
   30.39
```

6.
```
   1 1
   71.44
+  12.86
   84.30
```

Math Journal, p. 7P

▶ Practicing U.S. Traditional Addition for Decimals

(*Math Journal 1* or *2,* pp. 5P–8P; *Student Reference Book,* p. 40A)

When students are ready, have them solve Problems 2–7 on journ page 5P. They may find the example on *Student Reference Book,* page 40A helpful.

Journal pages 6P–8P provide students with additional practice using U.S. traditional addition. Use these journal pages as necessary.

2 Extending the Project

Solving Decimal Addition Problems

INDEPENDENT ACTIVITY

(Online Additional Practice, pp. 8A–8D; *Student Reference Book,* pp. 34–36 and 40A)

Online practice pages 8A–8D provide students with additional practice solving decimal addition problems. Use these pages as necessary.

Encourage students to use the focus algorithm (partial-sums addition) to solve the problems on practice page 8A. Invite them to use any algorithm they wish to solve the problems on the remaining pages.

Students may find the examples on *Student Reference Book,* pages 34–36 and 40A helpful.

Go to www.everydaymathonline.com to access the additional practice pages.

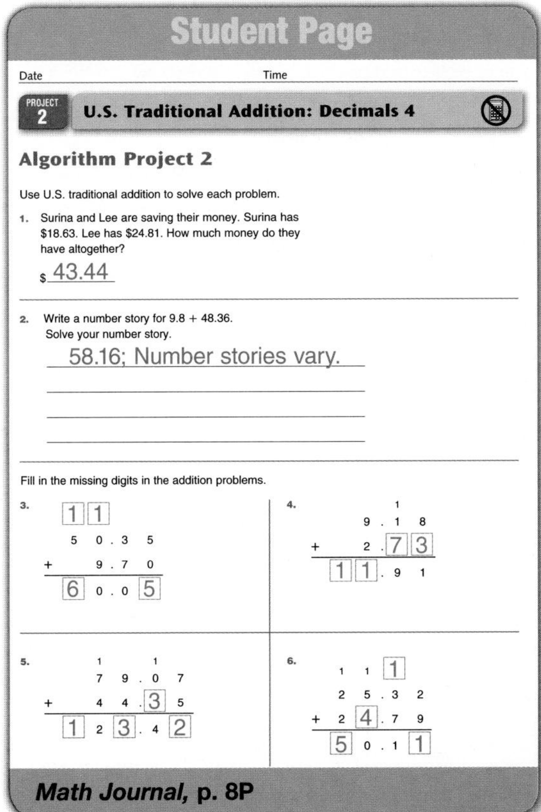

Student Page

Date Time

PROJECT 2 **U.S. Traditional Addition: Decimals 4**

Algorithm Project 2

Use U.S. traditional addition to solve each problem.

1. Surina and Lee are saving their money. Surina has \$18.63. Lee has \$24.81. How much money do they have altogether?

   \$ 43.44

2. Write a number story for 9.8 + 48.36. Solve your number story.

   58.16; Number stories vary.

Fill in the missing digits in the addition problems.

3.
```
  1 1
  5 0 . 3 5
+   9 . 7 0
  6 0 . 0 5
```

4.
```
      1
    9 . 1 8
+   2 . 7 3
  1 1 . 9 1
```

5.
```
  1     1
  7 9 . 0 7
+ 4 4 . 3 5
1 2 3 . 4 2
```

6.
```
  1 1 1
  2 5 . 3 2
+ 2 4 . 7 9
  5 0 . 1 1
```

Math Journal, p. 8P

Online Master

Name Date Time

PROJECT 2 **Partial-Sums Addition: Decimals**

Online Additional Practice

Algorithm Project 2

Use partial-sums addition to solve the problems.

1. Malik had \$89.72 in the bank. He earned \$14 this week. How much money does Malik have now?

   \$ 103.72

2. 99.01 = 67.12 + 31.89

3. 18.68 + 5.7 = 24.38

4. 2.08 + 9.9 = 11.98

5. \$72.81 + \$7.71 = \$ 80.52

6. 17.83 = 4.11 + 13.72

7. 67.42 = 5.59 + 61.83

Online Additional Practice, p. 8A

Algorithm 3 Project

U.S. Traditional Subtraction

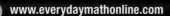

Objective To introduce U.S. traditional subtraction.

www.everydaymathonline.com

eToolkit

Algorithms Practice

EM Facts Workshop Game™

Family Letters

Assessment Management

Common Core State Standards

Curriculum Focal Points

Interactive Teacher's Lesson Guide

1 Doing the Project

Recommended Use After Lesson 2•9

Key Concepts and Skills

- Identify places in whole numbers and the values of the digits in those places.
  [Number and Numeration Goal 1]
- Use subtraction facts to find differences of multidigit whole numbers.
  [Operations and Computation Goal 1]
- Subtract multidigit numbers.
  [Operations and Computation Goal 2]
- Write and solve subtraction number stories.
  [Operations and Computation Goal 2]

Key Activities

Students explore and practice U.S. traditional subtraction with multidigit whole numbers.

Key Vocabulary

U.S. traditional subtraction

Materials

- *Math Journal 1* or *2,* pp. 9P–12P
- *Student Reference Book,* p. 24B
- play money (optional)
- base-10 blocks (optional)

2 Extending the Project

Students solve multidigit subtraction problems, first using the focus algorithm (trade-first subtraction) and then using any algorithm they choose.

Materials

- Online Additional Practice, pp. 12A–12D
- *Student Reference Book,* pp. 12–15 and 24B

1 Doing the Project

Solving a Subtraction Problem

(*Math Journal 1* or *2,* p. 9P)

Ask students to solve Problem 1 on journal page 9P. Tell them they may use base-10 blocks, play money, paper and pencil, or any other tools they wish, except calculators.

Discussing Solutions

(*Math Journal 1* or *2,* p. 9P)

Discuss students' solutions to Problem 1 on journal page 9P. 625 – 379 = 246 shirts Expect that students will use several different methods. Some may use base-10 blocks, play money, or other manipulatives. Others may use paper-and-pencil methods, including the same-change rule, counting up, partial-differences subtraction, and trade-first subtraction. Some students may also use U.S. traditional subtraction. *Possible strategies:*

▷ Using the same-change rule

$$\begin{array}{r} \mathbf{625} \\ -\ \mathbf{379} \\ \hline \end{array} \quad \begin{array}{c} \text{(add 21)} \\ \text{(add 21)} \end{array} \quad \begin{array}{r} 646 \\ -\ 400 \\ \hline \mathbf{246} \end{array}$$

▷ Counting up

$$379 \xrightarrow{+1} 380 \xrightarrow{+20} 400 \xrightarrow{+200} 600 \xrightarrow{+25} 625$$

$$\begin{aligned} 379 + 1 &= 380 \\ 380 + 20 &= 400 \\ 400 + 200 &= 600 \\ 600 + 25 &= 625 \end{aligned}$$

$$1 + 20 + 200 + 25 = 246$$

$$625 - 379 = 246$$

▷ Using partial-differences subtraction

		6 2 5
		– 3 7 9
Subtract the 100s.	600 – 300 →	+ 3 0 0
Subtract the 10s.	20 – 70 →	– 5 0
Subtract the 1s.	5 – 9 →	– 4
Find the total.	300 – 50 – 4 →	**2 4 6**

▷ Using trade-first subtraction

	11	
5	~~1~~	15
~~6~~	~~2~~	~~5~~
– 3	7	9
2	4	6

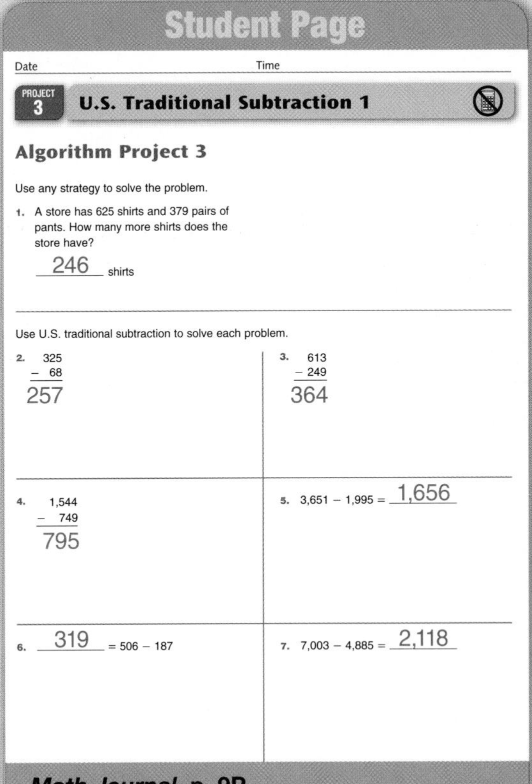
Student Page

Date Time

PROJECT 3 **U.S. Traditional Subtraction 1**

Algorithm Project 3

Use any strategy to solve the problem.

1. A store has 625 shirts and 379 pairs of pants. How many more shirts does the store have?
246 shirts

Use U.S. traditional subtraction to solve each problem.

2. 325 – 68 = 257
3. 613 – 249 = 364
4. 1,544 – 749 = 795
5. 3,651 – 1,995 = 1,656
6. 319 = 506 – 187
7. 7,003 – 4,885 = 2,118

Math Journal, p. 9P

▷ Using U.S. traditional subtraction

	11	
5	~~1~~	15
~~6~~	~~2~~	~~5~~
− 3	7	9
2	4	6

NOTE Trade-first subtraction resembles U.S. traditional subtraction, except that in trade-first subtraction, as the name implies, all the trading is done before any subtractions are carried out, allowing the person to concentrate on one task at a time.

▶ Introducing U.S. Traditional Subtraction

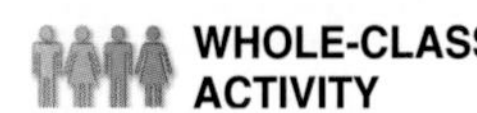

After you have discussed students' solutions, and even if one or more students used **U.S. traditional subtraction,** demonstrate it again as described below.

Example 1: 625 – 379

Step 1:

Start with the 1s.

Since 9 > 5, you need to regroup.

Trade 1 ten for 10 ones:
625 = 6 hundreds + 1 ten + 15 ones.

Subtract the 1s: 15 – 9 = 6.

	1	**15**
6	~~**2**~~	~~**5**~~
− 3	7	**9**
		6

Step 2:

Go to the 10s.

Since 7 > 1, you need to regroup.

Trade 1 hundred for 10 tens:
625 = 5 hundreds + 11 tens + 15 ones.

Subtract the 10s: 11 – 7 = 4.

	11	
5	~~**1**~~	15
~~**6**~~	~~2~~	~~5~~
− 3	**7**	9
	4	6

Step 3:

Go to the 100s. You don't need to regroup.

Subtract the 100s: 5 – 3 = 2.

625 – 379 = 246

There are 246 more shirts than pairs of pants.

	11	
5	~~1~~	15
~~6~~	~~2~~	~~5~~
− **3**	7	9
2	4	6

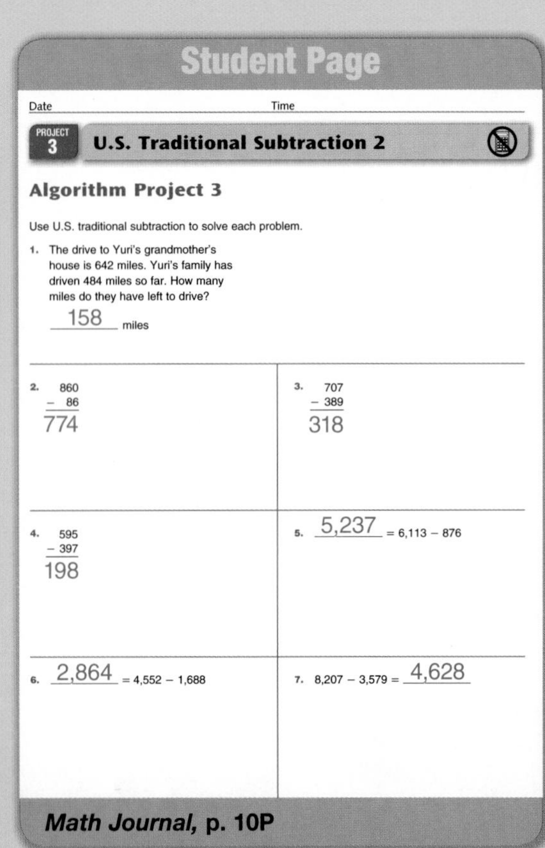

Student Page

Date Time

PROJECT 3 U.S. Traditional Subtraction 2

Algorithm Project 3

Use U.S. traditional subtraction to solve each problem.

1. The drive to Yuri's grandmother's house is 642 miles. Yuri's family has driven 484 miles so far. How many miles do they have left to drive?
158 miles

2. 860 − 86 = 774

3. 707 − 389 = 318

4. 595 − 397 = 198

5. 5,237 = 6,113 − 876

6. 2,864 = 4,552 − 1,688

7. 8,207 − 3,579 = 4,628

Math Journal, p. 10P

Example 2: 802 – 457

Step 1:

Start with the 1s.

Since 7 > 2, you need to regroup.

There are no tens in 802, so trade 1 hundred for 10 tens and then trade 1 ten for 10 ones: 802 = 7 hundreds + 9 tens + 12 ones.

Subtract the 1s: 12 – 7 = 5.

	9	
7	~~10~~	12
~~8~~	~~0~~	~~2~~
– 4	5	7
		5

Step 2:

Go to the 10s. You don't need to regroup.

Subtract the 10s: 9 – 5 = 4.

	9	
7	~~10~~	12
~~8~~	~~0~~	~~2~~
– 4	5	7
	4	5

Step 3:

Go to the 100s. You don't need to regroup.

Subtract the 100s: 7 – 4 = 3.

802 – 457 = 345

	9	
7	~~10~~	12
~~8~~	~~0~~	~~2~~
– 4	5	7
3	4	5

You may want to work several more examples with the whole class.

Suggestions:

▷ 75 – 48 = ? 27

▷ 711 – 36 = ? 675

▷ 342 – 148 = ? 194

▷ 402 – 327 = ? 75

▷ 7,243 – 2,977 = ? 4,266

▷ 6,004 – 4,735 = ? 1,269

Practicing U.S. Traditional Subtraction

PARTNER ACTIVITY

(*Math Journal 1* or *2,* pp. 9P–12P; *Student Reference Book,* p. 24B)

When students are ready, have them solve Problems 2–7 on journal page 9P. They may find the example on *Student Reference Book,* page 24B helpful.

Journal pages 10P–12P provide students with additional practice using U.S. traditional subtraction. Use these journal pages as necessary.

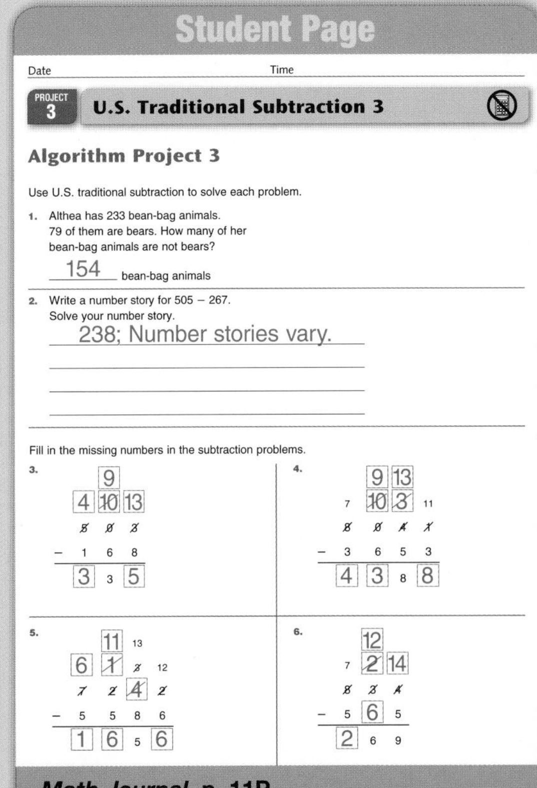

Student Page

Date Time

PROJECT 3 **U.S. Traditional Subtraction 3**

Algorithm Project 3

Use U.S. traditional subtraction to solve each problem.

1. Althea has 233 bean-bag animals. 79 of them are bears. How many of her bean-bag animals are not bears?
   154 bean-bag animals
2. Write a number story for 505 – 267. Solve your number story.
   238; Number stories vary.

Fill in the missing numbers in the subtraction problems.

3. 503 – 168 = 335
4. 8,041 – 3,653 = 4,388
5. 7,242 – 5,586 = 1,656
6. 834 – 565 = 269

Math Journal, p. 11P

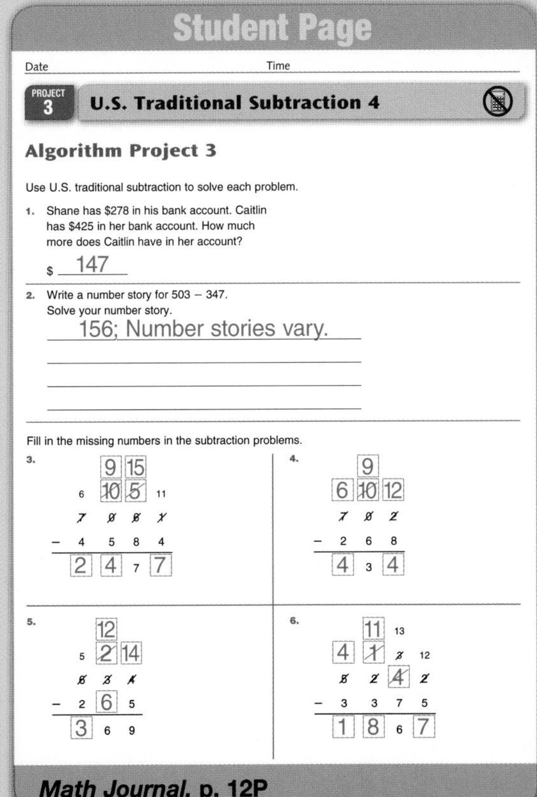

Student Page

Date Time

PROJECT 3 **U.S. Traditional Subtraction 4**

Algorithm Project 3

Use U.S. traditional subtraction to solve each problem.

1. Shane has $278 in his bank account. Caitlin has $425 in her bank account. How much more does Caitlin have in her account?
   $ 147
2. Write a number story for 503 – 347. Solve your number story.
   156; Number stories vary.

Fill in the missing numbers in the subtraction problems.

3. 7,061 – 4,584 = 2,477
4. 702 – 268 = 434
5. 634 – 265 = 369
6. 5,242 – 3,375 = 1,867

Math Journal, p. 12P

Go to www.everydaymathonline.com to access the additional practice pages.

2 Extending the Project

▶ Solving Multidigit Subtraction Problems

(Online Additional Practice, pp. 12A–12D; *Student Reference Book*, pp. 12–15 and 24B)

Online practice pages 12A–12D provide students with additional practice solving multidigit subtraction problems. Use these pages as necessary.

Encourage students to use the focus algorithm (trade-first subtraction) to solve the problems on practice page 12A. Invite them to use any algorithm they wish to solve the problems on the remaining pages.

Students may find the examples on *Student Reference Book,* pages 12–15 and 24B helpful.

Online Master

Name Date Time

PROJECT 3 **Trade-First Subtraction** Online Additional Practice

Algorithm Project 3

Use trade-first subtraction to solve each problem.

1. Mai's book has 316 pages. She has read 77 pages so far. How many pages does Mai have left to read?
 239 pages

2. 384 − 295 = 89

3. 512 − 144 = 368

4. 2,171 − 688 = 1,483

5. 6,645 − 3,896 = 2,749

6. 629 = 804 − 175

7. 7,006 − 5,117 = 1,889

Online Additional Practice, p. 12A

U.S. Traditional Subtraction: Decimals

Objective To introduce U.S. traditional subtraction with decimals.

Technology Resources www.everydaymathonline.com

eToolkit

Algorithms Practice

EM Facts Workshop Game™

Family Letters

Assessment Management

Common Core State Standards

Curriculum Focal Points

Interactive Teacher's Lesson Guide

1 Doing the Project

Recommended Use After Lesson 4•5

Key Concepts and Skills

- Identify places in whole numbers and decimals and the values of the digits in those places.
  [Number and Numeration Goal 1]
- Use subtraction facts to find differences of decimals.
  [Operations and Computation Goal 1]
- Subtract decimals.
  [Operations and Computation Goal 2]
- Write and solve subtraction number stories with decimals.
  [Operations and Computation Goal 2]

Key Activities

Students explore and practice U.S. traditional subtraction with decimals.

Materials

- *Math Journal 1* or *2,* pp. 13P–16P
- *Student Reference Book,* p. 40B
- $1 and $10 bills (*Math Masters,* p. 428; optional)
- dimes and pennies (optional)
- base-10 blocks (optional)

2 Extending the Project

Students solve decimal subtraction problems, first using the focus algorithm (trade-first subtraction) and then using any algorithm they choose.

Materials

- Online Additional Practice, pp. 16A–16D
- *Student Reference Book,* pp. 34–37 and 40B

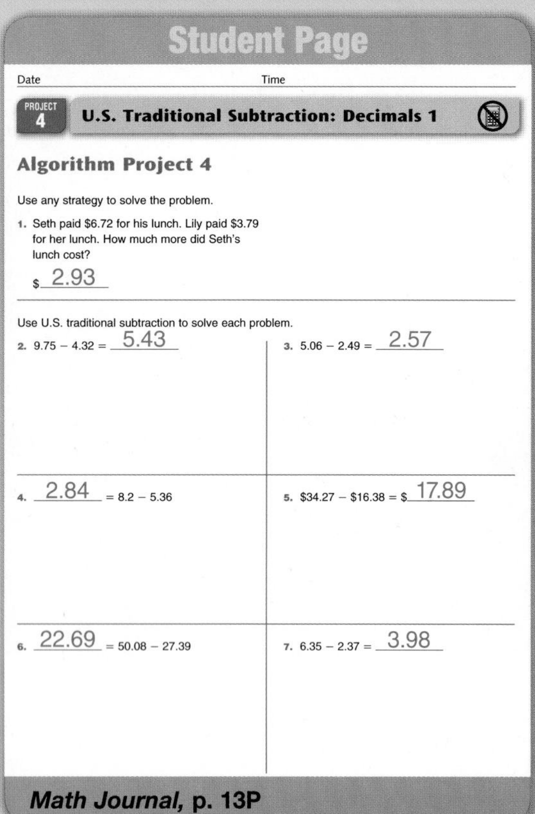
Student Page

Date Time

PROJECT 4 **U.S. Traditional Subtraction: Decimals 1**

Algorithm Project 4

Use any strategy to solve the problem.

1. Seth paid $6.72 for his lunch. Lily paid $3.79 for her lunch. How much more did Seth's lunch cost?
   $ 2.93

Use U.S. traditional subtraction to solve each problem.

2. 9.75 − 4.32 = 5.43
3. 5.06 − 2.49 = 2.57
4. 2.84 = 8.2 − 5.36
5. $34.27 − $16.38 = $ 17.89
6. 22.69 = 50.08 − 27.39
7. 6.35 − 2.37 = 3.98

Math Journal, p. 13P

1 Doing the Project

▶ Solving a Decimal Subtraction Problem

(*Math Journal 1* or *2,* p.13P)

Ask students to solve Problem 1 on journal page 13P. Tell them they may use base-10 blocks, play money, paper and pencil, or any other tools they wish, except calculators.

▶ Discussing Solutions

(*Math Journal 1* or *2,* p. 13P)

Discuss students' solutions to Problem 1 on journal page 13P. $6.72 − $3.79 = $2.93 Expect that students will use several different methods, including modeling with base-10 blocks, counting up, using partial-differences subtraction, and using trade-first subtraction. Some students may also use U.S. traditional subtraction. *Possible strategies:*

▷ Modeling with base-10 blocks

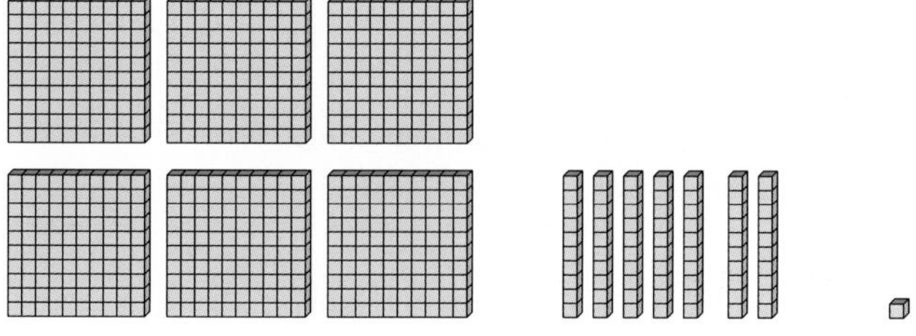

Show 6.72 with blocks.

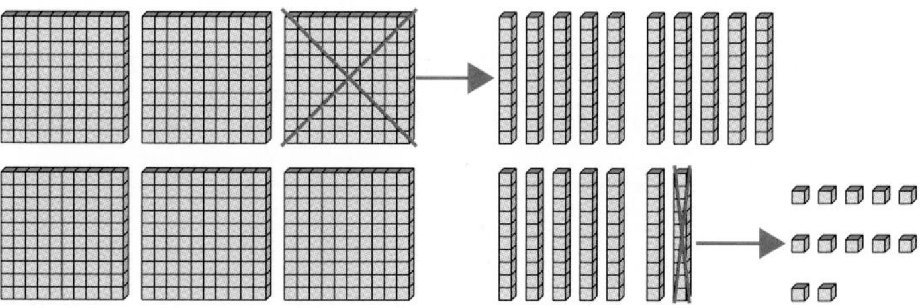

You want to take away 3.79. To do this, you need to first trade 1 flat for 10 longs and 1 long for 10 cubes.

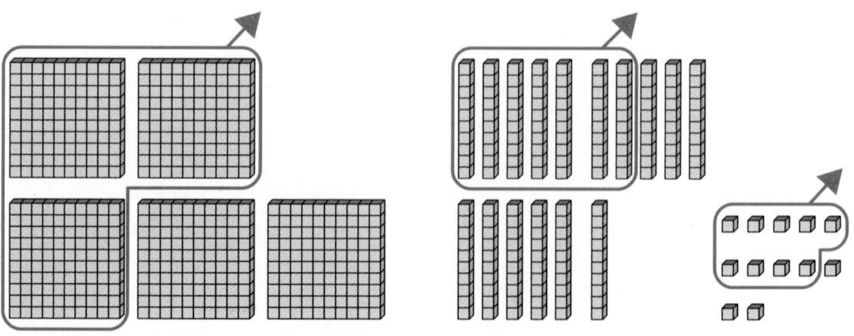

Now remove 3 flats, 7 longs, and 9 cubes (3.79). Two flats, 9 longs, and 3 cubes are left. These blocks show 2.93.

▷ Using shorthand pictures of base-10 blocks (*See margin.*)

▷ Counting up

$$\begin{array}{r} 3.79 \\ +\,\boxed{0.01} \\ \hline 3.80 \\ +\,\boxed{0.20} \\ \hline 4.00 \\ +\,\boxed{2.72} \\ \hline 6.72 \end{array} \qquad \begin{array}{r} 0.01 \\ 0.20 \\ +\ 2.72 \\ \hline 2.93 \end{array}$$

$6.72 − $3.79 = $2.93

▷ Using partial-differences subtraction

		6. 7 2
		− 3. 7 9
Subtract the 1s.	6 − 3 →	3. 0 0
Subtract the 0.1s.	0.7 − 0.7 →	0. 0 0
Subtract the 0.01s.	0.02 − 0.09 →	− 0. 0 7
Find the total.	3 − 0.07 →	**2. 9 3**

▷ Using trade-first subtraction

1s	0.1s	0.01s
	16	
5	~~6~~	12
~~6~~.	~~7~~	~~2~~
− 3.	7	9
2.	9	3

▷ Using U.S. traditional subtraction

1s	0.1s	0.01s
	16	
5	~~6~~	12
~~6~~.	~~7~~	~~2~~
− 3.	7	9
2.	9	3

NOTE Trade-first subtraction resembles U.S. traditional subtraction, except that in trade-first subtraction, as the name implies, all the trading is done before any subtractions are carried out, allowing the person to concentrate on one task at a time.

Introducing U.S. Traditional Subtraction for Decimals

WHOLE-CLASS ACTIVITY

After you have discussed students' solutions, and even if one or more students used U.S. traditional subtraction, demonstrate it again as described on the next page.

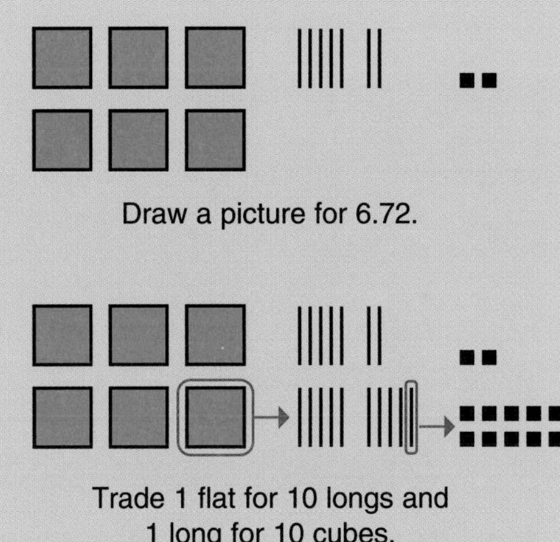
Draw a picture for 6.72.

Trade 1 flat for 10 longs and 1 long for 10 cubes.

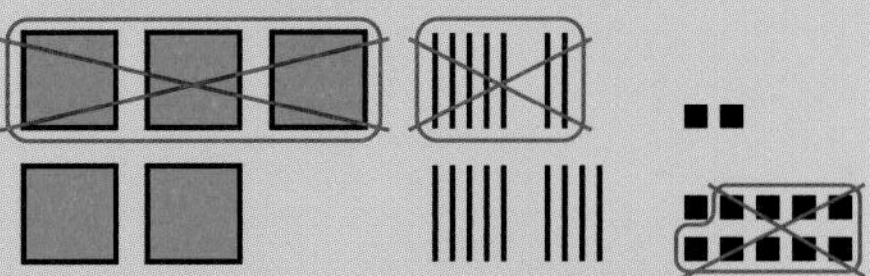
Remove 3 flats, 7 longs, and 9 cubes. The drawing shows 2.93.

Example 1: \$6.72 – \$3.79

Step 1:

Start with the 0.01s.

Since 9 > 2, you need to regroup.

Trade 1 tenth for 10 hundredths:
6.72 = 6 ones + 6 tenths + 12 hundredths.

Subtract the 0.01s: 12 – 9 = 3.

$$\begin{array}{r} {}^{6}\ {}^{12} \\ 6.\not{7}\not{2} \\ -\,3.7\,9 \\ \hline 3 \end{array}$$

Step 2:

Go to the 0.1s.

Since 7 > 6, you need to regroup.

Trade 1 one for 10 tenths:
6.72 = 5 ones + 16 tenths + 12 hundredths.

Subtract the 0.1s: 16 – 7 = 9.

$$\begin{array}{r} {}^{16}\ \ \\ {}^{5}\ \not{{}^{6}}\ {}^{12} \\ \not{6}.\not{7}\not{2} \\ -\,3.7\,9 \\ \hline 9\,3 \end{array}$$

Step 3:

Go to the 1s. You don't need to regroup.

Subtract the 1s: 5 – 3 = 2.

Remember to include the decimal point in the answer.

$$\begin{array}{r} {}^{16}\ \ \\ {}^{5}\ \not{{}^{6}}\ {}^{12} \\ \not{6}.\not{7}\not{2} \\ -\,3.7\,9 \\ \hline 2.9\,3 \end{array}$$

\$6.72 – \$3.79 = \$2.93

Seth's lunch cost \$2.93 more than Lily's lunch.

Example 2: 46.03 – 27.48

Step 1:

Start with the 0.01s.

Since 8 > 3, you need to regroup.

There are no tenths in 46.03, so trade 1 one for 10 tenths and then trade 1 tenth for 10 hundredths: 46.03 = 4 tens + 5 ones + 9 tenths + 13 hundredths.

Subtract the 0.01s: 13 – 8 = 5.

$$\begin{array}{r} {}^{9}\ \ \\ {}^{5}\ \not{{}^{10}}\ {}^{13} \\ 4\,\not{6}.\not{0}\not{3} \\ -\,2\,7.4\,8 \\ \hline 5 \end{array}$$

Step 2:

Go to the 0.1s.

You don't need to regroup.

Subtract the 0.1s: 9 – 4 = 5.

$$\begin{array}{r} {}^{9}\ \ \\ {}^{5}\ \not{{}^{10}}\ {}^{13} \\ 4\,\not{6}.\not{0}\not{3} \\ -\,2\,7.4\,8 \\ \hline 5\,5 \end{array}$$

Step 3:

Go to the 1s.

Since 7 > 5, you need to regroup.

Trade 1 ten for 10 ones: 46.03 = 3 tens + 15 ones + 9 tenths + 13 hundredths.

Subtract the ones: 15 – 7 = 8.

$$\begin{array}{r} {}^{15}\ {}^{9}\ \ \\ {}^{3}\ \not{{}^{5}}\ \not{{}^{10}}\ {}^{13} \\ \not{4}\,\not{6}.\not{0}\not{3} \\ -\,2\,7.4\,8 \\ \hline 8\,5\,5 \end{array}$$

Step 4:

Go to the 10s.
You don't need to regroup.
Subtract the 10s: 3 – 2 = 1.
Remember to include the decimal point in the answer.

```
     15  9
 3   5  10 13
 4   6 . 0  3
-2   7 . 4  8
-------------
 1   8 . 5  5
```

46.03 – 27.48 = 18.55

Example 3: 7.1 – 3.86

Step 1:

Write the problem in columns.
Be sure to line up the places correctly.
Since 3.86 has two decimal places, write 7.1 as 7.10.

```
  7 . 1  0
- 3 . 8  6
----------
```

Step 2:

Start with the 0.01s.
Since 6 > 0, you need to regroup.
Trade 1 tenth for 10 hundredths:
7.10 = 7 ones + 0 tenths + 10 hundredths.
Subtract the 0.01s: 10 – 6 = 4.

```
      0 10
  7 . 1  0
- 3 . 8  6
----------
         4
```

Step 3:

Go to the 0.1s.
Since 8 > 0, you need to regroup.
Trade 1 one for 10 tenths:
7.10 = 6 ones + 10 tenths + 10 hundredths.
Subtract the 0.1s: 10 – 8 = 2.

```
     10
  6   0 10
  7 . 1  0
- 3 . 8  6
----------
      2  4
```

Step 4:

Go to the 1s. You don't need to regroup.
Subtract the 1s: 6 – 3 = 3.
Remember to include the decimal point in the answer.

```
     10
  6   0 10
  7 . 1  0
- 3 . 8  6
----------
  3 . 2  4
```

7.1 – 3.86 = 3.24

You may want to work several more examples with the whole class.

Suggestions:

▷ $8.49 – $6.35 = ? $2.14

▷ 5.61 – 3.74 = ? 1.87

▷ 7.06 – 4.98 = ? 2.08

▷ 3.9 – 2.62 = ? 1.28

▷ $28.74 – $19.86 = ? $8.88

▷ 40.07 – 26.39 = ? 13.68

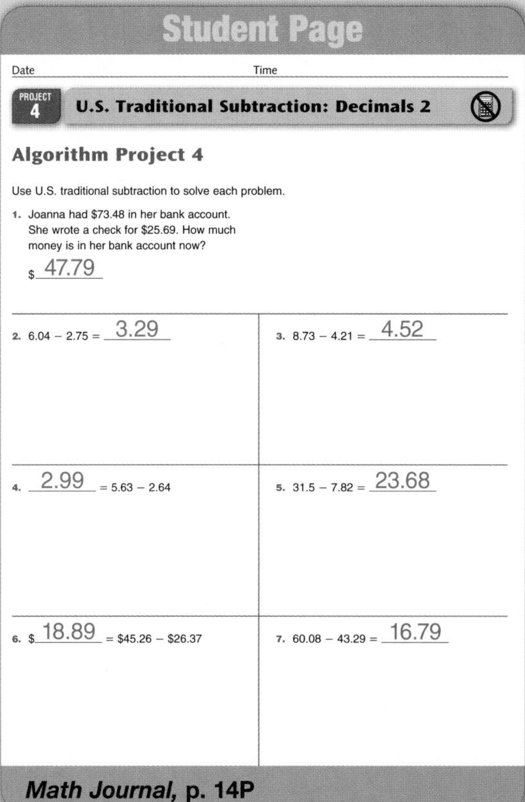

Student Page

Date Time

PROJECT 4 **U.S. Traditional Subtraction: Decimals 2**

Algorithm Project 4

Use U.S. traditional subtraction to solve each problem.

1. Joanna had $73.48 in her bank account. She wrote a check for $25.69. How much money is in her bank account now?
$ 47.79

2. 6.04 – 2.75 = 3.29

3. 8.73 – 4.21 = 4.52

4. 2.99 = 5.63 – 2.64

5. 31.5 – 7.82 = 23.68

6. $ 18.89 = $45.26 – $26.37

7. 60.08 – 43.29 = 16.79

Math Journal, p. 14P

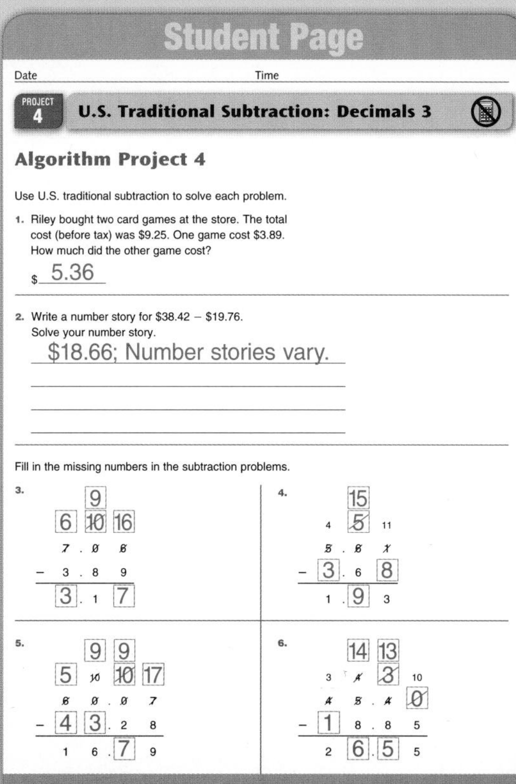

Student Page

Date Time

PROJECT 4 **U.S. Traditional Subtraction: Decimals 3**

Algorithm Project 4

Use U.S. traditional subtraction to solve each problem.

1. Riley bought two card games at the store. The total cost (before tax) was $9.25. One game cost $3.89. How much did the other game cost?
$ 5.36

2. Write a number story for $38.42 – $19.76. Solve your number story.
$18.66; Number stories vary.

Fill in the missing numbers in the subtraction problems.

3. 7.06 – 3.89 = 3.17

4. 5.61 – 3.68 = 1.93

5. 86.07 – 43.28 = 16.79

6. 45.40 – 18.85 = 26.55

Math Journal, p. 15P

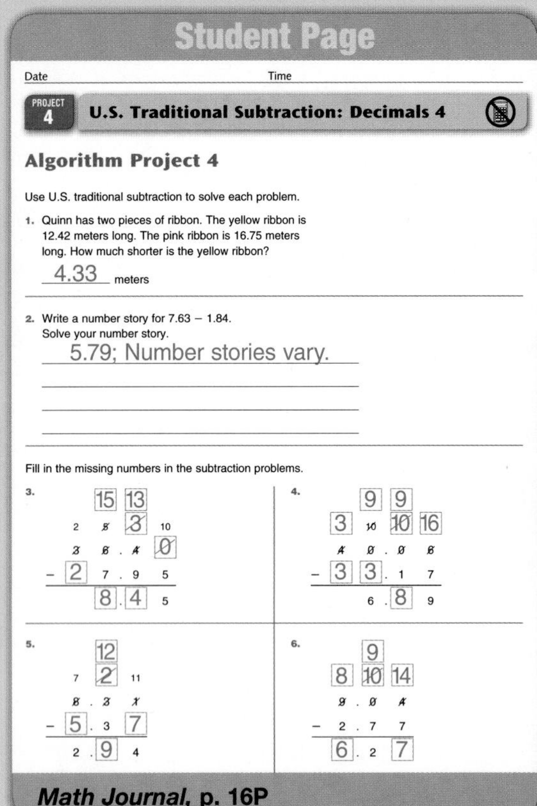
Student Page

Date Time

PROJECT 4 **U.S. Traditional Subtraction: Decimals 4**

Algorithm Project 4

Use U.S. traditional subtraction to solve each problem.

1. Quinn has two pieces of ribbon. The yellow ribbon is 12.42 meters long. The pink ribbon is 16.75 meters long. How much shorter is the yellow ribbon?
 4.33 meters

2. Write a number story for 7.63 − 1.84.
 Solve your number story.
 5.79; Number stories vary.

Fill in the missing numbers in the subtraction problems.

3. 3 8 . 4 [0] − [2] 7 . 9 5 = [8] . [4] 5
4. [3] 4 0 . 0 8 − [3] [3] . 1 7 = 6 . [8] 9
5. 8 . 3 1 − [5] . 3 [7] = 2 . [9] 4
6. 9 . 0 4 − 2 . 7 7 = [6] . 2 [7]

Math Journal, **p. 16P**

Go to www.everydaymathonline.com to access the additional practice pages.

Online Master

Name Date Time

PROJECT 4 **Trade-First Subtraction: Decimals** Online Additional Practice

Algorithm Project 4

Use trade-first subtraction to solve each problem.

1. Matthew was building a house for his dog. He had a board that was 2.45 meters long. He cut off 1.75 meters. How long is the board now?
 0.7 meters

2. 8.72 − 4.61 = 4.11
3. 9.02 − 5.87 = 3.15
4. 3.75 = 7.6 − 3.85
5. $82.43 − $56.77 = $25.66
6. 23.77 = 70.05 − 46.28
7. 6.54 − 3.59 = 2.95

Online Additional Practice, p. 16A

▶ Practicing U.S. Traditional Subtraction for Decimals

PARTNER ACTIVITY

(*Math Journal 1* or *2,* pp. 13P–16P; *Student Reference Book,* p. 40B)

When students are ready, have them solve Problems 2–7 on journal page 13P. They may find the example on *Student Reference Book,* page 40B helpful.

Journal pages 14P–16P provide students with additional practice using U.S. traditional subtraction. Use these journal pages as necessary.

2 Extending the Project

▶ Solving Decimal Subtraction Problems

INDEPENDENT ACTIVITY

(Online Additional Practice, pp. 16A–16D; *Student Reference Book,* pp. 34–37 and 40B)

Online practice pages 16A–16D provide students with additional practice solving decimal subtraction problems. Use these pages as necessary.

Encourage students to use the focus algorithm (trade-first subtraction) to solve the problems on practice page 16A. Invite them to use any algorithm they wish to solve the problems on the remaining pages.

Students may find the examples on *Student Reference Book,* pages 34–37 and 40B helpful.

Algorithm
5
Project

U.S. Traditional Multiplication

Objective To introduce U.S. traditional multiplication.

www.everydaymathonline.com

eToolkit

Algorithms Practice

EM Facts Workshop Game™

Family Letters

Assessment Management

Common Core State Standards

Curriculum Focal Points

Interactive Teacher's Lesson Guide

1 Doing the Project

Recommended Use After Lesson 5•7

Key Concepts and Skills

- Identify places in whole numbers and the values of the digits in those places.
  [Number and Numeration Goal 1]
- Use multiplication facts to find products of multidigit whole numbers.
  [Operations and Computation Goal 3]
- Multiply multidigit whole numbers.
  [Operations and Computation Goal 4]
- Write and solve multiplication number stories.
  [Operations and Computation Goal 4]

Key Activities

Students explore and practice U.S. traditional multiplication with multidigit whole numbers.

Key Vocabulary

U.S. traditional multiplication

Materials

- *Math Journal 1* or *2,* pp. 17P–20P
- *Student Reference Book,* pp. 24C and 24D

2 Extending the Project

Students solve multidigit multiplication problems, first using the focus algorithm (partial-products multiplication) and then using any algorithm they choose.

Materials

- Online Additional Practice, pp. 20A–20D
- *Student Reference Book,* pp. 18, 19, 24C, and 24D

Student Page

Date Time

PROJECT 5 **U.S. Traditional Multiplication 1**

Algorithm Project 5

Use any strategy to solve the problem.

1. Mountain View Elementary School held a food drive. Each student donated 4 cans of food. There are 676 students at the school. How many cans of food did the students donate altogether?
2,704 cans

Use U.S. traditional multiplication to solve each problem.

2. 2 * 413 = 826
3. 265 * 4 = 1,060
4. 14,122 = 46 * 307
5. 278 * 43 = 11,954
6. 18 * 72 = 1,296
7. 18,360 = 459 * 40

Math Journal, p. 17P

1 Doing the Project

Solving a Multiplication Problem

INDEPENDENT ACTIVITY

(*Math Journal 1* or *2,* p. 17P)

Ask students to solve Problem 1 on journal page 17P. Tell them they may use any methods they wish, except calculators.

Discussing Solutions

WHOLE-CLASS ACTIVITY

(*Math Journal 1* or *2,* p. 17P)

Discuss students' solutions to Problem 1 on journal page 17P. 4 * 676 = 2,704 cans Expect that students will use several different methods, including partial-products multiplication and lattice multiplication. Some students may also use U.S. traditional multiplication. *Possible strategies:*

▷ Using partial-products multiplication

```
               6 7 6
           *       4
4 * 600 →    2 4 0 0
 4 * 70 →      2 8 0
  4 * 6 →  +     2 4
             2 7 0 4
```

▷ Using lattice multiplication

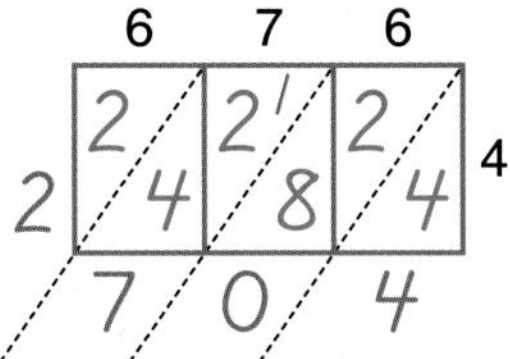

▷ Using U.S. traditional multiplication

```
   3 2
   6 7 6
 *     4
 2 7 0 4
```

Introducing U.S. Traditional Multiplication

WHOLE-CLASS ACTIVITY

After you have discussed students' solutions, and even if one or more students used **U.S. traditional multiplication,** demonstrate it again as described below.

Example 1: 4 ∗ 676

Step 1:

Multiply the ones.
4 ∗ 6 ones = 24 ones = 2 tens + 4 ones
Write 4 in the 1s place below the line.
Write 2 above the 7 in the 10s place.

$$\begin{array}{r} {\scriptstyle 2\;\;} \\ 67\mathbf{6} \\ * \quad \mathbf{4} \\ \hline \mathbf{4} \end{array}$$

Step 2:

Multiply the tens.
4 ∗ 7 tens = 28 tens
Remember the 2 tens from Step 1.
28 tens + 2 tens = 30 tens in all
30 tens = 3 hundreds + 0 tens
Write 0 in the 10s place below the line.
Write 3 above the 6 in the 100s place.

$$\begin{array}{r} {\scriptstyle \mathbf{3}\,\mathbf{2}\;\;} \\ 6\mathbf{7}6 \\ * \quad \mathbf{4} \\ \hline \mathbf{0}4 \end{array}$$

Step 3:

Multiply the hundreds.
4 ∗ 6 hundreds = 24 hundreds
Remember the 3 hundreds from Step 2.
24 hundreds + 3 hundreds = 27 hundreds
27 hundreds = 2 thousands + 7 hundreds
Write 7 in the 100s place below the line.
Write 2 in the 1,000s place below the line.

$$\begin{array}{r} {\scriptstyle \mathbf{3}\,2\;\;} \\ \mathbf{6}76 \\ * \quad \mathbf{4} \\ \hline \mathbf{27}04 \end{array}$$

4 ∗ 676 = 2,704

The students donated 2,704 cans.

NOTE U.S. traditional multiplication is so familiar that the details of its working may appear more meaningful than they are. Consider the following example:

$$\begin{array}{r} {\scriptstyle 1\,2\;} \\ {\scriptstyle 3\,5\;} \\ 147 \\ * \quad 38 \\ \hline 1176 \\ +\,4410 \\ \hline 5586 \end{array}$$

Many people, when asked why the "2" carried from "3 ∗ 7" is written in the 10s place, will explain that it stands for "2 tens." But this "2" really means "2 hundreds" since the "3" is really "3 tens." U.S. traditional multiplication is efficient—though not as efficient as a calculator—but it is not, despite its familiarity, conceptually transparent.

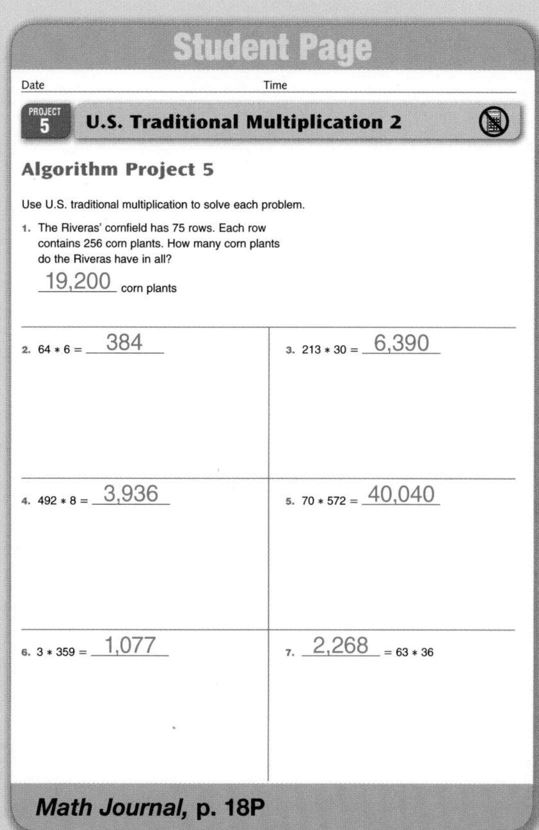

Student Page

Date Time

PROJECT 5 **U.S. Traditional Multiplication 2**

Algorithm Project 5

Use U.S. traditional multiplication to solve each problem.

1. The Riveras' cornfield has 75 rows. Each row contains 256 corn plants. How many corn plants do the Riveras have in all?
19,200 corn plants

2. 64 ∗ 6 = 384
3. 213 ∗ 30 = 6,390
4. 492 ∗ 8 = 3,936
5. 70 ∗ 572 = 40,040
6. 3 ∗ 359 = 1,077
7. 2,268 = 63 ∗ 36

Math Journal, p. 18P

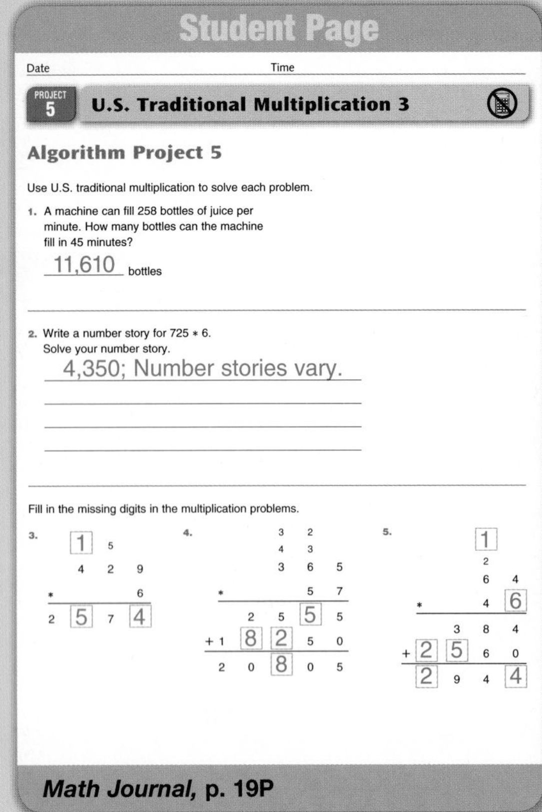
Student Page

Date Time

PROJECT 5 **U.S. Traditional Multiplication 3**

Algorithm Project 5

Use U.S. traditional multiplication to solve each problem.

1. A machine can fill 258 bottles of juice per minute. How many bottles can the machine fill in 45 minutes?

11,610 bottles

2. Write a number story for 725 * 6. Solve your number story.

4,350; Number stories vary.

Fill in the missing digits in the multiplication problems.

3.
```
   1 5
   4 2 9
 *     6
 2 5 7 4
```

4.
```
      3 2
      4 3
      3 6 5
 *      5 7
    2 5 5 5
 + 1 8 2 5 0
   2 0 8 0 5
```

5.
```
        1
        2
      6 4
 *    4 6
    3 8 4
 + 2 5 6 0
   2 9 4 4
```

Math Journal, p. 19P

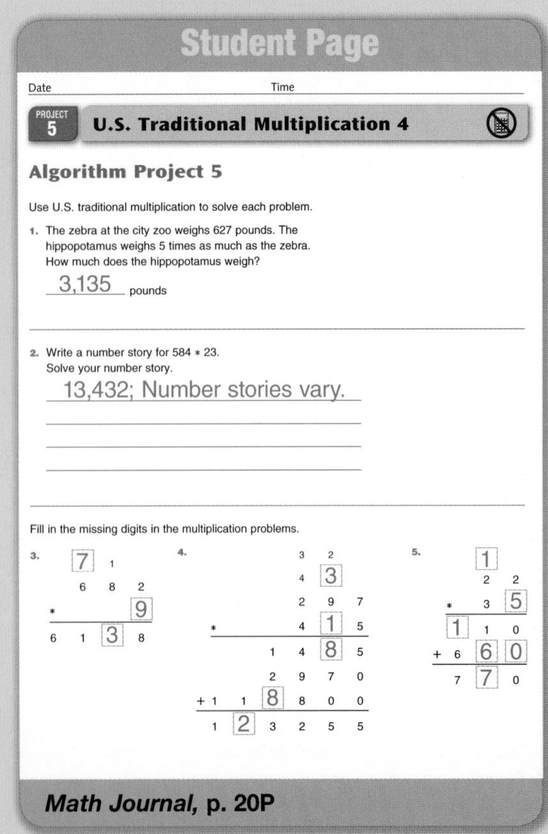
Student Page

Date Time

PROJECT 5 **U.S. Traditional Multiplication 4**

Algorithm Project 5

Use U.S. traditional multiplication to solve each problem.

1. The zebra at the city zoo weighs 627 pounds. The hippopotamus weighs 5 times as much as the zebra. How much does the hippopotamus weigh?

3,135 pounds

2. Write a number story for 584 * 23. Solve your number story.

13,432; Number stories vary.

Fill in the missing digits in the multiplication problems.

3.
```
   7 1
   6 8 2
 *     9
 6 1 3 8
```

4.
```
          3 2
          4 3
          2 9 7
 *        4 1 5
        1 4 8 5
        2 9 7 0
 + 1 1 8 8 0 0
   1 2 3 2 5 5
```

5.
```
        1
      2 2
 *    3 5
    1 1 0
 +  6 6 0
    7 7 0
```

Math Journal, p. 20P

Example 2: 487 * 35

Step 1:

Multiply 487 by the 5 in 35, as if the problem were 5 * 487.

```
     4 3
     4 8 7
 *     3 5
   2 4 3 5  ← The partial product
              5 * 487 = 2,435
```

Step 2:

Multiply 487 by the 3 in 35, as if the problem were 3 * 487.

The 3 in 35 stands for 3 tens, so write the partial product one place to the left.

Write a 0 in the 1s place to show you are multiplying by tens.

Write the new carries above the old carries.

```
      2 2
      4 3
      4 8 7
 *      3 5
    2 4 3 5
  1 4 6 1 0  ← 30 * 487 = 14,610
```

Step 3:

Add the two partial products to get the final answer.

```
      2 2
      4 3
      4 8 7
 *      3 5
    2 4 3 5
 + 1 4 6 1 0
   1 7 0 4 5  ← 35 * 487 = 17,045
```

35 * 487 = 17,045

You may want to work several more examples with the whole class.

Suggestions:

▷ 12 * 43 = ? 516

▷ 509 * 6 = ? 3,054

▷ 70 * 384 = ? 26,880

▷ 9 * 500 = ? 4,500

▷ 830 * 29 = ? 24,070

▷ 67 * 30 = ? 2,010

▶ Practicing U.S. Traditional Multiplication

PARTNER ACTIVITY

(*Math Journal 1* or *2,* pp. 17P–20P; *Student Reference Book,* pp. 24C and 24D)

When students are ready, have them solve Problems 2–7 on journal page 17P. They may find the examples on *Student Reference Book,* pages 24C and 24D helpful.

Journal pages 18P–20P provide students with additional practice using U.S. traditional multiplication. Use these journal pages as necessary.

2 Extending the Project

Solving Multidigit Multiplication Problems

INDEPENDENT ACTIVITY

(Online Additional Practice, pp. 20A–20D; *Student Reference Book,* pp. 18, 19, 24C, and 24D)

Online practice pages 20A–20D provide students with additional practice solving multidigit multiplication problems. Use these pages as necessary.

Encourage students to use the focus algorithm (partial-products multiplication) to solve the problems on practice page 20A. Invite them to use any algorithm they wish to solve the problems on the remaining pages.

Students may find the examples on *Student Reference Book,* pages 18, 19, 24C, and 24D helpful.

Go to www.everydaymathonline.com to access the additional practice pages.

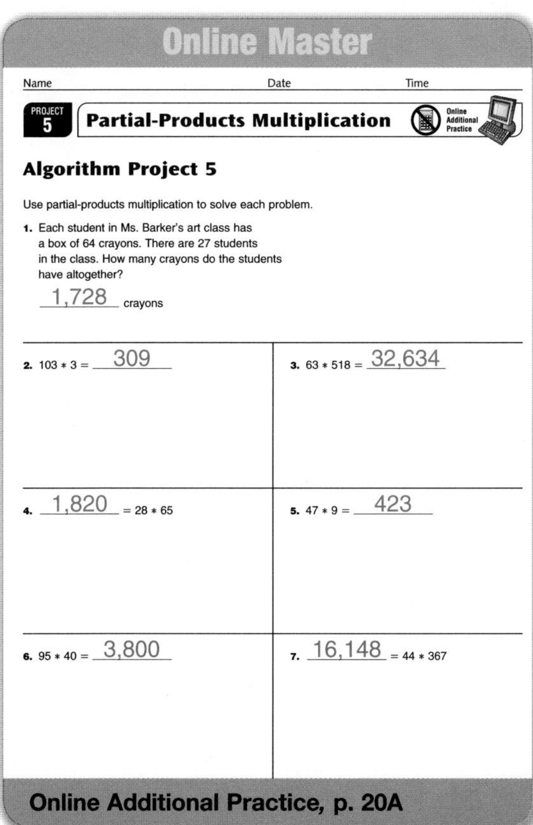

Online Master

Name Date Time

PROJECT 5 **Partial-Products Multiplication**

Algorithm Project 5

Use partial-products multiplication to solve each problem.

1. Each student in Ms. Barker's art class has a box of 64 crayons. There are 27 students in the class. How many crayons do the students have altogether?
   1,728 crayons

2. 103 * 3 = 309
3. 63 * 518 = 32,634
4. 1,820 = 28 * 65
5. 47 * 9 = 423
6. 95 * 40 = 3,800
7. 16,148 = 44 * 367

Online Additional Practice, p. 20A

Algorithm 6 Project

U.S. Traditional Multiplication: Decimals

Objective To introduce U.S. traditional multiplication for decimals.

Technology Resources www.everydaymathonline.com

eToolkit

Algorithms Practice

EM Facts Workshop Game™

Family Letters

Assessment Management

Common Core State Standards

Curriculum Focal Points

Interactive Teacher's Lesson Guide

1 Doing the Project

Recommended Use After Lesson 9•8

Key Concepts and Skills

- Identify places in whole numbers and decimals and the values of the digits in those places.
  [Number and Numeration Goal 1]
- Use multiplication facts to calculate products of decimals and whole-number multipliers.
  [Operations and Computation Goal 3]
- Write and solve multiplication number stories with decimals.
  [Operations and Computation Goal 4]

Key Activities

Students explore and practice U.S. traditional multiplication with decimals.

Materials

- *Math Journal 1* or *2,* pp. 21P–24P
- *Student Reference Book,* p. 40C
- $1 and $10 bills (*Math Masters,* p. 428; optional)
- dimes and pennies (optional)

2 Extending the Project

Students solve decimal multiplication problems, first using the focus algorithm (partial-products multiplication) and then using any algorithm they choose.

Materials

- Online Additional Practice, pp. 24A–24D
- *Student Reference Book,* pp. 37A, 37B, and 40C

1 Doing the Project

Solving a Decimal Multiplication Problem

(*Math Journal 1* or *2,* p. 21P)

Ask students to solve Problem 1 on journal page 21P. Tell them they may use play money, paper and pencil, or any other tools they wish, except calculators.

Discussing Solutions

(*Math Journal 1* or *2,* p. 21P)

Discuss students' solutions to Problem 1 on journal page 21P. $5.98 * 4 = $23.92 Expect that students will use several different methods, which may include modeling with play money, using repeated addition, using lattice multiplication, and using partial-products multiplication. Some students may also use U.S. traditional multiplication. *Possible strategies:*

▷ Modeling with play money

$1 $1 $1 $1 $1	$1 $1 $1 $1 $1	$1 $1 $1 $1 $1	$1 $1 $1 $1 $1
(D)(D)(D)(D)(D) (D)(D)(D)(D)	(D)(D)(D)(D)(D) (D)(D)(D)(D)	(D)(D)(D)(D)(D) (D)(D)(D)(D)	(D)(D)(D)(D)(D) (D)(D)(D)(D)
(P)(P)(P)(P)(P) (P)(P)(P)	(P)(P)(P)(P)(P) (P)(P)(P)	(P)(P)(P)(P)(P) (P)(P)(P)	(P)(P)(P)(P)(P) (P)(P)(P)

Use play money to show the cost of 4 sandwiches.

5 [$1] + 5 [$1] + 5 [$1] + 5 [$1] = 20 [$1] or 2 [$10]

Combine the bills.

9 (D) + 9 (D) + 9 (D) + 9 (D) = 36 (D) or 3 [$1] and 6 (D)

Combine the dimes.

8 (P) + 8 (P) + 8 (P) + 8 (P) = 32 (P) or 3 (D) and 2 (P)

Combine the pennies.

2 [$10] + 3 [$1] + 6 (D) + 3 (D) + 2 (P) = $23.92

Combine the bills and coins.

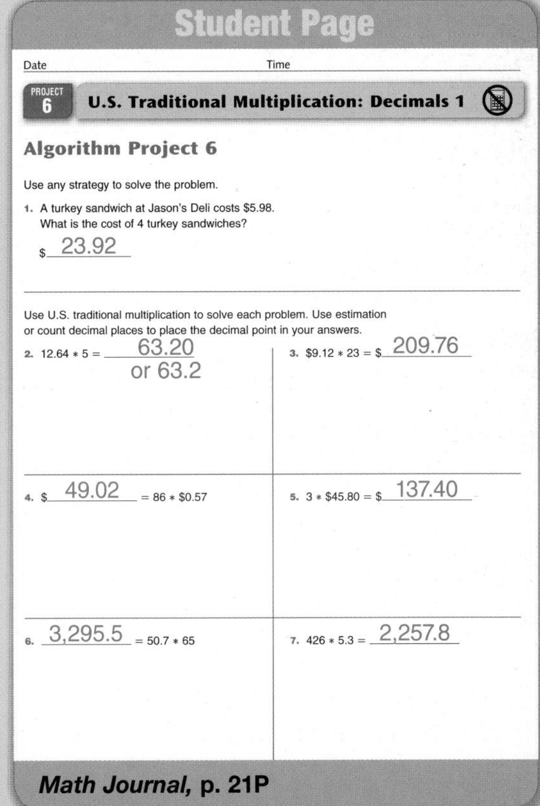

Student Page

Date Time

PROJECT 6 **U.S. Traditional Multiplication: Decimals 1**

Algorithm Project 6

Use any strategy to solve the problem.

1. A turkey sandwich at Jason's Deli costs $5.98. What is the cost of 4 turkey sandwiches?
   $ 23.92

Use U.S. traditional multiplication to solve each problem. Use estimation or count decimal places to place the decimal point in your answers.

2. 12.64 ∗ 5 = 63.20 or 63.2
3. $9.12 ∗ 23 = $ 209.76
4. $ 49.02 = 86 ∗ $0.57
5. 3 ∗ $45.80 = $ 137.40
6. 3,295.5 = 50.7 ∗ 65
7. 426 ∗ 5.3 = 2,257.8

***Math Journal,* p. 21P**

▷ Using repeated addition

\$5.98	\$11.96
+ \$5.98	+ \$11.96
\$10.00	\$22.00
\$1.80	\$1.80
+ \$0.16	+ \$0.12
\$11.96	\$23.92

▷ Using lattice multiplication

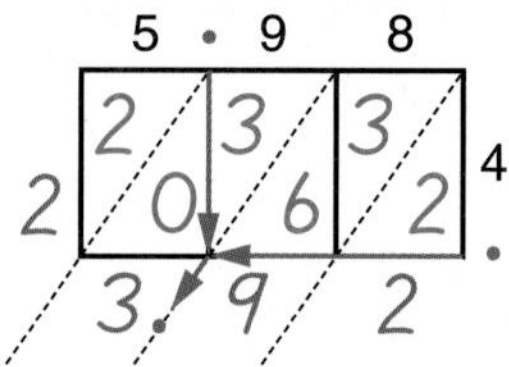

▷ Using partial-products multiplication

	\$5. 9 8
	* 4
4 [\$5.00]s →	2 0. 0 0
4 [\$0.90]s →	3. 6 0
4 [\$0.08]s →	+ 0. 3 2
	\$2 3. 9 2

▷ Using U.S. traditional multiplication

```
  3 3
 $5. 9 8
*      4
$2 3. 9 2
```

▶ Introducing U.S. Traditional Multiplication for Decimals

WHOLE-CLASS ACTIVITY

After you have discussed students' solutions, and even if one or more students used U.S. traditional multiplication, demonstrate it again as described below.

Example 1: \$5.98 * 4

Step 1:

Start with the pennies.

4 * 8 pennies = 32 pennies

32 pennies = 3 dimes + 2 pennies

```
    3
5 . 9 8
*     4
      2
```

Step 2:

Multiply the dimes.

4 * 9 dimes = 36 dimes

Remember the 3 dimes from Step 1.

36 dimes + 3 dimes = 39 dimes in all

39 dimes = \$3 + 9 dimes

```
3   3
5 . 9 8
*     4
    9 2
```

Step 3:

Multiply the dollars.

4 ∗ \$5 = \$20

Remember the \$3 from Step 2.

\$20 + \$3 = \$23 in all

\$23 = 2 [\$10]s + 3 [\$1]s

Remember to include the decimal point.

```
   3 3
   5.98
*     4
-------
  23.92
```

\$5.98 ∗ 4 = \$23.92

Four turkey sandwiches cost \$23.92.

One way to use U.S. traditional multiplication with decimals is to multiply the factors as though they were whole numbers and then use estimation to place the decimal point.

Example 2: 14.85 ∗ 6

Step 1:

Multiply as though both factors were whole numbers.

```
  2 5 3
  1485
*    6
------
  8910
```

Step 2:

Estimate the product: 14.85 is about 15, and 15 ∗ 6 = 90.

Step 3:

Use the estimate to place the decimal point in the answer. The estimate is 90, so place the decimal point to make the answer close to 90: 89.10 is close to 90.

14.85 ∗ 6 = 89.10

Another way to use U.S. traditional multiplication with decimals is to multiply as though both factors were whole numbers and then find the total number of places to the right of the decimal points of both factors to determine where to place the decimal point.

Example 3: 35 ∗ 8.62

Step 1:

Multiply as though both factors were whole numbers.

```
      1
     31
    862
*    35
-------
   4310
+ 25860
-------
  30170
```

Step 2:

Count the total number of places to the right of the decimal points of both factors. There are 0 places to the right of the decimal point in 35. There are 2 places to the right of the decimal point in 8.62. There are 2 decimal places in all.

Step 3:

Place the decimal point 2 places from the right.

3 0 1 . 7 0

35 ∗ 8.62 = 301.70

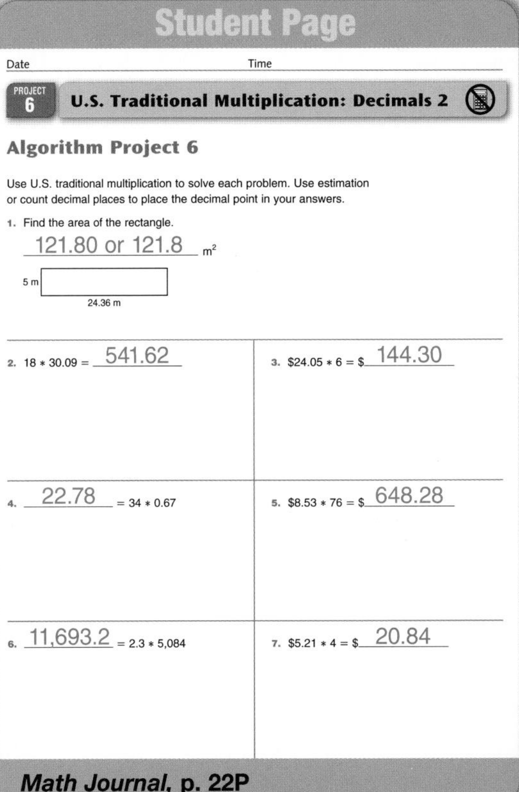

Student Page

Date Time

PROJECT 6 **U.S. Traditional Multiplication: Decimals 2**

Algorithm Project 6

Use U.S. traditional multiplication to solve each problem. Use estimation or count decimal places to place the decimal point in your answers.

1. Find the area of the rectangle.
   121.80 or 121.8 m^2
   (rectangle: 5 m by 24.36 m)
2. 18 ∗ 30.09 = 541.62
3. \$24.05 ∗ 6 = \$ 144.30
4. 22.78 = 34 ∗ 0.67
5. \$8.53 ∗ 76 = \$ 648.28
6. 11,693.2 = 2.3 ∗ 5,084
7. \$5.21 ∗ 4 = \$ 20.84

Math Journal, p. 22P

NOTE This second method for multiplying decimals (used in Example 3) is useful when there are many decimal places in the factors, making it difficult to estimate the answer. For example, 0.078 ∗ 0.029 = 0.002262.

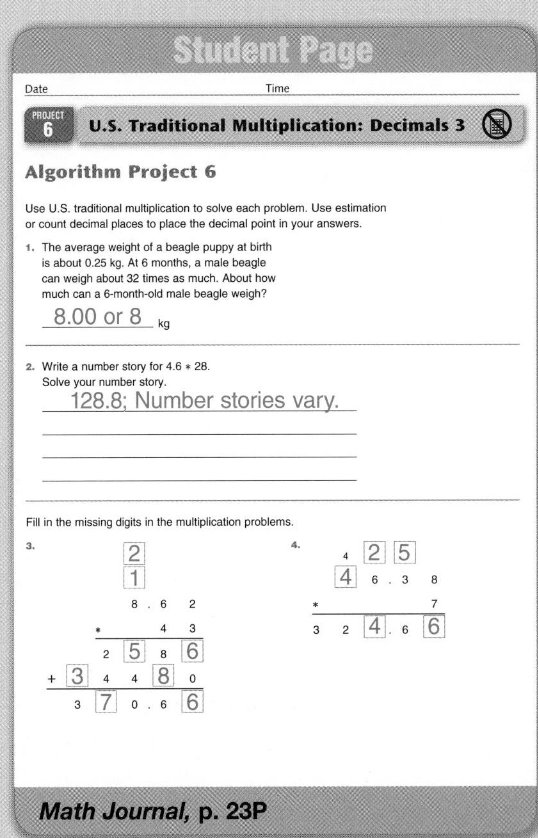

Student Page

Date Time

PROJECT 6 **U.S. Traditional Multiplication: Decimals 3**

Algorithm Project 6

Use U.S. traditional multiplication to solve each problem. Use estimation or count decimal places to place the decimal point in your answers.

1. The average weight of a beagle puppy at birth is about 0.25 kg. At 6 months, a male beagle can weigh about 32 times as much. About how much can a 6-month-old male beagle weigh?
   8.00 or 8 kg
2. Write a number story for 4.6 ∗ 28. Solve your number story.
   128.8; Number stories vary.

Fill in the missing digits in the multiplication problems.

3.
```
      2
      1
    8.62
*     43
--------
   25.86
+ 344.80
--------
  370.66
```

4.
```
   4 2 5
    46.38
*       7
---------
   324.66
```

Math Journal, p. 23P

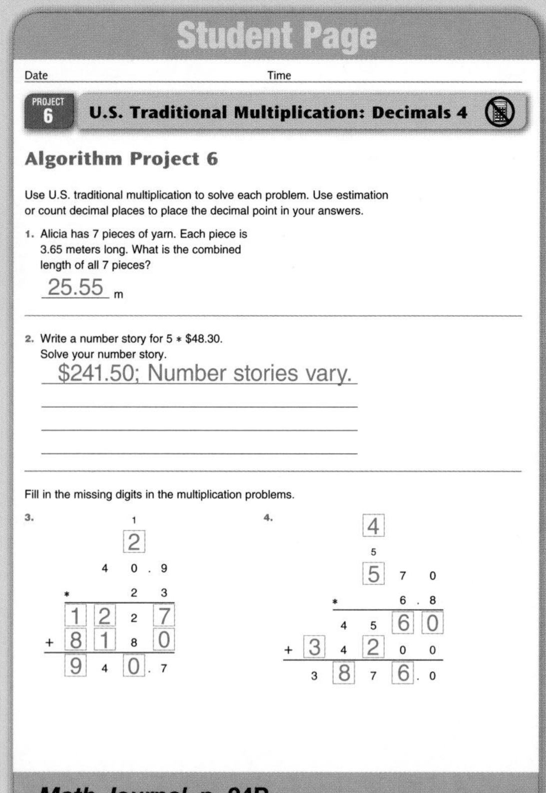
Student Page

Date Time

PROJECT 6 **U.S. Traditional Multiplication: Decimals 4**

Algorithm Project 6

Use U.S. traditional multiplication to solve each problem. Use estimation or count decimal places to place the decimal point in your answers.

1. Alicia has 7 pieces of yarn. Each piece is 3.65 meters long. What is the combined length of all 7 pieces?
   25.55 m

2. Write a number story for 5 * $48.30. Solve your number story.
   $241.50; Number stories vary.

Fill in the missing digits in the multiplication problems.

3.
```
      1
      2
    4 0 . 9
  *     2 3
  1 2 2 7
+ 8 1 8 0
  9 4 0 . 7
```

4.
```
        4
        5
      5 7 0
  *   6 . 8
    4 5 6 0
+ 3 4 2 0 0
  3 8 7 6 . 0
```

Math Journal, p. 24P

Go to www.everydaymathonline.com to access the additional practice pages.

Online Master

Name Date Time

PROJECT 6 **Partial-Products Multiplication: Decimals** Online Additional Practice

Algorithm Project 6

Use partial-products multiplication to solve each problem. Use estimation to place the decimal point in your answers.

1. A pack of 12 party invitations costs $8.95. Mrs. Becker bought 15 packs. How much money did she spend?
   $ 134.25

2. $0.46 * 83 = $ 38.18
3. 7 * 39.04 = 273.28
4. $ 633.15 = 63 * $10.05
5. 71.21 * 4 = 284.84
6. 60.48 = 7.56 * 8
7. 9,406 * 2.8 = 26,336.8

Online Additional Practice, p. 24A

You may want to work several more examples with the whole class.

Suggestions:

▷ 7.46 ∗ 3 = ? 22.38

▷ 3 ∗ $43.21 = ? $129.63

▷ $0.67 ∗ 5 = ? $3.35

▷ 8 ∗ 17.04 = ? 136.32

▷ 23 ∗ $40.06 = ? $921.38

▷ 5.6 ∗ 70 = ? 392

▶ Practicing U.S. Traditional Multiplication for Decimals

PARTNER ACTIVITY

(*Math Journal 1* or *2,* pp. 21P–24P; *Student Reference Book,* p. 40C)

When students are ready, have them solve Problems 2–7 on journal page 21P. They may find the examples on *Student Reference Book,* page 40C helpful.

Journal pages 22P–24P provide students with additional practice using U.S. traditional multiplication. Use these journal pages as necessary.

2 Extending the Project

▶ Solving Decimal Multiplication Problems

INDEPENDENT ACTIVITY

(Online Additional Practice, pp. 24A–24D; *Student Reference Book,* pp. 37A, 37B, and 40C)

Online practice pages 24A–24D provide students with additional practice solving decimal multiplication problems. Use these pages as necessary.

Encourage students to use the focus algorithm (partial-products multiplication) to solve the problems on practice page 24A. Invite them to use any algorithm they wish to solve the problems on the remaining pages.

Students may find the examples on *Student Reference Book,* pages 37A, 37B, and 40C helpful.

Algorithm 7 Project

U.S. Traditional Long Division, Part 1

Objective To introduce U.S. traditional long division.

Technology Resources www.everydaymathonline.com

eToolkit

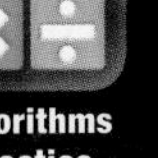
Algorithms Practice

EM Facts Workshop Game™

Family Letters

Assessment Management

Common Core State Standards

Curriculum Focal Points

Interactive Teacher's Lesson Guide

1 Doing the Project

Recommended Use After Lesson 6•10

Key Concepts and Skills

- Subtract multidigit numbers.
  [Operations and Computation Goal 2]
- Apply multiplication facts to long-division situations.
  [Operations and Computation Goal 3]
- Solve equal-sharing division problems and number stories.
  [Operations and Computation Goal 4]

Key Activities

Students explore and practice U.S. traditional long division with two- and three-digit whole numbers divided by single-digit whole numbers.

Key Vocabulary

U.S. traditional long division ◆ dividend ◆ divisor ◆ quotient ◆ remainder

Materials

- *Math Journal 1* or *2,* pp. 25P–27P
- *Student Reference Book,* pp. 24E–24H
- \$1 and \$10 bills (*Math Masters,* p. 428; optional)
- \$100 bills (optional)
- coins (optional)
- base-10 blocks (optional)
- index cards (optional)

2 Extending the Project

Students write and solve division number stories using U.S. traditional long division.

For additional practice, students solve division problems, first using the focus algorithm (partial-quotients division) and then using any algorithm they choose.

Materials

- *Student Reference Book,* pp. 22–24 and 24E–24H
- Online Additional Practice, pp. 27A–27C

Advance Preparation

If you intend to have students use coins and bills to model the division problems, you will need \$100 bills. Make several copies of Grade 3 *Math Masters,* page 401. Alternatively, use index cards to create \$100 bills.

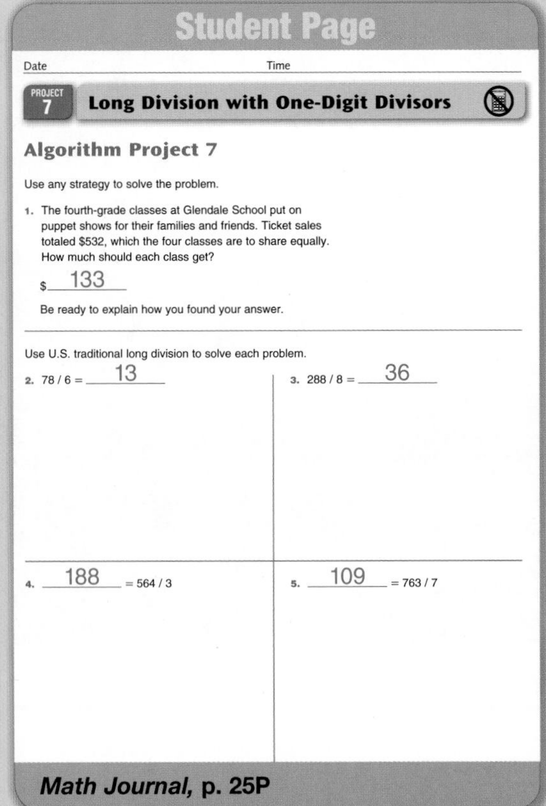
Student Page

Date Time

PROJECT 7 **Long Division with One-Digit Divisors**

Algorithm Project 7

Use any strategy to solve the problem.

1. The fourth-grade classes at Glendale School put on puppet shows for their families and friends. Ticket sales totaled $532, which the four classes are to share equally. How much should each class get?

   $ 133

   Be ready to explain how you found your answer.

Use U.S. traditional long division to solve each problem.

2. 78 / 6 = 13
3. 288 / 8 = 36
4. 188 = 564 / 3
5. 109 = 763 / 7

Math Journal, p. 25P

1 Doing the Project

▶ Solving a Division Problem

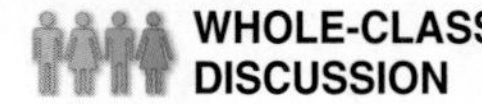
WHOLE-CLASS DISCUSSION

(*Math Journal 1* or *2*, p. 25P)

Ask students to solve Problem 1 on journal page 25P. Tell them they may use play money, paper and pencil, or any other tools they wish except calculators.

Discuss students' solutions. $532 / 4 = $133 Expect that students will use several different methods, including sharing or other actions with play money or other manipulatives, various informal paper-and-pencil methods, and partial-quotients division. Some students may also use U.S. traditional long division. *For example:*

▷ Sharing play money

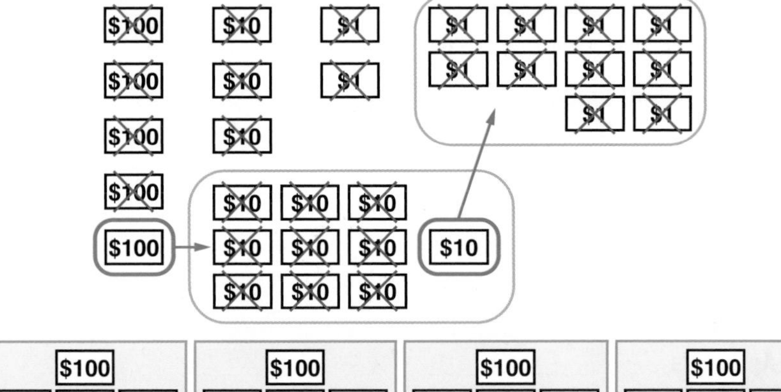

$532 / 4 = $133

▷ Sharing base-10 blocks

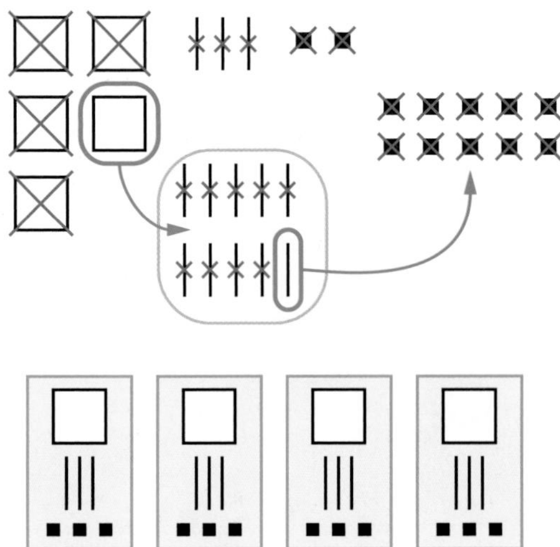

$532 / 4 = $133

▷ Using an informal paper-and-pencil method (*See margin.*)

▷ Using partial-quotients division

4)532	
− 400	100
132	
− 80	20
52	
− 40	10
12	
− 12	3
0	133

▷ Using U.S. traditional long division

```
   133
4)532
 − 4
   13
 − 12
    12
  − 12
     0
```

532	
− 100	← $25 for each class
432	
− 100	← $25 for each class
332	
− 100	← $25 for each class
232	
− 100	← $25 for each class
132	
− 100	← $25 for each class
32	
− 32	← $8 for each class
0	

$25 + $25 + $25 + $25 + $25 + $8 = $133

NOTE Long division is very demanding. Encourage students who may be overwhelmed to make a table of easy multiples of the divisor. For example:

1 * 4	4
2 * 4	8
3 * 4	12
4 * 4	16
5 * 4	20
6 * 4	24
7 * 4	28
8 * 4	32
9 * 4	36

▸ Introducing Long Division

WHOLE-CLASS ACTIVITY

After discussing students' solutions, regardless of whether one or more students used **U.S. traditional long division,** demonstrate it again as described below. Illustrate each step with pictures and, if possible, act out the problem using play money. Help students make connections between the steps in the algorithm and the actions of sharing the money.

Step 1:

Set up the problem. Think about sharing actual bills: 5 [$100]s, 3 [$10]s, and 2 [$1]s.

4)5 3 2 ← $532 is to be shared. We say $532 is the **dividend.** Think of $532 as 5 [$100]s, 3 [$10]s, and 2 [$1]s.

↑

The money is to be shared by four classes. We say 4 is the **divisor.**

Step 2:

Share the [$100]s. There are 5 [$100]s, so each class gets 1 [$100]. That uses up 4 [$100]s and leaves 1 [$100].

```
   1    ← Each class gets 1 [$100].
4)5 3 2
 − 4    ← 1 [$100] each for 4 classes = 4 [$100]s
   1    ← 1 [$100] is left.
```

Step 1

Money to be Shared	Ms. A's Class	Ms. B's Class	Ms. C's Class	Mr. D's Class
$100 $100 $100 $100 $100 $10 $10 $10 $1 $1				

Step 2

Money to be Shared	Ms. A's Class	Ms. B's Class	Ms. C's Class	Mr. D's Class
$100 $10 $10 $10 $1 $1	$100	$100	$100	$100

Step 3

Money to be Shared	Ms. A's Class	Ms. B's Class	Ms. C's Class	Mr. D's Class
$10 $10 $10 $10 $10 $10 $10 $10 $10 $10 $10 $10 $10 $1 $1	$100	$100	$100	$100

Step 3:

Trade the remaining [$100] for 10 [$10]s. That makes 13 [$10]s in all.

```
  1
4)5 3 2
 -4  ↓
  1 3   ← After trading the [$100] for 10 [$10]s, there are
          13 [$10]s in all.
```

Step 4

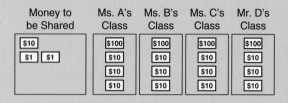

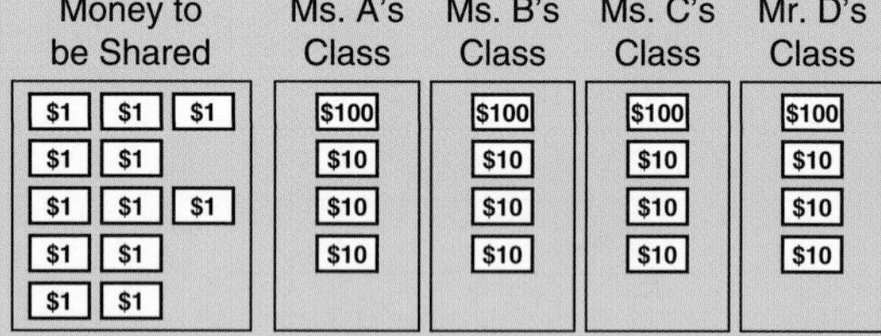

Step 4:

Share the 13 [$10]s. Each class gets 3 [$10]s. That leaves 1 [$10] still to be shared.

```
  1 3   ← Each class gets 3 [$10]s.
4)5 3 2
 -4
  1 3
 -1 2   ← 3 [$10]s each for 4 classes = 12 [$10]s
    1   ← 1 [$10] is left.
```

Step 5

Money to be Shared	Ms. A's Class	Ms. B's Class	Ms. C's Class	Mr. D's Class
$1 $1 $1 $1 $1 $1 $1 $1 $1 $1 $1 $1	$100 $10 $10 $10	$100 $10 $10 $10	$100 $10 $10 $10	$100 $10 $10 $10

Step 5:

Trade the last [$10] to be shared for 10 [$1]s. That makes 12 [$1]s in all.

```
  1 3
4)5 3 2
 -4   ↓
  1 3 ↓
 -1 2 ↓
    1 2 ← After trading the [$10] for 10 [$1]s, there are
          12 [$1]s in all.
```

Step 6

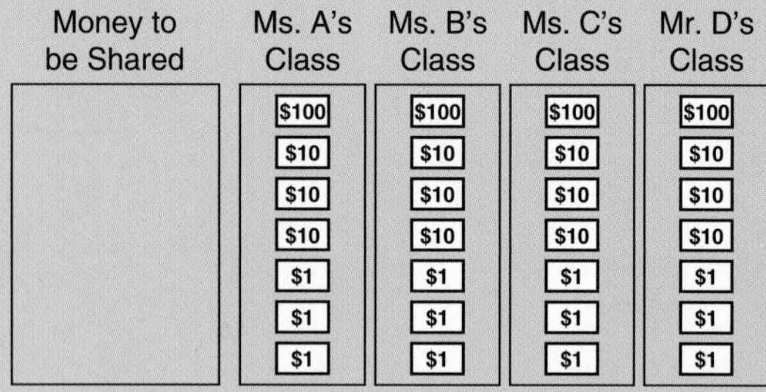

Step 6:

Share the 12 [$1]s. Each class gets 3 [$1]s.

```
  1 3 3 ← Each class gets 3 [$1]s.
4)5 3 2
 -4
  1 3
 -1 2
    1 2
   -1 2 ← 3 [$1]s each for 4 classes = 12 [$1]s
      0 ← 0 [$1]s are left.
```

Step 7:

Each class gets \$133. We say \$133 is the **quotient.** A number model is a good way to show the answer. Since there is no **remainder,** either

\$532 / 4 → \$133

or

\$532 / 4 = \$133

would be an acceptable number model for this problem.

U.S. traditional long division is complicated, so you may want to work more examples with the whole class. For now, continue to use sharing money as a context and continue drawing pictures and, if possible, acting out the problems with play money. Later, the algorithm can be generalized to non-money contexts.

Suggestions:

- ▷ \$84 / 7 \$12
- ▷ \$785 / 5 \$157
- ▷ \$122 / 8 \$15 R\$2
- ▷ \$807 / 4 \$201 R\$3
- ▷ 86 / 7 12 R2
- ▷ 468 / 5 93 R3

Solving Long Division Problems with One-Digit Divisors

PARTNER ACTIVITY

(*Math Journal 1* or *2,* pp. 25P–27P; *Student Reference Book,* pp. 24E–24H)

When students are ready, have them use U.S. traditional long division to solve Problems 2–13 on journal pages 25P–27P. They may find the examples on *Student Reference Book,* pages 24E–24H helpful. Students should note that Problems 6–9 involve remainders.

2 Extending the Project

Writing and Solving Division Number Stories

PARTNER ACTIVITY

(*Student Reference Book,* pp. 24E–24H)

Have students write division number stories for a partner to solve using U.S. traditional long division. Again, students may find the examples on *Student Reference Book,* pages 24E–24H helpful.

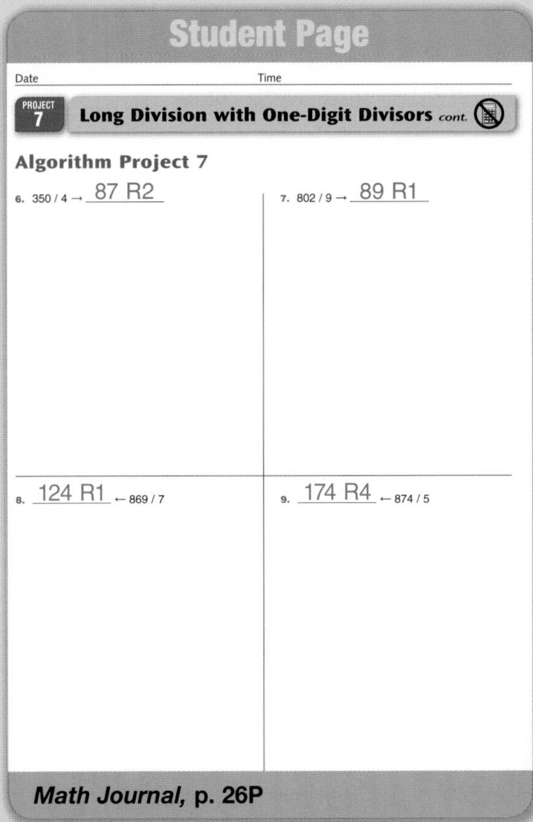
Student Page

Date Time

PROJECT 7 Long Division with One-Digit Divisors *cont.*

Algorithm Project 7

6. 350 / 4 → 87 R2

7. 802 / 9 → 89 R1

8. 124 R1 ← 869 / 7

9. 174 R4 ← 874 / 5

Math Journal, p. 26P

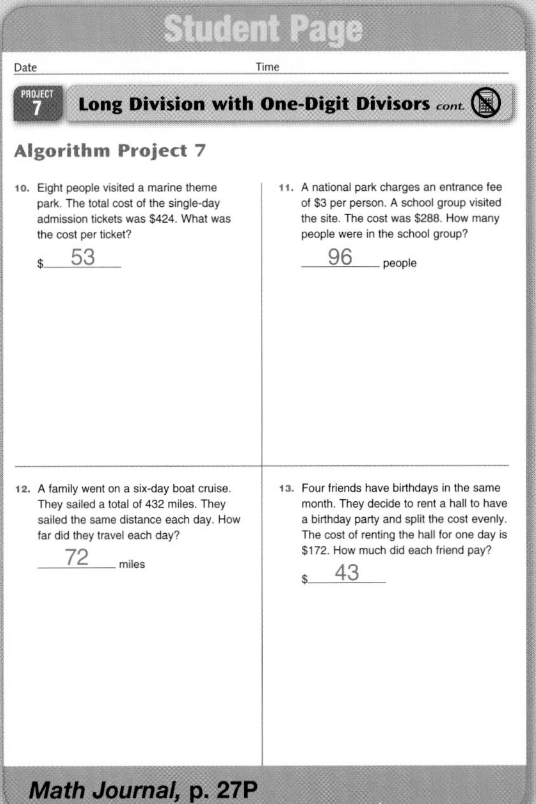
Student Page

Date Time

PROJECT 7 Long Division with One-Digit Divisors *cont.*

Algorithm Project 7

10. Eight people visited a marine theme park. The total cost of the single-day admission tickets was \$424. What was the cost per ticket?
\$ 53

11. A national park charges an entrance fee of \$3 per person. A school group visited the site. The cost was \$288. How many people were in the school group?
96 people

12. A family went on a six-day boat cruise. They sailed a total of 432 miles. They sailed the same distance each day. How far did they travel each day?
72 miles

13. Four friends have birthdays in the same month. They decide to rent a hall to have a birthday party and split the cost evenly. The cost of renting the hall for one day is \$172. How much did each friend pay?
\$ 43

Math Journal, p. 27P

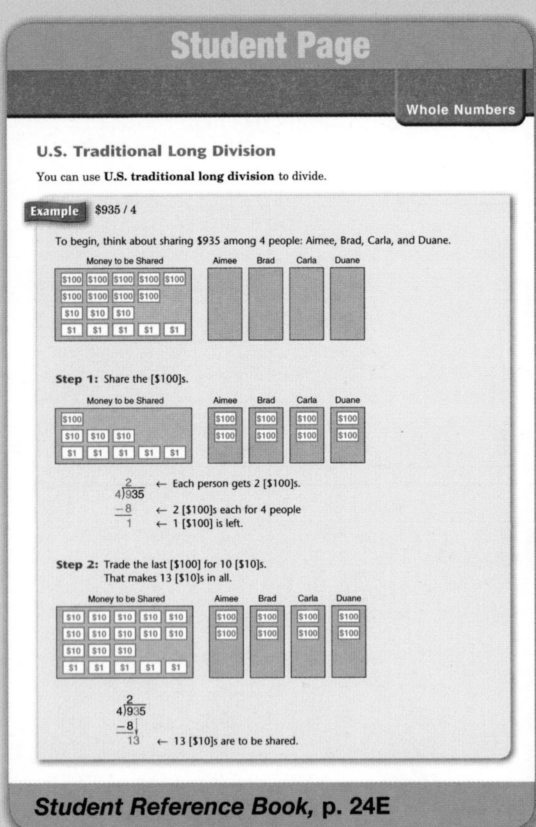

Student Page

Whole Numbers

U.S. Traditional Long Division

You can use **U.S. traditional long division** to divide.

Example $935 / 4

To begin, think about sharing $935 among 4 people: Aimee, Brad, Carla, and Duane.

Step 1: Share the [$100]s.

$4\overline{)935}$ with quotient 2 ← Each person gets 2 [$100]s.
−8 ← 2 [$100]s each for 4 people
1 ← 1 [$100] is left.

Step 2: Trade the last [$100] for 10 [$10]s. That makes 13 [$10]s in all.

$4\overline{)935}$ with quotient 2
−8
13 ← 13 [$10]s are to be shared.

Student Reference Book, **p. 24E**

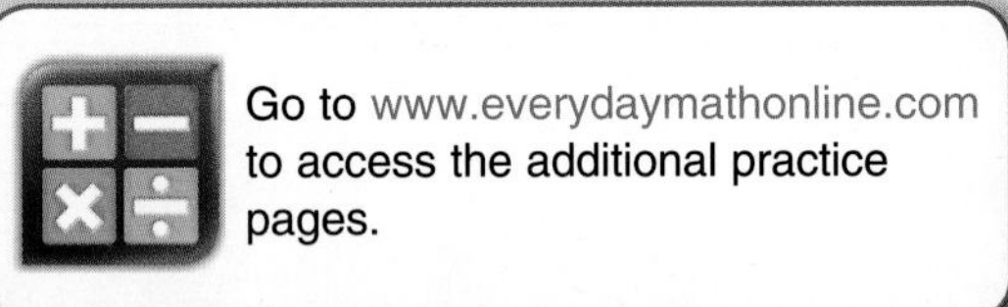

Go to www.everydaymathonline.com to access the additional practice pages.

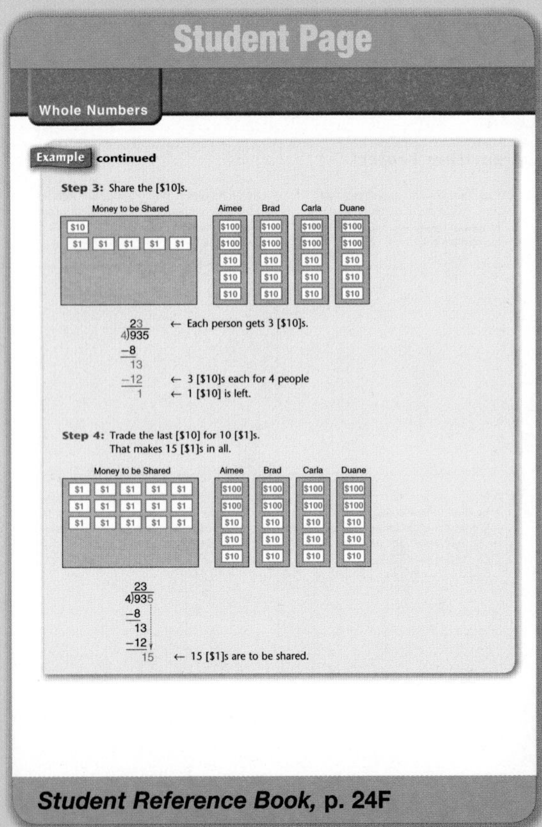

Student Page

Whole Numbers

Example continued

Step 3: Share the [$10]s.

$4\overline{)935}$ with quotient 23 ← Each person gets 3 [$10]s.
−8
13
−12 ← 3 [$10]s each for 4 people
1 ← 1 [$10] is left.

Step 4: Trade the last [$10] for 10 [$1]s. That makes 15 [$1]s in all.

$4\overline{)935}$ with quotient 23
−8
13
−12
15 ← 15 [$1]s are to be shared.

Student Reference Book, **p. 24F**

Solving Division Problems

(Online Additional Practice, pp. 27A–27C; *Student Reference Book,* pp. 22–24 and 24E–24H)

Online practice pages 27A–27C provide students with additional practice solving division problems. Use these pages as necessary.

Encourage students to use the focus algorithm (partial-quotients division) to solve the problems on practice page 27A. Invite them to use any algorithm they wish to solve the problems on the remaining pages. Students may find the examples on *Student Reference Book,* pages 22–24 and 24E–24H helpful.

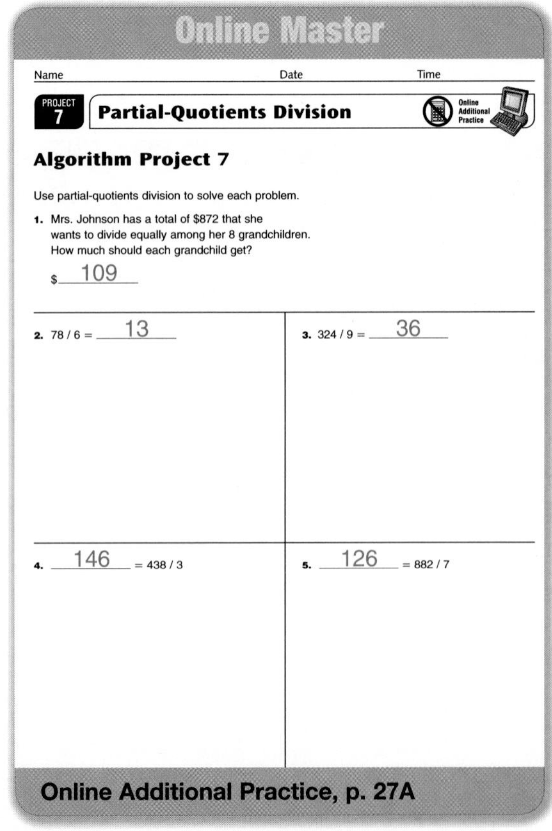

Online Master

Name Date Time

PROJECT 7 **Partial-Quotients Division**

Algorithm Project 7

Use partial-quotients division to solve each problem.

1. Mrs. Johnson has a total of $872 that she wants to divide equally among her 8 grandchildren. How much should each grandchild get?
$ 109

2. 78 / 6 = 13

3. 324 / 9 = 36

4. 146 = 438 / 3

5. 126 = 882 / 7

Online Additional Practice, p. 27A

Algorithm **8** Project

U.S. Traditional Long Division, Part 2

Objective To extend U.S. traditional long division with single-digit divisors to four- and five-digit dividends and dividends in dollars-and-cents notation.

Technology Resources www.everydaymathonline.com

eToolkit

Algorithms Practice

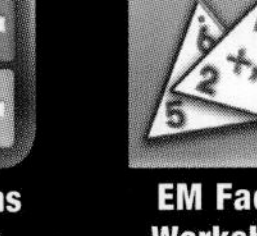
EM Facts Workshop Game™

Family Letters

Assessment Management

Common Core State Standards

Curriculum Focal Points

Interactive Teacher's Lesson Guide

1 Doing the Project

Recommended Use After Lesson 9•9 and after Algorithm Project 7

Key Concepts and Skills

- Subtract multidigit numbers. [Operations and Computation Goal 2]
- Apply multiplication facts to long-division situations. [Operations and Computation Goal 3]
- Solve equal-sharing division problems and number stories. [Operations and Computation Goal 4]
- Divide decimals by whole numbers. [Operations and Computation Goal 4]

Key Activities

Students explore and practice U.S. traditional long division with single-digit divisors, four- and five-digit dividends, and dividends in dollars-and-cents notation.

Key Vocabulary

quotient ◆ dividend

Materials

- *Math Journal 1* or *2,* pp. 28P–30P
- *Student Reference Book,* pp. 24E–24J and 40D–40F
- $1 and $10 bills (*Math Masters,* p. 428; optional)
- $100 and $1,000 bills (optional)
- coins (optional)
- base-10 blocks (optional)
- index cards (optional)

2 Extending the Project

Students write division number stories and use U.S. traditional long division to solve them.

For additional practice, students solve division problems, first using the focus algorithm (partial-quotients division) and then using any algorithm they choose.

Materials

- *Student Reference Book,* pp. 22–24 and 24E–24H
- Online Additional Practice, pp. 27A–27C

Additional Information

Today there are no longer any bills larger than $100 in circulation, but it was not always so. Beginning in the late 1920s and early 1930s the U.S. Treasury issued a small number of large bills, including $500, $1,000, $5,000, $10,000, and $100,000 bills. By the mid-1940s, the Treasury stopped making these bills, and in 1969 President Nixon removed them from circulation because they were rarely used and attractive to counterfeiters.

Advance Preparation

If you intend to have students use coins and bills to model the division problems, you will need $100 and $1,000 bills. Make several copies of Grade 3 *Math Masters,* page 401 for the $100 bills or use index cards to create them. Use index cards to create $1,000 bills.

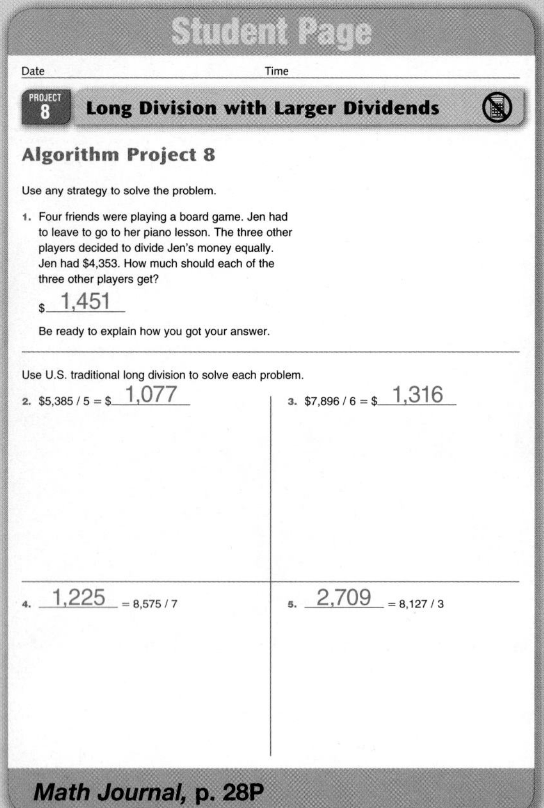

Student Page

Date Time

PROJECT 8 **Long Division with Larger Dividends**

Algorithm Project 8

Use any strategy to solve the problem.

1. Four friends were playing a board game. Jen had to leave to go to her piano lesson. The three other players decided to divide Jen's money equally. Jen had $4,353. How much should each of the three other players get?

   $ 1,451

   Be ready to explain how you got your answer.

Use U.S. traditional long division to solve each problem.

2. $5,385 / 5 = $ 1,077
3. $7,896 / 6 = $ 1,316
4. 1,225 = 8,575 / 7
5. 2,709 = 8,127 / 3

Math Journal, p. 28P

```
3)4353
 - 3000 | 1000
   1353 |
 - 1200 |  400
    153 |
 - 150  |   50
      3 |
    - 3 |    1
      0 | 1451
```

Partial-quotients division

1 Doing the Project

▶ Solving a Division Problem

WHOLE-CLASS DISCUSSION

(*Math Journal 1* or *2*, p. 28P)

Ask students to solve Problem 1 on journal page 28P. Tell them they may use paper and pencil or any tools they wish, except calculators.

Have students discuss and share solutions. $4353 / 3 = $1451 Expect a variety of approaches, including U.S. traditional long division, which was introduced in Algorithm Project 7. Have students explain why each of the steps in their procedures make sense. *For example:*

▷ Sharing play money or base-10 blocks

▷ Using an informal paper-and-pencil method

```
  4353
- 3000 ← $1000 for each player
  1353
 - 300 ← $100 for each player
  1053
 - 300 ← $100 for each player
   753
 - 300 ← $100 for each player
   453
 - 300 ← $100 for each player
   153
 - 150 ← $50 for each player
     3
   - 3 ← $1 for each player
     0
```

$1000 + $100 + $100 + $100 + $100 + $50 + $1 = $1451

▷ Using partial-quotients division (*See margin.*)

▷ Using U.S. traditional long division

```
  1451
3)4353
 - 3
   13
 - 12
    15
  - 15
     03
    - 3
      0
```

▶ Extending Long Division to Larger Dividends

WHOLE-CLASS ACTIVITY

After you have discussed students' solutions, regardless of whether some students used U.S. traditional long division, demonstrate it again as described on the next page. Illustrate each step in the algorithm with pictures of play money. Help students make connections between the steps in the algorithm and the actions of sharing money.

Step 1:

Set up the problem. Think about sharing actual bills:
4 [$1,000]s, 3 [$100]s, 5 [$10]s, and 3 [$1]s.

3)4 3 5 3 ← $4,353 is to be shared.

↑

Three players will share Jen's money.

Step 2:

Share the [$1,000]s. Each player gets 1 [$1,000]. There is 1 [$1,000] left.

1 ← Each player gets 1 [$1,000].
3)4 3 5 3
– 3 ← 1 [$1,000] each for 3 players = 3 [$1,000]s
1 ← 1 [$1,000] is left.

Step 3:

Trade the 1 [$1,000] for 10 [$100]s.

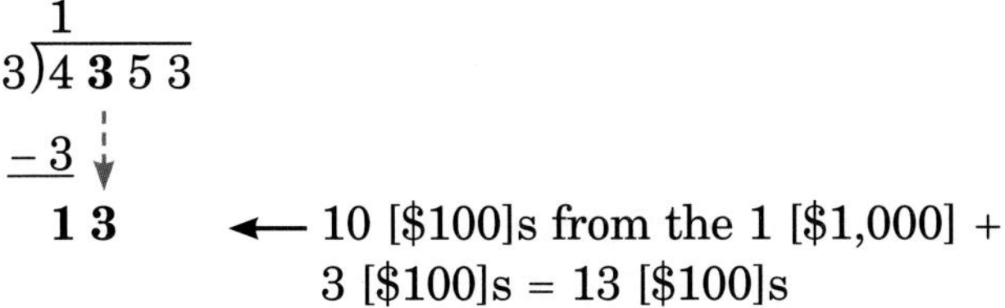

1
3)4 **3** 5 3
– 3 ↓
1 3 ← 10 [$100]s from the 1 [$1,000] + 3 [$100]s = 13 [$100]s

Step 4:

Share the 13 [$100]s. Each player gets 4 [$100]s; 1 [$100] is left.

1 **4** ← Each player gets 4 [$100]s.
3)4 3 5 3
– 3
1 3
– 1 2 ← 4 [$100]s each for 3 players = 12 [$100]s.
1 ← 1 [$100] is left.

Step 5:

Trade the 1 [$100] for 10 [$10]s.

1 4
3)4 3 **5** 3
– 3
1 3
– 1 2 ↓
1 5 ← 10 [$10]s from the 1 [$100] + 5 [$10]s = 15 [$10]s

Step 1

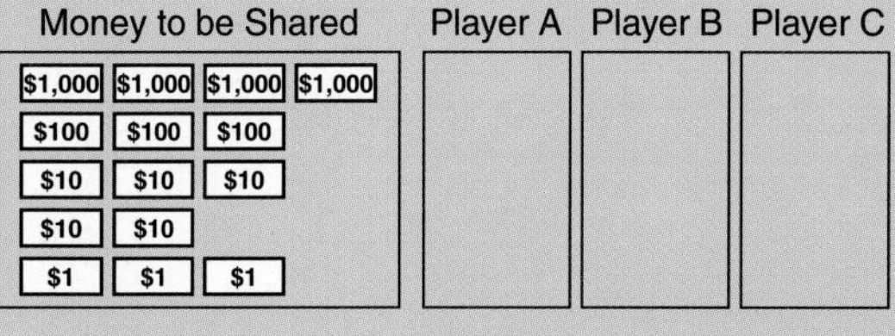

Step 2

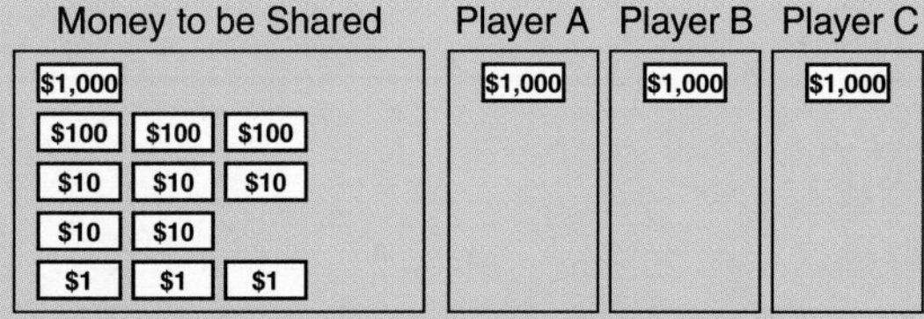

Step 3

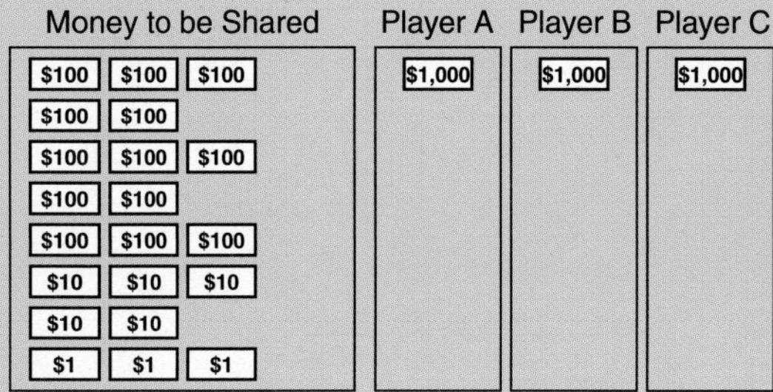

Step 4

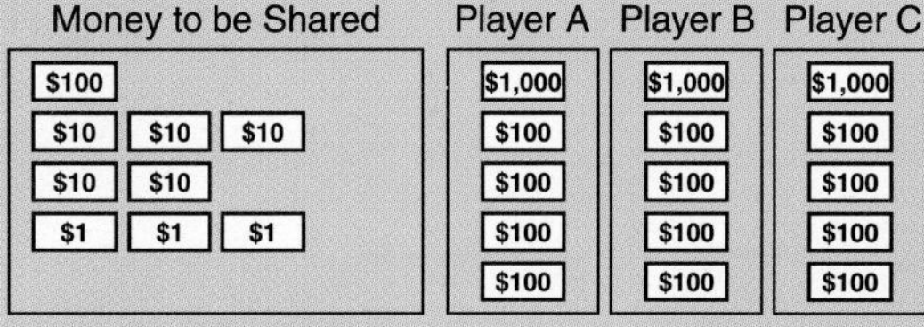

Step 5

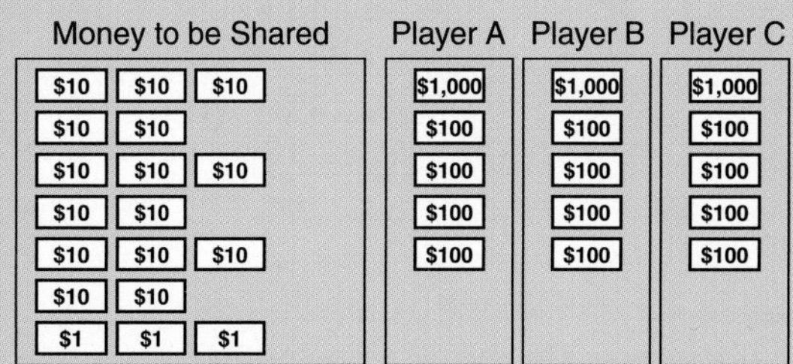

Step 6

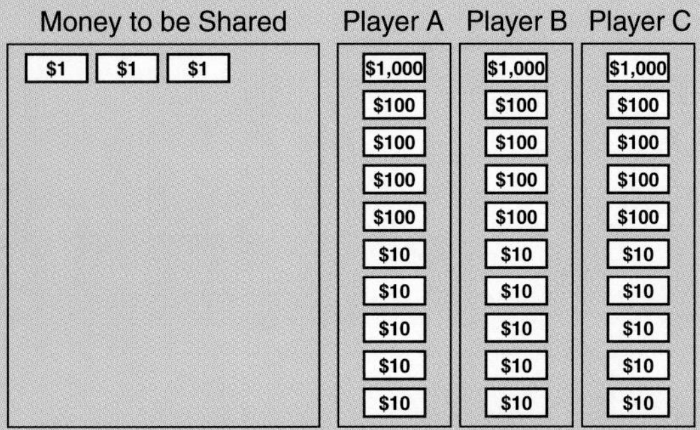

Step 7

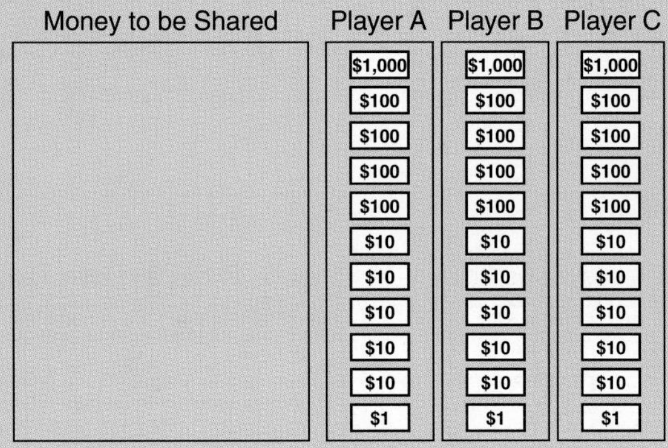

Student Page

Date Time

PROJECT 8 **Long Division with Larger Dividends** *cont.*

Algorithm Project 8

Fill in the missing numbers.

6.
```
   1 7 3 9
5)8 6 9 5
 - 5
   3 6
 - 3 5
     1 9
   - 1 5
       4 5
     - 4 5
         0
```

7.
```
     5 4 2
6)3 2 5 2
 -3 0
    2 5
  - 2 4
      1 2
    - 1 2
        0
```

8. Jai is saving money to go to sleep-away camp next summer. The total cost is $1,092. He is earning money by walking dogs in his neighborhood.

a. At $4 per walk, how many dogs will Jai need to walk to earn $1,092? 273 dogs

b. At $7 per walk, how many dogs will Jai need to walk to earn $1,092? 156 dogs

Math Journal, p. 29P

Step 6:

Share the 15 [$10]s. Each player gets 5 [$10]s.

```
  1 4 5      ← Each player gets 5 [$10]s.
3)4 3 5 3
 -3
  1 3
 -1 2
    1 5
  - 1 5      ← 5 [$10]s each for 3 players = 15 [$10]s
      0      ← 0 [$10]s are left.
```

Step 7:

Share the 3 [$1]s. Each player gets 1 [$1].

```
  1 4 5 1    ← Each player gets 1 [$1].
3)4 3 5 3
 -3
  1 3
 -1 2
    1 5
  - 1 5
      0 3    ← 3 [$1]s are to be shared.
      - 3    ← 1 [$1] each for 3 players = 3 [$1]s
        0    ← 0 [$1]s are left to be shared.
```

$4,353 / 3 = $1,451

Each of the continuing players gets $1,451.

Solving Long Division Problems

PARTNER ACTIVITY

(*Math Journal 1* or *2,* pp. 28P and 29P; *Student Reference Book,* pp. 24E–24J)

Have partners use U.S. traditional long division to solve the problems on journal pages 28P and 29P. Students may find the examples on *Student Reference Book,* pages 24E–24J helpful.

Extending Long Division to Dollars-and-Cents Notation

WHOLE-CLASS DISCUSSION

(*Math Journal 1* or *2,* p. 30P; *Student Reference Book,* pp. 40D–40F)

Have students solve Problem 1 on journal page 30P. As a class, discuss how Dennis solved the problem. Be sure to include the following points:

- Long division for dollars and cents looks almost exactly the same as for whole numbers.
- The money in Dennis's method would include dimes and pennies, not just bills as in whole-number long division with money.

▷ There are decimal points separating dollars from cents in Dennis's **quotient** and **dividend.** In whole-number long division there were no decimal points.

▷ With Dennis's method, we know exactly where the decimal point belongs. If we use partial-quotients division to solve the problem, we use estimation to place the decimal point. For example, to solve $9.45 / 7 by partial quotients:

- Estimate the answer. $9.45 / 7 would be more than $1 but less than $2.
- Divide as though the dividend were a whole number. 945 / 7 = 135
- Use the estimate to place the decimal point in the quotient. Since the answer must be between $1 and $2, the decimal point must go between the 1 and the 3; $1.35.

Have students complete Problems 2–5 on page 30P. Pose additional problems such as the following. Review *Student Reference Book,* pages 40D–40F as necessary.

▷ $1.72 / 4 $0.43
▷ $7.05 / 5 $1.41
▷ $9.27 / 3 $3.09
▷ $9.42 / 6 $1.57
▷ $8.01 / 3 $2.67
▷ $6.93 / 7 $0.99
▷ $8.66 / 2 $4.33
▷ $6.90 / 6 $1.15

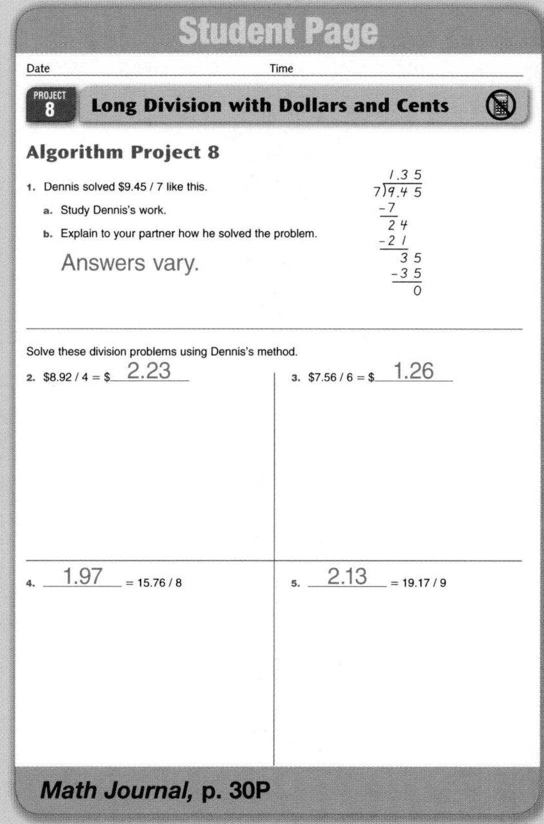
Student Page

Date Time

PROJECT 8 **Long Division with Dollars and Cents**

Algorithm Project 8

1. Dennis solved $9.45 / 7 like this.
   a. Study Dennis's work.
   b. Explain to your partner how he solved the problem.

   Answers vary.

Solve these division problems using Dennis's method.

2. $8.92 / 4 = $ 2.23
3. $7.56 / 6 = $ 1.26
4. 1.97 = 15.76 / 8
5. 2.13 = 19.17 / 9

Math Journal, p. 30P

2 Extending the Project

Writing and Solving Division Number Stories

PARTNER ACTIVITY

(*Student Reference Book,* pp. 24E–25J and 40D–40F)

Have students write division number stories that include single-digit divisors, four-and five-digit dividends, and dividends in dollars-and-cents notation. Partners use U.S. traditional long division to solve them. Students may find the examples on *Student Reference Book,* pages 24E–24J and 40D–40F helpful.

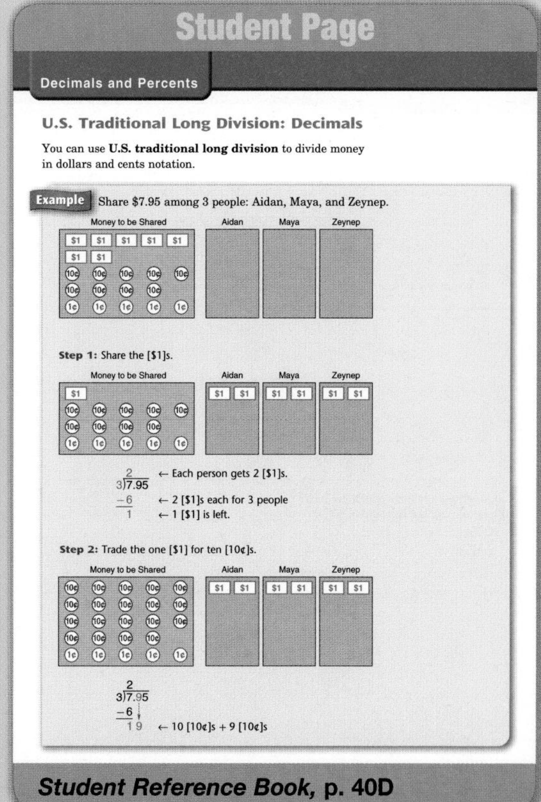
Student Page

Decimals and Percents

U.S. Traditional Long Division: Decimals

You can use **U.S. traditional long division** to divide money in dollars and cents notation.

Example Share $7.95 among 3 people: Aidan, Maya, and Zeynep.

Step 1: Share the [$1]s.

← Each person gets 2 [$1]s.
← 2 [$1]s each for 3 people
← 1 [$1] is left.

Step 2: Trade the one [$1] for ten [10¢]s.

← 10 [10¢]s + 9 [10¢]s

Student Reference Book, p. 40D

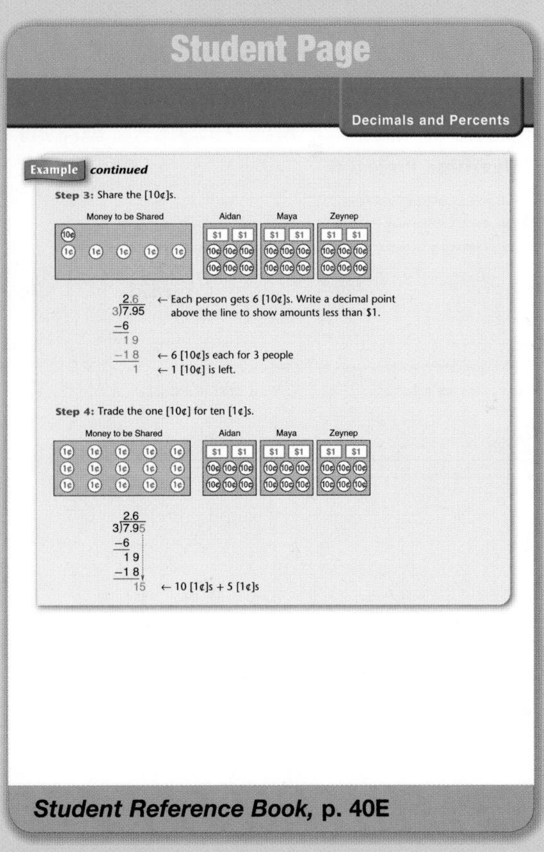

Student Page

Decimals and Percents

Example *continued*

Step 3: Share the [10¢]s.

Money to be Shared	Aidan	Maya	Zeynep

```
   2.6    ← Each person gets 6 [10¢]s. Write a decimal point
 3)7.95     above the line to show amounts less than $1.
  -6
   1 9
  -1 8    ← 6 [10¢]s each for 3 people
     1    ← 1 [10¢] is left.
```

Step 4: Trade the one [10¢] for ten [1¢]s.

Money to be Shared	Aidan	Maya	Zeynep

```
   2.6
 3)7.95
  -6
   1 9
  -1 8
     15   ← 10 [1¢]s + 5 [1¢]s
```

***Student Reference Book,* p. 40E**

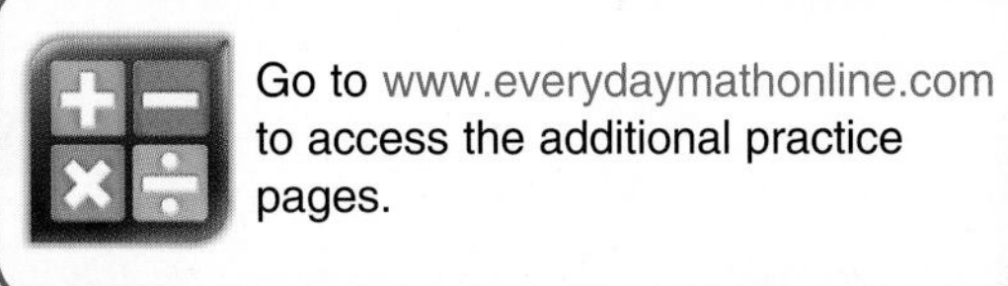

Go to www.everydaymathonline.com to access the additional practice pages.

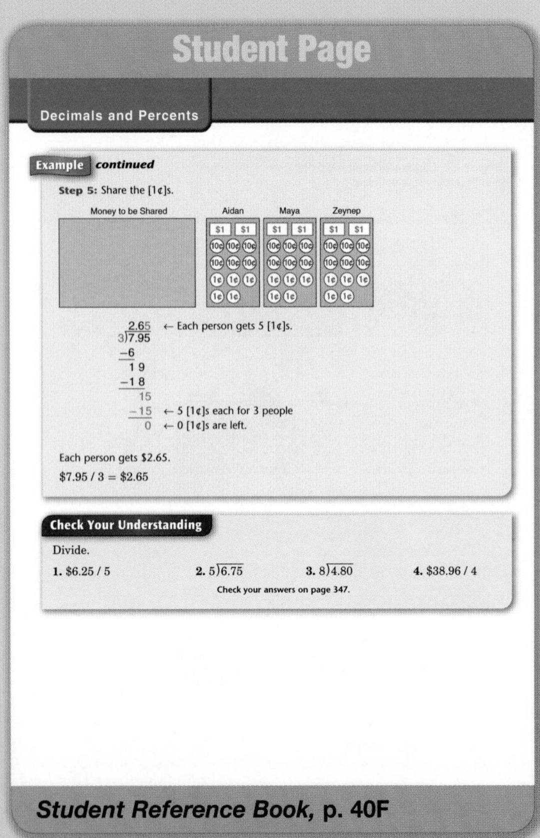

Student Page

Decimals and Percents

Example *continued*

Step 5: Share the [1¢]s.

Money to be Shared	Aidan	Maya	Zeynep

```
   2.65   ← Each person gets 5 [1¢]s.
 3)7.95
  -6
   1 9
  -1 8
     15
    -15   ← 5 [1¢]s each for 3 people
      0   ← 0 [1¢]s are left.
```

Each person gets $2.65.

$7.95 / 3 = $2.65

Check Your Understanding

Divide.

1. $6.25 / 5
2. 5)6.75
3. 8)4.80
4. $38.96 / 4

Check your answers on page 347.

***Student Reference Book,* p. 40F**

▶ Solving Division Problems

INDEPENDENT ACTIVITY

(Online Additional Practice, pp. 30A–30C; *Student Reference Book,* pp. 22–24, 24E–24J, and 40D–40F)

Online practice pages 30A–30C provide students with additional practice solving division problems. Use these pages as necessary.

Encourage students to use the focus algorithm (partial-quotients division) to solve the problems on practice page 30A. Invite them to use any algorithm they wish to solve the problems on the remaining pages. Students may find the examples on *Student Reference Book,* pages 22–24, 24E–24J, and 40D–40F helpful.

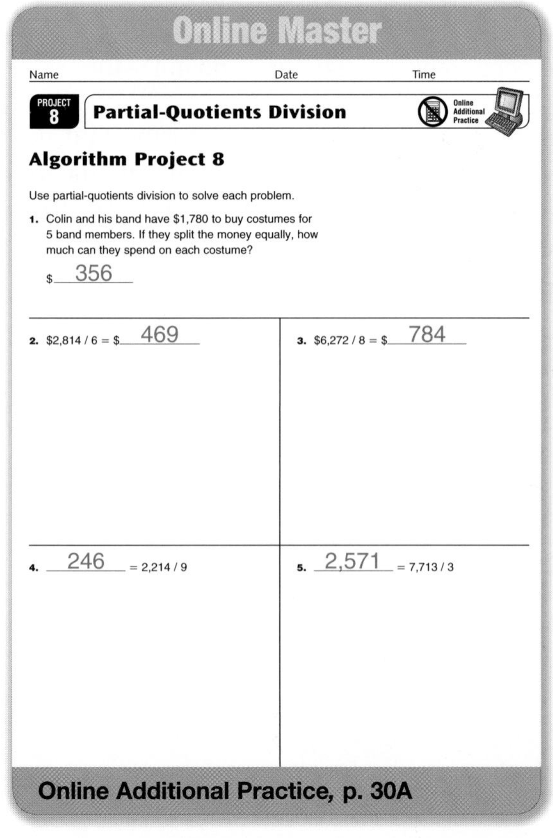

Online Master

Name　　Date　　Time

PROJECT 8 **Partial-Quotients Division**

Online Additional Practice

Algorithm Project 8

Use partial-quotients division to solve each problem.

1. Colin and his band have $1,780 to buy costumes for 5 band members. If they split the money equally, how much can they spend on each costume?
   $ 356
2. $2,814 / 6 = $ 469
3. $6,272 / 8 = $ 784
4. 246 = 2,214 / 9
5. 2,571 = 7,713 / 3

Online Additional Practice, p. 30A

Fourth Grade Key Vocabulary

For a more comprehensive glossary that includes additional entries and illustrations, please refer to the *Teacher's Reference Manual*.

NOTE: In a definition, terms in italics are defined elsewhere in this glossary.

acute angle An *angle* with a measure less than 90°.

Acute angles

algorithm A set of step-by-step instructions for doing something, such as carrying out a computation or solving a problem. The most common algorithms are those for basic arithmetic computation, but there are many others. Some mathematicians and many computer scientists spend a great deal of time trying to find more efficient algorithms for solving problems.

altitude (1) In *Everyday Mathematics*, same as *height* of a figure. (2) Distance above sea level.

angle A figure formed by two *rays* or two *line segments* with a common *endpoint* called the *vertex* of the angle. The rays or segments are called the *sides* of the angle. An angle is measured in degrees between 0 and 360. One side of an angle is the *rotation* image of the other side through a number of degrees. Angles are named after their vertex point alone as in ∠*A* below; or by three points, one on each side and the vertex in the middle as in ∠*BCD* below.

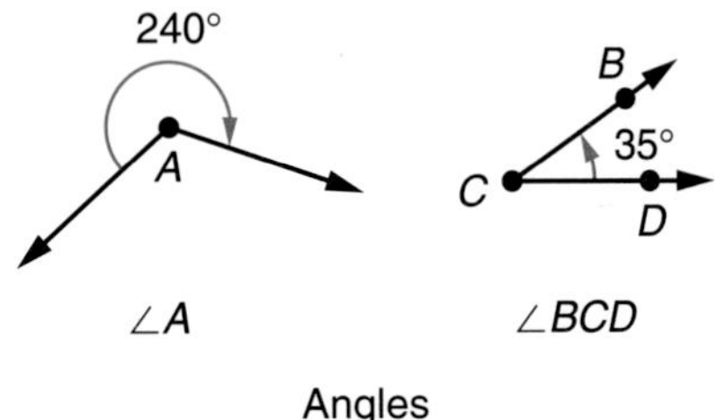

Angles

area The amount of surface inside a 2-dimensional figure. The figure might be a triangle or rectangle in a plane, the curved surface of a cylinder, or a state or country on Earth's surface. Commonly, area is measured in *square units* such as square miles, square inches, or square centimeters.

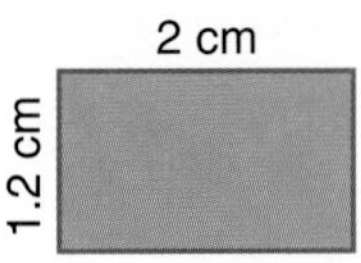

A rectangle with area
1.2 cm ∗ 2 cm = 2.4 cm^2

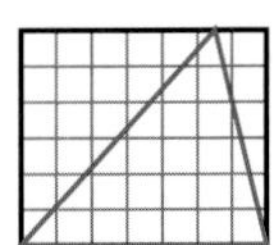

A triangle with area
21 square units

The area of the United States is about 3,800,000 square miles.

average A typical value for a set of numbers. In everyday life, average usually refers to the *mean* of the set, found by adding all the numbers and dividing by the number of numbers.

axis of a coordinate grid Either of the two number lines used to form a *coordinate grid*. Plural is axes.

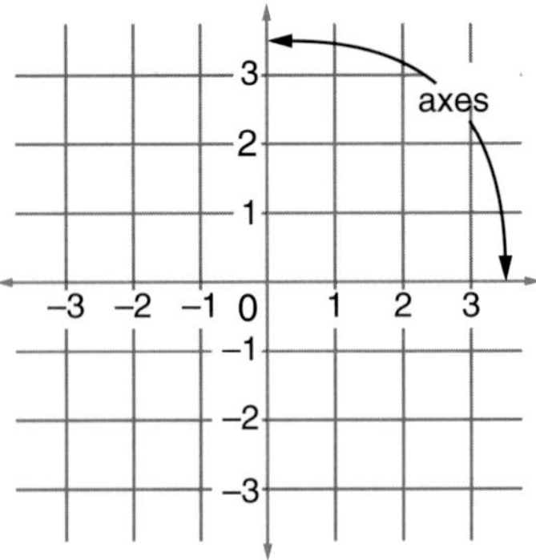

axis of rotation A *line* about which a solid figure rotates.

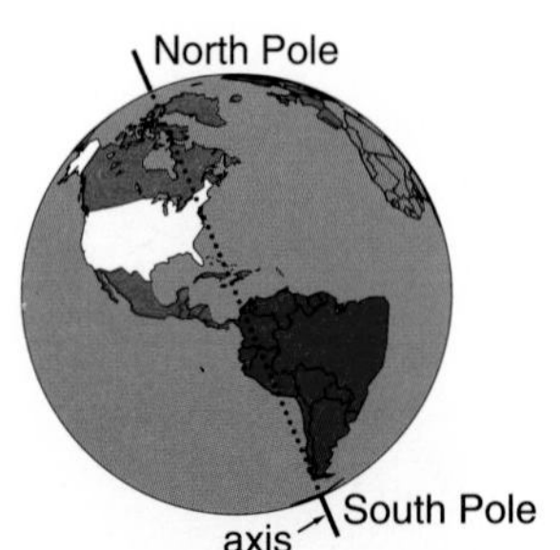

bar graph A graph with horizontal or vertical bars that represent data.

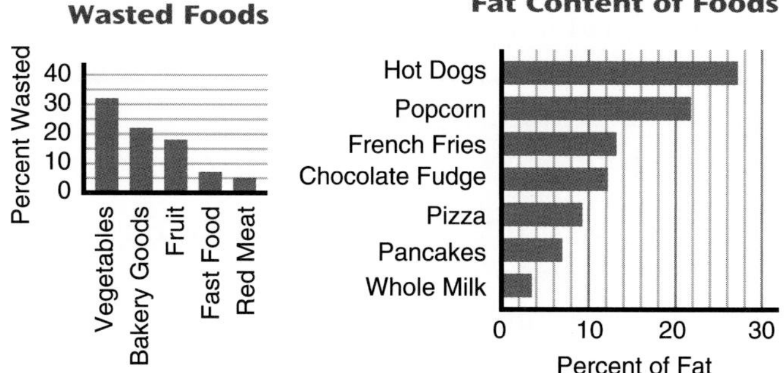

Source: The Garbage Product *Source:* The New York Public Library Desk Reference

base (in exponential notation) A number that is raised to a *power.* For example, the base in 5^3 is 5.

base of a parallelogram (1) The side of a *parallelogram* to which an altitude is drawn. (2) The length of this side. The area of a parallelogram is the base times the altitude or height perpendicular to it.

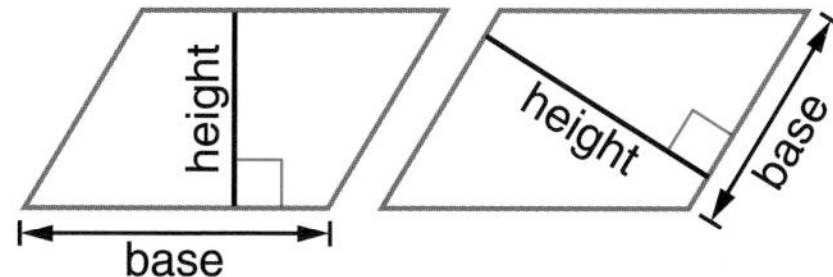

base of a prism or cylinder Either of the two parallel and congruent *faces* that define the shape of a *prism* or *cylinder.* In a cylinder, the base is a circle.

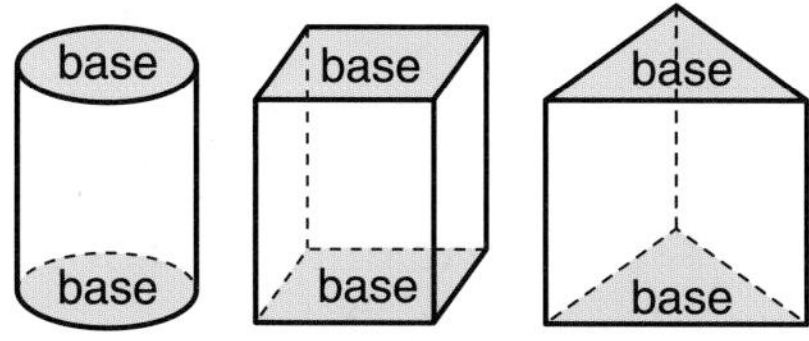

base of a pyramid or cone The *face* of a pyramid or cone that is opposite its apex (the vertex opposite the base). The base of a cone is a circle.

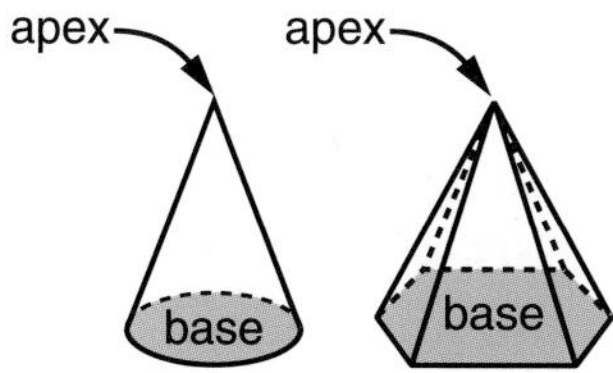

base of a rectangle (1) One of the sides of a *rectangle.* (2) The length of this side. The area of a rectangle is the base times the *altitude* or height.

base of a triangle (1) Any side of a *triangle* to which an *altitude* is drawn. (2) The length of this side. The area of a triangle is half the base times the altitude or height.

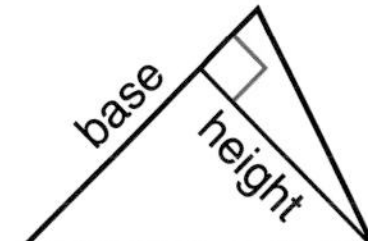

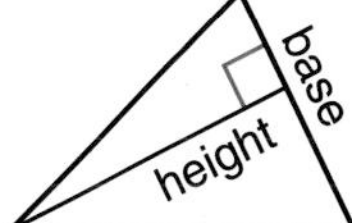

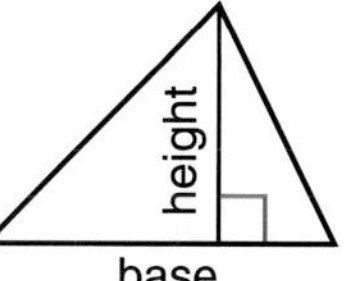

capacity (1) The amount of space occupied by a 3-dimensional figure. Same as *volume.* (2) Less formally, the amount a container can hold. Capacity is often measured in units such as quarts, gallons, cups, or liters.

centimeter (cm) A metric unit of *length* equivalent to 10 millimeters, $\frac{1}{10}$ of a decimeter, and $\frac{1}{100}$ of a *meter.*

circle The set of all *points* in a plane that are equally distant from a fixed point in the plane called the center of the circle. The distance from the center to the circle is the *radius* of the circle. The *diameter* of a circle is twice its radius. Points inside a circle are not part of the circle. A circle together with its interior is called a disk or a circular region.

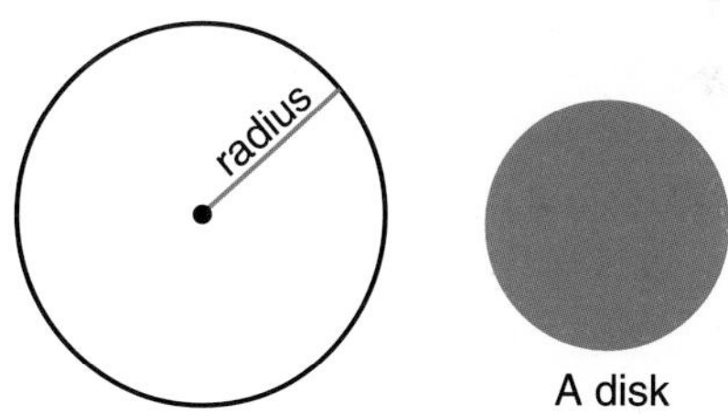

clockwise rotation The direction in which the hands move on a typical analog clock; a turn to the right.

column addition An addition *algorithm* in which the addends' digits are first added in each place-value column separately, and then 10-for-1 trades are made until each column has only one digit. Lines may be drawn to separate the place-value columns.

compass (1) A tool used to draw *circles* and arcs and copy *line segments.* Certain geometric figures can be drawn with compass-and-straightedge constructions.

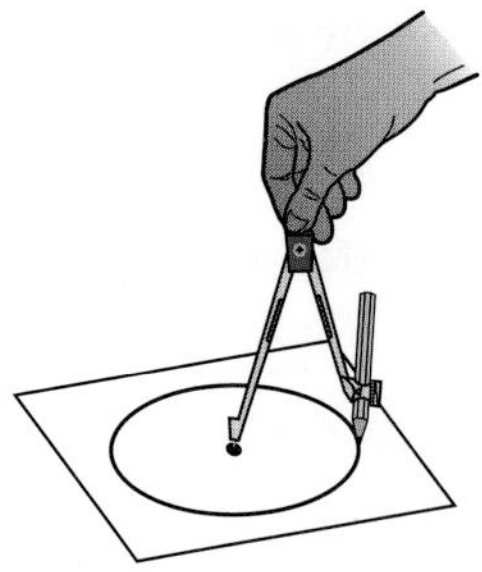

A directional compass

(2) A tool used to determine geographic direction.

composite number A *counting number* greater than 1 that has more than two *factors.* For example, 10 is a composite number because it has four factors; 1, 2, 5, and 10. A composite number is divisible by at least three whole numbers. Compare to *prime number.*

concave polygon A *polygon* on which there are at least two *points* that can be connected with a *line segment* that passes outside the polygon. For example, segment *AD* is outside the hexagon between *B* and *C*. Informally, at least one *vertex* appears to be "pushed inward." At least one interior angle has a measure greater than 180°. Same as *nonconvex polygon.* Compare to *convex polygon.*

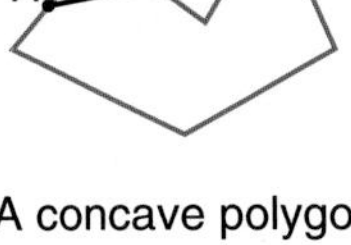

A concave polygon

concentric circles *Circles* that have the same center but have *radii* of different lengths.

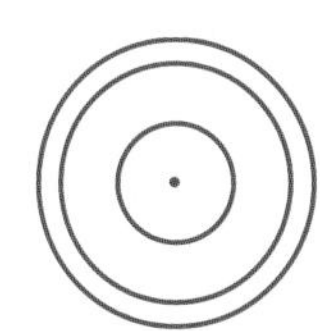

Concentric circles

convex polygon A *polygon* on which no two *points* can be connected with a *line segment* that passes outside the polygon. Informally, all *vertices* appear to be "pushed outward." Each angle in the polygon measures less than 180°. Compare to *concave polygon.*

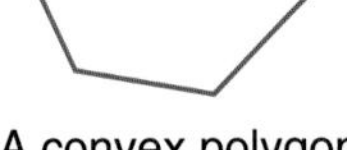

A convex polygon

coordinate (1) A number used to locate a *point* on a number line; a point's distance from an origin. (2) One of the numbers in an *ordered pair* or triple that locates a point on a *coordinate grid* or in coordinate space, respectively.

coordinate grid (rectangular coordinate grid) A reference frame for locating *points* in a plane by means of *ordered pairs* of numbers. A rectangular coordinate grid is formed by two number lines that intersect at *right angles* at their zero points.

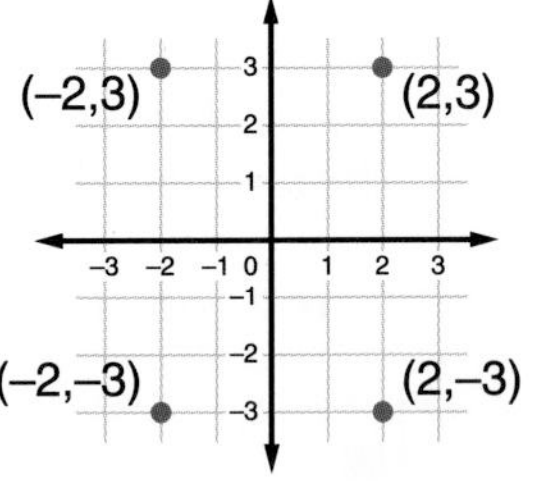

A coordinate grid

counterclockwise rotation Opposite the direction in which the hands move on a typical analog clock; a turn to the left.

counting numbers The numbers used to count things. The set of counting numbers is {1, 2, 3, 4, . . .}. Sometimes 0 is included, but not in *Everyday Mathematics.* Counting numbers are in the sets of *whole numbers,* integers, rational numbers, and real numbers, but each of these sets include numbers that are not counting numbers.

cylinder A geometric solid with two congruent, parallel circular regions for *bases* and a curved *face* formed by all the segments with an endpoint on each circle that are parallel to a segment with endpoints at the centers of the circles. Also called a circular cylinder.

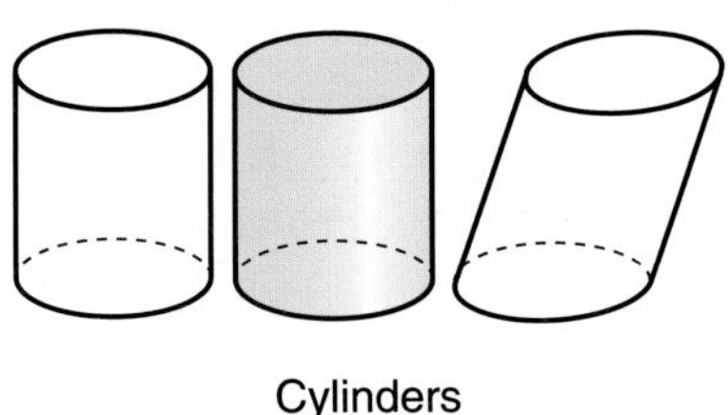

Cylinders

D

decimeter (dm) A metric unit of *length* equivalent to $\frac{1}{10}$ *meter* or 10 *centimeters.*

degree (°) (1) A unit of measure for *angles* based on dividing a *circle* into 360 equal parts. *Lines of latitude* and *longitude* are measured in degrees, and these degrees are based on angle measures. (2) A unit for measuring temperature.

denominator The nonzero *divisor* b in a fraction $\frac{a}{b}$ and a/b. In a part-whole fraction, the denominator is the number of equal parts into which the *whole,* or *ONE,* has been divided. Compare to *numerator*.

diameter (1) A *line segment* that passes through the center of a *circle* or *sphere* and has endpoints on the circle or sphere. (2) The length of such a segment. The diameter of a circle or sphere is twice the *radius.*

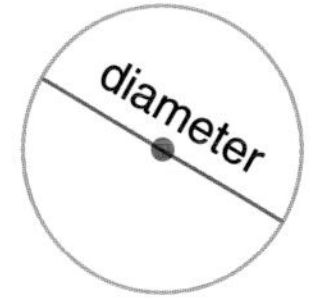

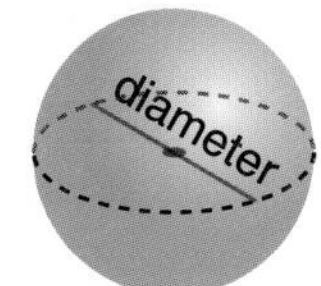

Distributive Property of Multiplication over Addition A property relating multiplication to a sum of numbers by distributing a *factor* over the terms in the sum. For example, $2 * (5 + 3) = (2 * 5) + (2 * 3) = 10 + 6 = 16$. In symbols:

For any numbers a, b, and c:
$a * (b + c) = (a * b) + (a * c)$
or $a(b + c) = ab + ac$

dividend The number in division that is being divided. For example, in 35 / 5 = 7, the dividend is 35.

dividend → 35 / 5 = 7 ← quotient; divisor ↓ 5

dividend → 40 ÷ 8 = 5 ← quotient; divisor ↓ 8

quotient → 3; divisor → 12)36 ← dividend

divisor In division, the number that divides another number, the *dividend*. For example, in 35 / 7 = 5, the divisor is 7. See the diagram under the definition of *dividend*.

E

endpoint A point at the end of a *line segment, ray,* or arc (part of a *circle* between and including two endpoints on the circle). These shapes are usually named using their endpoints. For example, the segment shown is "segment *TL*" or "segment *LT*."

endpoints
T ——— *L*

equal-groups notation In *Everyday Mathematics,* a way to denote a number of equal-size groups. The size of each group is shown inside square brackets and the number of groups is written in front of the brackets. For example, 3 [6s] means 3 groups with 6 in each group. In general, n [bs] means n groups with b in each group.

equally likely outcomes *Outcomes* of a chance experiment or situation that have the same *probability* of happening. If all the possible outcomes are equally likely, then the probability of an event is equal to:

$$\frac{\text{number of favorable outcomes}}{\text{number of possible outcomes}}$$

equation A *number sentence* that contains an equal sign. For example, $5 + 10 = 15$ and $P = 2l + 2w$ are equations.

equator An imaginary circle around Earth halfway between the North Pole and the South Pole. The equator is the 0° *line* for *latitude.*

equilateral triangle A *triangle* with all three sides equal in length. Each angle of an equilateral triangle measures 60°, so it is also called an equiangular triangle.

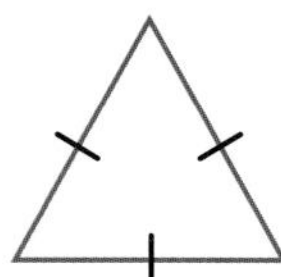
An equilateral triangle

equivalent fractions Fractions with different *denominators* that name the same number.

equivalent names Different ways of naming the same number. For example, 2 + 6, 4 + 4, 12 – 4, 18 – 10, 100 – 92, 5 + 1 + 2, eight, VIII, and HHT /// are all equivalent names for 8. See *name-collection box.*

estimate (1) An answer close to, or approximating, an exact answer. (2) To make an estimate.

event A set of possible *outcomes* to an experiment. For example, in an experiment flipping two coins, getting 2 HEADS is an event, as is getting 1 HEAD and 1 TAIL.

expanded notation A way of writing a number as the sum of the values of each digit. For example, 356 is 300 + 50 + 6 in expanded notation.

expected outcome The average *outcome* over a large number of repetitions of a random experiment. For example, the expected outcome of rolling one die is the average number of spots landing up over a large number of rolls. Because each face of a fair die has equal probability of landing up, the expected outcome is $\frac{(1+2+3+4+5+6)}{6} = \frac{21}{6} = 3\frac{1}{2}$. This means that the average of many rolls of a fair die is expected to be about $3\frac{1}{2}$. More formally, the expected outcome is defined as an average over infinitely many repetitions.

exponent A small raised number used in *exponential notation* to tell how many times the *base* is used as a *factor.* For example, in 5^3, the base is 5, the exponent is 3, and $5^3 = 5 * 5 * 5 = 125$. Same as *power.*

exponential notation A way of representing repeated multiplication by the same *factor.* For example, 2^3 is exponential notation for $2 * 2 * 2$. The *exponent* 3 tells how many times the *base* 2 is used as a factor.

expression (1) A mathematical phrase made up of numbers, *variables,* operation symbols, and/or *grouping symbols.* An expression does not contain relation symbols such as =, >, and ≤. (2) Either side of an *equation* or inequality.

$2 + 3$

$\sqrt{2ab}$

πr^2

$9x - 2$

Expressions

extended facts Variations of basic arithmetic facts involving multiples of 10, 100, and so on. For example, $30 + 70 = 100$, $40 * 5 = 200$, and $560 / 7 = 80$ are extended facts.

face (1) In *Everyday Mathematics,* a flat surface on a 3-dimensional figure. Some special faces are called *bases.* (2) More generally, any 2-dimensional surface on a 3-dimensional figure.

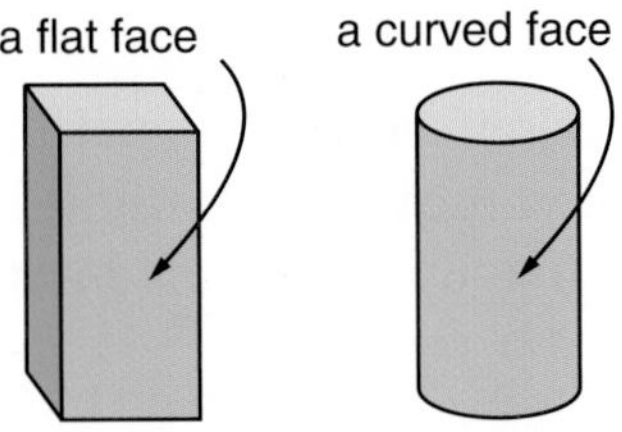

fact family A set of related arithmetic facts linking two inverse operations. For example,

$$5 + 6 = 11$$
$$6 + 5 = 11$$
$$11 - 5 = 6$$
$$11 - 6 = 5$$

are an addition/subtraction fact family.

Similarly,

$$5 * 7 = 35$$
$$7 * 5 = 35$$
$$35 / 7 = 5$$
$$35 / 5 = 7$$

are a multiplication/division fact family. Same as *number family.*

factor (1) Each of the two or more numbers in a *product.* For example, in $6 * 0.5$, 6 and 0.5 are factors. (2) To represent a number as a product of factors. For example, factor 21 by rewriting as $7 * 3$.

factor of a counting number *n* A *counting number* whose product with some other counting number equals *n.* For example, 2 and 3 are factors of 6 because $2 * 3 = 6$. But 4 is not a factor of 6 because $4 * 1.5 = 6$, and 1.5 is not a counting number.

factor pair Two *factors of a counting number* n whose product is *n.* A number may have more than one factor pair. For example, the factor pairs for 18 are 1 and 18, 2 and 9, and 3 and 6.

fair Free from bias. Each side of a fair die or coin will land up about equally often. Each region of a fair spinner will be landed on in proportion to its area.

favorable outcome An *outcome* that satisfies the conditions of an *event* of interest. For example, suppose a 6-sided die is rolled and the event of interest is "roll an even number." There are six possible outcomes: roll 1, 2, 3, 4, 5, or 6. Of these, 3 are favorable: roll 2, 4, or 6.

flip An informal name for a *reflection.*

formula A general rule for finding the value of something. A formula is usually an *equation* with quantities represented by letter *variables.* For example, a formula for distance traveled *d* at a rate *r* over a time *t* is $d = r * t$. The area of a triangle *A* with base length *b* and height *h* is given below.

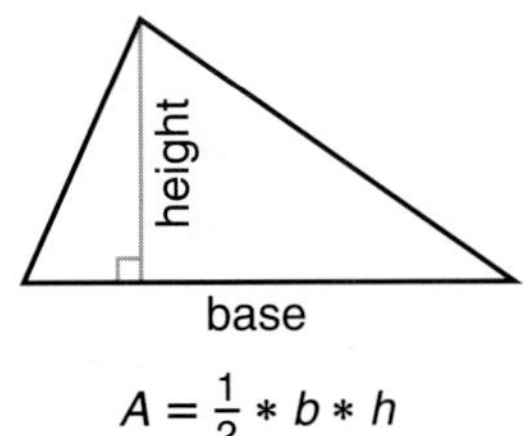

G

grouping symbols Parentheses ( ), brackets [ ], braces { }, and similar symbols that define the order in which operations in an *expression* are to be done. Nested grouping symbols are groupings within groupings, and the innermost grouping is done first. For example, in

(3 + 4) ∗ [(8 + 2) / 5], the group (8 + 2) is nested within [(8 + 2) / 5] and is done first. So (3 + 4) ∗ [(8 + 2) / 5] simplifies as follows:

$$(3 + 4) * [(8 + 2) / 5]$$
$$(3 + 4) * [10 / 5]$$
$$7 * 2$$
$$14$$

H

height (1) A *perpendicular* segment from one *side* of a geometric figure to a *parallel* side or from a *vertex* to the opposite side. (2) The length of this segment. In *Everyday Mathematics,* same as *altitude.*

height of a parallelogram (1) The *length* of the shortest *line segment* between a *base of a parallelogram* and the *line* containing the opposite *side*. The height is *perpendicular* to the base. (2) The line segment itself.

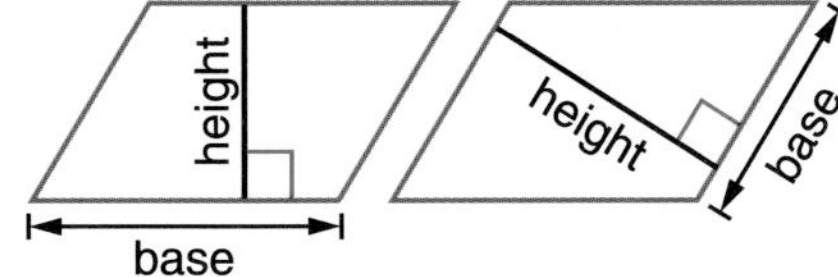

height of a prism or cylinder The *length* of the shortest *line segment* from a *base of a prism* or *cylinder* to the plane containing the opposite base. The height is *perpendicular* to the bases. (2) The line segment itself.

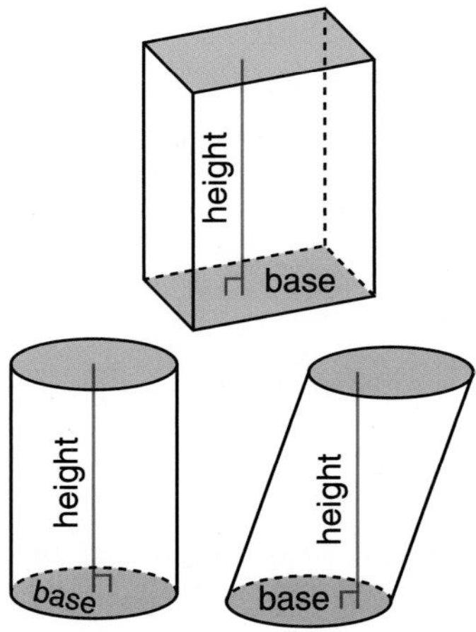

height of a pyramid or cone The *length* of the shortest *line segment* from the apex of a pyramid or cone to the plane containing the *base.* The height is *perpendicular* to the base. (2) The line segment itself.

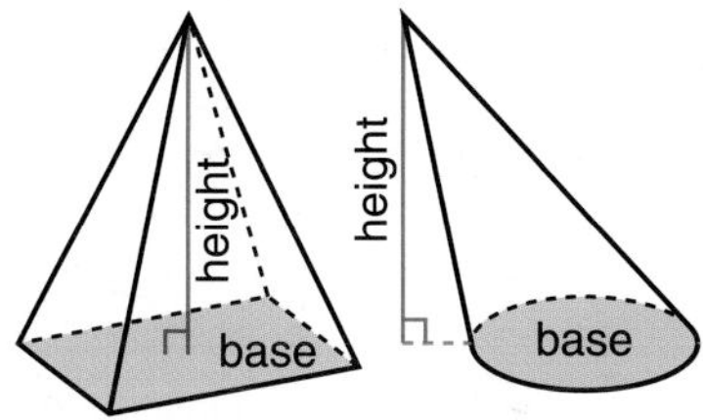

height of a rectangle The *length* of a *side perpendicular* to a *base of a rectangle.* Same as altitude of a rectangle.

height of a triangle The *length* of the shortest segment from a *vertex* of a triangle to the line containing the opposite *side.* The height is *perpendicular* to the base. (2) The line segment itself.

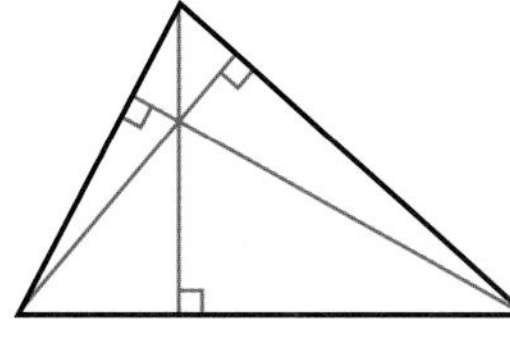

The heights of the triangle are blue.

heptagon A 7-sided *polygon.*

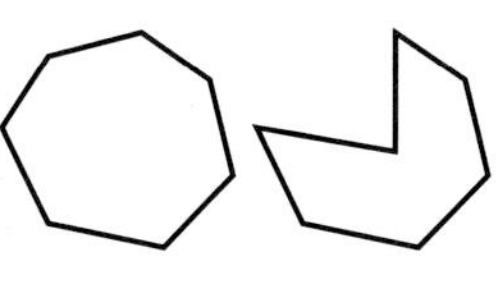

Heptagons

hexagon A 6-sided *polygon.*

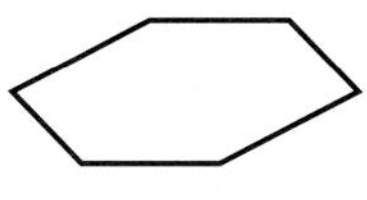

A hexagon

I

index of locations A list of places together with a reference frame for locating them on a map. For example, "Billings, D3," means that Billings is in the rectangle to the right of D and above 3 on the map below.

Section of Map of Montana

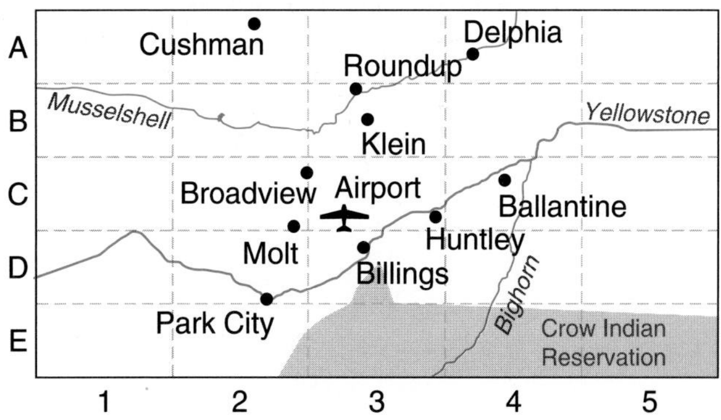

inscribed polygon A *polygon* whose vertices are all on the same *circle.*

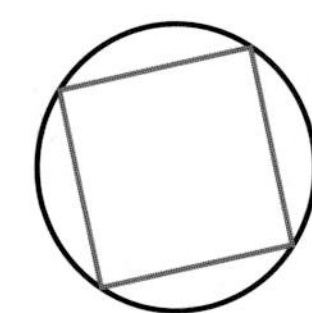

An inscribed square

interest A charge for using someone else's money. Interest is usually a *percent* of the amount borrowed.

interior of a figure (1) The set of all *points* in a plane bounded by a closed 2-dimensional figure, such as a *polygon* or *circle.* (2) The set of all points in space bounded by a closed 3-dimensional figure, such as a *polyhedron* or *sphere.* The interior is usually not considered to be part of the figure.

intersect To share a common *point* or points.

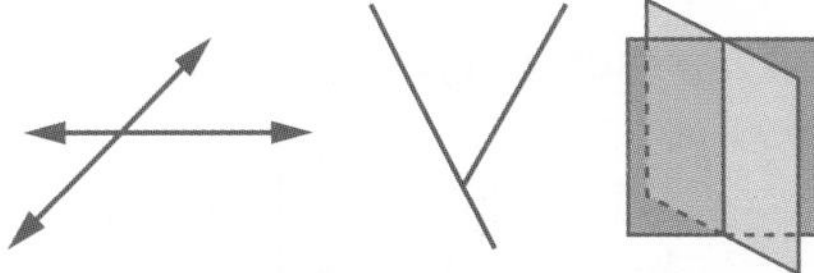

Intersecting lines and line segments — Intersecting planes

isosceles triangle A *triangle* with at least two sides equal in length. Angles opposite the congruent sides are congruent to each other.

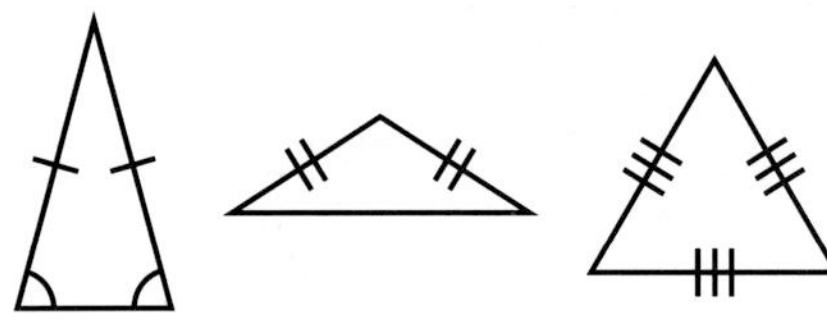

Isosceles triangles

K

kite A *quadrilateral* with two distinct pairs of adjacent sides of equal length. In *Everyday Mathematics,* the four sides cannot all have equal length; that is, a *rhombus* is not a kite. The diagonals of a kite are *perpendicular.*

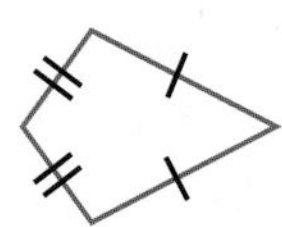

A kite

L

landmark In *Everyday Mathematics,* a notable feature of a data set. Landmarks include the *median, mode, mean, maximum, minimum,* and *range.*

latitude A *degree* measure locating a place on Earth north or south of the *equator.* A location at 0° latitude is on the equator. The North Pole is at 90° north latitude, and the South Pole is at 90° south latitude. Compare to *longitude.* See *lines of latitude.*

lattice multiplication A very old *algorithm* for multiplying multidigit numbers that requires only basic *multiplication facts* and addition of 1-digit numbers in a lattice diagram.

length of a rectangle Typically, but not necessarily, the longer dimension of a *rectangle.*

letter-number pair An *ordered pair* in which one of the *coordinates* is a letter. Often used to locate places on maps.

line In *Everyday Mathematics,* a 1-dimensional straight path that extends forever in opposite directions. A line is named using two *points* on it or with a single, italicized lower-case letter such as *l*. In formal Euclidean geometry, line is an undefined geometric term.

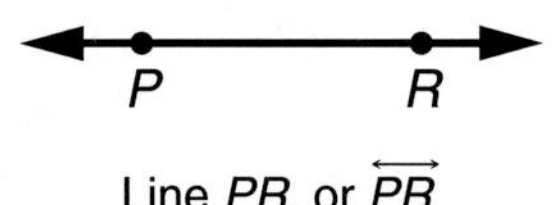

Line *PR,* or $\overleftrightarrow{PR}$

line plot A sketch of data in which check marks, Xs, or other symbols above a labeled line show the frequency of each value.

line segment (or **segment**) A part of a *line* between and including two *points,* called *endpoints* of the segment. A line segment is often named by its endpoints.

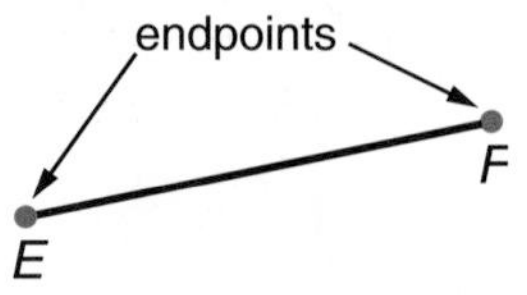

Segment *EF,* or $\overline{EF}$

lines of latitude Lines of constant *latitude* drawn on a 2-dimensional map or circles of constant latitude drawn on a globe. Lines of latitude are also called "parallels" because they are parallel to the *equator* and to each other. On a globe, latitude lines (circles) are intersections of planes parallel to the plane through the equator. Compare to *lines of longitude.*

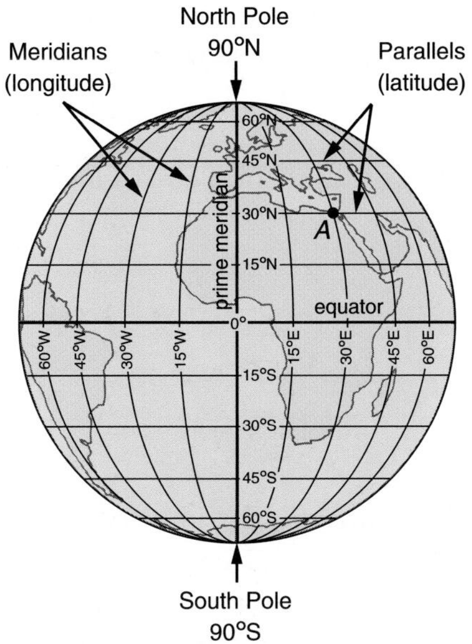

Point A is located at 30°N, 30°E.

lines of longitude Lines of constant *longitude* drawn on a 2-dimensional map or semicircles of constant longitude drawn on a globe connecting the North and South Poles. Lines of longitude are also called "meridians." Compare to *lines of latitude.*

liter (L) A metric unit of *volume* or *capacity* equal to the volume of a cube with 10-cm-long edges. 1 L = 1,000 mL = 1,000 cm^3. A liter is a little larger than a quart.

longitude A *degree* measure locating a place on Earth east or west of the *prime meridian.* A location at 0° longitude is on the prime meridian. A location at 180° east or west longitude is on or near the international date line, which is based on the imaginary semicircle opposite the prime meridian. Compare to *latitude.* See *lines of longitude.*

M

magnitude estimate A rough *estimate* of whether a number is in the tens, hundreds, thousands, or other powers of 10. For example, the U.S. national debt per person is in the tens of thousands of dollars. In *Everyday Mathematics,* students give magnitude estimates for problems such as *How many dimes are in $200?* or *How many halves are in 30?*

map scale The ratio of a distance on a map, globe, or drawing to an actual distance. For example, 1 inch on a map might correspond to 1 real-world mile. A map scale may be shown on a segment of a number line, given as a ratio of distances such as $\frac{1}{63{,}360}$ or 1:63,360 when an inch represents a mile, or by an informal use of the = symbol such as "1 inch = 1 mile."

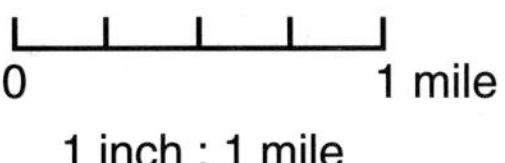

maximum The largest amount; the greatest number in a set of data. Compare to *minimum.*

mean For a set of numbers, their sum divided by the number of numbers. Often called the average value of the set. Compare to the other data *landmarks median* and *mode.*

median The middle value in a set of data when the data are listed in order from smallest to largest or vice versa. If there is an even number of data points, the median is the *mean* of the two middle values. Compare to other data *landmarks mean* and *mode.*

meridian bar A device on a globe that shows degrees of *latitude* north and south of the *equator,* called a meridian bar because it is in the same orientation as meridians (*lines of longitude*).

meter (m) The basic metric unit of *length* from which other metric units of length are derived. Originally, the meter was defined as $\frac{1}{10{,}000{,}000}$ of the distance from the North Pole to the *equator* along a meridian passing through Paris. From 1960 to 1983, the meter was redefined as 1,630,763.73 wavelengths of orange-red light from the element krypton. Today, the meter is defined as the distance light travels in a vacuum in $\frac{1}{299{,}792{,}458}$ second. One meter is equal to 10 decimeters, 100 *centimeters,* or 1,000 millimeters.

milliliter (mL) A metric unit of *volume* or *capacity* equal to $\frac{1}{1000}$ of a *liter,* or 1 cubic centimeter.

minimum The smallest amount; the smallest number in a set of data. Compare to *maximum.*

minuend In subtraction, the number from which another number is subtracted. For example, in 19 − 5 = 14, the minuend is 19. Compare to *subtrahend.*

mixed number A number that is written using both a *whole number* and a fraction. For example, $2\frac{1}{4}$ is a mixed number equal to $2 + \frac{1}{4}$.

mode The value or values that occur most often in a set of data. Compare to other *landmarks median* and *mean.*

multiple of a number *n* (1) A *product* of *n* and a *counting number.* For example, the multiples of 7 are 7, 14, 21, 28, ... (2) A product of *n* and an *integer*. For example, the multiples of 7 are . . ., –21, –14, –7, 0, 7, 14, 21, ...

multiplication/division diagram A diagram used in *Everyday Mathematics* to model situations in which a total number is made up of equal-size groups. The diagram contains a number of groups, a number in each group, and a total number. Also called a multiplication diagram for short.

rows	chairs per row	total chairs
15	25	?

A multiplication/division diagram

multiplication fact The *product* of two 1-digit numbers, such as $6 * 7 = 42$.

name-collection box In *Everyday Mathematics,* a diagram that is used for collecting *equivalent names* for a number.

25
37 – 12
20 + 5
HHT HHT HHT HHT HHT
twenty-five
veinticinco

***n*-gon** Same as *polygon,* where *n* is the number of sides. Polygons that do not have special names like squares and pentagons are usually named using *n*-gon notation, such as 13-gon or 100-gon.

nonagon A 9-sided *polygon.*

nonconvex polygon Same as *concave polygon.*

number family Same as *fact family.*

number model A *number sentence, expression,* or other representation that models a number story or situation. For example, the story *Sally had $5, and then she earned $8* can be modeled as the number sentence $5 + 8 = 13$, as the expression $5 + 8$, or by

$$\begin{array}{r} 5 \\ +\ 8 \\ \hline 13 \end{array}$$

number sentence Two *expressions* with a relation symbol. For example,

$$5 + 5 = 10$$
$$2 - ? = 8$$
$$16 \leq a * b$$
$$a^2 + b^2 = c^2$$

Number sentences

numerator The *dividend a* in a fraction $\frac{a}{b}$ or *a*/*b*. In a part-whole fraction, in which the *whole* (the *ONE* or *unit whole*) is divided into a number of equal parts, the numerator is the number of equal parts being considered. Compare to *denominator.*

obtuse angle An *angle* with measure between 90° and 180°.

octagon An 8-sided *polygon.*

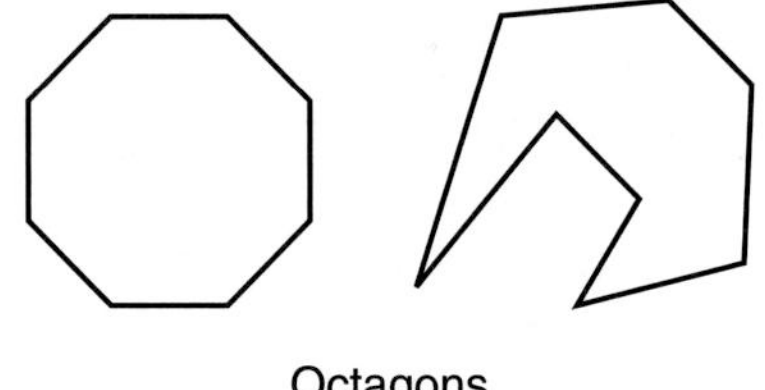

Octagons

ONE In *Everyday Mathematics,* same as *whole* or *unit whole.*

open sentence A *number sentence* with one or more *variables.* An open sentence is neither true nor false. For example, 9 + ______ = 15, ? – 24 < 10, and $7 = x + y$ are open sentences.

ordered pair (1) Two numbers, or *coordinates,* used to locate a *point* on a rectangular *coordinate grid.* The first coordinate *x* gives the position along the horizontal axis of the grid, and the second coordinate *y* gives the position along the vertical axis. The pair is written (x,y). (2) Any pair of objects or numbers in a particular order, as in letter-number spreadsheet-cell names or map coordinates.

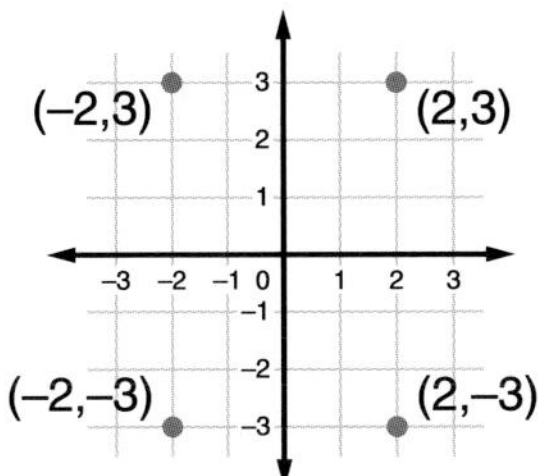

Ordered pairs

outcome A possible result of a chance experiment or situation. For example, HEADS and TAILS are the two possible outcomes of flipping a coin.

P

parallel lines *Lines* in a plane that never meet. Two parallel lines are always the same distance apart. *Line segments* or *rays* on parallel lines are parallel to each other.

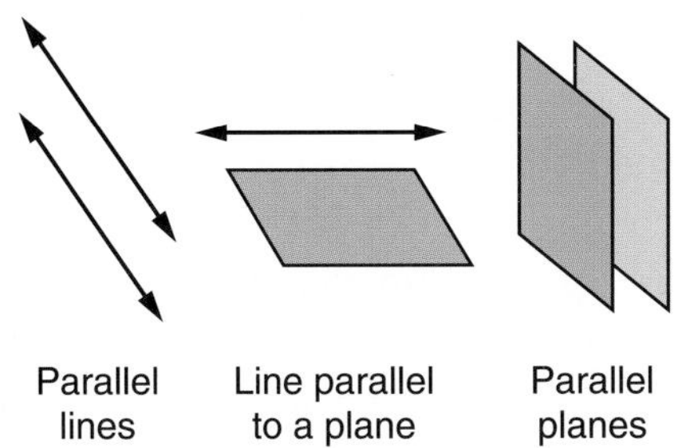

Parallel lines | Line parallel to a plane | Parallel planes

parallelogram A *quadrilateral* with two pairs of parallel sides. Opposite sides of a parallelogram have the same length and opposite *angles* have the same measure. All *rectangles* are parallelograms, but not all parallelograms are rectangles because parallelograms do not necessarily have *right angles*.

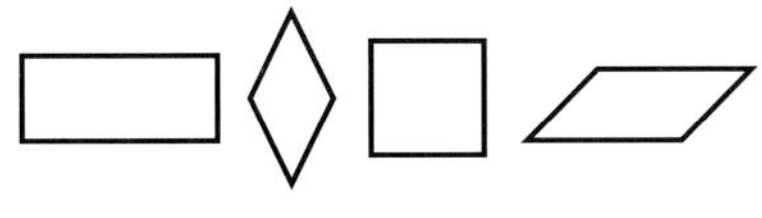

Parallelograms

partial-differences subtraction A subtraction *algorithm* in which separate differences are computed for each *place value* of the numbers and then added to get a final difference.

partial-products multiplication A multiplication *algorithm* in which partial products are computed by multiplying the value of each digit in one *factor* by the value of each digit in the other factor. The final *product* is the sum of the partial products.

partial-quotients division A division *algorithm* in which a partial quotient is computed in each of several steps. The final *quotient* is the sum of the partial quotients.

partial-sums addition An addition *algorithm* in which separate sums are computed for each *place value* of the numbers and then added to get a final sum.

pentagon A 5-sided *polygon.*

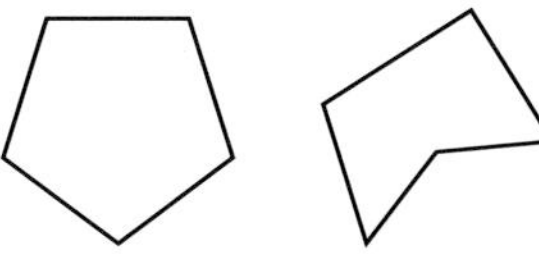

Pentagons

percent (%) Per hundred, for each hundred, or out of a hundred. $1\% = \frac{1}{100} = 0.01$. For example, *48% of the students in the school are boys* means that, on average, 48 of every 100 students in the school are boys.

perimeter The distance around the boundary of a 2-dimensional figure. The perimeter of a *circle* is called its circumference. A *formula* for the perimeter P of a *rectangle* with length l and width w is $P = 2 * (l + w)$. Perimeter comes from the Greek words for "around measure."

perpendicular (⊥) Two *lines* or two planes that *intersect* at *right angles. Line segments* or *rays* that lie on perpendicular lines are perpendicular to each other. The symbol ⊥ means "is perpendicular to."

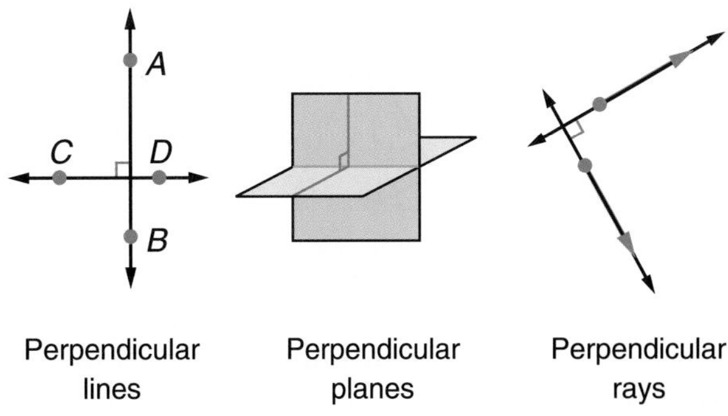

Perpendicular lines | Perpendicular planes | Perpendicular rays

place value A system that gives a digit a value according to its position, or place, in a number. In our standard, base-10 (decimal) system for writing numbers, each place has a value 10 times that of the place to its right and 1 tenth the value of the place to its left.

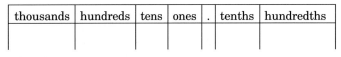

thousands	hundreds	tens	ones	.	tenths	hundredths

A place-value chart

point In *Everyday Mathematics,* an exact location in space. Points are usually labeled with capital letters. In formal Euclidean geometry, a point is an undefined geometric term.

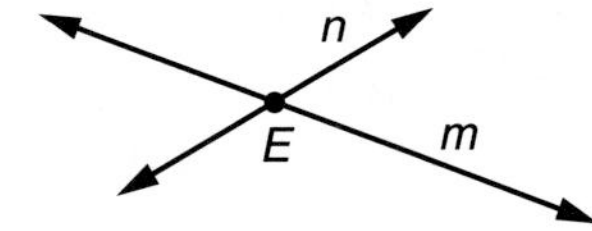

Lines *m* and *n* intersect at point *E*.

polygon A 2-dimensional figure formed by three or more *line segments* (*sides*) that meet only at their *endpoints* (*vertices*) to make a closed path. The sides may not cross one another.

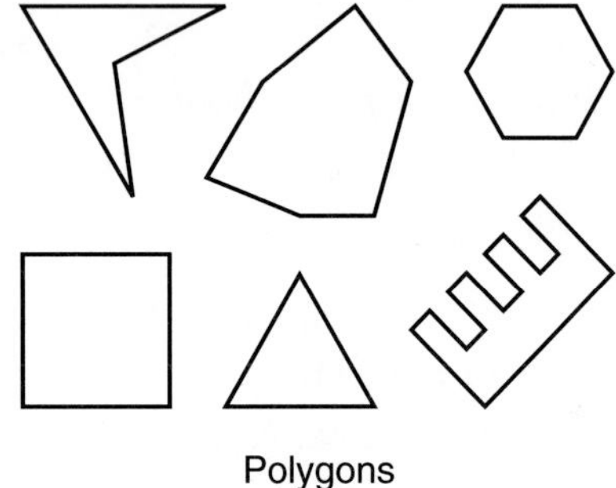

Polygons

polyhedron A 3-dimensional figure formed by *polygons* with their *interiors* (*faces*) and having no holes. Plural is polyhedrons or polyhedra.

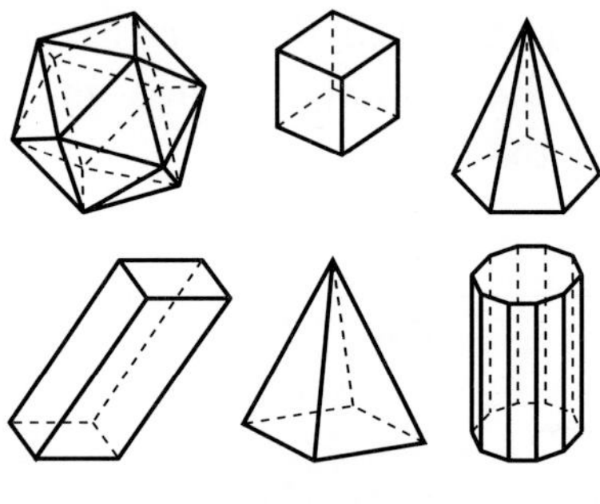

Polyhedrons

positive power of 10 A number that can be written in the form 10^a, where *a* is a *counting number,* that is, the numbers 10, 100, 1,000, and so on, that can be written using only 10s as factors.

prime meridian An imaginary semicircle on Earth that connects the North and South Poles through Greenwich, England. See *lines of longitude.*

prime number A *counting number* greater than 1 that has exactly two whole-number *factors,* 1 and itself. For example, 7 is a prime number because its only factors are 1 and 7. The first five prime numbers are 2, 3, 5, 7, and 11. Also simply called primes. Compare to *composite number.*

prism A *polyhedron* with two *parallel* and congruent polygonal regions for *bases* and lateral *faces* formed by all the *line segments* with *endpoints* on corresponding edges of the bases. The lateral faces are all *parallelograms*. Lateral faces intersect at lateral edges. In a right prism, the lateral faces are rectangular. Prisms get their names from the shape of their bases.

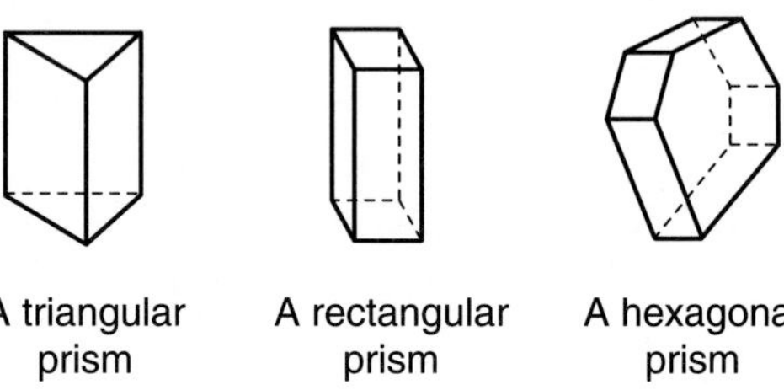

A triangular prism A rectangular prism A hexagonal prism

probability A number from 0 through 1 giving the likelihood that an *event* will happen. The closer a probability is to 1, the more likely the event is to happen. The closer a probability is to 0, the less likely the event is to happen. For example, the probability that a *fair* coin will show HEADS is $\frac{1}{2}$.

product The result of multiplying two numbers, called *factors.* For example, in $4 * 3 = 12$, the product is 12.

Q

quadrangle Same as *quadrilateral.*

quadrilateral A 4-sided *polygon.*

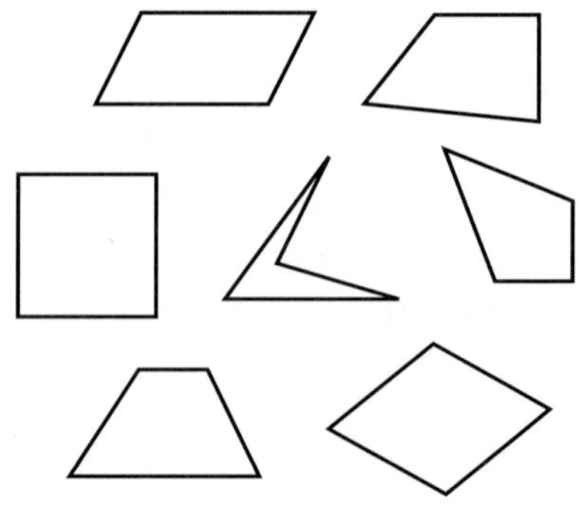

Quadrilaterals

quotient The result of dividing one number by another number. For example, in 10 / 5 = 2, the quotient is 2.

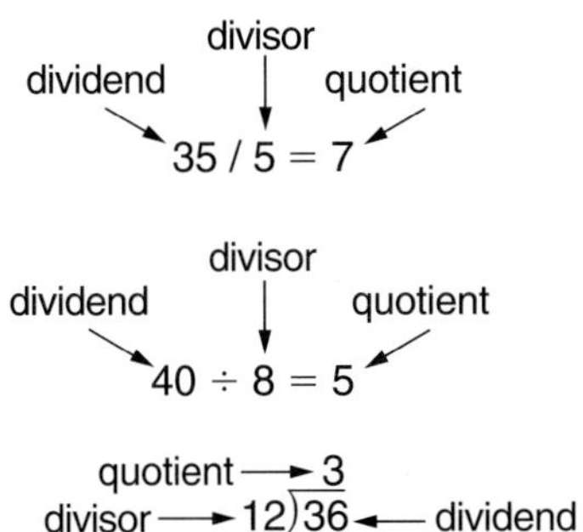

radius (1) A *line segment* from the center of a *circle* (or *sphere*) to any point on the circle (or sphere). (2) The length of this *line segment.* The length of a radius is half the length of a *diameter.* Plural is radiuses or radii.

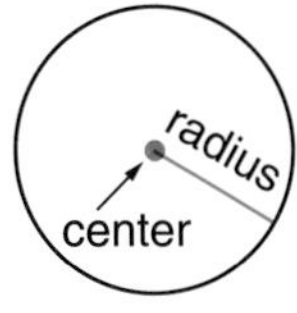

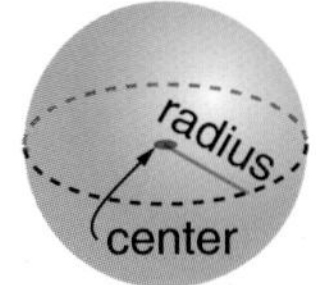

range The difference between the *maximum* and the *minimum* in a set of data. Used as a measure of the spread of the data.

rate A comparison by division of two quantities with different *units*. For example, traveling 100 miles in 2 hours is an average rate of $\frac{100 \text{ mi}}{2 \text{ hr}}$, or 50 miles per hour.

ray A part of a *line* starting at the ray's *endpoint* and continuing forever in one direction. A ray is often named by its endpoint and another *point* on it.

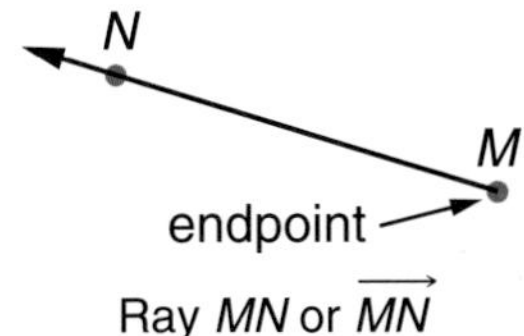

Ray *MN* or $\overrightarrow{MN}$

rectangle A *parallelogram* with all *right angles.*

reflection A point *A′* is a reflection image of a point *A* over a line of reflection *l* if *A′* and *A* are the same distance from *l* on a line *perpendicular* to it. If all *points* on one figure are reflection images of all the points on another figure over the same line, the figures are reflection images. Informally called a *flip.*

reflex angle An *angle* with a measure between 180° and 360°.

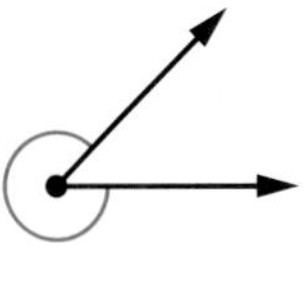

A reflex angle

regular polygon A *polygon* in which all *sides* are the same length and all *angles* have the same measure.

remainder An amount left over when one number is divided by another number. For example, in 16 / 3 → 5 R1, the *quotient* is 5 and the remainder R is 1.

rhombus A *parallelogram* with all sides the same length. All rhombuses are parallelograms. Every *square* is a rhombus, but not all rhombuses are squares. Also called a diamond. Plural is rhombuses or rhombi.

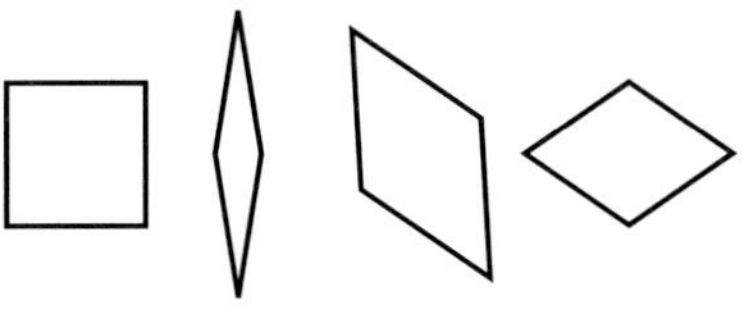

Rhombuses

right angle A 90° *angle.*

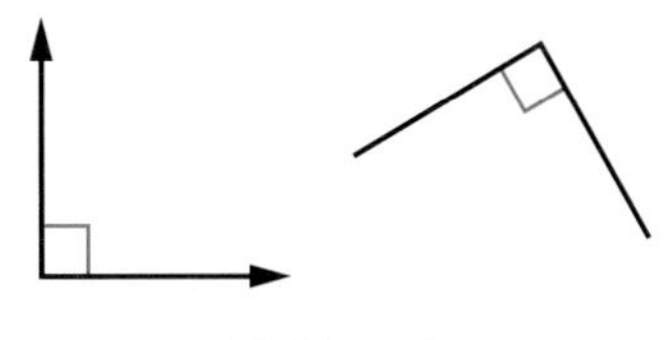

Right angles

right triangle A *triangle* with a *right angle.*

rotation (1) A point *P′* is a rotation image of a point *P* around a center of rotation *C* if *P′* is on the *circle* with center *C* and radius *CP*. If all the *points* in one figure are rotation images of all the points in another figure around the same center of rotation and with the same angle of rotation, the figures are rotation images. The center can be inside or outside of the original image. Informally called a *turn.* (2) If all points on the image of a 3-dimensional figure are rotation images around a point on a *line* called the axis of rotation, then the image is a rotation image of the original figure.

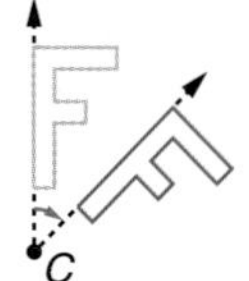

A rotation

round (1) To approximate a number to make it easier to work with, or to make it better reflect the precision of the data. "Rounding up" means to approximate larger than the actual value. "Rounding down" means to approximate smaller than the actual value. (2) Circular in shape.

scale (1) The relative size of something. (2) A tool for measuring weight. See *map scale.*

scale drawing A drawing of an object in which all parts are drawn to the same *scale* to the object. For example, architects and builders use scale drawings traditionally called "blueprints." A map is a scale drawing of a geographical region.

A woodpecker (8 in.) to $\frac{1}{4}$ scale

scalene triangle A *triangle* with sides of three different lengths. The three angles of a scalene triangle have different measures.

side (1) One of the *line segments* that make up a *polygon.* (2) One of the *rays* or *segments* that form an *angle.* (3) One of the *faces* of a *polyhedron.*

slide An informal name for a *translation.*

solution of an open sentence A value or values for the *variable(s)* in an *open sentence* that make the sentence true. For example, 7 is the solution of $5 + n = 12$. Although *equations* are not necessarily open sentences, the solution of an open sentence is commonly referred to as a "solution of an equation."

sphere The set of all *points* in space that are an equal distance from a fixed point called the center of the sphere. The distance from the center to the sphere is the *radius* of the sphere. The *diameter* of a sphere is twice its radius. Points inside a sphere are not part of the sphere.

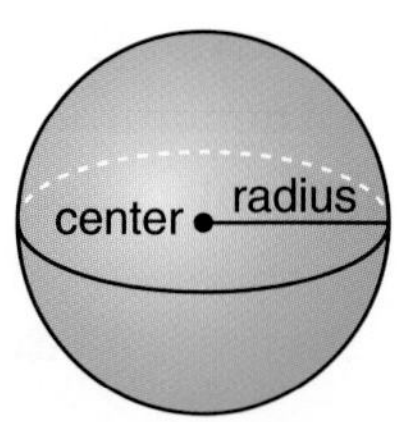

A sphere

square A *rectangle* with all sides of equal length. All angles in a square are *right angles.*

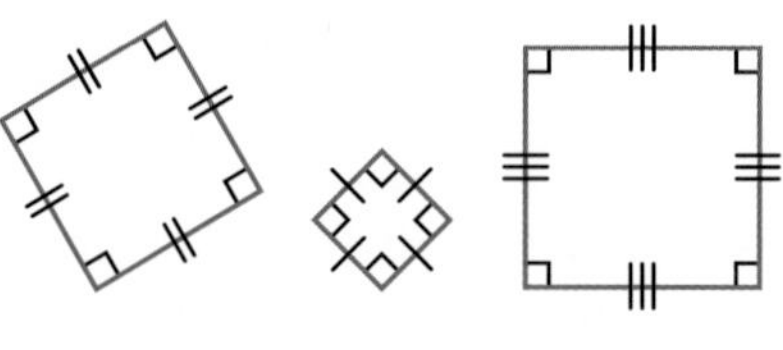

Squares

square numbers Figurate numbers (numbers that can be illustrated by specific geometric patterns) that are the product of a *counting number* and itself. For example, 25 is a square number because $25 = 5 * 5$. A square number can be represented by a square array and as a number squared, such as $25 = 5^2$.

square unit A unit to measure *area.* A model of a square unit is a square with each side a related unit of *length.* For example, a square inch is the area of a square with 1-inch sides. Square units are often labeled as the length unit squared. For example, 1 cm^2 is read "1 square centimeter" or "1 centimeter squared."

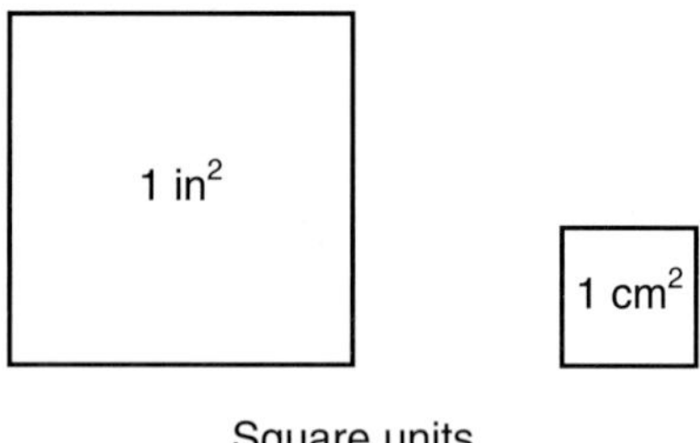

Square units

straight angle A 180° *angle.*

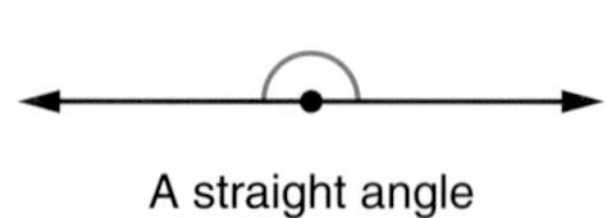

A straight angle

subtrahend The number being taken away in a subtraction problem. For example, in $15 - 5 = 10$, the subtrahend is 5.

symmetric figure A figure that exactly matches with its image under a *reflection* or *rotation.*

tally chart A table to keep track of a tally, typically showing how many times each value appears in a set of data.

Number of Pull-Ups	Number of Children
0	~~////~~ /
1	~~////~~
2	////
3	//

A tally chart

trade-first subtraction A subtraction *algorithm* in which all necessary trades between places in the numbers are done before any subtractions are carried out. Some people favor this algorithm because they can concentrate on one thing at a time.

translation A transformation in which every point in the *image* of a figure is at the same distance in the same direction from its corresponding point in the figure. Informally called a *slide*.

trapezoid A *quadrilateral* that has exactly one pair of *parallel* sides. In *Everyday Mathematics,* both pairs of sides cannot be parallel; that is, a *parallelogram* is not a trapezoid.

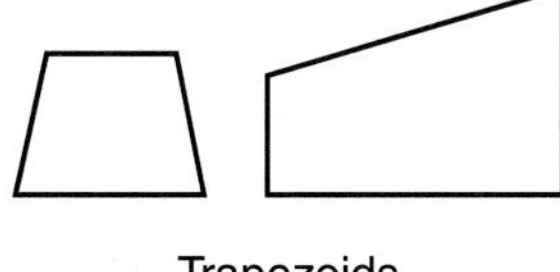

Trapezoids

triangle A 3-sided *polygon.*

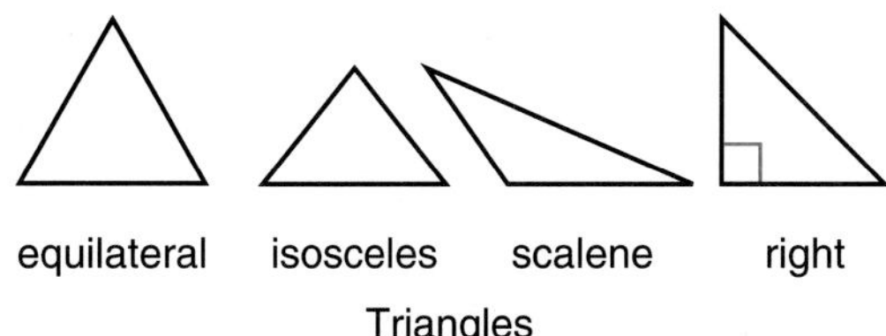

Triangles

turn An informal name for a *rotation.*

turn-around facts A pair of multiplication (or addition) facts in which the order of the *factors* (or addends) is reversed. For example, $3 * 9 = 27$ and $9 * 3 = 27$ are turn-around *multiplication facts,* and $4 + 5 = 9$ and $5 + 4 = 9$ are turn-around addition facts. There are no turn-around facts for subtraction or division. Turn-around facts are instances of the Commutative Properties of Addition and Multiplication.

unit A label used to put a number in context. In measuring length, for example, inches and centimeters are units. In a problem about 5 apples, apple is the unit. In *Everyday Mathematics,* students keep track of units in unit boxes.

unit fraction A fraction whose *numerator* is 1. For example, $\frac{1}{2}, \frac{1}{3}, \frac{1}{8}, \frac{1}{12}$, and $\frac{1}{20}$ are unit fractions. Unit fractions are especially useful in converting among units within measurement systems. For example, because 1 foot = 12 inches, you can multiply a number of inches by $\frac{1}{12}$ to convert to feet.

unit whole Same as *whole* or *ONE.*

variable A letter or other symbol that represents a number. A variable can represent a single number, as in $5 + n = 9$, because only $n = 4$ makes the sentence true. A variable may also stand for many different numbers, as in $x + 2 < 10$, because any number x less than 8 makes the sentence true. In *formulas* and properties, variables stand for all numbers. For example, $a + 3 = 3 + a$ for all numbers a.

vertex The *point* at which the *rays* of an angle, the *sides* of a polygon, or the edges of a *polyhedron* meet. Plural is vertexes or vertices. In *Everyday Mathematics,* same as corner.

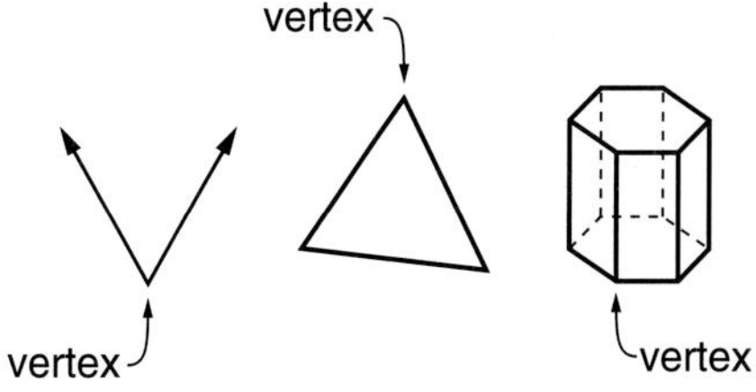

volume (1) The amount of space occupied by a 3-dimensional shape. Same as *capacity*. (2) Less formally, the amount a container can hold. Volume is often measured in cubic units, such as cm^3, cubic inches, or cubic feet.

"What's My Rule?" problem In *Everyday Mathematics,* a problem in which two of the three parts of a function (input, output, and rule) are known, and the third is to be found out.

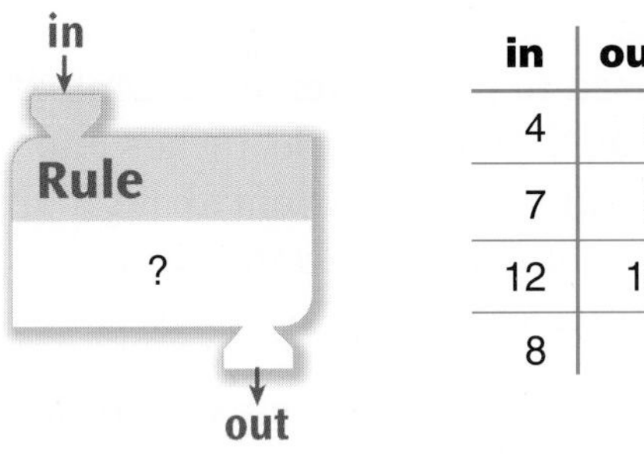

in	out
4	2
7	5
12	10
8	

A "What's My Rule?" problem

whole An entire object, collection of objects, or quantity being considered in a problem situation; 100%. Same as *ONE* and *unit whole.*

whole numbers The *counting numbers* and 0. The set of whole numbers is {0, 1, 2, 3, . . .}.

width of a rectangle The length of one side of a *rectangle* or rectangular object, typically the shorter side.

Grade-Level Goals

Everyday Mathematics organizes content through Program Goals and Grade-Level Goals. The Grade-Level Goals Chart shows the units in which goal content is taught and then practiced and applied. For more information, see the *Assessment Handbook.*

The Grade-Level Goals are divided according to the content strands below.

Content Strands

How to Read the Grade-Level Goals Chart

Each section of the chart includes Grade-Level Goals organized by content strand. The three grade-level columns divided into units indicate in which units the goals are addressed.

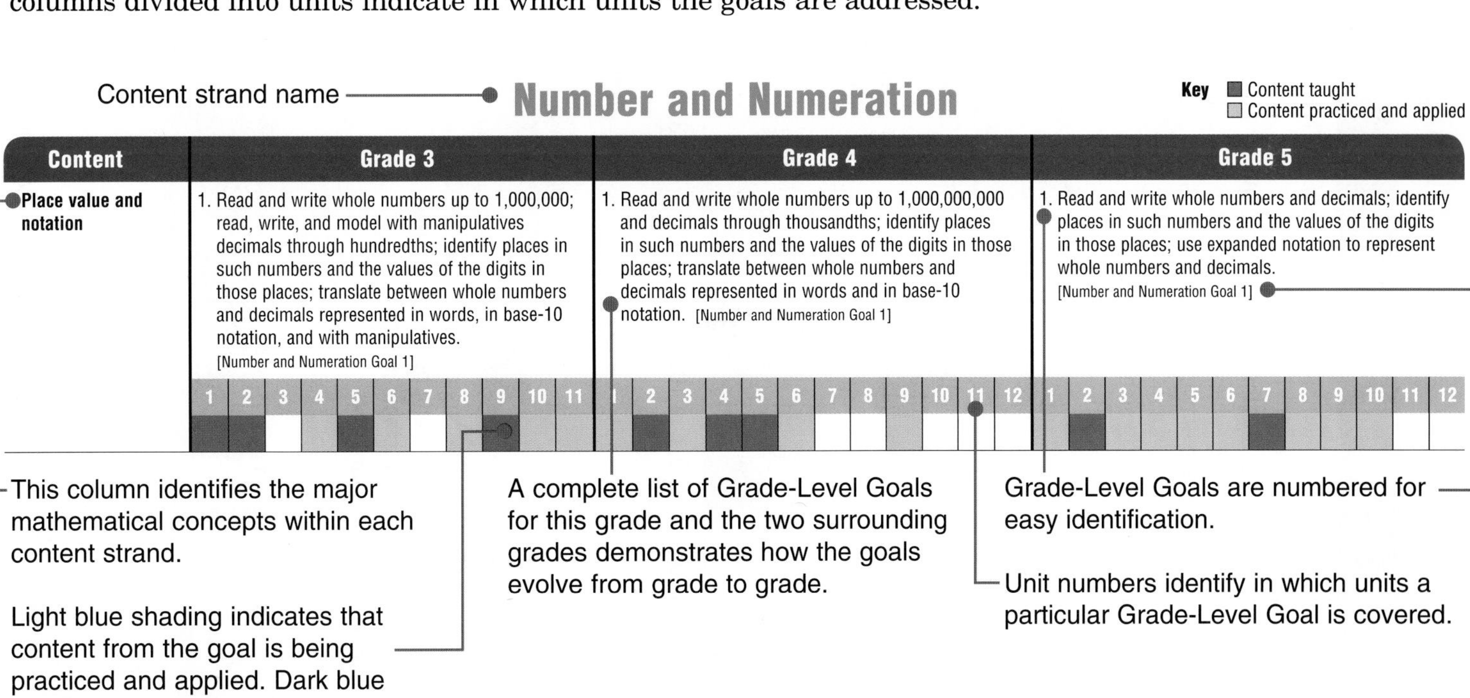

Content strand name
Number and Numeration
Key
Content taught
Content practiced and applied
Content
Grade 3
Grade 4
Grade 5
Place value and notation
1. Read and write whole numbers up to 1,000,000; read, write, and model with manipulatives decimals through hundredths; identify places in such numbers and the values of the digits in those places; translate between whole numbers and decimals represented in words, in base-10 notation, and with manipulatives. [Number and Numeration Goal 1]
1. Read and write whole numbers up to 1,000,000,000 and decimals through thousandths; identify places in such numbers and the values of the digits in those places; translate between whole numbers and decimals represented in words and in base-10 notation. [Number and Numeration Goal 1]
1. Read and write whole numbers and decimals; identify places in such numbers and the values of the digits in those places; use expanded notation to represent whole numbers and decimals. [Number and Numeration Goal 1]
1 2 3 4 5 6 7 8 9 10 11
1 2 3 4 5 6 7 8 9 10 11 12
1 2 3 4 5 6 7 8 9 10 11 12
This column identifies the major mathematical concepts within each content strand.
Light blue shading indicates that content from the goal is being practiced and applied. Dark blue shading indicates that content from the goal is being taught.
A complete list of Grade-Level Goals for this grade and the two surrounding grades demonstrates how the goals evolve from grade to grade.
Grade-Level Goals are numbered for easy identification.
Unit numbers identify in which units a particular Grade-Level Goal is covered.

Number and Numeration

Key
- Content taught
- Content practiced and app

Content	Grade 3	Grade 4	Grade 5
Place value and notation	1. Read and write whole numbers up to 1,000,000; read, write, and model with manipulatives decimals through hundredths; identify places in such numbers and the values of the digits in those places; translate between whole numbers and decimals represented in words, in base-10 notation, and with manipulatives. [Number and Numeration Goal 1] 1 2 3 4 5 6 7 8 9 10 11	1. Read and write whole numbers up to 1,000,000,000 and decimals through thousandths; identify places in such numbers and the values of the digits in those places; translate between whole numbers and decimals represented in words and in base-10 notation. [Number and Numeration Goal 1] 1 2 3 4 5 6 7 8 9 10 11 12	1. Read and write whole numbers and decimals; identi places in such numbers and the values of the digits in those places; use expanded notation to represent whole numbers and decimals. [Number and Numeration Goal 1] 1 2 3 4 5 6 7 8 9 10 11
Meanings and uses of fractions	2. Read, write, and model fractions; solve problems involving fractional parts of a region or a collection; describe strategies used. [Number and Numeration Goal 2] 1 2 3 4 5 6 7 8 9 10 11	2. Read, write, and model fractions; solve problems involving fractional parts of a region or a collection; describe and explain strategies used; given a fractional part of a region or a collection, identify the unit whole. [Number and Numeration Goal 2] 1 2 3 4 5 6 7 8 9 10 11 12	2. Solve problems involving percents and discounts; describe and explain strategies used; identify the un whole in situations involving fractions. [Number and Numeration Goal 2] 1 2 3 4 5 6 7 8 9 10 11
Number theory	3. Find multiples of 2, 5, and 10. [Number and Numeration Goal 3] 1 2 3 4 5 6 7 8 9 10 11	3. Find multiples of whole numbers less than 10; identify prime and composite numbers; find whole-number factors of numbers. [Number and Numeration Goal 3] 1 2 3 4 5 6 7 8 9 10 11 12	3. Identify prime and composite numbers; factor numbers; find prime factorizations. [Number and Numeration Goal 3] 1 2 3 4 5 6 7 8 9 10 11
Equivalent names for whole numbers	4. Use numerical expressions involving one or more of the basic four arithmetic operations to give equivalent names for whole numbers. [Number and Numeration Goal 4] 1 2 3 4 5 6 7 8 9 10 11	4. Use numerical expressions involving one or more of the basic four arithmetic operations and grouping symbols to give equivalent names for whole numbers. [Number and Numeration Goal 4] 1 2 3 4 5 6 7 8 9 10 11 12	4. Use numerical expressions involving one or more of the basic four arithmetic operations, grouping symbols, and exponents to give equivalent names for whole numbers; convert between base-10, exponential, and repeated-factor notations. [Number and Numeration Goal 4] 1 2 3 4 5 6 7 8 9 10 11

Content	Grade 3	Grade 4	Grade 5
Equivalent names for fractions, decimals, and percents	5. Use manipulatives and drawings to find and represent equivalent names for fractions; use manipulatives to generate equivalent fractions. [Number and Numeration Goal 5]	5. Use numerical expressions to find and represent equivalent names for fractions and decimals; use and explain a multiplication rule to find equivalent fractions; rename fourths, fifths, tenths, and hundredths as decimals and percents. [Number and Numeration Goal 5]	5. Use numerical expressions to find and represent equivalent names for fractions, decimals, and percents; use and explain multiplication and division rules to find equivalent fractions and fractions in simplest form; convert between fractions and mixed numbers; convert between fractions, decimals, and percents. [Number and Numeration Goal 5]
Comparing and ordering numbers	6. Compare and order whole numbers up to 1,000,000; use manipulatives to order decimals through hundredths; use area models and benchmark fractions to compare and order fractions. [Number and Numeration Goal 6]	6. Compare and order whole numbers up to 1,000,000,000 and decimals through thousandths; compare and order integers between –100 and 0; use area models, benchmark fractions, and analyses of numerators and denominators to compare and order fractions. [Number and Numeration Goal 6]	6. Compare and order rational numbers; use area models, benchmark fractions, and analyses of numerators and denominators to compare and order fractions and mixed numbers; describe strategies used to compare fractions and mixed numbers. [Number and Numeration Goal 6]

Operations and Computation

Key
- Content taught
- Content practiced and applied

Content	Grade 3	Grade 4	Grade 5
Addition and subtraction facts	1. Demonstrate automaticity with all addition and subtraction facts through 10 + 10; use basic facts to compute fact extensions such as 80 + 70. [Operations and Computation Goal 1]	1. Demonstrate automaticity with addition and subtraction fact extensions. [Operations and Computation Goal 1]	
Addition and subtraction procedures	2. Use manipulatives, mental arithmetic, paper-and-pencil algorithms and models, and calculators to solve problems involving the addition and subtraction of whole numbers and decimals in a money context; describe the strategies used and explain how they work. [Operations and Computation Goal 2]	2. Use manipulatives, mental arithmetic, paper-and-pencil algorithms and models, and calculators to solve problems involving the addition and subtraction of whole numbers and decimals through hundredths; describe the strategies used and explain how they work. [Operations and Computation Goal 2]	1. Use manipulatives, mental arithmetic, paper-and-pencil algorithms and models, and calculators to solve problems involving the addition and subtraction of whole numbers, decimals, and signed numbers; describe the strategies used and explain how they work. [Operations and Computation Goal 1]

Operations and Computation (cont.)

Key ■ Content taught □ Content practiced and applied

Content	Grade 3	Grade 4	Grade 5
Multiplication and division facts	3. Demonstrate automaticity with multiplication facts through 10 × 10. [Operations and Computation Goal 3]	3. Demonstrate automaticity with multiplication facts through 10 * 10 and proficiency with related division facts; use basic facts to compute fact extensions such as 30 * 60. [Operations and Computation Goal 3]	2. Demonstrate automaticity with multiplication and division fact extensions. [Operations and Computation Goal 2]
Units 1–12	Content taught: 4, 7; Content practiced and applied: 3, 5, 6, 8, 9, 10, 11	Content taught: 3, 4, 5, 6; Content practiced and applied: 2, 11, 12	Content taught: 1, 4; Content practiced and applied: 2, 3
Multiplication and division procedures	4. Use arrays, mental arithmetic, paper-and-pencil algorithms and models, and calculators to solve problems involving the multiplication of 2- and 3-digit whole numbers by 1-digit whole numbers; describe the strategies used. [Operations and Computation Goal 4]	4. Use manipulatives, mental arithmetic, paper-and-pencil algorithms and models, and calculators to solve problems involving the multiplication of multidigit whole numbers by 2-digit whole numbers and the division of multidigit whole numbers by 1-digit whole numbers; describe the strategies used and explain how they work. [Operations and Computation Goal 4]	3. Use manipulatives, mental arithmetic, paper-and-pencil algorithms and models, and calculators to solve problems involving the multiplication of whole numbers and decimals and the division of multidigit whole numbers and decimals by whole numbers; express remainders as whole numbers or fractions as appropriate; describe the strategies used and explain how they work. [Operations and Computation Goal 3]
Units 1–12	Content taught: 4, 7, 9; Content practiced and applied: 10, 11	Content taught: 3, 5, 6, 7; Content practiced and applied: 8, 9, 10, 11, 12	Content taught: 1, 2, 4; Content practiced and applied: 3, 5, 6, 7, 8, 9, 10, 11, 12
Procedures for addition and subtraction of fractions		5. Use manipulatives, mental arithmetic, and calculators to solve problems involving the addition and subtraction of fractions and mixed numbers; describe the strategies used. [Operations and Computation Goal 5]	4. Use mental arithmetic, paper-and-pencil algorithms and models, and calculators to solve problems involving the addition and subtraction of fractions and mixed numbers; describe the strategies used and explain how they work. [Operations and Computation Goal 4]
Units 1–12		Content taught: 7; Content practiced and applied: 8, 9, 10, 11	Content taught: 5, 6, 8; Content practiced and applied: 7, 9, 10
Procedures for multiplication and division of fractions			5. Use area models, mental arithmetic, paper-and-pencil algorithms and models, and calculators to solve problems involving the multiplication of fractions and mixed numbers; use visual models, paper-and-pencil methods, and calculators to solve problems involving the division of fractions; describe the strategies used. [Operations and Computation Goal 5]
Units 1–12			Content taught: 8; Content practiced and applied: 9, 12

Content	Grade 3	Grade 4	Grade 5
Computational estimation	5. Make reasonable estimates for whole number addition, subtraction, multiplication, and division problems; explain how the estimates were obtained. [Operations and Computation Goal 5] 1 2 3 4 5 6 7 8 9 10 11	6. Make reasonable estimates for whole number and decimal addition and subtraction problems, and whole number multiplication and division problems; explain how the estimates were obtained. [Operations and Computation Goal 6] 1 2 3 4 5 6 7 8 9 10 11 12	6. Make reasonable estimates for whole number and decimal addition, subtraction, multiplication, and division problems and fraction and mixed number addition and subtraction problems; explain how the estimates were obtained. [Operations and Computation Goal 6] 1 2 3 4 5 6 7 8 9 10 11 12
Models for the operations	6. Recognize and describe change, comparison, and parts-and-total situations; use repeated addition, arrays, and skip counting to model multiplication; use equal sharing and equal grouping to model division. [Operations and Computation Goal 6] 1 2 3 4 5 6 7 8 9 10 11	7. Use repeated addition, skip counting, arrays, area, and scaling to model multiplication and division. [Operations and Computation Goal 7] 1 2 3 4 5 6 7 8 9 10 11 12	7. Use repeated addition, arrays, area, and scaling to model multiplication and division; use ratios expressed as words, fractions, percents, and with colons; solve problems involving ratios of parts of a set to the whole set. [Operations and Computation Goal 7] 1 2 3 4 5 6 7 8 9 10 11 12

Data and Chance

Key
- Content taught
- Content practiced and applied

Content	Grade 3	Grade 4	Grade 5
Data collection and representation	1. Collect and organize data or use given data to create charts, tables, graphs, and line plots. [Data and Chance Goal 1] 1 2 3 4 5 6 7 8 9 10 11	1. Collect and organize data or use given data to create charts, tables, graphs, and line plots. [Data and Chance Goal 1] 1 2 3 4 5 6 7 8 9 10 11 12	1. Collect and organize data or use given data to create graphic displays with reasonable titles, labels, keys, and intervals. [Data and Chance Goal 1] 1 2 3 4 5 6 7 8 9 10 11 12
Data analysis	2. Use graphs to ask and answer simple questions and draw conclusions; find the maximum, minimum, range, mode, and median of a data set. [Data and Chance Goal 2] 1 2 3 4 5 6 7 8 9 10 11	2. Use the maximum, minimum, range, median, mode, and graphs to ask and answer questions, draw conclusions, and make predictions. [Data and Chance Goal 2] 1 2 3 4 5 6 7 8 9 10 11 12	2. Use the maximum, minimum, range, median, mode, and mean, and graphs to ask and answer questions, draw conclusions, and make predictions. [Data and Chance Goal 2] 1 2 3 4 5 6 7 8 9 10 11 12

Data and Chance (cont.)

Content	Grade 3	Grade 4	Grade 5
Qualitative probability	3. Describe events using *certain, very likely, likely, unlikely, very unlikely, impossible,* and other basic probability terms; explain the choice of language. [Data and Chance Goal 3]	3. Describe events using *certain, very likely, likely, unlikely, very unlikely, impossible,* and other basic probability terms; use *more likely, equally likely, same chance, 50-50, less likely,* and other basic probability terms to compare events; explain the choice of language. [Data and Chance Goal 3]	3. Describe events using *certain, very likely, likely, unlikely, very unlikely, impossible* and other basic probability terms; use *more likely, equally likely, same chance, 50-50, less likely,* and other basic probability terms to compare events; explain the choice of language. [Data and Chance Goal 3]
	1 2 3 4 5 6 7 8 9 10 11	1 2 3 4 5 6 7 8 9 10 11 12	1 2 3 4 5 6 7 8 9 10 11 12
Quantitative probability	4. Predict the outcomes of simple experiments and test the predictions using manipulatives; express the probability of an event by using "_____ out of _____" language. [Data and Chance Goal 4]	4. Predict the outcomes of experiments and test the predictions using manipulatives; summarize the results and use them to predict future events; express the probability of an event as a fraction. [Data and Chance Goal 4]	4. Predict the outcomes of experiments, test the predictions using manipulatives, and summarize the results; compare predictions based on theoretical probability with experimental results; use summaries and comparisons to predict future events; express the probability of an event as a fraction, decimal, or percent. [Data and Chance Goal 4]
	1 2 3 4 5 6 7 8 9 10 11	1 2 3 4 5 6 7 8 9 10 11 12	1 2 3 4 5 6 7 8 9 10 11 12

Measurement and Reference Frames

Key
- Content taught
- Content practiced and applied

Content	Grade 3	Grade 4	Grade 5
Length, weight, and angles	1. Estimate length with and without tools; measure length to the nearest $\frac{1}{2}$ inch and $\frac{1}{2}$ centimeter; draw and describe angles as records of rotations. [Measurement and Reference Frames Goal 1]	1. Estimate length with and without tools; measure length to the nearest $\frac{1}{4}$ inch and $\frac{1}{2}$ centimeter; use tools to measure and draw angles; estimate the size of angles without tools. [Measurement and Reference Frames Goal 1]	1. Estimate length with and without tools; measure length with tools to the nearest $\frac{1}{8}$ inch and millimeter; estimate the measure of angles with and without tools; use tools to draw angles with given measures. [Measurement and Reference Frames Goal 1]
	1 2 3 4 5 6 7 8 9 10 11	1 2 3 4 5 6 7 8 9 10 11 12	1 2 3 4 5 6 7 8 9 10 11 12

Key ■ Content taught □ Content practiced and applied

Content	Grade 3	Grade 4	Grade 5
Area, perimeter, volume, and capacity	2. Describe and use strategies to measure the perimeter of polygons; find the areas of rectangles. [Measurement and Reference Frames Goal 2]	2. Describe and use strategies to measure the perimeter and area of polygons, to estimate the area of irregular shapes, and to find the volume of rectangular prisms. [Measurement and Reference Frames Goal 2]	2. Describe and use strategies to find the perimeter of polygons and the area of circles; choose and use appropriate methods, including formulas, to find the areas of rectangles, parallelograms, and triangles, and the volume of a prism; define *pi* as the ratio of a circle's circumference to its diameter. [Measurement and Reference Frames Goal 2]
	1 2 3 4 5 6 7 8 9 10 11	1 2 3 4 5 6 7 8 9 10 11 12	1 2 3 4 5 6 7 8 9 10 11 12
Units and systems of measurement	3. Describe relationships among inches, feet, and yards; describe relationships between minutes in an hour, hours in a day, days in a week. [Measurement and Reference Frames Goal 3]	3. Describe relationships among U.S. customary units of measure and among metric units of measure. [Measurement and Reference Frames Goal 3]	3. Describe relationships among U.S. customary units of measure and among metric units of measure. [Measurement and Reference Frames Goal 3]
	1 2 3 4 5 6 7 8 9 10 11	1 2 3 4 5 6 7 8 9 10 11 12	1 2 3 4 5 6 7 8 9 10 11 12
Time	4. Tell and show time to the nearest minute on an analog clock; tell and write time in digital notation.* [Measurement and Reference Frames Goal 4]		
	1 2 3 4 5 6 7 8 9 10 11	1 2 3 4 5 6 7 8 9 10 11 12	1 2 3 4 5 6 7 8 9 10 11 12
Coordinate systems		4. Use ordered pairs of numbers to name, locate, and plot points in the first quadrant of a coordinate grid. [Measurement and Reference Frames Goal 4]	4. Use ordered pairs of numbers to name, locate, and plot points in all four quadrants of a coordinate grid. [Measurement and Reference Frames Goal 4]
	1 2 3 4 5 6 7 8 9 10 11	1 2 3 4 5 6 7 8 9 10 11 12	1 2 3 4 5 6 7 8 9 10 11 12

*Children record their start time at the top of journal pages on a daily basis.

Geometry

Key ■ Content taught ■ Content practiced and applied

Content	Grade 3	Grade 4	Grade 5
Lines and angles	1. Identify and draw points, intersecting and parallel line segments and lines, rays, and right angles. [Geometry Goal 1]	1. Identify, draw, and describe points, intersecting and parallel line segments and lines, rays, and right, acute, and obtuse angles. [Geometry Goal 1]	1. Identify, describe, compare, name, and draw right, acute, obtuse, straight, and reflex angles; determine angle measures in vertical and supplementary angles by applying properties of sums of angle measures in triangles and quadrangles. [Geometry Goal 1]
	1 2 3 4 5 6 7 8 9 10 11	1 2 3 4 5 6 7 8 9 10 11 12	1 2 3 4 5 6 7 8 9 10 11 12
Plane and solid figures	2. Identify, describe, model, and compare plane and solid figures including circles, polygons, spheres, cylinders, rectangular prisms, pyramids, cones, and cubes using appropriate geometric terms including the terms *face, edge, vertex,* and *base.* [Geometry Goal 2]	2. Describe, compare, and classify plane and solid figures, including polygons, circles, spheres, cylinders, rectangular prisms, cones, cubes, and pyramids, using appropriate geometric terms including *vertex, base, face, edge,* and *congruent.* [Geometry Goal 2]	2. Describe, compare, and classify plane and solid figures using appropriate geometric terms; identify congruent figures and describe their properties. [Geometry Goal 2]
	1 2 3 4 5 6 7 8 9 10 11	1 2 3 4 5 6 7 8 9 10 11 12	1 2 3 4 5 6 7 8 9 10 11 12
Transformations and symmetry	3. Create and complete two-dimensional symmetric shapes or designs; locate multiple lines of symmetry in a two-dimensional shape. [Geometry Goal 3]	3. Identify, describe, and sketch examples of reflections; identify and describe examples of translations and rotations. [Geometry Goal 3]	3. Identify, describe, and sketch examples of reflections, translations, and rotations. [Geometry Goal 3]
	1 2 3 4 5 6 7 8 9 10 11	1 2 3 4 5 6 7 8 9 10 11 12	1 2 3 4 5 6 7 8 9 10 11 12

Patterns, Functions, and Algebra

Key
- Content taught
- Content practiced and applied

Content	Grade 3	Grade 4	Grade 5
Patterns and functions	1. Extend, describe, and create numeric patterns; describe rules for patterns and use them to solve problems; use words and symbols to describe and write rules for functions involving addition, subtraction, and multiplication and use those rules to solve problems. [Patterns, Functions, and Algebra Goal 1]	1. Extend, describe, and create numeric patterns; describe rules for patterns and use them to solve problems; use words and symbols to describe and write rules for functions that involve the four basic arithmetic operations and use those rules to solve problems. [Patterns, Functions, and Algebra Goal 1]	1. Extend, describe, and create numeric patterns; describe rules for patterns and use them to solve problems; write rules for functions involving the four basic arithmetic operations; represent functions using words, symbols, tables, and graphs and use those representations to solve problems. [Patterns, Functions, and Algebra Goal 1]
Algebraic notation and solving number sentences	2. Read, write, and explain number sentences using the symbols $+$, $-$, $\times$, $\div$, $=$, $>$, and $<$; solve number sentences; write expressions and number sentences to model number stories. [Patterns, Functions, and Algebra Goal 2]	2. Use conventional notation to write expressions and number sentences using the four basic arithmetic operations; determine whether number sentences are true or false; solve open sentences and explain the solutions; write expressions and number sentences to model number stories. [Patterns, Functions, and Algebra Goal 2]	2. Determine whether number sentences are true or false; solve open number sentences and explain the solutions; use a letter variable to write an open sentence to model a number story; use a pan-balance model to solve linear equations in one unknown. [Patterns, Functions, and Algebra Goal 2]
Order of operations	3. Recognize that numeric expressions can have different values depending on the order in which operations are carried out; understand that grouping symbols can be used to affect the order in which operations are carried out. [Patterns, Functions, and Algebra Goal 3]	3. Evaluate numeric expressions containing grouping symbols; insert grouping symbols to make number sentences true. [Patterns, Functions, and Algebra Goal 3]	3. Evaluate numeric expressions containing grouping symbols and nested grouping symbols; insert grouping symbols and nested grouping symbols to make number sentences true; describe and use the precedence of multiplication and division over addition and subtraction. [Patterns, Functions, and Algebra Goal 3]
Properties of the arithmetic operations	4. Describe and apply the Commutative and Associative Properties of Addition and Multiplication, and the Multiplicative Identity; apply the Distributive Property of Multiplication over Addition. [Patterns, Functions, and Algebra Goal 4]	4. Describe and apply the Distributive Property of Multiplication over Addition. [Patterns, Functions, and Algebra Goal 4]	4. Describe and apply properties of arithmetic. [Patterns, Functions, and Algebra Goal 4]

Scope and Sequence Chart

Throughout *Everyday Mathematics*, students repeatedly encounter skills in each of the content strands. Each exposure builds on and extends students' understanding. They study important concepts over consecutive years through a variety of formats. The Scope and Sequence Chart shows the units in which these exposures occur. The symbol ● indicates that the skill is introduced or taught. The symbol ■ indicates that the skill is revisited, practiced, or extended. These levels refer to unit content within the *K–6 Everyday Mathematics* curriculum.

The skills are divided according to the content strands below.

Content Strands — Pages

How to Read the Scope and Sequence Chart

Each section of the chart includes a content strand title, three grade-level columns divided by units or sections, and a list of specific skills grouped by major concepts.

Number and Numeration — Content Strand

Key: ● Content taught ■ Content practiced

	Grade 4 Units												Grade 5 Units												Grade 6 Units									
Rote Counting	1	2	3	4	5	6	7	8	9	10	11	12	1	2	3	4	5	6	7	8	9	10	11	12	1	2	3	4	5	6	7	8	9	10
Count by tenths and hundredths				●																														
Place Value and Notation	1	2	3	4	5	6	7	8	9	10	11	12	1	2	3	4	5	6	7	8	9	10	11	12	1	2	3	4	5	6	7	8	9	10
Read and write numbers to hundred millions		●	■	■	■		■						■	■	●	■			■							●	■		■					
Read and write numbers to billions		●			●									■	■											●	■		■					

This row identifies the major mathematical concepts within each content strand. A list of related concepts and skills appear below this head.

Find specific skills in this list and then follow across the row to find where they appear at each grade level.

The colored circle indicates where the skill is introduced or taught.

The colored square indicates where the skill is primarily revisited, practiced, or extended.

Number and Numeration

Key ● Content taught ■ Content practiced

	Grade 4 Units												Grade 5 Units												Grade 6 Units									
Rote Counting	**1**	**2**	**3**	**4**	**5**	**6**	**7**	**8**	**9**	**10**	**11**	**12**	**1**	**2**	**3**	**4**	**5**	**6**	**7**	**8**	**9**	**10**	**11**	**12**	**1**	**2**	**3**	**4**	**5**	**6**	**7**	**8**	**9**	**10**
Count by tenths and hundredths				●																														
Place Value and Notation	**1**	**2**	**3**	**4**	**5**	**6**	**7**	**8**	**9**	**10**	**11**	**12**	**1**	**2**	**3**	**4**	**5**	**6**	**7**	**8**	**9**	**10**	**11**	**12**	**1**	**2**	**3**	**4**	**5**	**6**	**7**	**8**	**9**	**10**
Read and write numbers to hundred millions		●	■	■	■		■						■	■	●	■			■							●	■		■					
Read and write numbers to billions		●			●									■	■											●	■		■					
Explore numbers to trillions					●									●					●						■	●	■				■			
Investigate or identify place value in numbers to hundred millions		●	■	■			■						■	■	■	■			■						■	●	■						■	
Identify place value in numbers to billions		●			●									■	■								■		■	●	■						■	
Name the values of digits in numbers to billions		●			●										■										■	●	■						■	
Make exchanges among place values		●		■										■			■	■	■							■					■			
Investigate and apply powers of 10					■								■	■	■				●							●	■	■						■
Investigate and apply expanded notation		■			■									●		■		■	●							■			■	■				
Read and write numbers to trillions in standard and expanded notation		●	■		●																				●	●	■				■			■
Investigate, use, or apply exponential notation					●	■		■					●	■			■	■	●							●	■	■	■	■		■		■
Investigate and apply scientific notation																			●							●	■	■		■				■
Use dollar-and-cents notation			■	●		■	●	■	●		■	●																						
Explore uses of decimals				■																														
Model decimals with base-10 materials				●																														
Read and write decimals to ten-thousandths in standard and expanded notation				●	■				●					●	■				■						■	●			■					
Identify place value in decimals through ten-thousandths; compare decimals				●	■	■							■	●	■	■			■		■	■			●	●	■	●				●	●	
Investigate and apply expanded notation of decimals				■											■					■						●								
Translate words into numerical expressions													■		■															●				
Meanings and Uses of Fractions	**1**	**2**	**3**	**4**	**5**	**6**	**7**	**8**	**9**	**10**	**11**	**12**	**1**	**2**	**3**	**4**	**5**	**6**	**7**	**8**	**9**	**10**	**11**	**12**	**1**	**2**	**3**	**4**	**5**	**6**	**7**	**8**	**9**	**10**
Explore uses of fractions			■				●										●					■		■										

Key ● Content taught ■ Content practiced

Meanings and Uses of Fractions (cont.)	1	2	3	4	5	6	7	8	9	10	11	12	1	2	3	4	5	6	7	8	9	10	11	12	1	2	3	4	5	6	7	8	9	10
Identify fractional parts of regions					■	■	●	■	●	■							●	■		●					■			●						
Identify fractional parts of a set				●		■	●	■									●			■									■	■	■			
Decompose a fraction							●																											
Identify the whole for fractions							●		●						■		●	■	■	●								■				●		
Identify fractions on a number line						■	●	■				■					●	●									■							
Identify/find fractional parts of units of money							■													●												●		
Find a fraction of a number				●		■	●		●								●	■	■	●			■	●				●	■	■	■		■	
Use percents to describe real-life situations								■	●																							■		
Find a percent of a number								■	●			■					■	■	■	●			■	■			●	●	■	■	●	●	●	
Find the whole, given a percent of the whole									●											●				■								●	■	
Solve percent problems								■	■	■							●			●						■	●	●	■	■	●	●	●	
Estimate and calculate percent								■	●								●			●						■	●	●	■	■	●	●	●	
Find the unit fraction or unit percent to calculate unit prices												●								●		●									■	●		
Determine the better buy												●								■			●				●					●	■	
Number Theory	**1**	**2**	**3**	**4**	**5**	**6**	**7**	**8**	**9**	**10**	**11**	**12**	**1**	**2**	**3**	**4**	**5**	**6**	**7**	**8**	**9**	**10**	**11**	**12**	**1**	**2**	**3**	**4**	**5**	**6**	**7**	**8**	**9**	**10**
Identify even and odd numbers													●																	■				
Find the factors of numbers			●		■		■					■	●	■	■	■	■			■			■	●			■	■					●	
Investigate, identify, or apply the concepts of prime and composite numbers			●										●											●				●		■				
Find the prime factorization of numbers													●	■	■	■	■				■		■	●				■						
Find multiples of a number or the least common multiple of two numbers			●	■							■		●					■		■	■			●			■	●		●		■		
Find the greatest common factor of two numbers													●							■				●			■	●			●		●	
Investigate or identify square numbers, square roots, and absolute value			●										●										■				■			●			●	
Understand properties of rational numbers																					■		■			■				●	■			

Number and Numeration (cont.)

Key ● Content taught ■ Content practiced

	Grade 4 Units												Grade 5 Units												Grade 6 Units									
Equivalent Names for Whole Numbers	1	2	3	4	5	6	7	8	9	10	11	12	1	2	3	4	5	6	7	8	9	10	11	12	1	2	3	4	5	6	7	8	9	10
Find equivalent names for numbers	■	●	■	■	■	■				■		■	●	■	■	●	■	■	●		■	■			●	●		■				■	●	■
Rename numbers written in exponential notation					●	■							●						●							●	■	■	■	■		■		■
Equivalent Names for Fractions, Decimals, and Percents	1	2	3	4	5	6	7	8	9	10	11	12	1	2	3	4	5	6	7	8	9	10	11	12	1	2	3	4	5	6	7	8	9	10
Find equivalent fractions						■	●	■	■							■	●	●	■	●			■	●				●			■	●		
Rename fractions as decimals				●			●		●	■				■			●	■									■	●	●	■	■	■		
Relate fractions and decimals				●			●	■	●	■		■					●								●	●		●	■	■	■	■	■	
Convert between fractions and decimals							●	■	●	■							●			■							■	●	■	■	■	■		
Estimate equivalent percents for fractions																	●											●	●	■	■	●	■	
Rename fractions and mixed numbers in simplest forms																	■	●	■	●			■	■			■	●		■	■	■	■	
Convert between fractions, mixed numbers, decimals, and/or percents			●	●			■		●	■			■	■	■		●	●		●	■			■	●	■	■	●	■	●	●	●	■	
Use a calculator to rename any fraction as a decimal or percent									●								●	●									■	●	●		●	●		
Comparing and Ordering Numbers	1	2	3	4	5	6	7	8	9	10	11	12	1	2	3	4	5	6	7	8	9	10	11	12	1	2	3	4	5	6	7	8	9	10
Compare numbers using <, >, and = symbols	■	■	■	■	■	■	●	■			■	■	■					●	●	●	■		■	■	●	■		●		●			■	
Compare larger numbers					●	■								■					●						■	■								
Compare and order decimals			■	●	■	■			■			■	■		■	■	■		■		■			■		●	■			■		■		
Compare and order integers										●	■	■							●						●	■			■	●	■	■		
Compare and order fractions with or without benchmarks							●		■	■		■		■		■	●	●	■	●	■			■			■	●		■		■		
Plot and compare decimals on a number line																									●	■				■				
Explore uses for positive and negative numbers										●	●								●		●								■	●	■			
Use properties of positive and negative numbers										●	■	■							●							■	●		■	●	■			
Explore reference points for zero										●	■												●	●			■			■				

Operations and Computation

Key ● Content taught ■ Content practiced

	Grade 4 Units												Grade 5 Units												Grade 6 Units									
Addition and Subtraction Facts	1	2	3	4	5	6	7	8	9	10	11	12	1	2	3	4	5	6	7	8	9	10	11	12	1	2	3	4	5	6	7	8	9	10
Practice basic facts and extended facts	■	■											■	■		■			■			■	■			■			●		■	■		
Practice extensions of basic facts		■													■											■				■				
Add/subtract multiples of 10 or 100		●																																
Addition and Subtraction Procedures	1	2	3	4	5	6	7	8	9	10	11	12	1	2	3	4	5	6	7	8	9	10	11	12	1	2	3	4	5	6	7	8	9	10
Use addition/subtraction algorithms		●		●	■								■	●	■										■	●	■			■		■		
Add/subtract using a calculator		●		●																						■					■	■		
Add/subtract multidigit numbers	■	●	●		●								■	●	■										■	●		■	■		■			
Solve addition/subtraction number stories		■	●	■	●									●	■										■							■		
Add/subtract multidigit whole numbers and decimals		●	■	●	■		■							●	■	■					■	■			■	●	■			■		■		
Use estimation or algorithms to add/subtract money amounts/decimals; make change			■	●		■				●	●	●		●	■	■	■	■	■	■					■	●	■	■					■	
Solve decimal addition/subtraction number stories				●															■							●								
Add/subtract positive and negative numbers; model addition and subtraction on a number line										●	●	■							●			■	■				●	■	●	●		■		
Compute with positive and negative integers											■	■							●								■			●	■	■		
Multiplication and Division Facts	1	2	3	4	5	6	7	8	9	10	11	12	1	2	3	4	5	6	7	8	9	10	11	12	1	2	3	4	5	6	7	8	9	10
Use a Multiplication/Division Facts Table			●										■																					
Practice multiplication/division facts			●	■	■	■	■						●	■	■	●			■	■		■	■			●	●	●	■	●		●		
Practice extended multiplication/division facts			●		●	■							■	■	■	●						■				●	■					■		
Solve multiplication/division problems involving multiples of 10, 100, and 1,000					●	■							■	●	■	●									■	●	■	●	■		■	■		
Understand the relationship between multiplication and division			●			●							■			●				■			■	■						●				
Multiplication and Division Procedures	1	2	3	4	5	6	7	8	9	10	11	12	1	2	3	4	5	6	7	8	9	10	11	12	1	2	3	4	5	6	7	8	9	10
Model multiplication with arrays			■		■								●																					
Use mental arithmetic to multiply/divide		■		■	●									■	■	●		■					■	■	●	●				■		■		
Use multiplication/division algorithms					●	●	■	■	●					●	■	●					■	■		■	●	●	■	■	■		■	●		

Operations and Computation (cont.)

Key ● Content taught ■ Content practiced

	Grade 4 Units												Grade 5 Units												Grade 6 Units									
Multiplication and Division Procedures (cont.)	1	2	3	4	5	6	7	8	9	10	11	12	1	2	3	4	5	6	7	8	9	10	11	12	1	2	3	4	5	6	7	8	9	10
Relate fractions and division			■						●								■	■	●								■	●	■	■		■		
Divide by 1-digit numbers						●			■				●			●		■						■	■	●				■		■		
Divide by 2-digit numbers						●			■							●	■									●				■		■		
Use a calculator to multiply/divide					■							●	●			●		■	■			■			●	●		●	■			■	■	
Identify or investigate square numbers			●										●														■						●	
Solve multiplication/division number stories		■	■		■	●			■		■	●				●	■	■								●		■	■			■	■	
Solve multidigit multiplication/division problems					●	■								●	■	●					■	■		■	●	●	■				■			
Multiply/divide decimals by powers of 10														■	■				■			■				●	■	●		■		■		
Multiply decimals by whole numbers									●	■	■			●	■			■	■						●	●		●	■			●		
Divide decimals by whole numbers									●	■	■					●		■								●	■					■		
Multiply/divide money amounts						■			●	●		●		●		●				●	■	●				●	■					●	●	
Solve multiplication/division decimal number stories									●														■					●				■	●	
Interpret a remainder in division problems					■	●			■			●				●	■									■		●				■		
Express remainders as fractions or decimals						●						■				●										●	■	●		■		■	■	
Express quotients as mixed numbers or decimals						●											■	■								●	■	●		■		■		
Locate the decimal point in a product or quotient									●	■	■			●												●		●	■					
Round a decimal quotient to a specified place																		■			■					●		●				●		
Multiply decimals by decimals														●											■	●						●		
Multiply by positive and negative powers of 10																			●		■					●	■							
Multiply/divide positive and negative numbers																											■			●	■	■		
Use divisibility tests to determine if a number is divisible by another number													●		■	■	■	■			■	■				■	■	●						
Procedures for Addition and Subtraction of Fractions	1	2	3	4	5	6	7	8	9	10	11	12	1	2	3	4	5	6	7	8	9	10	11	12	1	2	3	4	5	6	7	8	9	10
Use benchmarks to add and subtract fractions																		●		■	■													
Use models to add/subtract fractions and mixed numbers							●		■	■	■						●	●	■	●								■						

Key ● Content taught ■ Content practiced

Procedures for Addition and Subtraction of Fractions (cont.)	1	2	3	4	5	6	7	8	9	10	11	12	1	2	3	4	5	6	7	8	9	10	11	12	1	2	3	4	5	6	7	8	9	10
Add/subtract fractions with like denominators							●	■	■	■								●		●							■	●			●	■	●	
Add/subtract fractions with unlike denominators							●	■	■	■								●		●	■			■				●	■	■	●	■	●	
Solve fraction addition/subtraction number stories; model addition and subtraction with pictures or words							●				■						●	■	■	■	■			■				●	■			■		
Use an algorithm to add/subtract mixed numbers with like denominators							●													●				■			■	●						
Use an algorithm to add/subtract mixed numbers with unlike denominators							●										■	■	■	●				■				●	■			■		
Procedures for Multiplication and Division of Fractions	**1**	**2**	**3**	**4**	**5**	**6**	**7**	**8**	**9**	**10**	**11**	**12**	**1**	**2**	**3**	**4**	**5**	**6**	**7**	**8**	**9**	**10**	**11**	**12**	**1**	**2**	**3**	**4**	**5**	**6**	**7**	**8**	**9**	**10**
Find common denominators																		●		●				■				●	■	●	●	■		
Use an algorithm to multiply fractions by whole numbers							●	■		■										●								■		■				
Use an algorithm to multiply fractions																				●	■			■				●	■	●	●	●	■	■
Use an algorithm to multiply mixed numbers																				●	■			■				●	■	●		●		■
Solve multiplication/division fraction number stories							●			■										●	■							■	■			●		
Solve "fraction-of-a-fraction" problems																				●										■	●	■	■	
Use a common denominator to divide fractions																			■	●														
Use an algorithm to multiply/divide fractions and mixed numbers; use area models to demonstrate							●													●	■							●	■	●		●	■	■
Understand the effect of multiplying fractions by a number less than 1, equal to 1, or greater than 1																				●														
Computational Estimation	**1**	**2**	**3**	**4**	**5**	**6**	**7**	**8**	**9**	**10**	**11**	**12**	**1**	**2**	**3**	**4**	**5**	**6**	**7**	**8**	**9**	**10**	**11**	**12**	**1**	**2**	**3**	**4**	**5**	**6**	**7**	**8**	**9**	**10**
Round whole numbers to a given place				■	●	■							■	■		●		■							■	●	■						●	
Use estimation to add/subtract		●	■	●	●									●						●	■							■		●		●		
Use estimation to multiply/divide					●			■						●	●	●								■	■		■	■						■
Make magnitude estimates to solve *, ÷ problems					●									●		●		●				■			■	■		■						■
Estimate sums/differences of fractions																				■	■	■						■						
Round decimals to a given place									■		■	■		●	■	●										●	■	●	■			●	■	

Operations and Computation (cont.)

Key ● Content taught ■ Content practiced

	Grade 4 Units												Grade 5 Units												Grade 6 Units									
Computational Estimation (cont.)	1	2	3	4	5	6	7	8	9	10	11	12	1	2	3	4	5	6	7	8	9	10	11	12	1	2	3	4	5	6	7	8	9	10
Estimate costs				■		■			■								■								■									
Estimate products and multiply decimals									●	■	■			●										■	■	●								■
Estimate the quotient and divide a decimal by a whole number									●	■	■					●	■									●	■	●		■				
Models for the Operations	1	2	3	4	5	6	7	8	9	10	11	12	1	2	3	4	5	6	7	8	9	10	11	12	1	2	3	4	5	6	7	8	9	10
Understand multiplicative comparisons		■	●	●	●	■		●					■		■	■				■														
Understand additive comparisons				●	●																													
Find unit rates												●										●					■				■	●	■	
Collect and compare rate data; evaluate reasonableness of rate data												●										●		●			●					●		
Use rate tables to solve problems												●										●		●			●					●		
Represent rates with formulas, tables, and graphs												●										●		●			●			■	■	●	■	
Solve rate and ratio number stories; find equivalent ratios												●								■		●		●			●				■	●	●	
Explore uses of ratios and ways of expressing ratios; differentiate between rate and ratio												●										●		●							■	●	●	
Find opposites and reciprocals of numbers																				■							●			●		■		
Solve problems involving a size-change factor																																●	●	
Write open proportions to solve model problems																								●							■	●	●	
Use cross-multiplication to solve open proportions																															■	●	■	

Data and Chance

	Grade 4 Units												Grade 5 Units												Grade 6 Units									
Data Collection and Representation	1	2	3	4	5	6	7	8	9	10	11	12	1	2	3	4	5	6	7	8	9	10	11	12	1	2	3	4	5	6	7	8	9	10
Collect data by counting/interviewing		●							●			●					●	●							●		■	■						
Collect data from print sources		●	●	■	■	■	■	■	■	■	■	■						■	■						●	■								
Collect data from a map			●	■	●	●						■			■			●					■									●		

Key ● Content taught ■ Content practiced

Data Collection and Representation (cont.)	1	2	3	4	5	6	7	8	9	10	11	12
Find locations on a map or globe		●	●		●	●	■		■		■	
Collect and compare rate data												●
Conduct a survey									●			
Organize and tabulate survey data									●			
Make a tally chart		●										
Record data in a table/chart		●	●						●	■		●
Record data on a map									●			
Record/compare numerical data		●					●	■	●			●
Create/interpret bar graphs		●		■	■	■			■	■	■	■
Create/interpret box plots												
Create/interpret broken-line graphs and line plots		■	●				■				■	■
Create/interpret circle graphs with or without a Percent Circle			■	■	■	■						
Create/interpret step graphs												
Create/interpret Venn diagrams	■		■		■						■	
Create/interpret number-line plots		●					●				●	
Create/interpret stem-and-leaf plots		■										
Interpret mystery graphs												
Use technology to create graphs												
Use a spreadsheet												
Explore misleading ways of presenting data												
Data Analysis	**1**	**2**	**3**	**4**	**5**	**6**	**7**	**8**	**9**	**10**	**11**	**12**
Interpret tables, graphs, and maps	■		●	■	■	■			●			
Use a map scale			●	■	■	●	■	●	■			
Use a mileage map					●							
Make and interpret scale drawings								●				
Identify locations for given latitudes and longitudes						●						

Data Collection and Representation (cont.)	1	2	3	4	5	6	7	8	9	10	11	12
Find locations on a map or globe									●			
Collect and compare rate data										●		●
Conduct a survey						●		●				
Organize and tabulate survey data						●						
Make a tally chart						●						
Record data in a table/chart						●		■		●	●	●
Record data on a map												
Record/compare numerical data		●				●						●
Create/interpret bar graphs		■			●	●						
Create/interpret box plots												
Create/interpret broken-line graphs and line plots		●				●	●	■	■	●	■	●
Create/interpret circle graphs with or without a Percent Circle				■	●	●		■		■	■	
Create/interpret step graphs												
Create/interpret Venn diagrams					■		●				●	■
Create/interpret number-line plots		●				●						
Create/interpret stem-and-leaf plots						●	■			●		
Interpret mystery graphs										●		
Use technology to create graphs												
Use a spreadsheet												
Explore misleading ways of presenting data												
Data Analysis	**1**	**2**	**3**	**4**	**5**	**6**	**7**	**8**	**9**	**10**	**11**	**12**
Interpret tables, graphs, and maps		●	■	■	●	●	●	●	■	●	■	●
Use a map scale		●		●								
Use a mileage map		●		●								
Make and interpret scale drawings									■			
Identify locations for given latitudes and longitudes									●			

Data Collection and Representation (cont.)	1	2	3	4	5	6	7	8	9	10
Find locations on a map or globe										
Collect and compare rate data			●					●		
Conduct a survey	●	■								
Organize and tabulate survey data	●									
Make a tally chart							■			
Record data in a table/chart	●		●			■	■	■	●	
Record data on a map										
Record/compare numerical data	●		●	●				■		
Create/interpret bar graphs	●	■		■			■			
Create/interpret box plots	●	■	■							
Create/interpret broken-line graphs and line plots	●	■	●			■	■			
Create/interpret circle graphs with or without a Percent Circle	●	■		●	●	■		■		
Create/interpret step graphs	●									
Create/interpret Venn diagrams					■		●	■		
Create/interpret number-line plots	●	■								
Create/interpret stem-and-leaf plots	●	■		■					■	
Interpret mystery graphs		■	■			■			■	
Use technology to create graphs	■									
Use a spreadsheet			●	■				■	●	
Explore misleading ways of presenting data	●	■								
Data Analysis	**1**	**2**	**3**	**4**	**5**	**6**	**7**	**8**	**9**	**10**
Interpret tables, graphs, and maps	●	■	●	■				●	■	
Use a map scale								●	●	
Use a mileage map								●		
Make and interpret scale drawings								●	●	
Identify locations for given latitudes and longitudes										

Data and Chance (cont.)

Key ● Content taught ■ Content practiced

	Grade 4 Units												Grade 5 Units												Grade 6 Units									
Data Analysis (cont.)	1	2	3	4	5	6	7	8	9	10	11	12	1	2	3	4	5	6	7	8	9	10	11	12	1	2	3	4	5	6	7	8	9	10
Find latitude and longitude for given locations						●			■												●													
Summarize and interpret data		■		■				■				●		●				●	●	●		●		●	●	■	●	■				■	■	
Compare two sets of data; compare graphical representations of the same data		■						■	■			■		●	●		●	●	●	●		●		●	●	■	■							
Make predictions about data		■					●		●			■						●				●		●	●		●	●			●			
Find/use the minimum/maximum		●		■				●		■			■	●	●	■	■	●	■		■	■	■	●	●	■	■						■	
Find/use the range		●	■	■	■		■			■			■	●	■		■	●	■		■		■	●	●	■	■						■	
Find/use the median		●	●		■		■	●		■		●	■	●	●	■	■	●	■			●	■	●	●	■	■	■					■	
Find/use the mode		●		■			■	●		■				●	■	■	■	●			■		■		●	■	■						■	
Find/use the mean		■	●	■			■					■		●	■	■	■	●			■		■		●	■	●	■	●				■	
Find/use the lower quartile, upper quartile, and the interquartile range																									●	■	■							
Understand how sample size or outliers affect results		■					■											●							●	■		■						
Determine whether the mean, median, or mode provides the most useful information in a given situation		■	■									■						●							●	■	■	■						
Use data in problem solving		■	●					■				●						●				●			●	■	●				■	■		
Qualitative Probability	1	2	3	4	5	6	7	8	9	10	11	12	1	2	3	4	5	6	7	8	9	10	11	12	1	2	3	4	5	6	7	8	9	10
Explore likelihood of events						■	●		■		■	■		●										●						■	●			
Explore fair and unfair games							●										■	●													●			
Quantitative Probability	1	2	3	4	5	6	7	8	9	10	11	12	1	2	3	4	5	6	7	8	9	10	11	12	1	2	3	4	5	6	7	8	9	10
Predict outcomes; solve problems involving chance outcomes							●	■	■					●				■						●						■	●	■		
Conduct experiments							●							●				■						●							●			
Record outcomes							●							●				■						●							●	■		
Use fractions to record probabilities of events							●		■															●						■	■	■		
Compute the probability of equally-likely outcomes							●	■	■		■			■										●						■	●	■		
Calculate and express the probability of simple events						■	●	■	■	■	■	■					■		■		■			●						■	●			

Key ● Content taught ■ Content practiced

Quantitative Probability (cont.)	1	2	3	4	5	6	7	8	9	10	11	12	1	2	3	4	5	6	7	8	9	10	11	12	1	2	3	4	5	6	7	8	9	10
Understand and apply the concept of random numbers to probability situations																															●			
Understand how increasing the number of trials affects experimental results																		●						■	●						●	■		
Investigate/apply the Multiplication Counting Principle, tree diagrams, lists, and other counting strategies to identify all possible outcomes for a situation			■																					●						■	●	■		
Explore random sampling									●									●							●						●			

Measurement and Reference Frames

	Grade 4 Units												Grade 5 Units												Grade 6 Units									
Length, Weight, and Angles	1	2	3	4	5	6	7	8	9	10	11	12	1	2	3	4	5	6	7	8	9	10	11	12	1	2	3	4	5	6	7	8	9	10
Add and subtract units of length, weight, and capacity			●		■		■				■												■											
Estimate and compare lengths/heights of objects			■	●	■		■																●										●	●
Measure to the nearest foot								●																										
Measure to the nearest inch			■				■									●								●										
Measure to the nearest $\frac{1}{2}$ inch			●																■						■							●	●	●
Measure to the nearest $\frac{1}{4}$ inch					■	■		●						■		■	●			■					■				■			●	●	
Measure to the nearest $\frac{1}{8}$ inch														■				■							■			●	■	●		●	●	
Draw or measure line segments to the nearest centimeter		●	■	●				●								■		●							■				■				■	
Measure to the nearest $\frac{1}{2}$ centimeter		●		■																														
Draw or measure line segments to the nearest millimeter				●	■	■												●		■					■				■			●	●	
Investigate the meter				●																														
Express metric measures with decimals				●																						■								
Estimate and compare distances			●	●	●	●		●						●		●					■													●
Solve length/height/distance number stories			●		■		■		■		■										■					■						●	■	
Estimate and compare weights										■	●																					■		

Measurement and Reference Frames (cont.)

Key ● Content taught ■ Content practiced

	Grade 4 Units												Grade 5 Units												Grade 6 Units									
Length, Weight, and Angles (cont.)	1	2	3	4	5	6	7	8	9	10	11	12	1	2	3	4	5	6	7	8	9	10	11	12	1	2	3	4	5	6	7	8	9	10
Estimate/weigh objects in ounces or grams											●																			■				
Use a pan balance/spring scale											●											●												
Solve weight number stories											●											●	●											
Estimate the measure of an angle			■			■	■			■					●	■												■	■					■
Use full-circle and half-circle protractors to measure and draw angles						●	■	■	■	■					●		■	●										■	●			■		
Measure angles with degree units to within 2°						●	■							■	●	■	■	●	■									■	●				■	■
Area, Perimeter, Volume, and Capacity	1	2	3	4	5	6	7	8	9	10	11	12	1	2	3	4	5	6	7	8	9	10	11	12	1	2	3	4	5	6	7	8	9	10
Investigate area and perimeter			■				■	●	■												●			■	●	■	●					■	●	
Find the areas of regular shapes								●	■	■							■			■	●	■	●		●	■	●	●		●		■	●	
Find the perimeters of regular shapes			■					●	■	■					■		■				■		■		■	■	●					■	●	
Find the areas of irregular shapes								●													●		■					■					■	
Find the perimeters of irregular shapes								■	■												■		■										■	■
Estimate area								●													●							■					●	
Compare perimeter and area								■	■			■									■		■	■	■								●	
Find the area of a figure by counting unit squares and fractions of unit squares inside the figure							■	●													●					■							■	
Use formulas to find areas of rectangles, parallelograms, and triangles; understand the relationship between these formulas								●	■												●		●		■	■	●			●		■	●	■
Find the surface areas of prisms, cylinders, and pyramids																					■		●					●					■	
Investigate/understand the concept of volume of a figure											●										●	■	■										●	■
Understand the relationships between the volumes of pyramids and prisms, and the volumes of cones and cylinders																							●										●	
Estimate volume or surface area								●			●										●												●	
Find and use an approximate value for π (pi)																						●											●	
Use a formula to find the circumference of a circle																						■	■	■									●	■

Key ● Content taught ■ Content practiced

Area, Perimeter, Volume, and Capacity (cont.)	1	2	3	4	5	6	7	8	9	10	11	12	1	2	3	4	5	6	7	8	9	10	11	12	1	2	3	4	5	6	7	8	9	10
Use a formula to find the area of a circle																						●	●	■			●					■	●	■
Distinguish between circumference and area of a circle																						●	■	■									●	
Solve cube-stacking volume problems with unit cubes and fractions of unit cubes											■										●	■	■										■	
Use formulas to calculate volumes of 3-dimensional shapes											●	■									●	■	●			■					■		●	■
Investigate/understand the concept of capacity											●	■									●		●								■		●	
Estimate and calculate capacity											●	■									●		●								■		●	■
Solve capacity number stories											●	■											●								■		●	■
Units and Systems of Measurement	**1**	**2**	**3**	**4**	**5**	**6**	**7**	**8**	**9**	**10**	**11**	**12**	**1**	**2**	**3**	**4**	**5**	**6**	**7**	**8**	**9**	**10**	**11**	**12**	**1**	**2**	**3**	**4**	**5**	**6**	**7**	**8**	**9**	**10**
Identify equivalent customary units of length	■	■	■					●	■		■			●							■	■										●	●	■
Identify equivalent metric units of length				●		■												■			■	■			■						■	■	●	
Convert between metric/customary measures			■	●				■		■	●	■						■							●	●				■		■	●	■
Use personal references for metric/customary units of length				●	■										■			●			●													
Identify equivalent customary units of weight										■	●											■	■									■		
Identify equivalent metric units of weight				■							●											■	●									■		
Identify metric units of capacity											●	■									●	■	●										●	
Identify equivalent metric units of capacity											●	■									●	■	●									■	●	
Examine the relationships among the liter, milliliter, and cubic centimeter																					●		●										●	
Use personal references for common units of area																					●				■			■					■	
Money	**1**	**2**	**3**	**4**	**5**	**6**	**7**	**8**	**9**	**10**	**11**	**12**	**1**	**2**	**3**	**4**	**5**	**6**	**7**	**8**	**9**	**10**	**11**	**12**	**1**	**2**	**3**	**4**	**5**	**6**	**7**	**8**	**9**	**10**
Compare money amounts	■		■	■					■			●																						
Temperature	**1**	**2**	**3**	**4**	**5**	**6**	**7**	**8**	**9**	**10**	**11**	**12**	**1**	**2**	**3**	**4**	**5**	**6**	**7**	**8**	**9**	**10**	**11**	**12**	**1**	**2**	**3**	**4**	**5**	**6**	**7**	**8**	**9**	**10**
Read, record, and convert units of temperature									■													■					●					■	●	
Time	**1**	**2**	**3**	**4**	**5**	**6**	**7**	**8**	**9**	**10**	**11**	**12**	**1**	**2**	**3**	**4**	**5**	**6**	**7**	**8**	**9**	**10**	**11**	**12**	**1**	**2**	**3**	**4**	**5**	**6**	**7**	**8**	**9**	**10**
Investigate 1-minute intervals						●						●																						

Measurement and Reference Frames (cont.)

Key ● Content taught ■ Content practiced

	Grade 4 Units												Grade 5 Units												Grade 6 Units									
Time (cont.)	1	2	3	4	5	6	7	8	9	10	11	12	1	2	3	4	5	6	7	8	9	10	11	12	1	2	3	4	5	6	7	8	9	10
Calculate elapsed time		■	●		■	●																●												
Convert units of time		■			●													●		■				■								■		
Solve time number stories			●		●								■																					
Coordinate Systems	1	2	3	4	5	6	7	8	9	10	11	12	1	2	3	4	5	6	7	8	9	10	11	12	1	2	3	4	5	6	7	8	9	10
Plot ordered number pairs on a one or four-quadrant coordinate grid						●	■	■	■	■		■								■	●	■		●	■	■	■		●		■		■	
Use ordered number pairs to name points in four quadrants																				■	●	■			■	■	■		■			■		■
Find distances between ordered number pairs along lines																													●	●				■

Geometry

	Grade 4 Units												Grade 5 Units												Grade 6 Units									
Lines and Angles	1	2	3	4	5	6	7	8	9	10	11	12	1	2	3	4	5	6	7	8	9	10	11	12	1	2	3	4	5	6	7	8	9	10
Identify and name points	●														■										■			■	●					■
Identify and name line segments	●		■												■					■								■	●				■	
Draw line segments to a specified length	●	●													●						■				■				●					
Identify parallel and nonparallel line segments	●				■										■														●	■		■	■	
Identify and name lines	●														■														●	■		■	■	
Identify and name intersecting lines					■										■														●	■		■	■	
Identify and name rays	●			■																														
Name, draw, and label line segments, lines, and rays	●														■										■			■	●					■
Identify and name acute, obtuse, right, straight, and reflex angles	●					●			■					■	●	■				■				■				■	●				●	
Identify and describe right angles, parallel lines, skew lines, and line segments	●													■	■													■	●			■	■	
Use full-circle and half-circle protractors to measure and draw angles						●	■	■	■	■					●		■	●										■	●			■		■
Use a compass and a protractor to draw and measure angles formed by intersecting lines															●														●					■
Solve degree problems						●	■	■	■						■														●				■	

Key ● Content taught ■ Content practiced

Lines and Angles (cont.)	1	2	3	4	5	6	7	8	9	10	11	12	1	2	3	4	5	6	7	8	9	10	11	12	1	2	3	4	5	6	7	8	9	10
Determine angle measures based on relationships among common angles					■	●	■	■	■						●													■	●					■
Find angle sums for geometric shapes						■									●														●				■	■
Apply properties of adjacent, supplementary, complementary, and vertical angles; recognize properties in real-world settings						●	■		■						●														●	■		■	●	■
Apply properties of sums of angle measures of triangles and quadrilaterals															●	■								■				■	●			■	■	■
Apply properties of angles of parallelograms															●														●				■	●
Apply properties of angles formed by two parallel lines and a transversal																													●	■		■	■	■
Explore the relationship between endpoints and midpoints																													●					
Make turns and fractions of turns; relate turns to angles						●				■					●									■					●				■	●
Solve construction problems															●														●			■		
Plane and Solid Figures	**1**	**2**	**3**	**4**	**5**	**6**	**7**	**8**	**9**	**10**	**11**	**12**	**1**	**2**	**3**	**4**	**5**	**6**	**7**	**8**	**9**	**10**	**11**	**12**	**1**	**2**	**3**	**4**	**5**	**6**	**7**	**8**	**9**	**10**
Explore shape relationships	●						●	●		●					●						■								■			●	●	■
Identify characteristics of 2-dimensional shapes; use symbolic notation to denote these characteristics	●						●	●	■	●				■	●						●					■			●			●	●	
Identify 2-dimensional shapes	●	■	■				●	●							●					■	■					■			●			■	●	■
Construct/draw 2-dimensional shapes; create designs with 2-dimensional shapes	●	■					■	●		●					●										■				●			●	●	
Use a compass and a straightedge to construct geometric figures	●	■					■	■							●														●			■		
Identify the bases and heights of triangles and parallelograms								●													●											■	●	■
Use a compass to draw a circle with a given radius or diameter, and angles formed by intersecting lines															●														●				■	
Investigate the relationship between circumference and diameter																						●					■						■	
Form shapes by combining polygons							●	■																										
Identify properties and characteristics of polygons	●	■	■	■	■			●	■	●				■	●	●					■				■	■			●			●	●	●
Classify and name polygons	●						●	●	■						●					■	■				■				●				■	■
Classify triangles and quadrilaterals according to side and angle properties	●							●							●					■					■				●				●	●

Geometry (cont.)

Key ● Content taught ■ Content practiced

	Grade 4 Units												Grade 5 Units												Grade 6 Units									
Plane and Solid Figures (cont.)	**1**	**2**	**3**	**4**	**5**	**6**	**7**	**8**	**9**	**10**	**11**	**12**	**1**	**2**	**3**	**4**	**5**	**6**	**7**	**8**	**9**	**10**	**11**	**12**	**1**	**2**	**3**	**4**	**5**	**6**	**7**	**8**	**9**	**10**
Name, draw, and label angles, triangles, and quadrilaterals	●							●							●					■					●			■	●					■
Identify types of triangles								●							●	■				■					■									
Verify and apply the Pythagorean Theorem																																	●	
Solve problems involving 2-dimensional shapes	■	■					●	●							●						●				■				●			●	●	
Identify and classify 3-dimensional shapes											●									■	●		●						■				●	
Identify characteristics of 3-dimensional shapes; compare them with their 2-D faces											●										●	■	●						■				●	
Construct 3-dimensional shapes											●										●		●										●	
Describe properties of geometric solids											●										●		●						■				●	■
Identify faces, edges, vertices, and bases of prisms and pyramids											●	■											●						■				●	
Perform and identify topological transformations																													■					●
Identify congruent figures															●					■			■					●	●	■		●		●
Draw or form a figure congruent to a given figure										●					●						■								●					■
Identify and draw similar figures								■							●														■			●	●	
Describe relationships among angles, side lengths, perimeter, and area of similar polygons								■																						■	■	●	●	
Transformations and Symmetry	**1**	**2**	**3**	**4**	**5**	**6**	**7**	**8**	**9**	**10**	**11**	**12**	**1**	**2**	**3**	**4**	**5**	**6**	**7**	**8**	**9**	**10**	**11**	**12**	**1**	**2**	**3**	**4**	**5**	**6**	**7**	**8**	**9**	**10**
Identify lines of reflection, reflected figures, and figures with line symmetry										●											●								●					■
Use a transparent mirror to draw the reflection of a figure										●																								■
Identify symmetrical figures										●											■													■
Identify lines of symmetry									■	●											■												■	■
Translate figures on a coordinate grid																					●								●					●
Rotate figures										■	■										●								●					●
Model clockwise/counterclockwise turns/rotations						●				■														■					●					
Explore transformations of geometric figures in a plane; identify preimage and image											■										●								●				■	●
Explore rotation and point symmetry										■					●																			●

Patterns, Functions, and Algebra

Key ● Content taught ■ Content practiced

	Grade 4 Units												Grade 5 Units												Grade 6 Units									
Patterns and Functions	1	2	3	4	5	6	7	8	9	10	11	12	1	2	3	4	5	6	7	8	9	10	11	12	1	2	3	4	5	6	7	8	9	10
Explore and extend visual patterns	■						●			●			●							●	●	■							●					●
Create patterns with 2-dimensional shapes	■						●			●																								■
Define and create tessellations/frieze patterns										●					●																		■	●
Identify and use notation for semiregular tessellations																																	■	●
Identify regular tessellations															●																		■	●
Find and extend numerical patterns		■	■		■						●				■			■	■	■		●				●	●	■	●			●	●	
Make/complete a sequence with a number line		●		●	■		●	■				■	●			■		■				■												
Solve "What's My Rule?" (function machine) problems; find a rule for a set of problems		■	●	■	■	■	■		■	■							●	■	●	●	■					●	■			■			■	■
Solve pan-balance problems		■																				●	■	■						●	■		●	
Describe a pattern with a number sentence that has one to three variables																											●			●		■	●	■
Find patterns in addition, subtraction, multiplication, and division facts		■	■		■								●								■					●	■	●		●	■	●	●	
Find number patterns in data; complete a table of values								●				●										●		●		●	●	●				●	●	
Solve and graph solutions for inequalities																														●	■		■	
Combine like terms to simplify expressions and equations																																	●	■
Write and identify equivalent expressions and equivalent equations													●				■	■			●								●	●			●	
Write and solve equations that represent problem situations			●		■	●	●	■	■	■						●											■			●		■	●	■
Algebraic Notation and Solving Number Sentences	1	2	3	4	5	6	7	8	9	10	11	12	1	2	3	4	5	6	7	8	9	10	11	12	1	2	3	4	5	6	7	8	9	10
Compare numbers using <, >, and = symbols	■	■	■	■	■	■	●	■			■	■						●	●	●			■	■	●			●	■	●			■	
Evaluate expressions using <, >, =, and ≈ symbols																■						■			●		●	●	■	●	■	●	●	
Translate number stories into expressions			●		■	●	●	■	■	■				●		●			●			●		●			●	■	■	●			●	
Write/solve addition and subtraction number sentences	■	●			■		■						■	●	■						■				■	■	●	■	■	●			●	
Write/solve multiplication/division number sentences			●		■	■			■				■	●		●					■				■	■	●		■	●		●	●	■
Use variables to describe general patterns																											●	■		●		●	●	

Patterns, Functions, and Algebra (cont.)

Key ● Content taught ■ Content practiced

	Grade 4 Units												Grade 5 Units												Grade 6 Units									
Algebraic Notation and Solving Number Sentences (cont.)	1	2	3	4	5	6	7	8	9	10	11	12	1	2	3	4	5	6	7	8	9	10	11	12	1	2	3	4	5	6	7	8	9	10
Determine the value of a variable		■		■		■		■		■	■	■		●	■	●		■	■	■	■	●	■	●			●	●	●	●	■	●	●	
Write and solve open sentences or number sentences with variables			●		■	●		■	■		■	■		●	■	●	■		●	●	■	●	■	●			●	●	●	●	■	●	●	
Determine if number sentences are true or false		■	●	■	■												■		●	■									■	●	■	■		
Write or evaluate algebraic expressions and formulas to describe situations			●		■	●			■													●		■			●	■		●		■	●	■
Use variables and formulas in spreadsheets																											●	■				■	●	
Evaluate formulas																					●		●			■	●	■		●		■	●	■
Use formulas to solve problems																					●		●			■	●	●		●		■	●	■
Identify dependent and independent variables																											●							
Order of Operations	1	2	3	4	5	6	7	8	9	10	11	12	1	2	3	4	5	6	7	8	9	10	11	12	1	2	3	4	5	6	7	8	9	10
Apply the use of parentheses in number sentences			●	■	■	■	■		■		■							■	●	■	■			■	■		●		■	●		■	●	■
Understand and apply the order of operations to evaluate expressions and solve number sentences																			●	■	■	●	■		■	●		■	■	●	■	■	●	■
Simplify expressions and equations that have parentheses																			●										■	●		■	●	■
Properties of Arithmetic Operations	1	2	3	4	5	6	7	8	9	10	11	12	1	2	3	4	5	6	7	8	9	10	11	12	1	2	3	4	5	6	7	8	9	10
Investigate properties of multiplication/division			●			■							●	■		●										■				●	■	■	■	
Understand and apply the Commutative Property for addition and multiplication																				■										●	■		●	
Apply the Distributive Property					●	■	■	■	■																			●		●		■	●	■
Understand and apply the Identity Property for multiplication																												●		●		●		
Understand and apply the Associative Property for addition and multiplication																	●	●			■		●					●		●			●	

Index

A

B

M

O

P

Q

S

Notes

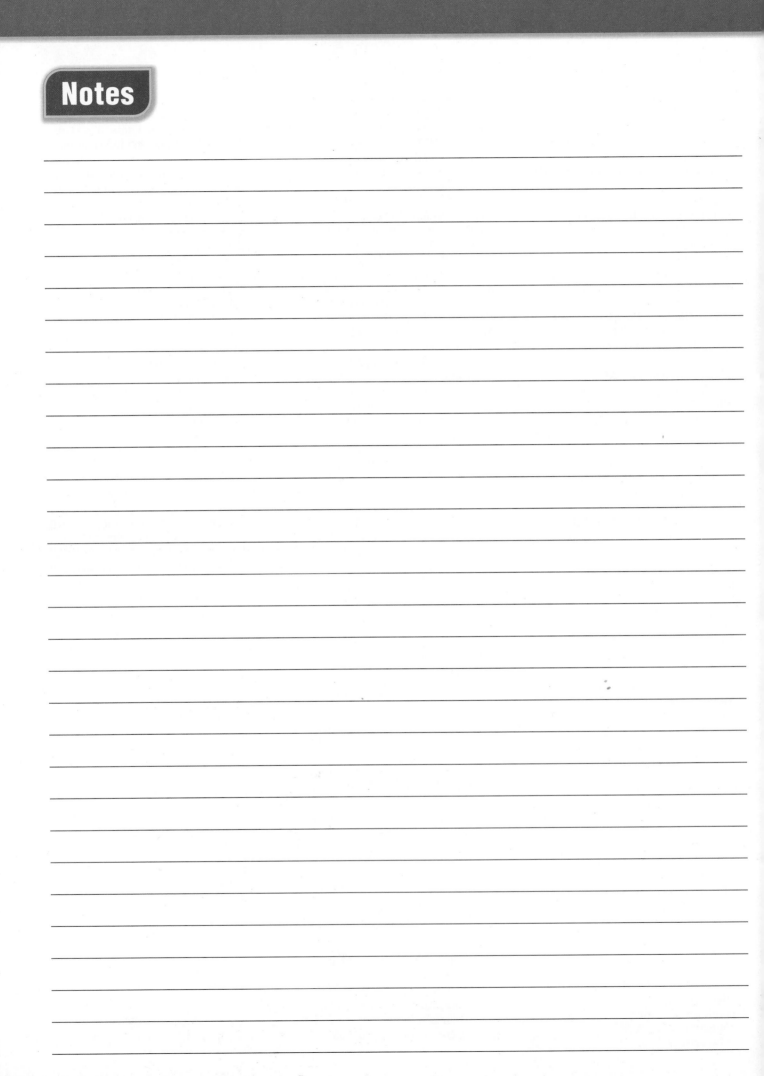